SPREAD SPECTRUM COMMUNICATIONS HANDBOOK

Marvin K. Simon
Jet Propulsion Laboratory

Jim K. Omura
Cylink Corporation, Sunnyvale, California

Robert A. Scholtz
University of Southern California

Barry K. Levitt
Jet Propulsion Laboratory

Revised Edition

McGraw-Hill, Inc.

New York San Francisco Washington, D.C. Auckland Bogotá
Caracas Lisbon London Madrid Mexico City Milan
Montreal New Delhi San Juan Singapore
Sydney Tokyo Toronto

Library of Congress Cataloging-in-Publication Data

Spread spectrum communications handbook / Marvin K. Simon . . . [et al.].—rev. ed.
p. cm.
Rev. ed. of: Spread spectrum communications. 1985.
Includes bibliographical references and index.
ISBN 0-07-057629-7
1. Spread spectrum communications. I. Simon, Marvin Kenneth, date. II. Title: Spread spectrum communications.
TK5103.45.S77 1994
621.382—dc20 94-5803
CIP

The previous edition was published in three volumes by Computer Science Press in 1985 under the title *Spread Spectrum Communications*.

1 2 3 4 5 6 7 8 9 0 DOC/DOC 9 0 9 8 7 6 5 4

ISBN 0-07-057629-7

The sponsoring editor for this book was Stephen S. Chapman, the editing supervisor was David E. Fogarty, and the production supervisor was Suzanne W. Babeuf. It was set in Times Roman by Techna Type, Inc.

Printed and bound by R. R. Donnelley & Sons Company.

This book is printed on acid-free paper.

CONTENTS

PART 2 CLASSICAL SPREAD-SPECTRUM COMMUNICATIONS

PREFACE

In the nine years since the publication of the first edition of *Spread Spectrum Communications,* the world's political situation has changed considerably. The U.S. Department of Defense has reduced its support for the development of new communication systems as well as their acquisition. One might question the need for a second edition of a book written about robust techniques for anti-jamming (AJ) and low-probability-of-intercept (LPI) communications.

However, while it is already painfully clear that the close of the Cold War has not ended warfare, the past decade has also ushered in a new era of mobile communications. The qualities that make spread-spectrum techniques useful in military communications—fine time-resolution, low power-density, privacy, and a high immunity to interference—are also extremely desirable in today's mobile communications systems. Encouraged by enlightened FCC actions, spread-spectrum technology is being transferred from the Department of Defense to the arena of commercial mobile cellular communications. The emerging markets for spread-spectrum systems have the potential to dwarf those of the past.

Are the design techniques for military communication systems truly applicable to the commercial environment? Does yesteryear's jammer have anything to teach us about managing multiple-user noise in a spread-spectrum multiple-access radio network? The answer—an unqualified "yes"—is attested to by the successes of companies that are penetrating the commercial marketplace with spread-spectrum products.

This revised edition contains new material on the emerging commercial applications of spread-spectrum techniques as well as minor modifications to the book's original fourteen chapters. We believe that since it is based on sound engineering principles and is not bound to a particular implementation technology, it will retain its usefulness for the foreseeable future.

Marvin K. Simon
Jim K. Omura
Robert A. Scholtz
Barry K. Levitt

PREFACE TO FIRST EDITION

Not more than a decade ago, the discipline of spread-spectrum (SS) communications was primarily cloaked in secrecy. Indeed, most of the information available on the subject at that time could be found only in documents of a classified nature.

Today the picture is noticeably changed. The open literature abounds with publications on SS communications, special issues of the *IEEE Transactions on Communications* have been devoted to the subject, and the formation of an annual conference on military communications, MILCOM, now offers a public forum for presentation of unclassified (as well as classified) papers dealing with SS applications in military systems. On a less formal note, many tutorial and survey papers have recently appeared in the open literature, and presentations on a similar level have taken place at major communications conferences. Finally, as further evidence we cite the publication of several books dealing either with SS communications directly or as part of the more general electronic countermeasures (ECM) and electronic counter-counter measures (ECCM) problem. References to all these forms of public documentation are given in Section 1.7 of Chapter 1, Part 1.

The reasons for this proliferation can be traced to many sources. While it is undoubtedly true that the primary application of SS communications still lies in the development of enemy jam-resistant communication systems for the military, largely within the confines of classified programs, the emergence of other applications, in which both the military and civilian sectors are involved, is playing a role of ever-increasing importance. For example, to minimize mutual interference, the flux density of transmissions from radio transmitters must often be maintained at acceptably low radiation levels. A convenient way to meet these requirements is to spread the power spectrum of the signal before transmission and despread it after reception—the non-hostile equivalent of the military low-probability-of-intercept (LPI) signal design.

Another instance in which SS techniques are particularly useful in a non-anti-jam application is in multiple-access communications in which many users share a single communication channel. The assignment of a unique SS sequence to each user allows him or her to transmit simultaneously over the common channel with a minimum of mutual interference, simplifying the network control requirements.

Extremely accurate positioning can be computed by using signals from several satellites in synchronous and asynchronous orbits. Satellites transmitting pseudorandom noise sequences modulated onto the transmitted carrier signal provide the means for accomplishing the required range and distance determination at any point on the earth.

Finally, SS techniques can improve the reliability of transmission in frequency-selective fading and multipath environments. Spreading the bandwidth of the transmitted signal over a wide range of frequencies reduces its vulnerability to interference and often provides some diversity gain at the receiver.

At the heart of all these potential applications lies the increasing use of digital forms of modulation for transmitting information, driven by the tremendous advances made over the last decade in microelectronics. This trend no doubt will continue, and thus it should not be surprising that more and more applications for spread-spectrum techniques will continue to surface. Indeed, the state-of-the-art is advancing so rapidly (e.g., witness the recent improvements in frequency synthesizers boosting frequency hop rates from the Khops/sec to the Mhops/sec ranges over SS bandwidths in excess of a GHz) that today's primarily theoretical concepts will be realized tomorrow.

Unclassified research and developments in spread-spectrum communications have arrived at a point of maturity necessary to justify a textbook on SS communications that goes far beyond the level of those available on today's market. Such is the purpose of *Spread Spectrum Communications*. Contained within the fourteen chapters of its three volumes is an in-depth treatment of SS communications that should appeal to the specialist already familiar with the subject as well as the neophyte with little or no background in the area. The book is organized into five parts, within which the various chapters are for the most part self-contained. The exception is Chapter 3, Part 1, which deals with basic concepts and system models and serves as a basis for many of the other chapters that follow. As would be expected, the more traditional portions of the subject are treated in the first two parts, while the latter three parts deal with more specialized aspects. The authors envision that an introductory one-semester course in SS communications taught at a graduate level in a university might cover all or parts of Chapters 1, 3, 4, 5 of Part 1, Chapters 1 and 2 of Part 2, and Chapters 1 and 2 of Part 4.

In composing the technical material presented in *Spread Spectrum Communications*, the authors have intentionally avoided referring by name to specific modern SS systems that employ techniques such as those discussed in many of the chapters. Such a choice was motivated by the desire to offer a unified approach to the subject that stresses fundamental principles rather than specific applications. Nevertheless, the reader should feel confident that the broad experience of the four authors ensures that the material is practical as well as academically inspiring.

In writing a book of this magnitude, we acknowledge many whose efforts should not go unnoticed. Credit is due to Paul Green for originally suggesting the research that uncovered the material in Chapter 2, Part 1, and to Bob Price for the tireless sleuthing which led to much of the remarkable information presented there. Chapter 5, Part 1 benefitted significantly from the comments of Lloyd Welch, whose innovative research is responsible for some of the elegant sequence designs presented there. Per Kullstam helped clarify the material on DS/BPSK analysis in Chapter 1, Part 2. Paul Crepeau contributed substantially to the work on list detectors. Last but by no means least, the authors would like to thank James Springett, Gaylord Huth, and Richard Iwasaki for their contributions to much of the material presented in Chapter 4, Part 5.

Several colleagues of the authors have aided in the production of a useful book by virtue of critical reading and/or proofing. In this regard, the efforts of Paul Crepeau, Larry Hatch, Vijay Kumar, Sang Moon, Wei-Chung Peng, and Reginaldo Polazzo, Jr. are greatly appreciated.

It is often said that a book cannot be judged by its cover. The authors of *Spread Spectrum Communications* are proud to take exception to this commonly quoted cliche. For the permission to use the historically significant noise-wheel cover design (see Chapter 2, Part 1, Section 2.2.5), we gratefully acknowledge the International Telephone and Telegraph Corp.

Marvin K. Simon
Jim K. Omura
Robert A. Scholtz
Barry K. Levitt

Part 1

INTRODUCTION TO SPREAD-SPECTRUM COMMUNICATION

Chapter 1

A SPREAD-SPECTRUM OVERVIEW

Over thirty years have passed since the terms spread-spectrum (SS) and noise modulation and correlation (NOMAC) were first used to describe a class of signalling techniques possessing several desirable attributes for communication and navigation applications, especially in an interference environment. What are these techniques? How are they classified? What are those useful properties? How well do they work? Preliminary answers are forthcoming in this introductory chapter.

We will motivate the study of spread-spectrum systems by analyzing a simple game, played on a finite-dimensional signal space by a communications system and a jammer, in which the signal-to-interference energy ratio in the communication receiver's data detection circuitry serves as a payoff function. The reader is hereby forewarned that signal-to-interference ratio calculations alone cannot illustrate many effects which, in subtle ways, degrade more realistic performance ratios, e.g., bit-error-rate in coded digital SS systems. However, the tutorial value of the following simple energy calculations soon will be evident.

1.1 A BASIS FOR A JAMMING GAME

The following abstract scenario will be used to illustrate the need for spectrum spreading in a jamming environment, to determine fundamental design characteristics, and to quantify one measure of SS system performance. Consider a synchronous digital communication complex in which the communicator has K transmitters available with which to convey information to a cooperating communicator who possesses K matching receivers (see Figure 1.1). Assume for simplicity that the communication signal space has been "divided equally" among the K transmitters. Hence, with a bandwidth W_{ss} available for communicating an information symbol in a T_s second interval $(0, T_s)$, the resultant transmitted-signal function space of dimension approximately $2T_sW_{ss}$ is divided so that each transmitter

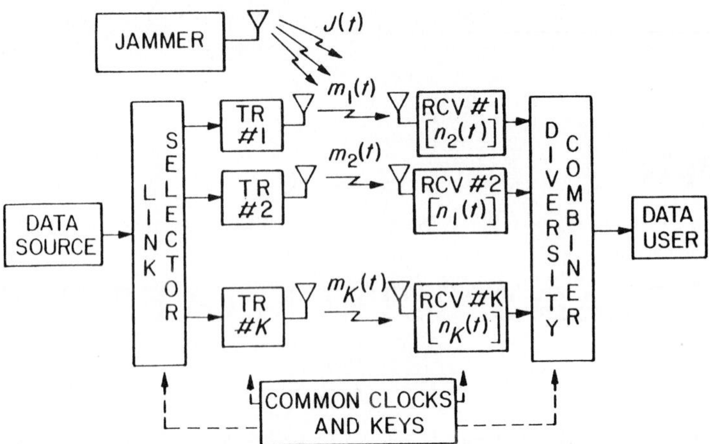

Figure 1.1. The scenario for a game between a jammer and a communication system complex.

has a D-dimensional subspace, $D = 2T_s W_{ss}/K$, in which to synthesize its output signal. Denote an orthonormal basis for the total signal space by $\psi_k(t)$, $k = 1, 2, \ldots, 2T_s W_{ss}$, i.e.,

$$\int_0^{T_s} \psi_j(t)\psi_k^*(t)\,dt = \begin{cases} 1, & j = k \\ 0, & j \neq k \end{cases} \tag{1.1}$$

where the basis functions may be complex valued, and ( )* denotes conjugation. Then the signal emitted by the k-th transmitter is of the form

$$m_k(t) = \sum_{j \in \mathcal{N}_k} a_j \psi_j(t), \tag{1.2}$$

where

$$\mathcal{N}_k = \{ j\colon (k-1)D < j \le kD \} \tag{1.3}$$

and $\{a_j\}$ is a data-dependent set of coefficients. We will refer to the above as an *orthogonal communication system complex of multiplicity K*.

Of course, real systems generally radiate real signals. The reader may wish to view $m_k(t)$ as the modulation on the radiated signal $\mathrm{Re}\{m_k(t)\exp(j\omega_c t + \theta)\}$. Without loss of generality, we can dispense with the shift to RF during this initial discussion.

In a simplified jamming situation, the signal $z_i(t)$ observed at the i-th receiver in the receiving complex might be

$$z_i(t) = \sum_{k=1}^{K} m_k(t) + J(t) + n_i(t), \tag{1.4}$$

where $n_i(t)$ represents internally generated noise in the i-th receiver, $J(t)$ is an externally generated jamming signal, and the K-term sum represents the total output signal of the transmitter complex. One signal processing strategy for the i-th receiver is to project the received signal onto the set of basis functions for the i-th transmitter's signal space, thereby calculating

$$z_j = \int_0^{T_s} z_i(t)\psi_j^*(t)\,dt \quad \text{for all } j \in \mathcal{N}_i. \tag{1.5}$$

In the absence of jamming and receiver noise, the properties of the orthonormal basis insure that $z_j = a_j$, and thus, the i-th receiver correctly discovers the data dependent set of coefficients $\{a_j\}$, $j \in \mathcal{N}_i$, used by the i-th transmitter.

Both the jamming and receiver noise signals can be expanded in terms of the orthonormal basis as

$$J(t) = \sum_{j=1}^{2T_sW_{ss}} J_j\psi_j(t) + J_0(t), \tag{1.6}$$

$$n_i(t) = \sum_{j=1}^{2T_sW_{ss}} n_{ij}\psi_j(t) + n_{0i}(t), \tag{1.7}$$

where $J_0(t)$ represents that portion of the jamming signal orthogonal to all of the $2T_sW_{ss}$ basis functions used in producing the composite signal. The receiver noise component $n_{0i}(t)$ likewise is orthogonal to all possible transmitted signals. These representations indicate that, in general, the projection (1.5) of $z_i(t)$ onto $\psi_j(t)$ in the i-th receiver produces

$$z_j = a_j + J_j + n_{ij} \quad \text{for all } j \in \mathcal{N}_i. \tag{1.8}$$

The everpresent thermal noise random variable n_{ij}, assumed complex Gaussian, independent, and identically distributed for different values of i and/or j, represents the relatively benign receiver perturbations in the absence of jamming. The jamming signal coefficients J_j are less easily classified, and from the jammer's point of view, hopefully are unpredictable by the receiver.

The total energy E_J in the jamming signal $J(t)$ over the time interval $(0, T_s)$ is given by

$$E_J = \int_0^{T_s} |J(t)|^2\,dt = \sum_{j=1}^{2T_sW_{ss}} |J_j|^2 + \int_0^{T_s} |J_0(t)|^2\,dt. \tag{1.9}$$

Obviously, the energy term involving $J_0(t)$ serves no useful jamming purpose, and henceforth, will be assumed zero. (In keeping with this conservative aspect of communication system design, we also assume that the jammer has full knowledge of timing and of the set $\{\psi_j(t)\}$ of basis functions.) The sum in (1.9) can be partitioned into K parts, the i-th part representing the energy E_{Ji} used to jam the i-th receiver. Thus,

$$E_J = \sum_{i=1}^{K} E_{Ji}, \quad E_{Ji} = \sum_{j\in\mathcal{N}_i} |J_j|^2. \tag{1.10}$$

A similar partition holds for the total transmitted signal energy E_s, namely

$$E_S = \sum_{i=1}^{K} E_{Si}, \quad E_{Si} = \sum_{j \in \mathcal{N}_i} |a_j|^2, \tag{1.11}$$

E_{Si} being the energy used by the i-th transmitter. The additive partitions (1.10), (1.11) are a direct result of the orthogonality requirement placed on the signals produced by the transmitter complex.

The above signal representations and calculations have been made under the assumption that the channel is ideal, causing no attenuation, delay, or distortion in conveying the composite transmitted signal to the receiver complex, and that synchronous clocks are available at the transmitter and receiver for determining the time interval $(0, T_s)$ of operation. Hence, important considerations have been suppressed in this initial discussion, so that we may focus on one major issue facing both the communication system designer and the jammer designer, namely their allocations of transmitter energy and jammer energy over the K orthogonal communication links.

1.2 ENERGY ALLOCATION STRATEGIES

Within the framework of an orthogonal communication system complex of multiplicity K, let's consider the communicator and jammer to use the following strategies for allocating their available energies, E_S and E_J respectively, to the K links.

> *Communicators' strategy*: Randomly select K_S links, $K_S \leq K$, for equal energy allocations, each receiving E_S/K_S units. The remaining links are not utilized.
>
> *Jammer's strategy*: Randomly select K_J receivers for equal doses of jamming energy, each receiving E_J/K_J units. The remaining channels are not jammed.

The quantity K_S is referred to as the *diversity factor* of the communication system complex. When K_S exceeds unity, the receiver must employ a diversity combining algorithm to convert the outputs of the K_S chosen links into a single output for the system user. The performance measure to be employed here, in determining the effectiveness of these strategies, will not depend on specifying a particular diversity combining algorithm.

The randomness required of these strategies should be interpreted as meaning that the corresponding adversary has no logical method for predicting the choice of strategy, and must consider all strategies equally likely. Furthermore, random selection of communication links by the transmitter should not affect communication quality since all available links are assumed to have equal attributes. (Examples of link collections with non-uniform attributes will be considered in Part 2, Chapter 2.)

The receiving complex, having knowledge of the strategy selected for communication, will collect all E_S units of transmitted energy in the K_S receivers remaining in operation. However, the amount of jamming energy collected by those same K_S receivers is a random variable whose value is determined by which of the $\binom{K}{K_J}$ jamming strategies is selected ($\binom{\cdot}{\cdot}$ denotes a binomial coefficient). Under the equally likely strategy assumption, the probability that the jammer strategy will include exactly N of the K_S receivers in use, is given by

$$\Pr(N) = \begin{cases} \dfrac{\binom{K_S}{N}\binom{K-K_S}{K_J-N}}{\binom{K}{K_J}}, & N_{\min} \le N \le N_{\max} \\ 0, & \text{otherwise} \end{cases} \tag{1.12}$$

where

$$N_{\min} = \max(0, K_J + K_S - K) \tag{1.13}$$

$$N_{\max} = \min(K_S, K_J). \tag{1.14}$$

Using (1.12)–(1.14), it is possible to compute the expected total effective jamming energy $E_{J\text{eff}}$ sensed by the K_S receivers, namely

$$E_{J\text{eff}} = \frac{E_J}{K_J}\mathbf{E}\{N\}, \tag{1.15}$$

E being the expected value operator. Despite the complicated form of $\Pr(N)$, it can be verified that

$$\mathbf{E}\{N\} = \frac{K_J K_S}{K}, \tag{1.16}$$

and hence, that

$$E_{J\text{eff}} = \frac{E_J K_S}{K}. \tag{1.17}$$

More generally, it can be verified that when the communicators use the strategy described above, (1.17) is the average total effective jamming energy for any arbitrary distribution of jamming energy.

This idealized situation leads one to conclude, based on (1.17), that the receiver can minimize the jammer's effectiveness energy-wise by not using diversity, i.e., by using $K_S = 1$. Furthermore, the multiplicity K of the orthogonal communication system complex should be made as large as possible to reduce $E_{J\text{eff}}$, i.e., the complex should be designed to use all of the available bandwidth. The energy-optimal communication strategy ($K_S = 1$) using a single one of the K available communication links, is called a *pure spread-spectrum strategy*. This strategy, with its accompanying threat to use any of K orthogonal links, increases the total signal-to-jamming ratio from E_S/E_J at each receiving antenna's terminals to KE_S/E_J at the output of the designated receiver, and therefore qualifies as an *anti-jam* (AJ) modulation technique.

The improvement $E_J/E_{J\text{eff}}$ in signal-to-jamming ratio will be called the *energy gain EG* of the signalling strategy played on the orthogonal communication system complex.

$$EG = \frac{E_J}{E_{J\text{eff}}} = \frac{K}{K_S} = \frac{2T_sW_{ss}}{K_SD}. \tag{1.18}$$

Hence, the energy gain for a pure SS strategy is the multiplicity factor of the complex. In this fundamental form (1.18), the energy gain is the ratio of the signal space dimension $2T_sW_{ss}$ perceived by the jammer for potential communication use to the total dimension K_SD of the K_S links' D-dimensional signal spaces which the receiver must observe. For a fixed T_sW_{ss} product, this definition of energy gain makes no distinction between diversity and SS strategies using the same signal space dimension K_SD. The reader may recognize the fact that the quantity called the multiplicity factor, or energy gain in this chapter, is sometimes referred to as the processing gain of the SS system. This nomenclature is by no means universally accepted, and we will instead identify the term *processing gain PG* with the ratio W_{ss}/R_b, where R_b is the data rate in bits/second. It is easily verified from (1.18) that processing gain and energy gain are identical when $R_b = K_SD/2T_s$, e.g., for binary orthogonal signalling ($D = 2$) with no diversity ($K_S = 1$).

Two key assumptions were made in showing that the pure SS strategy is best: (1) The channel is ideal and propagates all signals equally well, and (2) the proper performance measure is the total effective jamming energy. If either of the above assumptions is not acceptable, then the jammer's strategy may influence the performance measure, and the optimum diversity factor K_S may be greater than one. Indeed, in later chapters it is shown that the use of bit-error rate (BER) as a performance measure implies that the optimum diversity factor can exceed unity.

Let's summarize the requirements characteristic of a digital spread-spectrum communication system in a jamming environment:

1. The bandwidth (or equivalently the link's signal-space dimension D) required to transmit the data in the absence of jamming is much less than the bandwidth W_{ss} (or equivalently the system's signal space dimension $2T_sW_{ss}$) available for use.
2. The receiver uses inner product operations (or their equivalent) to confine its operation to the link's D-dimensional signal space, to demodulate the signal, and thereby to reject orthogonal jamming waveform components.
3. The waveforms used for communication are randomly or pseudorandomly selected, and equally likely to be anywhere in the available

bandwidth (or equivalently, anywhere in the system's $2T_sW_{ss}$ dimensional signal space).

The term *pseudorandom* is used specifically to mean random in appearance but reproducible by deterministic means.

We will now review a sampling of the wide variety of communication system designs which possess SS characteristics.

1.3 SPREAD-SPECTRUM SYSTEM CONFIGURATIONS AND COMPONENTS

A pure spread-spectrum strategy, employing only a single link at any time, can be mechanized more efficiently than the system with potential diversity factor K, shown in Figure 1.1. In an SS system, the K transmitter-receiver pairs of Figure 1.1 are replaced by a single wideband communication link having the capability to synthesize and detect all of the waveforms potentially generated by the orthogonal communication system complex. The pure SS strategy of randomly selecting a link for communication is replaced with an equivalent approach, namely, selecting a D-dimensional subspace for waveform synthesis out of the system's $2T_sW_{ss}$-dimensional signal space. This random selection process must be independently repeated each time a symbol is transmitted. Independent selections are necessary to avoid exposing the communication link to the threat that the jammer will predict the signal set to be used, will confine his jamming energy to that set, and hence, will reduce the apparent multiplicity and energy gain to unity.

Three system configurations are shown in Figure 1.2, which illustrate basic techniques that the designer may use to insure that transmitter and receiver operate synchronously with the same apparently random set of signals. The portions of the SS system which are charged with the responsibility of maintaining the unpredictable nature of the transmission are double-boxed in Figure 1.2. The *modus operandi* of these systems is as follows:

1. *Transmitted reference* (TR) systems accomplish SS operation by transmitting two versions of a wideband, unpredictable carrier, one ($x(t)$) modulated by data and the other ($r(t)$) unmodulated (Figure 1.2(a)). These signals, being separately recovered by the receiver (e.g., one may be displaced in frequency from the other), are the inputs to a correlation detector which recovers the data modulation. The wideband carrier in a TR-SS system may be a truly random, wideband noise source, unknown by transmitter and receiver until the instant it is generated for use in communication.

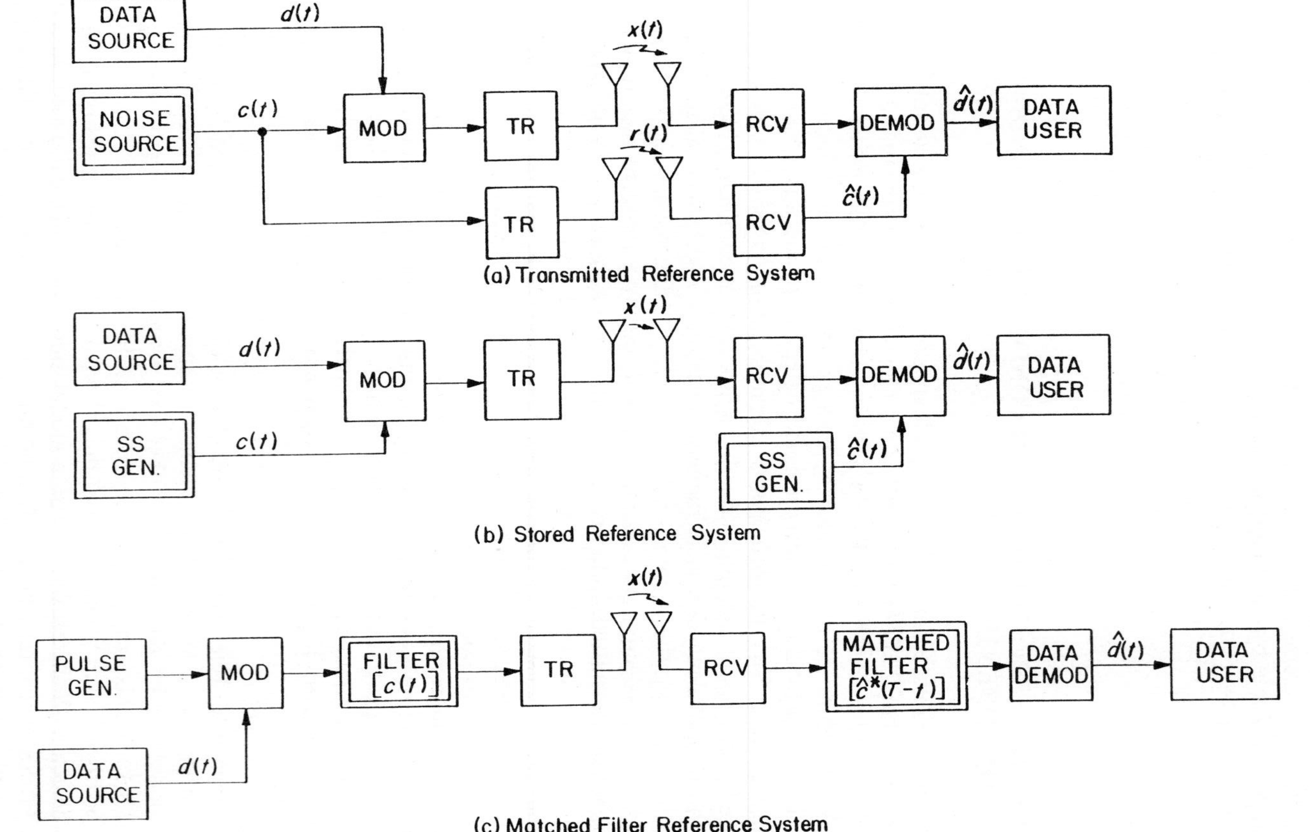

Figure 1.2. Simple SS system configurations. (The notation $\hat{z}(t)$ is used to denote an estimate of $z(t)$.)

2. *Stored reference* (SR) systems require independent generation at transmitter and receiver of pseudorandom wideband waveforms which are identical in their essential characteristics (Figure 1.2(b)). The receiver's SS waveform generator is adjusted automatically to keep its output in close synchronism with the arriving SS waveform. Data detection, then, is accomplished by cross-correlation. The waveform generators are initialized prior to use by setting certain parameters in the generating algorithm, thereby denying the jammer knowledge of the waveform set being used (even if the jammer has succeeded in determining the generator's structure).
3. *Matched filter* (MF) systems generate a wideband transmitted signal by pulsing a filter having a long, wideband, pseudorandomly controlled impulse response (Figure 1.2(c)). Signal detection at the receiver employs an identically pseudorandom, synchronously controlled, matched filter which performs the correlation computation. Matched filter systems differ from SR systems primarily in the manner in which the inner-product detection process is mechanized, and hence, have externally observed properties similar to those of SR systems.

Certainly, a pure TR system has several fundamental weaknesses including: (1) The system is easily spoofed since a jammer can in principle transmit a pair of waveforms which are accepted by the receiver, (2) relatively poor performance occurs at low signal levels because noise and interference are present on both signals which are cross-correlated in the receiver, (3) the data is easily determined by any listener who has access to both transmitted signals, and (4) the TR system's two channels may require extra bandwidth and may be difficult to match. Some of the problems associated with TR systems may be mitigated by randomly changing parameters of one of the communication links (e.g., by protecting one of the TR wideband links with an SR-like technique). Historical examples of SR-protected TR systems will be given in the next chapter.

Spread-spectrum waveform generators for SR systems employing the following general modulation formats have been built. The output of an SS waveform generator is given the generic name $c(t)$ and is a (possibly complex-valued) baseband representation of the SS waveform.

1. *Recorded modulation*: The waveform $w(t)$ of duration T_p is recorded, and if necessary, extended periodically to give
$$c(t) = \sum_n w(t - nT_p). \tag{1.19}$$
The utility of this type of signal is limited by the problem of distributing recordings to transmitter and receiver so that reuse of a waveform is not necessary.
2. *Frequency hopping* (FH): Assuming that $p(t)$ is a basic pulse shape of duration T_h (usually called the *hop time*), frequency-hopping modulation

has the form

$$c(t) = \sum_n \exp[j(2\pi f_n t + \phi_n)]\, p(t - nT_h). \tag{1.20}$$

In all likelihood, the complex baseband signal $c(t)$ never physically appears in the transmitter or receiver. Instead, the pseudorandomly generated sequence $\{f_n\}$ of frequency shifts will drive a frequency synthesizer to produce a real-valued IF or RF carrier-modulated version of $c(t)$. The sequence $\{\phi_n\}$ of random phases is a by-product of the modulation process.

3. *Time hopping* (TH): Assuming that the pulse waveform $p(t)$ has duration at most T_s/M_T, a typical time hopping waveform might be

$$c(t) = \sum_n p\left(t - \left(n + \frac{a_n}{M_T}\right)T_s\right). \tag{1.21}$$

In this example, time has been segmented into T_s second intervals, with each interval containing a single pulse pseudorandomly located at one of M_T locations within the interval.

4. *Direct sequence* (DS) *modulation*: Spread-spectrum designers call the waveform

$$c(t) = \sum_n c_n p(t - nT_c) \tag{1.22}$$

direct sequence modulation. Here, the output sequence $\{c_n\}$ of a pseudorandom number generator is linearly modulated onto a sequence of pulses, each pulse having a duration T_c called the *chip time.*

5. *Hybrid modulations*: Each of the above techniques possesses certain advantages and disadvantages, depending on the system design objectives (AJ protection is just one facet of the design problem). Potentially, a blend of modulation techniques may provide better performance at the cost of some complexity. For example, the choice

$$c(t) = \prod_i c^{(i)}(t) \tag{1.23}$$

may capture the advantages of the individual wideband waveforms $c^{(i)}(t)$ and mitigate their individual disadvantages.

Three schemes seem to be prevalent for combining the data signal $d(t)$ with the SS modulation waveform $c(t)$ to produce the transmitted SS signal $x(t)$.

1. *Multiplicative modulation*: Used in many modern systems, the transmitted signal for multiplicative modulation is of the form

$$x(t) = \text{Re}\{d(t)c(t)e^{j(\omega_c t + \phi_T)}\}. \tag{1.24}$$

Mechanization simplicity usually suggests certain combinations of data and SS formats, e.g., binary phase-shift-keyed (BPSK) data on a DS signal, or multiple frequency-shift-keyed (MFSK) data on a FH signal. These modulation schemes are the ones of primary interest in this book.

2. *Delay modulation*: Suggested for use in several early systems, and a natural for mechanization with TH-SS modulation, this technique transmits the signal

$$x(t) = \mathrm{Re}\{c(t - d(t))e^{j(\omega_c t + \phi_T)}\}. \tag{1.25}$$

3. *Independent (switching) modulation*: Techniques (1) and (2) are susceptible to a jamming strategy in which the jammer forwards the transmitted signal to the receiver with no significant additional delay (a severe geometric constraint on the location of the jammer with respect to the transmitter and receiver), but with modified modulation. This repeater strategy, which if implementable, clearly reduces the multiplicity factor K of the SS system to unity, can be nullified by using a transmitted signal of the form

$$x(t) = \mathrm{Re}\{c^{(d(t))}(t)e^{j(\omega_c t + \phi_T)}\}. \tag{1.26}$$

Here the data signal, quantized to M levels, determines which of M distinct SS modulations $c^{(d)}(t)$, $d = 1, \ldots, 2, \ldots, M$, is transmitted. The key assumption here is that even though the jammer can observe the above waveform, it cannot reliably produce an alternate waveform $c^{(j(t))}(t)$, $j(t) \neq d(t)$, acceptable to the receiver as alternate data modulation. The cost of independent data modulation is a clearly increased hardware complexity.

The data demodulation process in a digital SS system must compute inner products in the process of demodulation. That is, the receiver must mechanize calculations of the form

$$(m_T, m_R) = \int_0^{T_S} m_T(t) m_R^*(t)\, dt \tag{1.27}$$

where in general $m_T(t)$ and $m_R(t)$ represent complex baseband signals and (m_T, m_R) is their inner product. However, one or both of these complex baseband signals usually appears in modulated form as a real IF or RF signal

$$x_i(t) = \mathrm{Re}\{m_i(t)e^{j(\omega_i t + \phi_i)}\}, \quad i = T, R. \tag{1.28}$$

The inner product (1.27) can be recovered from the modulated signal(s) in several ways, as illustrated in Figure 1.3. For example, the receiver can first demodulate the signal $x_T(t)$ to recover the real and imaginary parts of $m_T(t)$ and then proceed with straightforward correlation or matched filtering operations using baseband signals. On the other hand, as indicated in Figures 1.3(c) and 1.3(d), there are alternative ways to compute the inner product, which do not require that both signals be shifted to baseband first.

In all cases, the heart of the SS receiver is its synchronization circuitry, and the heartbeats are the clock pulses which control almost all steps in

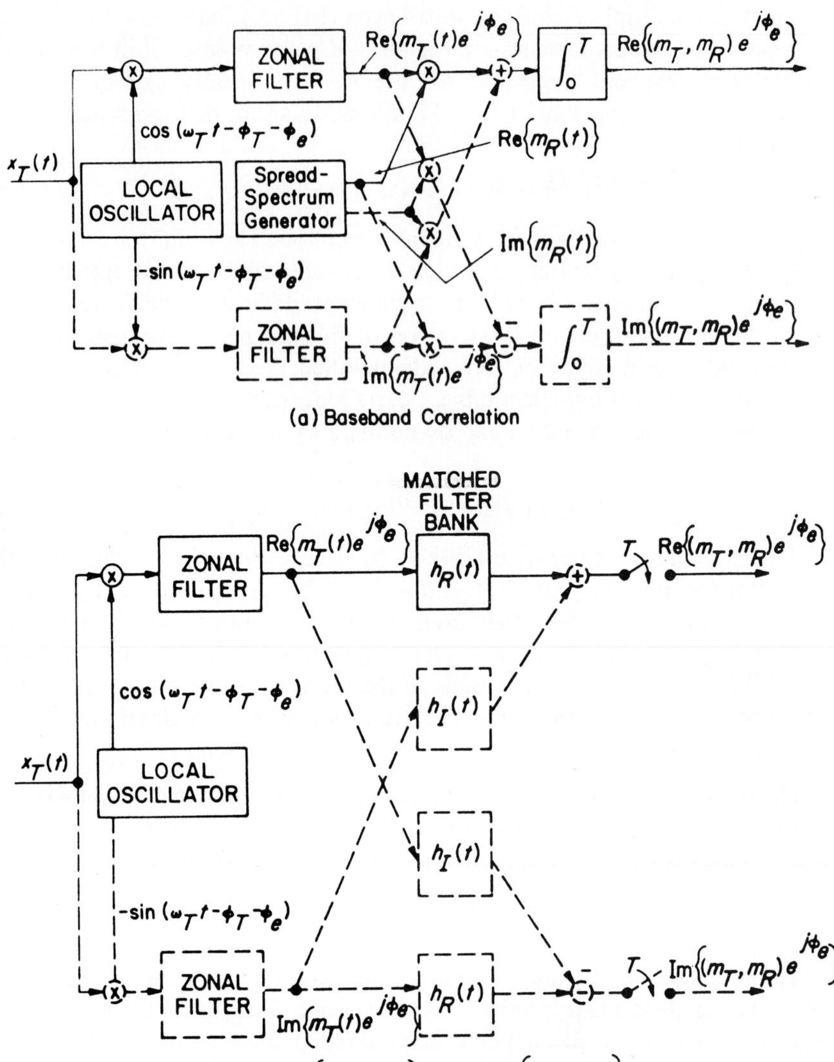

Figure 1.3. Examples of correlation-computing block diagrams. The dashed portions of the diagrams can be eliminated when the modulations $m_T(t)$ and $m_R(t)$ are real and, in addition, the local oscillator is phase-coherent, i.e., $\phi_e \approx 0$. Solid line processing is often called the "in-phase" channel, while the dashed line processing is called the "quadrature" channel.

ZONAL BANDPASS FILTER
$\int_0^T$
$\mathrm{Re}\{(m_T, m_R)e^{j\phi_e}\}$
$\cos(\omega_1 t + \phi_1)$
$\mathrm{Re}\{m_R(t)\}$
$\cos[(\omega_T - \omega_1)t + (\phi_T - \phi_1 - \phi_e)]$
$x_T(t)$
LOCAL OSCILLATOR
Spread-Spectrum Generator
LOCAL OSCILLATOR
$-\sin(\omega_1 t + \phi_1)$
$-\sin[(\omega_T - \omega_1)t + (\phi_T - \phi_1 - \phi_e)]$
$\mathrm{Im}\{m_R(t)\}$
ZONAL BANDPASS FILTER
$\int_0^T$
$\mathrm{Im}\{(m_T, m_R)e^{j\phi_e}\}$
$\mathrm{Re}\{m_T(t)m_R^*(t)e^{j[(\omega_T - \omega_1)t + (\phi_T - \phi_1)]}\}$

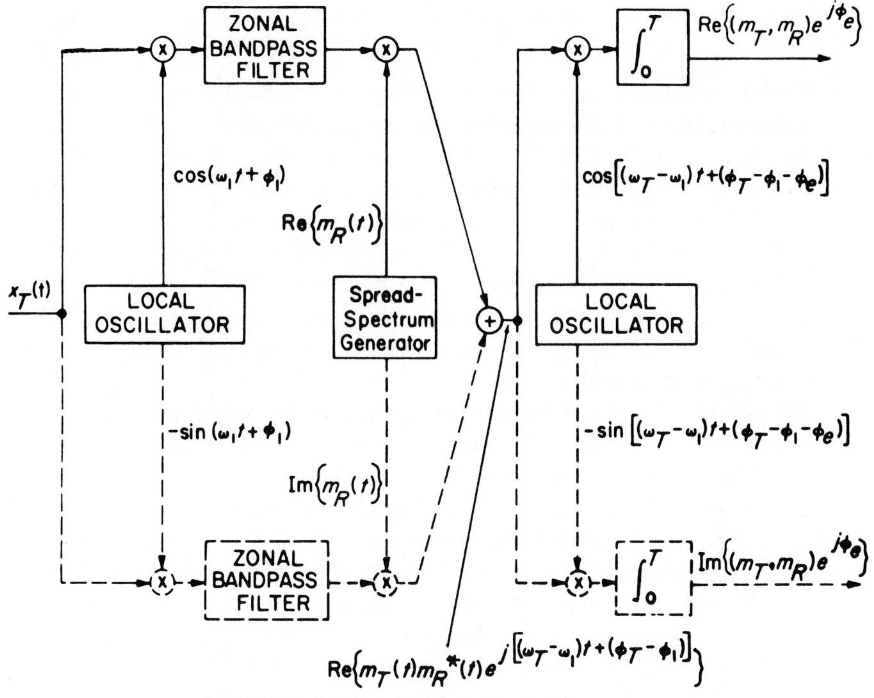

(c) IF Multiplication, Baseband Integration

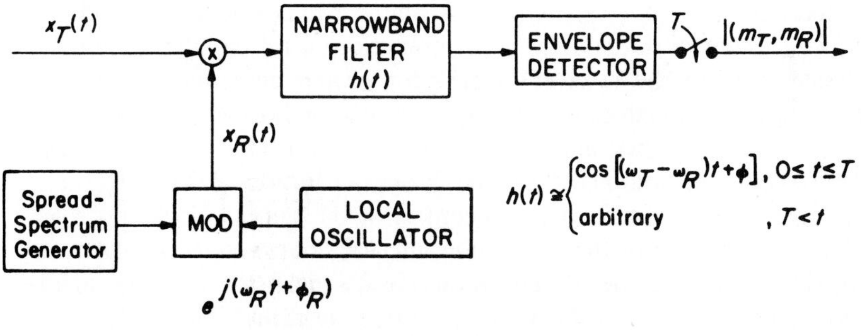

$x_T(t)$
NARROWBAND FILTER $h(t)$
ENVELOPE DETECTOR
T
$|(m_T, m_R)|$
$x_R(t)$
$h(t) \cong \begin{cases} \cos[(\omega_T - \omega_R)t + \phi], & 0 \le t \le T \\ \text{arbitrary}, & T < t \end{cases}$
Spread-Spectrum Generator
MOD
LOCAL OSCILLATOR
$e^{j(\omega_R t + \phi_R)}$

(d) IF Multiplication and Integration
(Bandpass Correlator)

Figure 1.3. *Continued.*

forming the desired inner product. Recovery of $\text{Re}\{(m_T, m_R)\}$ and $\text{Im}\{(m_T, m_R)\}$ requires three levels of synchronization.

1. *Correlation interval synchronization*: Correlators require pulses to indicate when the interval of integration is to begin and when it is to end. In the bandpass correlator of Figure 1.3(d), interval sync not only provides the timing for the sampling operation, but also initializes the narrowband filter's state to zero at the beginning of each correlation interval. Typically, in DS systems these signals correspond to the data symbol clock pulses. In FH systems in which the data symbol time exceeds the hop time, the interval sync pulses must indicate the duration of a single frequency, since correlation operations spanning random phase transitions are not generally useful.
2. *SS generator synchronization*: Timing signals are required to control the epoch of the system's SS waveform generator's output and the rate at which that output is produced. Direct sequence systems employ a clock ticking at the chip rate $1/T_c$ for this purpose, while FH systems have a similar clock operating at the hopping rate $1/T_h$.
3. *Carrier synchronization*: Ideal reduction of the SS signal to baseband in the receiver is possible if a local oscillator (or oscillator network) is available whose output is in frequency and phase synchronism with the received signal's carrier (i.e., $\phi_e = 0$ in Figure 1.3). The above level of carrier sync is often available in DS systems, but usually only frequency synchronism is attained in FH systems.

In some SS systems, the above synchronization signals are derived from a single clock; in others, the carrier local oscillator is independent of the clock signals which control its modulation. Automatic control circuitry generally is included to align the receiver's clocks for proper demodulation of the incoming signal, although some systems have been built in which ultrastable clocks are initially aligned and then are allowed to drift in a free-running mode until communication is concluded. Proper operation of the correlation computing circuits generally requires control of the symbol clock epoch to within a small fraction of the correlation interval's duration T. Similarly, it is necessary to adjust the SS generator clock's ticks to within a small fraction of the reciprocal of the SS modulation's short-term bandwidth, i.e., the bandwidth of the energy spectrum of the SS reference waveform within a correlation interval. Section 1.5.3 will indicate that the SS generator clock error for DS and FH systems must be a small fraction of T_c and T_h, respectively, to maintain correlator operation at nearly maximum output signal levels, as required.

Frequency synchronous operation of correlation detectors requires that the phase drift between the incoming carrier (excluding SS modulation) and the receiver's local oscillator, over a correlation interval, be a fraction of radian, i.e., the quantity ϕ_e in Figure 1.3 may be assumed nearly constant during the correlation computation. (Phase synchronism of the local oscillator requires, in addition, that ϕ_e be near zero.) The bandpass correlator is a frequency synchronous device requiring that the input to its narrowband filter be centered in its passband to an error tolerance of a fraction of the reciprocal of the correlation time.

Output threshold crossing techniques, similar to those used in radar detection, are an alternative to MF output sampling in Figure 1.3(b), and may have higher tolerance to synchronization errors than SR/DS systems. However, any realized tolerance to synchronization errors implies a potential weakness to repeater jamming.

1.4 ENERGY GAIN CALCULATIONS FOR TYPICAL SYSTEMS

The following examples illustrate the energy gain calculation for basic SS systems. In each case, the SS system is viewed (in the terminology of Section 1.2) as replacing an orthogonal communication system complex, and its multiplicity factor K determined, thereby evaluating the energy gain of the system via (1.18).

Example 1.1. Let's examine a SS system using binary (± 1) DS spreading modulation as in (1.22), multiplicative data modulation (1.24), and single-channel phase-synchronous detection (solid line portion of Figure 1.3(a)) over the data symbol duration T_s of N_c chip times, i.e., $T_s = N_c T_c$. Hence, the pseudorandom quantities which are known to the receiver, but unknown to the jammer, are the DS pulse modulation sequence $c_1, c_2, \ldots, c_{N_c}$ and the carrier phase ϕ_T. The inner product of two such waveforms with different pseudorandom variables and data modulations is given by

$$\begin{aligned}
&\int_0^{T_s} \mathrm{Re}\{ dc(t) e^{j(\omega_c t + \phi_T)} \} \mathrm{Re}\Big\{ d'c'(t) e^{j(\omega_c t + \phi'_T)} \Big\}\, dt \\
&\quad = \frac{dd' \cos\big(\phi_T - \phi'_T \big)}{2} \int_0^{T_s} c(t) c'(t)\, dt \\
&\quad = \frac{dd' \cos\big(\phi_T - \phi'_T \big)}{2} \sum_{n=1}^{N_c} c_n c'_n \int_0^{T_c} |p(t)|^2\, dt. \qquad (1.29)
\end{aligned}$$

For any particular choice of $[c_1, \ldots, c_{N_c}]$ and ϕ_T, and regardless of the values of the data modulation d and d', constants over $(0, T_s)$, the two signals are orthogonal if either $\phi_T - \phi'_T = \pi/2$ or $[c'_1, \ldots, c'_{N_c}]$ is orthogonal to $[c_1, \ldots, c_{N_c}]$. Since the set of real N_c-tuples forms an N_c-dimensional space (and furthermore an orthogonal basis of vectors with ± 1 entries can be found when N_c is a multiple of 4), and since carrier phase differences of magnitude $\pi/2$ cause orthogonality, the jammer is forced to view his waveform selection problem as being defined for an orthogonal communication system complex with multiplicity factor K given by

$$K = 2N_c = 2T_s/T_c. \tag{1.30}$$

Example 1.2. Suppose that two independently hopped SS waveforms, $c^{(0)}(t)$ and $c^{(1)}(t)$, of the form (1.20) are employed in a switching modulation scheme as in (1.26) to transmit binary data. The data symbols' duration T_s spans M_D hop times. Frequency-synchronous correlation computations in the receiver are then carried out over individual hop times, and the correlator's sync clock produces a pulse every T_h seconds. The signal parameters, known to the receiver but not to the jammer, are the two pseudorandom hopping sequences $f_{01}, f_{02}, \ldots, f_{0M_D}$ and $f_{11}, f_{12}, \ldots, f_{1M_D}$ which represent the two possible data symbols. Two similar FH waveforms have inner product

$$\begin{aligned}
&\int_0^{T_h} \cos(2\pi(f_c + f_{d1})t + \phi_1)\cos(2\pi(f_c + f_{d'1})t + \phi_1')\,dt \\
&\quad = \frac{1}{2}\int_0^{T_h} \cos(2\pi(f_{d1} - f_{d'1})t + (\phi_1 - \phi_1'))\,dt \\
&\quad = \frac{1}{4\pi(f_{d1} - f_{d'1})}\big[\cos(\phi_1 - \phi_1')\sin(2\pi(f_{d1} - f_{d'1})T_h) \\
&\qquad\qquad + \sin(\phi_1 - \phi_1')(\cos(2\pi(f_{d1} - f_{d'1})T_h) - 1)\big].
\end{aligned} \tag{1.31}$$

Orthogonality between two such waveforms is guaranteed, regardless of the values of the phases (ϕ_1, ϕ_1') and data symbols (d, d'), provided that

$$f_{d1} - f_{d'1} = \frac{k}{T_h} \tag{1.32}$$

where k is any non-zero integer, for all d, d' in $\{0, 1\}$. We assume that two such orthogonal frequency waveforms are used by the communication system as f_{0n} and f_{1n}, with a different pair for each n, $1 \le n \le M_D$.

If the transmitter and receiver are capable of producing and observing M_F distinct orthogonal tones (assume M_F is even for convenience), it is clear that during each hop the jammer must contemplate combatting a pure SS strategy on an orthogonal communication system complex of multiplicity $M_F/2$. Therefore, during each hop time a single link in the orthogonal system complex requires four dedicated orthonormal basis functions (e.g., sines and cosines at two distinct frequencies), and uses $4M_D$ such functions over M_D hops. By the same reasoning the number of basis functions available to the entire complex is $2M_F M_D$, and hence, the energy gain of (1.18) is given by

$$EG = \frac{2M_F M_D}{4M_D} = \frac{M_F}{2}. \tag{1.33}$$

Example 1.3. One possible hybrid SS communication system employs TH, FH, and DS modulations to produce the wideband waveform

$$c^{(d(t))}(t) = \sum_n e^{j(2\pi f_n t + \phi_n)} \sum_{m=1}^{N_c} c_{nmd_n} p\left(t - mT_c - \left(n + \frac{b_n}{M_T}\right)T_s\right) \tag{1.34}$$

in which $p(t)$ is a unit-amplitude rectangular pulse of chip time duration T_c. A total of N_c pulses, modulated by the sequence $\{c_{nmd_n}\}$, are concatenated to produce a DS waveform of duration T_h, which in turn is frequency-hopped to one of M_F frequencies and time-hopped to one of M_T time intervals within the symbol time T_s. Hence,

$$T_s = M_T T_h = M_T N_c T_c. \tag{1.35}$$

Modulation by the n-th M-ary data symbol d_n is accomplished by switching the DS modulation to the d_n-th of M orthogonal vectors $c_{n1d_n}, \ldots, c_{nN_cd_n}$.

Two such hybrid SS signals have inner product given by

$$\begin{aligned}
&\int_0^{T_S} \sum_{m=1}^{N_c} c_{0md_0} p\left(t - mT_c - \frac{b_0}{M_T}T_s\right)\cos(2\pi(f_c + f_0)t + \phi_0) \\
&\quad \times \sum_{m'=1}^{N_c} c'_{0m'd'_0} p\left(t - m'T_c - \frac{b'_0}{M_T}T_s\right)\cos\left(2\pi(f_c + f'_0)t + \phi'_0\right) dt \\
&= \delta_{b_0 - b'_0} \cdot \frac{1}{4\pi(f_0 - f'_0)}\left[\cos(\phi_0 - \phi'_0)\sin\left(2\pi(f_0 - f'_0)T_c\right)\right. \\
&\quad \left. + \sin(\phi_0 - \phi'_0)\left(\cos\left(2\pi(f_0 - f'_0)T_c\right) - 1\right)\right] \sum_{m=1}^{N_c} c_{0md_0} c'_{0md'_0}.
\end{aligned} \tag{1.36}$$

Here δ_z is the Kronecker delta function, which is one if $z = 0$ and is zero otherwise. Orthogonality of these waveforms can be achieved, regardless of the data values (d, d') and random phase values (ϕ_0, ϕ'_0), if one or more of the following conditions holds:

1. $$\sum_{m=1}^{N_c} c_{0md} c'_{0md} = 0, \text{ for all } d, d'. \tag{1.37}$$

2. $$b_0 \neq b'_0. \tag{1.38}$$

3. $$f_0 - f'_0 = \frac{k}{T_c}, \text{ for } k \text{ integer, } k \neq 0. \tag{1.39}$$

The signal variables, known *a priori* to the receiver, but not the jammer, are the pseudorandom DS chip values $\{c_{0md}\colon\ d = 1, 2, \ldots, M, m = 1, 2, \ldots, N_c\}$, the hop frequency f_0, and the time interval index b_0. Hence, the receiver must observe the signal in a $2M$-dimensional space whose basis over the interval $(0, T_s)$ consists of $\mathrm{Re}\{c^{(d)}(t)\exp(j2\pi f_c t)\}$ evaluated for each of the M values of d, with the random hop phase ϕ_0 set at 0 and at $\pi/2$. The jammer, however, must choose his waveform to jam a signal space of dimension $2N_c M_F M_T$, whose basis consists of the sines and cosines of N_c orthogonal *DS* modulations hopped over M_F orthogonal tones and M_T disjoint time intervals. Therefore, the nominal energy gain EG of this system is

$$EG = \frac{N_c M_F M_T}{M}. \tag{1.40}$$

The nominal minimum bandwidth W_{ss} required to implement the orthogonality requirements (1 − 3) is determined by the minimum hop frequency spacing $1/T_c$ to be M_F/T_c. Using this fact and substituting (1.35) into (1.40) indicates that the energy gain for this hybrid SS system in a closely packed design is $T_s W_{ss}/M$.

1.5 THE ADVANTAGES OF SPECTRUM SPREADING

We have seen the advantages of making a jammer counteract an ensemble of orthogonal communication systems. The bandwidth increase which must accompany this SS strategy has further advantages which we will outline here.

1.5.1 Low Probability of Intercept (LPI)

Spectrum spreading complicates the signal detection problem for a surveillance receiver in two ways: (1) a larger frequency band must be monitored, and (2) the power density of the signal to be detected is lowered in the spectrum-spreading process. The signal may have further desirable attributes based in part on LPI, such as low probability of position fix (LPPF) which includes both intercept and direction finding (DFing) in its evaluation, or low probability of signal exploitation (LPSE) which may append additional effects, e.g., source identification.

For now let's simply evaluate the power spectral density (PSD) of an SS signal to determine its general properties. Consider a signal of the form

$$x(t) = \mathrm{Re}\left\{m_T(t)e^{j(2\pi f_c t + \phi_T)}\right\}, \tag{1.41}$$

where $m_T(t)$ represents the total modulation as a result of data and spectrum-spreading effects, and ϕ_T is a random phase variable uniformly distributed on $(-\pi, \pi)$. The PSD $S_x(f)$ of the waveform $x(t)$ is defined as

$$S_x(f) \triangleq \lim_{T\to\infty} \frac{1}{2T}\mathbf{E}\{|\mathbf{F}_{2T}\{x(t)\}|^2\}. \tag{1.42}$$

Here $\mathbf{F}_{2T}$ is the time-limited Fourier transform

$$\mathbf{F}_{2T}\{x(t)\} \triangleq \int_{-T}^{T} x(t)e^{-j2\pi ft}\,dt, \tag{1.43}$$

and hence, $\mathbf{E}\{|\mathbf{F}_{2T}\{x(t)\}|^2\}$ is the average energy spectral density of a $2T$ second signal segment. Conversion of this energy density to a power density is accomplished by division by $2T$, and $S_x(f)$ then is simply the limiting form as T becomes large. Averaging over the random phase ϕ_T leads to the relation

$$S_x(f) = \tfrac{1}{4}[S_m(f-f_c) + S_m(-f-f_c)], \tag{1.44}$$

where $S_m(f)$ is the PSD of the modulation $m_T(t)$. We will now evaluate $S_m(f)$ for two basic SS modulation designs.

1. *DS/BPSK modulation*: The waveform corresponding to a DS signal antipodally modulated by binary data is

$$m_T(t) = \sum_n c_n d_{\lfloor n/N_c \rfloor} p(t - nT_c), \tag{1.45}$$

in which the data value $d_{\lfloor n/N_c \rfloor}$ has the opportunity to change every N_c chip times ($\lfloor x \rfloor$ denotes the integer part of x), and $p(t)$ is a pulse shape which is non-zero only in the interval $(0, T_c)$. The calculation of $S_m(f)$ is simplified by letting the limit parameter T grow in multiples of the symbol time N_cT_c. Hence,

$$S_m(f) = \lim_{K\to\infty} \frac{1}{2KN_cT_c}\mathbf{E}\left\{|\mathbf{F}_{2KN_cT_c}\{m_T(t)\}|^2\right\}. \tag{1.46}$$

By converting the sum index n in (1.45) to $kN_c + m$ where k ranges from $-K$ to $K-1$ and m ranges between 0 and $N_c - 1$, it is possible to show that

$$\mathbf{F}_{2KN_cT_c}\{m_T(t)\} = P(f)\sum_{k=-K}^{K-1} d_k e^{-j2\pi fkN_cT_c} \sum_{m=0}^{N_c-1} c_{kN_c+m} e^{-j2\pi fmT_c}, \tag{1.47}$$

where $P(f)$ is the Fourier transform of the chip pulse $p(t)$. Inserting this transform into (1.46) and ensemble averaging over the data sequence $\{d_k\}$ which we assume to be composed of independent binary random variables, each equally likely to be $+1$ or -1, gives

$$S_m(f) = \lim_{K\to\infty}\frac{1}{2K}\sum_{k=-K}^{K-1}\frac{|P(f)|^2}{T_c} \times \frac{1}{N_c}\mathbf{E}\left\{\left|\sum_{m=0}^{N_c-1} c_{kN_c+m} e^{-j2\pi fmT_c}\right|^2\right\}. \tag{1.48}$$

We consider two possible assumptions regarding the nature of the direct sequence $\{c_n\}$.

a. *Random DS Modulation*: If $\{c_n\}$ is a sequence of independent, identically distributed random variables, each equally likely to be $+1$ or -1, then the ensemble average in (1.48) simplifies to N_c, and

$$S_m(f) = \frac{|P(f)|^2}{T_c}. \tag{1.49}$$

This PSD is sketched in Figure 1.4 for several possible pulse shapes. Note that $1/T_c$ is a rough measure of the widths of these spectra.

b. *Periodic DS Modulation*: When $\{c_n\}$ is generated by a finite state device acting as a pseudorandom number generator, then $\{c_n\}$ must be periodic with some period N, i.e.,

$$c_{n+N} = c_n \quad \text{for all } n. \tag{1.50}$$

Hence, nothing random remains in (1.48) and the expected value operator can be dropped. Furthermore, the value of the sum on m in (1.48) must also be a periodic function of K, with period P_c corre-

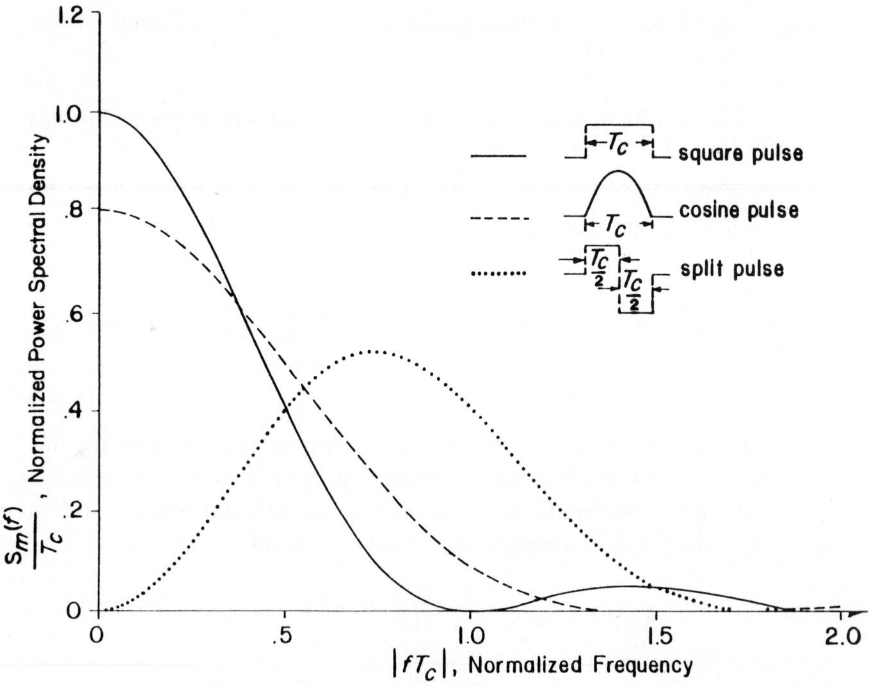

Figure 1.4. The power spectral density of random DS/BPSK modulation for three different chip pulse shapes.

sponding to the smallest value of k such that kN_c is a multiple of N. Hence,

$$P_c = \frac{\mathrm{lcm}(N, N_c)}{N_c}, \tag{1.51}$$

where lcm$(\cdot,\cdot)$ denotes the least common integer multiple of its arguments, and

$$S_m(f) = \frac{|P(f)|^2}{T_c} \times \frac{1}{P_c}\sum_{k=0}^{P_c-1}\frac{1}{N_c}\left|\sum_{m=0}^{N_c-1} c_{kN_c+m}e^{-j2\pi fmT_c}\right|^2. \tag{1.52}$$

When $P_c = N$, then (1.52) can be simplified still further by taking the k-sum inside the two sums of the squared absolute value, to give,

$$S_m(f) = \frac{|P(f)|^2}{NN_cT_c}\sum_{m=0}^{N_c-1}\sum_{m'=0}^{N_c-1} R_c(m-m')e^{-j2\pi f(m-m')T_c}, \tag{1.53}$$

where $R_c(\cdot)$ is the periodic autocorrelation function of the sequence $\{c_n\}$, i.e.,

$$R_c(k) \triangleq \sum_{m=0}^{N-1} c_{m+k}c_m = \sum_{m=0}^{N-1} c_{mN_c+k}c_{mN_c}. \tag{1.54}$$

The latter sum in (1.54) is the periodic correlation function of the sequence $\{c_{mN_c}\}$ which is called the *decimation* of $\{c_m\}$ by N_c. Such decimations preserve the periodic autocorrelation properties of the sequence when the greatest common divisor of N and N_c is unity. Summing like terms in (1.53) and using the symmetry of $R_c(k)$ gives

$$S_m(f) = \frac{|P(f)|^2}{T_c} \times \frac{1}{N}\left[R_c(0) + 2\sum_{k=1}^{N_c-1} R_c(k)\left(1-\frac{k}{N_c}\right)\cos(2\pi fkT_c)\right]. \tag{1.55}$$

Since $\{c_n\}$ is composed of ± 1 elements, then $R_c(0) = N$, and this PSD is identical to that of random DS modulation provided that $R_c(k) = 0$ for $k = 1, 2, \ldots, N_c - 1$. This latter condition is one reasonable objective for pseudorandom number generator design.

2. *FH/FSK modulation*: The use of M-ary data, frequency-shift-keyed onto an FH signal at a rate of M_D hops per data symbol, creates the modulation

$$m_T(t) = \sum_n e^{j[2\pi(f_n + d_{\lfloor n/M_D\rfloor})t + \phi_n]}p(t - nT_h), \tag{1.56}$$

where $p(t)$ is a hop pulse waveform which is non-zero only in the interval $(0, T_h)$, $\{f_n\}$ is the sequence of frequency hop values, $\{d_k\}$ is the data sequence, and $\{\phi_n\}$ is a sequence of independent, uniformly distributed, random phase variables.

In calculating $S_m(f)$ using the approach in (1.42) we will take the limit as the integer $K = T/T_h$ becomes large. Hence,

$$S_m(f) = \lim_{K\to\infty} \frac{1}{2KT_h} \mathbf{E}\{|\mathbf{F}_{2KT_h}\{m_T(t)\}|^2\}. \tag{1.57}$$

The required Fourier transform is given by

$$\mathbf{F}_{2KT_h}\{m_T(t)\} = \sum_{n=-K}^{K-1} e^{j\phi_n}\mathbf{F}\{e^{j2\pi(f_n + d_{\lfloor n/M_D \rfloor})t}p(t - nT_h)\} \tag{1.58}$$

where $\mathbf{F}$ denotes the ordinary Fourier transform. Evaluating the transform in (1.58), substituting in (1.57), and averaging over the random phase sequence, gives

$$S_m(f) = \lim_{K\to\infty} \frac{1}{2KT_h} \sum_{n=-K}^{K-1} \mathbf{E}\{|P(f - f_n - d_{\lfloor n/M_D \rfloor})|^2\}, \tag{1.59}$$

where $P(f)$ is the transform of the hop pulse. Assuming that the data sequence elements are independent, identically distributed random variables chosen from the set $\mathscr{D}$ with probability function $P_D(\cdot)$, gives

$$S_m(f) = \sum_{d\in\mathscr{D}} P_D(d) \lim_{K\to\infty} \frac{1}{2KT_h} \sum_{n=-K}^{K-1} \mathbf{E}\{|P(f - f_n - d)|^2\}. \tag{1.60}$$

We now consider two models for the hopping sequence.

a. *Random Hopping*. When $\{f_n\}$ is a sequence of identically distributed random variables with values selected from a frequency set $\mathscr{F}$ according to a probability distribution function $P_F(\cdot)$, then

$$S_m(f) = \frac{1}{T_h} \sum_{d\in\mathscr{D}} \sum_{f'\in\mathscr{F}} P_D(d)P_F(f')|P(f - f' - d)|^2. \tag{1.61}$$

b. *Periodic Hopping*. If $\{f_n\}$ is sequence of frequencies with period N, generated by a finite state machine, and if $N_{f'}$ denotes the number of occurrences of the frequency value f' in one sequence period, then

$$S_m(f) = \frac{1}{T_h} \sum_{d\in\mathscr{D}} \sum_{f'\in\mathscr{F}} P_D(d)\frac{N_{f'}}{N}|P(f - f' - d)|^2. \tag{1.62}$$

Notice that the PSD of the deterministically generated sequence will match that of the randomly generated sequence with $P_F(f) = N_f/N$. Furthermore, the number of hops M_D spanned by a data symbol is not a factor in the spectral density of the resultant signal in either case.

A rough measure of the hop pulse transform's width is $1/T_h$. Since integer multiples of $1/T_h$ are required for orthogonal randomly phased tones of duration T_h, the assumption that the radiated tones $d + f$, $f \in \mathscr{F}$ and $d \in \mathscr{D}$, are orthogonal leads to the conclusion that the minimum required bandwidth is approximately MM_F/T_h, $|\mathscr{F}| = M_F$, $|\mathscr{D}| = M$.

The PSDs which we have just calculated correspond to asymptotically long-term ensemble-averaged, time-normalized, energy spectra. Attempts at interception of these signals in reality will be made over short time intervals, usually much shorter than the periods of the pseudorandom number generators driving the SS waveform generator. Hence, signals with comparable PSDs may have differing short-term energy density characteristics, and hence, different LPI capabilities.

1.5.2 Independent Interference Rejection and Multiple-Access Operation

We have already discussed the energy gain achievable against a jammer whose radiated signal is generated without knowledge of the key parameters used in generating the SS transmitter's modulation. We refer to this type of interference as *independent*, the connotation also applying to in-band interference from other friendly communication systems.

The ability of a SS system to reject independent interference is the basis for the multiple-access capability of SS systems, so called because several SS systems can operate in the same frequency band, each rejecting the interference produced by the others by a factor approximately equal to its energy gain. This asynchronous form of spectrum sharing is often called *spread-spectrum multiple-access* (SSMA) or *code-division multiple-access* (CDMA).

As an illustration of SSMA operation, consider a transmitted signal $x_T(t)$,

$$x_T(t) = \mathrm{Re}\left\{\sqrt{P_T}\, m_T(t) e^{j(2\pi f_c t + \phi_T)}\right\}, \tag{1.63}$$

and an interfering signal $x_t(t)$,

$$x_I(t) = \mathrm{Re}\left\{\sqrt{P_I}\, m_I(t - t_I) e^{j(2\pi(f_c + \Delta)t + \phi_I)}\right\}, \tag{1.64}$$

impinging on a receiver which is frequency synchronous with the transmitted signal and which computes the inner product of the received signal with a reference modulation $m_R(t)$. We assume without loss of generality that $m_T(t)$, $m_I(t)$, and $m_R(t)$ are unit power waveforms, i.e., the time-averaged and ensemble-averaged value of $|m_j(t)|^2$ is one for $j = T, I, R$. The output of the receiver correlator is the sum of two terms, corresponding to the desired inner product $\sqrt{P_T}\, v_T$ and the interference inner product $\sqrt{P_I}\, v_I$. These terms for the k-th correlation interval $((k-1)T, kT)$, normalized to unit input power, are

$$v_T(k) = (m_T, m_R) = \int_{(k-1)T}^{kT} m_T(t) m_R^*(t)\, dt \cdot e^{j\phi_e}, \tag{1.65}$$

$$v_I(k) = (m_I, m_R) = \int_{(k-t)T}^{kT} m_I(t - t_I) m_R^*(t) e^{j2\pi\Delta t}\, dt\, e^{j(\phi_I - \phi_T + \phi_e)}, \tag{1.66}$$

where ϕ_e is the phase tracking error in the receiver (see Figure 1.3), and Δ is the carrier frequency offset between the interference and the transmitted signal. The average signal-to-interference energy at the input to the correlator is simply

$$\mathrm{SIR}_{\mathrm{in}} \triangleq \frac{\left\langle \mathbf{E}\left\{ P_T \int_{(k-1)T}^{kT} |m_T(t)|^2\, dt \right\}\right\rangle}{\left\langle \mathbf{E}\left\{ P_I \int_{(k-1)T}^{kT} |m_I(t)|^2\, dt \right\}\right\rangle} = \frac{P_T}{P_I}, \tag{1.67}$$

and the frequency-synchronous correlator's output signal-to-interference measurement ratio is

$$\mathrm{SIR}_{\mathrm{out(freq\ sync)}} = \frac{\langle \mathbf{E}\{ |v_T(k)|^2 \}\rangle}{\langle \mathbf{E}\{ |v_I(k)|^2 \}\rangle} \cdot \mathrm{SIR}_{\mathrm{in}}. \tag{1.68}$$

Here $\langle \cdot \rangle$ denotes discrete time averaging over the parameter k.

The above calculation is based on the supposition that outputs from both the in-phase and quadrature channels of the correlator are necessary, i.e., both the real and imaginary parts of $v_T(k)$ are necessary in the reception process. If instead reception is phase-synchronous, then $v_T(k)$ is real, and on the average only half of the interference power contributes to the disturbance of $\mathrm{Re}\{v_T(k)\}$. Hence, for phase-synchronous detection,

$$\mathrm{SIR}_{\mathrm{out}(\phi\ \mathrm{sync})} = 2 \cdot \mathrm{SIR}_{\mathrm{out(freq\ sync)}}. \tag{1.69}$$

The key to further analysis is the evaluation of the interference level at the correlator output.

$$\mathbf{E}\{ |v_I(k)|^2 \} = \mathbf{E}\left\{ \iint_{(k-1)T}^{kT} m_I(t - t_I) m_I^*(t' - t_I) e^{j2\pi\Delta(t-t')} \times m_R^*(t) m_R(t')\, dt\, dt' \right\}. \tag{1.70}$$

The variable t_I denotes an arbitrary time shift of the interference modulation relative to the reference modulation, this shift being inserted to model the fact that the interference is assumed asynchronous with respect to all clocks generating the transmitted signal. Stored reference modulations (e.g., $m_I(t)$ if the interference is SSMA in nature) are generally *cyclo-stationary*, i.e., they may be made stationary by inserting a time-shift random variable (e.g., t_I) which is uniformly distributed on a finite interval. Hence, we assume that t_I is uniformly distributed on a finite interval which makes $m_I(t - t_I)$ a wide-sense stationary random process. This assumption and the further assumption that any random variables in $m_I(t)$ are independent of any in $m_R(t)$, effectively allow us to treat asynchronous multiple-access interference and jamming identically in average power calculations.

Averaging (1.70) over t_I gives

$$\mathbf{E}\{|v_I(k)|^2\} = \iint_{(k-1)T}^{kT} R_I(t-t')e^{j2\pi\Delta(t-t')}\mathbf{E}\{m_R^*(t)m_R(t')\}\,dt\,dt'$$

$$= \int_{-\infty}^{\infty} S_I(f-\Delta)\mathbf{E}\{|M_{Rk}(f)|^2\}\,df, \tag{1.71}$$

where $R_I(\cdot)$ and $S_I(\cdot)$ are the autocorrelation function and PSD respectively of the unit power process $m_I(t-t_I)$. That is,

$$R_I(\tau) = \mathbf{E}\{m_I(t+\tau-t_I)m_I^*(t-t_I)\} = \int_{-\infty}^{\infty} S_I(f)e^{j2\pi f\tau}\,df, \tag{1.72}$$

and $M_{Rk}(f)$ is the Fourier transform of the reference modulation $m_R(t)$ in the k-th correlation interval.

$$M_{Rk}(f) = \int_{(k-1)T}^{kT} m_R(t)e^{-j2\pi ft}\,dt. \tag{1.73}$$

Certainly when the correlation time T is not a multiple of the reference modulation generator's period (and this must be the case to avoid problems with simple repeater jammers), then $|M_{Rk}(f)|^2$ will vary with k.

Using the fact that the modulation forms are normalized to unit energy, and combining (1.65)–(1.68) and (1.71), demonstrates that the improvement in signal-to-interference ratio achieved in the correlation calculation is

$$\frac{\mathrm{SIR}_{\text{out(freq sync)}}}{\mathrm{SIR}_{\text{in}}} = \frac{\left\langle \mathbf{E}\left\{\left|\int_{(k-1)T}^{kT} m_T(t)m_R^*(t)\,dt\right|^2\right\}\right\rangle}{\int_{-\infty}^{\infty} S_I(f-\Delta)\langle\mathbf{E}\{|M_{Rk}(f)|^2\}\rangle\,df}. \tag{1.74}$$

Again we emphasize that (1.74) applies both to asynchronous multiple-access interference and independent jamming.

Example 1.4. Suppose that a DS/BPSK communication system employs binary antipodal modulation and phase coherent reception over a symbol time T_s. Hence, in the k-th correlation interval, $m_T(t)$ in (1.45) is equal to $c(t)$ or $-c(t)$, and reception is performed by correlating the received signal with $c(t)$ as given in (1.22). Then,

$$M_{Rk}(f) = \mathbf{F}\left\{\sum_{n=(k-1)N_c}^{kN_c-1} c_n p(t-nT_c)\right\}$$

$$= P(f)\sum_{n=(k-1)N_c}^{kN_c-1} c_n e^{-j2\pi fnT_c}, \tag{1.75}$$

where again N_c denotes the number of chips per data bit, $\mathbf{F}$ denotes the Fourier transform operation, and $P(f)$ is the Fourier transform of the chip pulse $p(t)$. Denoting the period of $\{c_n\}$ by N and time-averaging the squared magnitude of $M_{Rk}(f)$ over k gives

$$\langle |M_{Rk}(f)|^2 \rangle = \frac{1}{P_c} \sum_{k=0}^{P_c-1} |M_{Rk}(f)|^2$$

$$= T_s S_m(f), \qquad (1.76)$$

where P_c is defined in (1.51) and $S_m(f)$ is given by (1.52). This result can be verified analytically, despite the fact that $S_m(f)$ is the PSD of the data-modulated waveform $m_T(t)$ while (1.76) represents an average of short-term energy spectra of $m_R(t)$. However, this result is reasonable because averaging over the zero-mean independent data symbols, which leads to the result (1.52), breaks up the PSD calculation into a time average of short-term energy spectra.

The SIR improvement ratio for a DS/BPSK system is determined by substituting (1.76) into (1.74) and using the fact that $m_T(t) = dm_R(t)$ in a correlation interval.

$$\frac{\text{SIR}_{\text{out}(\phi\text{ sync})}}{\text{SIR}_{\text{in}}} = 2\left[\frac{1}{T_s}\int_{-\infty}^{\infty} S_I(f-\Delta) S_m(f)\, df\right]^{-1}. \qquad (1.77)$$

Since both $S_I(f)$ and $S_m(f)$ have fixed areas and are non-negative, the worst-case interference PSD $S_I(f-\Delta)$ in (1.77) is a Dirac delta function located at the frequency which maximizes $S_m(f)$. Therefore,

$$\frac{\text{SIR}_{\text{out(freq sync)}}}{\text{SIR}_{\text{in}}} \geq 2\left[\frac{1}{T_s}\max_f S_m(f)\right]^{-1}. \qquad (1.78)$$

A well-designed spreading sequence $\{c_n\}$ should result in a PSD $S_m(f)$ close to that of a purely random sequence, namely $|P(f)|^2/T_c$. In keeping with our power normalizations, let's assume that

$$p(t) = \begin{cases} 1, & 0 \leq t < T_c \\ 0, & \text{otherwise} \end{cases} \qquad |P(f)| = \left|\frac{\sin(\pi f T_c)}{\pi f}\right|, \qquad (1.79)$$

and hence, $\max_f |P(f)| = T_c$. Therefore, a well-designed spreading sequence has $\max_f S_m(f) = T_c$, and from (1.78)

$$\frac{\text{SIR}_{\text{out}(\phi\text{ sync})}}{\text{SIR}_{\text{in}}} \geq \frac{2T_s}{T_c} = 2N_c. \qquad (1.80)$$

This lower bound on signal-to-interference ratio improvement is the energy gain indicated in Example 1.1.

When the interference is spectrally similar to the transmitted signal, e.g., in the SSMA case, and both signals possess the spectra of a purely random binary sequence modulated on rectangular chip pulses (1.79), then

$$\frac{\mathrm{SIR}_{\mathrm{out}(\phi\,\mathrm{sync})}}{\mathrm{SIR}_{\mathrm{in}}} = 2\left[\frac{1}{T_s}\int_{-\infty}^{\infty} S_m^2(f)\,df\right]^{-1}$$

$$= 2\left[\frac{1}{T_s T_c^2}\int_{-\infty}^{\infty} |P(f)|^4\,df\right]^{-1} = 3N_c. \qquad (1.81)$$

The above example illustrates the following points concerning SIR improvement calculations based on long-term energy averages:

1. The jammer can minimize the signal-to-interference ratio by transmitting a single tone at the frequency of the transmitter spectrum's peak. However, this is not the best jamming strategy if the receiver has an additional notch filtering capability, or if the designer is interested in the more significant bit-error-rate (BER) design criterion.
2. The above SIR improvement calculation is valid even if $m_I(t) = m_T(t)$, randomization by time shift t_I being enough to make $m_T(t - t_I)$ and $m_T(t)$ quite distinct on the average. This suggests that several systems could use identical SS waveforms, provided the probability that they arrive in near synchronism at a receiver (for any reason, natural or jam-motivated) is virtually zero.
3. Cross-correlation functions and cross-spectra between asynchronous interference and desired signal are not a specific factor in the signal-to-interference ratio improvement based on long-term averages.

Clearly the use of long-term averages in a SIR-based figure-of-merit has led to these simple results.

Similar results can be achieved for other forms of SS modulation. The DS example was particularly simple because the receiver used only one correlator. Corresponding analyses of SS systems using higher dimensional signal sets, e.g., FH/FSK, must consider the total signal energy and total interference energy collected in a set of correlators.

1.5.3 High-Resolution Time-of-Arrival (TOA) Measurements

Not all interference waveforms satisfy the independence and randomly asynchronous assumptions used in Section 1.5.2 to reaffirm the energy gain capability of SS systems. Here are some examples which are illustrated pictorially in Figure 1.5.

1. *Multipath*: Additional propagation paths from transmitter to receiver may produce undesirable interference in a correlator synchronized to a signal arriving via a specified path. For example, a single additional path may produce an interfering signal of the form (1.64) with

$$m_I(t) = m_T(t), \qquad (1.82)$$

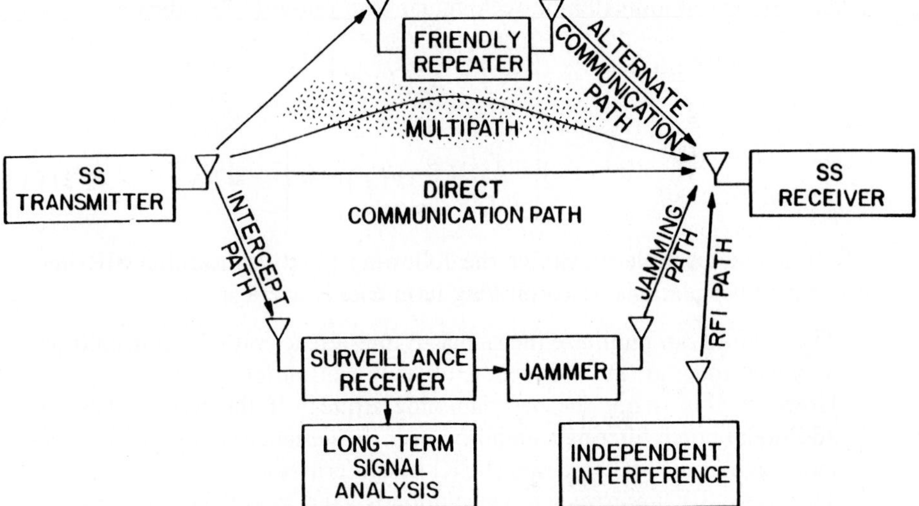

Figure 1.5. A scenario for SS link operation.

at a fixed delay t_I corresponding to the incremental propagation delay between the interference path and the communication signal path.

2. *Repeater Jamming*: This is a form of artificial multipath, in which the jammer attempts to receive the SS signal, somehow alter the data modulation, and then broadcast the result. Hence, if the modulation is multiplicatively changed, then the signal retransmitted by the jammer may be of the form (1.64) with

$$m_I(t) = d'(t)m_T(t). \tag{1.83}$$

In this case, t_I corresponds to the additional propagation delay encountered over the propagation path through the surveillance/jamming system.

In both of these cases, the time shift parameter t_I and frequency offset Δ of (1.64) are nearly constant or slowly varying over restricted ranges. The interference's incremental delay t_I is a positive quantity when a direct natural propagation path is used for communication. On the other hand, communication via a friendly repeater or an indirect path may result in a negative value for t_I.

The average response of a correlation detector to the above types of signal-related interference can be determined by evaluating (1.66) or (1.71), e.g.,

$$\langle \mathbf{E}\{|v_I(k)|^2\}\rangle = \left\langle \mathbf{E}\left\{\left|\int_{(k-1)T}^{kT} m_I(t-t_I)m_R^*(t)e^{j2\pi\Delta t}\,dt\right|^2\right\}\right\rangle. \tag{1.84}$$

Here it is assumed that the receiver's correlator reference signal $m_R(t)$ is synchronized to the signal arriving via the communication path, and that t_I and Δ are the incremental time and frequency shifts incurred by the interference signal during the k-th correlation interval. At this point, we must depart from the analysis of the previous section, because t_I is fixed within a limited range in this interference scenario and cannot be used as an averaging variable.

The shape of $\langle \mathbf{E}\{|v_I(k)|^2\}\rangle$ as a function of t_I and Δ will indicate the time and frequency *resolution* capability of the SS signal structure, i.e., the ability of the receiver's correlation detector to discriminate against versions of the transmitted signal which do not arrive in synchronism with the receiver's clocks. The mean-squared value of the integral in (1.84) is the *cross-ambiguity function* of the waveforms $m_I(t)$ and $m_R(t)$ at offsets t_I and Δ, and hence, we are embarking on a study of the time- and ensemble-averaged ambiguity function provided by an SS waveform/modulation system. The theory of auto-ambiguity functions (i.e., $m_I(t) = m_R(t)$) states that the time-width of the function's central and largest peak at $t_I = 0$ and $\Delta = 0$ is inversely proportional to the rms bandwidth of the signal upon which the correlator acts. Hence, one might expect under certain conditions that SS receivers are especially sensitive to synchronization errors, and possess high time-of-arrival (TOA) resolution capabilities.

The evaluation of (1.84) for repeater modulation of the form (1.83), under the assumption that the added modulation $d'(t)$ is an independent stationary random process, yields

$$\begin{aligned}\langle \mathbf{E}\{|v_{RJ}(k)|^2\}\rangle &= \Big\langle \mathbf{E}\Big\{\iint_{(k-1)T}^{kT} R_{d'}(t-t')e^{j2\pi\Delta(t-t')} \\ &\qquad \times m_T(t-t_I)m_R^*(t)m_T^*(t'-t_I)m_R(t')\,dt\,dt'\Big\}\Big\rangle \\ &= \int_{-\infty}^{\infty} S_{d'}(f)\langle \mathbf{E}\{|v_M(k)|^2\}\rangle df \qquad (1.85)\end{aligned}$$

where $R_{d'}(\cdot)$ and $S_{d'}(\cdot)$ are the autocorrelation function and PSD, respectively, of $d'(t)$; $v_{RJ}(k)$ and $v_M(k)$ are the values of $v_I(k)$ for repeater jamming (1.83) and multipath (1.84) respectively, and

$$|v_M(k)|^2 = \left|\int_{(k-1)T}^{kT} m_T(t-t_I)m_R^*(t)e^{j2\pi(f+\Delta)t}\,dt\right|^2. \qquad (1.86)$$

Henceforth, for simplicity we set

$$\nu \triangleq f + \Delta. \qquad (1.87)$$

Equation (1.85) indicates that the effect of the jammer's added modulation $d'(t)$ is to average an equivalent multipath interference measure $\langle \mathbf{E}\{|v_M(k)|^2\}\rangle$ at offsets t_I and $f+\Delta$ over f (weighted by $S_{d'}(f)$) to determine the repeater jamming measure $\langle \mathbf{E}\{|v_{RJ}(k)|^2\}\rangle$.

We will now evaluate the multipath interference measure for two basic SS waveform designs.

1. *DS/BPSK modulation*: In this case $m_T(t)$ is given by (1.45) and $m_R(t)$ is simply the SS code $c(t)$ in (1.22). Breaking up the integral over the data symbol interval of duration $T = T_s$ in (1.86) into a sum of integrals over the chip intervals of $m_R(t)$, gives

$$|v_M(k)|^2 = \left| \sum_{n=(k-1)N_c}^{kN_c-1} \sum_{m=-\infty}^{\infty} d_{\lfloor m/N_c \rfloor} c_m c_n \times \int_{nT_c}^{(n+1)T_c} p(t - t_I - mT_c) p^*(t - nT_c) \cdot e^{j2\pi\nu t}\, dt \right|^2. \quad (1.88)$$

The integral in (1.88) can be simplified by using the fact that the pulse shape $p(t)$ is non-zero only in $(0, T_c)$ and by defining the quantities N_I (and integer) and τ_I to satisfy

$$-t_I = N_I T_c + \tau_I, \qquad 0 \le \tau_I < T_c. \quad (1.89)$$

Then

$$\int_{nT_c}^{(n+1)T_c} p(t - t_I - mT_c) p^*(t - nT_c) e^{j2\pi\nu t}\, dt$$

$$= \begin{cases} X_p(\tau_I, \nu; T_c) e^{j2\pi\nu n T_c}, \\ \quad \text{for } m = N_I + n \\ X_p(\tau_I - T_c, \nu; T_c) e^{j2\pi\nu n T_c}, \\ \quad \text{for } m = N_I + n + 1 \\ 0, \text{ otherwise} \end{cases} \quad (1.90)$$

where $X_p(\tau, \nu; T)$ is the ambiguity function of the pulse waveform $p(t)$ generally defined as

$$X_p(\tau, \nu; T) = \int_0^T p(t + \tau) p^*(t) e^{j2\pi\nu t}\, dt \quad (1.91)$$

for pulse waveforms $p(t)$ non-zero only in the time interval $(0, T)$. The limited values of m which produce non-zero results in (1.90) further simplify (1.88) to

$$|v_M(k)|^2 = \left| \sum_{n=(k-1)N_c}^{kN_c-1} e^{j2\pi\nu n T_c} \Big[d_{\lfloor (N_I+n)/N_c \rfloor} c_{N_I+n} c_n X_p(\tau_I, \nu; T_c) + d_{\lfloor (N_I+n+1)/N_c \rfloor} c_{N_I+n+1} c_n X_p(\tau_I - T_c, \nu; T_c) \Big] \right|^2. \quad (1.92)$$

Equation (1.92) is a convenient starting point for time and ensemble averaging operations.

We will carry out the ensemble-averaging process under the assumption that the spectrum-spreading sequence $\{c_n\}$ is composed of independent, identically distributed random variables, equally likely to be $+1$ or -1, and that the independent data sequence $\{d_k\}$ likewise, is composed solely of $+1$'s and -1's. The expansion of (1.92) then requires the moments

$$\mathbf{E}\{d_{\lfloor (N+m)/N_c \rfloor} d_{\lfloor (N+n)/N_c \rfloor} c_{N+m} c_m c_{N+n} c_n\} = \begin{cases} 1 & \text{if } N = 0 \\ 1 & \text{if } N \neq 0,\ n = m \\ 0 & \text{otherwise} \end{cases} \tag{1.93}$$

$$\mathbf{E}\{d_{\lfloor (N+m)/N_c \rfloor} d_{\lfloor (N+n+1)/N_c \rfloor} c_{N+m} c_m c_{N+n+1} c_n\} = 0 \text{ for all } N, m, n, \tag{1.94}$$

and the fact that

$$\left| \sum_{n=(k-1)N_c}^{kN_c - 1} e^{j2\pi \nu n T_c} \right|^2 = \left| \frac{\sin(\pi \nu T_s)}{\sin(\pi \nu T_c)} \right|^2. \tag{1.95}$$

Expanding the squared sum in (1.92) as a double sum and simplifying, gives

$$\mathbf{E}\{|v_M(k)|^2\} = \begin{cases} \left| \dfrac{\sin(\pi \nu T_s)}{\sin(\pi \nu T_c)} \right|^2 |X_p(\tau_I, \nu; T_c)|^2 + N_c |X_p(\tau_I - T_c, \nu; T_c)|^2, \\ \qquad \text{for } N_I = 0, \\ \left| \dfrac{\sin(\pi \nu T_s)}{\sin(\pi \nu T_c)} \right|^2 |X_p(\tau_I - T_c, \nu; T_c)|^2 + N_c |X_p(\tau_I, \nu; T_c)|^2, \\ \qquad \text{for } N_I = -1, \\ N_c\left[|X_p(\tau_I, \nu; T_c)|^2 + |X_p(\tau_I - T_c, \nu; T_c)|^2 \right], \\ \qquad \text{otherwise.} \end{cases} \tag{1.96}$$

Because of the manner in which we modelled $\{c_n\}$ and $\{d_k\}$, the above mean-squared value of $v_M(k)$ is not a function of k, and hence, no further averaging is necessary.

When the chip pulse $p(t)$ is unit amplitude and rectangular in shape, with duration T, then

$$|X_p(\tau, \nu; T_c)|^2 = \begin{cases} \left| \dfrac{\sin[\pi \nu (T - |\tau|)]}{\pi \nu} \right|^2, & |\tau| < T \\ 0, \text{ otherwise.} \end{cases} \tag{1.97}$$

With the aid of (1.89) and (1.97), the average ambiguity surface (1.96) can be evaluated as a function of t_I and ν, and the results are displayed in Figure 1.6 for the case $N_c = 100$.

When there is no time or frequency mismatch, i.e., when $t_I = 0$ and $\nu = 0$, then the normalized detector output (1.96) is $N_c^2 T_c^2$. Alternatively, when $|t_I| \geq T_c$, then (1.96) is upper-bounded by $N_c T_c^2$. Hence, multipath and repeater jamming are reduced by a factor $1/N_c$ when the interference's incremental delay exceeds a chip time. This is a firm basis for stating that the TOA resolution of a high energy gain DS/BPSK system is approximately one chip time.

2. *FH/FSK modulation*: When FH signalling of the form (1.56) is employed, a correlator set to detect the data frequency d_R correlates the received signal with the reference

$$m_R(t) = \sum_n e^{j[2\pi(f_n + d_R)t + \phi'_n]} p(t - nT_h). \tag{1.98}$$

where $p(t)$ is a hop pulse of duration T_h which is non-zero only on $(0, T_h)$, and $\{\phi'_n\}$ is a sequence of uniformly distributed phase variables. The correlator resets every hop interval, i.e., $T = T_h$, and the squared

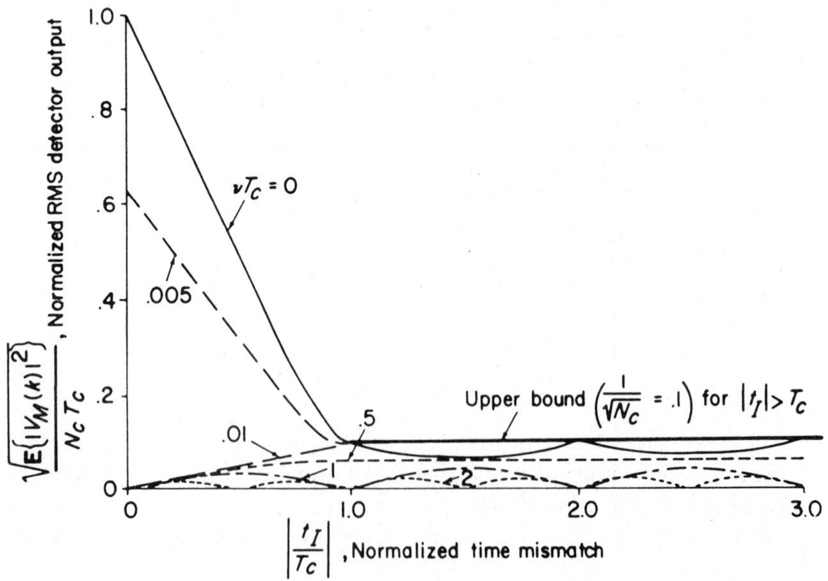

Figure 1.6. Normalized RMS detector output as a function of normalized time mismatch t_I/T_c for several values of normalized frequency mismatch νT_c. Random DS modulation is assumed, with an energy gain of $N_c = 100$ and square chip pulses.

k-th correlator output (1.86) is

$$|v_M(k)|^2 = \left| \int_{(k-1)T_h}^{kT_h} \sum_m e^{j[2\pi(f_m + d_{\lfloor m/M_D \rfloor})(t-t_I)+\phi_m]} p(t - t_I - mT_h) \right.$$
$$\left. \times e^{-j[2\pi(f_{k-1}+d_R)t+\phi'_{k-1}]} p^*(t-(k-1)T_h) e^{j2\pi\nu t}\, dt \right|^2 . \quad (1.99)$$

Only two terms in the sum over m contribute to the value of $|v_M(k)|^2$ for a given k. Defining the integer N_I and τ_I to satisfy

$$-t_I = N_I T_h + \tau_I, \qquad 0 \le \tau_I < T_h, \quad (1.100)$$

and using techniques similar to those seen earlier, result in

$$|v_M(k)|^2 = |e^{j\theta} X_p\big(\tau_I, f_{N_I+k-1} + d_{\lfloor (N_I+k-1)/M_D \rfloor} - f_{k-1} - d_R + \nu; T_h\big)$$
$$+ e^{j\theta'} X_p\big(\tau_I - T_h, f_{N_I+k} + d_{\lfloor (N_I+k)/M_D \rfloor}$$
$$- f_{k-1} - d_R + \nu; T_h\big)|^2, \quad (1.101)$$

where θ and θ' are independent, uniformly distributed phase variables, and $X_p(\cdot, \cdot; \cdot)$ is defined by (1.91).

We continue on the assumption that $\{f_n\}$ is a sequence of random variables, each chosen from a set $\mathscr{F}$ of possible frequencies according to the probability distribution $P_F(\cdot)$. Averaging over θ, θ', and $\{f_n\}$ in (1.101), produces a variety of expressions depending on the values of N and the data-induced frequency shifts. For simplicity, we assume that all the involved data variables are equal. Ensemble-averaging (1.101) produces

$$\mathbf{E}\{|v_M(k)|^2\} = \begin{cases} |X_p(\tau_I, \nu; T_h)|^2 + \overline{|X_p(\tau_I - T_h, \nu; T_h)|^2}, & N_I = 0 \\ |X_p(\tau_I - T_h, \nu; T_h)|^2 + \overline{|X_p(\tau_I, \nu; T_h)|^2}, & N_I = -1 \\ \overline{|X_p(\tau_I, \nu; T_h)|^2} + \overline{|X_p(\tau_I - T_h, \nu; T_h)|^2}, & \text{otherwise} \end{cases} \quad (1.102)$$

for $d_R = d_{\lfloor (N_I+k-1)/M_D \rfloor} = d_{\lfloor (N_I+k)/M_D \rfloor}$, where

$$\overline{|X_p(\tau, \nu; T_h)|^2} \triangleq \sum_{f' \in \mathscr{F}} \sum_{f'' \in \mathscr{F}} P_F(f') P_F(f'') |X_p(\tau, f' + f'' + \nu; T_h)|^2. \quad (1.103)$$

We will use (1.102) as a basis for evaluating the TOA resolution capability of FH signals.

Before proceeding, we will develop a useful upper bound on (1.103). For this purpose we assume that $\mathscr{F}$ is composed of M_F frequencies, equally likely and uniformly spaced $1/T_h$ Hz apart (the minimum spacing required for orthogonality over a hop time). For this calculation's purposes, this assumption is conservative in the sense that the hop frequencies in an operational system may be further apart to support FSK data and maintain the orthogonality of all possible waveforms. Assuming that the pulse shape is rectangular, the corresponding ambiguity function (1.97) can be overbounded by

$$|X_p(\tau, \nu; T_h)|^2 \leq \begin{cases} T_h^2, & \nu < \dfrac{1}{\pi T_h}, \\ \left(\dfrac{1}{\pi \nu}\right)^2, & \nu \geq \dfrac{1}{\pi T_h}. \end{cases} \tag{1.104}$$

Now define the integer k_0 such that

$$\left|\frac{k_0}{T_h} + \nu\right| = \min_k \left|\frac{k}{T_h} + \nu\right| \tag{1.105}$$

or equivalently

$$\nu = -\frac{k_0}{T_h} + \frac{\delta}{T_h}, \qquad |\delta| \leq \frac{1}{2}. \tag{1.106}$$

Noting that there are $M_F - k_0$ frequency pairs (f', f''), each from $\mathscr{F}$, for which $f' - f'' = k_0/T_h$, it can be shown that

$$\begin{aligned} \overline{|X_p(\tau, \nu; T_h)|^2} &\leq \frac{1}{M_F^2}\left[(M_F - k_0)T_h^2 + \sum_{\substack{f' \in \mathscr{F} \\ f' - f'' \neq k_0/T_h}} \sum_{f'' \in \mathscr{F}} \frac{1}{\pi^2 (f' - f'' + \nu)^2}\right] \\ &\leq \frac{1}{M_F^2}\left[(M_F - k_0)T_h^2 \right. \\ &\quad \left. + \sum_{\substack{k_1 = 1 \\ k_1 - k_2 \neq k_0}}^{M_F} \sum_{k_2 = 1}^{M_F} \frac{T_h^2}{\pi^2 (|k_1 - k_2 - k_0| - 1/2)^2}\right]. \end{aligned} \tag{1.107}$$

The last inequality in (1.107) follows from (1.105) and (1.106), and worst case choice of δ. The weakest bound (1.107) occurs when ν is close to zero and $k_0 = 0$, and hence, considering that case and letting $m = k_1 -$

k_2, gives

$$\overline{|X_p(\tau, \nu; T_h)|^2} \le \frac{1}{M_F^2}\left[M_F T_h^2 + \frac{T_h^2}{\pi^2}\sum_{m=-M_F+1}^{M_F-1}(M_F - |m|)\left(\frac{2}{2|m|-1}\right)^2\right]$$

$$< \frac{T_h^2}{M_F}\left[1 + \frac{8}{\pi^2}\sum_{m=1}^{\infty}\frac{1}{(2m-1)^2}\right] = \frac{2T_h^2}{M_F}. \tag{1.108}$$

The resolution capability of FH/SS communication system can now be estimated by noting from (1.102) and (1.108) that

$$\frac{\mathbf{E}\{|v_M(k)|^2\}\big|_{t_I=0,\,\nu=0}}{\mathbf{E}\{|v_M(k)|^2\}\big|_{|t_I|\ge T_h}} > \frac{M_F}{2}. \tag{1.109}$$

This is the basis for stating that a high energy gain FH/FSK communication system has TOA resolution on the order of T_h. That is, (1.109) indicates that frequency-synchronous correlation detectors should be able to reject the desired FH/FSK signal, if it arrives out of time synchronism by more than T_h seconds.

1.6 DESIGN ISSUES

Based on the analyses presented in this chapter, spread-spectrum techniques promise an attractive approach to the design of communication systems which must operate in an interference environment. However, major design issues have been obscured thus far by the apparent simplicity of the concept.

1. How does the receiver acquire and retain synchronization with the received signal's clocks, especially in the presence of interference?
2. Can the appearance of randomness in modulation selection be achieved deterministically by a stored-reference SS system?
3. In what ways does the communication vs. jamming game change when the payoff function is bit-error rate?
4. What are the effects of imperfect system operation/modelling (e.g., synchronization errors, non-uniform channel characteristics across the communication band) on performance estimates?
5. How should data detectors be designed when the nature of the interference is not known *a priori*?

These are a sample of the questions which must be answered before a realistic system design can be achieved.

Several truths have been demonstrated by this introductory treatment. First, excess bandwidth is required to employ randomized signalling strategies against interference. That is, spreading the spectrum is necessary in this gaming approach to interference rejection. Secondly, if either side, communicator or jammer, fails to completely randomize its signalling strategy, the opponent in principle may observe this fact, adapt to this failing, and take advantage of the situation. Barring this event, the energy gain of the SS system on the average will be achieved by the communicator unless the jammer can avoid complying with a rule of the game.

1.7 REFERENCES

In most cases the results of this chapter and the issues raised herein will be fully discussed in greater detail in later chapters. The references listed here are general references to background material, tutorials, and paper collections.

1.7.1 Books on Communication Theory

[1] W. B. Davenport, Jr., and W. L. Root, *Random Signals and Noise*. New York: McGraw-Hill, 1958.

[2] D. Middleton, *An Introduction to Statistical Communication Theory*. New York: McGraw-Hill, 1960.

[3] S. W. Golomb, ed., *Digital Communications with Space Applications*. Englewood Cliffs, NJ: Prentice-Hall, 1964.

[4] J. M. Wozencraft and I. M. Jacobs, *Principles of Communication Engineering*. New York: John Wiley, 1965.

[5] M. Schwartz, W. R. Bennett, and S. Stein, *Communication Systems and Techniques*. New York: McGraw-Hill, 1966.

[6] A. J. Viterbi, *Principles of Coherent Communication*. New York: McGraw-Hill, 1966.

[7] S. Stein and J. J. Jones, *Modern Communication Principles*. New York: McGraw-Hill, 1967.

[8] H. L. Van Trees, *Detection, Estimation, and Modulation Theory* (3 vols.). New York: McGraw-Hill, 1968.

[9] G. L. Turin, *Notes on Digital Communication*. New York: Van Nostrand Reinhold, 1969.

[10] J. B. Thomas, *An Introduction to Statistical Communication Theory*. New York: John Wiley, 1969.

[11] J. J. Stiffler, *Theory of Synchronous Communication*. Englewood Cliffs, NJ: Prentice-Hall, 1971.

[12] W. C. Lindsey, *Synchronization Systems in Communication and Control*. Englewood Cliffs, NJ: Prentice-Hall, 1972.

[13] W. C. Lindsey and M. K. Simon, *Telecommunication Systems Engineering*. Englewood Cliffs, NJ: Prentice-Hall, 1973.

[14] R. E. Ziemer and W. H. Tranter, *Principles of Communications*. Boston, MA: Houghton Mifflin, 1976.

[15] J. J. Spilker, Jr., *Digital Communications by Satellite*. Englewood Cliffs, NJ: Prentice-Hall, 1977.
[16] S. Haykin, *Communication Systems*. New York: John Wiley, 1978.
[17] A. J. Viterbi and J. K. Omura, *Principles of Digital Communication and Coding*. New York: McGraw-Hill, 1979.
[18] J. G. Proakis, *Digital Communication*. New York: McGraw-Hill, 1983.

1.7.2 Books on Resolution and Ambiguity Functions

[19] C. E. Cook and M. Bernfeld, *Radar Signals*. New York: Academic Press, 1967.
[20] A. W. Rihaczek, *Principles of High Resolution Radar*. New York: McGraw-Hill, 1969.
[21] G. W. Deley, "Waveform Design," in *Radar Handbook*, M. Skolnik, ed., New York: McGraw-Hill, 1970.

1.7.3 Recent Books and Proceedings on Spread-Spectrum Communications

[22] *Proceedings of the 1973 Symposium on Spread Spectrum Communications*. Naval Electronics Laboratory Center, San Diego, CA, March 13–16, 1973.
[23] *Spread Spectrum Communications*. Lecture Series No. 58, Advisory Group for Aerospace Research and Development, North Atlantic Treaty Organization, July 1973 (AD 766914).
[24] R. C. Dixon, ed., *Spread Spectrum Techniques*. New York: IEEE Press, 1976.
[25] R. C. Dixon, *Spread Spectrum Systems*. New York: John Wiley, 1976.
[26] L. A. Gerhardt and R. C. Dixon, eds., "Special Issue on Spread Spectrum Communications," *IEEE Trans. Commun.*, COM-25, August 1977.
[27] D. J. Torrieri, *Principles of Military Communication Systems*. Dedham, MA: Artech House, 1981.
[28] C. E. Cook, F. W. Ellersick, L. B. Milstein, and D. L. Schilling, eds., "Special Issue on Spread Spectrum Communications," *IEEE Trans. Commun.*, COM-30, May 1982.
[29] J. K. Holmes, *Coherent Spread Spectrum Systems*. New York: John Wiley, 1982.
[30] R. H. Pettit, *ECM and ECCM Techniques for Digital Communication Systems*. Belmont, CA: Lifelong Learning Publications, 1982.
[31] *MILCOM Conference Record*, 1982 IEEE Military Communications Conference, Boston, MA, October 17–20, 1982.
[32] *Proceedings of the 1983 Spread Spectrum Symposium*, Long Island, NY. Sponsored by the Long Island Chapter of the IEEE Commun. Soc., 807 Grundy Ave., Holbrook, NY.

1.7.4 Spread-Spectrum Tutorials and General Interest Papers

[33] R. A. Scholtz, "The spread spectrum concept," *IEEE Trans. Commun.*, COM-25, pp. 748–755, August 1977.
[34] M. P. Ristenbatt and J. L. Daws, Jr., "Performance criteria for spread spectrum

communications," *IEEE Trans. Commun.*, COM-25, pp. 756–763, August 1977.

[35] C. L. Cuccia, "Spread spectrum techniques are revolutionizing communications," *MSN*, pp. 37–49, Sept. 1977.

[36] J. Fawcette, "Mystic links revealed," *MSN*, pp. 81–94, Sept. 1977.

[37] W. F. Utlaut, "Spread spectrum—principles and possible application to spectrum utilization and allocation," *ITU Telecommunication J.*, vol. 45, pp. 20–32, Jan. 1978. Also see *IEEE Commun. Mag.*, Sept. 1978.

[38] "Spread Spectrum: An Annotated Bibliography," National Telecommunications and Information Administration, Boulder, CO, May 1978 (PB 283964).

[39] J. J. Spilker, "GPS signal structure and performance characteristics," *Navigation*, vol. 25, pp. 121–146, Summer 1978.

[40] W. M. Holmes, "NASA's tracking and data relay satellite system," *IEEE Commun. Mag.*, vol. 16, pp. 13–20, Sept. 1978.

[41] R. E. Kahn, S. A. Gronemeyer, J. Burchfield, and R. C. Kunzelman, "Advances in packet radio technology," *Proc. IEEE*, vol. 66, pp. 1468–1496, Nov. 1978.

[42] A. J. Viterbi, "Spread spectrum communications—myths and realities," *IEEE Commun. Mag.*, vol. 17, pp. 11–18, May 1979.

[43] P. W. Baier and M. Pandit, "Spread spectrum communication systems," *Advances in Electronics and Electron Physics*, vol. 53, pp. 209–267. Sept. 1980.

[44] R. L. Pickholtz, D. L. Schilling, and L. B. Milstein, "Theory of spread spectrum communications—a tutorial," *IEEE Trans. Commun.*, COM-30, pp. 855–884, May 1982.

[45] N. Krasner, "Optimal detection of digitally modulated signals," *IEEE Trans. Commun.*, COM-30, pp. 885–895, May 1982.

[46] C. E. Cook and H. S. Marsh, "An introduction to spread spectrum," *IEEE Commun. Mag.*, vol. 21, pp. 8–16, March 1983.

[47] M. Spellman, "A comparison between frequency hopping and direct sequence PN as antijam techniques," *IEEE Commun. Mag.*, vol. 21, pp. 26–33, July 1983.

[48] A. B. Glenn, "Low probability of intercept," *IEEE Commun. Mag.*, vol. 21, pp. 26–33, July 1983.

Chapter 2

THE HISTORICAL ORIGINS OF SPREAD-SPECTRUM COMMUNICATIONS[1]

"Whuh? Oh," said the missile expert. "I guess I was off base about the jamming. Suddenly it seems to me that's so obvious, it must have been tried and it doesn't work."

"Right, it doesn't. That's because the frequency and amplitude of the control pulses make like purest noise–they're genuinely random. So trying to jam them is like trying to jam FM with an AM signal. You hit it so seldom, you might as well not try."

"What do you mean, random? You can't control anything with random noise."

The captain thumbed over his shoulder at the Luanae Galaxy. "They can. There's a synchronous generator in the missiles that reproduces the same random noise, *peak by pulse. Once you do that, modulation's no problem. I don't know* how *they do it. They just do. The Luanae can't explain it; the planetoid developed it."*

England put his head down almost to the table. "The same random," he whispered from the very edge of sanity.

–from "The Pod in the Barrier" by Theodore Sturgeon, in *Galaxy*, Sept. 1957; reprinted in *A Touch of Strange* (Doubleday, 1958).

Led by the Global Positioning System (GPS) and the Joint Tactical Information Distribution System (JTIDS), the spread-spectrum (SS) concept has

[1]Major portions of the material in this chapter have been adapted from three historical papers [1] © 1982 IEEE, [2] © 1983 IEEE, [3] © 1983 IEEE with the permission of the Institute of Electrical and Electronic Engineers.

emerged from its cloak of secrecy. And yet the history of this robust military communication technique remains largely unknown to many modern communication engineers. Was it a spark of genius or the orderly evolution of a family of electronic communication systems that gave birth to the spread-spectrum technique? Was it, as Frank Lehan said, an idea whose time had come? Was the spread-spectrum technique practiced in World War II, as Eugene Fubini declares? Was it invented in the 1920s as the U.S. Patent Office records suggest? Was Theodore Sturgeon's lucid description of a jam-proof guidance system precognition, extrasensory perception, or a security leak? Let's examine the evidence, circa 1900–1960, concerning the development of spread-spectrum communications.

2.1 EMERGING CONCEPTS

Before we can assess the ingenuity which went into the development of the first spread-spectrum systems, we must examine the development of communication theory and technology. When all the data has been reviewed, a case can be made for evolution and selection as the method by which progress has been made. A search for the origin of SS communications can become mired in the "definitionsmanship" (a word coined by Robert Price in [3]) attendant to classification by order, genus, and species. The following will provide a database from which the reader may draw conclusions.

2.1.1 Radar Innovations

From the 1920s through World War II, many systems incorporating some of the characteristics of spread-spectrum systems were studied. The birth of RADAR, i.e., RAdio Detection And Ranging, occurred in the mid-1920s when scientists used echo sounding to prove the existence of an ionized gas layer in the upper atmosphere. British scientists E. V. Appleton and M. A. F. Barnett performed this feat by transmitting a frequency modulated wave upward and listening for the return echo [4]. Applications of this concept to aircraft instrumentation were obvious and FM altimetry became a reality in the 1930s, with all major combatants in World War II making use of this technology [5]. Typically, linear-sawtooth or sinusoidal modulations were used in these early systems. The frequency modulation generally serves two purposes: 1) it ameliorates the problem of interference leakage of the transmitted signal directly into the receiver, and 2) it makes possible the measurement of propagation delay and, hence, range.

Historically, the development of pulsed radars has received more attention than that of continuous wave (CW) radars, since isolation of the transmitting and receiving systems is a lesser problem in this case. By the end of World War II, the Germans were developing a linear FM pulse compression (chirp) system called Kugelschale, and a pulse-to-pulse frequency-hopping radar called Reisslaus [6]. In the 1940s, Prof. E. Huttman was issued a German patent on a chirp pulse radar, while U.S. patents on this type of system were first filed by R. H. Dicke in 1945 and by S. Darlington in 1949 [7]. The mid-1940s also saw the formulation of the matched filter concept for maximum signal-to-noise ratio (SNR) pulse detection by North [8] and Van Vleck and Middleton [9]. This development indicated that the performance of optimum signal detection procedures in the presence of white noise depends only on the ratio of signal energy to noise power spectral density, thus, leaving the choice of waveform open to satisfy other design criteria (e.g., LPI or AJ). Resolution, accuracy, and ambiguity properties of pulse waveforms finally were placed on a sound theoretical basis by P. M. Woodward [10] in the early 1950s.

Spectrum spreading was a natural result of the Second World War battle for electronic supremacy, a war waged with jamming and anti-jamming tactics. On the Allied side by the end of the war, every heavy bomber, excluding Pathfinders, on the German front was equipped with at least two jammers developed by the Radio Research Laboratory (RRL) at Harvard [11]. The use of chaff was prevalent, the Allies consuming 2000 tons per month near the end. On the German side, it is estimated that at one time, as many as 90 percent of all available electronic engineers were involved in some way in a tremendous, but unsuccessful, AJ program. Undoubtedly Kugelschale and Reisslaus were products of this effort.

In a postwar RRL report [11], the following comment on AJ design is notable:

> In the end, it can be stated that the best anti-jamming is simply good engineering design and the spreading of the operating frequencies.

Certainly, spectrum spreading for jamming avoidance (AJ) and resolution, be it for location accuracy or signal discrimination (AJ), was a concept familiar to radar engineers by the end of the war.

In the late 1950s and early 1960s, the East German scientist F. H. Lange toured Europe and the United States collecting (unclassified) material for a book on correlation techniques. Published first in 1959 with its third edition being translated into English [12] a few years later, Lange's book contains some references all but unnoticed by researchers on this side of the Atlantic. The most intriguing of these is to the work of Gustav Guanella (Figure 2.1) of Brown, Boveri, and Company in Switzerland. Among Guanella's approximately 100 patents is one [13] filed in 1938, containing all the technical characteristics of an SR-SS radar! The radiated signal in Guanella's CW radar is "composed of a multiplicity of different frequencies the energies of which are small compared with the total energy" of the signal. His prime examples of such signals are acoustic and electrical noise, and an oscillator whose frequency is "wobbled at a high rate between a lower and upper limit."

Ranging is accomplished by adjusting an internal signal delay mechanism to match the external propagation delay experienced by the transmitted

Figure 2.1. Gustav Guanella, Swiss pioneer of noise-modulated radar and speech privacy systems. (Photo courtesy of I. Wigdorovits.)

signal (see Figure 2.2(c)). Delay matching errors are detected by cross correlating the internally delayed signal with a 90 degree phase-shifted (across the whole transmission band) version of the received signal. Thus, if the transmitted signal is of the form

$$\sum_n a_n \cos(\omega_n t + \phi_n),$$

the propagation delay is τ_p, and the internal delay is τ_i, then the measured error is proportional to

$$\sum_n a_n^2 \sin\left[\omega_n(\tau_p - \tau_i)\right].$$

This ensemble of phase locked loops, all rolled up into one neat package, possesses a tracking-loop S-curve which looks like the Hilbert transform of the transmitted signal's autocorrelation function. Undoubtedly, Guanella's patent contains possibly the earliest description of a delay-locked loop. Guanella used the same type of error-sensing concept in an earlier patent filed in 1936 [14]. Many of his inventions are cited as prior art in later patents.

In addition to accurate range measurement, the noise-radar patent indicates improved performance against interference. Guanella evidently did not pursue these intriguing claims, but instead turned his innovative talents to the field of speech scrambling.

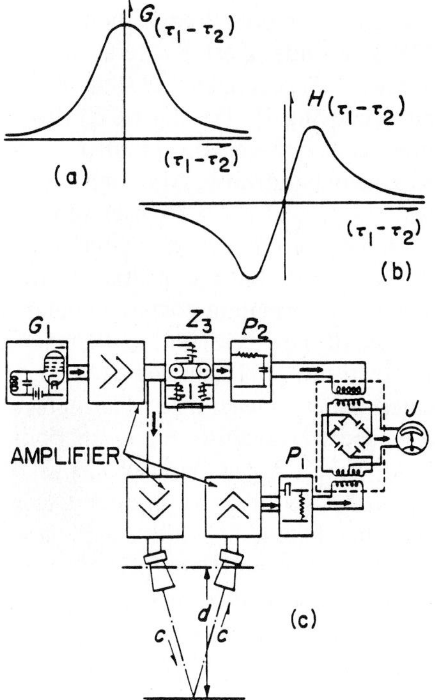

Figure 2.2. Guanella's noise radar patent [13] (redrawn). Part (c) shows a noise source (G_1), recording media (Z_3) for mechanizing the adjustable internal delay, filters (P_1 and P_2) whose design controls the measurement characteristic read on meter J. Parts (a) and (b) show two possible characteristics as functions of the time delay mismatch $\tau_1 - \tau_2$. The characteristic of part (b) was used later in the disclosure to describe delay-lock feedback control of the internal delay.

2.1.2 Developments in Communication Theory

In 1915, E. T. Whittaker concluded his search for a distinctive function among the set of functions, all of which take on the same specified values at regularly spaced points along the real line [16]. This "function of royal blood whose distinguished properties set it apart from its bourgeois brethren" [17] is given by

$$x(t) = \sum_n x(n/2W)\sin[\pi(2Wt - n)]/[\pi(2Wt - n)]$$

where $x(n/2W)$ represents the specified values and $x(t)$ is the cardinal function of the specified values, a function whose Fourier transform is strictly band limited in the frequency domain [15]—[18]. Based on this result, the sampling theory used in a communication context by Hartley [19], Nyquist [20], Kotelnikov [21], and Shannon [22] states that a function band limited to W Hz can be represented without loss of information by samples spaced $1/(2W)$ seconds apart. Generalizations [23], [24] of this result indicate that a set of approximately $2TW$ orthogonal functions of T seconds duration and occupying W Hz can be constructed. In SS theory, this provides the connection between the number of possible orthogonal signaling formats and system bandwidth. Although earlier, Nyquist [20] and later Gabor [25] both had argued using Fourier series that $2TW$ samples should be sufficient to represent a T-second segment of such a band-limited signal, it was Shannon who made full use of this classical tool.

Probabilistic modeling of information flow in communication and control systems was the brainchild of the preeminent mathematican Norbert Wiener of the Massachusetts Institute of Technology (M.I.T.). In 1930, Wiener published his celebrated paper "Generalized Harmonic Analysis" [26] developing the theory of spectral analysis for nonperiodic infinite-duration functions. When World War II began, Wiener was asked by the National Defense Research Committee (NDRC) to produce a theory for the optimal design of servomechanisms. Potential military applications for this theory existed in many gunfire control problems [27]. The resultant work [28], published initially in 1942 as a classified report and often referred to as the "Yellow Peril," laid the groundwork for modern continuous-parameter estimation theory. By 1947, Wiener's filter design techniques were in the open literature [29].

Claude E. Shannon, who had known Wiener while a graduate student at M.I.T., joined the Bell Telephone Laboratories (BTL) in 1941, where he began to establish a fundamental theory of communication within a statistical framework. Much of his work, motivated in good part by the urge to find basic cryptographic and cryptanalytic design principles [30], was classified well past the end of the Second World War. In a paper [22] first presented in 1947, Shannon invoked the cardinal expansion in formulating a capacity for delivering information (negentropy [31]) over channels perturbed solely by additive Gaussian noise. He showed that this channel capacity was maximized by selectively spreading the signaling spectrum so that wherever deployed within designated bandwidth confines–but only there–the sum of its power spectral density plus that of the independent noise should lie as uniformly low as possible, yet utilize all the average transmitter power available (see Figure 2.3). Moreover, this capacity was met by sending a set of noise-like waveforms and distinguishing between them at the receiver via a minimum-distance criterion akin to correlation-testing the observed signal against locally stored waveform replicas.

Even though Shannon's theory [22] did not apply directly to many jamming/interference situations, his result might be construed as the solution to a game theory problem in a jamming situation. When queried in 1982 by Robert Price [3], Shannon replied that there could well have been such a military application in the back of his mind. Regardless of his research motives, Shannon's remarkable concepts and results profoundly

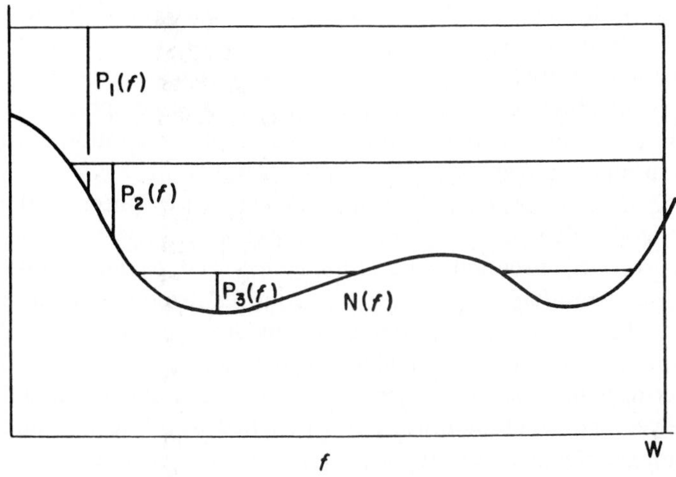

Figure 2.3. This "water pouring" illustration redrawn from Shannon's thought-provoking paper [22] depicts the communication-capacity-maximizing densities ($P_i(f)$) over the available bandwidth W, as a function of frequency f, for three different power levels. The optimal distribution may be viewed as the gravity-driven result of pouring a fluid, having a total volume proportional to the available transmitter power, into a rectangular vessel of width W, whose bottom profile in the f direction corresponds uniformly, and by the same proportion, to the power density $N(f)$ of the additively interfering Gaussian noise.

influenced communication engineers' thinking. Nearly a decade later, further applications of game theory to jamming situations were presented by William Root [32], [33], Nelson Blachman [34], [35], and Lloyd Welch [36], all then associated with SS system developments.

Driven by the intense interest in the theories of Wiener and Shannon, the Institute of Radio Engineers (IRE) formed the Professional Group on Information Theory, which commenced publishing in 1953 [37]. The first three chairmen of this Group were, in order, Nathan Marchand, William G. Tuller, and Louis deRosa. Marchand and deRosa, close friends, were at that time playing key roles in the development of SS systems; Tuller had independently but rather heuristically arrived at one of Shannon's capacity formulas.

2.1.3 Correlator Mechanization

One of the difficult problems which Guanella faced (by this account without any knowledge of Wiener's work) was to fabricate a device which will perform a weighted correlation computation on two inputs. Specifically, a means was needed for taking two inputs $x_1(t)$ and $x_2(t)$ and computing

$$y(t) = \int^t x_1(u)x_2(u)w(t-u)\,du$$

where $y(t)$ is the device output and $w(t)$ is the weighting function. The difficulty here is not with the weighting (i.e., filtering) operation, but with the prior multiplication of $x_1(t)$ by $x_2(t)$, and in particular with the range of inputs over which accurate multiplication can be accomplished. As shall be seen later, the ability to mechanize the correlation operation precisely is essential in building high-performance SS systems.

In 1942, Nathan Marchand, then a 26-year-old engineer working for ITT's Federal Telephone and Radio Corporation in New York, discussed his radio receiver invention with ITT engineer and patent attorney Paul Adams. Marchand had developed a converter for demodulating a received FM signal of known frequency wobbulation by mixing it with a time-aligned, heterodyned replica of the wobbulated signal to produce a signal of constant intermediate frequency (IF) which could then be narrow-band filtered. The receiver's anti-multipath attributes designed by Marchand and additional anti-interference features suggested by Adams appear in a 1947 patent [38]. Later during World War II, after studying Wiener's "Yellow Peril," Marchand was able to dub his converter a bandpass correlator.

However, Marchand was neither the first nor the last to propose the bandpass correlator, a similar device being contained in Purington's 1930 patent application [39].

At M.I.T. in 1947, Prof. Yuk Wing Lee commenced research into the implications of Wiener's theories and the new directions they inspired for engineering science. Soon thereafter, Lee was joined by Jerome Wiesner and Thomas Cheatham, and their collective efforts led to the development of the first high-performance electronic correlators. In August 1949, they applied for a patent [40] and in October they reported applications of correlation techniques to detection problems [41]. Continuing this work, Henry Singleton proceeded to innovate an all-digital correlator [42].

2.1.4 Protected Communications

It has been found [6], [43, p. 1] that secrecy, jamming, and anti-jamming had each begun to stir attention as early as 1901. (Note: For further details see [44, pp. 38—39], where also a recommendation is mentioned that "the homing-pigeon service should be discontinued as soon as some system of wireless telegraphy is adopted.") The first two of these three differing adversary-recourses were astutely exercised together in reporting, by "wireless," the America's Cup yacht race of that year. They were invoked by a thereby countermeasures-pioneering engineer who was competing against both Guglielmo Marconi and Lee De Forest for live coverage of this nautical event.

Even earlier, in 1899, Marconi had experimented with frequency-selective reception in response to worries about radio interference [6], [43]. The Navy, whose due concern had prompted this most basic advance in the radio art, reemphasized its apprehensions by warnings "... during 1904 on the dangers of relying on wireless in war" that "raised the questions of enemy intercept and interference which were to remain and grow into the major research and operational fields of radio intelligence and radio countermeasures" [45, p. 1243].

The earliest patent [46] presently construed by the U.S. Patent Office as being spread spectrum in character was filed in 1924 by Alfred N. Goldsmith, one of the three founders of the IRE. Goldsmith proposed to counteract the multipath-induced fading effects encountered in shortwave communication by

> radiating a certain range of wave frequencies which are modulated in accordance with the signal and actuating a receiver by means of energy collected on all the frequencies, preferably utilizing a wave which is continuously varied in wave frequency over a certain range of cycles recurring in a certain period.

Certainly, we can identify this as a form of FM-SS transmission. However, the envisioned data modulation was by amplitude (AM) with reception by a broadly tuned AM receiver. Hence, the correlation detector necessary to achieve the full benefits of SS operation was not inherent in Goldsmith's disclosure. For a World War II disclosure on an FM-SS chirp communication system with a more sophisticated receiver, claiming a primitive form of diversity reception for multipath signals and a capability against narrow-band interference, see [47].

In 1935, Telefunken engineers Paul Kotowski and Kurt Dannehl applied for a German patent on a device for masking voice signals by combining them with an equally broad-band noise signal produced by a rotating generator [48]. The receiver in their system had a duplicate rotating generator, properly synchronized so that its locally produced noise replica could be used to uncover the voice signal. The U.S. version of this patent was issued in 1940, and was considered prior art in a later patent [49] on DS-SS communication systems. Certainly, the Kotowski-Dannehl patent exemplifies the transition from the use of key-stream generators for discrete data encryption [50] to pseudorandom signal storage for voice or continuous signal encryption. Several elements of the SS concept are present in this patent, the obvious missing notion being that of purposeful bandwidth expansion.

The Germans used Kotowski's concept as the starting point for developing a more sophisticated capability that was urgently needed in the early years of World War II. Gottfried Vogt, a Telefunken engineer under Kotowski, remembers testing a system for analog speech encryption in 1939. This employed a pair of irregularly slotted or sawtoothed disks turning at different speeds, for generating a noise-like signal at the transmitter, to be modulated/multiplied by the voice signal. The receiver's matching disks were synchronized by means of two transmitted tones, one above and one below the encrypted voice band. This system was used on a wire link from

Germany, through Yugoslavia and Greece, to a very- and/or ultra-high frequency (VHF/UHF) link across the Mediterranean to General Erwin Rommel's forces in Derna, Libya.

In January 1943, British troops captured, from General Rommel's forces in North Africa, a communication transceiver called the "Optiphone" (or "Photophone"). Developed in Germany in the mid-1930s (and covered by U.S. Patent No. 2010313 to the Zeiss works), this system could provide voice communications over a light-path up to four miles long under reasonably clear atmospheric conditions [51]. While it would be far-fetched to view such (prelaser) incoherent optical communications as SS in nature, the interesting aspect here is that this apparatus seems to have been a further example of Rommel's employment of relatively advanced technology in secure communications.

Dr. Richard Gunther, an employee of the German company Siemens and Halske during World War II, recalls another speech encryption system involving bandwidth expansion and noise injection. In a fashion similar to the Western Electric B1 Privacy System, the voice subbands were pseudorandomly frequency scrambled to span 9 kHz and pure noise was added to fill in the gaps. The noise was later eliminated by receiver filtering in the speech restoration process. Tunis was the terminus of a link operated at 800 MHz and protected by this system.

In turning next to another battlefield of the Second World War, the following point of explanation is appropriate. Classical wideband FM systems have not been classified within the particular species described as "modern spread-spectrum communications" since this bandwidth expanding FM technique does not encompass all of the attributes described in Chapter 1. However, there is no doubt that wideband FM belongs to the genus of spectrum-spreading systems, and in fact fulfilled an urgent need for jam-resistant communications during a crisis in the war. This singular event took place at the late-1944 "Battle of the Bulge" which surged past the crossroads town of Bastogne, in the Belgian Ardennes, where extended American forces had been trapped and General George S. Patton's Third Army was storming to their rescue. Quoting at some length from [52, pp. 163–164]:

> On 26 December Patton succeeded in forcing a narrow corridor through the German tanks ringing Bastogne. It was only three hundred yards wide, but it opened the way to the American troops cut off there and punctured the German bulge, which began slowly to deflate under combined British and American pressure.
>
> Now came the first and only battle test of Jackal, the high-powered airborne radio jammer AN/ART-3 developed by the Signal Corps for the AAF [Army Air Forces]. The First and Third U.S. Armies had been reluctant to try Jackal jamming because a portion of the frequency band used by their tank radios overlapped into the German band to be jammed. Earlier tests in

> England had indicated somewhat inconclusively that little or no interference would be caused, since American radio for armored forces was FM while similar German sets and Jackal were AM [amplitude modulation]. Now that nearly the whole of the German *Sixth Panzer Army* was in the Ardennes fighting, it seemed a good opportunity to test Jackal.
>
> Accordingly, beginning on 29 December and continuing through 7 January [1945], Eighth Air Force B-24's based in England and bearing the Jackal jammers blaring full blast, flew in relays over the battle area, coinciding with a Third Army counterthrust in the vicinity of Bastogne. The first results seemed inconclusive, but, according to later reports from German prisoners, Jackal effectively blanketed German armored communications during these crucial days. Nor were the American tankmen inconvenienced or made voiceless by the overlap in frequencies. The jammer effectively filled the German AM receivers with a meaningless blare, while the American FM sets heard nothing but the voices of the operators.

This intriguing FM episode dramatized in real life (as twice again referred to in [52, p. 318, footnote 57; p. 324]) the simple FM/AM analogy later given in Theodore Sturgeon's science-fiction portrayal of SS communications, given at the beginning of this chapter. That FM radio (and FM radio-relay, too, each unique to the U.S. Army in this worldwide war, per [52, pp. 21, 107] was even available, "beyond anything either the enemy or the other allied nations possessed" [52, p. 631], was due in large measure to three men. Through experiments conducted in the mid-1930s with the close cooperation of its inventor, Edwin Armstrong, (the then) Col. Roger B. Colton and Maj. James D. O'Connell recognized the clear superiority of this modulation method and pushed hard to have it ready for communicators on the battlefield. One colonel exclaimed: "I feel that every soldier that lived through the war with an Armored Unit owes a debt that he does not even realize to General Colton" [52, p. 631]. Armstrong patriotically donated to every military service of the United States, free of any royalty payments, license to the use of all his inventions. (Note: Additional information on Maj. Armstrong's contributions to the Signal Corps is given in [53].)

The Allies' voice communication system that supplied the highest level of voice security for Roosevelt, Churchill, Truman, and others [3], [54], [55], [232] in top secret conversations, was developed by Bell Telephone Laboratories at the beginning of the war. Officially called the X-System or Project X-61753 at Bell Labs, nicknamed the "Green Hornet," and codenamed "Sigsaly" by the Signal Corps, this system contained several significant innovations related to the signal processing contained in its novel vocoding apparatus [55], [255]. (Other early vocoders are discussed in [56].)

The most striking security feature of the X-System, was its use of non-repeating, prerecorded keys which were combined modulo 6 with elaborately generated speech samples, to provide the complete security of a one-time-pad crypto-system, at a data rate of 1500 bps. Copies of each key were pressed on phonograph discs by Muzak, and the best studio-quality turntables for playing these records were incorporated into the thirty racks of equipment making up a Sigsaly radio station. The weight of the million dollar station, i.e., the operational equipment, a 30 kw power source, air conditioning, a complete set of spare parts including duplicates of the required 1100 + vacuum tubes, and other ancillary equipment, has been informally estimated at a staggering 80 tons. The official government designation for this station was the RC-220-T1 Terminal.

The use of pseudorandom keys in combination with speech bandwidth compression and re-expansion into a pulse-code modulation (PCM) format to utilize the full bandwidth of a telephone channel could be viewed as a SR spectrum-spreading system. The intended application, admirably achieved, was unbreakable enciphered telephony; the system "contained no anti-jamming provisions, and for the most part, did not require any" [55]. Surprisingly, synchronization of the turntables was not as difficult as expected, because of the use of excellent frequency standards.

Both Claude Shannon of Bell Laboratories and Alan Turing of the Government Code and Cypher School at Bletchley Park, England, independently verified the security of the X-System [3], [225]. Robert C. Mathes [57] and Ralph K. Potter [58] applied for patents on X-System apparatus in 1941, the disclosures being immediately placed under secrecy order. Thirty more patents, with X-System applications, followed [225, p. 297].

BTL continued its work on key-stream generation and in the mid-1940s filed for patents on all-electronic key generators which combined several short keys of relatively prime lengths to produce key streams possessing long periods [59], [60]. Such schemes also had been studied by Shannon [30] at BTL, but his comments on these were deleted before republication of his declassified report on secrecy systems in the *Bell System Technical Journal.* All of these BTL patent filings remained under secrecy order until the 1970s when the orders were rescinded and the patents issued.

Alan Turing, who had seen the enormous amount of equipment required by the X-System and heard Shannon explain the sampling theorem, considered the vocoder a non-essential part of its electronics. This led to his conception of the Delilah, a secure voice communication system named for the biblical "deceiver of men" [231]. The idea in Turing's design was to perform modular addition of a random key directly to time samples of speech, at a rate high enough to allow eventual speech reconstruction at the receiver, as indicated by the Whittaker-Shannon sampling theorem. The Delilah signal processors were built and laboratory tested by the end of 1944, with random noise from an antennaless radio wired directly to the transmitter and receiver key inputs during the tests. Turing then devised a sophisticated key-stream generator for the system (rather than accept the key distribution problems associated with one-time pads), and tackled the key synchronization problem. The effort was not completed in time for use during the war.

Gustav Guanella, the Swiss inventor who held pre-World War II patents on radars and direction finders employing noise-like signals [13], [14], also applied his innovative talents in the related field of speech scrambling systems [61]. A 1946 NDRC report [56] in fact discusses his designs and the level of security which they provide. No direct mention of the ultra-secret X-System was included in this report, which does include descriptions of noise-masking systems and multiplicative signal-modifying systems, as well as methods for protecting the reference signals in TR systems. (An example of good TR-technique is the subject of the next vignette.) It was further noted that if a short-period signal was used as a multiplicative signal in an effort to disguise a speech waveform, then the transmission was quite vulnerable to "cryptanalysis." Several long-period code generators were discussed.

The historically useful reports [27], [56], [62], [63] of the NDRC were undoubtedly precursors of the postwar demobilization of that civilian organization. Military officials, recognizing the major contributions of the academic world during the war just ended, and realizing the need for a continued strong research base, initiated a program of support for advanced research in the nation's universities [64, p. 98]. First installed at M.I.T., Harvard, Columbia, and Stanford, this joint Services Electronics Program now sponsors research at many major U.S. institutions.

One can view the advanced Telefunken system as an avatar of a TR system since specialized signals are transmitted to solve the disk synchronization problem. Another novel variation of TR voice communication was conceived in the U.S. during the war years by W. W. Hansen. This Sperry/M.I.T. Radiation Laboratory scientist is noted for his invention of the microwave cavity resonator and for his joint effort with the Varian brothers in originating the Klystron. In a 1943 patent application [65], Hansen describes a two-channel system (see Figure 2.4) with the reference channel used solely for the transmission of noise, and the intelligence channel bearing the following signal (in complex notation):

$$\exp\left\{ j \int^{t} [\omega_1 + An(t')]\, dt' \right\} \cdot \exp\left\{ j \int^{t} [\omega_2 + Bv(t')]\, dt' \right\}$$

where $n(t)$ is a filtered version of the noise communicated via the reference channel, $v(t)$ is the voice signal, and assuming $n(t)$ and $v(t)$ are at comparable levels, $A \gg B$. The intelligence signal is the result of combining a wide-swing noise-modulated FM waveform with a narrow-swing voice-modulated FM waveform in a device "similar in principle of operation to the mixers used in superheterodyne receivers."

At the receiver, the reference channel signal is used to reconstruct the first of the above factors, and that in turn is mixed with the received intelligence signal to recover the voice-modulated waveform represented by the second factor. This receiver mixer appears to be similar in many respects to Marchand's bandpass correlator.

To overcome some of the fundamental weaknesses of TR systems (see Chapter 1, Section 3), Hansen threw in an additional twist: The filtering of

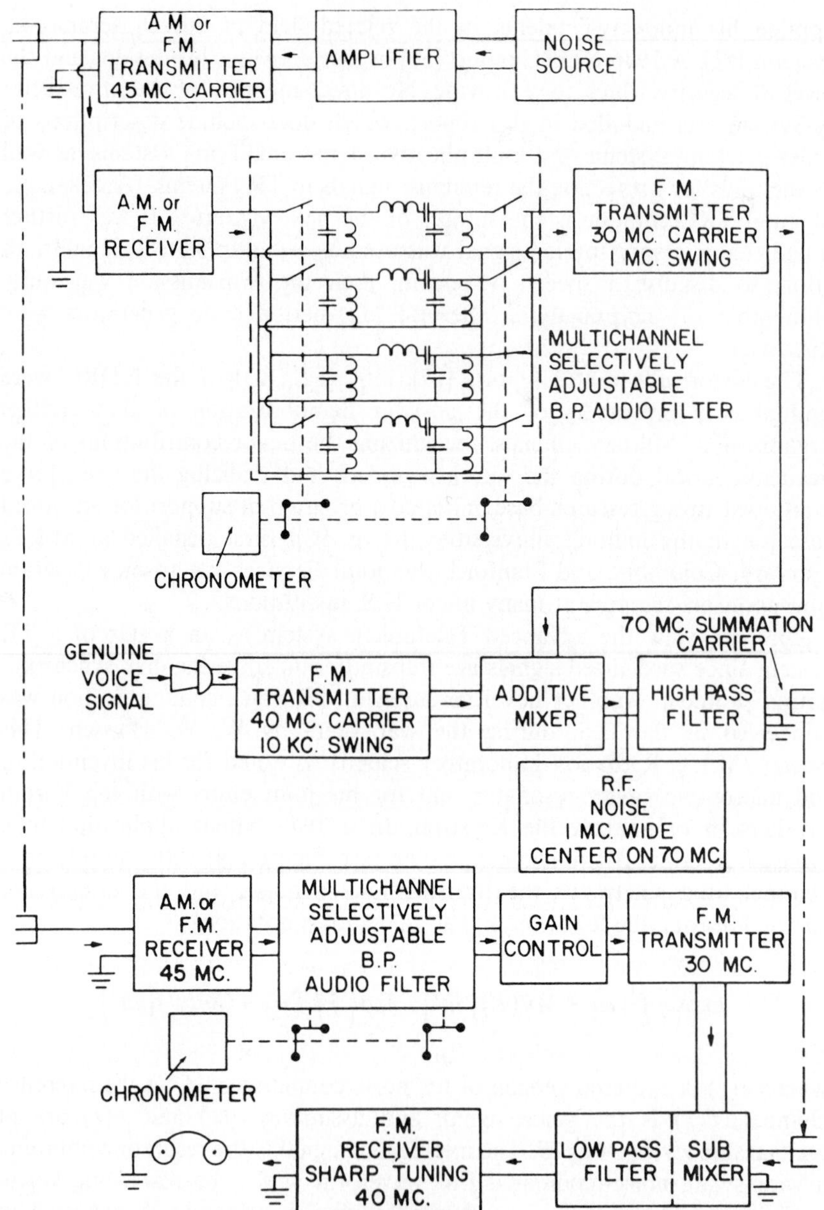

Figure 2.4. This TR-FM-SS block diagram redrawn from Hansen's patent [65] illustrates one method for denying an unauthorized listener direct access to the reference signal used by the receiver to detect the information bearing transmission.

the reference channel signal, used to generate $n(t)$, was made time dependent, with transmitter and receiver filters required to change structure in virtual synchronism under the control of a chronometer. This structural change could not be detected in any way by observing the reference channel.

When presenting his design along the TR-FM-SS lines, Hansen notes that the intelligence signal cannot be heard by unauthorized narrow-band receivers because "such wide-swing modulations in effect tune the transmitted wave outside the frequency band of the unauthorized listener's receiver for the greater portion of the time and thus make such a receiver inoperative." Concerned about the fact that a wide-band FM receiver might conceivably recover the signal $An(t) + Bv(t)$, he also concludes that "if therefore the noise $[n(t)]$ has important components throughout the range of signal frequencies and if the swing due to the noise is large compared to the swing due to the signal $[v(t)]$, deciphering is impossible."

Curiously enough, as a result of the use of an exponential form of modulation, Hansen's design is constructed as a TR-FM-SS communication system at radio frequency (RF), but equivalently at demodulated baseband, it is simply a "typical noise masking" add/subtract TR system. (This latter appraisal of [65] is from the case file—open to the public as for any issued patent—in Crystal City on an SR-SS invention [49] of major importance to a later period in this history.) Moreover, except for its TR vulnerabilities, Hansen's system is good AJ design, and as he points out, a large amount of additional noise can be injected at the RF output of the transmitter's intelligence channel for further masking without seriously degrading system performance.

Surprisingly, without the spectral spreading and chronometer-controlled reference signal filters, Hansen's system would bear a strong resemblance to a TR-FM system described in 1922 by Chaffee and Purington [66]. Hence, the concept of transmitting a reference signal to aid in the demodulation of a disguised information transmission is over sixty years old!

E. M. Deloraine's history [67] of the early years at ITT contains segments recounting the efforts and risks undergone in France during World War II to protect valuable information, and to eventually transport it to the United States. In a daring move, Louis Chereau, then Director of Patents and Information under Deloraine at ITT's Paris Laboratories, indicates [2] that he visited the French Patent Office in Vichy just before the Germans crossed the demarcation line, for the purpose of removing Henri Busignies' MTI patent application on "Elimination of fixed echoes," filed in Lyon on May 27, 1942, and also Ferdinand Bac's LORAN application. The MTI application was based on a Busignies memorandum, dated October 24, 1940, and the memorandum in turn was motivated by a "brainstorming session" initiated by Chereau who had put forth the idea of echo cancellation. The memorandum was written shortly before Deloraine and Busignies, along with Emile Labin and Georges Chevigny and their families, escaped via

Marseilles, Algiers, Casablanca, Tangier, and Lisbon to New York, arriving on New Year's Eve, the last day of 1940. Busignies filed his application in the United States on March 5, 1941, and was granted U.S. Patent 2 570 203.

Busignies, a remarkably prolific inventor who over his lifetime was granted about 140 patents, soon collaborated with Edmond Deloraine and Louis deRosa in applying for a patent [68] on a facsimile communication system with intriguing anti-jam possibilities here set forth:

> [The system uses a transmitter which sends each character] a plurality of times in succession, [and a receiver in which the character signals are visually reproduced,] one on top another... to provide a cumulative effect. [If] the interference signals are not transmitted to provide such a cumulative effect, the interference will form only a bright background but will not prevent the signals from being read.

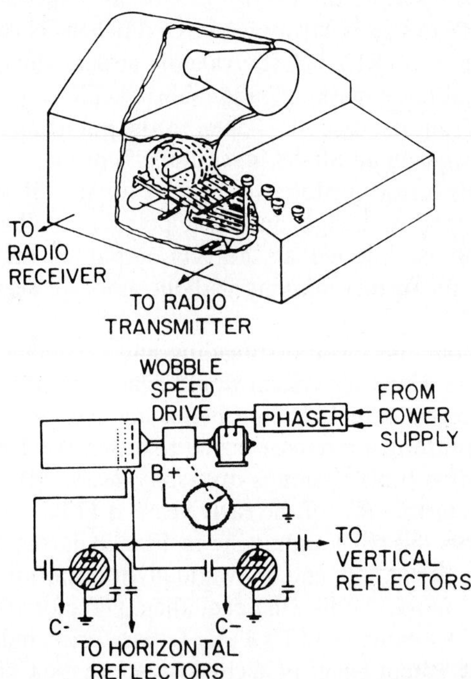

Figure 2.5. The core of Deloraine, Busignies, and deRosa's time-wobbling system consisted of a drum containing a slot track for each transmittable character. When the drum is turned at a constant speed, the signal produced by reading a track with a light beam was that required to create a character on a CRT screen. For security, the drum's rotation rate was "wobbled" and compensating variations in the CRT beam deflection voltages were inserted, so that interference, being wobbled on receive only, could not easily produce a bright screen signal. (Redrawn from [68], [69].)

From a jamming viewpoint, the real novelty in the the disclosure is in the fact that the mechanisms which read the characters at the transmitter and write the characters at the receiver synchronously vary in rate of operation (see Figure 2.5). Thus, attempts to jam the system with periodic signals which might achieve the "cumulative effect" at the receiver output will be unsuccessful.

In a sequel patent filed six weeks later [69], it is specified that the facsimile pulse modulation should have a low average duty cycle, be characterized by steep wavefronts, and have high peak-to-average power, in order to attain superior protection. This time-wobbling system is obviously an early relative of modern TH-SS systems. Concurrently with these efforts, deRosa covered similar applications in the field of radar by filing what may be the first patent on random jittering of pulse repetition frequencies [70].

Another study of protected communications was launched when ITT submitted Proposal 158A to the NDRC for consideration. Although the original proposal only suggested the use of redundancy in time or frequency as a possible AJ measure, a 1944 report [71] stated with regard to jamming that

> The enemy can be forced to maintain a wide bandwidth if we use a coded frequency shifting of our narrower printer bandwidth so that it might at any time occupy any portion of a wider band.

This clear suggestion of FH-SS signaling was not explored further in the last year of the contract. Several different tone signalling arrangements were considered for communication to a printer at rates on the order of one character per second. Synchronization of these digital signalling formats was accomplished in open-loop fashion using precision tuning forks as reference clocks.

> These forks are temperature compensated over a wide range and are mounted in a partial vacuum, so that their rate is not affected by the low barometric pressures encountered at high altitudes. Their accuracy is of the order of one part in a million, so that once the receiving distributor was phased with the transmitted signal, it remained within operable limits for two hours or more. A differential gear mechanism, operated by a crank handle on the front panel, was provided for rephasing the receiving distributor whenever this became necessary.

The receiving distributor controlled the reinitializing of *L-C* tank circuits tuned to detect transmitted tones. Because of their high *Q*, these circuits performed an integrate-and-dump operation during each distributor cycle. This detector was a significant improvement over the prior art, a fact indeed recognized intuitively by ITT, rather than derived from correlation principles.

ITT's printer communication system was tested at Rye Lake Airport on February 21, 1945. The printer performed well in the presence of jamming

11 dB stronger than the desired signal, and under conditions where voice on the same channel was not intelligible [72]. The interference in this test consisted of an AM radio station. Test results of the printer system are mentioned briefly in a 1946 NDRC Division 15 report [62] which also points out in a radar context that

> There is factual evidence that tunability is foremost as an AJ measure. Frequency spread of radars, which serves the same function, is a corollary and equally important. [With regard to communications,] RF carrier frequency scrambling and time modulation of pulses with time scrambling [are possible communication anti-jam measures].

The report's final recommendations state that "any peacetime program to achieve protection against jamming should not be concerned with the type of equipment already in service, but should be permitted an unrestricted field of development." This was sensible advice to follow, when practical, in the post-war years.

An explicit description of an FH system was put forward in early January 1943, when U.S. Army Signal Corps officer Henry P. Hutchinson applied for a patent on FH signaling for "maintaining secrecy of telephone conversations" or for "privately transmitting information" [73]. His scheme employed on-line cryptographic machines to produce a pseudorandom hopping pattern on demand. Although the subject of the patent is secrecy and privacy, Hutchinson has stated [3] that he was aware of the advantage his concept could have for avoiding interference. The patent application, which received official review [74], was held under secrecy order by the U.S. Patent Office until 1950.

As will soon be seen, Hutchinson's landmark patent was preceded in time, and eclipsed in human interest, by another true SR-FH-SS patent application filed by a rising Hollywood star!

2.1.5 Remote Control and Missile Guidance

Interest in radio guidance dates back to the turn of the century. Notable pioneering efforts took place at the Hammond Radio Research Laboratory, a privately organized research group. Its founder, John Hays Hammond, Jr., an inventor whose "...development of radio remote control served as the basis for modern missile guidance systems," also "...developed techniques for preventing enemy jamming of remote control and invented a radio-controlled torpedo..." [75]. By 1914, he was actively exploring means to "...greatly minimize the possibility of an enemy determining the wave lengths used in the control of the craft and thereupon interfering with the control thereof" [76]. In the radio guidance of remote vehicles, Hammond was following in the footsteps of Adm. Bradley A. Fiske and of Nikola Tesla [77, p. iii]. (Note: See [44, ch. XXIX] for more background on Hammond, Fiske, and Tesla.) The efforts against jamming were, initially, pursued by Benjamin F. Miessner, Hammond's sole coworker during 1912, who had invented a primitive form of SS signaling [77, p. 32] which was quite likely the earliest to be thus "... transmitted in a peculiar way" [77, p. 65].

The Miessner-Hammond carrier broadening was incorporated into a military transmitter, which with its associated receiver (that additionally introduced amplitude-limiting action) was delivered to the U.S. Army in France just before World War I ended. There, Maj. Edwin H. Armstrong verified the Hammond system's ability to communicate in the face of powerful enemy interference, a challenge officially recognized as "... one of the most important matters connected with the war" [78, footnote 48].

From the First World War on into World War II, the furtherance of wideband techniques continued at the Hammond Laboratory, with concentration on frequency-wobbling methods to send secret signals which sounded like "... some new kind of man-made static ... " [78, p. 1203]. The anti-jamming attribute of spectrum spreading became obvious as the frequency deviation of the wobbling increased so that its "... wider swing reduced the amount of time that a given narrow-band disturbance could affect the intermediate-frequency circuit of the receiver ... " [78, p. 1202]. Contributions of this kind, originating in that era from the Hammond group (additionally to [66]), are documented in patents on TR and SR wobbling which were filed, respectively, by Emory L. Chaffee [79] in 1922 and Ellison S. Purington [39] in 1930.

The Chaffee patent claims that his invention, involving "rapid and erratic" wobbling, is useful for "secret radio telephony" and for "... telegraphic signals or radio-dynamic control." With respect to the Purington patent [39] (which seems somehow to have been overlooked in the chronicles [78] and [80]), that SR invention for obtaining "secrecy in which a rapid variation rate is necessary ... " for the wobbling was a sequel to Hammond/Navy experiments of 1921–1922 which "... established points of interest regarding information theory when the interference greatly exceeds the signal" [78, p. 1202]. Also, circa 1920, the Hammond company had contracts from the U.S. Army to show that "noninterferable characteristics" could be secured for the radio control of aircraft [80, p. 1262].

During World War II, the NDRC entered the realm of guided missiles with a variety of projects [81] including the radio control in azimuth only (AZON) of conventionally dropped bombs (VB's) which trailed flares for visibility, radar-controlled glide bombs (GB's) such as the Pelican and the Bat, and the remotely controlled ROC VB-10 using a television link. Now documented mostly through oral history and innocuous circuit patents, one of several secure radio guidance efforts took place at Colonial Radio, predecessor of the Sylvania division at Buffalo, NY. This project was under the direction of Madison Nicholson, with the help of Robert Carlson, Alden Packard, Maxwell Scott, and Ernest Burlingame. The secret communications system concept was stimulated, so Carlson thinks, by talks with Navy people who wanted a system like the "Flash" system which the Germans used for U-boat transmissions. However, it wasn't until the Army Air Force at Wright Field posed the following problem that the Colonial Radio effort began seriously.

The airfoil surfaces of the glide bombs were radio controlled by a mother plane some distance away, sometimes with television display (by RCA) relayed back to the plane so that closed-loop guidance could be performed. It was feared that soon the Germans would become adept at jamming the control. To solve this problem Colonial Radio developed a secure guidance system based on a pulsed waveform which hopped over two diverse frequency bands. This dual band operation led to the system's nickname, Janus, after the Roman god possessing two faces looking in opposite directions. Low duty cycle transmission was used, and although the radio link was designed to be covert, the system could withstand jamming in one of its two frequency bands of operation and still maintain command control.

The Colonial Radio design's transmitter for the mother aircraft was designated the AN/ARW-4, and the corresponding glide bomb receiver was the AN/CRW-8. Testing of the radio guidance system took place at Wright Field in 1943, under the direction of Lt. Leonhard Katz, Capts. Walter Brown and Theodore Manley, and Project Engineer Jack Bacon. The contract, including procurement of two transmitters and seven receivers, was completed by June 1944 [82].

ITT also participated in these World War II guidance programs, notably with a system called Rex [63]. One patent, evidently resulting from this work and filed in 1943 by Emile Labin and Donald Grieg [83], is interesting because it suggests CDMA operation in pulse code modulation (PCM) systems by slight changes in the pulse repetition frequency. In addition, the patent notes the jammer's inherent problem of trying to deliver its interference to the victim receiver in synchronism with the transmitted pulse train. However, the notion of multiplicity factor or spectrum spreading is not mentioned.

A third guidance system for the control of VB's and GB's was proposed by the Hammond Laboratory. The Hammond system used a complicated modulation format which included a carrier wobbled over 20 kHz to protect against tone interference, and FM control signals amplitude modulated onto this frequency-modulated carrier [63]. More notable in this history than the system itself is the fact that Ellison Purington in 1948 came close to describing a TH and FH carrier for a radio control system in a patent application [84] (see Figure 2.6). The actual details describe a TH-SS system with control signals coded into the transmission using frequency patterns. Magnetic or optical recording "on a rotating member driven by a constant speed motor" was one suggestion for the storage of different time hopping patterns, while another possibility mentioned involves delay line generation of pulse train patterns. Control keys are hidden in the way that the patterns

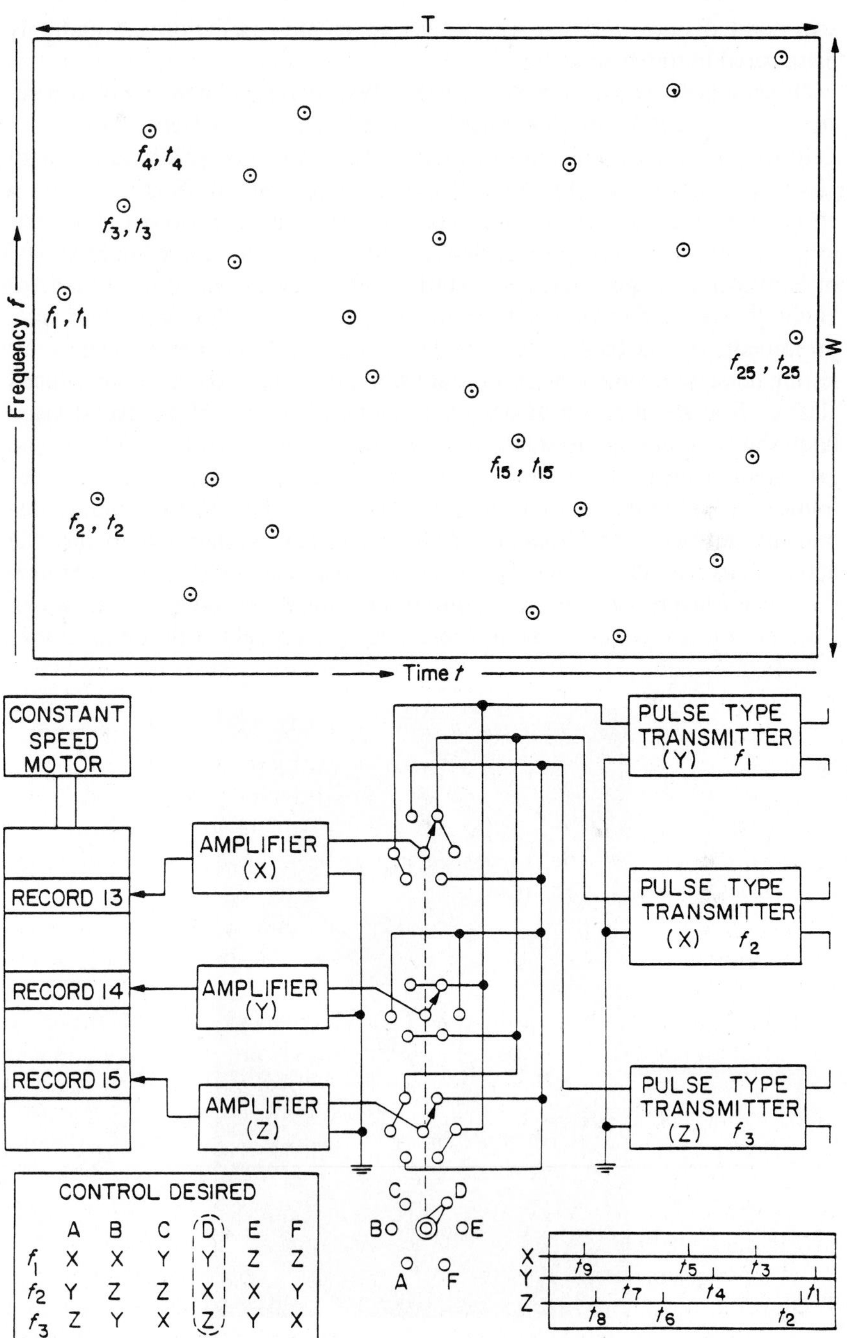

Figure 2.6. Purington's time-frequency chart definitely suggests a hybrid TH and FH system. However, the illustrated transmitter uses the assignment of TH patterns to frequency tracks as a method for signal encoding. (Redrawn from [84]).

are mapped onto different frequencies to create "radiations...randomly distributed in time and in frequency."

Other salient patents, based on World War II AJ and command/control efforts, include those of Hoeppner [85] and Krause and Cleeton [86].

In mid-1941 an application for the FH patent [87], [232] was filed by Hedy K. Markey (see Figure 2.7) and George Antheil. Neither inventor was an engineer, conversant with the prior art, e.g., the broad FH method [88] invented a dozen years earlier. Being at that time a recent ex-spouse of Hollywood scriptwriter Gene Markey, Hedy Markey had been baptized Hedwig Eva Maria Kiesler. Growing up in Austria, this only child of a prominent Vienna banker had shown, at age 16, a flair for innovation by letting herself be filmed in total nudity while starring in the Czech-produced classic, *Ecstasy* (the fifth of her many motion pictures [89]). Several years later she was one of the small minority among non-Jewish Austrians who saw great danger to the world in Germany's early-1938 *Anschluss* of her homeland. That year, permanently leaving her country and her munitions-magnate husband, Friedrich A. "Fritz" Mandl, as washouts to Hitler, the actress came to the United States on a seven-year contract from Metro-Goldwyn-Mayer. There, she legalized her stage-renaming (by Louis B. Mayer) to Hedy Lamarr. The now-escaped wife brought with her memories

Figure 2.7. Hedy Lamarr, inventress of the first frequency-hopping spread-spectrum technique explicitly conceived for anti-jamming communications. (Photo courtesy of Kenneth Galente, The Silver Screen, New York.)

of company films, which she had witnessed, of difficulties Mandl and his factory managers were encountering in getting their "aimlessly" unguided torpedoes to hit evasive targets.

Once settled in southern California but still greatly concerned by the war then impending for the United States, Lamarr sought out the versatile and volatile symphony composer Antheil [90, ch. 32]. Quickly stimulating a new application of his creative talents, she led him to their joint conception of a radio-control scheme in which the transmitted carrier frequency would jump about via a prearranged, randomized, and nonrepeating FH code. A torpedo carrying a properly synchronized receiver could thereby be secretly guided from its launch site all the way to its target. Hedy Lamarr and George Antheil thought such a stealthy "dirigible craft" capability, for missiles as well as torpedoes, would soon be needed by Germany's opponents.

Drawing large diagrams while stretched out on Lamarr's carpeted floor, she and Antheil concentrated on them for weeks until they arrived at a secure and feasible FH-SS concept. The system design took special advantage of the composer's know-how, in their plan to synchronize the radio transmission and reception frequencies by means of twin, identically crypto-code slotted, paper music rolls like those used in player piano, audio-frequency (!) mechanisms (see Figure 2.8). Indeed, Antheil had already achieved such synchronization precisely in his multi-player-piano opus of the 1920s, *Ballet Mécanique* [90, p. 185]. Their invention disclosure points out that an FH repertoire of eighty-eight radio frequencies could readily be accommodated.

The Lamarr-Antheil invention promised to be "sturdy and foolproof," and well within the manufacturing capabilities of the 1940s, and its FH secrecy features were enhanced by the inventors' advocacy of short-pulse transmission to provide low detectability. But what seems, for that day, to

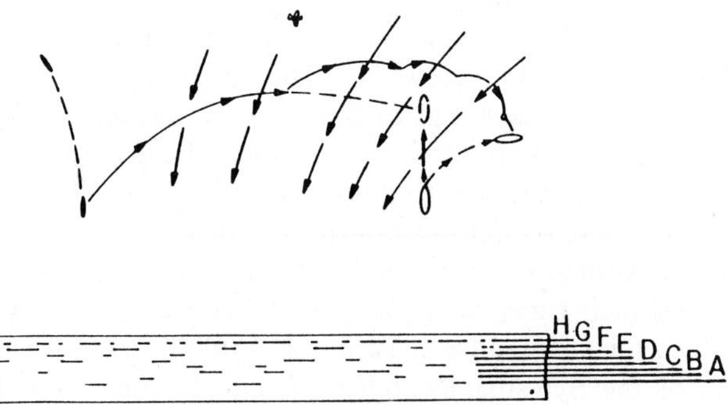

Figure 2.8. Redrawn from the Markey-Antheil patent [87]. Upper figure shows midcourse corrections to a torpedo course, made by FH-SR-SS communication from an observing aircraft. A "piano-roll" recording of the frequency hopping sequence is illustrated in the lower drawing.

be most perceptive in the initial installment [91] of the invention disclosure is presented quite boldly:

> ...it is veritably impossible for an enemy vessel to 'jam' or in any way interfere with the radio-direction of such a previously synchronized torpedo because, simply, no ship may have enough sending stations aboard or nearby to 'jam' every air-wavelength possible or to otherwise succeed except by barest accident to deflect the course of the oncoming radio controlled torpedo —unless, of course, it happened to have the exact synchronization pattern between sender-ship and torpedo.

(Minor, mostly typographical improvements have been made here within this quote while dropping its originally all-capitals lettering; in the patent itself [87], "block control" is said rather than "jam.")

Lamarr next brought her and Antheil's secret system concept to the attention of the then newly government-established National Inventors Council, which soon (quoting from [92]) "...classed Miss Lamarr's invention as in the 'red hot' category. The only inkling of what it might be was the announcement that it was related to remote control of apparatus employed in warfare." That is how it was guardedly publicized by the U.S. Department of Commerce after being scrutinized by Charles F. Kettering, the noted General Motors inventor who was also a pioneer (with Elmer A. Sperry) in remotely piloted vehicles.

Despite this first reaction of enthusiasm mixed with caution, the Lamarr (Markey)-Antheil patent appears to have been routinely issued and published, curiously without imposition of a Secrecy Order. It may be that such potential restraint from the U.S. Patent Office was precluded by the fact that Lamarr's continuing (until 1953) Austrian citizenship rendered her an "enemy alien" during most of World War II. Although this personal circumstance is indeed reflected in the patent case file [93], it seems to have been a mere technicality, which did not impair her screen-actress career nor her image to the American public.

At one of the many war-bond rallies through which she expressed her loyalty, Hedy Lamarr told a crowd of 10,000 in Elizabeth, NJ, that "...she knew what Nazism would mean to this country because she knew what it did to her native country, Austria. 'I'm giving all I can because I have found a home here and want to keep it'" [94]. She had certainly tried to contribute to the war effort, too, by her inventiveness.

Lamarr and Antheil seem, however, to have been more than a score of years ahead of their time, considering that FH-SS evidently was not used operationally against intentional jamming until the 1963 exercise, by the U.S. Navy, of the Sylvania BLADES system. It appears that no coded-paper-hole implementation ever resulted from their FH invention, and that in the decades since the issuance of its patent, whatever scant notice it has received has been confined to the popular press [95].

As far as technology is concerned, all of the above communication systems share a common propensity for the use of electromechanical devices, especially where signal storage and synchronization are required. Undoubtedly in the 1940s the barriers to be overcome in the development of SS communications were as much technological as they were conceptual. The emergence of missile guidance as a potential weapon delivery technique requiring light-weight, rugged construction, did much to drive communication technology toward all-electronic and eventually all-solid state systems. Furthermore the use of guided weapons placed communication jamming and AJ in a more serious light [52]:

> radio jamming, in World War II generally did not require, and did not receive, much attention. Everyone was far more concerned [for intelligence analysis] with listening in. However, when... inhuman radio-guided missiles put in their terrifying appearance, the electromagnetic frequencies employed by the new military engines became suddenly too dangerous to neglect.

2.2 EARLY SPREAD-SPECTRUM SYSTEMS

The following accounts of early SS developments are given to some extent as system genealogies. As we shall see, however, the blood lines of these system families are not pure, there being a great deal of information exchange at the conceptual level despite the secrecy under which these systems were developed. Approximate SS system time lines for several of the research groups tracked here are shown in Figure 2.9. Since the SS concept was developed gradually during the same period that Shannon's work on information theory became appreciated, J.R. Pierce's commentary [96] on the times should be borne in mind:

> It is hard to picture the world before Shannon as it seemed to those who lived in it. In the face of publications now known and what we now read into them, it is difficult to recover innocence, ignorance, and lack of understanding. It is easy to read into earlier work a generality that came only later.

2.2.1 WHYN

Many of the roots of SS system work in the U.S.A. can be traced back to the pioneering of FM radar by Major Edwin Armstrong during the early phases of World War II. The Armstrong technique involved transmitting a sinusoidally modulated wide-band FM signal, and then heterodyne-mixing the return from the target with the transmitted signal at a frequency offset. When the frequency of the modulation was properly adjusted so that the round-trip propagation delay corresponded to one modulation period, the output of the mixer was very narrow-band and the one-period difference between the transmitted modulation and that of the replica then gave a measure of the two-way propagation delay to the target. Certainly, this created a bandwidth expansion and compression methodology, primitive though it was, since the FM wobbulation was simply a sine wave. Sylvania's

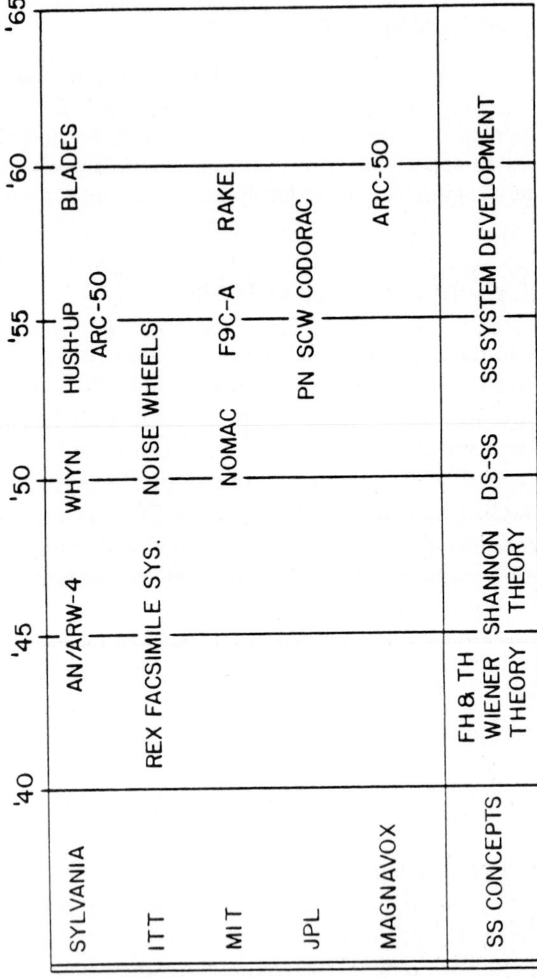

Figure 2.9. Approximate time lines for the systems and concepts feature in this history.

Bayside Laboratories on Long Island received the contract in World War II to continue development of the Armstrong radar.

In 1946, Sylvania received a subcontract from Republic Aviation under Army Air Force Project MX-773 to develop a guidance system for a 500–1500 mile surface-to-surface missile. Although celestial and inertial navigation were possibilities, it was decided that a radio-controlled system using FM ranging would be the most easily realized.

Accurate high-frequency (HF) ranging requires that the receiver extract the ground wave propagation and ignore the potentially strong skywave multipath, as well as ambient noise and jamming. The MX-773 subcontract specifications called for satisfactory discrimination against intereferences of the following types:

1. Skywave, identical in modulation to the ground wave guidance signal but forty times greater in amplitude and delayed 100–250 μs.
2. Other guidance signals identical in modulation, but fifteen times greater in amplitude and differing in arrival time by 50–2000 μs.
3. Unmodulated, pulse, or noise-modulated interference up to twenty times the guidance signal in amplitude.

These time resolution and interference rejection requirements eventually motivated the use of wide-band modulation techniques.

Norman Harvey, the leader in this development effort, states:

> The MX-773 project started out in a strictly study phase, with no special linkage to the FM radar project. It was the specification of 0.5 mile accuracy at 1500 miles that initially gave us the greatest concern. At the time, DECCA (England) was operating a pure cw, cycle-matching navigation system that attracted our interest because it promised that kind of accuracy under ideal conditions. Bob Bowie, John Wilmarth of Republic Aviation, and I went to England in the spring of 1946 to attend the Provisional International Conference on Air Organization (PICAO), to look particularly at DECCA, but also to see if there were other systems that might be adapted to meet our requirements.
>
> Not long after that, the idea of combining a DECCA-type cycle matching system (for accuracy) with FM modulation techniques (for resolution), occurred to me, and the WHYN concept was born.

At least two classes of navigation systems were studied, the first being a circular-navigation, two-ground station system in which the range to each station was determined separately. The second technique measured the relative delay between two identically modulated ground station transmissions (see Figure 2.10). Measured accurately, this information located the receiver on a hyperbolic curve. The acronym WHYN, coined by Harvey for this latter system, stands for Wobbulated HYperbolic Navigation. From the receiver's viewpoint, the WHYN system might be considered a primitive form of TR-FM-SS communication, with information contained in the relative signal delays.

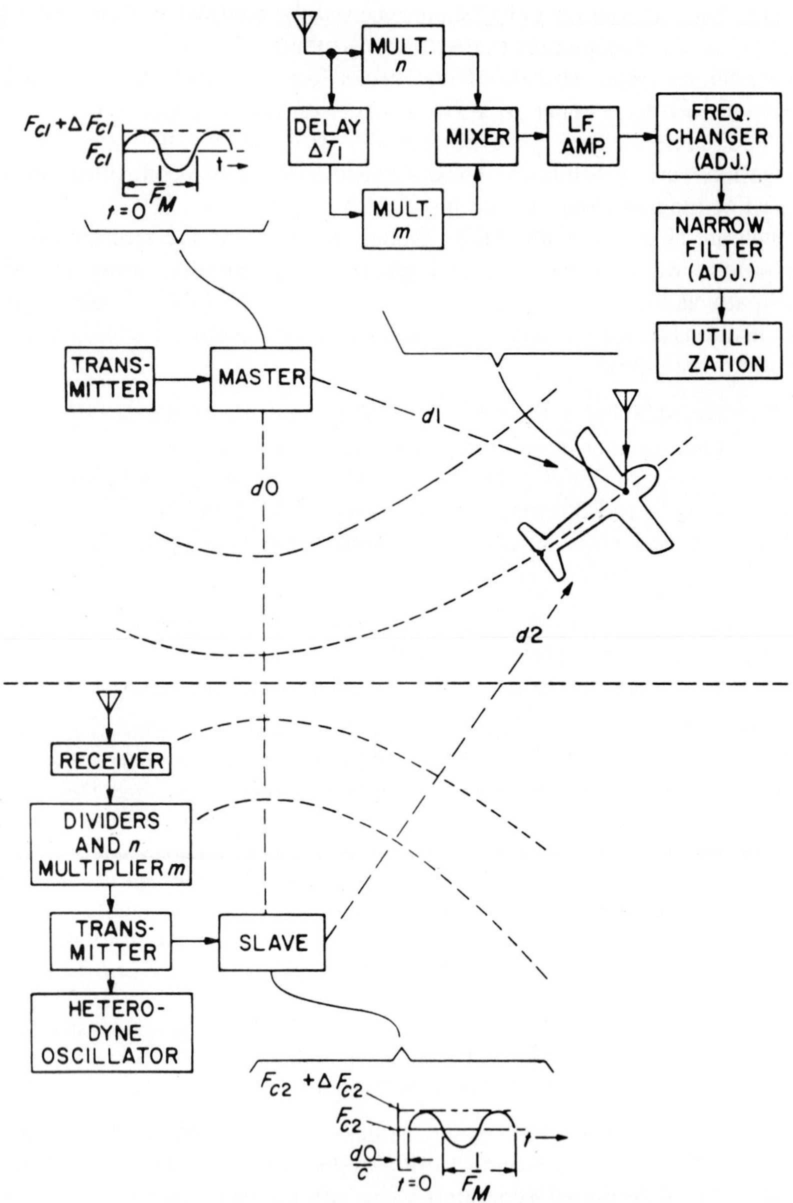

Figure 2.10. Harvey's WHYN system concept is shown here with a plane flying along a hyperbolic curve. Knowing the appropriate ΔT_1 setting for its destination, the aircraft could employ this curve-following tactic to navigate, using only two ground-station transmissions. A third station would be required to provide unambiguous location information. Note that the mixer-i.f. amplifier circuitry acts as the correlating mechanism in the aircraft's receiver. (Diagram abstracted from [107]).

The Bayside engineering team, headed by Harvey, Walter Serniuk, and Meyer Leifer, and joined in 1947 by Nathan Marchand, felt that an FM signal with a more complex modulation than Armstrong's would satisfy requirements. The concept was bench tested via analog simulation with perfect guidance signal synchronization being wired in. Using multiple tone modulation under a maximum frequency deviation constraint of 10 kHz, no simple multitone FM modulation satisfying the contractual constraints could be found. However, low-frequency noise modulation was shown on the bench test to give "an excellent discrimination function with no secondary peaks."

The Sylvania team recognized that noise modulation was "very appealing from the antijamming and security aspects," but its utility in WHYN was questionable since the recording and reproduction requirement in the actual system would be severe. Accordingly, electronic generation of a reproducible multitone modulation function remained the preferred approach. Although the above are quoted from [97], these revealing results were in classified print by October 1948 [98], simultaneously with Shannon's open publication of pseudorandom signalling.

When Republic Aviation's missile development was discontinued, Sylvania work proceeded on WHYN under the auspices of the Air Force's Watson Laboratories [later to become the Rome Air Development Center (RADC)] with this support spanning the 1948–1952 time frame. Noise modulation never made it into the WHYN system, but correlation detection certainly did. In fact, it was noted [99] in 1950 that "Had the full significance of cross-correlation been realized [at the beginning], it is probable that the name [WHYN] would be different." Advocacy (see Figure 2.11) of correlation detection reached an artistic peak when the following classified Sylvania jingle was heard at a 1950 autumn meeting in Washington.

Correlation is the best,
It outdoes all the rest,
Use it in your guided missile
And all they'll hear will be a whistle.
Whistle, whistle, whistle...

Sung to the tune of a popular Pepsi-Cola commercial, this bit of creativity may have been inspired by the arrival, at Sylvania's helm, of Pepsi's chief executive.

The earliest public disclosure of the concept which had evolved in the first WHYN study appears circumspectly in the last paragraph of an October 1950, article by Leifer and Marchand in the *Sylvania Technologist* [101]:

> ...The factors determining signal bandwidth and receiver noise bandwidth are entirely different; in the former it is resolution and in the latter, rate of flow of information. A signal that provides good resolution and, hence, has fairly large bandwidth, should be made more complex in nature within this bandwidth for anti-jamming characteristics. Finally, it is important to note

Figure 2.11. Nathan Marchand, organizer and first chairman of the IRE Information Theory Group, early practitioner of correlation techniques, and codesigner of the WHYN system. He was the lyricist of the classified jingle presented at a Washington meeting where radar correlation-detection methodology was discussed [100]. (Photo courtesy of N. Marchand.)

> that nowhere has the type of modulation of the signals been specified; the conclusions apply equally to pulse-, frequency-, and phase-modulated signals.

Similar views are expressed by Harvey in a companion paper [102]. Ideas and analyses which were prompted by the Sylvania Bayside work appeared in the literature [103]–[106], in two Harvey patents, the first on WHYN [107] and the second on a collision warning radar [108] which could employ noise modulation, and in another patent [109] on spectrum shaping for improving TOA measurement accuracy in correlation detectors. With continued study, the need for bandwidth expansion to improve system performance became even more apparent, and it was declared that [110]

> Jamming signals which are noise modulated or non-synchronous cw or modulated signals are rejected to the same extent that general noise is rejected, the improvement in signal over interference in terms of power being equivalent to the ratio of the transmission bandwidth to the receiver bandwidth.

This improvement property of SS systems is usually referred to as processing gain, which nominally equals the multiplicity factor of the system. By suitably setting these bandwidth parameters, acceptable receiver operation from 40 to 60 dB interference-to-signal ratio was reported in laboratory tests, and navigation receivers operating at -25 dB SNR were predicted [111].

2.2.2 A Note on CYTAC

WHYN was one of the competitors in the development of LORAN (LOng RAnge Navigation), a competition which was eventually won by Sperry Gyroscope Company's CYTAC [112]. Developed in the early 1950s, the CYTAC system and its CYCLAN predecessor had many of the attributes of WHYN, but signal-wise, CYTAC was different in two regards. First, pulse modulation was used so that earliest arriving skywaves could be rejected by gating, and second, phase coding of the pulses was innovated to reject multihop skywaves. These same properties, designed into the system and later patented by Robert Frank and Solomon Zadoff [113], were also used to discriminate between signals from different LORAN stations. The polyphase codes originally designed for CYTAC's pulse modulation were patented separately by Frank [114], but were eventually replaced in LORAN-C by biphase codes to reduce complexity [115]. A certain degree of receiver mismatching also was employed for enhancing time resolution, a similar strategem having been used for the WHYN system [109].

Since narrow-band interference was a potential problem in LORAN, the anti-interference capabilities of this pulse-compression type of signaling were appreciated and reported in 1951 [116]. To further improve performance against in-band CW interference, manually tuned notch filters were added to CYTAC in 1955, and automatic anti-CW notch filters [117], [118] were added to LORAN-C in 1964. To indicate progress, Frank notes that LORAN receivers with four automatically tunable notch filters are now on the market, some for under $1600.

2.2.3 Hush-Up

In the summer of 1951, Madison Nicholson (see Figure 2.12) of Sylvania Buffalo headed a proposal effort for the study of a communication system which he called "Hush-Up." Undoubtedly, the SS ideas therein were distilled versions of those brought to Colonial Radio from the WHYN project by Norman Harvey shortly before that subsidiary lost its identity and was absorbed by Sylvania in February 1950. Nicholson coaxed his old colleague, Robert M. Brown, who had worked at Bayside on the Armstrong radar in World War II while Nicholson had led the AN/ARW-4 team at Colonial, back to Sylvania to work with him and Allen Norris for the duration of the proposal effort. Harvey, by then chiefly responsible for commercial television work, left the realm of military communications research and development. In due course Wright Air Development Center (WADC) gave Sylvania a contract beginning in May 1952, and Nicholson's team went "behind closed doors" to begin work.

Having boned up on Sylvania Bayside's WHYN reports, the engineers at Buffalo set out to verify that a noise-like signal could be used as a carrier, and received coherently, without causing insoluble technical problems.

Figure 2.12. One of the last snapshots of Madison "Mad" Nicholson, at age 51, on a cold Easter Sunday in 1958. As a tribute to this dedicated scientist who died suddenly in Mid-January, 1959, the library at Sylvania's Amherst Laboratory was named the Madison G. Nicholson, Jr., Memorial Library. (Photo courtesy of Dana Cole.)

Independently adopting a pattern of experimentation which was being pursued secretly by other researchers at the time, detector operation was initially examined in the laboratory using a broad-band carrier whose source was thermal noise generated in a 1500 Ω resistor. This wide-band carrier signal was wired directly to the receiver as one input of the correlation detector, thereby temporarily bypassing the remaining major technical problem, the generation of a noise-like carrier at the transmitter and the internal production of an identical, synchronous copy of the same noise-like carrier at the receiver.

In 1953, as the follow-on contract for Hush-Up commenced, James H. Green was hired specifically to develop digital techniques for producing noise-like carriers. John Raney, a Wright Field Project Engineer who had worked on WHYN, also joined Nicholson as System Engineer in early 1953. Nicholson and Raney almost certainly deserve the credit for coining the now universally recognized descriptor "spread spectrum," which Sylvania termed their Hush-Up system as early as 1954, (see [3], footnote 2).

During the second contractual period, which lasted into 1957, Green and Nicholson settled on the form of noise-like carrier which Hush-Up would employ in place of WHYN's FM, namely, a pseudorandomly generated binary sequence PSK-modulated (0 or 180 degrees) onto an RF sinusoid. Such binary sequences with two-level periodic correlation were called "perfect words" by Nicholson. In the end, a variety of perfect word known as an m-sequence was advocated for implementation (more on m-sequences later). Synchronization of the DS-SS signal was accomplished by a sinusoidally dithered tau tracker (τ = delay). Nicholson and Green's tau tracker invention has been, until recently, under patent secrecy order [119] (see Figure 2.13).

As development progressed, the system evolving from the Hush-Up effort was officially designated the ARC-50. Sylvania engineer Everard Book fabricated the ARC-50/XA-2 "flying breadboards." In 1956, flight testing began at Wright-Patterson Air Force Base (WPAFB) with WADC Project Engineers Lloyd Higginbotham and Charles Arnold at the ground end of the ARC-50/XA-2 test link and Capt. Harold K. Christian in the air. The assigned carrier frequency for the tests was the WPAFB tower frequency; the ground terminal of the ARC-50 was about 100 yards from the tower antenna, and communication with the airborne terminal was acceptable at ranges of up to 100 miles. Vincent Oxley recalls that tower personnel, and the aircraft with whom they were conducting normal business, were never aware of ARC-50 transmissions. While the tests were successful, it must have been disheartening to Buffalo engineers when Sylvania failed to win the development/production contract for the ARC-50.

2.2.4 BLADES[2]

In the mid-1950s, Madison Nicholson spent part of his considerable creative energies in the development of methods for generating signals having selectable frequency deviation from a reference frequency. Nicholson achieved this goal with notable accuracy by creating an artificial Doppler effect using a tapped delay line. Even though patent searches uncovered similar frequency-synthesis claims by the Hammond Organ Company, the resulting inventions [120], [121] were a breakthrough for Sylvania engineers working on SS systems.

In addition to being used to slew the time base in the Hush-Up receiver, Nicholson's "linear modulator" (or "cycle adder") was an essential part of another system which Jim Green named the Buffalo Laboratories Application of Digitally Exact Spectra, or BLADES for short. Initiated with company funds in 1955, and headed by Green and Nicholson, the BLADES effort was originally intended to fill Admiral Raeburn's Polaris submarine communications requirements.

Perhaps concern for the serious distortions that multipath could produce in long-range HF communication caused the ARC-50 DS configuration to

[2] It is convenient to recount this Sylvania system next, even though chronologically it would belong toward the end of this chapter.

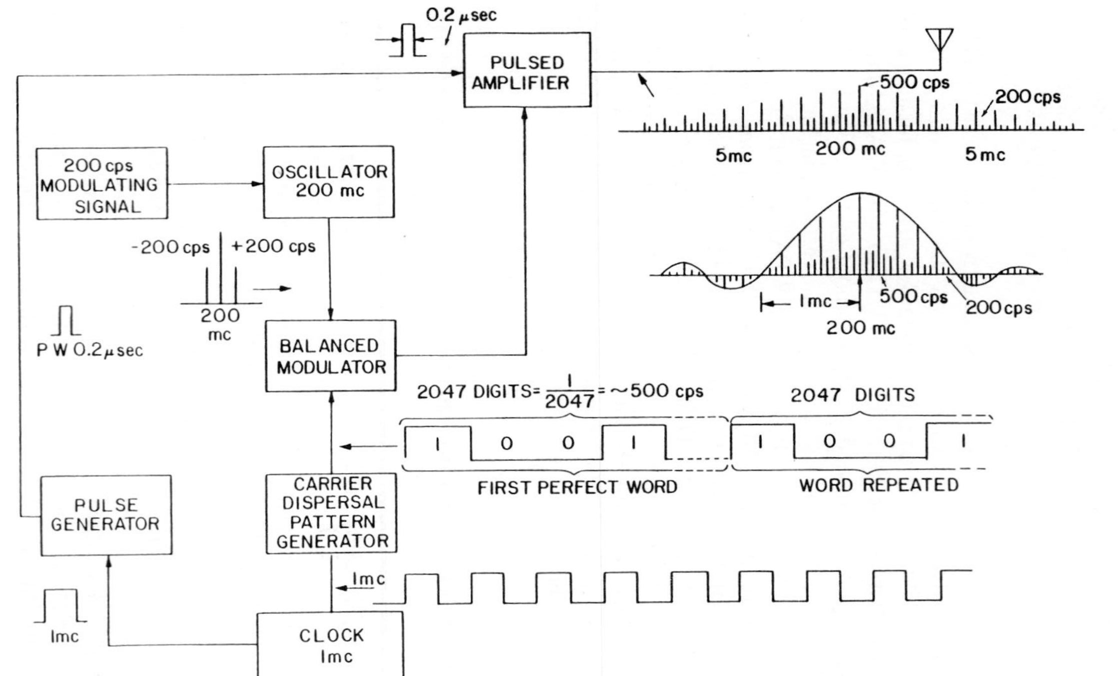

Figure 2.13 (a). Green and Nicholson's SS transmitter contains an *m*-sequence generator, shown here as a "carrier-dispersal-pattern" generator. Data is keyed onto this SS carier by means of a 200 Hz oscillator. The lower of the two displayed output amplitude spectra corresponds to PSK suppressed carrier modulation by the 1 MHz-clocked *m*-sequence. The upper spectrum shows the effect of further spreading by modulating the same carrier dispersal pattern onto .2 μsec pulses. This latter technique for band-spreading probably was employed, since 1950s technology could not reliably support higher-speed *m*-sequence generators.

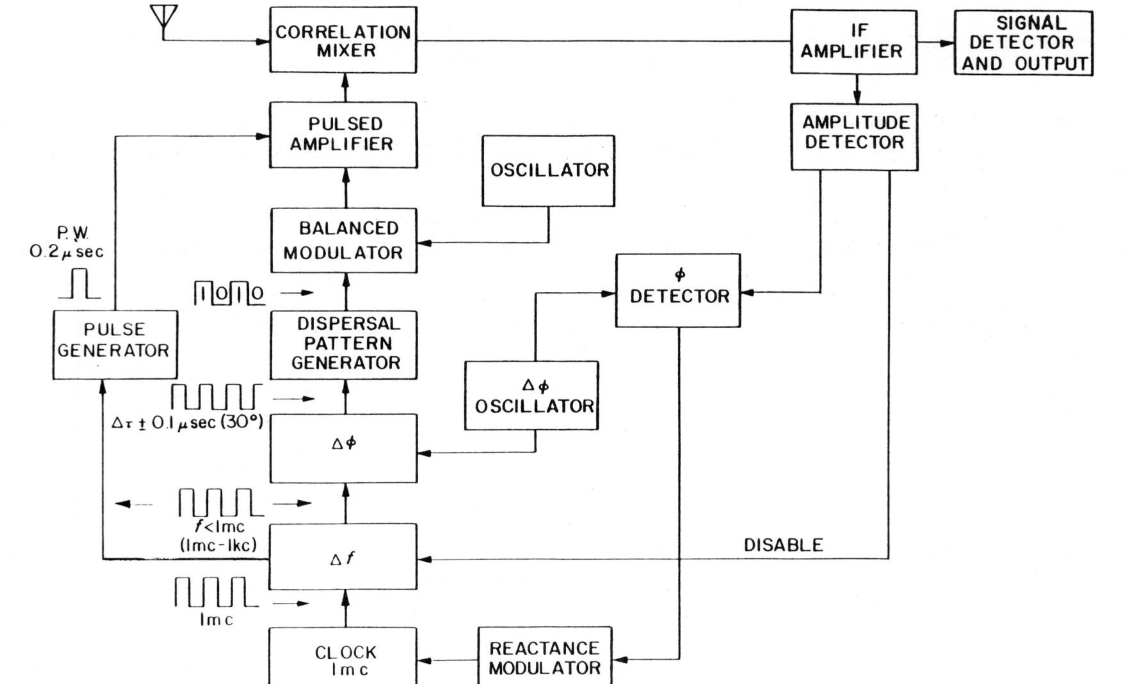

Figure 2.13 (b). The receiver's τ-dither tracker is built around a correlator which compares a locally generated replica of the transmitted carrier to the received signal. Superimposed on the 1 MHz clock driving the carrier dispersal pattern generator is a sinusoidal phase variation controlled by the $\Delta\phi$ oscillator, which in turn produces a corresponding oscillation of the correlator's output amplitude. The phase of this amplitude oscillation, relative to that of the $\Delta\phi$ oscillator, provides an error signal for clock correction. (Both diagrams are abstracted from [119].)

be abandoned in favor of an FH-SS system. In 1957, a demonstration of the breadboard system, operating between Buffalo, NY, and Mountain View, CA, was given to a multiservice group of communications users. Vincent Oxley was system engineer on this development, as well as for the follow-on effort in 1958 to produce a packaged prototype.

The original breadboard contained only an FH-SS/FSK anti-jam mode. The system achieved its protection ratio (Sylvania's then current name for processing gain) by using the code generator to select two new frequencies for each baud, the final choice of frequency being dictated by the data bit to be transmitted. To be effective, a jammer would have to place its power on the other (unused) frequency, or as an alternative, to place its power uniformly over all potentially usable frequencies. Because of the possibility that a jammer might put significant power at the unused frequency, or that the selected channel frequency might be in a fade, a (15, 5) error-correcting code was developed and implemented for the prototype, and was available as an optional mode with a penalty of reducing the information transmission rate to one-third.

While apparently no unclassified descriptions of BLADES are available, glimpses of the system can be seen in several "sanitized" papers and patents produced by Sylvania engineers. Using the results of Pierce [122], Jim Green, David Leichtman, Leon Lewandowski, and Robert Malm [123] analyzed the performance improvements attainable through the diversity achieved by FH combined with coding for error correction. Sylvania's expertise in coding at that time is exemplified by Green and San Soucie's [124] and Fryer's [125] descriptions of a triple-error-correcting (15,5) code (see Figure 2.14), Nicholson and Smith's patent on a binary error-correction system [126], and Green and Gordon's patent [127] on a selective calling system. All are based on properties of the particular perfect words called m-sequences, which were investigated in Sylvania Buffalo's Hush-Up studies. Also involved in BLADES development were R. T. Barnes, David Blair, Ronald Hileman, Stephen Hmelar, James Lindholm, and Jack Wittman at Sylvania, and Project Engineers Richard Newman and Charles Steck at the Navy's Bureau of Ships.

The prototype design effort was aimed at equipment optimization. Extremely stable, single quartz crystal, integrate-and-dump filters were developed. Based on their success, a bank of thirty-two "channel" filters was implemented for an M-ary FSK optional mode to transmit a full character (five bits) per baud. Loss of a single baud in this case meant loss of a full character because the (15,5) decoder could only correct three bit errors per codeword. A "noodle slicer" was implemented to avoid this problem by interleaving five different codewords, so that each baud carried one bit from each word. This interleaving technique was the subject of a patent filed in 1962 by Sylvania engineers Vincent Oxley and William De Lisle [128]. Noodle slicing was never employed in the FH binary FSK mode.

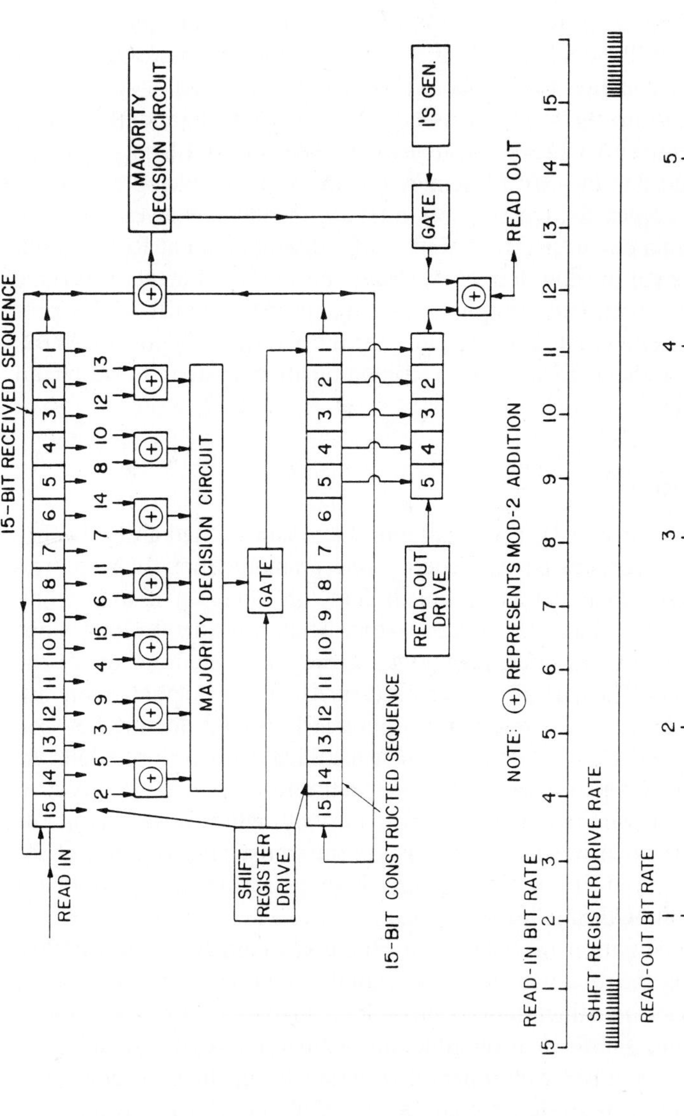

Figure 2.14. The (15, 5) error-correcting code used in BLADES consisted of a (15, 4) code and its complement. The (15, 4) code in turn was composed of the all-zeros 15-tuple and the fifteen cyclic shifts of a length-15 *m*-sequence. Fryer's description of the (15, 5) decoder (shown above) indicated that the received word was majority-logic decoded as a member of the (15, 4) code, using the two 15-stage registers, and the result compared to the received code word. The complement of the decoded word was assumed transmitted if and only if more than seven bit changes were made in the (15, 4) decoding process. (Diagram from [125].)

BLADES occupied nearly 13 kHz of bandwidth in its highest protection mode. In addition to being a practical AJ system, as Vincent Oxley recalls, during initial breadboard on-air tests, the system also served very well as an unintentional jammer, efficiently clearing all other users from the assigned frequency band.

After considerable in-house and on-air testing between the Amherst Laboratories at Williamsville, NY, and San Juan, PR, the packaged prototype was finally delivered for shipboard testing in 1962. Such a system was evidently carried into the blockade associated with the Cuban missile crisis, but a radio silence order prevented its use. In 1963, BLADES was installed on the command flagship Mt. McKinley for operational development tests. Successful full-duplex field trials over intercontinental distances were observed by Sylvania engineer Gerry Meiler, who disembarked at Rota, Spain, leaving the system in the hands of Navy personnel. Further into the Mediterranean, intentional jamming was encountered, and BLADES provided the only useful communication link for the McKinley. Thus, BLADES was quite likely the earliest FH-SS communication system to reach an operational state.

2.2.5 Noise Wheels

At the end of World War II, ITT reorganized and constructed a new facility at Nutley, NJ, incorporated as Federal Telecommunication Laboratories (FTL), with Henri Busignies as Technical Director. There, in 1946, a group of engineers in Paul Adam's R-16 Laboratory began working on long-range navigation and communication techniques to meet the requirements of the expanding intercontinental air traffic industry. In the available frequency bands, it was expected that multipath generated by signal ducting between the ionosphere and the earth would cause significant distortion, while the prime source of independent interference at the receiver would consist of atmospheric noise generated for the most part by lightning storms in the tropics. A major effort was initiated to study the statistical properties of the interference and to learn how to design high performance detectors for signals competing with this interference.

This was the situation in 1948 when Shannon's communication philosophy, embracing the idea that noise-like signals could be used as bearers of information, made a distinct impression on FTL engineers. Mortimer Rogoff, one of the engineers in R-16 at the time, was an avid photographic hobbyist. He conceived of a novel experimental program using photographic techniques for storing a noise-like signal and for building a nearly ideal cross correlator. Supported by ITT funds and doing some work in a makeshift home lab, Rogoff prepared a 4 in. $\times$ 5 in. sheet of film whose transmissivity varied linearly in both directions, thus creating a mask whose transmission characteristic at every point (X, Y) was proportional to the product XY. Two signals then were correlated by using them as the X and Y inputs to the oscilloscope, reading the light emitted from the masked oscilloscope face with a photomultiplier, and low-pass filtering the resultant output.

Rogoff's noise-like carrier came straight from the Manhattan telephone directory. Selecting at random 1440 numbers not ending in 00, he radially plotted the middle two of the last four digits so that the radius every fourth of a degree represented a new random number (see Figure 2.15). This drawing was transferred to film which, in turn, when rotated past a slit of light, intensity-modulated a light beam, providing a stored noise-like signal to be sensed by a photocell.

In initial experiments, Rogoff mounted two identical noise wheels on a single axle driven by a Diehl 900 rpm synchronous motor (see Figure 2.16). Designed and assembled by Rogoff and his colleague, Robert Whittle, separate photocell pickups were placed on each wheel, one stationary and one on an alidade, so that the relative phase between the two signals could be varied for test purposes. Using time-shift keying (an extra pickup required) to generate MARK or SPACE, one noise wheel's signal was modulated and then combined with interference to provide one correlator input, while the other input came directly from the second noise wheel. These baseband experiments, with data rates on the order of a bit per second and, hence, a multiplicity factor of well over 40 dB, indicated that a noise-like signal hidden in ambient thermal noise could still accurately convey information.

In another part of FTL, highly compartmentalized for security purposes, Louis deRosa headed the R-14 Electronic Warfare Group. DeRosa, who earlier had collaborated with Busignies and Deloraine, and who had exchanged many friendly arguments with Nathan Marchand concerning the

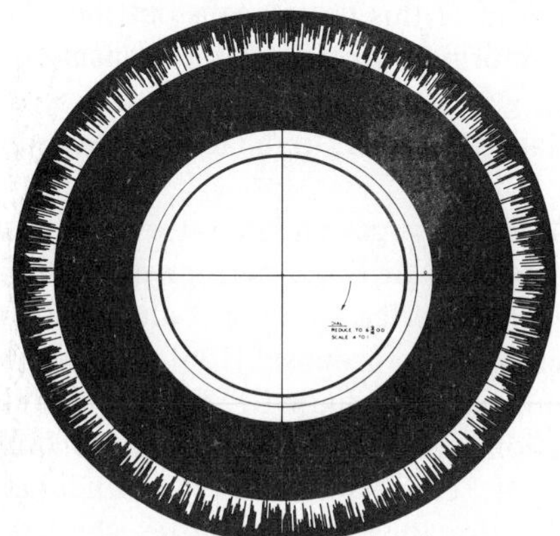

Figure 2.15. Only two copies of Rogoff's secret noise wheel, shown here, were made to support ITT's early research on spread-spectrum systems. The noise wheel concept was revived briefly in 1963 when two more wheels were produced and tested in a system at ITT. (Photo from [130], courtesy of ITT.)

Figure 2.16. ITT's equipment constructed for bench-testing a communication system based on noise-like carriers stored on wheels. (Photo from [130], courtesy of ITT.)

merits of IF correlation (à la Marchand [38]) versus baseband correlation via homodyning (deRosa's favorite), held an umbrella contract through Dr. George Rappaport, Chief of the Electronic Warfare Branch at WADC, to pursue a variety of electronic countermeasures and counter-countermeasures. The contract, codenamed Project Della Rosa, spanned the 1947–1951 time frame and, hence, was concurrent with Rogoff's work.

The first written indication of deRosa's visualization of an SR-SS technique occurs in one of this prolific inventor's patents, filed in January 1950, with L. G. Fischer and M. J. DiToro [129], and kept under secrecy order for some time. The fine print of this patent calls out the possibility of using an arbitrarily coded waveform generated at the transmitter and an identical, synchronous, locally generated waveform at the receiver to provide a reference for a correlation detector, to reliably recover signals well below the noise level.

On August 1, 1950, de Rosa gave a laboratory demonstration of Rogoff's noise wheels to visiting U.S. Air Force personnel, with the system extracting signals 35 dB below the interfering noise. Later the same month, deRosa and Rogoff produced a secret proposal [130] outlining Rogoff's work and proposing several refinements including PSK data modulation, wider bandwidth carrier generation (either by scaling Rogoff's original system or by introducing flying spot scanners reading a pseudorandom image), and quicker-response drives for the receiver's noise wheel synchronizing servo. This proposal also contains a performance analysis resulting in a processing gain representation as a ratio of transmission bandwidth to data bandwidth.

Whittle recalls that in mid-1951 the wheels were separated by about 200 yards in the first test of his synchronization system for the noise wheel drives. During these tests, Bing Crosby's crooning on radio station WOR provided the jamming as Morse code was successfully transmitted at −30 dB SNR. Tapes of the test were made and taken on unsuccessful Washington, DC, marketing trips, where there was considerable interest but evidently the government could not grasp the full significance of the results.

In 1952, an FTL Vice President, retired General Peter C. Sandretto, established relations between deRosa and Eugene Price, then Vice President of Mackay Marine, whereby Mackay facilities in Palo Alto, CA, were made available for transcontinental tests of the FTL equipment. Testing began in late November and ended before Christmas 1952, with Whittle and Frank Lundburg operating an ARC-3 Collins transmitter at the Mackay installation, and deRosa and Frank Bucher manning the receiver at Telegraph Hill, NJ.

Coordination of these field trials was done by telephone using a codeword jargon, with

"crank it" = bring up transmitter power,

"take your foot off" = reduce transmitter power,

"ring it up" = advance the sync search phase,

"the tide is running" = severe fading is being encountered,

"go north" = increase transmission speed.

Initial synchronization adjustments typically took 3–5 min. Matched tuning forks, ringing at a multiple of 60 Hz, provided stable frequency sources for the drives with the receiver synchronizer employing a war-surplus Bendix size-10 selsyn resolver for phase-shifting purposes. Rogoff's original noise wheels were retained for the transcontinental tests, as was his photo-optical multiplier, although the multiplier was improved to handle both positive and negative inputs. Using ionospheric prediction charts, transmission was near the maximum usable frequency (where multipath is least), in the 12–20 MHz range, without FCC license. The system bandwidth was fixed at 8 kHz, the data rate varied down to a few bits per second, and the transmitter power was adjustable between 12 and 25 W.

Although documentation of the test results has not yet been made available, Whittle recalls that during a magnetic storm that happened to occur, a 50 kW Mackay transmitter could not communicate with the East Coast using its conventional modulation, while FTL's test system operated successfully on 25 W. Often the noise-wheel system communicated reliably, even while interference in the same frequency band was provided by the high-power Mackay transmitter. Air Force observer Thomas Lawrence, Project Engineer on Della Rosa and Chief of the Deceptive Countermeasures Section at WADC (another WADC team member was Frank Catanzarite), also recalls witnessing these capabilities.

However, some problems were encountered. In addition to the FTL system once being detected out-of-band (probably in the vicinity of the transmitter), propagation effects apparently caused trouble at times. The signals received at Telegraph Hill were preserved by a speed-lock tape recorder which had been built from scratch to have adequate stability. In the months following the transcontinental tests, John Groce performed correlation recovery experiments on the taped signals, experiencing considerable difficulty with multipath.

Government-decreed project isolation prevented Rogoff from being told about the above tests of his noise wheels. In fact, Rogoff could not follow developments after 1950, except to participate in a patent application with deRosa, for which [130] served as the disclosure. With the help of patent attorney Percy Lantzy, the application, which described a full-fledged SR-SS single-sideband communication system based on Rogoff's noise wheels, was filed in March 1953 (see Figure 2.17). The original patent claims placed few restrictions on the DS modulation technique to be employed, but subsequently these were struck out in favor of single-sideband specification.

In June 1953, the Bureau of Ships placed a secrecy order against the application, which stood until July 1966, when the Navy recommended recision of the order and issuance of the patent. Technically, this was accomplished in November 1966, but before the printing presses in the U.S. Patent Office had begun to roll, a civil servant at the National Security Agency (NSA) noted the invention and was able to get secrecy reimposed. This order stood until 1978, when NSA permitted wholesale recision on scores of patents including at least a dozen on SS techniques. The deRosa-Rogoff patent [49] was finally awarded in November 1979, nearly thirty years after the invention's conception.

The emphasis in both invention and early experimental work at FTL was on covert communication and on suppressing atmospheric noise. It is impossible to determine exactly when FTL engineers appreciated the fully robust AJ capabilities of their system. In 1950, they suspected that broadband noise jamming would be the best attack against the receiver's signal processor, while the receiver itself might be disabled by any strong signal if it did not possess sufficient dynamic range. The deRosa-Rogoff patent, although using the phrase "secrecy and security" several times, never specifically claims AJ capabilities. However, during the course of their work, FTL engineers coined the term "chip" to denote an elementary pulse which is modulated by a single random or pseudorandom variable, and they realized that high performance against atmospheric noise, or when hiding beneath a strong signal like radio station WOR, required many chips per data bit of transmission.

For unknown reasons, FTL was unable to capitalize significantly on this early entrance into the SS field. When in June 1970, as an Assistant

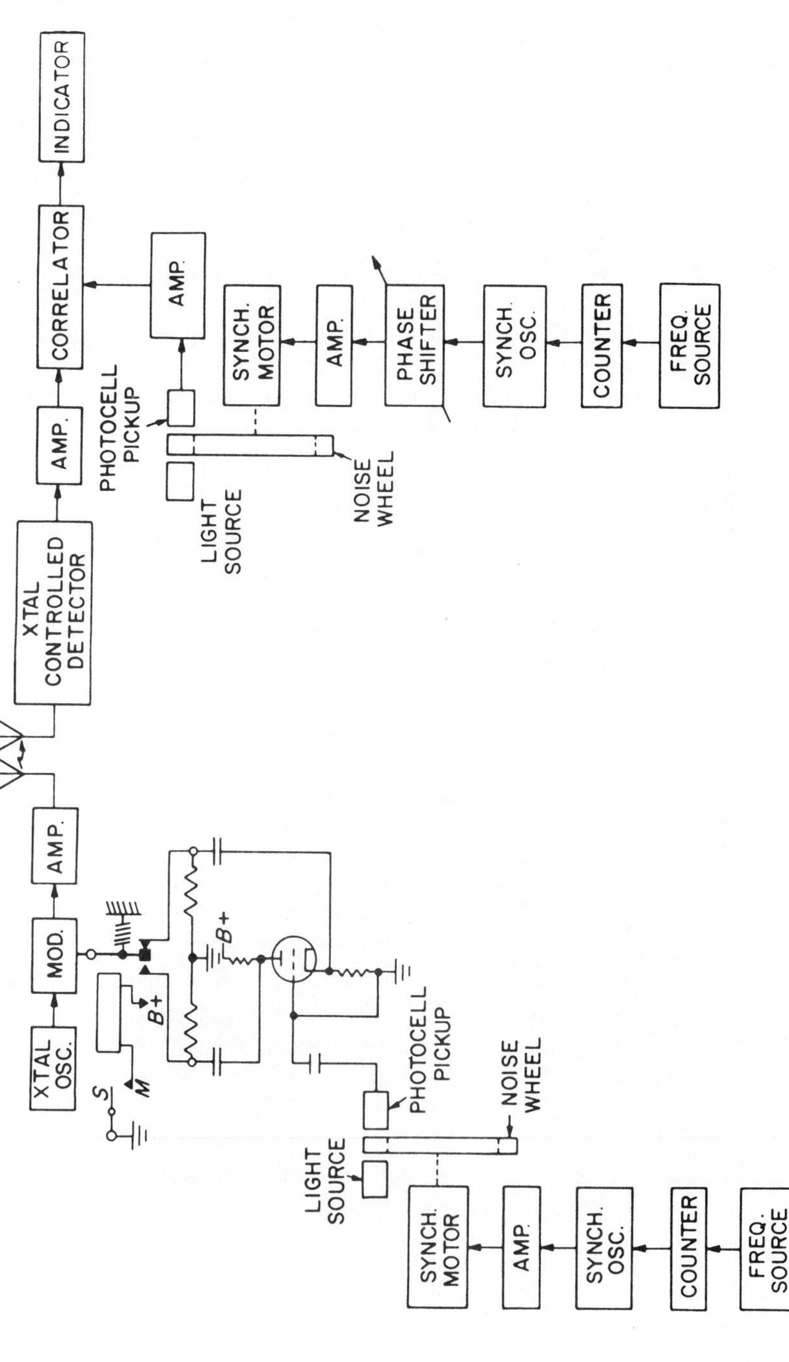

Figure 2.17. This diagram from the deRosa-Rogoff patent [49] shows Rogoff's identical noise wheels serving as signal storage, with matched frequency sources used to control the speed of their synchronous motor drives.

Secretary of Defense, Louis deRosa (see Figure 2.18) was asked about later developments involving the FTL system, he mentioned only Project Dog, a U.S. Navy covert communications operation in the North Korean theater.

2.2.6 The Hartwell Connection

In January 1950, the Committee on Undersea Warfare of the National Research Council addressed a letter to Admiral C. B. Monsen, Assistant Chief of Naval Operations, in which the committee urged the determination of a long-range program against submarines [131]. This was the beginning of a sequence of events which led to the formation of a classified study program known as Project Hartwell, held at M.I.T. in June through August 1950. Under the direction of Prof. Jerrold Zacharias, the study brought together highly qualified experts from the military, industry, and universities, to find new ways to protect overseas transportation.

A subsequent history [132] of the Research Laboratory of Electronics (RLE) at M.I.T. indicates that Hartwell was possibly the most successful of M.I.T.'s summer study projects, motivating the development of "the Mariner class of merchant vessels; the SOSUS submarine detection system; the atomic depth charge; a whole new look at radar, sonar and magnetic detection; and a good deal of research on oceanography." This 1966 history omitted (perhaps because of classification) the fact that transfer of an important concept in modern military communications took place at Hartwell.

Figure 2.18. Louis deRosa remained with ITT until 1966 when he joined the Philco-Ford Corporation as Director of Engineering and Research. In 1970, he left a Corporate Vice President position at Philco-Ford to be sworn in (above) by Melvin Laird as Assistant Secretary of Defense for Telecommunications, the first holder of that office. He died unexpectedly in 1971 after a long workout on the tennis court. (Photo courtesy of Mrs. Louis deRosa, standing next to Secretary Laird.)

One of the many ideas considered was the possibility of hiding fleet communication transmissions so that enemy submarines could not utilize them for direction finding. Appendix G of the secret final report on Project Hartwell suggested that a transmitter modulated by a wide band of noise be employed, reducing the energy density of the transmitted signal "to an arbitrarily small value." If at the same time the actual intelligence bandwidth was kept small, covert communications should be possible in certain situations.

Three systems for accomplishing covert communications were described in the report. One, acknowledged to be the suggestion of FTL's Adams and deRosa (Adams alone was an attendee), was an SR-SS system. A second system, attributed to J. R. Pierce of BTL, used very narrow pulses to achieve frequency spreading, pulse pair spacing to carry intelligence, and coincidence detection at the receiver. It was noted that if synchronized (random) pulse sources were available at transmitter and receiver, then cryptographic-like effects were possible, presumably by transmitting only the second of each pulse pair.

A third system, with no proponent cited, is the only one described by a block diagram in the final report (see Figure 2.19). To avoid the synchronization problems inherent in stored reference systems, it was proposed that the noise-like carrier alone be transmitted on one channel, and that an information-bearing delay-modulated replica of the carrier also be trans-

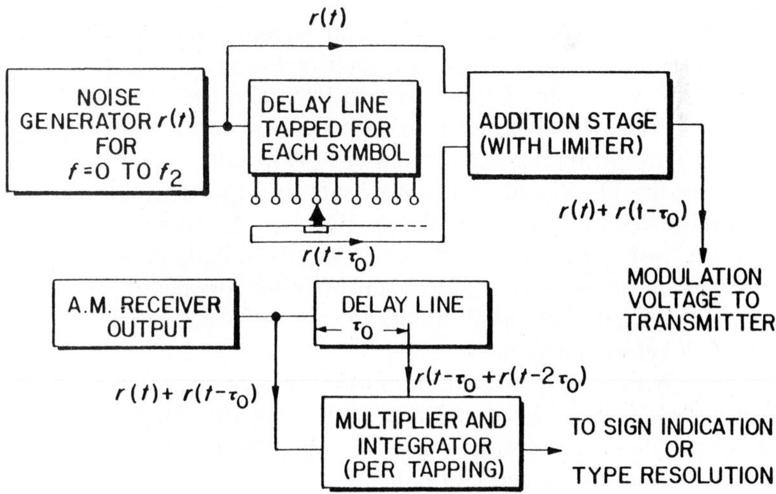

Figure 2.19. Block diagram of a basic transmitted reference system using pure noise as a carrier and time-shift keying for data modulation. No effort has been made to separate the data and reference channels in this system proposed by the East German Professor F. H. Lange. His configuration is nearly identical to that secretly suggested in Project Hartwell a decade earlier. (Redrawn from [12].)

mitted at either the same frequency or at an offset frequency. A cross-correlation receiver still would be employed in this TR-SS system, but the carrier storage and synchronization problems of an SR-SS system would be traded for the headaches of a second channel.

The Hartwell report noted that the SR system was cryptographically more secure than the TR system, which transmitted a copy of the wide-band carrier in the clear. Furthermore, it would be improper to transmit the intelligence-free wide-band carrier on the same channel as the intelligence-modulated carrier with a fixed delay τ between them, since this delay-line addition would impose a characteristic $\cos(\pi f \tau)$ periodic ripple on the power spectral density of the transmitted signal. This ripple might be detectable on a panoramic receiver, compromising the covertness of the transmission. Although not mentioned in the report, it was realized at about the same time that multipath could produce a similar delay-line effect with similar results on any wide-band signal, including SR-SS transmissions.

To close this revealing discussion of noise modulation, the Hartwell report suggested that several of these kinds of systems, using different wide-band carriers, could operate simultaneously in the same band with little effect on each other. This concept, which, it is noted, would eliminate the cooperative synchronization required in time-division multiple-access (TDMA) systems, is one of the earliest references to CDMA operation.

While the authorship of Appendix G is not indicated explicitly in the Hartwell report, it is clear that the main contributors to this portion of the study effort were Jerome B. Wiesner, Edward E. David, Harald T. Friis, and Ralph K. Potter. Wiesner and David went on from M.I.T. to become science advisers to Presidents Kennedy and Nixon, respectively. Friis and Potter were already well-known for their accomplishments at BTL, the latter being a prime innovator of the X-System [58]. There is considerable evidence that Wiesner, then professor of electrical engineering and Associate Director of RLE at M.I.T., was the author of Appendix G, and most likely the source of the TR-SS and SS-CDMA concepts set forth in this report [3].

Concerning Wiesner's place in the development of modern communications, it was later said by an M.I.T. professor [133], "Perhaps one might put it that Wiener preached the gospel and Wiesner organized the church. Jerry's real strength... lies in his ability to spot the potential importance of an idea long before others do."

Certainly Wiesner appreciated the possibilities of the wide-band communication systems discussed at Hartwell. Shortly after Hartwell, Wiesner met Robert Fano in a hallway near the Building 20 bridge entrance to the RLE secret research area and told Fano of a "Navy study idea" for using a noise-modulated carrier to provide secure military communications. Even though Fano was familiar with Shannon's precepts and had been an early contributor to the new field of information theory, this made a profound impression on him. He in turn discussed the concept with Wilbur Davenport, a then recent recipient of the Sc.D. degree from M.I.T. They decided to split the research possibilities, with Fano studying radar applications and

Davenport developing the communication applications. This was a fortunate juxtaposition with radar work alongside communications since covertness could not be maintained in radar applications and jamming was always a possibility. The AJ potential of SS systems was appreciated immediately and reported in a series of RLE secret Quarterly Progress Reports.

The year 1951 saw another secret summer study, known as Project Charles, in action at M.I.T. Under the direction of F. W. Loomis of the University of Illinois, Project Charles investigated air defense problems, including electronic warfare. Appendix IV-1 of the Charles Report [134], written by Harry Nyquist of BTL, suggests that carrier frequencies be changed in accordance with a predetermined random sequence, and that by using this FH pattern over a wide band, the effects of jamming could be minimized. In the next section of Appendix IV, the Charles Report proposes that a ground wave radar use a noise-modulated CW carrier to achieve security against countermeasures, and indicates that M.I.T. is investigating this technique (this is over a decade after Gustav Guanella's original conception).

2.2.7 NOMAC

Correlation methodology is so basic to modern communications that it may be difficult to imagine a time when the technique was not widely accepted. Fano, commenting on that era, has said, "There was a heck of a skepticism at the time about crosscorrelation...it was so bad that in my own talks I stopped using the word crosscorrelation. Instead I would say, 'You detect by multiplying the signals together and integrating.'" Nevertheless, by the outset of the 1950s, M.I.T. researchers had become leading proponents of correlation techniques, and were finding more and more problems which correlation might help solve [40]–[42], [151], [229], [230].

It was into this climate that Wiesner brought the noise-like wide-band carrier concept from Project Hartwell to M.I.T. researchers. Within a year of this event, Lincoln Laboratory received its organizational charter and commenced operation, its main purpose being the development of the SAGE (Semi-Automatic Ground Environment) air defense system defined by Project Charles. Soon thereafter, the classified work at RLE was transferred to Lincoln Laboratory and became Division 3 under the direction of William Radford. There, fundamental SS research was performed, to a significant extent by M.I.T. graduate students, guided by Group Leaders Fano and Davenport. The acronym NOMAC, classified confidential at the time and standing for "NOise Modulation And Correlation," was coined by one of these students, Bennett Basore, to describe the SS techniques under study. The term "spread spectrum" was never heard at M.I.T. in those days.

Basore's secret Sc.D. thesis [135], the first on NOMAC systems, was completed under Fano, Davenport, and Wiesner in 1952. Basore recalls that his research was motivated by a desire to "examine how the probability of error for correlation-detection compared with the probability computed by Rice [228], which Rice showed approached zero under conditions consistent with Shannon theory." His thesis, which documented the results of this effort, consisted of a comparison of the performances of transmitted- and stored-reference systems operating in the presence of broad-band Gaussian noise. An RF simulation of a NOMAC system with multiplicity factors up to 45 dB was used to back up theoretical analyses. As in Nicholson's and Rogoff's initial experiments, the synchronization problem of the SR system was bypassed in the experimental setup. The carrier was obtained by amplifying thermal and tube noise, while the interfering noise was produced by some old radar RF strips made originally for M.I.T.'s Radiation Laboratory. Data were on-off keyed. A bandpass correlator was employed in which two inputs at offset frequencies were inserted into an appropriate nonlinearity, the output signal then observed at the difference frequency through a narrow bandpass integrating filter, and the result envelope-detected to recover correlation magnitude. Basore's conclusion was that the effect of noise in the reference channel was to reduce the receiver's output SNR by the ratio of the signal power level to the signal-plus-noise power level in the reference channel.

While the advantages of TR systems have since dwindled as a result of the development of synchronization techniques for the SR system, the disadvantages of TR systems are to a great extent fundamental. Considerable experimental work on TR-NOMAC systems was performed at M.I.T. in the 1950–1952 time frame. Davenport's Group 34 at Lincoln Laboratory developed several TR-SS systems, including one called the P9D. An HF version of the P9D was tested between Lincoln Laboratory and a Signal Corps site in New Jersey and, according to Davenport, worked "reasonably well." This led to the development of a VHF version intended for an ionospheric scatter channel to a Distant Early Warning (DEW) radar complex near Point Barrow, AK. Since the need for LPI and AJ was marginal, SS modulation was not considered necessary and the DEW-Line link was eventually served by more conventional equipment.

A TR system study also was carried out by U.S. Army Signal Corps Capt. Bernard Pankowski in a secret Master's degree thesis [136], under the direction of Davenport. Published at the same time as Basore's thesis, Pankowski's work details several ideas concerning jamming, multiplexing, and CDMA operation of TR-NOMAC systems. In particular, it noted that jamming a TR system is accomplished simply by supplying the receiver with acceptable alternative reference and data signals, e.g., a pair of sine waves in the receiver's pass-bands at the appropriate frequency separation.

Bernie Pankowski offered three possible solutions to the jamming problem, namely, going to the MF or SR systems which others were studying at the time, or developing a hybrid pure noise-TR, FH-SR system with one of the two channels frequency hopped to deny offset frequency knowledge to the jammer. Similarly, CDMA operation was achieved by assigning each transmitter-receiver pair a different frequency offset between their data and reference channels. Laboratory experiments on various single-link TR system configurations with two multiplexed circuits sharing the same reference channel were carried out for a channel bandwidth of 3000 Hz and a data bandwidth of 50 Hz.

There were several exchanges of ideas with other research groups during the period following Basore's and Pankowski's theses. For example, at Lincoln Laboratory on October 2, 1952, Sylvania, Lincoln, and Air Force personnel participated in discussions led by Meyer Leifer and Wilbur Davenport on the subject of secure communications [137]. In February 1953, Sylvania, Lincoln and Jet Propulsion Laboratory researchers attended the (Classified) RDB Symposium on the Information Theory Applications to Guided Missile Problems at the California Institute of Technology [111], [138]. Detailed records of these kinds of exchanges appear to be virtually nonexistent. (RDB: the Pentagon's Research and Development Board.)

As Group 34 studied the TR approach, it became apparent that the SR approach had advantages that could not be overlooked. The task of solving the key generation and synchronization problems for an SR system was given to another of Davenport's Sc.D. candidates, Paul Green. Green's secret thesis [139] is a clearly written comparison of several NOMAC system configurations, the aim of which is to determine a feasible SR design. Comparisons are based on the relationship between input and output signal-to-noise (or jamming) ratios for the receiver's signal processor, and the degradations in this relationship as a result of synchronization error and multipath. Green deduced that correlation at baseband would require a phase-locked carrier for good correlator performance, while correlation at IF à la Basore, with the correlator output being the envelope of the bandpass-filtered IF signal, would require SS carrier sync error to be bounded by the reciprocal of the SS carrier bandwidth.

Green then designed and built (see Figure 2.20) a digitally controlled SS carrier generator in which five stagger-tuned resonant circuits were shock-excited by pseudorandom impulse sequences which in turn were generated from fifteen stored binary sequences of lengths 127, 128, and 129 (see Figure 2.21). The resultant signal had a long period and noise-like qualities in both the time and frequency domains, yet was storable and reproducible at an electronically controlled rate at both ends of a communication link. The proposed SS carrier synchronization procedure at the receiver was quite similar to then contemporary tracking-radar practice, progressing through search, acquisition, and track modes with no change in signal structure. Tracking error was sensed by differencing correlator outputs for slightly different values of clock oscillator phase. Based on Green's results which indicated that an SR system was feasible, and on jamming tests which confirmed TR system vulnerability [140], Group 34 resources were turned toward prototyping an SR system. This marked the end of TR system research at Lincoln Laboratory.

Figure 2.20. These two racks of equipment constitute the transmitter and receiver used to carry out the experimental portion of Paul Green's secret Sc.D. dissertation. The SS carrier generators occupy the upper half of each rack, with the plug boards allowing the operator to change the structure of the 15 stored binary sequences. Later in the F9C system, these plug boards were replaced by punched card readers. (Photo from [139], courtesy of M.I.T. Lincoln Laboratory.)

2.2.8 F9C-A / Rake

The prototype SR-NOMAC system developed for the Army Signal Corps by Lincoln Laboratory was called the F9C. Its evolution to a final deployed configuration, which spanned the 1953–1959 time frame, was carried out in cooperation with the Coles Signal Laboratory at Ft. Monmouth, in particular with the aid of Harold F. Meyer, Chief of the Long Range Radio Branch, and Bernard Goldberg, Chief of the Advanced Development Section, and also Lloyd Manamon and Capt. H. A. ("Judd") Schulke, all of that laboratory. This effect had the whole-hearted support of Lt. Genl. James D. O'Connell, then Chief Signal Officer of the U.S. Army.

Paul Green remained at Lincoln Lab after completing his thesis, and was placed in charge of building and testing F9C equipment. Included in the group of engineers contributing to the development of the F9C were Bob Berg, Bill Bergman, John Craig, Ben Eisenstadt, Phil Fleck, Bill McLaughlin, Bob Price, Bill Smith, George Turin, and Charles Wagner (originator of the Wagner "code," the simplest version of the Viterbi algorithm).

The F9C system [141] occupied 10 kHz of bandwidth and originally employed frequency-shift data modulation at a rate of approximately 22

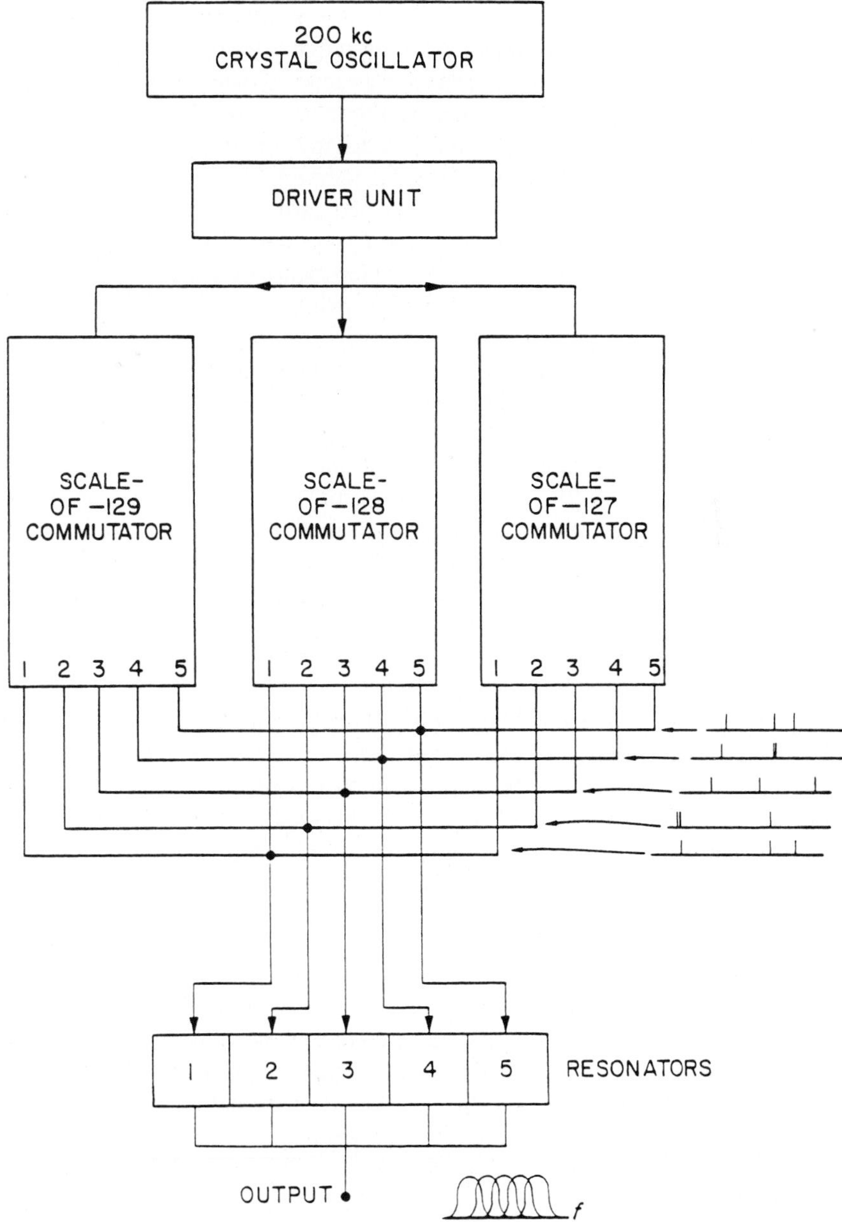

Figure 2.21. The boxes in the above diagram of Paul Green's SS signal generator are located so that they correspond to the physical layout in the equipment racks of Figure 2.20. An SS signal generator similar to the one shown here, combining waveforms of relatively prime periods, was chosen for the F9C system. (Redrawn from [139].)

ms/bit. This resulted in a multiplicity factor greater than 200. The F9C radioteletype system was intended for long-range fixed-plant usage over HF channels. Initially, SS signal generation was accomplished by combining the 28 outputs of four 7-stage counters (fixed to have periods 117, 121, 125, and 128) using an array of AND gates, and driving a bandpass filter with the resultant pulse train. For security against jamming, the gate array connections were controlled by changeable punched cards and this served the role of a key for the system. At the time, there were discussions concerning the possibility of making the SS signal provide cryptographic security as well, but this idea was eventually dropped in favor of conventional data encryption before modulation.

Both the SS signal generator and data modulation technique were later modified to improve spectral and correlation characteristics and change the SS signal period, thereby increasing AJ and privacy capabilities [142]. (For a discussion of the effects encountered in combining sequences of different periods, see [143]–[145].) Also, in a 1955 secret report [226], Price proposed improving DS-SS by resorting to error correction coding in combination with soft or hard decisions against CW or pulse jammers. This first conceptualization of error correction in an AJ strategy was not implemented in the F9C system.

At the suggestion of Signal Corps Capt. John Wozencraft, the bandpass filter in Basore's bandpass correlator was replaced by an active filter [146] employing a diode-quenched high-Q L-C tank circuit, thereby attaining true IF integrate-and-dump correlation operation. A different circuit achieving the same matched-filter-type improvement on sinusoids was developed independently by M. L. Doelz for the Collins Radio Company [147].

Synchronization of the SS signal was accomplished initially by sending a tone burst at a preagreed frequency to start the four 7-stage counters in near synchronism. A fine search then began to bring the receiver's SS modulation clock into precise alignment with the received modulation. When synchronism was achieved, a tracking loop was closed to maintain sync. The fine search was conducted at a rate of 1000 s for each second of relative delay being swept. The frequency standards used in the system were stable enough that even with propagation variations, a disablement of the tracking loop for a day would cause a desynchronization of at most 10 ms. Eventually it was demonstrated [148] that the tone burst was not necessary and the four 7-stage clocks were approximately aligned by time of day at 5 min intervals in initial search situations.

Transcontinental field trials of the F9C system commenced in August, 1954 [142]. The transmitter was located in Davis, CA, and the receiver in Deal, NJ, to provide an eastbound HF link for F9C tests. A conventional teletype link was supplied for westbound communication (see Figure 2.22). Initial tests verified what many suspected, namely, that multipath could severely reduce the effectiveness of SS systems. While at low data rates an ordinary FSK receiver would operate based on the energy received over all propagation paths, the high time resolution inherent in an SS receiver would force the receiver to select a single path for communication, resulting in a considerable loss in signal level. Based on these early trials, several of the previously mentioned modifications were made, and in addition, it was decided to add diversity to the system to combat multipath. Two receivers with antennas displaced by 550 feet were used for space diversity tests, and two correlators were employed to select signals propagated by different paths, in tau-diversity (time delay) tests.

A second set of field trials began in February 1955 to determine the effects of these changes on performance of the transcontinental link. Results showed that an ordinary FSK system with space diversity and integrate-and-dump reception still significantly outperformed the F9C, with tau-diversity showing some hope of improving F9C performance. Both local and remote jamming tests were conducted in this second series, the interfering signal being an in-band FSK signal with MARK and SPACE frequency spacing identical to that of the F9C data modulation. The remote jammers were located at Army Communication Station ABA in Honolulu, HI, and at the Collins Radio Company in Cedar Rapids, IA. With tau-diversity, the F9C achieved a rough average of 17 dB improvement over FSK against jamming in the presence of multipath, justifying transition to an F9C-A production phase.

```
RGR
PHIL MOVED YESTERDAY MOST OF HIS JUNK THAT IS THOUGH HE IS STILL AT
ROBINSON RD
THERE IS NOT TOO MUCH DOING AT THE LAB AT THE MOMENT
WE ARE TRYING TO FIND EQUIPMENT FOR THE ATLATIC PULSE TESTS
THE IPSWICH SITE IS COMING ALONG SLOWLY BECAUSE OF THE LONG DELAY IN
STARTING
MARIE WILL BE FLYING OUT TO SFO ON MONDAY
SHE SAYS R  THAT SHE WILL GIVE YOU A CALL WHEN SHE GETS TR  THERE
 I DONT KNOW IF SHE HAS A JOB YET

RGR I WAS WONDERING WHEN SHE WOULD ARRIVE OUT HERE AND ALSO IF I COULD
BE OF ANY ASSISTANCE TO HERE  I WILL WAIT FOR HER CALL AT EDL ON MONDAY
IN REGARD TO MY OWN PLANS I PLAN TO STAY OUT HERE UNTIL THE FIRST EQUIP
AT EDL IS SHOWN TO BE OK AND THE IF TIME PERMITS WILL GO BACK TO THE

LAB FOR A SHORT STAY  IT WILL BE SHORT SINCE I AM GOING UP TO TACOME
TO BE MARRIED ON THE 25 OF AUGUST AND THEN I PLAN TO GO TO SWEDEN ON
THE 20 OF SEPTEMBER FOR AT LEST A MONTH
SO I WILL BE ON VACATION FOR ABOUT THREE MONTHS  GA

OH REALLY ??
YES
WE ARE ALL BREAKING OUR NECKS TRYING TO GT  GET AT THIS

MACHINE TO SAY CONGRATULATIONS!

AND HER I EXPECTED PITY  MMMMMM

WELL THIS IS RATHER SUDDEN AS THE GIRLS SAY

YEP

HELLO BOB THIS IS P GREEN     I KNEW IT WOULD COME TO THIS SOME DAY

CHEER UP THE SORST IS YET TO COME     CONGRATULZYIONS

CI
  YES I UNDERST,$ 5-5
[illegible]SHOULD HOPE FOR THE BEST AND BE SATE  SATISFIR  SATIS[illegible]
M
AND BE SATISFIED WITH THE WORST  GA
```

Figure 2.22. This duplex teletype output, made during coast-to-coast tests of the F9C system, includes undoubtedly the first wedding announcement afforded the security of spread-spectrum communications. (Copy courtesy of the announcer at the West Coast station, Robert Berg.)

While initially the F9C MARK-SPACE modulation was FSK, this was eventually changed to another, equally phase-insensitive form of orthogonal signaling, which might be called the "mod-clock" approach. The mod-clock format, conceived by Neal Zierler and Bill Davenport, consisted of either transmitting the SS code in its original form (MARK), or transmitting it with every other pulse from the SS code generator inverted (SPACE) (see Figure 2.23).

Perhaps it was a case of serendipity that several years earlier Fano had suggested communication-through-multipath as an Sc.D. thesis topic to Bob Price. In any event, after a particularly frustrating day of field tests in which they encountered highly variable F9C performance, Price and Green got together in their Asbury Park boarding house to discuss multipath problems. Price already knew the optimal answers to some questions that were to come up that evening. Since receiving his doctorate and having been rehired by Davenport after trying his hand at radio astronomy in Australia, he had been polishing his dissertation with "lapidary zeal" (Green's witticism). Price had, in fact, statistically synthesized a signal processing technique for minimum-error-probability reception of signals sent over a channel disturbed by time-varying multipath as well as noise [150].

Green separately had been trying to determine how to weight the outputs of a time-staggered bank of correlators in order to improve F9C performance, and, acting on Jack Wozencraft's suggestion, had decided to choose weights to maximize the resultant transversal filter's output signal-to-noise ratio. Of course, the TOA resolution capability of the F9C was sufficient to guarantee that the outputs of different correlators in the bank represented signals arriving via different paths. Thus, the problem was one of efficiently recombining these signals. It took little time for Price and Green to realize that the results of their two approaches were nearly identical, and from that evening onward, the "Rake" (coined by Green) estimator-correlator became part of their plans for the F9C. Price took charge of building the Rake prototype, with the assistance of John Craig and Robert Lerner.

Related to Wiesner and Lee's work on system function measurements using cross correlation [151], Brennan's work on signal-combining techniques [152], and Turin's multipath studies [153], the Rake receiver could in turn be viewed as a predecessor of adaptive equalizers [154]. The Rake processor [155]–[157] (patented at Davenport's prompting) is adaptive in the sense that the weight on each MARK-SPACE tap pair is determined by the outputs of that MARK-SPACE tap pair, averaged over a multipath stability time constant. (See Figure 2.24). In its ultimate form, the magnetostrictive tapped delay line (patented by Nicholson [158]), around which the processor was built, contained fifty taps spanning 4.9 ms, the spacing being the reciprocal of the NOMAC signal bandwidth.

In addition to solving the multipath dilemma and thereby securing the full 23 dB of potential processing gain, Rake also allowed the sync search rate to be increased so that only 25 s were necessary to view one second of

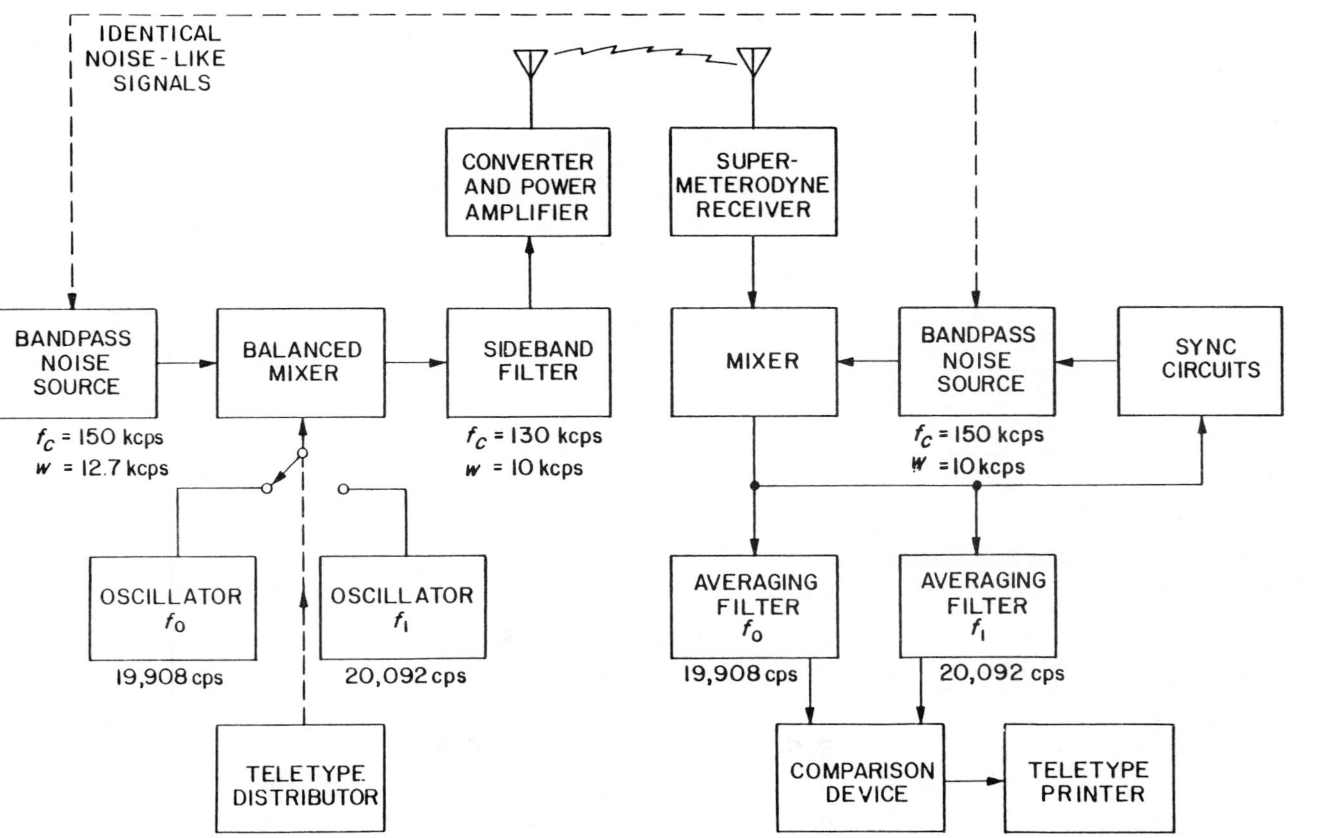

Figure 2.23 (a). Original F9C block diagram with FSK data modulation. (Redrawn from [141], [142].)

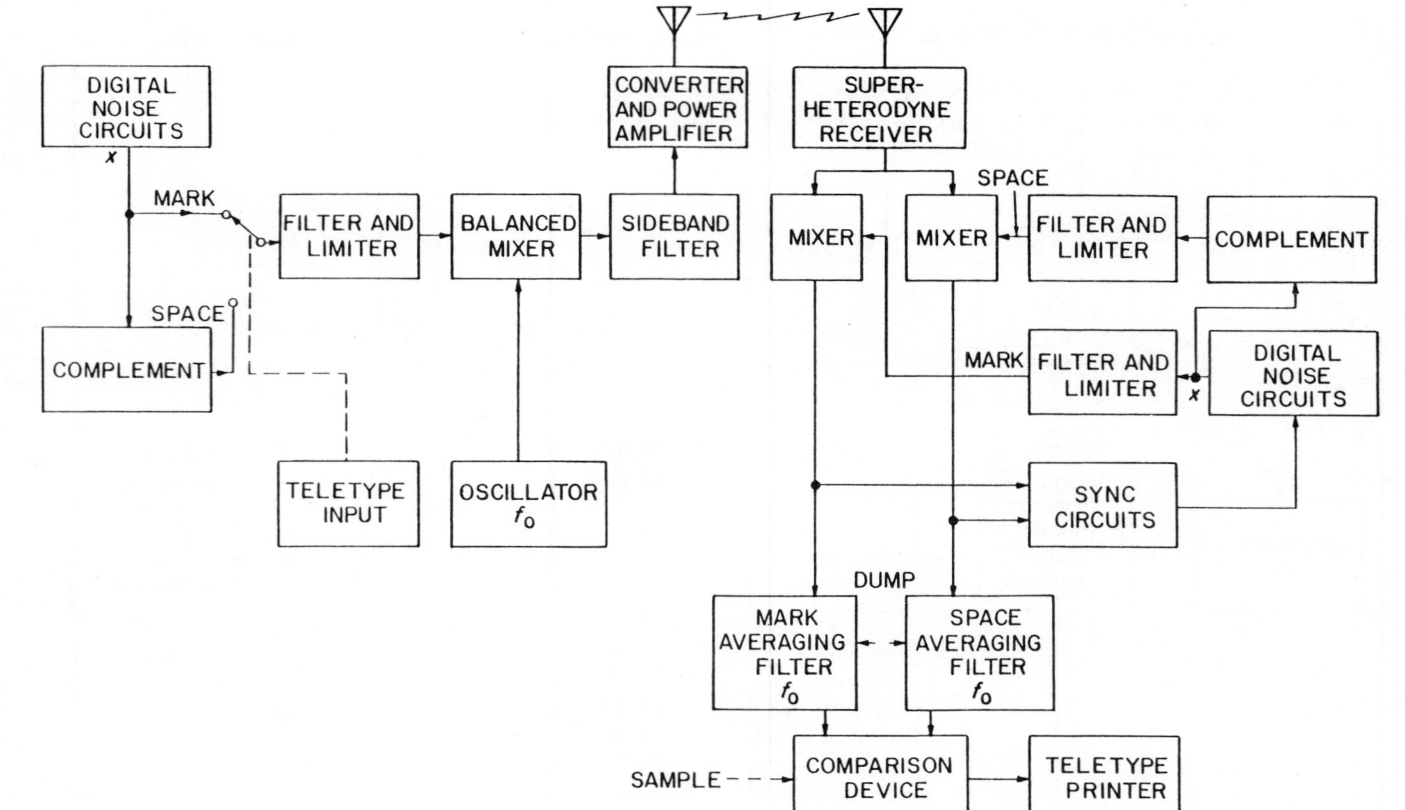

Figure 2.23 (b). Revised F9C block diagram with alternate chip inversion for the creation of orthogonal MARK and SPACE signals. (Redrawn from [142].)

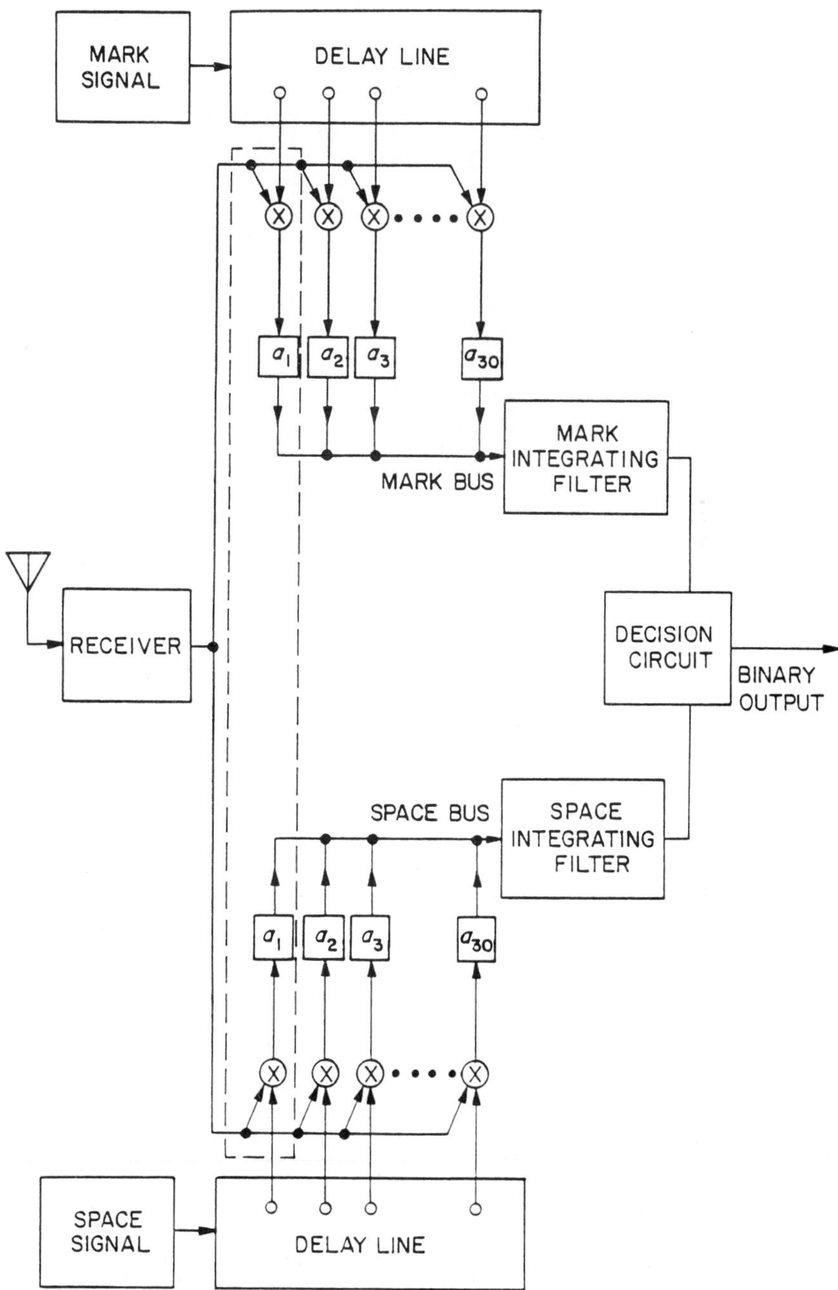

Figure 2.24 (a). This two-delay line version of Rake shows how signals arriving via different path delays are recombined for MARK and SPACE correlation detection. In practice, a single delay line configuration was adopted.

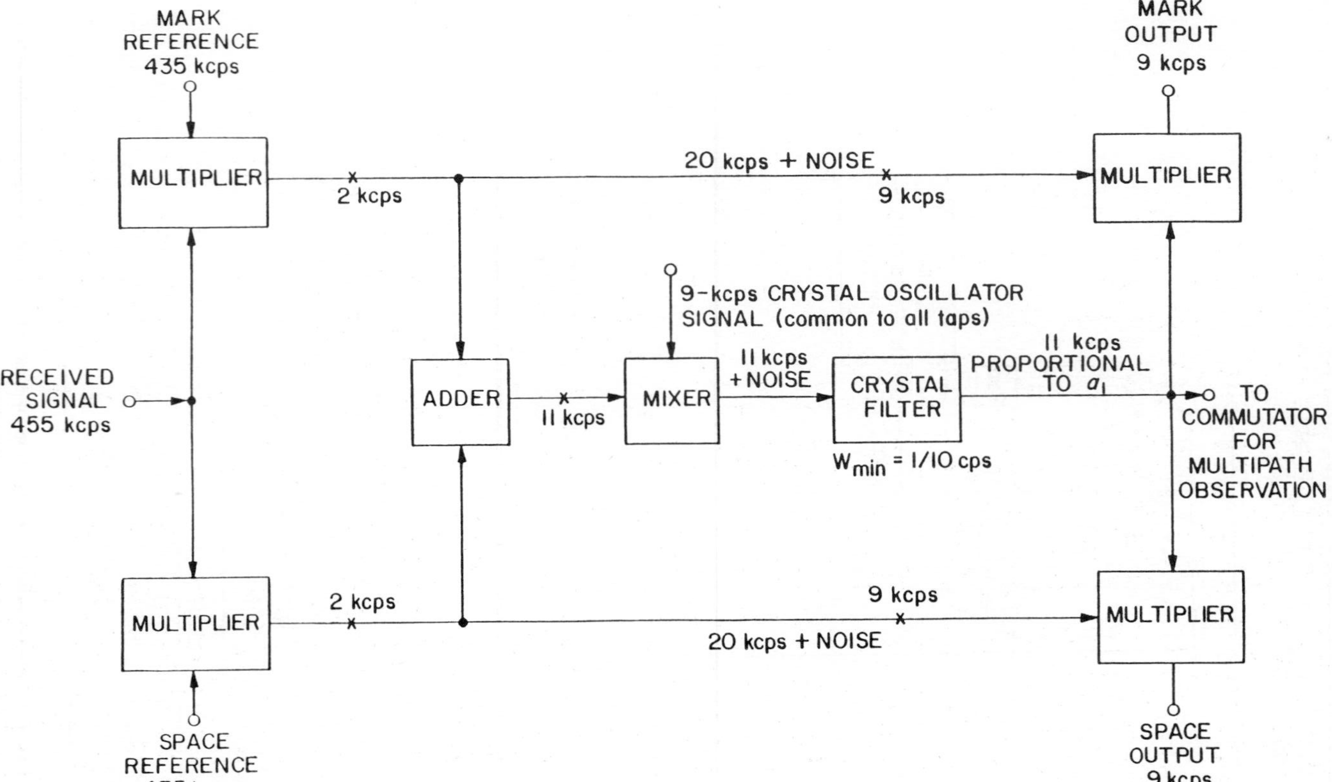

Figure 2.24 (b). The tap unit diagrammed here includes a long-time-constant crystal filter whose output signal envelope is proportional to the combining weight (a_i). This processing corresponds to that shown in the dashed box in (**a**). Rejection traps to eliminate undesirable cross products are shown by ×'s.

Figure 2.24 (c). This Rake rack contains thirty tap units, two helical magnetostrictive delay lines, and a commutator chassis. (Diagrams redrawn from [155], photo courtesy of M.I.T. Lincoln Laboratory.)

delay uncertainty [148]. (Readers of this early literature should note that to prevent disclosure of the actual F9C SS signal structure, all unclassified discussions of Rake, e.g., [156], invoked *m*-sequences for signal spreading. In addition, mod-clock MARK-SPACE modulation was never mentioned in this open literature.)

The F9C-A production contract was let to Sylvania Electronic Defense Laboratory (EDL) at Mountain View, CA, in 1955, with Judd Schulke acting as Project Engineer for the Signal Corps, and Bob Berg as Lincoln Lab's representative, resident at EDL. By December 1956, the first training manuals had been published [159]. Originally 16 F9C-A transmitter-receiver pairs were scheduled to be made, but funds ran out after production of only six pairs. The first installation was made for Washington, DC, near Woodbridge, VA/La Plata, MD. Worldwide strategic deployment commenced with the installation in Hawaii in January 1958, and was followed by installations in Germany (Pirmasens/Kaiserslautern, February 1958), Japan, and the Philippines. With the threat of a blockade of Berlin, the equipment assigned to Clark Field in the Philippines was moved in crates of Philippine mahogany to Berlin in the spring of 1959.

Rake appliques for the F9C-A receivers were fabricated later by the National Company of Malden, MA. These were produced with an improved, yet simplified, circuit configuration, invented at General Atronics [160], which employed tap units having a full 10 kHz of internal bandwidth instead of being structured as in Figure 2.24 (b). Additionally, the F9C-

A/Rake appliques introduced a novel method of ionospheric multipath display, in which the multipath-matched tap-combining weights were successively sensed by a short pulse traveling along the magnetostrictive delay line, the pulse duty cycle being low enough to have negligible effect on the Rake signal processing. Bernie Goldberg was the Project Director for this effort and Robert L. Heyd served as the Project Engineer. Together they also developed Goldberg's innovative "stored ionosphere" concept [161] in which the F9C-A/Rake's multipath measurement function was used to record ionospheric channel fluctuations for their later re-creation in testing short-wave apparatus. This measurement capability was also employed to assess multipath effects, between Hawaii and Tokyo, of a high altitude nuclear detonation in the Pacific in July 1962.

The F9C-A/Rake is no longer on-site, operational or supported by the Army.

2.2.9 A Note on PPM

As the Hartwell report indicated, J. R. Pierce of BTL had suggested that covertness be achieved by using extremely narrow pulses for communication, thereby spreading the transmission spectrum. This idea was undoubtedly based on BTL's postwar work on pulse position modulation (PPM) [96]. After discussing the CDMA idea generally in a 1952 paper, Pierce and Hopper make the following observations:

> There are a number of ways in which this sort of performance could be achieved. One way has been mentioned: the use of random or noise waveforms as carriers. This necessitates the transmission to or reproduction at the receiver of the carrier required for demodulation. Besides this, the signal-to-noise ratio in such a system is relatively poor even in the absence of interference unless the bandwidth used is many times the channel width... In the system discussed here, the signal to be sent is sampled at somewhat irregular intervals, the irregularity being introduced by means of a statistical or 'random' source. The amplitude of each of the samples is conveyed by a group of pulses, which also carries information as to which transmitter sent the group of pulses. A receiver can be adjusted to respond to pulse groups from one transmitter and to reject pulse groups from other transmitters.

This early unclassified reference [162] not only mentions an unpublished, noise-carrier-CDMA notion proposed by Shannon in 1949, but also indicates a PPM technique for achieving the CDMA property of an SS system. PPM systems evidently remained of interest to BTL engineers for some time (e.g., see [163]), and also formed the basis for some Martin Company designs [164], [165].

2.2.10 CODORAC

In 1952, the Jet Propulsion Laboratory (JPL) of the California Institute of Technology was attempting to construct a radio command link for the purpose of demonstrating remote control of the Corporal rocket. The two groups most closely connected with the formation of a system for accomplishing this task were the Telemetry and Control Section under Frank Lehan and the Guidance and Control Section under Robert Parks, both reporting to William Pickering.

One novel concept was formulated by Eberhardt Rechtin, a recent Caltech Ph.D. under Parks, who decided that the current radio design approach, calling for the IF bandwidth to match the Doppler spread of the signal, could be improved dramatically. Rechtin's solution was to adjust the receiver's local oscillator automatically to eliminate Doppler variations, thereby significantly reducing the receiver's noise bandwidth. This automated system used a correlator as its error detector, with the correlator inputs consisting of the received signal and the derivative of the estimate of the received signal. The resultant device, called a phase-locked loop (PLL), with its characteristics optimized for both transient and steady-state performance [166], was a key ingredient of all later JPL guidance and communication systems. Surprisingly, when attempts were made to patent an advanced form of PLL, the prior claim which precluded the award did not come from television, which also had synchronization problems, but came instead from a 1905 patent on feedback control. In retrospect, Eb Rechtin feels that perhaps his greatest contribution in this area consisted of "translating Wiener's 'Yellow Peril' into English," and converting these elegant results into practice.

In struggling with blind-range problems occurring in the integration of a tracking-range radar into the Corporal guidance system, Frank Lehan realized that his problems were due to the shape of the radar signal's autocorrelation function. The thought that the autocorrelation function of broad-band noise would be ideal led Lehan to formulate the concept of an elementary TR-SS communication system using a pure noise carrier. In May 1952, Lehan briefly documented his partially developed ideas and their potential for LPI and AJ in a memo to Bill Pickering. Lincoln Laboratory's NOMAC work was quickly discovered, since both JPL's and Lincoln's were sponsored by the Army, and the wealth of information contained in Lincoln's detailed reports was made available to JPL researchers.

By the spring of 1953, JPL had decided upon a DS-SS configuration for the Corporal guidance link, and Rechtin, noting applications for his tracking loop theory in SS code synchronization, transferred to Lehan's section to head a group studying this problem. Seeing the value of the M.I.T. documentation, JPL began a series of bimonthly progress reports in February 1953, these later being combined and annotated for historical purposes in 1958 [167] (see Figure 2.25).

The term "pseudonoise" with its abbreviation "PN" was used consistently from 1953 onward in JPL reports to denote the matched SS signals used in a DS system. Two PN generators initially were under consideration (see Figure 2.26), the first being a product of twelve digitally generated (± 1) square waves having relative periods corresponding to the first eleven primes. This type-I generator was eventually dropped because of its exces-

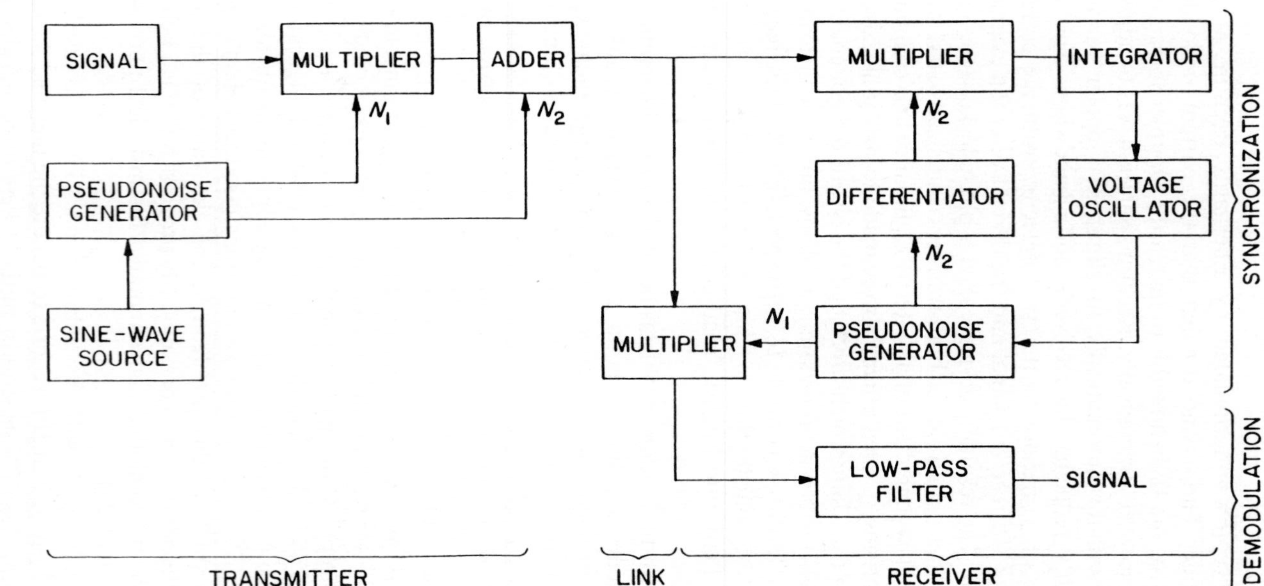

Figure 2.25. JPL's first attempt at a stored reference spread-spectrum design is shown here. This particular system uses one unmodulated noise signal N_2 for synchronizing the receiver's pseudonoise generator and another N_1 for carrying data. Most SR-SS systems do not use a separate signal for SS signal synchronization. (Redrawn from [167].)

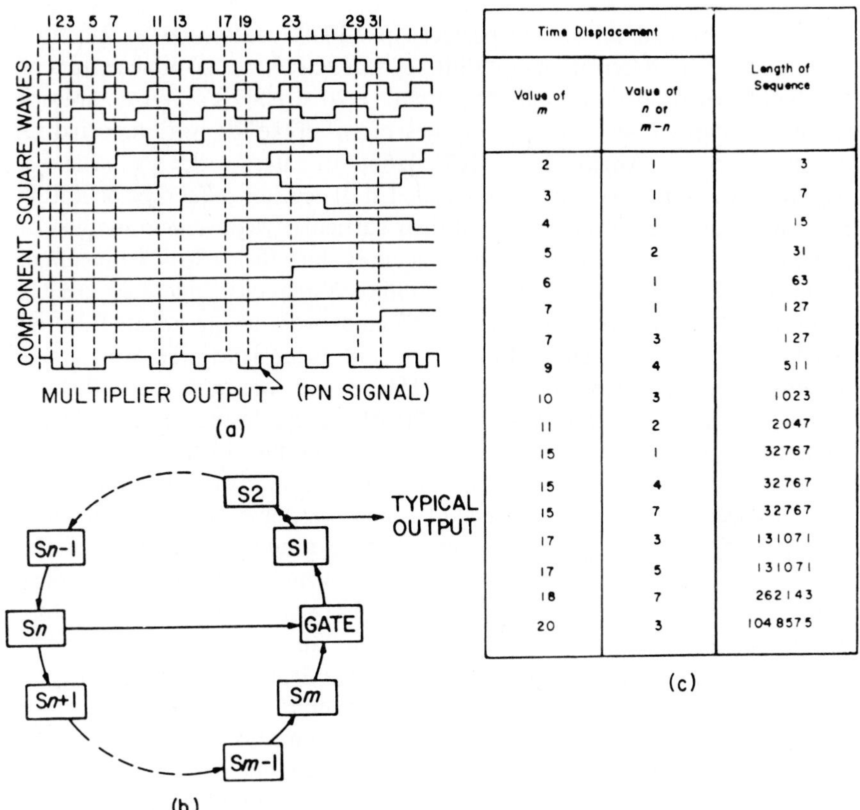

Time Displacement		Length of Sequence
Value of m	Value of n or $m-n$	
2	1	3
3	1	7
4	1	15
5	2	31
6	1	63
7	1	127
7	3	127
9	4	511
10	3	1023
11	2	2047
15	1	32767
15	4	32767
15	7	32767
17	3	131071
17	5	131071
18	7	262143
20	3	1048575

(c)

Figure 2.26(a). The type-I PN generator uses a multiplier to combine the outputs of binary (+1 or −1) signal shapers which in turn are driven by the outputs of relatively prime frequency dividers operating on the same sinusoid. The component square waves and the resultant PN product signal are shown here. (**b**) JPL's type-II generator was an m-stage linear-feedback shift register which produced binary (0 or 1) sequences of maximum period. The output of the mth and nth stages are added modulo 2 to produce the input of the first stage S1. (**c**) This first list of connections for the type-II generator was produced at JPL by hand and computer search. (Diagrams and table redrawn from [167].)

sive size and weight. The type-II PN generator was

> ...based on the equation
>
> $$x(t+m) = x(t)x(t+n)$$
>
> where t represents time, m and n are integers (m represents a time displacement greater than n), and the functions $x(t+m)$, $x(t)$, and $x(t+n)$ may equal ± 1 only.... If the correct values of m and n are chosen, the period before repeat is $2^m - 1$.... The correlation function of all type-II PN generators consists of a triangle of height unity and of a width equal to twice the shift time standing on a block of height $(2^m - 1)^{-1}$.

This origination of an almost perfect spike-like autocorrelation function, accompanied by descriptions of shift register hardware, positive results of baseband synchronization experiments at −20 dB SNR's and a table of suitable values of m and n for values of m up to 20, was reported as progress through August 1953 [167], [168]. In later works by other researchers, these PN sequences were called shift-register sequences or linear-recurring sequences as a reminder of their particularly convenient method of generation, and were also termed m-sequences since their period is maximal.

On January 18, 1954, a JPL PN radio system was operated over a 100-yard link and two independent commands were communicated. Initial synchronization was achieved with the aid of a land line which was disconnected after sync acquisition. The system was able to withstand jammer-to-signal power ratios of 15–20 dB before losing lock, against a wide variety of jamming threats. This test was the assurance that JPL engineers needed regarding the practicality of SR-SS communications.

At this point, work on the command system was temporarily dropped and a major effort was begun to optimize a pure ranging system, called the Scrambled Continuous Wave (SCW) system, which consisted of a "very narrow-band CW system scrambled externally by a PN sequence." On July 27, 1954, Corporal round 1276-83 carrying an SCW transponder was launched at White Sands Proving Ground. The transponder operated successfully from takeoff to near impact seventy miles away, providing range and range rate without loss of lock in the synchronization circuitry. Rechtin, engineer Walter Victor, and Lehan (who left JPL in 1954) later filed an invention disclosure based on the SCW system results from this test, and called the system a COded DOppler RAdar Command (CODORAC) system. This acronym was used to describe the radio guidance systems developed for the Sergeant and later the Jupiter missiles in the 1954–58 time frame.

Throughout this period one of the major problems in establishing one-way communication to a missile was to make the PN generator tough enough to withstand high temperatures and vibrations as well as small and light enough to fit into the missile design. A variety of devices (e.g., subminiature hearing aid tubes) and potting compounds were tested. In 1954, Signal Corps liaison official G. D. Bagley was able to obtain approximately 100 of the Western Electric type 1760 transistors (the first available outside BTL) for use by JPL engineer Bill Sampson in the construction of a PN generator. The resulting circuitry was an interesting combination of distributed-constant delay lines and transistor amplifiers and logic, chosen because it minimized the number of active elements required [169]. This general method of construction remained the norm at JPL through 1958.

Late in 1954, a separate group under Sampson was formed for the purpose of investigating possible countermeasures against the SCW system equipment designed by a group headed by Walt Victor. Created to make this phase of the program as objective as possible, this organization brought forth a thoroughly designed system with high countermeasures immunity. Here are three issues on which significant progress was made.

1. It was hoped that repeater jamming would be ineffective as a result of the high TOA resolution capability of SS and the excess propagation delay incurred by the repeater. The period of the PN sequence was made longer than the missile flight time so that it would be impossible for a repeater to store a PN coded signal for nearly a full period and deliver it to the victim receiver in synchronism with the directly transmitted PN sequence one period later. A weakness in this regard still existed in a simple m-sequence generator based on a linear recursion. Specifically, these sequences possessed a "cycle-and-add" property (see Chapter 5, Section 5.4.2) by which the modulo 2 sum of a sequence and a delayed version of that sequence results in the production of the same sequence at still another delay. The equivalent "shift-and-multiply" property for the ± 1 version of these m-sequences, satisfying the equation quoted earlier in this subsection, conceivably could be used by a jammer to produce an advance copy of the sequence without waiting a full period. In an effort to completely rule out this possibility, Caltech graduate student Lloyd Welch was hired in 1955 to study the generation of sequences which avoid the cycle-and-add property by resorting to nonlinear recursions [171]. Although laboratory system work continued to use linearly generated PN sequence for test purposes, final designs were to be based on nonlinear generators.
2. Initial jamming tests revealed weaknesses in the SCW system when confronted by certain narrow-band jammers. Most of these were due to problems in the mechanization of the multiplications required in the PN scrambler and correlator descrambler. For example, if the descrambler effectively mechanizes a multiplication of the jamming signal by a constant plus the receiver's PN sequence replica (the constant representing a bias or imbalance in the multiplicaton/modulation process), then the multiplier output will contain an unmodulated replica of the jamming signal which has a free ride into the narrowband circuitry following the descrambler. The sure cure for this problem is to construct better balanced multipliers/modulators since the processing gain achievable in an SS system is limited by the "feedthrough" (or bias) in its SS multipliers. In the mid-1950s, JPL was able to build balanced modulators which would support systems with processing gains near 40 dB.
3. Another major concern of system designers was the decibel range and rates of variation of signal strength, as a result of missile motion and pulsed or intermittent jamming. At the circuit level, the two approaches to controlling signal levels in critical subassemblies were automatic gain control (AGC) and limiting. The AGC approach suffers from the possibility that its dynamics may make it susceptible to pulse jamming, while limiters, although instantaneous in nature, generate harmonics which

might be exploited by a jammer. The eventual design rule-of-thumb was that limiters could be used when necessary on narrow-band signals (e.g., prior to PLL phase detectors), and that AGC techniques should be used in the wide-band portions of the system. Analytical support for this work came from JPL's own studies of AGC circuits [172], [173], and from Davenport's classic paper on limiters [174]. It was not realized until much later that in some instances the limiter theory was not appropriate for coherent signal processing analyses [175]. For further discussion of AGC capture by jamming, see [176].

Many of these kinds of problems remain with the designer today, the differences being in the technology available to solve them.

Both the Sergeant and Jupiter guidance programs were terminated when decisions were made to choose all-inertial jam-proof guidance designs as the baseline for those missile systems. However, CODORAC technology survived in the JPL integrated telemetry, command, tracking, and ranging system for the Deep Space Program, and in the later projects of subcontractors who had worked for JPL in the Jupiter program. A modified version of CODORAC became the Space Ground Link Subsystem (SGLS) now used routinely in U.S. Department of Defense missile and space instrumentation.

2.2.11 *M*-Sequence Genesis

The multiplicative PN recursion given in [167] and its linear recursion counterpart in modulo 2 arithmetic, namely

$$y(t+m) = y(t) \oplus y(t+n)$$

were among those under study by 1954 at several widely separated locations within the United States. Lehan recalls that the idea of generating a binary sequence recursively came out of a discussion which he had with Morgan Ward, Professor of Mathematics at Caltech, who had suggested a similar decimal arithmetic recursion for random number generation. It is hard to determine if this idea was mentioned at the (Classified) RDB Symposium held at Caltech in February 1953. Lincoln Laboratory's Bill Davenport remembers that the first time that he had seen a PN generator based on the above recursion was in Lehan's office on one of his trips west. This generator, built to Rechtin's specifications, was used to extend Rechtin's hand-calculated table of *m*-sequence generators from a shift register length of at most 7, to lengths up to 20 (see Figure 2.26).

Sol Golomb, then a summer hire at the Glenn L. Martin Company in Baltimore, MD, first heard of shift register-generated sequences from his supervisor, Tom Wedge, who in turn had run across them at a 1953 M.I.T. summer session course on the mathematical problems of communication theory. (This meeting included an elite group of the founding fathers of information theory and statistical communications. See Figure 2.27.)

On the other hand, Neal Zierler, who joined Lincoln Laboratory in 1953, recalls discovering shift register generation of PN sequences while looking for ways to simplify the SS signal generators used for the F9C system. Golomb's [170], [177], [178] and Zierler's [179]–[181] work established them as leading theorists in the area of pseudonoise generation. However, Zierler's shift register-generated sequences were never used in the F9C-A system since they possessed cryptanalytic weaknesses. Golomb's work gained further recognition after he joined JPL in August 1956.

Madison Nicholson's early attempts at PN sequence design date back to 1952 [137]. Nicholson's first exposure to the pseudorandomness properties of linearly recurring sequences probably came from Allen Norris, who remembers relating to Nicholson ideas developed from lectures by the noted mathematician, A. A. Albert, of the University of Chicago. Coworkers recollect that Nicholson used paper-and-pencil methods for finding a perfect word of length 43. Jim Green, in due course, joined in this exploration, and

Figure 2.27. Cut from a 1953 photograph of a summer session class on mathematical problems of communication theory, this picture salutes (from left to right) Yuk Wing Lee, Norbert Wiener, Claude Shannon, and Robert Fano. It is ironic that Wiener could not prevent the transfer of his theories, through meetings like the one at which this picture was taken, to the military research which he refused to support after World War II. (Photo courtesy of M.I.T.)

built demonstration hardware. Bob Hunting was assigned to investigate the generation of long *m*-sequences and spent a considerable amount of time exercising Sylvania's then-new UNIVAC 1 in the Corporate Computer Center at Camillus, NY, and eventually produced an extensive list of "perfect word" generators. R. L. San Soucie and R. E. Malm developed nonlinear sequence-combining techniques for the BLADES prototype, the result being an SS carrier with a period of about 8000 centuries. Oliver Selfridge of Lincoln Laboratory's Group 34 became the government representative whose approval was required on Sylvania's SS code designs for Air Force contracts, but was not involved with the Navy's BLADES effort.

Early work by others on linear-feedback shift registers includes that of Gilbert [182], Huffman [183], and Birdsall and Ristenbatt [184]. Additional insights were available from the prewar mathematical literature, especially from Ward [185], Hall [186], and Singer [187], [188]. Of course, in the top secret world of cryptography, key-stream generation by linear recursions may very well have been known earlier, particularly since Prof. Albert and others of similar stature were consultants to NSA. But it is doubtful that any of these had a direct impact on the pioneering applications to SS communication in 1953–54.

2.2.12 AN/ARC-50 DEVELOPMENT AT MAGNAVOX

In 1953, a group of scientists interested in the design of computers left the University of California at Los Angeles and formed a research laboratory under an agreement with the Magnavox Corporation. Their first contact with SS systems came when JPL approached them with the problem of building DS-SS code generators for the Jupiter missile's proposed radio navigation link. This exposure to JPL's work on PN sequences and their application to radio guidance paid dividends when Lloyd Higginbotham at WADC became interested in getting high-speed, long-period generators for the ARC-50 system which was emerging from the Hush-Up study at Sylvania Buffalo. At Sylvania, Hush-Up had started out under the premise of radio silence, and was aimed for an application to the then-new air-to-air refueling capability developed by the Strategic Air Command (SAC). After a demonstration of the wired system at Sylvania, a SAC representative made the "obvious" statement, "When you are in radar range, who needs radio silence?" From that time onward, the design was based on AJ considerations.

The AJ push resulted in NSA being brought into the program for their coding expertise. However, because of their nature, NSA passed technical judgment rather than providing any concrete guidance. The NSA view was that the SS codes had to be cryptographically secure to guarantee AJ capability, and Lincoln Laboratory had established that the proposed ARC-50 SS PN code was easily breakable. On this point, Lloyd Higginbotham says, "At that time we felt we were being treated unfairly because the system was still better than anything else then in existence."

By March 1958 Magnavox had parlayed their knowledge of high-speed PN generators into a development contract for the ARC-50 system, won in competition with Sylvania. Magnavox Research Laboratories operated out of a garage on Pico Boulevard in Santa Monica in those early days, with Jack Slattery as general manager and Ragnar Thorensen as technical director. From their few dozen employees, a team was organized to design the code generators and modem, while RF equipment was built at Magnavox's Fort Wayne facility. Shortly thereafter, Magnavox Research Laboratories moved to Torrance, CA, into a new facility sometimes referred to as "the house the ARC-50 built." Harry Posthumus came from Fort Wayne as program manager and teamed with system designers Tom Levesque, Bob Grady, and Gene Hoyt; system integrator Bob Dixon; and Bill Judge, Bragi Freymodsson, and Bob Gold.

Although retaining the spirit of the DS-SS system developed at Sylvania, technologically the design evolved through several more phases at Magnavox. Nowhere was this more obvious than in the design of the SS code generators, the heart of the system. The earliest Magnavox code generators were built using a pair of lumped constant delay lines, run in syncopated fashion to achieve a rate of 5 Mchips/s. This technology was expensive with a code generator costing about $5000, and was not technically satisfactory. The first improvement in this design came when the delay lines were transistorized, and a viable solution was finally achieved when 100 of the first batch of high-β, gold-doped, fast rise-time 2N753 transistors made by Texas Instruments were received and used to build a single-register code generator operating at 5 Mchips/s.

Originally to facilitate SS code synchronization, the system employed a synchronization preamble of 1023 chips followed by an m-sequence produced by a 31 stage shift register. Register length 31 was chosen because the period of the resultant m-sequence, namely 2,147,483,653, is prime, and it seemed unlikely that there would exist some periodic substructure useful to a jammer. Lacking knowledge of the proper connections for the shift register, a special machine was built which carried out a continuing search for long m-sequences. Problems were encountered involving false locks on correlation sidelobe peaks in the sync preamble (sometimes it seemed that a certain level of noise was necessary to make the system work properly), and concerning interference between different ARC-50 links as a result of poor cross-correlation properties between SS codes.

The ARC-50 was configured as a fully coherent system in which the SS code was first acquired, and the sinusoidal carrier was then synchronized using PLL techniques. Because of apprehension that jamming techniques might take advantage of coupling between the RF oscillator and the code chip clock, these two signals were generated independently in the transmitter. The receiver's PLL bandwidth was constrained by the fact that no frequency search was scheduled in the synchronization procedure; the assumption being that the pull-in range of the PLL was adequate to overcome both oscillator drifts and Doppler effects. Being a push-to-talk voice system which could operate either as a conventional AM radio or in an SS mode, a 5 s sync delay was encountered each time the SS modem was activated. Ranging up to 300 miles was possible with the measurement time taking about 40 s. To retain LPI capability in this AJ system, transmitter power was adjustable from minute fractions of a watt up to 100 W.

Testing of the Magnavox ARC-50 began in 1959. Bob Dixon, joined by John G. Smith and Larry Murphy of Fort Wayne, put the ARC-50 through preliminary trials at WPAFB, and later moved on to the Verona site at RADC. One radio was installed in a C131 aircraft and the other end of the link resided in a ground station along with a 10 kW, CW jammer (the FRT-49). Testing consisted of flying the aircraft in the beam of the jammer's 18 dB antenna while operating the ARC-50. Limited results in this partially controlled environment indicated that the receiver could synchronize at jammer-to-noise ratios near those predicted by theory.

Shortly after these flight tests, an upgraded version of the ARC-50 was developed with significantly improved characteristics. To alleviate SS-code correlation problems, a new design was adopted, including an *m*-sequence combining procedure developed by Bob Gold [189], [190] which guaranteed low SS-code cross correlations for CDMA operation. The SS sync delay was

Figure 2.28 (a). Examples of early- and mid-1960s technology. (**a**) SS code generator portion of a TH system developed by Brown, Boveri, and Company for surface-to-air missile guidance. (Photo courtesy of I. Wigdorovits of Brown, Boveri, and Co.)

Figure 2.28 (b). 1965 picture of the MX-118 applique, a member of the ARC-50 radio family and the first to use Gold codes. (Photo courtesy of Robert Dixon.)

reduced to one second and an improved ranging system yielded measurements in two seconds.

Even though the ARC-50 possessed obvious advantages over existing radios such as the ARC-27 or ARC-34, including a hundredfold improvement in mean time between failures, there was Air Force opposition to installing ARC-50's in the smaller fighter aircraft. The problem revolved around the fact that pilots were accustomed to having two radios, one being a backup for the other, and size-wise a single ARC-50 would displace both of the prior sets.

Certainly, the ARC-50 was a success, and Magnavox became an acknowledged leader in SS technology. Among the descendants of the ARC-50 are the GRC-116 troposcatter system which was designed free of a sync preamble, and the URC-55 and URC-61 ground-station modems for satellite channels. An applique, the MX-118, for the Army's VRC-12 family of VHF-FM radios was developed, but never was procured, partly as a result of inadequate bandwidth in the original radios (see Figure 2.28).

2.3 BRANCHES ON THE SS TREE

Many designs of the 1940s and 1950s have not yet been mentioned, but those described thus far seem in retrospect to have been exemplary pioneering efforts. It is time now to take notice of several SS systems left out of the previous accounting, some of which were never even prototyped.

2.3.1 Spread-Spectrum Radar

With the exception of the 1940s state-of-art descriptions of technology, we have made a distinction between the use of SS designs for communication and their use for detection and ranging on noncooperative targets, and have omitted a discussion of the latter. The signal strength advantage which the target holds over the radar receiver in looking for the radar's transmission versus its echo means that LPI is very difficult to achieve. Moreover, the fact that an adversary target knows *a priori* its relative location means that even with pure noise transmission the radar is vulnerable to false echo creation by a delaying repeater on the target.

Nonetheless, SS signaling has some advantages over conventional low time-bandwidth-product radar signaling: in better range (TOA) resolution for a peak-power-limited transmitter (via pulse compression techniques), in range ambiguity removal, in greater resistance to some nonrepeater jammers [7], and in a CDMA-like capability for sharing the transmission band with similar systems. Modern uses of SS radars include fusing (for a patent under wraps for twenty-four years, see [191]) and pulse compression, the latter's applications extending to high-resolution synthetic-aperture ground mapping.

2.3.2 Other Early Spread-Spectrum Communication Systems

Despite the security which once surrounded all of the advances described in previous sections, the SS system concept could not be limited indefinitely to a few companies and research institutions. The following notes describe several other early SS design efforts.

Phantom: An MF-SS system developed by General Electric (GE) for the Air Force, this system was built around tapped delay line filters. As shown in Costas and Widmann's patent [192], the tap weights were designed to be varied pseudorandomly for the purpose of defeating repeater jammers (see Figure 2.29). Constructed in the late 1950s, the Phantom spread its signal over 100 kHz. As with the F9C-A, this system was eventually used also to measure long-haul HF channel properties. For a description of other SS-related work performed at GE in the 1951–54 time frame, under the direction of Richard Shuey, see [193].

WOOF: This Sylvania Buffalo system hid an SS signal by placing within its transmission bandwidth a high-power, friendly, and overt transmitter. Thereby, the SS transmission would be masked by the friendly transmitter, either completely escaping notice or at least compounding the difficulties encountered by a reconnaissance receiver trying to detect it.

RACEP: Standing for Random Access and Correlation for Extended Performance, RACEP was the name chosen by the Martin Company to describe their asynchronous discrete address system that provided voice service for up to 700 mobile users [164]. In this system, the voice signal was first converted to pulse position modulation, and then each pulse in the resultant signal was in turn converted to a distinctive pattern of three narrow pulses and transmitted at one of a possible set of carrier frequencies. With the patterns serving also as addresses, this low duty cycle format possessed some of the advantages of SS systems.

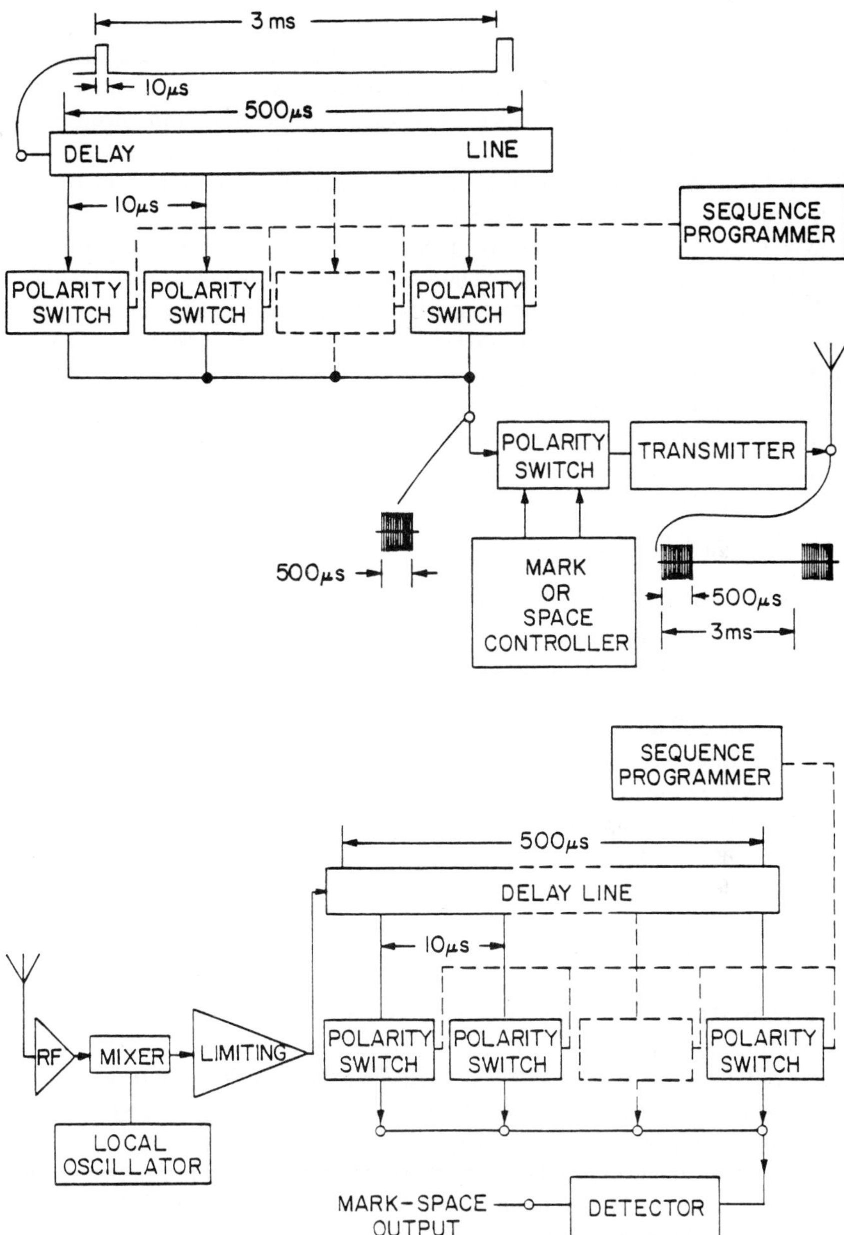

Figure 2.29. Costas and Widmann's Phantom system employs a pulsed delay line with pseudorandomly controlled taps summed to provide an SS signal for modulation. An identically structured system with a synchronous replica of the tap controller is used to construct a matched pseudorandom filter for data detection at the receiver. (Diagrams modified from [192].)

Cherokee: Also by the Martin Company, this was a PN system with a transmission bandwidth of nearly a megahertz and a processing gain of about 16 dB [164]. Both RACEP and Cherokee were on display at the 15th Annual Convention of the Armed Forces Communications and Electronics Association in June 1961.

MUTNS: Motorola's Multiple User Tactical Navigation System was a low frequency, hyperbolic navigation system employing PN signalling. Navigation was based on stable ground wave propagation with the SS modulation used to discriminate against the skywave, as it was in Sylvania's WHYN. Motorola, a subcontractor to JPL on the Jupiter CODORAC link, began Army-supported work on MUTNS in 1958. The first complete system flight test occurred on January 23, 1961 [194], [195].

RADA: RADA(S) is a general acronym for Random Access Discrete Address (System). Wide-band RADA systems developed prior to 1964 include Motorola's RADEM (Random Access DElta Modulation) and Bendix's CAPRI (Coded Address Private Radio Intercom) system, in addition to RACEP [196].

WICS: Jack Wozencraft, while on duty at the Signal Corps Engineering Laboratory, conceived WICS, Wozencraft's Iterated Coding System (see Figure 2.30). This teletype system was an SR-FH-SS system employing 155 different tones in a 10 kHz band to communicate at fifty words/min. Each bit was represented by two successively transmitted tones generated by either the MARK or the SPACE pseudorandomly driven frequency programmer. Bit decisions were made on detecting at least one of the two transmitted frequencies in receiver correlators, and parity checking provided further error correction capability. The subsequent WICS development effort by Melpar in the mid-1950s contemplated its tactical usage as an applique to radios then in inventory [148]. However, just as in ITT's early system concepts, the intended generation of pseudorandom signals via recording [197] did not result in a feasible production design.

Melpar Matched Filter System: A more successful mid-1950s development, this MF-SS design was largely conceived by Arthur Kohlenberg, Steve Sussman, David Van Meter, and Tom Cheatham. To transmit a MARK in this teletype system, an impulse is applied to a filter composed of a pseudorandomly selected, cascaded subset of the several hundred sections of an all-pass lumped-constant linear-phase delay line. The receiver's MARK matched filter is synchronously composed of the remaining sections of the delay line. The same technique was used to transmit SPACE [148] (see Figure 2.31). Patents [198], [199] filed on the system and its clever filter design, the latter invented by Prof. Ernst Guillemin who was a Melpar consultant, were held under secrecy along with the WICS patent until the mid-1970s. An unclassified discussion of an MF-SS system for use against multipath is given in [200].

Kathryn: Named after the daughter of the inventor, William Ehrich, and developed by General Atronics, Kathryn's novel signal processing effected

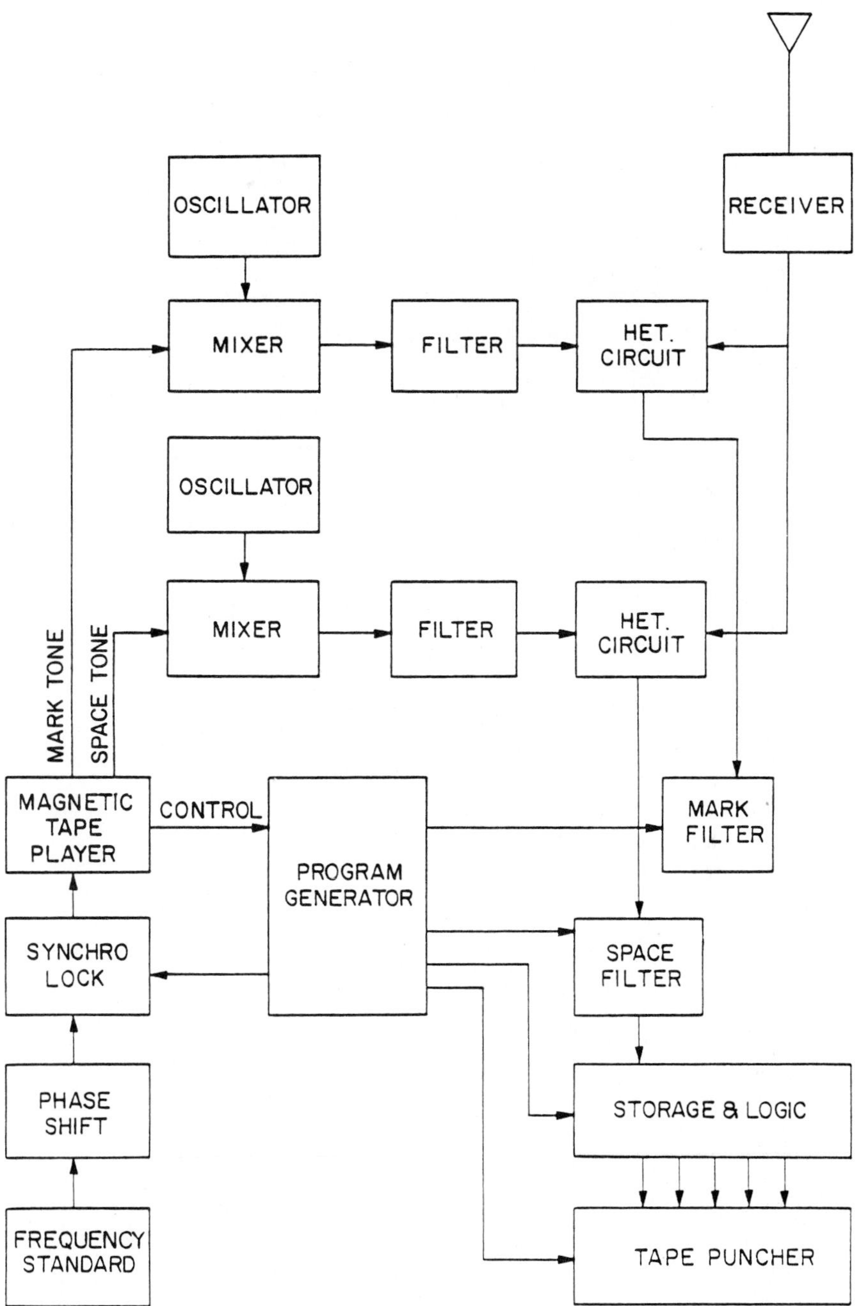

Figure 2.30. The receiver block diagram redrawn from Wozencraft's patent application [197] is shown here with magnetic tape used for storage of independent pseudo-random FH signals for MARK and SPACE reception.

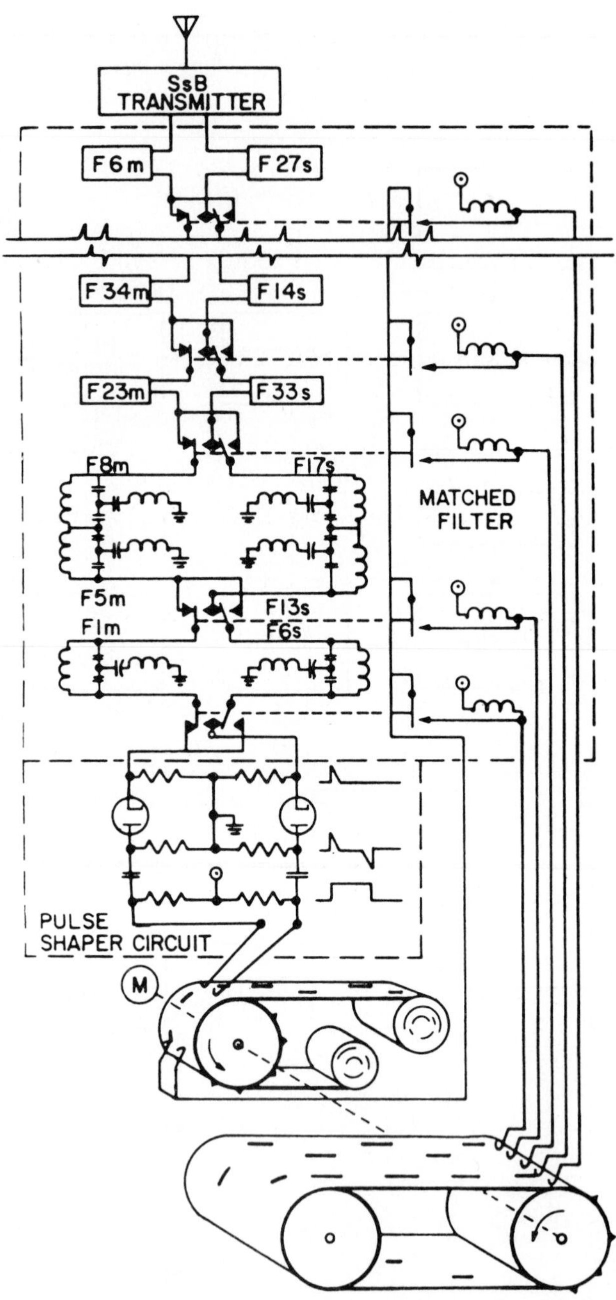

Figure 2.31. Guillemin's patented filter system design [199] is shown here imbedded in the transmitter's modulation generator described in the patent [198] of Kohlenberg, Sussman, and Van Meter. Filter sections were switched in and out according to a schedule recorded on an endless punched tape (and as shown here, punched tape was also used as a binary data source). The receiver contained a corresponding matched filter, synchronously controlled by an identical tape.

the transmission of the Fourier transform of a time-multiplexed set of channel outputs combined with a PN signal. Upon reception, the inverse transform yielded the original PN × multiplexed-signal product, now multiplied by the propagation medium's system function, thereby providing good or bad channels in accordance with that function. When jamming is present, the data rate is reduced by entering the same data bit into several or all data channels. In this case, a Rake-like combiner is used to remerge these channels at the output of the receiver's inverse Fourier transformer [148], [201]. The modern SS enhancement technique of adaptive spectral nulling against nonwhite jamming was at least implicitly available in this system.

Lockheed Transmitted Reference System: Of the several TR-SS systems patented, this one designed by Jim Spilker (see Figure 2.32) made it into production in time to meet a crisis in Berlin, despite the inherent weaknesses of TR systems [202]. The interesting question here is, "What circumstances would cause someone to use a TR system?" Evidently, extremely high chip rates are part of the answer. For an earlier TR patent that spent almost a quarter-century under secrecy order, see [203].

NOMAC Encrypted-Voice Communications: In 1952, Bob Fano and Bennett Basore, with the help of Bob Berg and Bob Price, constructed and briefly tested an IF model of a NOMAC-TR-FM voice system. At first surprised by the clarity of communication and lack of the self-noise which typifies NOMAC-AM systems, Basore soon realized that SS-carrier phase noise was eliminated in the heterodyne correlation process and that SS-carrier amplitude noise was removed by the limiting frequency-discriminator. Little more was done until years later when, in 1959, John Craig of Lincoln Laboratory designed an experimental SR-SS system based on low-deviation phase modulation of a voice signal onto an F9C-like noise carrier. The system provided fair quality voice with negligible distortion and an output SNR of about 15 dB, the ever-present noise deriving from system flaws. Simulated multipath caused problems in this low-processing-gain system, and it was postulated that Rake technology might alleviate the problem [204], [205], but the work was abandoned.

NOMAC Matched Filter System: In approximately October 1951, Robert Fano performed a remarkable acoustic pulse experiment involving high time-bandwidth-product matched filters (see Figure 2.33). At that time he disclosed a multiple matched-filter communication system to his colleagues [206]. Based on Fano's research, an MF-SS teletype communication system was suggested in 1952 [207]. Research at Lincoln Laboratory on this SS communication system type was confined to exploring a viable filter realization. This communication approach apparently was dropped when full-scale work began on the F9C system. Fano later patented [208] the wide-band matched filter system concept, claiming improved performance in the presence of multipath.

While Fano's invention, which originally suggested a reverse-driven magnetic-drum recording for signal generation, basically employed analog sig-

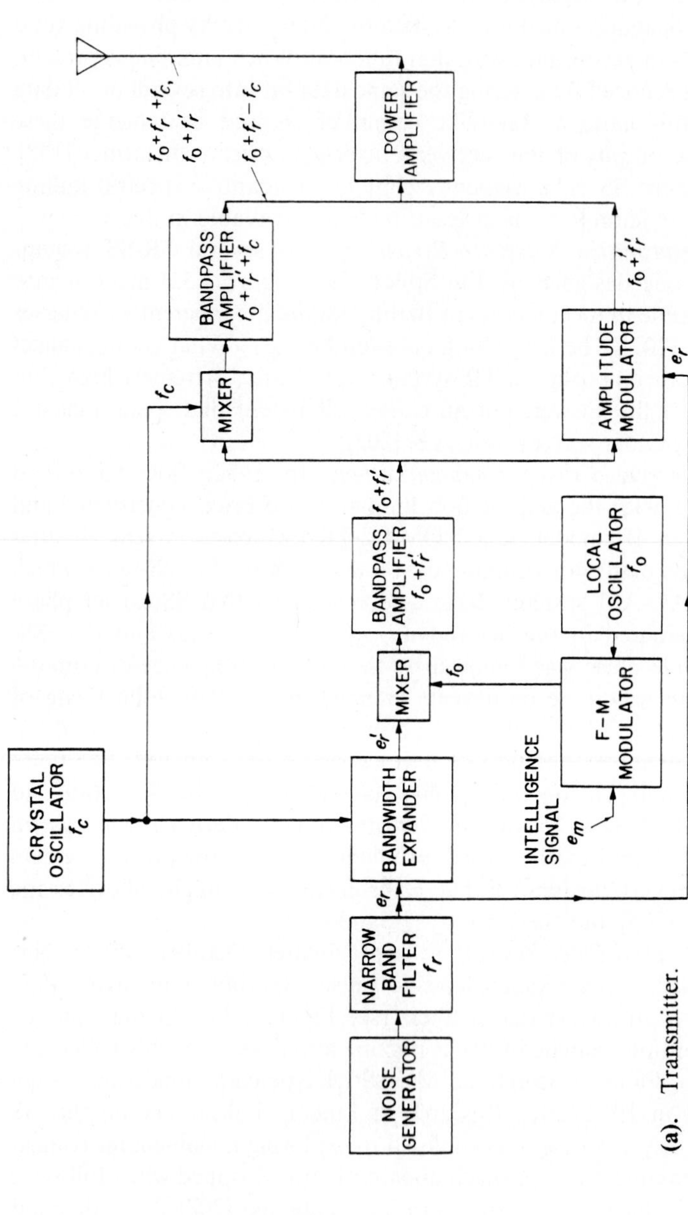

(a). Transmitter.

Figure 2.32. Spilker's patent on a TR-SS system uses a novel bandwidth expansion mechanism to generate a wideband reference signal e_r' from a random narrowband key signal e_r. Both transmitted signals (frequency offset by f_c Hz), contain the intelligence signal as FM modulation, and the signal at $f_0 + f_r'$ Hz additionally carries the key as AM modulation.

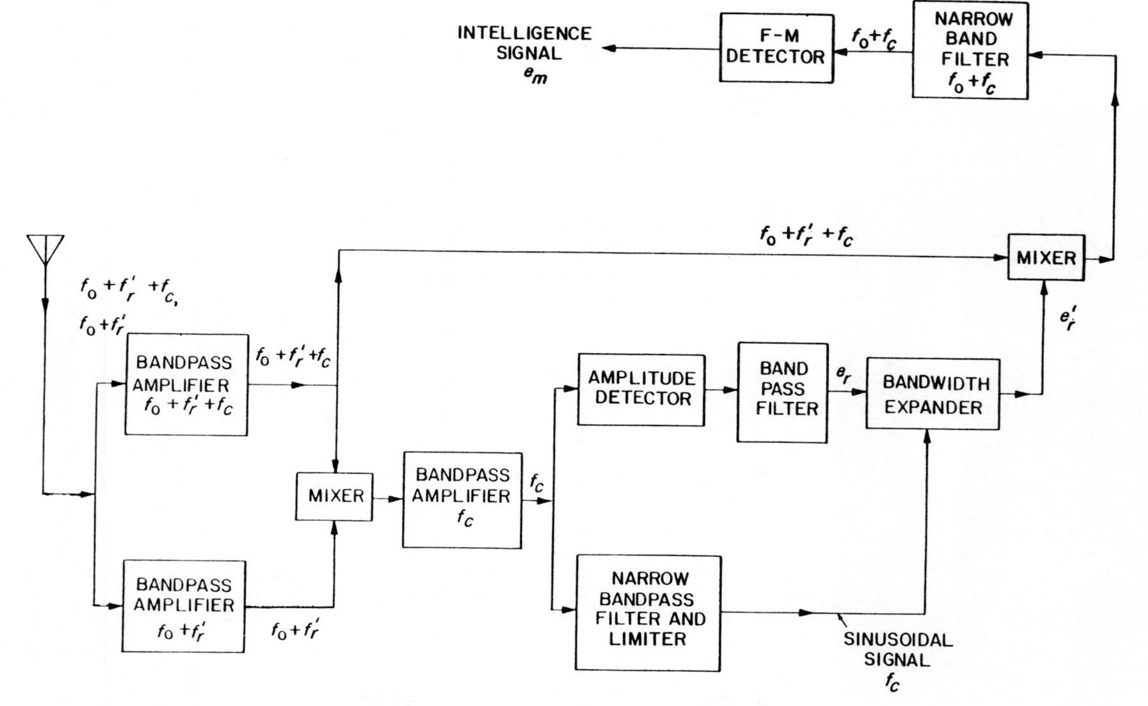

(b) Receiver.

Figure 2.32 (continued). To demodulate at the receiver, the two received signals are cross-correlated to recover the AM modulated key, which is then bandwidth-expanded to produce the wideband reference signal needed to demodulate the intelligence. (Diagrams from [202].)

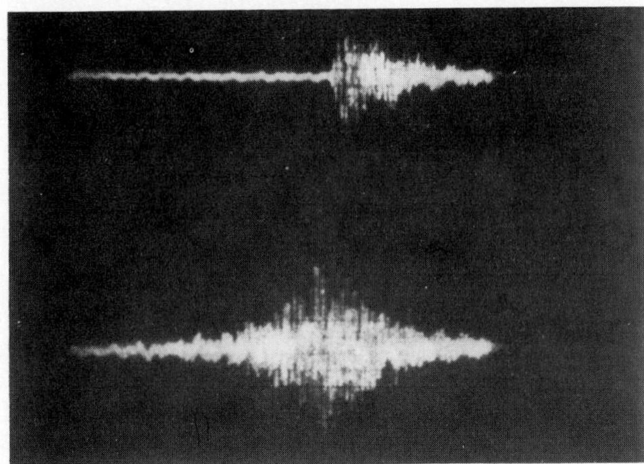

Figure 2.33. Fano's elegant matched filter experiment consisted of transmitting an acoustic pulse into a chamber containing many reflectors. The upper signal shown here represents the sound sensed by a microphone in the room, and tape recorded. The tape was then reversed (not rewound) and replayed into the chamber, the microphone this time sensing the lower of the above two signals, specifically intended to be the autocorrelation of the upper signal. Fano recalls being startled by his inability to see at first the extremely narrow peak of the autocorrelation function on the oscilloscope screen. The peak was soon discovered when the light were turned off. (Photo courtesy of Robert Fano.)

nals, another then contemporary matched-filter invention by Ronald Barker [227] definitely used digital signals. Barker's design employs the binary patterns, which now bear his name, as frame sync markers in digital data streams. While this application is not inherently bandwidth expanding, the waveform correlation design objectives in frame sync applications are quite similar to those for SS-MF communication applications, as well as to those for radar pulse-compression.

Spread Eagle: Philco Corporation developed this secure interceptor-control data link for WADC in the late 1950s. Eight hundred chips of a complex binary waveform, transmitted in 200 μsec, were used to represent each data bit, providing 29 db of improvement against jamming. The two possible waveforms, one for MARK and one for SPACE, were detected by a non-coherent MF receiver with in-phase and quadrature channels both containing synchronous matched filters.

The delay lines in the MF implementation were limited to 100 μsec, evidently for economy of size and weight. Hence, the 200 μsec waveforms actually consisted of repeated 100 μsec waveforms, the MF output being sampled twice in the detection process [176].

SECRAL: This ITT missile guidance system development of the late 1950s was a DS-SS design.

Longarm and Quicksilver: These are both early FH anti-multipath systems built by Hughes Aircraft Company, under the leadership of Samuel Lutz and Burton Miller, and sponsored by Edwin McCoppin of WPAFB.

2.3.3 Spread-Spectrum Developments Outside the United States

This historical review has concentrated on SS development in the United States for several reasons.

1. The theories of Wiener, and especially Shannon, which propounded the properties of and motivated the use of random and pseudorandom signals, were available in the U.S. before such basics were appreciated elsewhere (with the exception of Guanella). This gave U.S. researchers a significant lead time, an important factor near the outset of the Cold War when the Voice of America was being jammed intensively. Additional impetus for SS development came in urgent response to the threats posed by the onslaught of the Korean War and the tense confrontation over Berlin.
2. SS development occurred just after the Second World War, at a point in time when many of the world's technological leaders had suffered tremendous losses in both manpower and facilities, and additionally in Germany's case, political self-control. Research and industry in the U.S., on the other hand, were unscathed and the U.S. became the home for many leading European scientists, e.g., Henri Busignies and Wernher von Braun, to name two among many.
3. The available unclassified literature (virtually all the references in this history are now unclassified) points to the earliest SS developments having arisen in the United States.

We will now look at evidence of some SS beginnings outside the U.S.A.

Bill Davenport remembers a secret interchange with a visiting British delegation in which pre-Rake NOMAC concepts were discussed. Later, he was informed that the British had not pursued that approach to secure, long-range communication because they envisioned major problems from multipath [209]. Frank Lehan recalls a discussion with a British scientist who told him that the British had studied PN sequences several years before JPL developed the idea. Bob Dixon dates Canada's experimental Rampage system to the early 1950s, with no further details yet available [210]. So it seems that the closest friends of the U.S. were at least cognizant of the SS concept, knew something of PN generation, and to some extent had experimented with the idea. Further information on these early efforts has not been uncovered.

In neutral Switzerland, Brown, Boveri, and Company developed, starting in the late 1950s, an SS guidance system (see Figure 2.28). This was no doubt stimulated by Gustav Guanella, the pioneering inventor of noise-modulated radar [13] and of encryption schemes which the NDRC had sought to decipher during World War II. He quickly appreciated, and may well have seen, the true significance of the Rake concept upon its publication. Now, an intriguing question is, "When did the Soviet bloc become privy to the SS concept and realize its potential?"

In the mid-1950s some members of a high-level U.S. task force were convinced that the Russians knew about SS techniques and in fact might also be using them. For example, Eugene Fubini personally searched the U.S. Patent Office open files to see what a foreign country might be able to learn there of this new art; nomenclature was a problem and he had to look under "pulse communications" as well as many other patent classifications. (This difficulty was eased recently when the Patent Office created a special subclass 375-1 entitled *Spread Spectrum*.) Also curious about this issue, Paul Green determined to try to find out for himself the status of Russian knowledge about NOMAC techniques. After studying the language, he examined the Russian technical literature, surveying their work in information theory and attempting to uncover clues that might lie there to noise modulation concepts. Green came to believe that there was no plausible reason to suspect that the Soviets were then developing spread-spectrum systems, partly because of lack of technology and possibly because there was no perceived need for AJ communications capability.

Later Paul Green visited the Soviet Union and gave a talk in Russian on the use of Rake to measure properties of the ionosphere, which seemingly was accepted at face value. Because of this contact and his literature scrutiny, in the mid-1960s Green decided to postpone his plans to write an unclassified account of Lincoln Laboratory's NOMAC work, toward which full military clearances had already been granted.

The earliest Soviet reference (as cited in, e.g., [211]) proposing noise-like, intelligence-bearing signals is a 1957 publication by Kharkevich [212] on amplitude or frequency modulation of pure noise. Like Goldsmith's [46], Kharkevich's work is missing a key ingredient, namely, the attainment of synchronous detection via correlation with a stored or transmitted reference. Within a few months of the approved 1958 publication of the Rake concept for using wide-band signals ostensibly to counter multipath, that paper was translated into Russian, and hardly a year later an exposition of Rake appeared in Lange's first book *Korrelationselektronik* [213]. Thus began the revelation of the SS concept in the U.S. literature from scientific journals and conference proceedings to magazines such as *Electronics*, *Electronic Design*, and *Aviation Week*. Here is a small sample of U.S. open papers referenced in the Soviet literature:

1. March 1958. Rake remedy for multipath, using wideband signals [156].
2. December 1959. Use of wideband noise-like signals, CDMA, and jamming [214], [215].
3. Fall 1960. PN-controlled TH-SS command link for missile guidance [165].

4. January 1961. Analysis of a pure noise (TR) communications system [216].
5. March 1961. Discussion of RADA systems [217].
6. 1963. 200 Mcps PN generator construction [218].
7. December 1963. Wideband communication systems including Rake, RACEP, and RADEM [196].

It is clear from these citations and other evidence that the Russians were studying SS systems no later than 1963 [219], and by 1965 had carefully searched and reported [220] on the U.S. open literature discussing Rake, Phantom, and the various RADA systems. Between 1965 and 1971, the Soviets published several books [211], [221]–[224] concerned with SS principles and their applications to secure communication, command, and control.

2.4 A VIEWPOINT

One can paint the following picture of the development of spread-spectrum communications. During World War II the Allies and the Axis powers were in a desperate technological race on many fronts, one being secure communications. Jamming of communication and navigation systems was attempted by both sides and the need for reliable communication and accurate navigation in the face of this threat was real. One major AJ tactic of the war was to change carrier frequency often and force the jammer to keep looking for the right narrow band to jam. While this was possible to automate in the case of radar, communication frequency hopping was carried out by radio operators, in view of the major technological problem of providing an accurate synchronous frequency reference at the receiver to match the transmitter. Thus, at least frequency hopping and, to a similar extent, time hopping were recognized AJ concepts during the early 1940s.

Many of the early "secure" or "secret" non-SS communication systems seem to have been attempts to build analog equivalents of cryptographic machines and lacked the notion of bandwidth expansion (e.g., the Green Hornet, the Telefunken dual wheels system). The initial motivation for direct sequence systems appears, on the other hand, to have come from the need for accurate and unambiguous time-of-arrival measurements in navigation systems (e.g., WHYN and CODORAC), and from the desire to test or extend Shannon's random-signaling concept and, thus, communicate covertly (e.g., Rogoff's noise wheels experiment). The DS concept followed the FH and TH concepts by several years partly because the necessary correlation detection schemes were just emerging in the late 1940s.

Who first took these diverse system ideas and recognized the unifying essential requirements of a spread-spectrum system (e.g., high carrier-to-data bandwidth ratio, an unpredictable carrier, and some form of correlation detection)? From the available evidence, it appears that Shannon certainly had the insight to do it but never put it in print, and that two close friends, Nathan Marchand and Louis deRosa, both key figures in the formation of the IRE's Group on Information Theory, led Sylvania Bayside and FTL, respectively, toward a unified SS viewpoint. It seems that Sylvania Bayside had all the ingredients of the direct sequence concept as early as 1948, but did not have the technology to solve some of the signal processing problems. It remained for Mortimer Rogoff to provide a method for storing pseudonoise (a technique reminiscent of Telefunken's wheels), giving ITT the complete system assembled and tested under the Della Rosa contract and documented to a government agency.

Meanwhile, the idea either was propagated to, or was independently conceived by, several research and design groups, notably at M.I.T. in 1950 and at JPL in 1952. Group 34 at M.I.T. Lincoln Laboratory, sparked by Bill Davenport, Paul Green, and Bob Price, is generally credited with building the first successful SS communication system for several reasons.

1. The Rake system was the first wide-band pseudorandom-reference system to send messages reliably over the long-range HF multipath channel.
2. The F9C-A system, soon followed by the Rake applique, was probably the first deployed (nonexperimental) broad-band communication system which differed in its essentials from wide-deviation FM, PPM, or PCM.
3. The Rake system was the first such SR communication system to be discussed in the open literature, other than information theoretic designs.

JPL's radio control work, in competition with inertial guidance systems, did not reach a deployment stage until suitable applications appeared in the Space Program. In addition to opening new vistas in the development of PN generation techniques, JPL's contribution to SS technology has been the innovation of tracking loop designs which allow high-performance SS systems to be placed on high-speed vehicles with results comparable to those of stationary systems. Both the M.I.T. and JPL programs have left a legacy of excellent documentation on spread-spectrum signal processing, spectral analysis, and synchronization, and have provided some of the finest modern textbooks on communications.

A very successful long-term SS system investigation began at Sylvania Buffalo under Madison Nicholson and later under Jim Green, and ended up merging with some JPL-based experience at Magnavox in the development and production of the ARC-50 family of systems. The ARC-50 was the first deployed SS system with any of the following characteristics:

1. avionics packaging,
2. fully coherent reception (including carrier tracking),
3. a several megahertz chip rate, and
4. voice capability.

Figure 2.34. VIP's at the IEEE NAECON '81 included Robert Larson, Wilbur Davenport, Paul Green, B. Richard Climie, Mrs. Mortimer Rogoff, Mortimer Rogoff, Mrs. Louis deRosa, and Robert Price. Featured at this meeting was the presentation of the Pioneer Award to deRosa (posthumously), Rogoff, Green, and Davenport for their ground-breaking work in the development of spread-spectrum communications. (Photo courtesy of W. Donald Dodd.)

Although losing the ARC-50 final design and production contract to Magnavox, Sylvania continued on to develop BLADES, the earliest FH-SS communication system used operationally. Moreover, BLADES represented, by publication (e.g., [124]) and actual hardware, the start of real-world application of shift-register sequences to error correction coding, an algebraic specialty that would flourish in coming years.

Since the 1950s when the SS concept began to mature, the major advances in SS have been for the most part technological, with improvements in hardware and expansion in scope of application continuing to the present day. Now with the veil of secrecy being lifted, the contributions of some of the earliest pioneers of SS communications are being recognized (see Figure 2.34). We hope that this historical review has also served that purpose by highlighting the work of the many engineers who have figured prominently in the early conceptual development and implementation of spread-spectrum systems.

2.5 REFERENCES

[1] R. A. Scholtz, "The origins of spread-spectrum communications," *IEEE Trans. Commun.*, COM-30, pp. 822–854, May 1982 (Part I).

[2] R. A. Scholtz, "Notes on spread-spectrum history," *IEEE Trans. Commun.*, COM-31, pp. 82–84, Jan. 1983.

[3] R. Price, "Further notes and anecdotes on spread-spectrum origins," *IEEE Trans. Commun.*, COM-31, pp. 85–97, Jan. 1983.

[4] E. V. Appleton and M. A. F. Barnett, "On some direct evidence for downward atmospheric reflection of electric rays," *Proc. Roy. Soc. Ser. A*. vol. 109, pp. 621–641, Dec. 1, 1925.

[5] D. G. C. Luck, *Frequency Modulated Radar*, New York: McGraw-Hill, 1949.

[6] S. L. Johnston, "Radar ECCM history," *Proc. NAECON*, May 1980, pp. 1210–1214.

[7] G. R. Johnson, "Jamming low power spread spectrum radar," *Electron. Warfare*, pp. 103–112, Sept.–Oct. 1977.

[8] D. O. North, "An analysis of the factors which determine signal/noise discrimination in pulsed carrier systems," RCA Lab., Princeton, NJ. Rep. PTR-6C, June 25, 1943; see also *Proc. IEEE*, vol. 51, pp. 1015–1028, July 1963.

[9] J. H. Van Vleck and D. Middleton, "A theoretical comparison of the visual, aural, and meter reception of pulsed signals in the presence of noise," *J. Appl. Phys.*, vol. 17, pp. 940–971, Nov. 1946.

[10] P. M. Woodward, *Probability and Information Theory, with Applications to Radar*, New York: Pergamon, 1953.

[11] F. E. Terman, "Administrative history of the Radio Research Laboratory," Radio Res. Lab., Harvard Univ., Cambridge, MA. Rep. 411-299, Mar. 21, 1946.

[12] F. H. Lange, *Correlation Techniques*, Princeton, NJ: Van Nostrand, 1966.

[13] G. Guanella, "Distance determining system," U.S. Patent 2 253 975, Aug. 26, 1941 (filed in U.S. May 27, 1939; in Switzerland Sept. 26, 1938).

[14] _____, "Direction finding system," U.S. Patent 2 166 991, July 25, 1939 (filed in U.S. Nov. 24, 1937; in Switzerland Dec. 1, 1936).

[15] J. M. Whittaker, *Interpolatory Function Theory* (Cambridge Tracts in Mathematics and Mathematical Physics, no. 33), New York: Cambridge Univ. Press, 1935.

[16] E. T. Whittaker, "On the functions which are represented by the expansions of the interpolation theory," *Proc. Roy. Soc. Edinburgh*, vol. 35, pp. 191–194, 1915.

[17] J. McNamee, F. Stenger, and E. L. Whitney, "Whittaker's cardinal function in retrospect," *Math. Comput.*, vol. 25, pp. 141–154, Jan. 1971.

[18] A. J. Jerri, "The Shannon sampling theorem—Its various extensions and applications: A tutorial review," *Proc. IEEE*, vol. 65, pp. 1565–1596, Nov. 1977.

[19] R. V. L. Hartley, "The transmission of information," *Bell Syst. Tech. J.*, vol. 7, pp. 535–560, 1928.

[20] H. Nyquist, "Certain topics in telegraph transmission theory," *AIEE Trans.*, vol. 47, pp. 617–644, Apr. 1928.

[21] V. A. Kotelnikov, "Carrying capacity of 'ether' and wire in electrical communications" (in Russian), *Papers on Radio Communications, 1st All-Union Conv. Questions of Technical Reconstruction of Communications*, All-Union Energetics Committee, USSR, 1933, pp. 1–19.

[22] C. E. Shannon, "Communication in the presence of noise," *Proc. IRE*, vol. 37, pp. 10–21, Jan. 1949.

[23] D. Slepian, "On bandwidth," *Proc. IEEE*, vol. 64, pp. 292–300, Mar. 1976.

[24] A. H. Nuttall and F. Amoroso, "Minimum Gabor bandwidth of *M* orthogonal signals," *IEEE Trans. Inform. Theory*, vol. IT-11, pp. 440–444, July 1965.

[25] D. Gabor, "Theory of communication," *J. Inst. Elec. Eng.* (*London*), vol. 93, part 3, pp. 429–457, Nov. 1946.

[26] N. Wiener, "Generalized harmonic analysis," *Acta Math.*, vol. 55, pp. 117–258, May 9, 1930; reprinted in *Generalized Harmonic Analysis and Tauberian Theory* (*Norbert Wiener: Collected Work*, Vol. 2), P. Masani, ed. Cambridge, MA: M.I.T. Press, 1979.

[27] "Gunfire control," Nat. Defense Res. Committee, Office Sci. Res. Develop., Washington, DC, Summary Tech. Rep., Div. 7, 1946 (AD 200795).

[28] N. Wiener, *Extrapolation, Interpolation, and Smoothing of Stationary Time Series with Engineering Applications*, Cambridge, MA: M.I.T. Press, 1949.

[29] N. Levinson, "The Wiener rms (root mean square) error criterion in filter design and prediction," *J. Math. Phys.*, vol. 25, pp. 261–278, Jan. 1947.

[30] C. E. Shannon, "A mathematical theory of cryptography," Bell Tel. Lab., memo., Sept. 1, 1945; later published in expurgated form as "Communication theory of secrecy systems," *Bell. Syst. Tech. J.*, vol. 28, pp. 656–715, Oct. 1949.

[31] _____, "A mathematical theory of communication," *Bell Syst. Tech. J.*, vol. 27, pp. 379–423, July, and 623–656, Oct. 1948.

[32] W. L. Root, "Some notes on jamming, I," M.I.T. Lincoln Lab., Tech. Rep. 103, Jan. 3, 1956 (AD 090352; based on Lincoln Lab. Group Rep. 34–47, Dec. 15, 1955).

[33] _____, "Communications through unspecified additive noise," *Inform. Contr.*, vol. 4, pp. 15–29, 1961.

[34] N. M. Blachman, "Communication as a game," in *IRE Wescon Rec.*, San Francisco, CA, Aug. 20–23, 1957, part 2, pp. 61–66 (Note here a coincidental juxtaposition with a survey of U.S.S.R. literature, pp. 67–83—carried out *sub rosa* re SS by P. E. Green, Jr., as mentioned in Section 2.3.3). See also: N. M. Blachman, "On the effect of interference: prevarication vs. redundancy," Electronic Defense Laboratory, Sylvania Electric Products, Mountain View, CA, Tech. Memo EDL-M104, May 1, 1957 (AD 136152).

[35] _____, "On the capacity of a band-limited channel perturbed by statistically dependent interference," *IRE Trans Inform. Theory*, IT-8, pp. 48–55, Jan. 1962.

[36] L. R. Welch, "A game-theoretic model of communications jamming," Jet Propulsion Lab., Pasadena, CA, Memorandum No. 20-155, April 4, 1958.

[37] *Report of Proceedings, Symp. Inform. Theory*, London, England, Sept. 26–29, 1950; reprinted in *Trans. IRE Professional Group Inform. Theory*, vol. PGIT-1, Feb. 1953.

[38] N. Marchand, "Radio receiver," U.S. Patent 2 416 336, Feb. 25, 1947 (filed May 21, 1942).

[39] E. S. Purington, "Single side band transmission and reception," U.S. Patent 1 992 441, Feb. 26, 1935 (filed Sept 6, 1930).

[40] Y. W. Lee, J. B. Wiesner, and T. P. Cheatham, Jr., "Apparatus for computing correlation functions," U.S. Patent 2 643 819, June 30, 1953 (filed Aug. 11, 1949).

[41] Y. W. Lee, T. P. Cheatham, Jr., and J. B. Wiesner, "The application of correlation functions in the detection of small signals in noise," M.I.T. Res.

Lab. Electron., Tech. Rep. 141, Oct. 13, 1949 (ATI 066538, PB 102361).

[42] H. E. Singleton, "A digital electronic correlator," M.I.T. Res. Lab. Electron., Tech. Rep. 152, Feb. 21, 1950.

[43] S. L. Johnston, *Radar Electronic Counter-Countermeasures*, Dedham, MA: Artech House, 1979.

[44] L. S. Howeth, *History of Communications-Electronics in the United States Navy*. Washington, DC: U.S. Gov. Print. Off., 1963.

[45] J. D. O'Connell, A. L. Pachynski, and L. S. Howeth, "A summary of military communication in the United States—1860 to 1962," *Proc. IRE*, vol. 50, pp. 1241–1251, May 1962; see also [44].

[46] A. N. Goldsmith, "Radio signalling system," U.S. Patent 1 761 118, June 3, 1930 (filed Nov. 6, 1924).

[47] C. B. H. Feldman, "Wobbled radio carrier communication system," U.S. Patent 2 422 664, June 24, 1947 (filed July 12, 1944).

[48] P. Kotowski and K. Dannehl, "Method of transmitting secret messages," U.S. Patent 2 211 132, Aug. 13, 1940 (filed in U.S. May 6, 1936; in Germany May 9, 1935).

[49] L. A. deRosa and M. Rogoff, "Secure single sideband communication system using modulated noise subcarrier," U.S. Patent 4 176 316, Nov. 27, 1979 (filed Mar. 20, 1953); reissue appl. filed Sept. 4, 1981, Re. Ser. No. 299 469.

[50] D. Kahn, *The Codebreakers*, New York: Macmillan, 1967.

[51] L. Cranberg, "German Optiphone equipment 'Li-Spr-80.'" Memo., "Captured enemy equipment report no. 26." Signal Corps Ground Signal Agency, Bradley Beach, NJ, May 5, 1944 (PB 001531).

[52] G. R. Thompson and D. R. Harris, *The Signal Corps: The Outcome (Mid. 1943 Through 1945)* (*United States Army in World War II*, Vol. 6, Part 5: *The Technical Services*, vol. 3). Washington, DC, Off. Chief of Military History, U.S. Army, 1966.

[53] M. L. Marshall, ed., *The Story of the U.S. Army Signal Corps*, New York: Franklin Watts, 1965.

[54] S. V. Jones, "After 35 years, secrecy lifted on encoded calls," *New York Times*, p. 27, July 3, 1976.

[55] W. R. Bennett, "Secret Telephony as a historical example of spread-spectrum communication," *IEEE Trans. Commun.*, COM-31, pp. 98–104, January, 1983.

[56] "Speech and facsimile scrambling and decoding," Nat. Defense Res. Committee. Off. Sci. Res. Develop., Washington, DC. Summary Tech. Rep. Div. 13, vol. 3, 1946 (AD 221609); reprinted by Aegean Park Press, Laguna Hills, CA.

[57] R. C. Mathes, "Secret telephony," U.S. Patent 3 967 066, June 29, 1976 (filed Sept. 24, 1941).

[58] R. K. Potter, "Secret telephony," U.S. Patent 3 967 067, June 29, 1976 (filed Sept. 24, 1941).

[59] A. J. Busch, "Signalling circuit," U.S. Patent 3 968 454, July 6, 1976 (filed Sept. 27, 1944).

[60] A. E. Joel, Jr., "Pulse producing system for secrecy transmission," U.S. Patent 4 156 108, May 22, 1979 (filed Jan. 21, 1947).

[61] G. Guanella, "Methods for the automatic scrambling of speech," *Brown Boveri Review*, pp. 397–408, Dec. 1941.

[62] "Radio countermeasures," Nat. Defense Res. Committee, Office Sci. Res.

Develop., Washington, DC, Summary Tech. Rep. Div. 15, vol. I, 1946 (AD 221601).

[63] "Guided missiles and techniques," Nat. Defense Res. Committee, Office Sci. Res. Develop., Washington, DC, Summary Tech. Rep. Div. 5, vol. I, 1946 (AD 200781).

[64] H. A. Zahl, *Electrons Away, or Tales of a Government Scientist*, New York: Vantage, 1968.

[65] W. W. Hansen, "Secret communication," U.S. Patent 2 418 119 Apr. 1, 1947 (filed Apr. 10, 1943).

[66] E. Chaffee and E. Purington, "Method and means for secret radiosignalling," U.S. Patent 1 690 719, Nov. 6, 1928 (filed Mar. 31, 1922).

[67] M. Deloraine, *When Telecom and ITT Were Young*, New York: Lehigh, 1976; first published in French as *Des Ondes et des Hommes Jeunesse des Telecommunications et de l'ITT*, Paris, France: Flammarion, 1974.

[68] E. M. Deloraine, H. G. Busignies, and L. A. deRosa, "Facsimile system," U.S. Patent 2 406 811, Sept. 3, 1946 (filed Dec. 15, 1942).

[69] ____, "Facsimile system and method," U.S. Patent 2 406 812, Sept. 3, 1946 (filed Jan. 30, 1943).

[70] L. A. deRosa, "Random impulse system," U.S. Patent 2 671 896, Mar. 9, 1954 (filed Dec. 13, 1942).

[71] E. M. Deloraine, "Protected communication system," Fed. Radio Tel. Lab., New York, NY, Rep. 937-2, Apr. 28, 1944 (from the National Archives, Record Group 227; this report was written to Division 15 of the National Defense Research Committee, Office of Scientific Research and Development on Project RP-124) (ATI 014050).

[72] H. Busignies, S. H. Dodington, J. A. Herbst, and G. R. Clark, "Radio communication system protected against interference," Fed. Tel. Radio Corp., New York, NY, Final Rep. 937-3, July 12, 1945 (same source as [71]).

[73] H. P. Hutchinson, "Speech privacy apparatus," U.S. Patent 2 495 727, Jan. 31, 1950 (filed Jan. 7, 1943).

[74] D. O. Slater, "Speech privacy and synchronizing system devised by Captain Henry P. Hutchinson," Bell Tel. Lab., Rep. 20 under Project C-43 of NDRC (OSRD 4573B), July 31, 1943 (as cited in [56, p. 126]; available from U.S. Nat. Archives, Washington, DC).

[75] "John Hays Hammond, Jr." *Micropaedia*, vol. IV, *The New Encyclopaedia Britannica*, Chicago, IL: Encyclopaedia Britannica, 1975, pp. 877–878.

[76] J. H. Hammond, Jr., "System of aeroplane control," U.S. Patent 1 568 972, Jan. 12, 1926 (filed Mar. 7, 1914); see also Hammond's U.S. Patent 1 420 257 (filed 1910), and "Security of radio control," [78, pp. 1193–1197].

[77] B. F. Miessner, *On the Early History of Radio Guidance*. San Francisco, CA: San Francisco Press, 1964.

[78] J. H. Hammond, Jr. and E. S. Purington, "A history of some foundations of modern radio-electronic technology," *Proc. IRE*, vol. 45, pp. 1191–1208, Sept. 1957.

[79] E. L. Chaffee, "System of radio communication," U.S. Patent 1 642 663, Sept. 13, 1927 (filed Aug. 11, 1922).

[80] L. Espenschied *et al.*, "Discussion of 'A history of some foundations of modern radio-electronic technology,'" *Proc. IRE*, vol. 47, pp. 1253–1268, July 1959.

[81] B. Gunston, *Rockets and Missiles*, New York: Crescent, 1979.

[82] Air Force Corresp. File on Contr. W535-sc-707 with Colonial Radio Corp., May 1943–June 1944.

[83] E. Labin and D. D. Grieg, "Method and means of communication," U.S. Patent 2 410 350, Oct. 29, 1946 (filed Feb. 6, 1943).

[84] E. S. Purington, "Radio selective control system," U.S. Patent 2 635 228, Apr. 14, 1953 (filed June 2, 1948).

[85] C. H. Hoeppner, "Pulse communication system," U.S. Patent 2 999 128, Sept. 5, 1961 (filed Nov. 4, 1945).

[86] E. H. Krause and C. E. Cleeton, "Pulse signalling system," U.S. Patent 4 005 818, Feb. 1, 1977 (filed May 11, 1945).

[87] H. K. Markey and G. Antheil, "Secret communication system," U.S. Patent 2 292 387, Aug. 11, 1942 (filed June 10, 1941).

[88] W. Broertjes, "Method of maintaining secrecy in the transmission of wireless telegraphic messages," U.S. Patent 1 869 659, Aug. 2, 1932 (filed Nov. 14, 1929; in Germany, Oct. 11, 1929).

[89] C. Young, *The Films of Hedy Lamarr*, Secaucus, NJ: Citadel, 1978, pp. 92–97.

[90] G. Antheil, *Bad Boy of Music*, Garden City, NY: Doubleday, 1945.

[91] "Designs and ideas for a radio controlled torpedo," Dec. 23, 1940, contained in [93].

[92] *New York Times*, p. 24, Oct. 1, 1941.

[93] Case file for U.S. Patent Serial No. 397 412, supplied courtesy of J. D. McConaghy, Esq., Lyon and Lyon, Los Angeles, CA (per authorization of H. Lamarr–not publicly available).

[94] *New York Times*, p. 32, Sept. 6, 1942.

[95] *Time*, vol. 103, p. 52, Feb. 18, 1974; *Parade* (e.g., in *Boston Sunday Globe*), p. 16, Aug. 1, 1982. (Both items indicate only that the patent is in military or secret communications; no mention is made of frequency hopping or anti-jamming.)

[96] J. R. Pierce, "The early days of information theory," *IEEE Trans. Inform. Theory*, IT-19, pp. 3–8, Jan. 1973.

[97] "The WHYN guidance system," Phys. Lab., Sylvania Elec. Products, Bayside, NY, Final Eng. Rep., Modulation Wave Form Study & F-M Exciter Develop., Contr. W28-099ac465, June 1949 (AD895816).

[98] "The WHYN guidance system," Phys. Lab., Sylvania Elec. Products, Flushing, NY, Interim Eng. Rep. 5, Contr. W28-099ac465, Oct. 1948 (ATI 44524).

[99] "The WHYN guidance system," Phys. Lab., Sylvania Elec. Products, Bayside, NY, Final Eng. Rep., Equipment Develop. & East Coast Field Test, Contr. W28-099ac465, June 1950 (AD 895815).

[100] "Cross-correlation radar," Phys. Lab., Sylvania Elec. Products, Bayside, NY. Rep. YD-51-5, Feb. 1951.

[101] M. Leifer and N. Marchand, "The design of periodic radio systems," *Sylvania Technologist*, vol. 3, pp. 18–21, Oct. 1950.

[102] N. L. Harvey, "A new basis for the analysis of radio navigation and detection systems," *Sylvania Technologist*, vol. 3, pp. 15–18, Oct. 1950.

[103] N. Marchand and H. R. Holloway, "Multiplexing by orthogonal functions," presented at the IRE Conf. Airborne Electron., Dayton, OH, May 23–25, 1951.

[104] N. Marchand and M. Leifer, "Cross-correlation in periodic radio systems,"

presented at the IRE Conf. Airborne Electron., Dayton, OH, May 23–25, 1951.

[105] W. E. Budd, "Analysis of correlation distortion," M.E.E. thesis, Polytech. Inst. Brooklyn, Brooklyn, NY, May 1955.

[106] N. L. Harvey, M. Leifer, and N. Marchand, "The component theory of calculating radio spectra with special reference to frequency modulation," *Proc. IRE*, vol. 39, pp. 648–652, June 1951.

[107] N. L. Harvey, "Radio navigation system," U.S. Patent 2 690 558, Sept. 28, 1954 (filed Feb. 4, 1950).

[108] _____, "Collision warning radar," U.S. Patent 2 842 764, July 8, 1958 (filed Feb. 21, 1951).

[109] H. C. Harris, Jr., M. Leifer, and D. W. Cawood, "Modified cross-correlation radio system and method," U.S. Patent 2 941 202, June 14, 1960 (filed Aug. 4, 1951).

[110] "The WHYN guidance system," Phys. Lab., Sylvania Elec. Products, Bayside, NY, Final Eng. Rep., Equipment, Syst. Lab. Tests & Anal., Contr. W28-099ac 465, June 1953 (AD 024044).

[111] M. Leifer and W. Serniuk, "Long range high accuracy guidance system," presented at the RDB Symp. Inform. Theory Appl. Guided Missile Problems, California Inst. Technol., Pasadena, Feb. 2–3, 1953.

[112] W. P. Frantz, W. N. Dean, and R. L. Frank, "A precision multi-purpose radio navigation system," in *IRE Nat. Conv. Rec.*, New York, NY, Mar. 18–21, 1957, part 8, pp. 79–98.

[113] R. L. Frank and S. Zadoff, "Phase-coded hyperbolic navigation system," U.S. Patent 3 099 835, July 30, 1963 (filed May 31, 1956).

[114] R. L. Frank, "Phase-coded communication system," U.S. Patent 3 099 795, July 30, 1963 (filed Apr. 3, 1957).

[115] W. Palmer and R. L. Frank, in "1971 Pioneer Award," *IEEE Trans. Aerosp. Electron. Syst.*, vol. AES-7, pp. 1015–1021, Sept. 1971.

[116] [R. L. Frank and S. A. Zadoff], "Study and field tests of improved methods for pulse signal detection," Sperry Gyroscope, Great Neck, NY, Final Eng. Rep., Contr. AF28(099)-333, Sperry Eng. Rep. 5223-1245, June 1951 (ATI 150834).

[117] E. J. Baghdady, "New developments in FM reception and their application to the realization of a system of 'power-division' multiplexing," *IRE Trans. Commun. Syst.*, vol. CS-7, pp. 147–161, Sept. 1959.

[118] R. L. Frank, "Tunable narrowband rejection filter employing coherent demodulation," U.S. Patent 3 403 345, Sept. 24, 1968 (filed July 19, 1965).

[119] J. H. Green, Jr., and M. G. Nicholson, Jr., "Synchronizing System," U.S. Patent 4 361 890, Nov. 30, 1982 (filed June 17, 1958).

[120] M. G. Nicholson, Jr., "Apparatus for generating signals having selectable frequency deviation from a reference frequency," U.S. Patent 2 972 109, Feb. 14, 1961 (filed June 11, 1956).

[121] _____, "Generator of frequency increments," U.S. Patent 2 923 891, Feb. 2, 1960 (filed July 6, 1956).

[122] J. N. Pierce, "Theoretical diversity improvement in frequency shift keying," *Proc. IRE*, vol. 46, pp. 903–910, May 1958.

[123] J. H. Green, Jr., D. K. Leichtman, L. M. Lewandowski, and R. E. Malm, "Improvement in performance of radio-teletype systems through use of ele-

ment-to-element frequency diversity and redundant coding," presented at the 4th Annu. Symp. Global Commun., Washington, DC, Aug. 1–3, 1960.

[124] J. H. Green, Jr., and R. L. San Soucie, "An error correcting encoder and decoder of high efficiency," *Proc. IRE*, vol. 46, pp. 1741–1744, Oct. 1958.

[125] R. G. Fryer, "Analytical development and implementation of an optimum error-correcting code," *Sylvania Technologist*, vol. 13, pp. 101–110, July 1960.

[126] M. G. Nicholson, Jr., and R. A. Smith, "Data transmission systems," U.S. Patent 3 093 707, June 11, 1963 (filed Sept. 24, 1959).

[127] J. H. Green, Jr., and J. Gordon, "Selective calling system," U.S. Patent 3 069 657, Dec. 18, 1962 (filed June 11, 1958).

[128] V. C. Oxley and W. E. De Lisle, "Communications and data processing equipment," U.S. Patent 3 235 661, Feb. 15, 1966 (filed July 11, 1962).

[129] L. A. deRosa, M. J. DiToro, and L. G. Fischer, "Signal correlation radio receiver," U.S. Patent 2 718 638, Sept. 20, 1955 (filed Jan. 20, 1950).

[130] L. A. deRosa and M. Rogoff, Sect. I (Communications) of "Application of statistical methods to secrecy communication systems," Proposal 946, Fed. Telecommun. Lab., Nutley, NJ, Aug. 28, 1950.

[131] "A report on security of overseas transport," Project Hartwell, M.I.T., Cambridge, MA, Sept. 21, 1950 (ATI 205035, ATI 205036; not available from M.I.T.).

[132] "R.L.E.: 1946 + 20," M.I.T. Res. Lab. Electron., Cambridge, MA, May 1966.

[133] D. Lang, *An Inquiry into Enoughness*, New York: McGraw-Hill, 1965.

[134] "Problems of air defense," Project Charles, M.I.T., Cambridge, MA, Final Rep., Aug. 1, 1951 (ATI 139962; not available from M.I.T.).

[135] B. L. Basore, "Noise-like signals and their detection by correlation," M.I.T. Res. Lab. Electron. and Lincoln Lab., Tech. Rep. 7, May 26, 1952 (AD 004641).

[136] B. J. Pankowski, "Multiplexing a radio teletype system using a random carrier and correlation detection," M.I.T. Res. Lab. Electron. and Lincoln Lab., Tech. Rep. 5, May 16, 1952 (ATI 168857; not available from M.I.T.).

[137] "Engineering study and experimental investigation of secure directive radio communication systems," Sylvania Elec. Products, Buffalo, NY, Interim Eng. Rep., Contr. AF-33(616)-167. Aug. 5–Nov. 5, 1952 (AD 005243).

[138] W. B. Davenport, Jr., "NOMAC data transmission systems," presented at the RDB Symp. Inform. Theory Appl. Guided Missile Problems, California Inst. Technol., Pasadena, Feb. 2–3, 1953.

[139] P. E. Green, Jr., "Correlation detection using stored signals," M.I.T. Lincoln Lab., Tech. Rep. 33, Aug. 4, 1953 (AD 020524).

[140] B. M. Eisenstadt, P. L. Fleck, Jr., O. G. Selfridge, and C. A. Wagner, "Jamming tests on NOMAC systems," M.I.T. Lincoln Lab., Tech. Rep. 41, Sept. 25, 1953 (AD 020419).

[141] P. E. Green, Jr., "The Lincoln F9C radioteletype system," M.I.T. Lincoln Lab., Tech. Memo. 61, May 14, 1954 (not available from M.I.T.).

[142] P. E. Green, Jr., R. S. Berg, C. W. Bergman, and W. B. Smith, "Performance of the Lincoln F9C radioteletype system," M.I.T. Lincoln Lab., Tech. Rep. 88, Oct. 28, 1955 (AD 080345).

[143] N. Zierler, "Inverting the sum generator," M.I.T. Lincoln Lab., Group Rep. 34–48, Feb. 13, 1956 (AD 310397).

[144] B. M. Eisenstadt and B. Gold, "Autocorrelations for Boolean functions of

noiselike periodic sequences," *IRE Trans. Electron. Comput.*, vol. EC-10, pp. 383–388, Sept. 1961.

[145] R. C. Titsworth, "Correlation properties of cyclic sequences," Ph.D. dissertation, California Inst. Technol., Pasadena, 1962.

[146] J. M. Wozencraft, "Active filters," U.S. Patent 2 880 316, Mar. 31, 1959 (filed Mar. 21, 1955).

[147] M. L. Doelz and E. T. Heald, "A predicted wave radio teletype system," in *IRE Conv. Rec.*, New York, NY, Mar. 22–25, 1954, part 8, pp. 63–69.

[148] B. Goldberg, "Applications of statistical communications theory," presented at the Army Sci. Conf., West Point, NY, June 20–22, 1962 (AD 332048); republished in *IEEE Commun. Mag.*, vol. 19, pp. 26–33, July 1981.

[149] R. Price, "Statistical theory applied to communication through multipath disturbances," M.I.T. Res. Lab. Electron. Tech. Rep. 266 and M.I.T. Lincoln Lab. Tech. Rep. 34, Sept. 3, 1953 (AD 028497).

[150] R. Price, "Notes on ideal receivers for scatter multipath," M.I.T. Lincoln Lab., Group Rep. 34-39, May 12, 1955 (AD 224557).

[151] J. B. Wiesner and Y. W. Lee, "Experimental determination of system functions by the method of correlation," *Proc. IRE*, vol. 38, p. 205, Feb. 1950 (abstr.).

[152] D. G. Brennan, "On the maximum signal-to-noise ratio realizable from several noisy signals," *Proc. IRE*, vol. 43, p. 1530, Oct. 1955.

[153] G. L. Turin, "Communication through noisy, random-multipath channels," *IRE Conv. Rec.*, New York, NY, Mar. 19–22, 1956, part 4, pp. 154–166.

[154] P. Monsen, "Fading channel communications," *IEEE Commun. Mag.*, vol. 18, pp. 16–25, Jan. 1980.

[155] R. Price and P. E. Green, Jr., "An anti-multipath communication system," M.I.T. Lincoln Lab., Tech. Memo. 65, Nov. 9, 1956 (not available from M.I.T.).

[156] ——, "A communication technique for multipath channels," *Proc. IRE*, vol. 46, pp. 555–570, Mar. 1958.

[157] ——, "Anti-multipath receiving system," U.S. Patent 2 982 853, May 2, 1961 (filed July 2, 1956).

[158] M. G. Nicholson, Jr., "Time delay apparatus," U.S. Patent 2 401 094, May 28, 1946 (filed June 23, 1944).

[159] "Lincoln F9C-A radio teletype system," Sylvania Electron. Defense Lab., Mountain View, CA, Instruction Manual EDL-B8, Dec. 21, 1956.

[160] D. E. Sunstein and B. Steinberg, "Communication technique for multipath distortion," U.S. Patent 3 168 699, Feb. 2, 1965 (filed June 10, 1959).

[161] B. Goldberg, R. L. Heyd, and D. Pochmerski, "Stored ionosphere," *Proc. IEEE Int. Conf. Commun.*, Boulder, CO, June 1965, pp. 619–622.

[162] J. R. Pierce and A. L. Hopper, "Nonsynchronous time division with holding and with random sampling," *Proc. IRE*, vol. 40, pp. 1079–1088, Sept. 1952.

[163] A. R. Eckler, "The construction of missile guidance codes resistant to random interference," *Bell Syst. Tech. J.*, vol. 39, pp. 973–994, July 1960.

[164] A. Corneretto, "Spread spectrum com system uses modified PPM," *Electron. Design*, June 21, 1961.

[165] R. Lowrie, "A secure digital command link," *IRE Trans. Space Electron. Telem.*, vol. SET-6, pp. 103–114, Sept.–Dec. 1960.

[166] R. M. Jaffe and E. Rechtin, "Design and performance of phase-lock loops

capable of near optimum performance over a wide range of input signal and noise levels," Jet Propulsion Lab., Pasadena, CA, Progress Rep. 20-243, Dec. 1954; see also *IRE Trans. Inform. Theory*, IT-1, pp. 103–114, Mar. 1955.

[167] E. Rechtin, "An annotated history of CODORAC: 1953–1958," Jet Propulsion Lab., Pasadena, CA, Rep. 20-120, Contr. DA-04-495-Ord 18, Aug. 4, 1958 (AD 301248).

[168] Corporal Bimonthly Summary Rep. 37a (July 1–Sept. 1, 1953), Jet Propulsion Lab., Pasadena, CA, Oct. 1, 1953.

[169] W. F. Sampson, "Transistor pseudonoise generator," Jet Propulsion Lab., Pasadena, CA, Memo, 20-100, Dec. 7, 1954 (AD 056175).

[170] S. W. Golomb, *Shift Register Sequences*, San Francisco, CA: Holden-Day, 1967.

[171] B. L. Scott and L. R. Welch, "An investigation of iterative Boolean sequences," Jet Propulsion Lab., Pasadena, CA, Sect. Rep. 8-543, Nov. 1, 1955.

[172] Jupiter Bimonthly Summary No. 6 (Mar. 15–May 15, 1957), Jet Propulsion Lab., Pasadena, CA, June 1, 1957.

[173] W. K. Victor and M. H. Brockman, "The application of linear servo theory to the design of AGC loops," *Proc. IRE*, vol. 48, pp. 234–238, Feb. 1960.

[174] W. B. Davenport, Jr., "Signal-to-noise ratios in bandpass limiters," *J. Appl. Phys.*, vol. 24, pp. 720–727, June 1953.

[175] J. C. Springett and M. K. Simon, "An analysis of the phase coherent-incoherent output of the bandpass limiter," *IEEE Trans. Commun. Technol.*, CT 19, pp. 42–49, Feb. 1971.

[176] B. J. DuWaldt, "Survey of radio communications securing techniques," Space Technol. Lab., Los Angeles, CA, Tech. Rep. TR-59-0000-00789, Aug. 31, 1959 (AD 358618).

[177] S. W. Golomb, "Sequences with randomness properties," Glenn L. Martin Co., Baltimore, MD, Terminal Progress Rep., Contract Req. No. 639498, June 1955.

[178] _____, "Remarks on orthogonal sequences," Glenn L. Martin Co., Baltimore, MD, Interdepartment communication, July 28, 1954.

[179] N. Zierler, "Two pseudo-random digit generators," M.I.T. Lincoln Lab., Group Rep. 34-24, July 27, 1954.

[180] _____, "Several binary sequence generators," M.I.T. Lincoln Lab., Tech. Rep. 95, Sept. 12, 1955 (AD 089135).

[181] _____, "Linear recurring sequences," *J. SIAM*, vol. 7, pp. 31–48, Mar. 1959.

[182] E. N. Gilbert, "Quasi-random binary sequences," Bell Tel. Lab., unpublished memo., Nov. 27, 1953.

[183] D. A. Huffman, "Synthesis of linear sequential coding networks," presented at the 3rd London Symp. Inform. Theory, Sept. 12–16, 1955; published in *Information Theory*, C. Cherry, ed., New York: Academic, 1956.

[184] T. G. Birdsall and M. P. Ristenbatt, "Introduction to linear shift-register generated sequences," Univ. Michigan Res. Inst., Ann Arbor, Tech. Rep. 90, Oct. 1958 (AD 225380).

[185] M. Ward, "The arithmetical theory of linear recurring sequences," *Trans. Amer. Math. Soc.*, vol. 35, pp. 600–628, July 1933.

[186] M. Hall, "An isomorphism between linear recurring sequences and algebraic rings," *Trans. Amer. Math. Soc.*, vol. 44, pp. 196–218, Sept. 1938.

[187] J. Singer, "A theorem in finite projective geometry and some applications to number theory," *Trans. Amer. Math. Soc.*, vol. 43, pp. 377–385, May 1938.

[188] R. J. Turyn, "On Singer's parametrization and related matters," Appl. Res. Lab., Sylvania Electron. Syst., Waltham, MA, Eng. Note 197, Nov. 10, 1960.
[189] R. Gold, "Optimal binary sequences for spread spectrum multiplexing," *IEEE Trans. Inform. Theory*, IT-13, pp. 619–621, Oct. 1967.
[190] _____, "Maximal recursive sequences with 3-valued cross-correlation functions," *IEEE Trans. Inform. Theory*, IT-14, pp. 151–156, Jan. 1968.
[191] T. B. Whiteley and D. J. Adrian, "Random FM autocorrelation fuze system," U.S. Patent 4 220 952, Sept. 2, 1980 (filed Feb. 17, 1956).
[192] J. P. Costas and L. C. Widmann, "Data transmission system," U.S. Patent 3 337 803, Aug. 22, 1967 (filed Jan. 9, 1962).
[193] "Reliable tactical communications," General Electric Res. Lab., Schenectady, NY, Final Rep., Contr. DA-36-039sc-42693, Mar. 2, 1954 (AD 30344).
[194] E. J. Groth, "Notes on MUTNS, a hybrid navigation system," Conf. 6733 on Modern Navigation Systems, Univ. Michigan, Ann Arbor, Summer 1967 (Univ. Michigan Library Call No. VK 145.M624, 1967).
[195] E. J. Groth *et al.*, "Navigation, guidance, and control system for drone aircraft," Motorola, Final Eng. Rep., Contr. DA36-039sc78020, June 6, 1961 (AD 329101, AD 329102, AD 329103).
[196] L. S. Schwartz, "Wide-bandwidth communications," *Space/Aeronautics*, pp. 84–89, Dec. 1963.
[197] J. M. Wozencraft, "Reliable radio teletype coding," U.S. Patent 3 896 381, July 22, 1975 (filed Nov. 2, 1960).
[198] A. Kohlenberg, S. M. Sussman, and D. Van Meter, "Matched filter communication systems," U.S. Patent 3 876 941, Apr. 8, 1975 (filed June 23, 1961).
[199] E. Guillemin, "Matched filter communication systems," U.S. Patent 3 936 749, Feb. 3, 1976 (filed June 23, 1961).
[200] S. M. Sussman, "A matched filter communication system for multipath channels," *IRE Trans. Inform. Theory*, IT-6, pp. 367–373, June 1960.
[201] W. G. Ehrich, "Common channel multipath receiver," U.S. Patent 3 293 551, Dec. 20, 1966 (filed Dec. 24, 1963).
[202] J. J. Spilker, Jr., "Nonperiodic energy communication system capable of operating at low signal-to-noise ratios," U.S. Patent 3 638 121, Jan. 25, 1972 (filed Dec. 20, 1960).
[203] H. G. Lindner, "Communication security method and system," U.S. Patent 4 184 117, Jan. 25, 1980 (filed Apr. 16, 1956).
[204] J. W. Craig and R. Price, "A secure voice communication system," *Trans. Electron. Warfare Symp.*, 1959.
[205] J. W. Craig, Jr., "An experimental NOMAC voice communication system," M.I.T. Lincoln Lab., Rep. 34G-0007, Aug. 29, 1960 (AD 319610).
[206] R. M. Fano, "Patent disclosure," Nov. 14, 1951, disclosed orally to R. F. Schreitmueller, P. E. Green, Jr., and W. B. Davenport, Jr., Oct. 8, 1951.
[207] D. J. Gray, "A new method of teletype modulation," M.I.T. Lincoln Lab., Tech. Rep. 9, Sept. 22, 1952 (AD 000928).
[208] R. M. Fano, "Anti-multipath communication system," U.S. Patent 2 982 852, May 2, 1961 (filed Nov. 21, 1956).
[209] L. A. deRosa, M. Rogoff, W. B. Davenport, Jr., and P. E. Green, Jr., in "1981 Pioneer Award," *IEEE Trans. Aerosp. Electron. Syst.*, AES-18, pp. 153–160, Jan. 1982.
[210] R. C. Dixon, ed., *Spread Spectrum Techniques*, New York: IEEE Press, 1976.
[211] A. M. Semenov and A. A. Sikarev, *Shirokopolosnaya Radiosvyazy* [Wideband Radio Communications]. Moscow, USSR: Voyenizdat, 1970.

[212] A. A. Kharkevich, "The transmission of signals by modulated noise," *Telecommunications (USSR)*, vol. 11, no. 11, pp. 43–47, 1957.

[213] F. H. Lange, *Korrelationselektronik* [Correlation Electronics], Berlin, Germany: VEB Verlag Technik, 1959.

[214] J. P. Costas, "Poisson, Shannon, and the radio amateur," *Proc. IRE*, vol. 47, pp. 2058–2068, Dec. 1959.

[215] _____, "Author's comment," *Proc. IRE*, vol. 48, p. 1911, Nov. 1960 (see also "Information capacity of fading channels under conditions of intense interference," *Proc. IEEE*, vol. 51, pp. 451–161, Mar. 1963).

[216] P. Bello, "Demodulation of a phase-modulated noise carrier," *IRE Trans. Inform. Theory*, vol. IT-7, pp. 19–27, Jan. 1961.

[217] H. Magnuski, "Wideband channel for emergency communication," in *IRE Int. Conv. Rec.*, New York, NY, Mar. 20–23, 1961, part 8, pp. 80–84.

[218] R. A. Marolf, "200 Mbit/s pseudo random sequence generator for very wide band secure communication systems," in *Proc. NEC*, Chicago, IL, 1963, vol. 19, pp. 183–187.

[219] A. I. Alekseyev, "Optimum noise immunity of noise like signals," (in Russian), presented at the 19th All-Union Conf. Popov Society, May 1963; trans. in *Telecommun. Radio Eng. (USSR)*, pt. 2, vol. 19, pp. 79–83, Aug. 1965.

[220] M. K. Razmakhnin, "Wideband communication systems" (in Russian), *Zarubezhnaya Radioelektronika* [*Foreign Radio Electron.*], no. 8, pp. 3–29, 1965.

[221] N. T. Petrovich and M. K. Razmakhnin, *Sistemy Svyazi s Shumopodobnymi Signalami* [*Communication Systems with Noise-Like Signals*], Moscow: Sovetskoye Radio, 1969.

[222] A. I. Alekseyev, A. G. Sheremet'yev, G. I. Tuzov, and B. I. Glazov, *The Theory and Application of Pseudorandom Signals* (in Russian), Moscow: 1969.

[223] Yu. B. Okunev and L. A. Yakovlev, *Shirokopolosnye Sistemy Svyazi a Sostavnymi Signalami* [*Wideband Systems of Communication with Composite Signals*], Moscow: Svyaz, 1968.

[224] L. S. Gutkin, V. B. Pestryakov, and V. N. Tipugin, *Radioupravleniye* [*Radio Control*], Moscow: 1970.

[225] M. D. Fagen, ed., *A History of Engineering and Science in the Bell System, National Service in War and Peace (1925–1975)*, Bell Lab., Murray Hill, NJ, 1978, pp. 296–317.

[226] R. Price, "Coding for greater effectiveness against jamming in NOMAC systems," M.I.T. Lincoln Lab., Tech. Rep. 78, 30 Mar. 1955 (not available from M.I.T.).

[227] R. H. Barker, "Synchronising arrangements for pulse code systems," U.S. Patent 2 721 318, Oct. 18, 1955 (filed in U.S. Feb. 16, 1953; in Great Britain, Feb. 25, 1952).

[228] S. O. Rice, "Communication in the presence of noise; probability of error for two encoding schemes," *Bell System. Tech J.*, Jan. 1950.

[229] R. M. Fano, "Signal-to-noise ratio in correlation detectors," M.I.T. Res. Lab. Electron., Tech. Rep. 186, Feb. 19, 1951 (PB 110543, ATI 103043).

[230] Y. W. Lee and J. B. Wiesner, "Correlation functions and communication applications," *Electronics*, June 1950, pp. 86–92.

[231] A. Hodges, *Alan Turing: The Enigma*, New York: Simon & Schuster, 1983.

[232] D. Kahn, "Cryptology and the origins of spread spectrum," *IEEE Spectrum*, vol. 21, no. 9, pp. 70–80, September 1984.

Chapter 3

BASIC CONCEPTS AND SYSTEM MODELS

This chapter introduces the basic design approach for anti-jam communications and presents two simple idealized examples of such systems, specifically coherent direct-sequence spread, binary phase-shift-keying (DS/BPSK), and non-coherent frequency-hopped binary frequency-shift-keying (FH/BFSK) systems opposed by various jammer waveforms. Ideal signal parameter acquisition and synchronization is assumed throughout this chapter. Ground rules for system performance analysis are specified by stating assumptions regarding jammers and anti-jam systems along with definitions of the fundamental system parameters used throughout this three-volume work. Because coding and interleaving are extremely important in anti-jam system design, the impact of these techniques is illustrated with examples. The purpose of this chapter is to exemplify basic concepts with simple examples which serve as an introduction to the more advanced material in Part 1, Chapter 4, and Part 2, Chapters 1 and 2. The material in this and the previously mentioned chapters is based in part on the works of Jacobs and Viterbi [1], Houston [2], Scholtz [3], Viterbi [4], Clark and Cain [5], and Pickholtz et al. [6].

3.1 DESIGN APPROACH FOR ANTI-JAM SYSTEMS

How can a receiver overcome the effects of intentional jamming, particularly when the jammer has much more power than the transmitted signal? Classical communication theoretic investigations of the additive white Gaussian noise channel suggest the answer. White Gaussian noise is a mathematical model which has infinite power, spread uniformly over all frequencies. Effective communication is possible with this interfering noise of infinite power because only the finite power noise components in the "signal coordinates" can do any harm. Thus, as long as the noise components in the signal coordinates are not too large, reliable communication over an additive white Gaussian noise channel is achievable. For a typical narrowband signal, this simply means that only the noise in the signal bandwidth can degrade performance. This classical theory suggests the following design approach to combatting intentional jamming:

SELECT SIGNAL COORDINATES SUCH THAT THE JAMMER CANNOT ACHIEVE LARGE JAMMER-TO-SIGNAL POWER RATIO IN THESE COORDINATES.

If many signal coordinates are available to a communication link and only a small subset of them are used at any time, and if *the jammer cannot determine the subset in use*, then the jammer is forced to jam *all coordinates* with little power in each coordinate or to jam a *few coordinates* with more power in each of the jammed coordinates. Naturally, the more signal coordinates available, the better the protection against jamming. For signals of bandwidth W and duration T the number of coordinates is roughly [7]

$$N \cong \begin{cases} 2WT & \text{coherent signals} \\ WT & \text{non-coherent signals.} \end{cases} \tag{3.1}$$

T typically represents the time to send a basic symbol. For fixed T, to make N large, W is commonly made large by one of two techniques:

- Direct Sequence Spreading (DS)
- Frequency Hopping (FH).

The signals resulting from these basic forms are referred to as spread-spectrum signals. Various hybrids of these two spreading techniques and other spread-spectrum signals are possible, but their performance does not significantly differ from that of these two basic ones. Throughout this work, the stored reference systems are assumed and in this chapter two simple examples are studied.

The assumption that the jammer does not know which subset of the many possible signal coordinates the signal uses at any given time is generally achieved by having identical synchronized pseudorandom (PN) sequence generators at both the transmitter and receiver. These continuously running PN generators are used by the transmitter and receiver to choose signal coordinates that continuously change in time. This PN generator pair must use a common key without which they would not work in unison. Throughout this book, we assume that the PN generator key is available to the transmitter and intended receiver, but *not* to the jammer. This, in fact, is the only information not available to the jammer. Our basic assumption concerning the jammer is:

THE JAMMER HAS COMPLETE KNOWLEDGE OF THE SPREAD-SPECTRUM SYSTEM DESIGN EXCEPT HE DOES NOT HAVE THE KEY TO THE PSEUDORANDOM SEQUENCE GENERATORS.

Indeed, the jammer can have identical copies available (stolen perhaps) of the spread-spectrum transmitter and receiver, and certainly can try various keys; but without knowledge of the actual key used by the spread-spectrum system, the jammer cannot generate the same pseudorandom numbers used by the spread-spectrum transmitter and receiver. Chapter 5 of Part 1 reviews the properties and design of pseudorandom number generators.

3.2 MODELS AND FUNDAMENTAL PARAMETERS

The basic system is shown in Figure 3.1 where the following system parameters are fixed:

W_{ss} = total spread-spectrum signal bandwidth available

R_b = data rate in bits per second

$$\left.\begin{aligned} S &= \text{signal power} \\ J &= \text{jammer power} \end{aligned}\right\} \text{at input to the intended receiver} \tag{3.2}$$

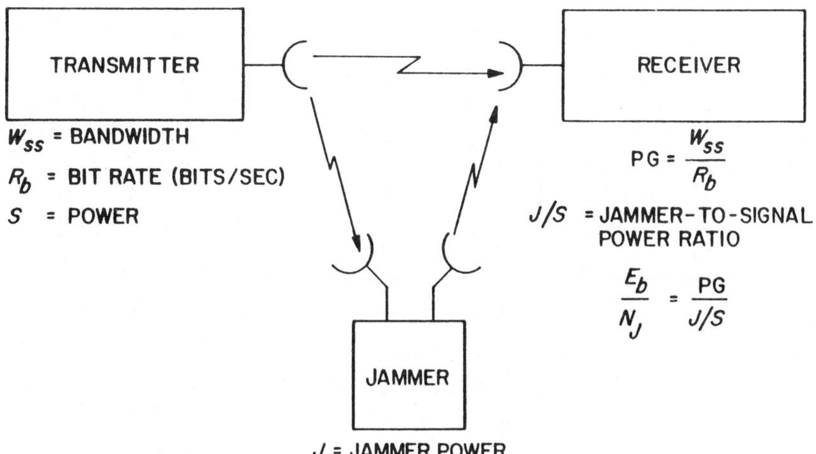

Figure 3.1. System overview.

The total spread-spectrum signal bandwidth available, W_{ss}, may not necessarily be contiguous; and it may be that a spread-spectrum system does not use all of this available bandwidth. Nevertheless, we define W_{ss} as the total available signal bandwidth and its definition is independent of how it is used. The data rate, R_b, is the uncoded information rate to be transmitted over the spread-spectrum communication link; this definition is independent of the use of coding. The signal power S and jammer power J are the time-averaged powers at the intended receiver. If, for example, the jammer transmits a pulsed signal where high peak power is achieved over short time intervals, the time-averaged power is still J. In practice, this relationship between peak power and average power may not always apply.

Regardless of the signal and jammer waveforms, an equivalent bit energy-to-jammer noise ratio is defined as

$$\frac{E_b}{N_J} = \frac{W_{ss}S}{R_b J} \tag{3.3}$$

where we define processing gain (PG)

$$\text{PG} = \frac{W_{ss}}{R_b} \tag{3.4}$$

and

$$\frac{J}{S} = \text{jammer-to-signal power ratio.} \tag{3.5}$$

In decibels (dB), the bit energy-to-jammer noise ratio is

$$\frac{E_b}{N_J}(\text{dB}) = [\text{PG}]_{\text{dB}} - [J/S]_{\text{dB}} \tag{3.6}$$

where

$$[\text{PG}]_{\text{dB}} = 10\log_{10}\left(\frac{W_{ss}}{R_b}\right)$$

$$[J/S]_{\text{dB}} = 10\log_{10}\left(\frac{J}{S}\right). \tag{3.7}$$

In this work, bit error bounds are derived as a function of this E_b/N_J for various spread-spectrum systems and various types of jamming waveforms.

Note again that all of these definitions are independent of the type of spread-spectrum system being used, including the use of coding. The purpose of defining all of these basic parameters, independent of specific system details, is so that the performance of different systems for the same set of overall system parameter values can be compared. The particular definition of processing gain given in (3.4) may not agree with the definition of processing gain as the ratio of spread bandwidth to unspread signal bandwidth. This latter definition depends on both the modulation and coding technique used and is not as fundamental as the definition (3.4) used throughout this work.

For most of the performance evaluations in this work, it is assumed that the jammer limits performance, and therefore the effects of receiver noise in the channel can be ignored. Thus, the performance results are generally based on the assumption that the jammer power is much larger than the noise in the receiver system. An exception to this is considered when we examine both non-uniform fading channels and multiple access channels where other user signals are taken into the analysis.

3.3 JAMMER WAVEFORMS

There are an infinite number of possible jamming waveforms that could be considered. A class of jamming waveforms is selected to illustrate the basic spread-spectrum communication concepts and includes (to a good approximation) the worst types of jammer to the spread-spectrum systems of interest. *There is no single jamming waveform that is worst for all spread-spectrum systems and there is no single spread-spectrum system that is best against all jamming waveforms.* For most of this work the following types of possible jammers are considered.

3.3.1 Broadband and Partial-Band Noise Jammers

A broadband noise jammer spreads Gaussian noise of total power J evenly over the total frequency range of the spread bandwidth W_{ss} as shown in Figure 3.2(a). This results in an equivalent single-sided noise power spectral density

$$N_J = \frac{J}{W_{ss}}. \tag{3.8}$$

Since the signal energy per bit is ST_b where $T_b = 1/R_b$,

$$E_b = \frac{S}{R_b}. \tag{3.9}$$

Thus, in this case, the general definition (3.3) is exactly the bit energy-to-jammer noise ratio.

The broadband noise jammer is a brute force jammer that does not exploit any knowledge of the anti-jam communication system except its spread bandwidth W_{ss}. The resulting bit error probability of the anti-jam system is the same as that with additive white Gaussian noise of one-sided spectral density equal to N_J. We refer to the performance with this jammer as the *baseline performance*. In the following sections, we will illustrate how much worse the performance can become with other jamming waveforms of the same power J. Coding and interleaving, however, can be used to recover most of the performance loss as a result of these other jammers and to reduce the jammer's effectiveness to that of the baseline broadband noise

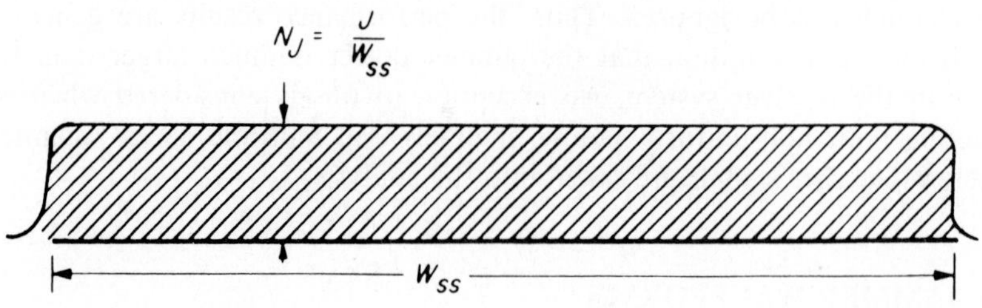

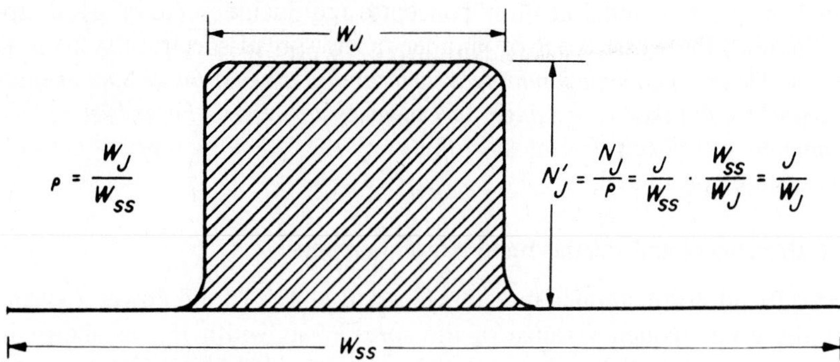

Figure 3.2. Noise jammer frequency distribution.

jammer case. *An effective anti-jam communication system is one that gives performance close to or better than the baseline performance, regardless of the type of jammer waveform used.*

A partial-band noise jammer, as shown in Figure 3.2(b), spreads noise of total power J evenly over some frequency range of bandwidth W_J, which is a subset of the total spread bandwidth W_{ss}. We define ρ as the ratio

$$\rho = \frac{W_J}{W_{ss}} \leq 1 \tag{3.10}$$

which is the fraction of the total spread-spectrum band that has noise of power spectral density

$$\begin{aligned} \frac{J}{W_J} &= \frac{J}{W_{ss}} \cdot \frac{W_{ss}}{W_J} \\ &= N_J/\rho . \end{aligned} \tag{3.11}$$

3.3.2 CW and Multitone Jammers

A CW jammer has the form

$$J(t) = \sqrt{2J}\cos[\omega t + \theta] \tag{3.12}$$

while multitone jammers using N_t equal power tones can be described by

$$J(t) = \sum_{l=1}^{N_t} \sqrt{2J/N_t}\cos[\omega_l t + \theta_l]. \tag{3.13}$$

These are shown in the frequency domain in Figures 3.3(a) and 3.3(b). All phases are assumed to be independent and uniformly distributed over $[0, 2\pi]$.

3.3.3 Pulse Jammer

Pulse jamming occurs when a jammer transmits with power

$$J_{\text{peak}} = \frac{J}{\rho} \tag{3.14}$$

for a fraction ρ of the time, and nothing for the remaining fraction $1 - \rho$ of the time. During the pulse interval, noise or tones can be transmitted while the time-averaged power is J.

3.3.4 Arbitrary Jammer Power Distributions

A natural generalization of the broadband and partial-band noise jammers given above is a Gaussian noise jammer with an arbitrary power spectral density of total power J. For most cases of interest, the power spectral

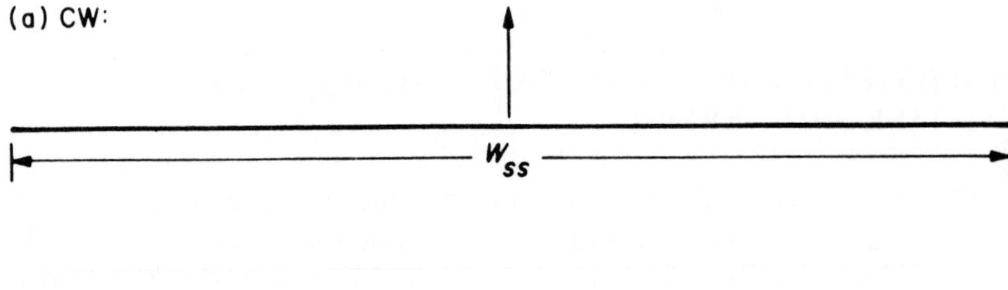

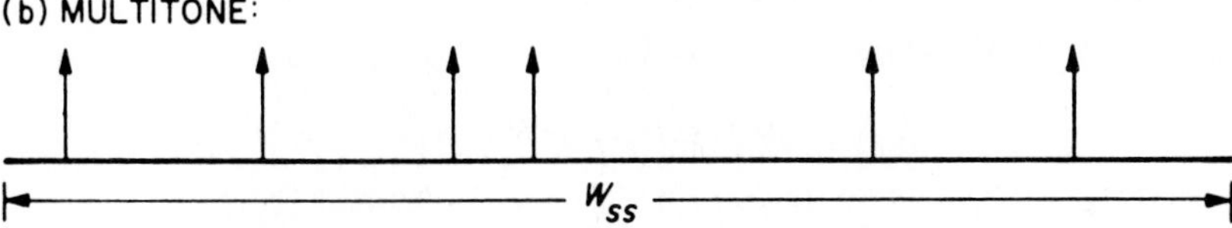

Figure 3.3. Tone jammer frequency distribution.

density that has the worst impact on the communicator has the simple partial-band form shown in Figure 3.2(b) for some corresponding worst case value of ρ. We illustrate this point in Part 2, Chapters 1 and 2. An exception to this occurs when the channel is non-uniform in the sense that the actual signal-to-noise ratio varies across the spread-spectrum band. This will be discussed in Part 2, Chapter 2, when modeling the high frequency (HF) channel that uses the skywave reflections off the ionosphere.

The pulse jammer discussed above can be generalized to include an arbitrary power distribution in time, keeping average power equal to J. Again, the worst case jammer is usually one that pulses on and off with a worst case value of ρ, the fraction of time the jammer is on with full peak power.

3.3.5 Repeat-Back Jammers

A repeat-back jammer first estimates parameters from the intercepted spread-spectrum signal and then transmits jamming waveforms that use this information. Such jammers are primarily effective against FH systems when the hop rate is slow enough for the repeat-back jammer to respond within the hop duration. *This type of jammer can be neutralized by increasing the hop rate or independently hopping each tone in the case of MFSK signals.* Here such jammers are sometimes referred to as "frequency-following jammers." An analysis of the average repeat-back jammer power reaching the receiver's data detection circuits is given in Scholtz [3].

In this work, the impact of repeat-back jammers is not discussed except to caution against low hop rates in an FH spread system. Generally the effectiveness of a repeat-back jammer depends on the hop rate and the distances between the transmitter, receiver, and jammer.

3.4 UNCODED DIRECT-SEQUENCE SPREAD BINARY PHASE-SHIFT-KEYING

To illustrate some basic concepts consider the example of an uncoded coherent, direct-sequence spread, binary phase-shift-keying (DS/BPSK) system. This type of anti-jam system is covered in greater detail in Part 2, Chapter 1.

Ordinary BPSK signals have the form

$$s(t) = \sqrt{2S}\,\sin[\omega_0 t + d_n \pi/2];$$
$$nT_b \le t < (n+1)T_b, \quad n = \text{integer}. \tag{3.15}$$

Here T_b is the data bit time and $\{d_n\}$ is the sequence of independent data bits where

$$d_n = \begin{cases} 1, & \text{with probability } \frac{1}{2} \\ -1, & \text{with probability } \frac{1}{2}. \end{cases} \tag{3.16}$$

Equation (3.15) can also be expressed in the form

$$\begin{aligned} s(t) &= d_n\sqrt{2S}\cos\omega_0 t; \\ nT_b &\le t < (n+1)T_b, \quad n = \text{integer}. \end{aligned} \tag{3.17}$$

Hence, we can view BPSK as phase modulation or amplitude modulation. Ordinary BPSK signals have a $(\sin^2 x)/x^2$ shaped power spectrum with one-sided first null bandwidth equal to $1/T_b$.

Direct sequence spreading of this BPSK signal is done with a pseudorandom (PN) binary sequence $\{c_k\}$ whose elements have values ± 1 and are generated by the PN sequence generator N times faster than the data rate. Thus, the time T_c of a PN binary symbol referred to as a "chip" is

$$T_c = \frac{T_b}{N}. \tag{3.18}$$

The PN chip rate might be several megabits per second while the data rate might be a few bits per second. The direct sequence spread-spectrum signal has the form

$$\begin{aligned} x(t) &= \sqrt{2S}\sin[\omega_0 t + d_n c_{nN+k}\pi/2] \\ &= d_n c_{nN+k}\sqrt{2S}\cos\omega_0 t; \\ nT_b + kT_c &\le t < nT_b + (k+1)T_c \\ k &= 0, 1, 2, \ldots, N-1 \\ n &= \text{integer}. \end{aligned} \tag{3.19}$$

This signal is similar to ordinary BPSK except that the apparent data rate is N times faster, resulting in a signal spectrum N times wider. Here the processing gain is simply

$$\text{PG} = \frac{W_{ss}}{R_b} = N, \tag{3.20}$$

where W_{ss} is again the direct sequence spread signal bandwidth.

Defining the data function

$$d(t) = d_n, \qquad nT_b \le t < (n+1)T_b \tag{3.21}$$

for all integers n, and PN function

$$c(t) = c_k, \qquad kT_c \le t < (k+1)T_c \tag{3.22}$$

for all integers k, the direct sequence spread BPSK signal can be expressed as

$$\begin{aligned} x(t) &= \sqrt{2S}\sin[\omega_0 t + c(t)d(t)\pi/2] \\ &= c(t)d(t)\sqrt{2S}\cos\omega_0 t. \end{aligned} \tag{3.23}$$

Figure 3.4 illustrates $d(t)$, $c(t)$, and $c(t)d(t)$ for $N = 6$. Figure 3.5(a) displays the normal form of the DS/BPSK modulator and Figure 3.5(b) shows a more convenient model for analysis. Note that in this latter form,

$$x(t) = c(t)s(t), \tag{3.24}$$

where

$$s(t) = d(t)\sqrt{2S}\cos\omega_0 t \tag{3.25}$$

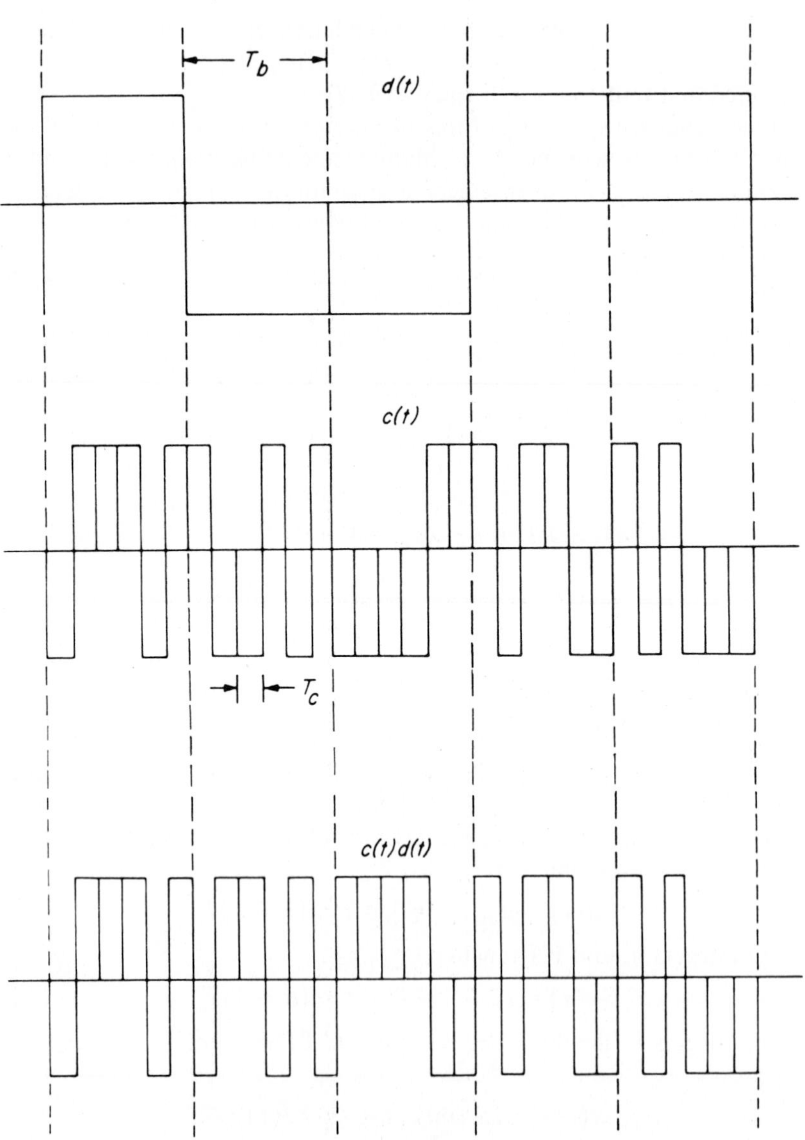

Figure 3.4. DS/BPSK waveforms.

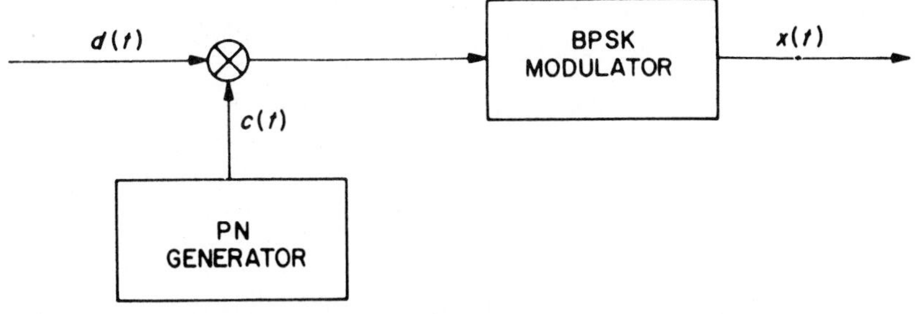

(a) Normal Form

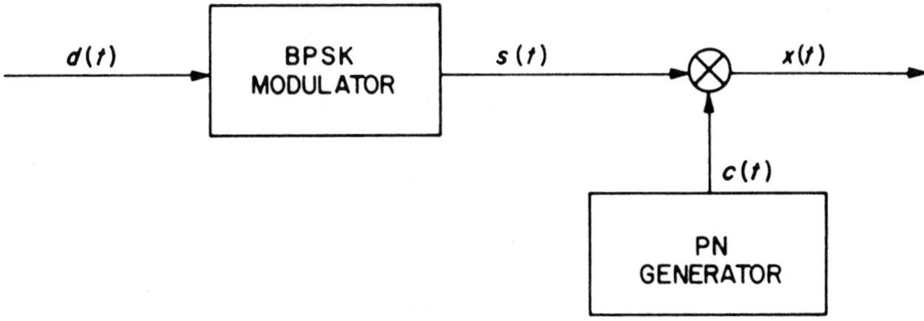

(b) Convenient Representation

Figure 3.5. DS/BPSK modulation.

is the ordinary BPSK signal. Also, since

$$c^2(t) = 1 \text{ for all } t, \tag{3.26}$$

it follows that

$$c(t)x(t) = s(t). \tag{3.27}$$

Assuming the intended receiver has a PN sequence generator that is synchronized to the one in the transmitter, $c(t)$ is available to both the transmitter and receiver.

3.4.1 Constant Power Broadband Noise Jammer

Suppose a jammer is transmitting a signal $J(t)$ with constant power J in the system shown in Figure 3.6. An ideal coherent BPSK demodulator is assumed to follow the received signal $y(t)$ multiplied by the PN sequence

$c(t)$. Here, the channel output is[1]

$$y(t) = x(t) + J(t) \tag{3.28}$$

which is multiplied by the PN sequence $c(t)$ to obtain

$$\begin{aligned} r(t) &= c(t)y(t) \\ &= c(t)x(t) + c(t)J(t) \\ &= s(t) + c(t)J(t). \end{aligned} \tag{3.29}$$

This is the ordinary BPSK signal imbedded in some additive noise given by $c(t)J(t)$. The BPSK detector output which is optimum for broadband interference [8] is

$$r = d\sqrt{E_b} + n \tag{3.30}$$

where d is the data bit for this T_b second interval. $E_b = ST_b$ is the bit energy, and n is the equivalent noise component given by

$$n = \sqrt{\frac{2}{T_b}} \int_0^{T_b} c(t)J(t)\cos\omega_0 t\,dt. \tag{3.31}$$

The typical BPSK decision rule is

$$\hat{d} = \begin{cases} 1, & \text{if } r > 0 \\ -1, & \text{if } r \le 0. \end{cases} \tag{3.32}$$

Hence, the bit error probability is

$$\begin{aligned} P_b &= \Pr\{r > 0 | d = -1\} \\ &= \Pr\left\{n > \sqrt{E_b}\right\} \end{aligned} \tag{3.33}$$

assuming, without loss of generality, that $d = -1$.

The noise term depends upon many PN chips, viz.,

$$n = \sum_{k=0}^{N-1} c_k \sqrt{\frac{2}{T_b}} \int_{kT_c}^{(k+1)T_c} J(t)\cos\omega_0 t\,dt. \tag{3.34}$$

Assuming the jammer transmits broadband Gaussian noise of one-sided power spectral density given by (3.8), the terms

$$n_k = \sqrt{\frac{2}{T_c}} \int_{kT_c}^{(k+1)T_c} J(t)\cos\omega_0 t\,dt \tag{3.35}$$

are independent zero-mean Gaussian random variables with variance $N_J/2$. Thus, n defined by (3.34) and rewritten as

$$n = \sum_{k=0}^{N-1} c_k \sqrt{\frac{T_c}{T_b}}\, n_k \tag{3.36}$$

[1]Receiver noise which is typically modeled as additive white Gaussian noise is ignored here since jammer interference is assumed to dominate. In Section 3.9 we discuss this assumption.

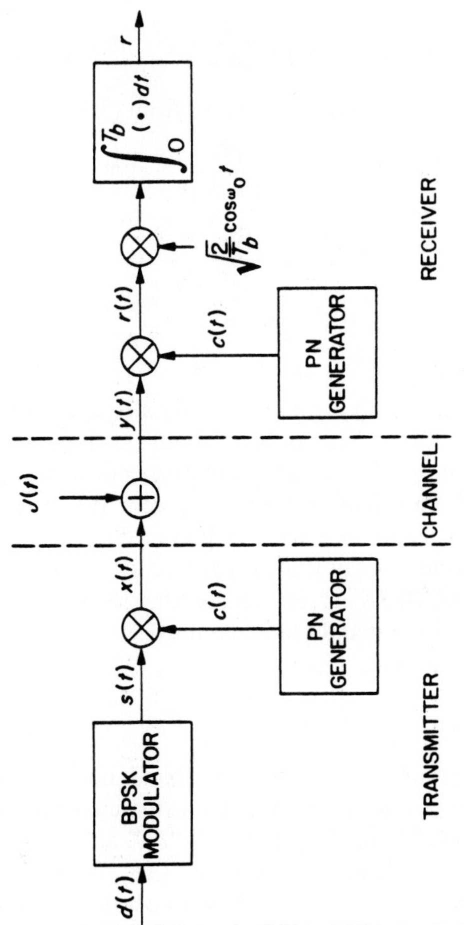

Figure 3.6. Uncoded DS/BPSK system.

is a zero-mean Gaussian random variable with variance $N_J/2$. For a continuous broadband noise jammer of constant power J the uncoded bit error probability is

$$P_b = Q\left(\sqrt{\frac{2E_b}{N_J}}\right) \tag{3.37}$$

where

$$Q(x) \triangleq \int_x^\infty \frac{1}{\sqrt{2\pi}} e^{-t^2/2}\, dt \tag{3.38}$$

is the Gaussian probability integral [8] and from (3.3) and (3.20),

$$\begin{aligned}\frac{E_b}{N_J} &= \frac{\text{PG}}{(J/S)} \\ &= \frac{(W_{ss}/R_b)}{(J/S)} \\ &= \frac{N}{(J/S)}.\end{aligned} \tag{3.39}$$

For large N, the above bit error probability also applies to most constant power jammer waveforms. This is based both on the assumption that the PN sequence $\{c_k\}$ is approximated as an independent binary sequence and the application of the Central Limit Theorem [9]. The details of this assumption are discussed in Part 1, Chapter 5 and Part 2, Chapter 1. Thus, this result *seems* to say that, regardless of the type of jammer, the performance of DS/BPSK is essentially the same as for the baseline jammer, namely the broadband Gaussian noise jammer. This is not true, as shown in the next example.

3.4.2 Pulse Jammer

Suppose that the jammer transmits broadband noise as in the previous section, but for only a fraction of the time with larger power. In particular, let ρ be the fraction of time the jammer is "on" and N_J/ρ be the jammer power spectral density where N_J is given by (3.8). Note that the time-averaged jammer power is assumed to be J, although the actual power during a jamming pulse duration is J/ρ. Also assume that the jammer pulse duration is greater than T_b, the data bit time, and that a particular transmitted data bit either encounters a channel with jammer "on" with probability ρ or jammer "off" with probability $1 - \rho$. We ignore the cases where the jammer might be "on" only a fraction of the transmitted data bit time.

We model the pulse jammer case as shown in Figure 3.6 with the detector output now given as

$$r = d\sqrt{E_b} + Zn \tag{3.40}$$

where n is the jammer noise term which is a Gaussian random variable with zero mean and variance $N_J/(2\rho)$. Here Z is a random variable independent of n that has probability,

$$\begin{aligned}\Pr\{Z=1\} &= \rho\\ \Pr\{Z=0\} &= 1-\rho.\end{aligned} \tag{3.41}$$

The random variable Z specifies whether or not the jammer is "on" during a particular T_b data bit time interval when one BPSK signal is transmitted.

The bit error probability is then

$$\begin{aligned}P_b &= \Pr\left\{Zn > \sqrt{E_b}\right\}\\ &= \Pr\left\{Zn > \sqrt{E_b}\,\middle|\,Z=1\right\}\Pr\{Z=1\}\\ &\quad + \Pr\left\{Zn > \sqrt{E_b}\,\middle|\,Z=0\right\}\Pr\{Z=0\}\\ &= \Pr\left\{n > \sqrt{E_b}\right\}\rho\\ &= \rho Q\left(\sqrt{\frac{2E_b}{N_J}\rho}\right)\end{aligned} \tag{3.42}$$

where with jammer pulse "off"

$$\Pr\left\{Zn > \sqrt{E_b}\,\middle|\,Z=0\right\} = 0. \tag{3.43}$$

This ignores the effects of noise and assumes the jammer signal "on" error term is much larger than the jammer signal "off" error term.

Figure 3.7 shows values of P_b versus $E_b/N_J = N/(J/S)$ for various values of ρ, the fraction of time the jammer pulse is on with power J/ρ. Note that the value of ρ that maximizes the bit error probability, P_b, decreases with increasing values of E_b/N_J. To see this analytically, differentiate (3.42) with respect to ρ to find that the value of ρ that maximizes P_b is

$$\rho^* = \begin{cases}\dfrac{0.709}{E_b/N_J}, & E_b/N_J > 0.709\\ 1, & E_b/N_J \le 0.709\end{cases} \tag{3.44}$$

which results in the maximum bit error probability

$$\begin{aligned}P_b^* &= \max_{0\le\rho\le 1} \rho Q\left(\sqrt{\frac{2E_b}{N_J}\rho}\right)\\ &= \rho^* Q\left(\sqrt{\frac{2E_b}{N_J}\rho^*}\right)\\ &= \begin{cases}\dfrac{0.083}{E_b/N_J}, & E_b/N_J > 0.709\\ Q\left(\sqrt{\dfrac{2E_b}{N_J}}\right), & E_b/N_J \le 0.709.\end{cases}\end{aligned} \tag{3.45}$$

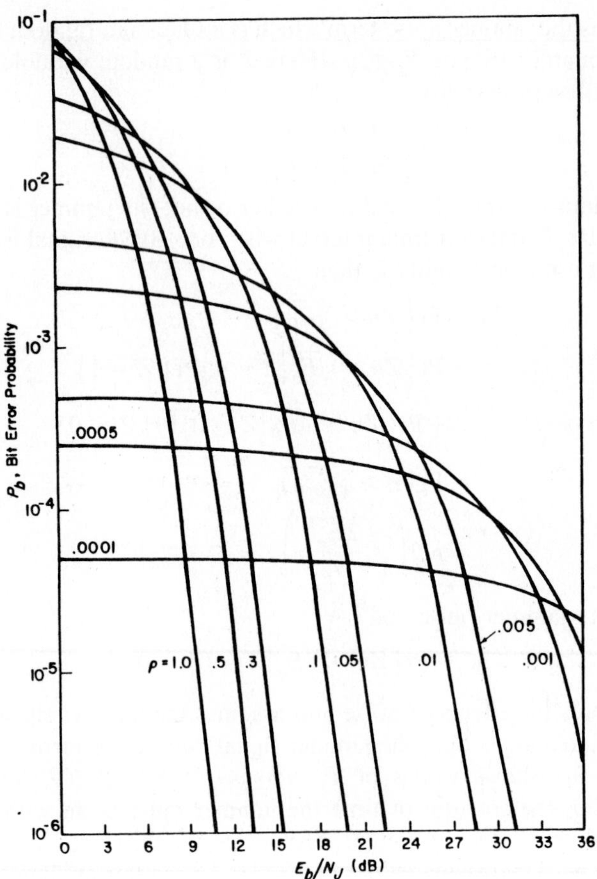

Figure 3.7. DS/BPSK pulse jammer.

Figure 3.8 illustrates the huge difference between a constant power jammer ($\rho = 1$) and the worst case pulse jammer with $\rho = \rho^*$ for uncoded DS/BPSK systems. Note that at a bit error probability of 10^{-6} there is almost a 40 dB difference in E_b/N_J. Here for the same fixed average power J, the jammer can do considerably more harm to an uncoded DS/BPSK anti-jam system with pulse jamming than with constant power jamming. This can be explained by noting in Figure 3.8 the rapidly dropping bit error probability curve for $\rho = 1$. A small decrease in E_b/N_J results in a large increase in P_b. The jammer can vary the value of E_b/N_J with pulse jamming, resulting in the net average bit error probability skewed toward the high error probabilities associated with the small values of E_b/N_J that occur during a pulse. In general, if the jammer were to vary its power over several values while maintaining time-averaged power J, the resulting bit error probability would be the weighted sum of the bit error probabilities at each of the possible jammer power levels. In this sum, the largest error

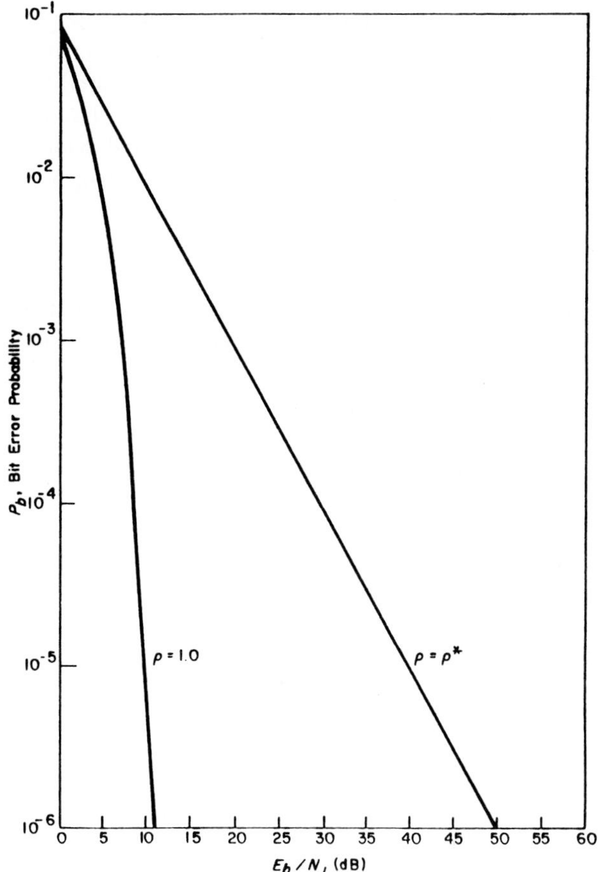

Figure 3.8. Constant power and worst case pulse jammer for DS/BPSK.

probabilities tend to dominate. We show in Volume II, Chapter 1 that the worst jammer power distribution is the "on" and "off" pulse jammer considered here.

In practice, the jammer may not be able to achieve small values of ρ or high peak power. Also when a jammer pulse length is shorter than a data bit time this analysis does not apply. In general, however, (3.45) represents an upper bound on the bit error probability.

3.5 CODED DIRECT-SEQUENCE SPREAD BINARY PHASE-SHIFT-KEYING

The impact of pulse jamming can be neutralized with coding techniques where the use of coding not only provides the usual coding gain but also forces the worst pulse jammer to be the constant power jammer. Thus, for example, at 10^{-6} bit error probability, the total coding gain against the worst pulse jammer is 40 dB as a result of pulse jammer neutralization plus the usual coding gain. This is a significant gain compared to the coding gain achieved in the usual additive white Gaussian noise channel.

Reducing the data rate or expanding the signal bandwidth is usually associated with coding since some form of redundancy is required. *For spread-spectrum signals it is not necessary to reduce the data rate or increase the signal bandwidth in order to use coding techniques.* To illustrate this consider a simple constraint length $K = 2$, rate $R = \frac{1}{2}$ bits per coded symbol convolutional code. For each data bit the encoder generates two coded bits. Let $\{d_n\}$ be the data bit sequence as before. For the k-th transmission time interval, the two coded bits are

$$\mathbf{a}_k = (a_{k1}, a_{k2}) \tag{3.46}$$

where

$$a_{k1} = d_k$$

$$a_{k2} = \begin{cases} 1; & d_k \neq d_{k-1} \\ -1; & d_k = d_{k-1}. \end{cases}$$

Suppose that T_b is the data bit time. Then each coded bit must be transmitted in $T_s = T_b/2$ seconds. Here T_s is the time of each coded symbol. Defining

$$a(t) = \begin{cases} a_{k1}, & kT_b \leq t < (k + \frac{1}{2})T_b \\ a_{k2}, & (k + \frac{1}{2})T_b \leq t < (k+1)T_b \end{cases}$$

$$k = \text{integer} \tag{3.47}$$

shown in Figure 3.9 is the uncoded waveform $d(t)$, coded waveform $a(t)$, and PN waveform $c(t)$ for $N = 6$. With ordinary BPSK modulation, the coded waveform will have twice the bandwidth of the uncoded waveform. However, when we multiply the PN waveform with the coded and uncoded waveform, we obtain $c(t)d(t)$ and $c(t)a(t)$ shown in Figure 3.10. At this point, the resulting spread-spectrum signals have the same bandwidth. Also shown here is the convolutional code diagram when $\{1, -1\}$ binary symbols are converted to $\{1, 0\}$ binary symbols.

To illustrate the impact of coding, consider the simplest of all coding techniques, the repeat code. This is a code of rate $R = 1/m$ bits per coded symbol for some integer m. For each data bit d this code is to simply transmit m bits

$$\mathbf{a} = (a_1, a_2, a_3, \ldots, a_m) \tag{3.48}$$

where

$$a_i = d; \qquad i = 1, 2, \ldots, m.$$

Thus, each coded bit a_i is transmitted within $T_s = T_b/m$ seconds. As we noted above, as long as $m < N$, the bandwidth of the direct sequence spread signal is unchanged by the use of this code.

The coded DS/BPSK system is sketched in Figure 3.11. Data bit d is encoded into a sequence of m coded bits each identical to d in value. The coded bits are scrambled in time by the interleaver and then BPSK modulated and direct sequence spread by the PN sequence $c(t)$. The transmitted DS/BPSK signal is given by (3.24) where $s(t)$ is the ordinary coded BPSK signal. The channel output is again $y(t)$ of (3.28) which after

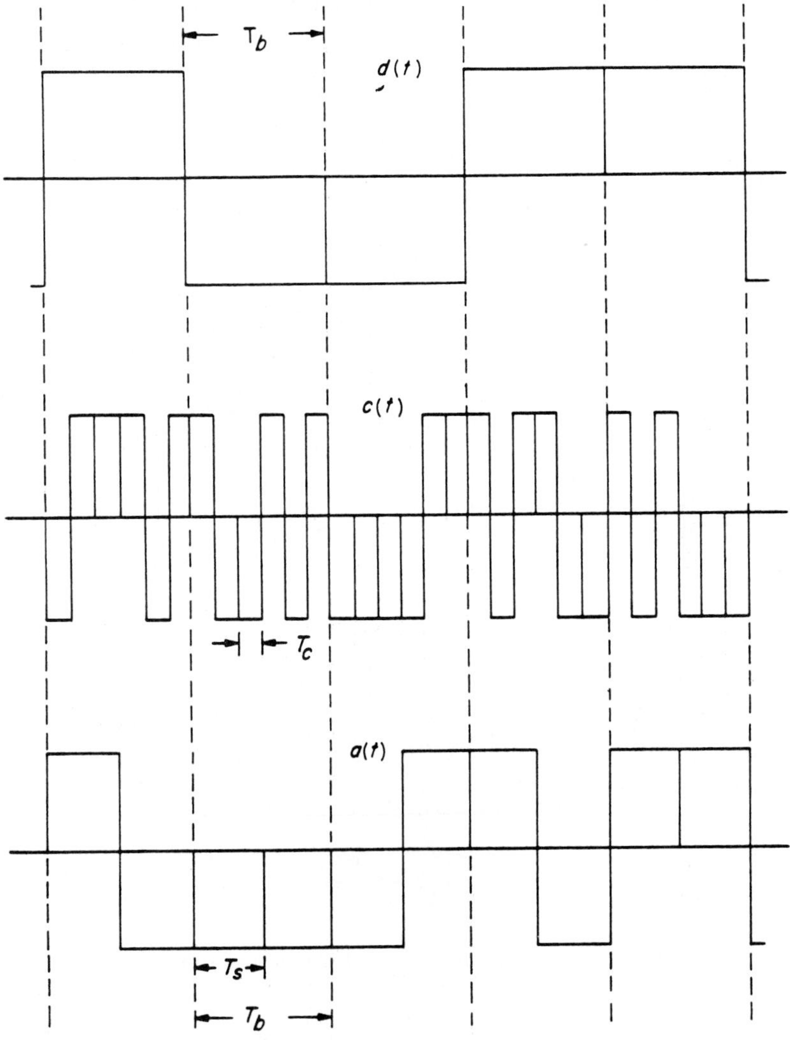

Figure 3.9. Coded and uncoded signals before spreading.

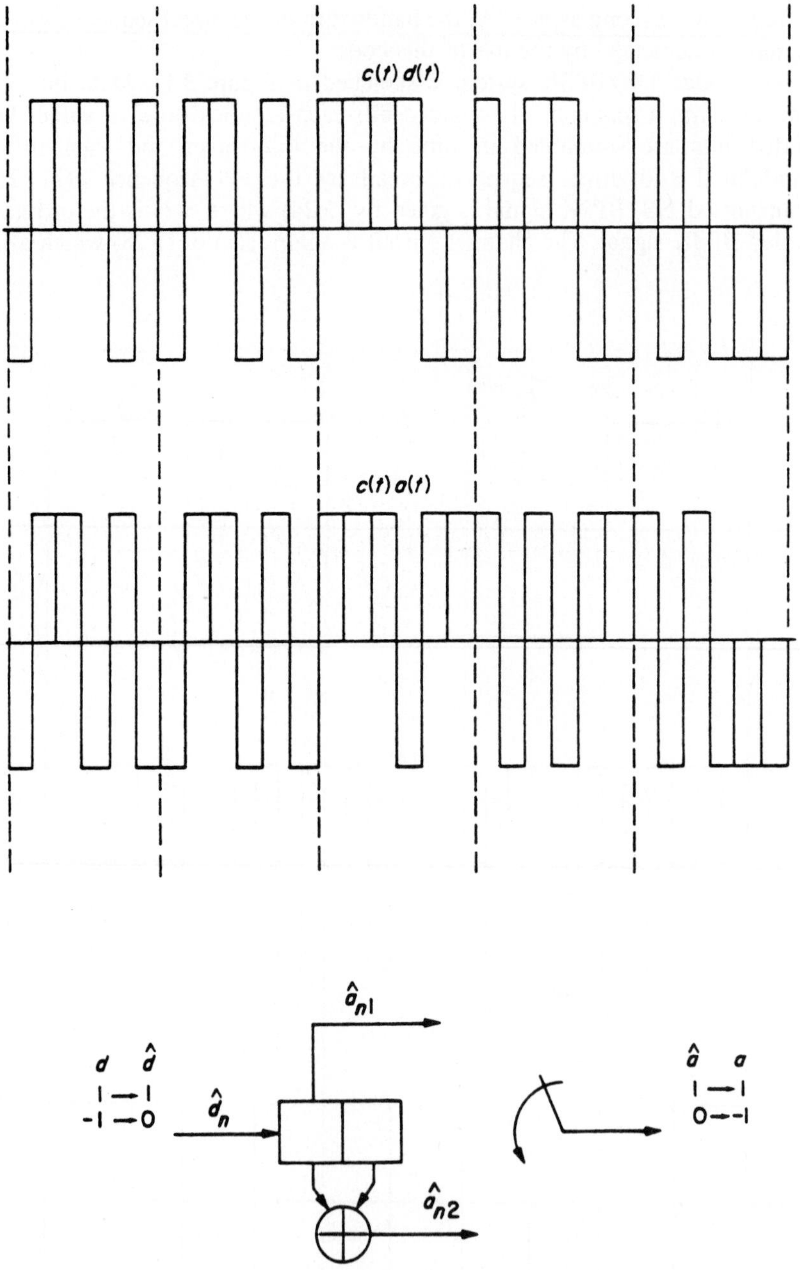

$c(t)\,d(t)$

$c(t)\,a(t)$

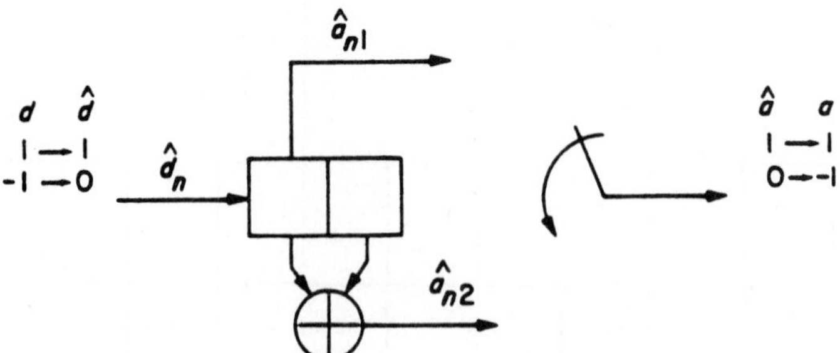

Figure 3.10. Coded and uncoded signals after spreading.

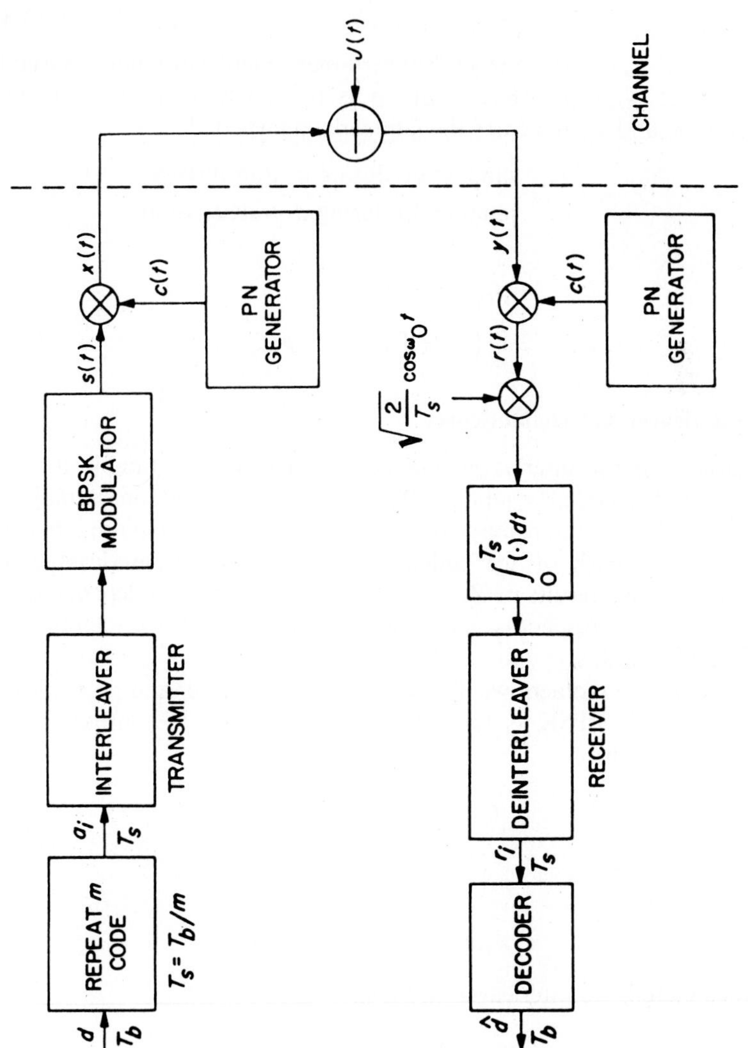

Figure 3.11. Repeat coded DS/BPSK system.

multiplication by $c(t)$ becomes $r(t)$ of (3.29). The detector for this signal consists of a correlator or matched filter with outputs, after deinterleaving, given by

$$r_i = a_i\sqrt{E_b/m} + Z_i n_i;$$
$$i = 1, 2, \ldots, m \tag{3.49}$$

where $n_1, n_2, \ldots, n_m$ are independent zero-mean Gaussian random variables with variance $N_J/(2\rho)$. Here again, ρ is the fraction of time the pulse jammer is on and Z_i indicates the jammer state where

$$Z_i = \begin{cases} 1, & \text{jammer on during } a_i \text{ transmission} \\ 0, & \text{jammer off during } a_i \text{ transmission} \end{cases} \tag{3.50}$$

and

$$\Pr\{Z_i = 1\} = \rho$$
$$\Pr\{Z_i = 0\} = 1 - \rho. \tag{3.51}$$

3.5.1 Interleaver and Deinterleaver

The purpose of the interleaver and deinterleaver is to scramble the time sequence of the coded symbols before transmission and unscramble the received signals after transmission so that the impact of the pulse jammer is independent in each of the coded symbols. For ideal interleaving and deinterleaving this results in $Z_1, Z_2, Z_3, \ldots, Z_m$ becoming independent random variables. In Appendix 3A, various forms of interleaver-deinterleaver pairs are discussed.

Suppose for the moment we did not have an interleaver and deinterleaver in the coded DS/BPSK system of Figure 3.11. Then the outputs of the channel have the form

$$r_i = d\sqrt{E_b/m} + Zn_i;$$
$$i = 1, 2, \ldots, m \tag{3.52}$$

where

$$a_i = d; \qquad i = 1, 2, \ldots, m$$

and since there is no interleaver and deinterleaver

$$Z_i = Z; \qquad i = 1, 2, \ldots, m. \tag{3.53}$$

This follows from the assumption that the jammer is either "on" or "off" during the whole transmission of a data bit. The interleaver-deinterleaver pair would normally scramble the coded bits over a large enough time span so that $Z_1, Z_2, \ldots, Z_m$ would come from widely spaced time segments and, thus, be independent of each other.

With no interleaver-deinterleaver pair the optimum decision rule is to form the sum

$$
\begin{aligned}
r &= \sum_{i=1}^{m} r_i \\
&= d\sqrt{mE_b} + Z\sum_{i=1}^{m} n_i
\end{aligned}
\tag{3.54}
$$

and make the bit decision $\hat{d}$ in accordance with (3.32). The bit error probability is, thus,

$$
\begin{aligned}
P_b &= \Pr\{\, r > 0 | d = -1\} \\
&= \Pr\left\{ Z\sum_{i=1}^{m} n_i > \sqrt{mE_b} \right\} \\
&= \Pr\left\{ Z\frac{1}{\sqrt{m}}\sum_{i=1}^{m} n_i > \sqrt{E_b} \right\} \\
&= \rho\Pr\left\{ Z\frac{1}{\sqrt{m}}\sum_{i=1}^{m} n_i > \sqrt{E_b} \,\middle|\, Z = 1 \right\} \\
&= \rho Q\left(\sqrt{\frac{2E_b}{N_J}\rho} \right).
\end{aligned}
\tag{3.55}
$$

This bit error probability is identical to that of the uncoded DS/BPSK system (see (3.42)). Thus, without interleaving and deinterleaving, there is no difference between the uncoded and simple repeat-coded systems.

In general, coding techniques are ineffective without interleaving and deinterleaving. Burst error correcting codes [10] may be effective against some pulse jammers, but would be useless against others. For robust system designs, interleavers and deinterleavers must be used with coding techniques so that the effect of the pulse jammer is independent among coded symbol transmissions. This is also true for other types of coded spread-spectrum systems and jammers. For the remainder of this work, ideal interleaving and deinterleaving is assumed where the impact of jamming is independent among transmitted coded symbols. (See Appendix 3A for more details.)

3.5.2 Unknown Channel State

With ideal interleaving and deinterleaving the channel outputs are as given in (3.49) where again $Z_1, Z_2, \ldots, Z_m$ and $n_1, n_2, \ldots, n_m$ are all independent random variables. The decoder takes $r_1, r_2, \ldots, r_m$ and makes a decision $\hat{d} = 1$ or $\hat{d} = -1$. With pulse jamming there is the possibility that the decoder may have additional information about the values $Z_1, Z_2, \ldots, Z_m$ that might aid the decision rule. This might be possible with channel measurements. Here, however, assume the decoder has no knowledge of $Z_1, Z_2, \ldots, Z_m$ and consider two standard decision rules.

3.5.2.1 Soft Decision Decoder

The soft decision decoder computes

$$r = \sum_{i=1}^{m} r_i$$
$$= d\sqrt{mE_b} + \sum_{i=1}^{m} Z_i n_i \tag{3.56}$$

and makes the decision in accordance with (3.32). The bit error probability

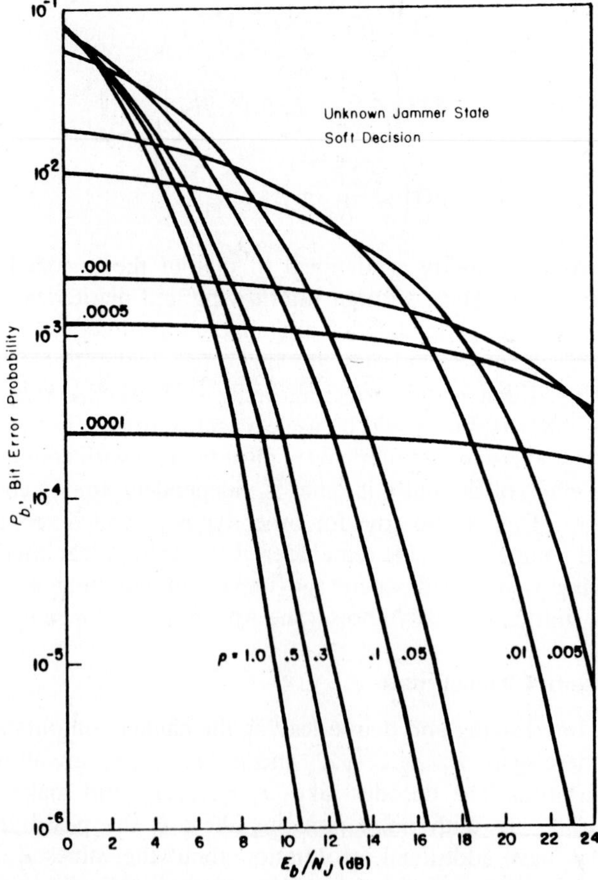

Figure 3.12. Repeat code $m = 5$ with unknown jammer state/soft decision.

is given by

$$P_b = \Pr\{ r > 0 | d = -1\}$$
$$= \Pr\left\{ \sum_{i=1}^{m} Z_i n_i > \sqrt{mE_b} \right\}. \tag{3.57}$$

To evaluate this, note that if k of the m coded symbols experience a pulse jammer then $\sum_{i=1}^{m} Z_i n_i$ is a sum of k independent Gaussian random variables each of variance $N_J/(2\rho)$. Using H_k to denote the condition of k pulse jammed symbols, we have

$$\Pr\left\{ \sum_{i=1}^{m} Z_i n_i > \sqrt{mE_b} \middle| H_k \right\} = Q\left(\sqrt{\frac{2mE_b}{kN_J}\rho} \right) \tag{3.58}$$

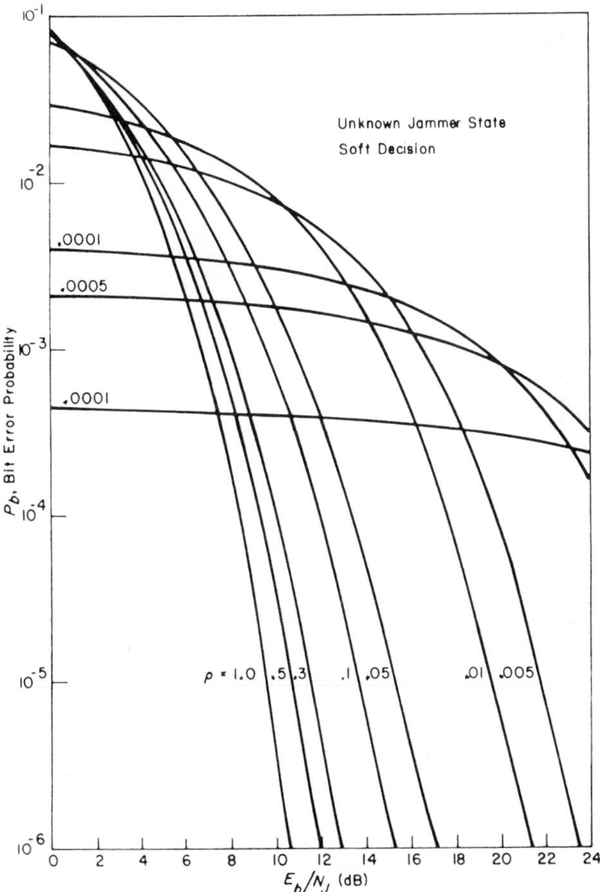

Figure 3.13. Repeat code $m = 9$ with unknown jammer state/soft decision.

where

$$\Pr\{H_k\} = \binom{m}{k}\rho^k(1-\rho)^{m-k};$$

$$k = 0, 1, \ldots, m. \tag{3.59}$$

The bit error probability is, thus,

$$P_b = \sum_{k=0}^{m} \binom{m}{k}\rho^k(1-\rho)^{m-k} Q\left(\sqrt{\frac{2mE_b}{kN_J}\rho}\right). \tag{3.60}$$

Figures 3.12 and 3.13 show P_b versus E_b/N_J for various values of ρ where $m = 5$ in Figure 3.12 and $m = 9$ for Figure 3.13. Comparing these with the uncoded case shown in Figure 3.7 there is only slight improvement with the repeat code. It is still clear that pulse jamming can cause much more degradation compared to constant power jamming ($\rho = 1$). Our conclusion is that *soft decision decoding with no jammer state knowledge is not very effective against pulse jammers.*

3.5.2.2 Hard Decision Decoder

The hard decision decoder makes a binary decision on each channel output symbol as follows:

$$\hat{d}_i = \begin{cases} 1, & r_i > 0 \\ -1, & r_i \le 0; \end{cases} \tag{3.61}$$

$$i = 1, 2, \ldots, m.$$

The final decision is then given by,

$$\hat{d} = \begin{cases} 1, & \sum_{i=1}^{m} \hat{d}_i > 0 \\ -1, & \sum_{i=1}^{m} \hat{d}_i \le 0. \end{cases} \tag{3.62}$$

For an odd integer m, the probability of error is the probability that $(m+1)/2$ or more of the m symbol decisions are in error. The probability that a particular coded symbol decision is in error is given by

$$\begin{aligned} \varepsilon &= \Pr\{r_i > 0 \mid d = -1\} \\ &= \Pr\left\{Z_i n_i > \sqrt{E_b/m}\right\} \\ &= \rho Q\left(\sqrt{\frac{2E_b}{mN_J}\rho}\right). \end{aligned} \tag{3.63}$$

The probability that more than half of the m coded symbol decisions are in error gives the overall bit error probability

$$P_b = \sum_{k=\frac{m+1}{2}}^{m} \binom{m}{k} \varepsilon^k (1-\varepsilon)^{m-k}. \tag{3.64}$$

Figures 3.14 to 3.16 show P_b as given by (3.64) versus E_b/N_J for various values of m. Here by increasing the value of m we can effectively combat pulse jamming. There is no loss in data rate nor any change in the spread-spectrum signal by increasing the number m of repeats of the data bit.

These results show that *against the worst pulse jammer the hard decision decoder does better than the soft decision decoder*. At first, this may seem like a contradiction of the fact that for the additive Gaussian noise channel, soft

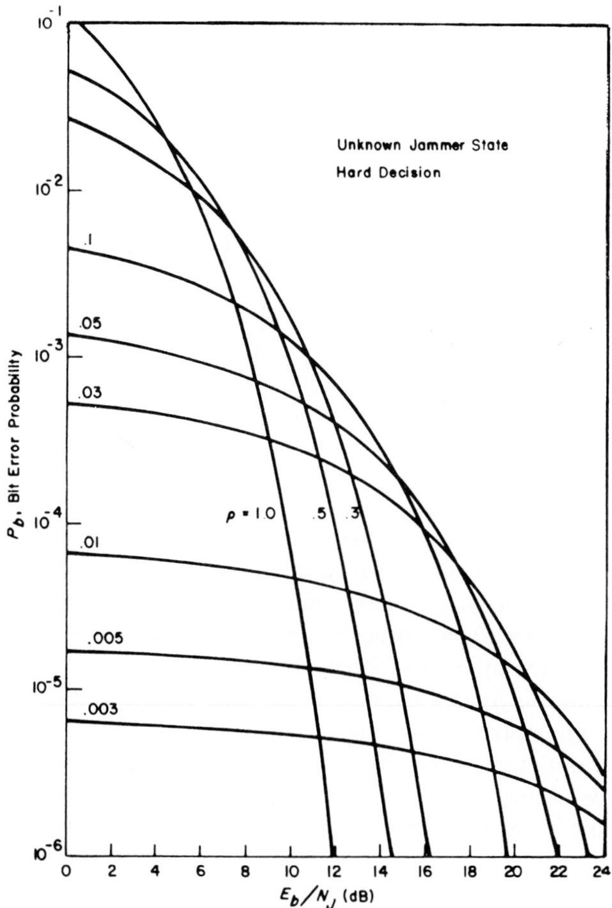

Figure 3.14. Repeat code $m = 3$ with unknown jammer state/hard decision.

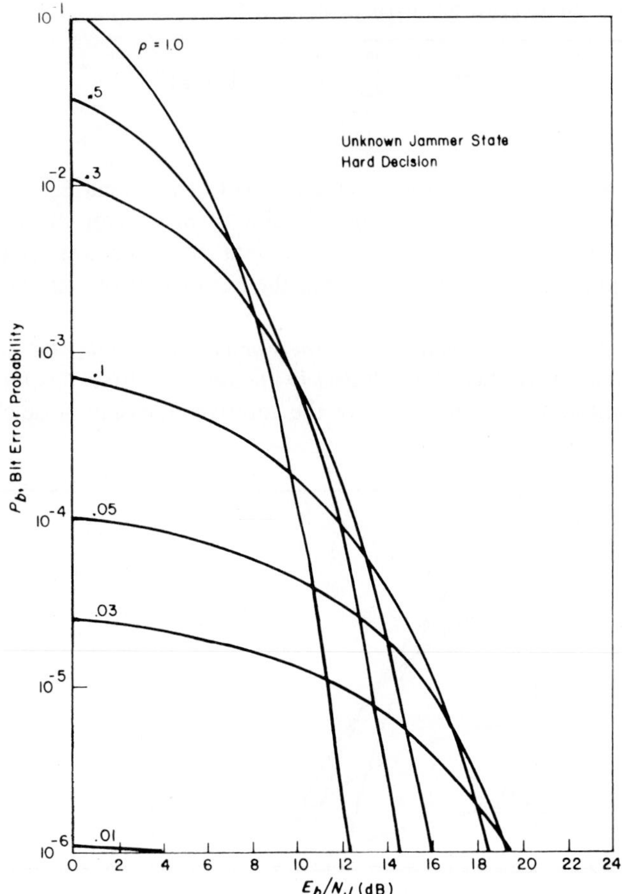

Figure 3.15. Repeat code $m = 5$ with unknown jammer state/hard decision.

decision decoders always do better than hard decision decoders. In our examples, the pulse jammer can do more harm to a soft decision decoder because it can place a lot more jammer noise power in the final decision statistics given by (3.56) through a single detector output. For the hard decision case, the amount of harm the pulse jammer can do to any given detector output is limited because of the hard decision. In general, decision rules that are optimum for the classical additive noise channel are not necessarily optimum over a channel with intentional jamming. Indeed, *there is no single decision rule that is optimum for all jamming signals.* A good decision rule is one that is robust in the sense that no jammer can degrade it very much. The soft decision rule can be degraded badly with high peak, low duty cycle pulses while the hard decision rule is less sensitive to pulse jamming. With coding, it is important to consider decision rules that limit the impact a single coded channel symbol output can have on the final

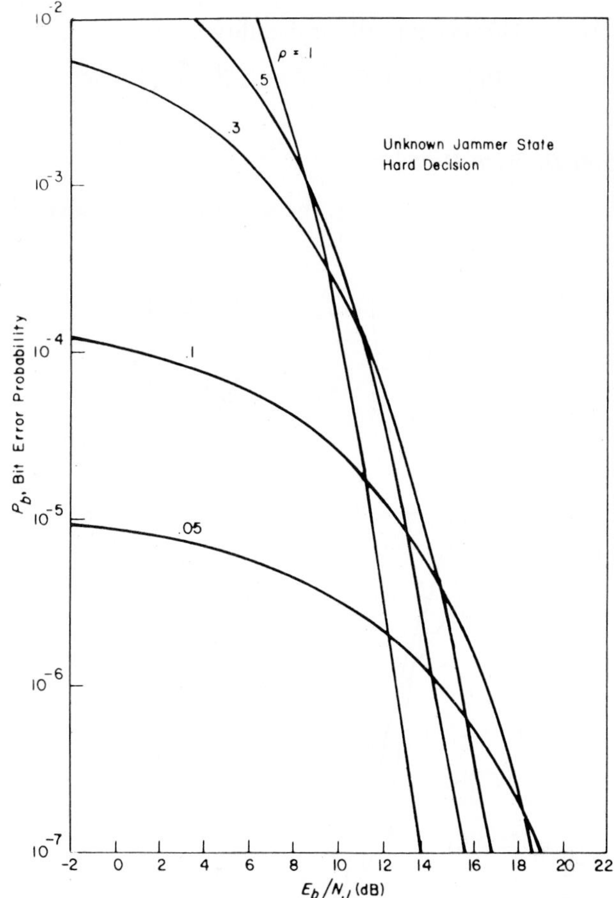

Figure 3.16. Repeat code $m = 9$ with unknown jammer state/hard decision.

decision. This usually means that some nonlinear function such as hard decisions or clipping must be used.

3.5.3 Known Channel State

Suppose that because of channel measurements, the decoder knows which of the m channel outputs $r_1, r_2, \ldots, r_m$ have a jammer term in them. This is equivalent to knowing the values of $Z_1, Z_2, \ldots, Z_m$ at the decoder. Naturally, when any $Z_i = 0$, then $r_i = d\sqrt{E_b/m}$ and d is known correctly. Hence, the only way an error can be made is when

$$Z_1 = Z_2 = \cdots = Z_m = 1. \tag{3.65}$$

That is, an error can only occur when all m coded symbols encounter a jamming pulse. This occurs with probability

$$\Pr\{Z_1 = 1, Z_2 = 1, \ldots, Z_m = 1\} = \rho^m. \tag{3.66}$$

3.5.3.1 Soft Decision Decoder

When $Z_1 = Z_2 = \cdots = Z_m = 1$, the soft decision decoder makes the decision

$$\hat{d} = \begin{cases} 1, & \sum_{i=1}^{m} r_i > 0 \\ -1, & \sum_{i=1}^{m} r_i \leq 0. \end{cases} \tag{3.67}$$

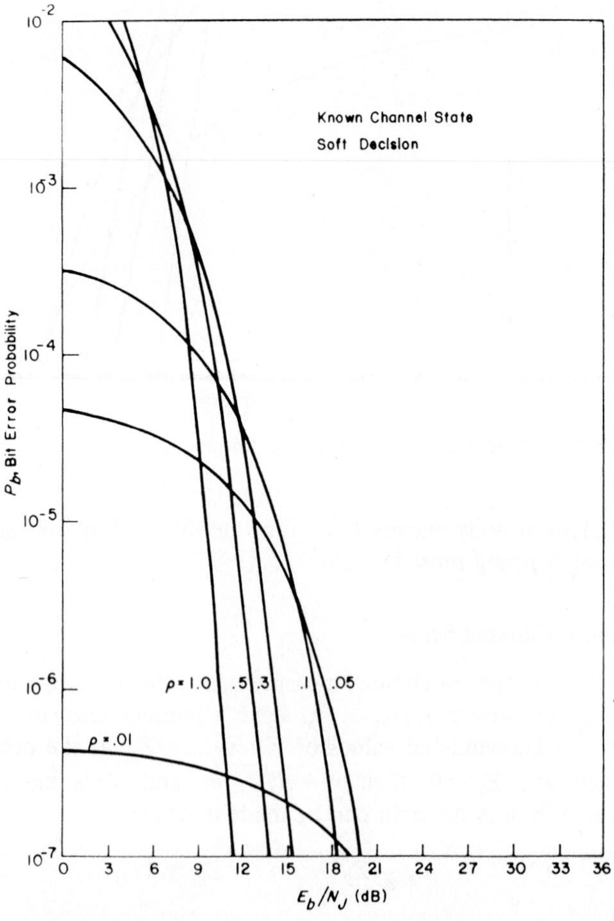

Figure 3.17. Repeat code $m = 3$ with known jammer state/soft decision.

Hence, the probability of a bit error is

$$P_b = \rho^m \Pr\left\{ \sum_{i=1}^{m} n_i > \sqrt{mE_b} \right\}$$

$$= \rho^m Q\left(\sqrt{\frac{2E_b}{N_J}\rho} \right). \tag{3.68}$$

Figures 3.17 to 3.19 show that for this case the impact of pulse jamming is effectively neutralized. For $m = 9$ and larger, for example, $\rho = 1$ gives the worst bit error probability for most values of interest. For $\rho = 1$, the repeat code gives the same performance as the uncoded DS/BPSK with constant power jamming. With more powerful codes, we can get coding gain in addition to neutralizing the degradation (40 dB at 10^{-6} bit error probability) as a result of worst case pulse jamming.

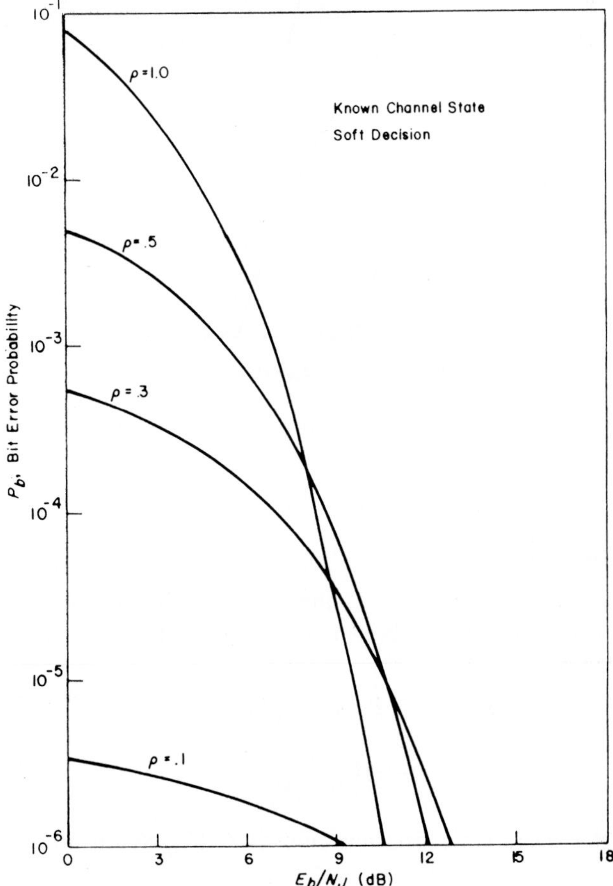

Figure 3.18. Repeat code $m = 5$ with known jammer state/soft decision.

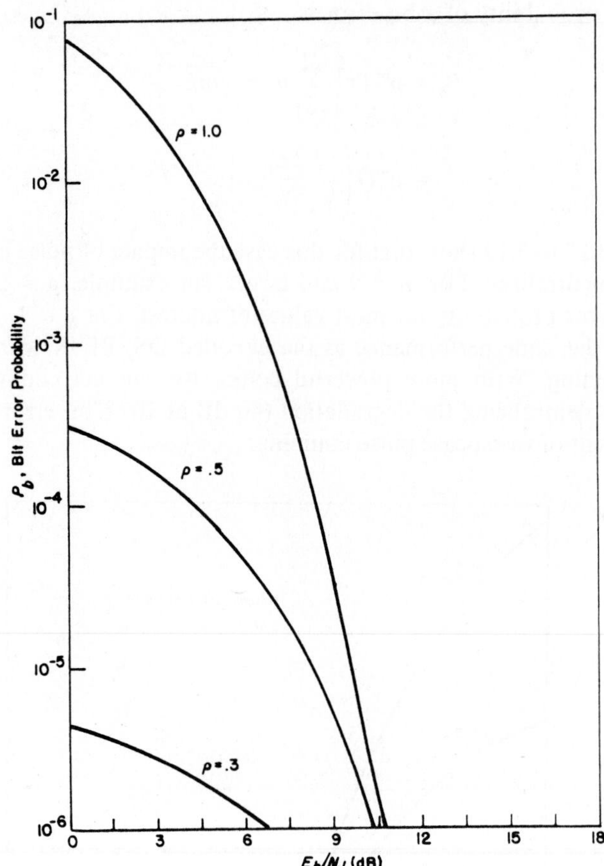

Figure 3.19. Repeat code $m = 9$ with known jammer state/soft decision.

3.5.3.2 Hard Decision Decoder

When $Z_1 = Z_2 = \cdots = Z_m = 1$, the hard decision decoder makes hard decisions on each coded symbol in accordance with (3.61), where a coded symbol error is

$$\begin{aligned}\varepsilon &= \Pr\left\{ n_i > \sqrt{E_b/m} \right\} \\ &= Q\left(\sqrt{\frac{2E_b}{mN_J}\rho} \right). \end{aligned} \tag{3.69}$$

Applying the overall bit decision rule of (3.62) results in the bit error probability

$$P_b = \rho^m \sum_{k=\frac{m+1}{2}}^{m} \binom{m}{k} \varepsilon^k (1-\varepsilon)^{m-k}. \tag{3.70}$$

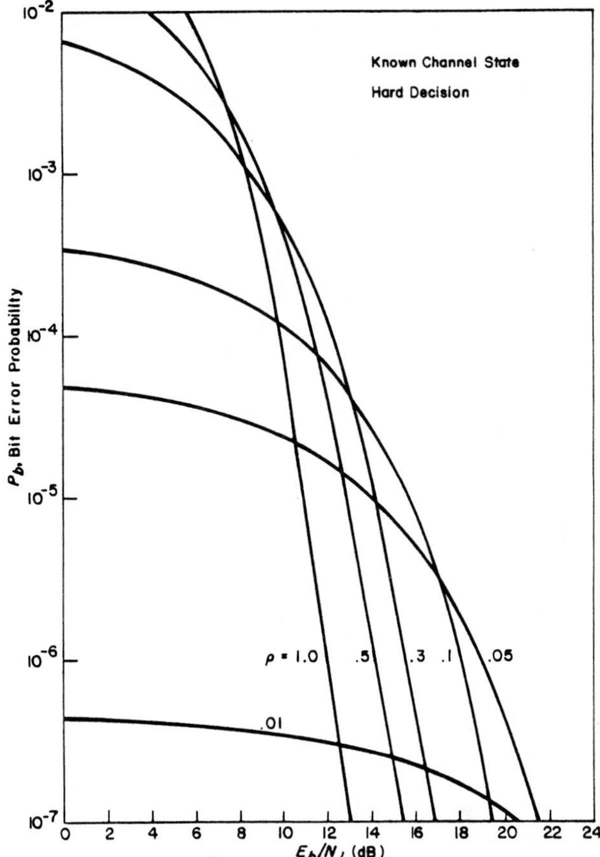

Figure 3.20. Repeat code $m = 3$ with known jammer state/hard decision.

Figures 3.20–3.22 show this bit error probability for various values of m. As expected, the bit error probabilities are smaller than the unknown channel state case for hard decision detectors. With jammer state knowledge the soft decision case yields better performance than the hard decision case.

3.6 UNCODED FREQUENCY-HOPPED BINARY FREQUENCY-SHIFT-KEYING

Taking a basic modulation technique and changing the carrier frequency in some pseudorandom manner is the frequency-hopping approach to generating a spread-spectrum signal. The most common modulations used with frequency hopping are the M-ary frequency-shift-keying (MFSK) modulations together with non-coherent reception. This section illustrates some

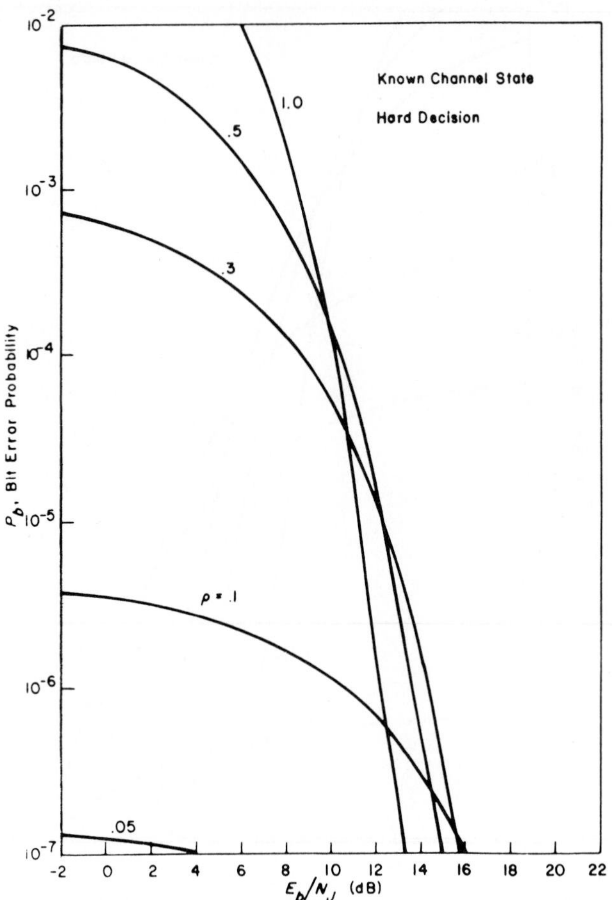

Figure 3.21. Repeat code $m = 5$ with known jammer state/hard decision.

additional basic concepts with the frequency-hopped binary frequency-shift-keying (FH/BFSK) spread-spectrum signals.

Ordinary BFSK signals have the form

$$s(t) = \sqrt{2S}\,\sin[\omega_0 t + d_n \Delta\omega t];$$
$$nT_b \leq t < (n+1)T_b, \qquad n = \text{integer}. \tag{3.71}$$

Here T_b is the data bit time and $\{d_n\}$ are the independent data bits where

$$d_n = \begin{cases} 1, & \text{with probability } \frac{1}{2} \\ -1, & \text{with probability } \frac{1}{2}. \end{cases} \tag{3.72}$$

Typically we choose

$$\Delta\omega T_b = \pi \tag{3.73}$$

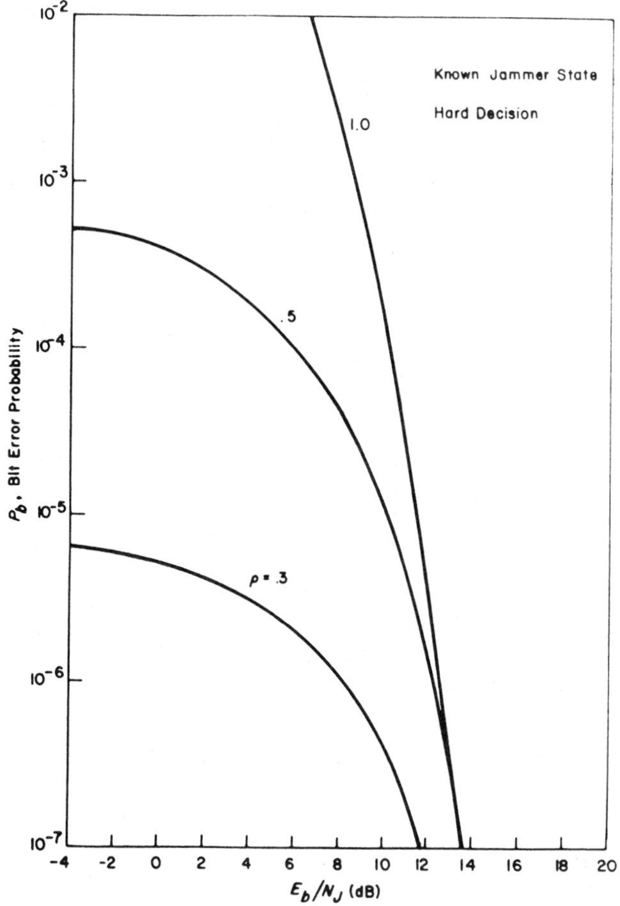

Figure 3.22. Repeat code $m = 9$ with known jammer state/hard decision.

so that the two possible transmitter tones are orthogonal for all relative phase shifts over the T_b second interval.

Frequency hopping of this BFSK signal is done with a pseudorandom binary sequence that is used to select a set of carrier frequency shifts resulting in the frequency-hopped signal

$$x(t) = \sqrt{2S}\,\sin[\omega_0 t + \omega_n t + d_n \Delta\omega t];$$
$$nT_b \leq t < (n+1)T_b, \qquad n = \text{integer} \tag{3.74}$$

where ω_n is the particular hop frequency chosen for the n-th transmission interval. Generally, if L pseudorandom binary symbols are used to select a frequency shift each T_b seconds, then there are at most 2^L distinct frequency shift values possible. The range of values taken by these frequency shifts defines the total spread-spectrum signal bandwidth W_{ss}. Although this total spread bandwidth need not be contiguous, it is assumed here that this band is a continuous frequency range.

Figure 3.23 illustrates the basic uncoded FH/BFSK system. For simplicity, assume the receiver's PN sequence generator is synchronized with that of the transmitter and, thus, the frequency dehop at the receiver removes the effects of the pseudorandom frequency shifts. A conventional non-coherent BFSK receiver follows the frequency dehop. Essentially, the transmitted signal is a conventional BFSK signal that has a shifting carrier frequency and the receiver has a conventional BFSK receiver that merely shifts its center frequency together with that of the transmitter.

The outputs of the energy detectors in Figure 3.23 are denoted e_+ and e_-. If there were no jamming signal present and if $d = 1$ were transmitted, these outputs would be $e_- = 0$ and $e_+ = ST_b$, the BFSK pulse energy. In general, the non-coherent decision rule based on the additive white Gaussian noise channel [8] is

$$\hat{d} = \begin{cases} 1, & e_+ > e_- \\ -1, & e_+ \leq e_-. \end{cases} \tag{3.75}$$

During any T_b second interval, the transmitted signal is a tone of duration T_b seconds and has a $(\sin^2 x)/x^2$ spectrum of bandwidth roughly $2/T_b$ centered at frequency $\omega_0 + \omega_n$. The transmitted signal would then be one of two possible tones separated in frequency by $2\Delta\omega$. This "instantaneous bandwidth" is generally a small fraction of the total spread-spectrum signal bandwidth W_{ss}, which is primarily determined by the range of frequency shift values generated by the frequency hopping.

For each T_b second interval, the particular bit error probability is determined by the amount of jammer power in the "instantaneous bandwidth" of the signal that contributes to the energy terms e_+ and e_-. The overall bit error probability is then the average of these particular bit error probabilities where the average is taken over all frequency-hopped shifts.

3.6.1 Constant Power Broadband Noise Jammer

Assume that the jammer transmits broadband noise over the total spread-spectrum band with constant power J. Thus, during any T_b second interval, regardless of the carrier frequency shift, there will be an equivalent white Gaussian noise process in the "instantaneous bandwidth" of the transmitted signal. The one-sided noise spectral density is $N_J = J/W_{ss}$.

Since an equivalent white Gaussian noise process is encountered in all parts of the total spread-spectrum band, the bit error probability for the uncoded FH/BFSK system of Figure 3.23 is the same as that for conventional BFSK in white Gaussian noise, namely

$$P_b = \tfrac{1}{2} e^{-(E_b/2N_J)} \tag{3.76}$$

where E_b/N_J is still given by (3.39). This is the baseline performance of the FH/BFSK system.

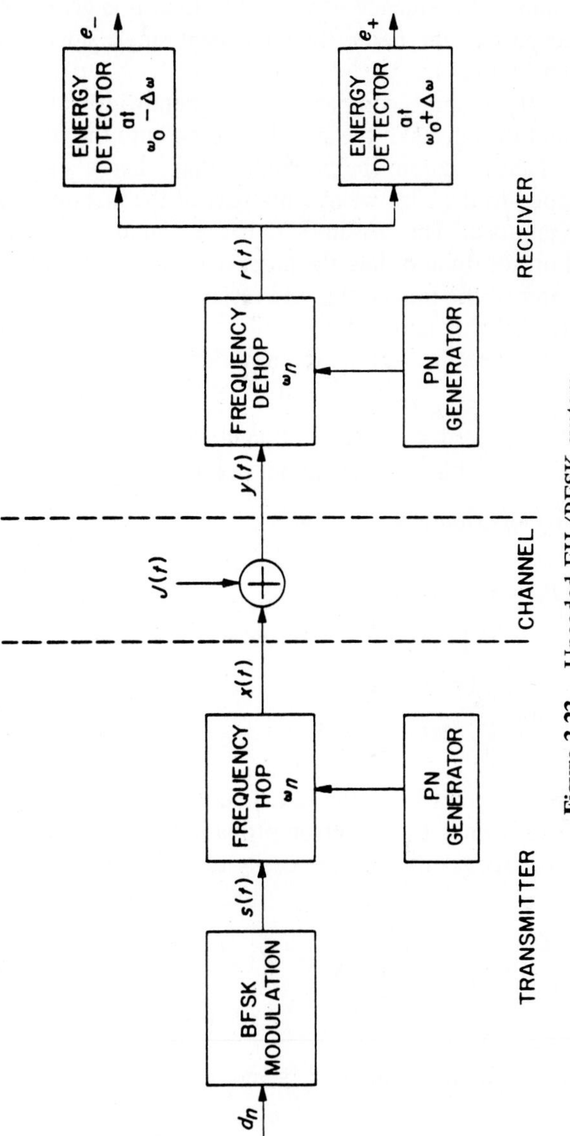

Figure 3.23. Uncoded FH/BFSK system.

3.6.2 Partial-Band Noise Jammer

Next, consider the impact of partial-band noise jamming where the jammer transmits noise over a fraction ρ of the total spread-spectrum signal band. Denoting the jammed frequency band by W_J, then ρ is given by (3.10) and in the jammed part of the band, the equivalent single-sided noise spectral density is given by (3.11).

Assume that W_J is large compared to the bandwidth of the unhopped BFSK signal and the effects of the signal hopping onto the edge of this band are negligible. That is, ignore the possibility that when a signal is sent it is frequency-hopped to the edge where only part of the instantaneous band of the signal is jammed. This assumes either a signal is hopped into the jammed band or not. In addition, the jammer is allowed to change the band it is jamming and so the transmitter and receiver never know *a priori* which frequency range is being jammed.

We again introduce the jammer state parameter Z for each T_b interval where now

$$Z = \begin{cases} 1, & \text{signal in jammed band} \\ 0, & \text{signal not in jammed band} \end{cases} \tag{3.77}$$

with probability distribution as in (3.41). The bit error probability is then given by

$$\begin{aligned} P_b &= \Pr\{e_+ > e_- | d = -1\} \\ &= \Pr\{e_+ > e_- | d = -1, Z = 1\}\Pr\{Z = 1\} \\ &\quad + \Pr\{e_+ > e_- | d = -1, Z = 0\}\Pr\{Z = 0\} \\ &= \frac{\rho}{2} e^{-\rho(E_b/2N_J)} \end{aligned} \tag{3.78}$$

where there are no errors when the signal hops out of the jammed band.

Figure 3.24 illustrates the bit error probability for various values of ρ. The value of ρ that maximizes P_b is easily obtained by differentiation and found to be

$$\rho^* = \begin{cases} \dfrac{2}{E_b/N_J}, & E_b/N_J > 2 \\ 1, & E_b/N_J \le 2. \end{cases} \tag{3.79}$$

This yields the maximum value of P_b given by

$$P_b = \begin{cases} \dfrac{e^{-1}}{E_b/N_J}, & E_b/N_J > 2 \\ \frac{1}{2} e^{-(E_b/2N_J)}, & E_b/N_J \le 2. \end{cases} \tag{3.80}$$

Figure 3.25 shows this worst case value of the bit error probability. Here at 10^{-6} bit error probability there is a 40 dB difference between broadband

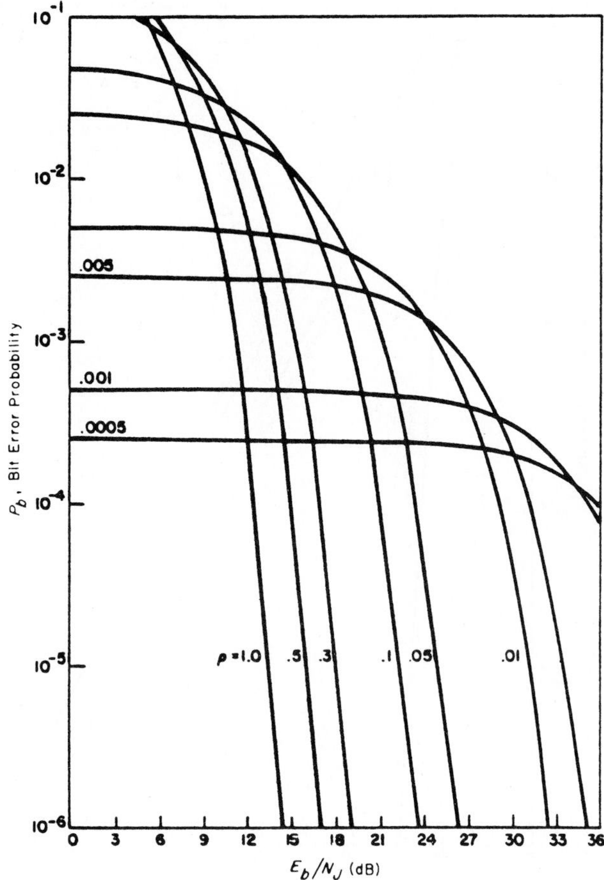

Figure 3.24. FH/BFSK—Partial-band noise jammer.

noise jamming and the worst case partial-band noise jamming for the same jammer power.

The partial-band noise jammer effect on the uncoded FH/BFSK system is analogous to the pulse noise jammer effect on the uncoded DS/BPSK system of Section 3.4. In both systems, these jammers cause considerable degradation by concentrating more jammer power on a fraction of the transmitted uncoded symbols. This potentially large degradation is explained by the fact that the uncoded bit error probability varies dramatically with small changes in the effective bit energy-to-jammer noise ratio, E_b/N_J. Thus, the jammer can cause high error probabilities for a fraction of the transmitted bits resulting in a high average bit error probability.

For the uncoded FH/BFSK system, pulse noise jamming and partial-band noise jamming have the same effect on performance. These are essentially equivalent ways of concentrating more jammer power on some fraction of

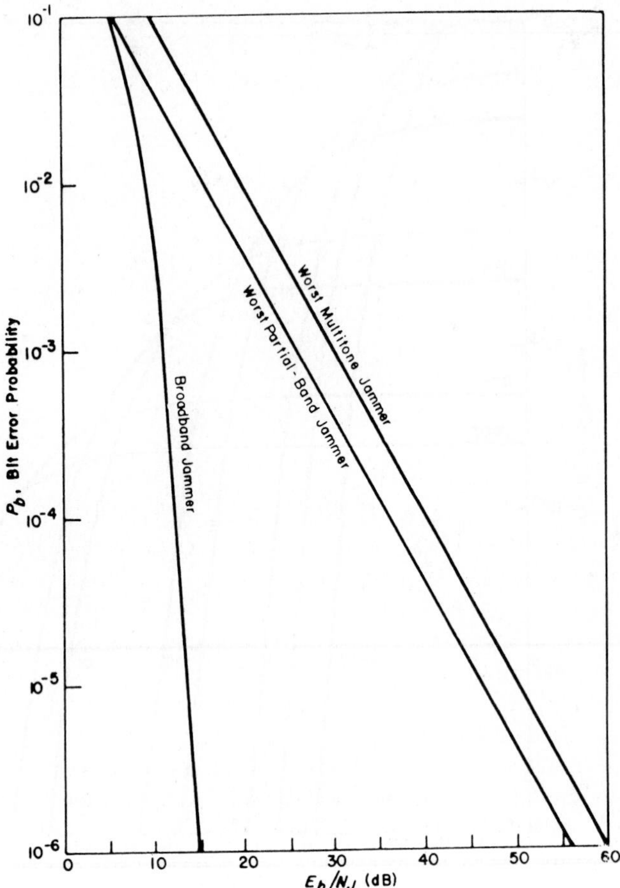

Figure 3.25. FH/BFSK—Against jammers.

the uncoded transmitted symbols. Using pulse noise jamming or a combination of pulse noise and partial-band noise jamming would give the same results as we found for partial-band noise alone.

3.6.3 Multitone Jammer

Recall that each signal tone of T_b second duration has one-sided first null bandwidth $1/T_b$. For the total spread-spectrum signal bandwidth W_{ss}, there are

$$N = W_{ss}T_b$$

possible orthogonal tone positions. Each FH/BFSK signal would then use an adjacent pair of these tone positions to transmit one data bit. The pair of tone positions selected at any data bit time is determined by the PN sequence generator.

Consider a jammer that transmits many tones each of energy $S_J T_b$. With total power J there are at most

$$N_t = \frac{J}{S_J} \tag{3.81}$$

jammer tones randomly scattered across the band. The probability that any given signal tone position is jammed with a jammer tone is, thus,

$$\begin{aligned} \rho &= \frac{N_t}{N} \\ &= \frac{J}{S_J W_{ss} T_b}. \end{aligned} \tag{3.82}$$

Here ρ is also the fraction of the signal tone positions that are jammed.

Assume that the jammer has exact knowledge of the N possible signal tone positions and places the N_t jamming tones in some subset of these N positions, where $N_t < N$ is always assumed.

During the transmission of a data bit, one of two possible adjacent tone positions is used by the transmitter. An error occurs if the detected energy in the alternate tone position not containing the transmitted signal tone is larger than the detected energy in the transmitted tone position. This can occur only if a jammer tone occurs in this alternative tone position. Here, ignore the smaller probability of a jammer tone in both positions and assume an error occurs if and only if a jammer tone with power $S_J \geq S$ occurs in the alternative tone position. Thus, the probability of a bit error is

$$P_b = \rho = \frac{J}{S_J W_{ss} T_b} \tag{3.83}$$

provided $S_J > S$. From the communicator's standpoint, the worst choice of S_J is $S_J = S$ resulting in the maximum bit error probability

$$\begin{aligned} P_b^* &= \frac{J}{S W_{ss} T_b} \\ &= \frac{1}{E_b/N_J}. \end{aligned} \tag{3.84}$$

This bit error probability is slightly larger than the worst partial-band noise jammer performance; the results are essentially the same. Figure 3.25 shows the bit error probabilities for broadband noise jamming, worst partial-band noise jamming, and worst multitone jamming. Part 2, Chapter 2, will examine these cases in greater detail.

3.7 CODED FREQUENCY-HOPPED BINARY FREQUENCY-SHIFT-KEYING

Figure 3.25 illustrates the up to 45 dB of degradation at 10^{-6} bit error probability that a jammer can cause to an uncoded FH/BFSK system using the same average power J. As was done for the DS/BPSK system, we show next how a simple repeat code can effectively neutralize the degradation because of multitone jamming. This same result is also shown for worst case partial-band noise jamming in Part 2, Chapter 2.

Assume that m FH/BFSK tones are transmitted for each data bit. In particular assume the simple repeat m code where for each data bit, m identical BFSK tones are sent where each of these tones are hopped separately. Referring to these tones or codeword components as "chips," m chips make up a single data bit. The chip duration is

$$T_c = \frac{T_b}{m}. \tag{3.85}$$

Requiring each of the chip tones to be orthogonal results in the total number of orthogonal chip tones to be

$$\begin{aligned} N_c &= W_{ss}T_c \\ &= W_{ss}T_b/m \end{aligned} \tag{3.86}$$

which is m times smaller than the uncoded case. As before, assume the jammer sends multiple tones where the number of jammer tones is still given by (3.81). Again, choose $S_J = S$ so that the probability that a particular chip tone position is jammed is given by

$$\begin{aligned} \delta &= \frac{N_t}{N_c} \\ &= \frac{J/S}{W_{ss}T_b/m} \\ &= \frac{m}{E_b/N_J}. \end{aligned} \tag{3.87}$$

After dehopping, the receiver is assumed to detect the energy in each of the two possible chip tone frequencies for every T_c second interval. The decoder adds up the chip energies for each of the two possible BFSK frequencies and makes a decision based on which of these has more total energy. In this case, an error is made only if a jammer tone occurs in all m of the chip tone frequencies corresponding to the BFSK frequency that was not transmitted. This occurs with probability

$$\begin{aligned} P_b &= \delta^m \\ &= \left(\frac{m}{E_b/N_J}\right)^m \end{aligned} \tag{3.88}$$

since each chip is independently hopped.

This analysis ignored the effects of jamming tones occurring in the same frequencies as the transmitted chips. Also, it could have considered the cases where the jammer tone power S_J is larger than S so that fewer than m jammed tones could still cause an error. These more general cases are examined in detail in Part 2, Chapter 2.

The bit error probability given in (3.88) is plotted in Figure 3.26 for various values of m. The $m = 1$ case is the uncoded case considered in the previous section. Note that there exists a value of m that achieves a bit error probability close to the baseline case of broadband noise jamming.

The repeat m code is a simple code of rate $R = 1/m$ bits per coded bit. It is also referred to as *diversity of order m*. Diversity techniques are useful in combatting deep fades in a fading channel. For similar reasons, diversity is effective for multitone jamming and for worst case partial-band jamming. We shall see later, however, that there are more effective codes than simple diversity.

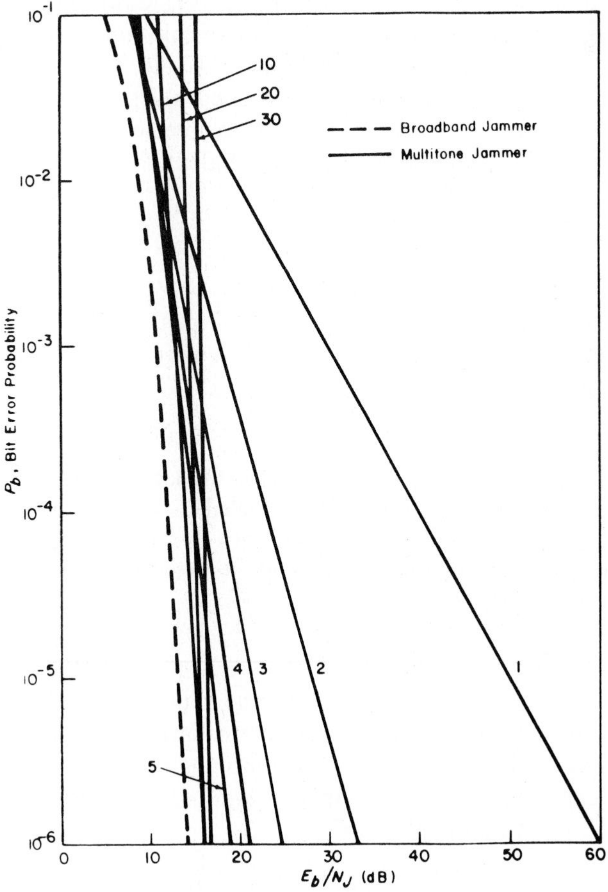

Figure 3.26. FH/BFSK with diversity—multitone jammer.

As with the DS/BPSK example, the use of coding here did not change the data rate or the total spread-spectrum bandwidth W_{ss}. Only the instantaneous bandwidth associated with each coded bit or chip became wider.

3.8 INTERLEAVER / HOP RATE TRADEOFF

In the coded FH/BFSK example considered above, the hop rate was increased from once every T_b seconds to once every $T_c = T_b/m$ seconds. Rather than increasing the hop rate by a factor of m, the same result can be achieved with an interleaver and deinterleaver. This is illustrated in Figure 3.27 with an example of $m = 3$.

Assume the frequency hop rate is fixed at once every T_b seconds, but $m = 3$ chip tones are transmitted during each hop. As illustrated in the frequency and time diagram of Figure 3.27, during each hop transmit chip tones corresponding to three different data bits. Thus, in three hop intervals of $3T_b$ seconds transmit nine chip tones where chip tones corresponding to the same data bit appear in different hop intervals. This ensures that the transmitted chips for each data bit are hopped independently. The performance achieved with this interleaver and deinterleaver is the same as the case where each transmitted chip is independently hopped at the rate of three times per T_b seconds.

3.9 RECEIVER NOISE FLOOR

In this chapter receiver noise was ignored. A more accurate model of the received signal is

$$y(t) = x(t) + J(t) + n(t) \tag{3.89}$$

where $x(t)$ is the transmitted signal, $J(t)$ is the jammer signal, and $n(t)$ is the receiver noise which is typically modeled as additive white Gaussian noise of single-sided spectral density N_0. With this receiver noise included in the analysis, the resulting bit error probability would have the form

$$P_b = f(E_b/N_J, E_b/N_0) \tag{3.90}$$

which is a function of the bit energy-to-noise ratio, E_b/N_0, as well as the effective bit energy-to-jammer power density ratio, E_b/N_J defined in (3.3).

The examples illustrated in this chapter assumed $N_0 = 0$ or $E_b/N_0 = \infty$, which is equivalent to assuming the jammer interference is much stronger than the receiver noise which can then be ignored. This resulted in bit error probability expressions of the form

$$P_b^* = f(E_b/N_J, \infty) \tag{3.91}$$

which were derived in this chapter for a few simple examples. Of course, if

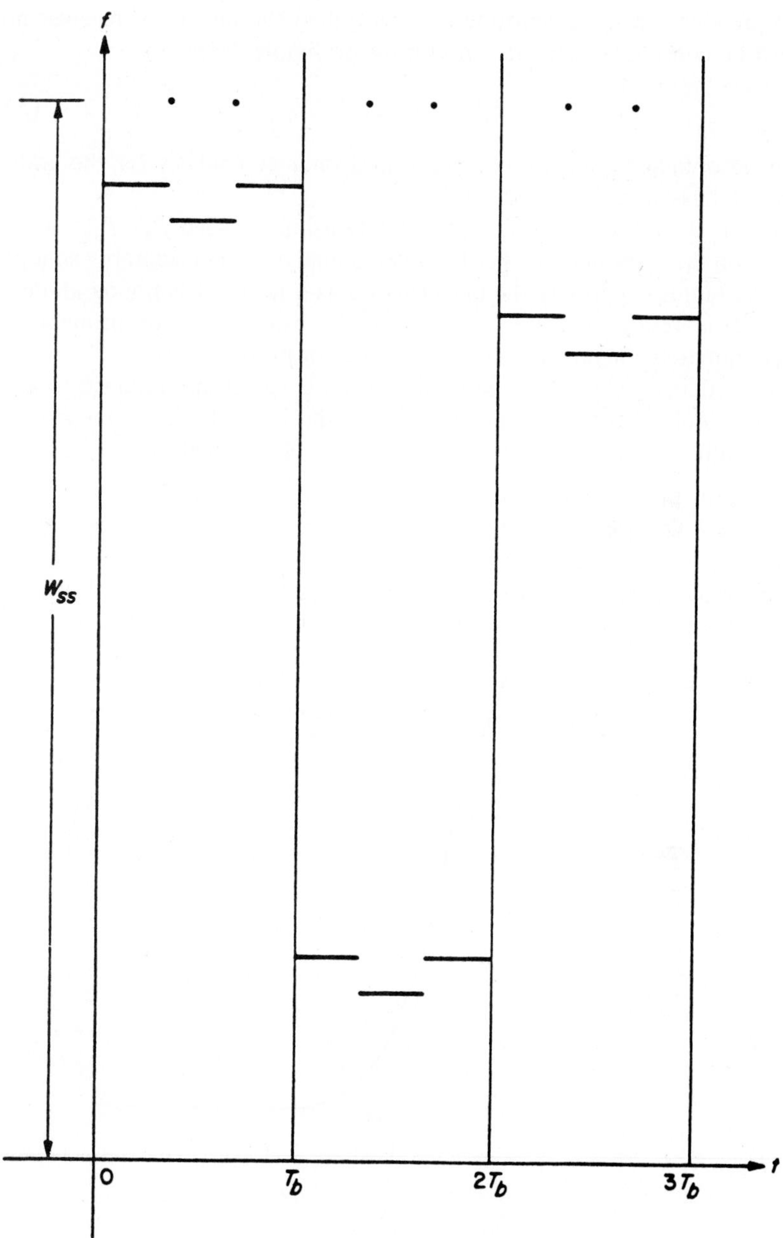

Figure 3.27. Interleaver for FH/BFSK.

the jammer is not transmitting ($N_J = 0$), then the impact of receiver noise must be considered since it is no longer negligible. Here,

$$P_b^{**} = f(\infty, E_b/N_0) \tag{3.92}$$

can be obtained using conventional performance analysis for the additive white Gaussian noise channel [8].

Figure 3.28 illustrates the typical relationship between P_b^*, P_b^{**}, and the exact bit error probability P_b. The overall analysis is considerably simplified by examining separately the performance as a result of jamming alone and then as a result of noise alone, since the exact bit error probability is approximately the larger of these two bit error probabilities.

The additive white Gaussian noise, $n(t)$, is sometimes referred to as the receiver noise floor implying that it sets the lower limit on the bit error probability when considering other types of channel interference. The

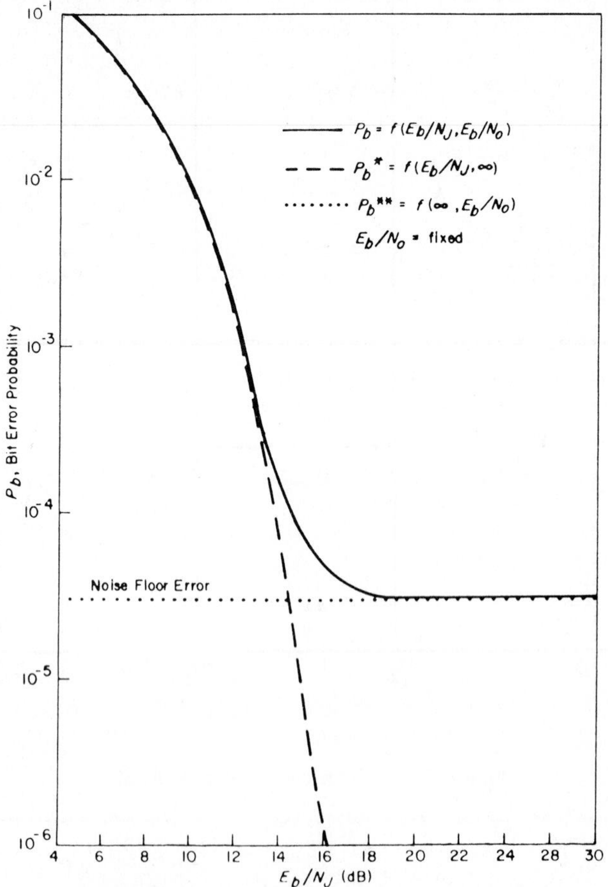

Figure 3.28. Impact of receiver noise.

analysis presented here and in Part 1, Chapter 4, and Part 2, Chapters 1 and 2, ignores this receiver noise and considers the impact of the jammer alone. Some receiver noise floor, as illustrated in Figure 3.28, will always exist and must ultimately be considered. We are primarily concerned with the impact of jamming which is assumed to be the primary limitation on anti-jam systems.

3.10 DISCUSSION

In this chapter we have stated basic assumptions and defined key system parameters for anti-jam communication systems and jamming signals. Concepts such as coding, interleaving, and diversity were illustrated with examples. Even simple repeat codes (diversity) were shown to effectively neutralize the over 40 dB of degradation at 10^{-6} bit error probabilities that some jammers can cause in uncoded anti-jam systems.

Also illustrated was the important fact that, in designing a coded anti-jam communication system, one ought to be careful in choosing the decoding metric. There is no single metric that is optimum for all types of jammers. We have seen that the maximum-likelihood metrics for the additive white Gaussian noise channel can cause the anti-jam system to be vulnerable to certain jammers and that a hard decision metric can yield much better performance than a soft decision metric. Also, having a decision rule that uses side information about when a channel is jammed or not can improve performance significantly. A good decision rule and associated metric is one that is robust in the sense that no jammer can degrade it much more than the baseline jammer.

Except for these very simple examples, coded spread-spectrum systems under attack by various jamming signals are difficult to analyze. Analysis becomes even more difficult when unconventional decoding metrics are used. In the next chapter, a general approach to the analysis of spread-spectrum communication systems is presented. It provides a means for handling these more difficult cases as well as placing the basic concepts of this chapter on firmer ground.

3.11 REFERENCES

[1] A. J. Viterbi and I. M. Jacobs, "Advances in coding and modulation for noncoherent channels affected by fading, partial band, and multiple access interference," in *Advances in Communication Systems*, vol. 4, New York: Academic Press, 1975, pp. 279–308.

[2] S. W. Houston, "Modulation techniques for communication, Part I: Tone and noise jamming performance of spread spectrum M ~ ary FSK and 2, 4 ~ ary DPSK waveforms," in *Proceedings of the IEEE National Aerospace and Electronics Conference* (NAECON '75), Dayton, Ohio, June 10–12, 1975, pp. 51–58.

[3] R. A. Scholtz, "The spread spectrum concept," *IEEE Trans. Commun.*, COM-25, pp. 748–755, August 1977.
[4] A. J. Viterbi, "Spread spectrum communication—Myths and realities," *IEEE Communications Magazine*, vol. 17, no. 3, pp. 11–18, May 1979.
[5] G. C. Clark, Jr., and J. B. Cain, *Error-Correction Coding for Digital Communications*, New York: Plenum Press, 1981.
[6] R. L. Pickholtz, D. L. Schilling, and L. B. Milstein, "Theory of spread-spectrum communications—A tutorial," *IEEE Trans. Commun.*, COM-30, no. 5, pp. 855–884, May 1982.
[7] H. J. Landau, and H. O. Pollak, "Prolate spheroidal wave functions, Fourier analysis, and uncertainty," *Bell Syst. Tech. J.*, Part II, vol. 40, 1961, pp. 65–84, Part III, in vol. 41, 1962, pp. 1295–1336.
[8] A. J. Viterbi and J. K. Omura, *Principles of Digital Communication and Coding*, New York: McGraw-Hill, 1979.
[9] A. Papoulis, *Probability, Random Variables, and Stochastic Processes*, New York: McGraw-Hill, 1965, Section 8-6.
[10] S. Lin and D. Costello, *Error Control Coding Fundamentals and Applications*, Englewood Cliffs, NJ: Prentice-Hall, 1983, chapter 14.
[11] J. L. Ramsey, "Realization of optimum interleavers," *IEEE Trans. Inform. Theory*, IT-6, pp. 338–345, May 1970.
[12] I. A. Richer, "A simple interleaver for use with Viterbi decoding," *IEEE Trans. Commun.*, COM-26, pp. 406–408, March 1978.

APPENDIX 3A. INTERLEAVING AND DEINTERLEAVING

The purpose of interleaving at the transmitter and deinterleaving at the receiver is to convert a channel with memory to one that is memoryless. In the pulse jammer example in Section 3.4.2, for example, it was assumed that the jammer pulse would jam several successive transmitted symbols resulting in a channel whose interference is not independent from symbol to symbol. By scrambling the order of channel symbols at the transmitter with interleaving and unscrambling it at the receiver with deinterleaving, an approximately memoryless channel is achieved where the impact of jamming or other channel disturbances is independent from transmitted symbol to symbol. Coding techniques are primarily designed for memoryless channels and, therefore, require interleaving and deinterleaving to be effective.

Interleaving is a form of time diversity which requires no knowledge of the channel memory other than its approximate length and is consequently very robust to changes in memory statistics. This is particularly important in a jamming environment where jammer waveforms may change. Since in all practical cases, memory decreases with time separation, if all symbols of a given codeword are transmitted at widely spaced intervals and the intervening spaces are filled similarly by symbols of other codewords, the statistical dependence between symbols of a given codeword can be effectively eliminated.

Figure 3A.1 illustrates an example of a block interleaver with depth $I = 5$ and interleaver span $N = 15$. Here the coded symbols are written into the interleaver memory filling it along columns while the transmitted symbols are read out of this memory along rows. Thus, if $x_1, x_2, x_3, x_4, \ldots$ are the coded symbols entering the interleaver, the inputs to the channel are $x_1, x_{16}, x_{31}, x_{46}, x_{61}, x_2, x_{17}, x_{32}, \ldots$. From this figure it is clear that the minimum separation is at least $I = 5$ for any two symbols entering the block interleaver within a separation of $N - 1 = 14$ symbols.

In general, with a block interleaver with depth I and span N, there are IN symbols of memory required. For synchronous transmission where one such memory is used to write in the symbols while another memory is used for reading out symbols into the channel, there is a total of $2IN$ symbols of memory required.

At the receiver, the deinterleaver simply performs the inverse operation where symbols are written into the deinterleaver by rows and read out by columns. Note that here a jamming pulse of b coded symbol duration where $b \leq I$ will result in these jammed symbols at the deinterleaver output separated by at least N symbols. Thus, if we had a block code of block-length $n \leq N$, there would be only one jammed symbol in a transmitted

$I = 5$ (columns); $N = 15$ (rows)

x_1	x_{16}	x_{31}	x_{46}	x_{61}
x_2	x_{17}	x_{32}	x_{47}	x_{62}
x_3	x_{18}	x_{33}	x_{48}	x_{63}
x_4	x_{19}	x_{34}	x_{49}	x_{64}
x_5	x_{20}	x_{35}	x_{50}	x_{65}
x_6	x_{21}	x_{36}	x_{51}	x_{66}
x_7	x_{22}	x_{37}	x_{52}	x_{67}
x_8	x_{23}	x_{38}	x_{53}	x_{68}
x_9	x_{24}	x_{39}	x_{54}	x_{69}
x_{10}	x_{25}	x_{40}	x_{55}	x_{70}
x_{11}	x_{26}	x_{41}	x_{56}	x_{71}
x_{12}	x_{27}	x_{42}	x_{57}	x_{72}
x_{13}	x_{28}	x_{43}	x_{58}	x_{73}
x_{14}	x_{29}	x_{44}	x_{59}	x_{74}
x_{15}	x_{30}	x_{45}	x_{60}	x_{75}

Read in by columns: $x_1, x_2, x_3, \ldots$
Read out by rows: $x_1, x_{16}, x_{31}, \ldots$

Figure 3A.1. Block interleaver example.

codeword as a result of this jammer pulse. For convolutional codes a similar result is obtained if N is larger than a constraint length. Clearly I should be chosen to be larger than the channel memory and N should be larger than the code memory measured in number of coded symbols.

Synchronization of the block interleaver requires some sort of standard frame synchronization technique. This requires some extra overhead symbols which are inserted periodically.

Another type of interleaver is the convolutional interleaver proposed by Ramsey [11]. This is illustrated in Figure 3A.2 for the same parameters $I = 5$ and $N = 15$. Here the coded symbols are switched between $I = 5$ tapped shift registers of the interleaver bank. The zero-th element of this bank provides no storage (the symbols are transmitted immediately), while each successive element provides $j = 3$ symbols more storage than the

x_1	—	—	—	—
x_6	—	—	—	—
x_{11}	—	—	—	—
x_{16}	x_2	—	—	—
x_{21}	x_7	—	—	—
x_{26}	x_{12}	—	—	—
x_{31}	x_{17}	x_3	—	—
x_{36}	x_{22}	x_8	—	—
x_{41}	x_{27}	x_{13}	—	—
x_{46}	x_{32}	x_{18}	x_4	—
x_{51}	x_{37}	x_{23}	x_9	—
x_{56}	x_{42}	x_{28}	x_{14}	—
x_{61}	x_{47}	x_{33}	x_{19}	x_5
x_{66}	x_{52}	x_{38}	x_{24}	x_{10}
x_{71}	x_{57}	x_{43}	x_{29}	x_{15}
x_{76}	x_{62}	x_{48}	x_{34}	x_{20}
⋮	⋮	⋮	⋮	⋮

$I = 5$
$j = 3$
$N = jI = 15$

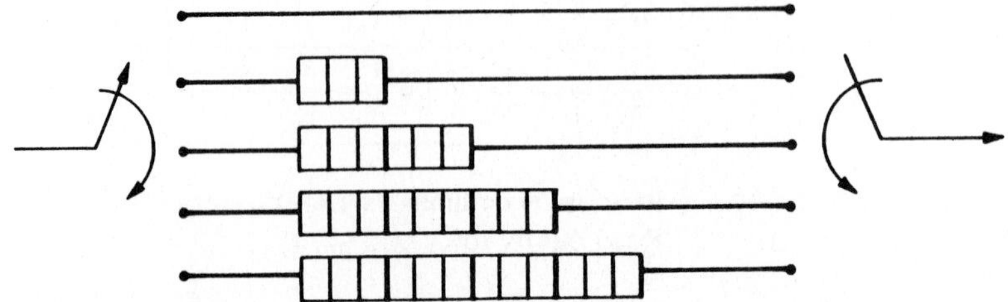

Figure 3A.2. Convolutional interleaver example.

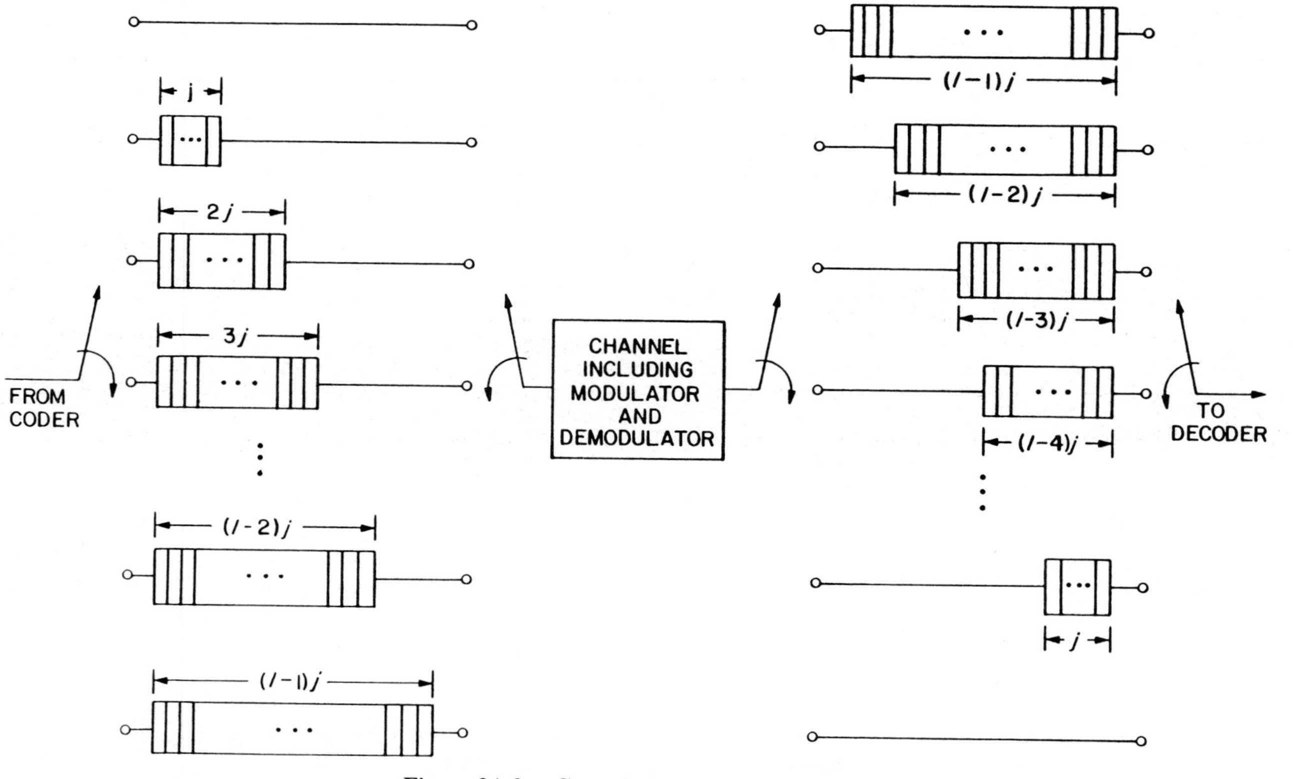

Figure 3A.3. Convolutional interleaver system.

preceding one. The input and output commutator switches move together from one register to the next. Again I is the minimum transmission separation provided for any two coded symbols entering the interleaver with a separation of less than $N = jI$ symbols.

In Figure 3A.2 the symbols entering the convolutional interleaver are $x_1, x_2, x_3, \ldots$. The interleaver outputs (coded channel input symbols) are shown by the rows of the diagram. Initially, there are some unused channel input slots until the shift registers in the interleaver fill up. After sixty channel symbols are transmitted the convolutional interleaver outputs are $x_{61}, x_{47}, x_{33}, x_{19}, x_5, x_{66}, x_{52}, \ldots$.

The convolutional deinterleaver inverts the action of the interleaver as shown in Figure 3A.3. Observables are fed in with each channel output going to a different shift register. Again, we have the property that a jamming pulse of b coded symbol duration where $b \leq I$ will result in these jammed symbols at the deinterleaver output being separated by at least N symbols.

From this it is clear that the convolutional interleaver requires roughly $IN/2$ symbols of memory compared to $2IN$ for the block interleaver memory for synchronous transmission. A fair comparison, however, must consider the fact that shift registers of varying lengths may be considerably more costly in terms of numbers of required integrated circuits than, for example, a random access memory (RAM) of larger size. Also, note that the deinterleaver memories for both approaches are often several times larger than the interleaver memory. This is because of the fact that channel output symbols are often quantized with more bits than the channel input symbols. For BPSK modulations, for example, each coded channel input symbol is one bit while the usual channel outputs are three bit quantized to eight levels.

With the deterministic interleaver and deinterleaver techniques described above, a jammer might cleverly pulse jam selected channel symbols in such a way that the deinterleaver outputs a burst of jammed symbols. This would dramatically degrade a coding system designed for independent channel disturbances. A pseudorandom interleaver/deinterleaver system can overcome this vulnerability.

A pseudorandom interleaver/deinterleaver is one where a pseudorandom sequence generator is used at the transmitter and receiver to pseudorandomly choose between many possible interleaver/deinterleaver structures. Typically for block interleaver techniques, coded symbols are written into a RAM and read out pseudorandomly. There may be several possible read out patterns, each stored in a read only memory (ROM). For each interleaved output block, a PN sequence can be used to select one of the read out patterns. (See Clark and Cain [5] and Richer [12].)

The main point of this discussion is that channels with memory can be converted into essentially memoryless channels at a cost of buffer storage and transmission delay. This cost can become prohibitive if the channel memory is very long compared to the transmission time per coded symbol.

Chapter 4

GENERAL ANALYSIS OF ANTI-JAM COMMUNICATION SYSTEMS

The evaluation of bit error probabilities for anti-jam communication systems is generally more difficult than for conventional communication systems. This is partly because of the fact that intentional jamming signals can be more varied than the additive Gaussian noise model which is typically assumed in conventional communication systems. In addition, most anti-jam communication systems use coding techniques where coding gains at 10^{-5} bit error rates are typically 30 dB to 60 dB compared to the 4 dB to 5 dB with the additive Gaussian noise channel. (This will be shown in greater detail in Part 2, Chapters 1 and 2). Even with conventional communication systems, the evaluation of exact coded bit error probabilities is usually difficult to do and, thus, easy-to-evaluate upper bounds are used [1], [2], [3].

The purpose of this chapter is to present a general expression for upper bounds on coded bit error probabilities which apply to all coded communication systems that use enough interleaving and deinterleaving so that the channel can be modeled as memoryless. We shall show that these error bounds are tight over ranges of interest by comparing them with exact bit error probabilities when they can be found. They are also applicable to arbitrary decoding decision metrics and a wide class of detectors. This generalization is necessary for anti-jam communication systems where there are no optimum detectors and maximum-likelihood decoding decision rules are not known at the receiver. Here, we are generally interested in robust detectors that are effective with all types of jammers and easy to compute decoding metrics. Under intentional jamming, it is unrealistic to assume that the receiver has complete knowledge of the jamming signal's statistical characteristics.

With channel measurements, the receiver may have some side information which can aid the decoding process. For example, the receiver may have knowledge of when a jammer signal is present or not during the transmission of a coded symbol. Side information may also include time-varying channel parameter values such as propagation conditions at HF frequencies measured with channel sounder equipment or the number of other active transmitters in a spread-spectrum multiple access environment. Such side information is included in the general formulation of the expression for upper bounds to coded bit error probabilities.

In summary, because for anti-jam communication systems exact bit error probabilities are difficult or impossible to evaluate, we derive general upper bounds to these probabilities that are tight and can be numerically evaluated. These bounds allow for receivers that have incomplete knowledge of the channel using any of several types of detectors and arbitrary decoding metrics. Channel measurements that provide additional side information can be included in the decision metrics and the impact of such side information can be evaluated with these upper bounds. Ideal signal acquisition and synchronization is assumed here.

4.1 SYSTEM MODEL

Consider the general anti-jam communication system illustrated in Figure 4.1. Here the channel can include noise, jamming, and possibly channel distortions such as fading and dispersion. The modulator is assumed to be memoryless in that any given modulation waveform depends only on one input coded symbol. In addition to modulation, the coded symbols are interleaved and the signal is spread in bandwidth for anti-jam protection. At the receiver, despreading is done first, followed by detection. The detector can have many possible forms including hard decision, soft decision, threshold, possibility of erasures, and for MFSK modulation, an ordered list of the energy detector outputs.

As shown in Figure 4.1, channel measurements may provide the decoder with side information. Long-term measurements can include slowly varying parameters of the channel such as propagation conditions. Short-term measurements will usually be used to determine if a particular coded symbol experienced jamming during transmission.

The part of the system shown inside the dotted lines in Figure 4.1 is called the coding channel. It is the effective channel as seen by the encoder and decoder system. Here a general coded bit error bound will be derived which will serve as a basis for evaluating the performance of all such complex communication systems. The key feature of this approach is the decoupling of the coding aspects of the system from the remaining part of the communication system. Specifically, the cutoff rate parameter [4], [5], [6], [7]

$$R_0 \text{ bits/channel use} \tag{4.1}$$

is computed. It represents the practically achievable reliable data rate per coded symbol. This cutoff rate will be a function of the equivalent channel

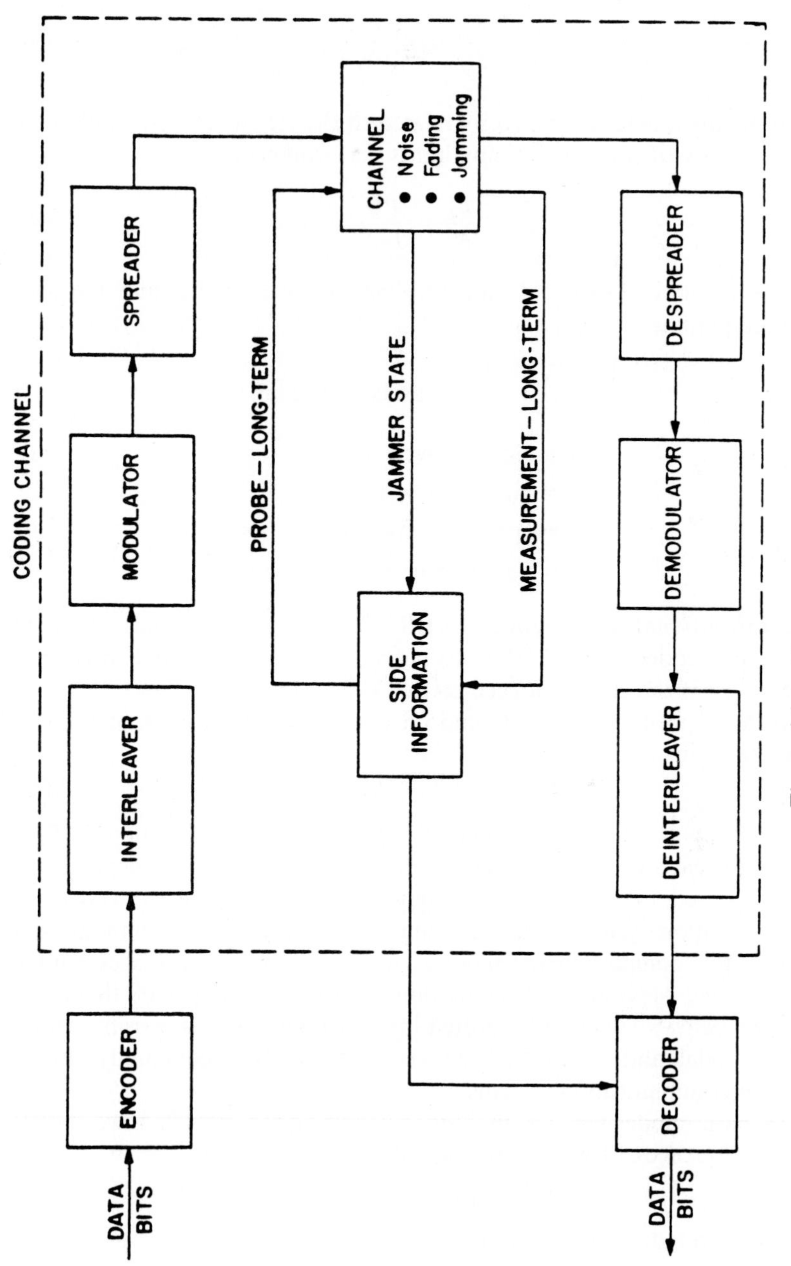

Figure 4.1. AJ system overview.

symbol energy-to-jammer noise ratio

$$\frac{E_s}{N_J} = R\left(\frac{E_b}{N_J}\right) \tag{4.2}$$

which is shown here to be directly related to the bit energy-to-jammer noise ratio given by (assuming jamming limits performance)

$$\frac{E_b}{N_J} = \frac{PG}{J/S}. \tag{4.3}$$

Here R is the code rate in data bits per channel symbol and the usual jamming parameters are

$$PG = \frac{W_{ss}}{R_b}, \quad \text{processing gain} \tag{4.4}$$

S = signal power

J = jammer power

W_{ss} = spread bandwidth

R_b = data rate in bits per second.

For conventional direct sequence (DS) coherent BPSK signals, E_s is the energy per coded symbol while for frequency-hopped (FH) non-coherent MFSK, E_s is the energy of each coded M-ary signal.

For any specific code the bound on the coded bit error probability will have the form

$$P_b \leq B(R_0) \tag{4.5}$$

which is only a function of the cutoff rate R_0. Since the function $B(R_0)$ is unique for each code and the cutoff rate parameter, R_0, is independent of the code used, we are able to decouple the coding from the rest of the communication system. Thus, to evaluate various anti-jam communication systems, first compare them using the cutoff rate parameter. Codes can then be evaluated separately. This decoupling of the codes and the coding channels (shown enclosed by dotted lines in Figure 4.1) is possible at least for antipodal and orthogonal signals such as those commonly used in anti-jam communication systems.

The basic model for this analysis is shown in Figure 4.2. Here a coded symbol sequence of length N is denoted

$$\mathbf{x} = (x_1, x_2, \ldots, x_N) \tag{4.6}$$

with corresponding channel output sequence

$$\mathbf{y} = (y_1, y_2, \ldots, y_N). \tag{4.7}$$

In addition, a corresponding side information sequence is denoted

$$\mathbf{z} = (z_1, z_2, \ldots, z_N). \tag{4.8}$$

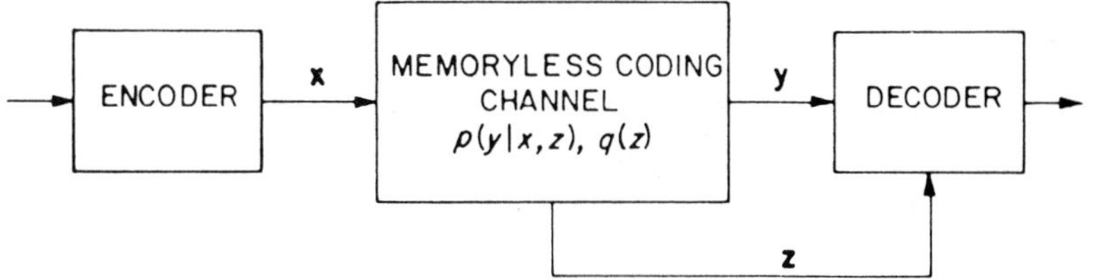

Figure 4.2. General memoryless channel.

With adequate interleaving and deinterleaving, assume that the coding channel is memoryless. That is, assume that the channel probabilities satisfy

$$p_N(\mathbf{y}|\mathbf{x},\mathbf{z}) = \prod_{n=1}^{N} p(y_n|x_n, z_n) \tag{4.9}$$

and

$$q_N(z) = \prod_{n=1}^{N} q(z_n). \tag{4.10}$$

For any coded communication, the decoding process uses a metric of the form $m(y, x; z)$ if side information is available and $m(y, x)$ if it is not available. To simplify the decoding process, the metric is required to have an additivity property where, for sequences of symbols, the total metric of the sequences is the sum of the metrics of each channel input and output pair of the sequence. Thus, for **x**, **y** and **z** given by (4.6), (4.7), and (4.8) the total metric is $m(y_1, x_1; z_1) + m(y_2, x_2; z_2) + \cdots + m(y_N, x_N; z_N)$ or $m(y_1, x_1) + m(y_2, x_2) + \cdots + m(y_N, x_N)$ depending on the availability of the side information sequence **z**. The metric is used by the decoder to make decisions as to which sequence was transmitted given the corresponding channel output sequences. The additivity property is important in reducing the decoder processing complexity.

In general in a jamming environment the receiver would most likely have incomplete knowledge of the channel conditional probabilities[1] $p(y|x, z)$. Thus, the maximum-likelihood metric

$$m(y, x; z) = \log p(y|x, z) \tag{4.11}$$

when side information is available or

$$m(y, x) = \log p(y|x) \tag{4.12}$$

[1]In a jamming environment, it is unrealistic to assume the jamming signal statistical characteristics are known. This is also true of many other cases and, thus, the receiver design is often "mismatched" to the actual channel.

when no side information is available, is not necessarily used in the decoder. Instead, an arbitrary metric denoted $m(y, x; z)$ when side information is available and $m(y, x)$ when it is not available is assumed in the following. (The case where no side information is available can be regarded as a special case where the metric $m(y, x; z)$ does not depend on z.)

4.2 CODED BIT ERROR RATE BOUND

Assume for the moment that there are only two possible coded sequences of length N given by (4.6) and

$$\hat{\mathbf{x}} = (\hat{x}_1, \hat{x}_2, \ldots, \hat{x}_N). \tag{4.13}$$

When the channel output sequence is (4.7) and side information is (4.8) the decoder decides $\hat{\mathbf{x}}$ is the transmitted sequence if

$$\sum_{n=1}^{N} m(y_n, \hat{x}_n; z_n) \geq \sum_{n=1}^{N} m(y_n, x_n; z_n). \tag{4.14}$$

Otherwise, it decides $\mathbf{x}$ is the transmitted sequence. Assuming $\mathbf{x}$ is the actual transmitted coded sequence, the probability that the decoder incorrectly decides $\hat{\mathbf{x}}$ is given by

$$P(\mathbf{x} \to \hat{\mathbf{x}}) = \Pr\left\{ \sum_{n=1}^{N} m(y_n, \hat{x}_n; z_n) \geq \sum_{n=1}^{N} m(y_n, x_n; z_n) \middle| \mathbf{x} \right\}. \tag{4.15}$$

This is called a *pairwise error probability*.

Applying the Chernoff bound (see Appendix 4A) (4.15) has the following bound:

$$\begin{aligned} P(\mathbf{x} \to \hat{\mathbf{x}}) &= \Pr\left\{ \sum_{n=1}^{N} [m(y_n, \hat{x}_n; z_n) - m(y_n, x_n; z_n)] \geq 0 \middle| \mathbf{x} \right\} \\ &\leq E\left\{ \exp\left(\lambda \sum_{n=1}^{N} [m(y_n, \hat{x}_n; z_n) - m(y_n, x_n; z_n)] \right) \middle| \mathbf{x} \right\} \\ &= E\left\{ \prod_{n=1}^{N} \exp(\lambda [m(y_n, \hat{x}_n; z_n) - m(y_n, x_n; z_n)]) \middle| \mathbf{x} \right\} \\ &= \prod_{n=1}^{N} E\{ \exp(\lambda [m(y_n, \hat{x}_n; z_n) - m(y_n, x_n; z_n)]) | \mathbf{x} \} \end{aligned} \tag{4.16}$$

for any $\lambda \geq 0$. For $\hat{x}_n = x_n$ it is clear that

$$E\{ \exp(\lambda [m(y_n, \hat{x}_n; z_n) - m(y_n, x_n; z_n)]) | \mathbf{x} \} = 1. \tag{4.17}$$

Antipodal and orthogonal waveforms commonly used in anti-jam communication systems and all metrics of interest have the important property,

$$E\{\exp(\lambda[m(y_n, \hat{x}_n; z_n) - m(y_n, x_n; z_n)])|\mathbf{x}\}\big|_{\hat{x}_n \neq x_n} = D(\lambda) \quad (4.18)$$

where $D(\lambda)$ is independent of x_n and $\hat{x}_n$ as long as $\hat{x}_n \neq x_n$. Thus, the pairwise error probability is bounded by

$$P(\mathbf{x} \to \hat{\mathbf{x}}) \leq [D(\lambda)]^{w(\mathbf{x}, \hat{\mathbf{x}})} \quad (4.19)$$

where $w(\mathbf{x}, \hat{\mathbf{x}})$ is the number of places where $\hat{x}_n \neq x_n$ $n = 1, 2, \ldots, N$. This is sometimes called the Hamming distance [1]. Since (4.19) applies for all $\lambda \geq 0$, define

$$\begin{aligned} D &= \min_{\lambda \geq 0} D(\lambda) \\ &= \min_{\lambda \geq 0} E\{\exp(\lambda[m(y, \hat{x}; z) - m(y, x; z)])|\mathbf{x}\}\Big|_{\hat{x} \neq x} \end{aligned} \quad (4.20)$$

which gives the final form of the pairwise error probability Chernoff bound,

$$P(\mathbf{x} \to \hat{\mathbf{x}}) \leq D^{w(\mathbf{x}, \hat{\mathbf{x}})}. \quad (4.21)$$

Note that the parameter D depends only on the coding channel and the choice of decoder metric.

In deriving the above results, we assumed a metric $m(y, x; z)$ which was arbitrary. For the special case of the maximum-likelihood metric of (4.11), (4.20) has the special form

$$D = E\left\{\sum_y \sqrt{p(y|x, z)p(y|\hat{x}, z)}\right\}\Bigg|_{\hat{x} \neq x} \quad (4.22\text{a})$$

where the expectation is over the jammer state random variable z. When there is no jammer state information and the maximum-likelihood metric (4.12) is used, then (4.20) has the form

$$D = \sum_y \sqrt{p(y|x)p(y|\hat{x})}\Bigg|_{\hat{x} \neq x} \quad (4.22\text{b})$$

When (4.22) is used in the pairwise error bound (4.21), this is referred to as the Bhattacharyya bound [2]. In order to analyze realistic cases where the channel conditional probabilities are not known and, thus, receivers are not based on the maximum-likelihood metric (mismatched receivers), the general form of D is given in (4.20).

The pairwise error probability is the basis of general bit error bounds for coded communication systems. This is based on the union bound where the bit error probability is upper bounded by the sum of the probabilities of all ways a bit error can occur. For any two coded sequences $\mathbf{x}$ and $\hat{\mathbf{x}}$ let $a(\mathbf{x}, \hat{\mathbf{x}})$ denote the number of bit errors occurring when $\mathbf{x}$ is transmitted and $\hat{\mathbf{x}}$ is chosen by the decoder. If $p(\mathbf{x})$ is the probability of transmitting sequence $\mathbf{x}$ then the coded bit error bound has the form

$$\begin{aligned} P_b &\le \sum_{\mathbf{x}, \hat{\mathbf{x}} \in \mathscr{C}}\sum a(\mathbf{x}, \hat{\mathbf{x}}) p(\mathbf{x}) P(\mathbf{x} \to \hat{\mathbf{x}}) \\ &\le \sum_{\mathbf{x}, \hat{\mathbf{x}} \in \mathscr{C}}\sum a(\mathbf{x}, \hat{\mathbf{x}}) p(\mathbf{x}) D^{w(\mathbf{x}, \hat{\mathbf{x}})} \end{aligned} \tag{4.23}$$

where $\mathscr{C}$ is the set of all coded sequences. Thus, we have the general form [2]

$$P_b \le G(D) \tag{4.24}$$

where $G(\cdot)$ is a function determined solely by the specific code whereas the parameter D depends only on the coding channel and the decoder metric.

The above coded bit error bound is based on two inequalities: the Chernoff bound (see Appendix 4A) and the union bound which has the general form

$$\Pr\left\{\bigcup_n A_n\right\} \le \sum_n \Pr\{A_n\}. \tag{4.25}$$

In addition, in many cases of interest we can reduce the bound based on these two inequalities by a factor of one-half. In all cases where the maximum-likelihood metric is used, the factor of one-half applies [8], [9]. This is shown in Appendix 4B. In all examples given in this book we will introduce this factor of one-half whenever it can be used.

4.3 CUTOFF RATES

The parameter D is directly related to the coding channel cutoff rate R_0. In general, the channel capacity is the theoretical upper limit on data rates where arbitrarily small bit error probabilities can be achieved with coding [2]. From a practical viewpoint, it is difficult to obtain small bit error probabilities with data rates near the channel capacity. Most practical coding techniques operate near the smaller data rate R_0. Thus, R_0 is known as the practically achievable data rate with coding. In addition, R_0 is easier to evaluate than the capacity of the coding channel.

Next we examine the relationship between R_0 and the pairwise error bound for the two coded sequences of length N denoted $\mathbf{x}$ and $\hat{\mathbf{x}}$. Assuming the code symbol alphabet consists of M distinct symbols, randomly select the $2N$ symbols of $\mathbf{x}$ and $\hat{\mathbf{x}}$ where each symbol is independently selected with uniform probability. The average of the pairwise error bound is then

$$\begin{aligned}\overline{P(\mathbf{x} \to \hat{\mathbf{x}})} &\le \overline{D^{w(\mathbf{x},\hat{\mathbf{x}})}} \\ &= \overline{\prod_{n=1}^{N} D^{w(x_n, \hat{x}_n)}} \\ &= \prod_{n=1}^{N} \overline{D^{w(x_n, \hat{x}_n)}} \\ &= \left\{\frac{1 + (M-1)D}{M}\right\}^N \end{aligned} \tag{4.26}$$

where the overbar indicates the average over the coded sequences.

The cutoff rate for this case is defined as

$$R_0 = \log_2 M - \log_2\{1 + (M-1)D\} \text{ bits/symbol} \tag{4.27}$$

so that the average pairwise error probability has the form

$$\overline{P(\mathbf{x} \to \hat{\mathbf{x}})} \le 2^{-NR_0}. \tag{4.28}$$

This definition of the cutoff rate is the natural generalization of the usual definition where the maximum-likelihood metric is assumed. Since from (4.20) D is defined for an arbitrary decoding metric, (4.27) likewise has been generalized to apply to arbitrary decoding metrics. For the special case where the maximum-likelihood metric is used and D is given by (4.22), we have the usual definition of R_0.

Note from (4.27) that there is a one-to-one relationship between R_0 and D where D can be expressed as

$$D = \frac{M2^{-R_0} - 1}{M - 1} \tag{4.29}$$

and for a specific code the bit error bound has the form

$$\begin{aligned}P_b &\le G(D) \\ &= G\left(\frac{M2^{-R_0} - 1}{M-1}\right) \\ &= B(R_0)\end{aligned} \tag{4.30}$$

where $B(\cdot)$ is a function determined solely by the specific code. In this final form of the coded bit error bound, the decoupling of the coding technique given by $B(\cdot)$ and the coding channel characterized by R_0, the cutoff rate is apparent.

In several cases of interest considered in this book, the parameter D is independent of the channel input alphabet size M whereas the cutoff rate given by (4.27) depends on both D and M. In these commonly occurring cases, the cutoff rate for an arbitrary code alphabet size M can be obtained from the cutoff rate for the binary alphabet special case where $M = 2$.

4.4 CONVENTIONAL COHERENT BPSK

For the usual coherent BPSK modulation with the additive white Gaussian noise channel the coding channel model is shown in Figure 4.3(a) where the additive noise component n is a zero-mean Gaussian random variable with variance

$$E\{n^2\} = \frac{N_0}{2}. \tag{4.31}$$

Here N_0 is the single-sided power spectral density of the additive white Gaussian noise process.

The quantizer is necessary when decoding with a digital processor. Here a "0" coded symbol results in a cosine waveform of energy E_s while a "1" coded symbol is a negative cosine waveform of energy E_s. If there is no quantizer in Figure 4.3(a) then the conventional maximum-likelihood metric is

$$m(y, x) = yx. \tag{4.32}$$

This is referred to as a soft decision channel. If x is the transmitted symbol then

$$y = x + n \tag{4.33}$$

and

$$\begin{aligned} D(\lambda) &= E\{ e^{\lambda[y(\hat{x}-x)]} | x \}\big|_{\hat{x}\neq x} \\ &= E\{ e^{\lambda(x+n)(\hat{x}-x)} \}\big|_{\hat{x}\neq x} \\ &= e^{-2\lambda E_s + \lambda^2 E_s N_0} \end{aligned} \tag{4.34}$$

or

$$\begin{aligned} D &= \min_{\lambda \geq 0} \left\{ e^{-2\lambda E_s + \lambda^2 E_s N_0} \right\} \\ &= e^{-E_s/N_0} \end{aligned} \tag{4.35}$$

where the minimum occurs for $\lambda = 1/N_0$.

Suppose next a hard decision channel sketched in Figure 4.3(b) is used where the quantizer forces a decision on each transmitted coded symbol. This results in the Binary Symmetric Channel (BSC) where the coded symbol error probability is

$$\begin{aligned} \varepsilon &= \Pr\left\{ n \geq \sqrt{E_s} \right\} \\ &= \Pr\left\{ \frac{n}{\sqrt{N_0/2}} \geq \sqrt{\frac{2E_s}{N_0}} \right\} \\ &= Q\left(\sqrt{\frac{2E_s}{N_0}} \right) \end{aligned} \tag{4.36}$$

where

$$Q(x) \triangleq \int_x^\infty \frac{1}{\sqrt{2\pi}} e^{-t^2/2}\, dt. \tag{4.37}$$

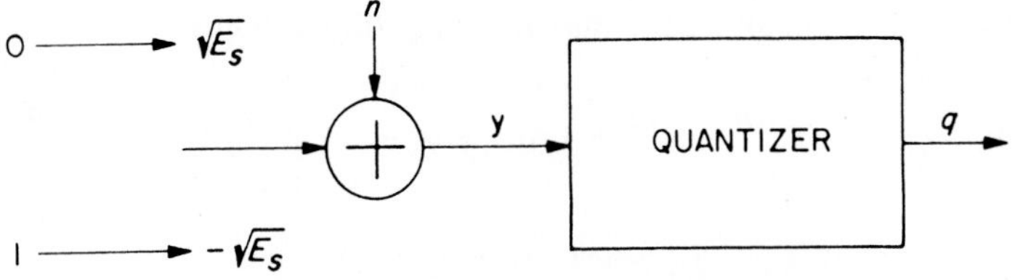

(a) General BPSK Coding Channel

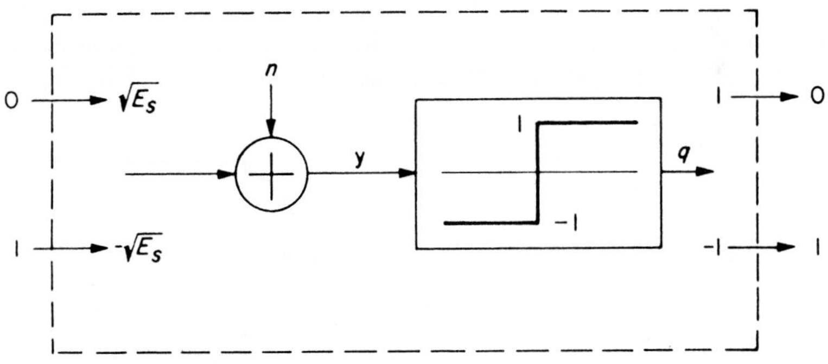

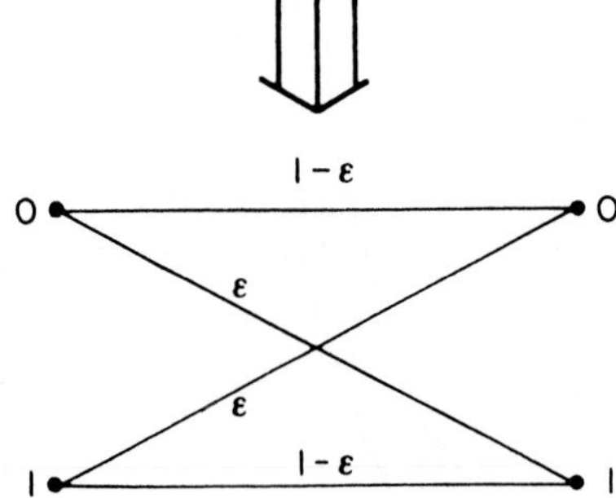

(b) Hard Decision BPSK Coding Channel

Figure 4.3. BPSK coding channels.

For the hard decision channel the maximum-likelihood metric is

$$m(y, x) = \begin{cases} 1, & y = x \\ 0, & y \neq x. \end{cases} \tag{4.38}$$

Hence,

$$\begin{aligned} D(\lambda) &= E\{ e^{\lambda[m(y,\hat{x}) - m(y,x)]} | x \} \big|_{\hat{x} \neq x} \\ &= \varepsilon e^{\lambda} + (1 - \varepsilon) e^{-\lambda} \end{aligned} \tag{4.39}$$

and

$$\begin{aligned} D &= \min_{\lambda \geq 0} \{ \varepsilon e^{\lambda} + (1 - \varepsilon) e^{-\lambda} \} \\ &= \sqrt{4\varepsilon(1 - \varepsilon)}\,. \end{aligned} \tag{4.40}$$

In general for binary symbols ($M = 2$),

$$R_0 = 1 - \log_2(1 + D) \text{ bits/symbol.} \tag{4.41}$$

Figure 4.4 shows R_0 versus E_s/N_0 for the soft and hard decision detectors. Note that there is roughly a 2 dB difference for most values of E_s/N_0.

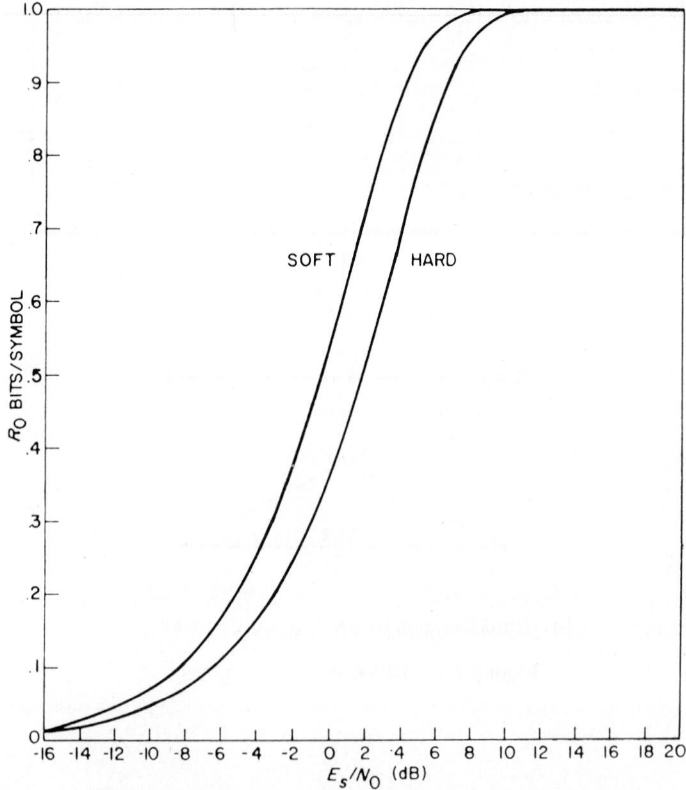

Figure 4.4. R_0 for hard and soft decision detectors.

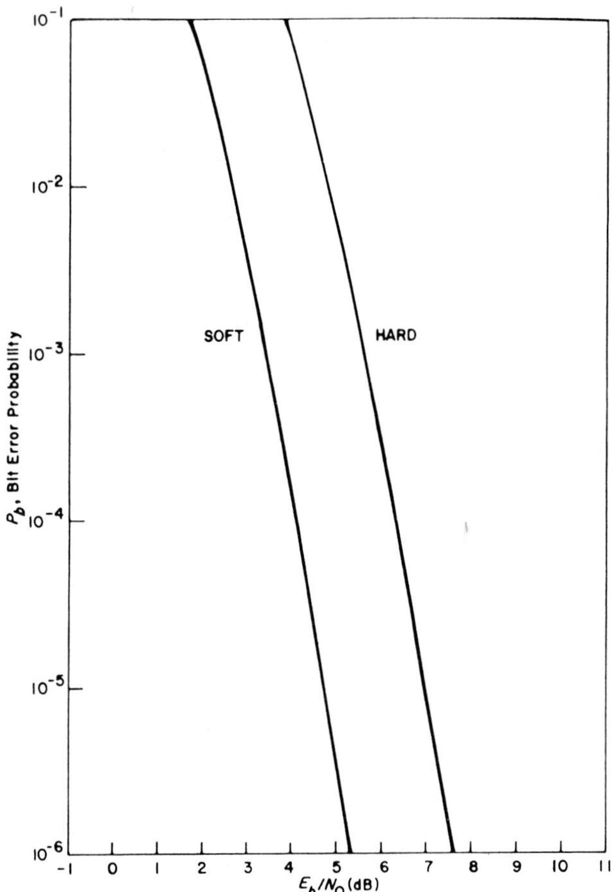

Figure 4.5a. $K = 7$, $R = 1/2$ binary convolutional code—BPSK.

The most commonly used code for coherent BPSK and QPSK modulations is the constraint length $K = 7$ rate $R = 1/2$ bits per coded bit convolutional code found by Odenwalder [10]. This code has the bit error bound[2]

$$P_b \leq \tfrac{1}{2}[36D^{10} + 211D^{12} + 1404D^{14} + 11633D^{16} + \cdots]. \quad (4.42)$$

Another common code is the $K = 7$, $R = 1/3$ convolutional code also found by Odenwalder where the bit error bound is given by

$$P_b \leq \tfrac{1}{2}[7D^{15} + 8D^{16} + 22D^{17} + 44D^{18} + \cdots]. \quad (4.43)$$

Figure 4.5 shows these two bit error bounds for the hard and soft decision

[2] The factor of one-half applies to all maximum-likelihood metrics considered here.

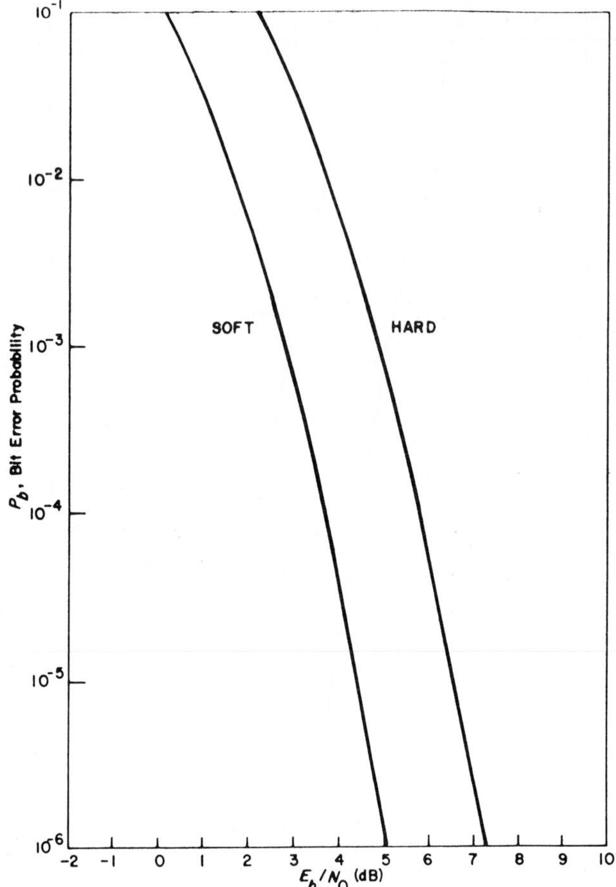

Figure 4.5b. $K = 7$, $R = 1/3$ binary convolutional code—BPSK.

detectors where the maximum-likelihood Viterbi decoders [2] are used for these convolutional codes.

Note that, regardless of the code used, the same difference in E_b/N_0 between hard and soft decision detectors occurs as seen in Figure 4.4 for R_0 versus E_s/N_0. The difference in E_s/N_0 for fixed value of R_0 directly translates to the difference in E_b/N_0 for the corresponding bound on bit error probability where E_s/N_0 and E_b/N_0 are related by (4.2) with N_J replaced by N_0.

One can view the uncoded case as a special case of coding where the code rate is $R = 1$. For this special case, for any transmitted sequence the maximum-likelihood receiver bases its decision on a symbol-by-symbol basis. That is, the optimum decision rule is to decide which particular symbol in a sequence was transmitted based only on the corresponding output symbol. This is the form of all memoryless channels with no coding since each channel output symbol depends only on the corresponding channel input symbol and all channel input symbols are independent of each other. With coding, of course, there are a restricted number of channel input sequences, thus introducing dependence among coded channel input sequences.

For the uncoded case, the symbol-by-symbol optimum decision rule is identical to the hard decision rule shown in Figure 4.3(b) where the exact bit error probability is

$$P_b = Q\left(\sqrt{\frac{2E_b}{N_0}}\right). \tag{4.44}$$

Note that these decisions assume the soft decision metric of (4.32). For the corresponding result using the general bound

$$\begin{aligned} P_b &\leq \tfrac{1}{2}D \\ &= \tfrac{1}{2}e^{-E_b/N_0}. \end{aligned} \tag{4.45}$$

Figure 4.6 shows both the exact bit error probability and this special case of

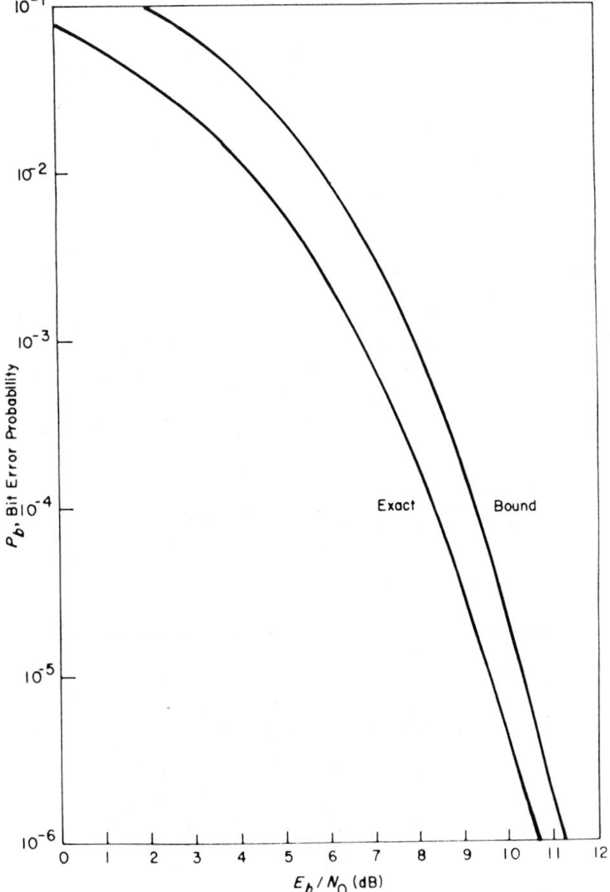

Figure 4.6. BPSK bit error probability.

the general coded bit error bound. For most values of E_b/N_0, there is approximately a 1 dB difference between the exact uncoded bit error probability and the bound.

4.5 DS/BPSK AND PULSE JAMMING

The previous results for the white Gaussian noise channel also apply to the case where there is continuous jamming of a direct sequence (DS) spread BPSK signal. The only difference is that N_J replaces N_0 in E_b/N_0 given by (4.3). Jamming, however, can take many forms. To illustrate the application of the general bounds presented in this chapter, consider the following example.

Suppose there is a pulse jammer with average power J/ρ for a fraction ρ of the time and zero power for a fraction $1 - \rho$ of the time. Assume that when the jammer is on, the channel is like an additive white Gaussian noise channel with power spectral density (one sided)

$$N_J' = \frac{J}{\rho W_{ss}} = \frac{N_J}{\rho} \tag{4.46}$$

where W_{ss} is the spread-spectrum signal bandwidth. During the transmission of a coded symbol define the jammer state random variable Z where

$$\Pr(Z = 1) = \rho$$

and

$$\Pr(Z = 0) = 1 - \rho. \tag{4.47}$$

This is the jammer state side information that may be available at the receiver where $Z = 1$ indicates a jammer is transmitting during a coded symbol time while $Z = 0$ indicates there is no jammer signal. With z available at the receiver, the metric we consider is

$$m(y, x; z) = c(z)yx \tag{4.48}$$

which is a weighted correlation metric.

Next compute the parameter

$$\begin{aligned} D(\lambda) &= E\{e^{\lambda[c(Z)y(\hat{x}-x)]}|x\}|_{\hat{x}\neq x} \\ &= \rho E\{e^{\lambda c(1)(x+n)(\hat{x}-x)}\}|_{\hat{x}\neq x} + (1-\rho)e^{\lambda c(0)x(\hat{x}-x)}|_{\hat{x}\neq x} \\ &= \rho \exp\{-2\lambda c(1)E_s + \lambda^2 c^2(1)E_s N_J/\rho\} \\ &\quad + (1-\rho)\exp\{-2\lambda c(0)E_s\}. \end{aligned} \tag{4.49}$$

If the receiver has jammer state side information (knowledge of z) then the metric can have $c(0)$ as large as possible to make the second term in (4.49) negligibly small. Also without loss of generality normalize $c(1) = 1$ to obtain

$$D(\lambda) = \rho \exp\{-2\lambda E_s + \lambda^2 E_s N_J/\rho\} \tag{4.50}$$

and

$$D = \min_{\lambda \geq 0} \left[\rho \exp\{ -2\lambda E_s + \lambda^2 E_s N_J/\rho \} \right]$$
$$= \rho e^{-\rho(E_s/N_J)}. \quad (4.51)$$

Suppose the receiver has no side information. Then the metric is independent of z, or equivalently has weighting $c(1) = c(0)$ which we can normalize to unity. Then, from (4.49)

$$D(\lambda) = \rho \exp\{ -2\lambda E_s + \lambda^2 E_s N_J/\rho \} + (1 - \rho)\exp\{ -2\lambda E_s \}$$
$$= e^{-2\lambda E_s} \left[\rho e^{\lambda^2 E_s N_J/\rho} + 1 - \rho \right] \quad (4.52)$$

and D is obtained by minimizing $D(\lambda)$ over $\lambda \geq 0$.

Both (4.50) and (4.52) correspond to soft decision detectors. The only difference between these two is the availability to the decoder of side information concerning the jammer state. The difference is shown in Figures 4.7 and 4.8 where $R_0 = 1 - \log_2(1 + D)$ is sketched versus E_s/N_J for various values of ρ. Clearly having jammer state knowledge helps improve the overall bit error probability. The special case where $\rho = 1$ coincides with the conventional soft decision curve shown in Figure 4.4. Similar results can be obtained for hard decision detectors. A complete discussion of DS/BPSK systems is covered in Chapter 1 of Part 2.

4.6 TRANSLATION OF CODED ERROR BOUNDS

The numerical evaluation of R_0 versus E_s/N_J is straightforward for most coding channels encountered in anti-jam communication systems. This cutoff rate parameter is independent of the specific code used, but can now be used to evaluate the coded bit error probability of any code whose standard bit error probability curve is available. For example, Figure 4.5 shows the coded bit error bounds for two codes commonly used over the additive white Gaussian noise channel. The basic modulation here is coherent BPSK or QPSK. Such curves are typically available in textbooks and published papers. For the standard additive white Gaussian noise channel, the standard cutoff rates are shown in Figure 4.4 for coherent BPSK modulation. The soft decision case in Figure 4.4 is the $\rho = 1$ case in Figures 4.7 and 4.8.

Suppose we now want to evaluate the coded bit error bound for the constraint length $K = 7$ rate $R = 1/2$ convolutional code used in a DS/BPSK anti-jam system where there is a pulse jammer with $\rho = .05$. Also, suppose the detector used was a soft decision detector and no jammer state information is available. Here we assume the metric used is simply that of (4.32). Figure 4.8 shows the R_0 versus E_s/N_J for this case. We can now translate the standard curve for this code shown in Figure 4.5 to determine the bit error bound with this same code for the new pulse jammed channel described above.

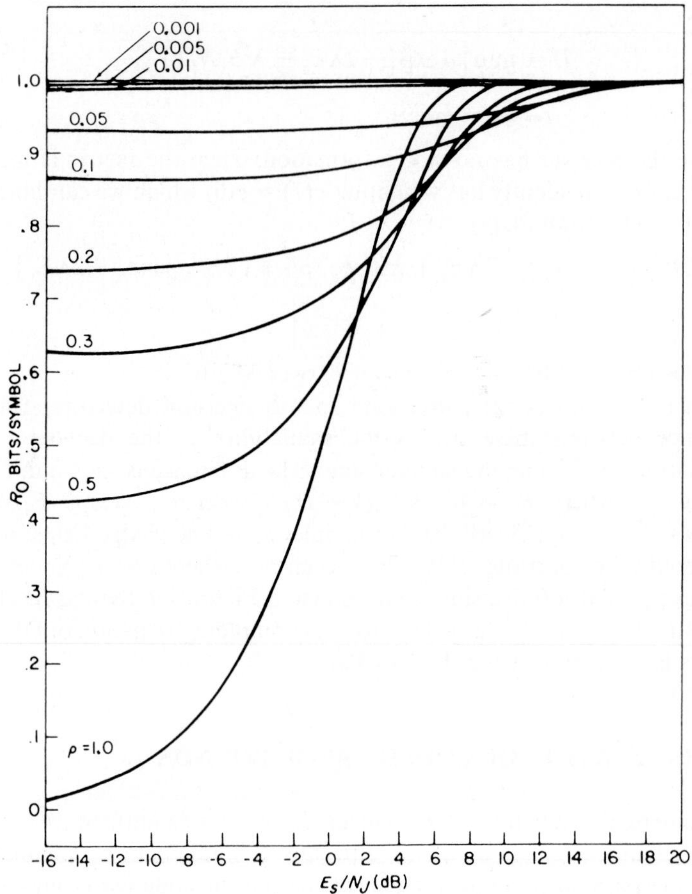

Figure 4.7. Soft decision with jammer state knowledge—DS/BPSK.

Note that for 10^{-6} coded bit error probability, the standard curve in Figure 4.5a shows a required

$$E_b/N_0 = 5.3 \text{ dB} \tag{4.53}$$

or since $E_s = E_b/2$ for $R = 1/2$,

$$E_s/N_0 = 2.3 \text{ dB}. \tag{4.54}$$

Next, for this choice of E_s/N_0, from Figure 4.4 we have that the cutoff rate required is (also see $\rho = 1$ curve in Figure 4.8)

$$R_0 = .76 \text{ bits/symbol}. \tag{4.55}$$

Recall that the coded bit error bound can always be expressed as a function of R_0 as shown in (4.5) or, more specifically for this code, by (4.42) where D is given by (4.29). Thus, if we have another coding channel with the same value of the cutoff rate parameter R_0, then the bit error bound is also the

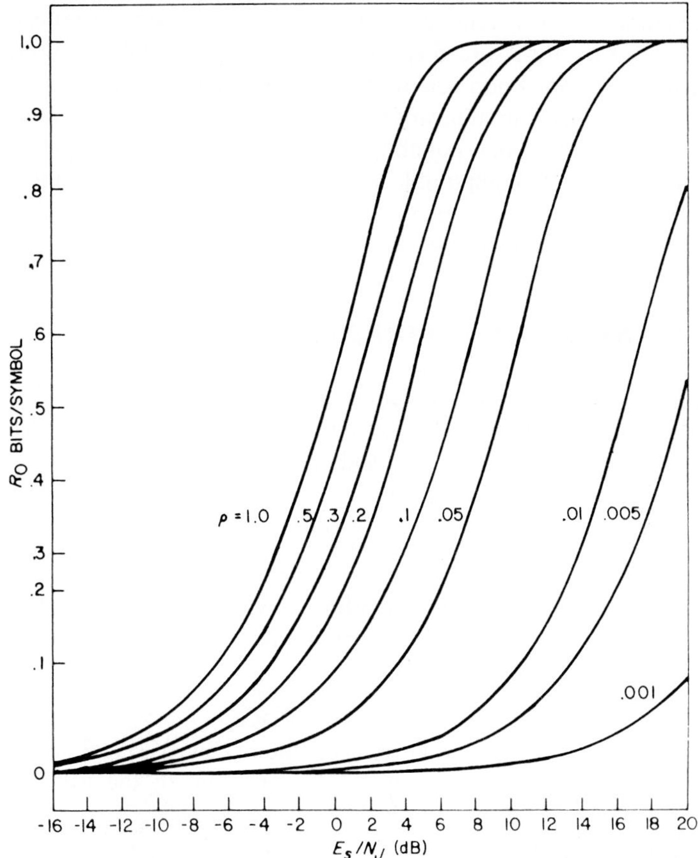

Figure 4.8. Soft decision with no jammer state knowledge—DS/BPSK.

same, which in this case is 10^{-6}. For our new coded channel, we determine from Figure 4.8 that for R_0 given by (4.55) and $\rho = .05$, the new required E_s/N_J is

$$E_s/N_J = 12.2 \text{ dB} \tag{4.56}$$

or

$$E_b/N_J = 15.2 \text{ dB}. \tag{4.57}$$

Thus, in this pulse jamming example, we require 15.2 dB of E_b/N_J defined by (4.3) to achieve 10^{-6} coded bit error probability with the given convolutional code. By continuing this translation for several bit error probabilities, we obtain the complete coded bit error bound for the case of interest by translating the standard coded bit error bound curve.

The translation of standard coded bit error bounds to obtain corresponding bit error bounds for different coding channels applies to all binary input coding channels. It also generalizes to M-ary input coding channels of the kind that arise in most spread-spectrum systems. This will be shown next with frequency-hopped non-coherent MFSK signals with partial-band jamming. For anti-jam communication systems, where jamming and receiver structures can take many possible forms, the general approach of first obtaining numerically computable values of the cutoff rate parameter and then translating standard error rate curves serves as a useful general approach to the analysis of anti-jam communication systems.

4.7 CONVENTIONAL NON-COHERENT MFSK

Conventional MFSK modulation consists of transmitting one of M symbols where the symbol is represented by one of M non-coherently orthogonal frequency tones of duration T_s seconds and energy E_s. We assume the M tones are separated in frequency by

$$\Delta f = \frac{1}{T_s}. \tag{4.58}$$

For MFSK modulation with the additive white Gaussian noise channel, the optimum non-coherent detector has the form shown in Figure 4.9. The detector output consists of

$$y = (e_1, e_2, \ldots, e_M) \tag{4.59}$$

where e_i is the normalized energy of the received signal at the i-th frequency. That is, e_i is the normalized energy out of the i-th frequency detector.

We denote the M modulation symbols by $\{1, 2, \ldots, M\}$ and a general input symbol into the modulator by x. Assuming $x = i$, which corresponds to the i-th frequency tone being transmitted, $e_1, e_2, \ldots, e_M$ are independent random variables where $r_i = \sqrt{e_i}$ has probability density functions [2],

$$p(r_i|x = i) = r_i e^{-r_i^2/2} e^{-E_s/N_0} I_0\left(\sqrt{\frac{2E_s}{N_0}}\, r_i\right) \tag{4.60}$$

for $r_i \geq 0$ where $I_0(\cdot)$ is the modified Bessel function of the first kind and zero-th order (this is a Rician density function) and

$$p(r_j|x = i) = r_j e^{-r_j^2/2} \tag{4.61}$$

for $r_j \geq 0$ and $j \neq i$ (these are Rayleigh density functions).

4.7.1 Uncoded

With no coding, the maximum-likelihood decision rule is: given channel output y given by (4.59), choose the transmitted symbol corresponding to the largest value of e_i; $i = 1, 2, \ldots, M$. This is equivalent to using a metric

$$m(y, x) = e_x. \tag{4.62}$$

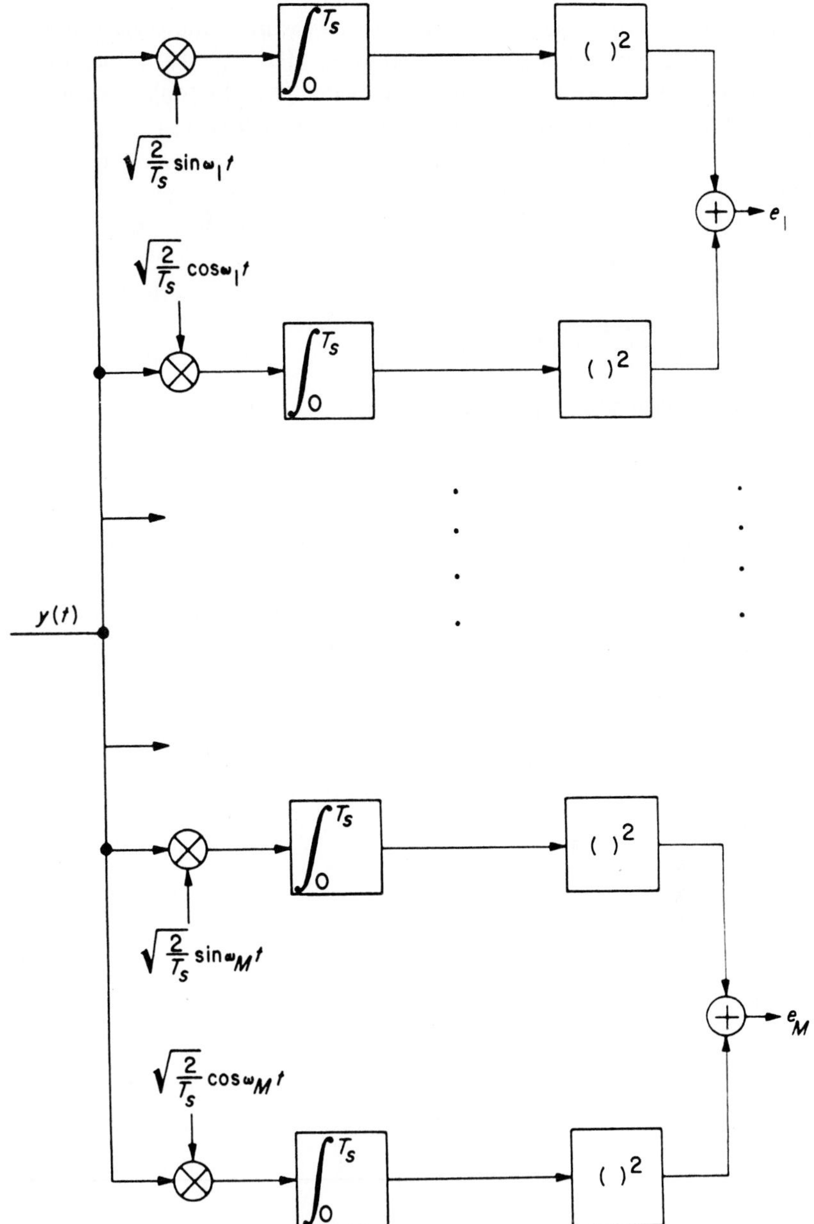

Figure 4.9. Non-coherent MFSK detector.

Note that, for the uncoded case, the decisions are made on a symbol-by-symbol basis without regard to sequences. Thus, we do not require the additivity property of metrics for the uncoded case. For this uncoded case, the probability of making a symbol decision error is [11]

$$\begin{aligned} P_s &= \Pr\{\hat{x} \neq x\} \\ &= \sum_{l=1}^{M-1} \binom{M-1}{l} (-1)^{l+1} \frac{1}{l+1} e^{-l(E_s/N_0)/(l+1)}. \end{aligned} \tag{4.63}$$

When $M = 2^K$, we can associate K data bits to each modulation symbol. Denoting E_b as the energy per data bit we have

$$E_s = KE_b \tag{4.64}$$

and the bit error probability [10]

$$\begin{aligned} P_b &= \frac{\frac{1}{2}M}{M-1} P_s \\ &= \frac{2^{K-1}}{2^K - 1} \sum_{l=1}^{2^K-1} \binom{2^K-1}{l} (-1)^{l+1} \frac{1}{l+1} e^{-lK(E_b/N_0)/(l+1)}. \end{aligned} \tag{4.65}$$

For the special case of binary symbols (BFSK), (4.65) becomes

$$P_b = \tfrac{1}{2} e^{-E_b/2N_0}. \tag{4.66}$$

Applying the general coded error bound to the special case of uncoded non-coherent MFSK with metric $m(y, x) = e_x$ yields

$$\begin{aligned} D(\lambda) &= E\{e^{\lambda[e_{\hat{x}} - e_x]}|x\}|_{\hat{x} \neq x} \\ &= E\{e^{\lambda e_{\hat{x}}}|x\}|_{\hat{x} \neq x} E\{e^{-\lambda e_x}|x\} \end{aligned} \tag{4.67}$$

where

$$\begin{aligned} E\{e^{-\lambda e_x}|x\} &= \int_0^\infty e^{-\lambda t^2} t e^{-t^2/2} e^{-E_s/N_0} I_0\left(\sqrt{\frac{2E_s}{N_0}}\, t\right) dt \\ &= \frac{1}{1+2\lambda} e^{-2\lambda(E_s/N_0)/(1+2\lambda)} \end{aligned} \tag{4.68}$$

and when $\hat{x} \neq x$,

$$\begin{aligned} E\{e^{\lambda e_{\hat{x}}}|x\}|_{\hat{x} \neq x} &= \int_0^\infty e^{\lambda t^2} t e^{-t^2/2}\, dt \\ &= \frac{1}{1-2\lambda} \end{aligned} \tag{4.69}$$

provided $2\lambda < 1$. Since λ is a free variable, substituting λ in place of 2λ results in the form,

$$D = \min_{0 \le \lambda \le 1} \left\{ \frac{1}{1-\lambda^2} e^{-\lambda(E_s/N_0)/(1+\lambda)} \right\}. \tag{4.70}$$

The pairwise error probability is, thus,

$$P(x \to \hat{x}) \le D \tag{4.71}$$

yielding the symbol error probability

$$P_s = \frac{1}{M}\sum_{i=1}^{M} \Pr\{e_i \le e_j \text{ for some } j \ne i | x = i\}$$
$$\le \tfrac{1}{2}(M-1)D. \tag{4.72}$$

This bound is based on the union bound with the factor of one-half applying. (See Appendix 4B). The bit error probability is then given by

$$P_b = \frac{\frac{1}{2}M}{M-1}P_s$$
$$\le \tfrac{1}{4}MD. \tag{4.73}$$

Figure 4.10 compares (4.65) and (4.73) for $M = 2, 4, 8, 16$, and 32. There is approximately a 1 dB difference between the exact bit error probability

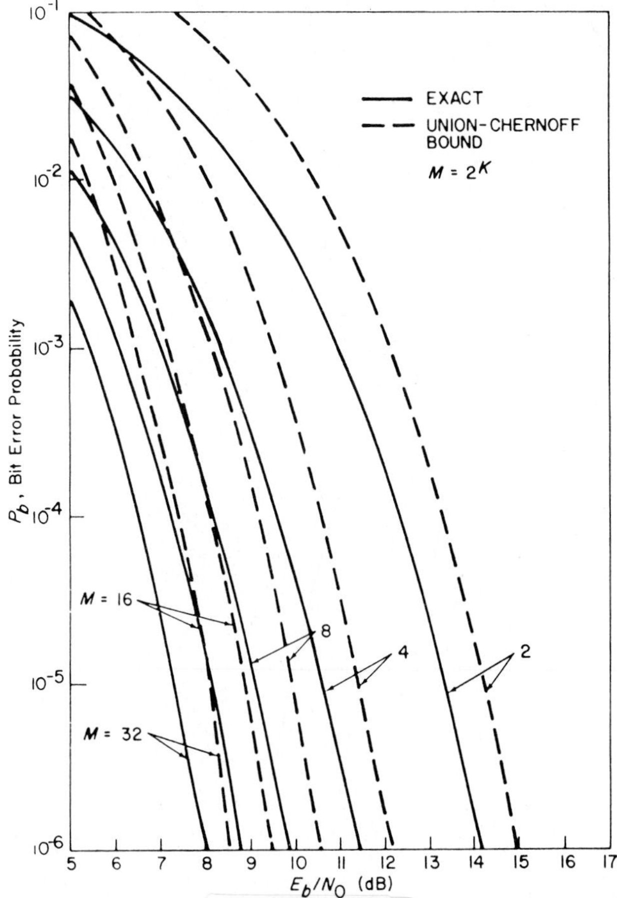

Figure 4.10. Exact versus union-Chernoff bound for uncoded MFSK bit error probability.

and the general coded bit error rate bound applied to this special case of no coding. Recall that the bound in (4.73) is based on the union bound (4.25) and the Chernoff bound (4.16). The 1 dB difference between the exact bit error probabilities and the bounds is due primarily to the Chernoff bound. For the uncoded case, we can derive the exact pairwise error probability which is given by

$$\Pr\{e_i \le e_j | x = i\} = \tfrac{1}{2}e^{-E_s/2N_0} \tag{4.74}$$

for $j \neq i$. This is just the two signal case equivalent to the BFSK bit error probability. The symbol error union bound is, thus,

$$\begin{aligned} P_s &\le \sum_{j \neq i} \Pr\{e_i \le e_j | x = i\} \\ &= (M-1)\tfrac{1}{2}e^{-E_s/2N_0} \end{aligned} \tag{4.75}$$

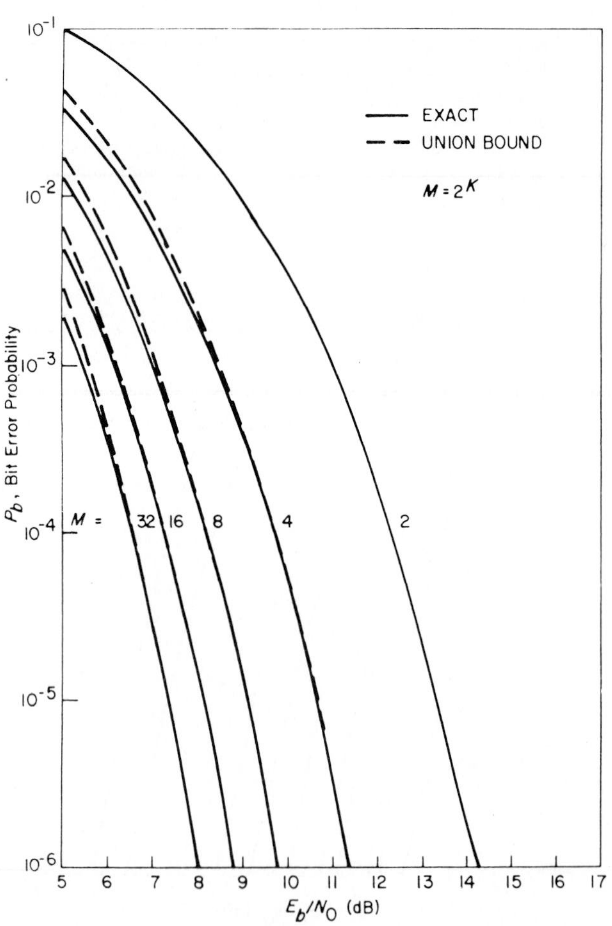

Figure 4.11. Exact versus union bound for uncoded MFSK bit error probability.

and the corresponding uncoded bit error bound using only the union bound is

$$P_b \leq \tfrac{1}{4} M e^{-E_s/2N_0}. \tag{4.76}$$

Figure 4.11 shows this bound and the exact bit error probability for $M = 2$, 4, 8, 16, and 32.

For the special case of no coding, the Chernoff bound was not required since an exact expression for the pairwise error probability is available. For the coded cases, however, the Chernoff bound for the pairwise error probabilities is needed since easy-to-evaluate exact pairwise error probability expressions are difficult to obtain.

4.7.2 Coded

With the use of coding, each coded MFSK symbol has an associated M-ary signal of energy denoted E_c and of duration T_c. With no coding these parameters become E_s and T_s as in the previous section.

The maximum-likelihood decision rule with coding requires a metric that includes a zero-th order Bessel function. This is because in order to have the additivity property, the maximum-likelihood metric is always proportional to the logarithm of the channel conditional probability which in this case has the form given in (4.60). Without coding where only symbol-by-symbol decisions are made, the maximum-likelihood metric can be any monotone function of the channel conditional probability such as (4.62).

For high signal-to-noise ratios the optimum metric can be approximated by (4.62). Although this is not the maximum-likelihood metric, it is the most commonly used metric for coded non-coherent MFSK systems. Volume II, Chapter 2 shows that it is the maximum-likelihood metric when there is Rayleigh fading in the channel. The choice of this metric results in the parameter D given by (4.70) with $E_c = RE_b$ where R is the code rate in bits per coded M-ary symbol.

For the binary alphabet ($M = 2$), the binary convolutional codes found by Odenwalder are given by (4.42) for rate $R = 1/2$ and by (4.43) for rate $R = 1/3$. Thus, for non-coherent BFSK with the metric given by (4.62), we would merely use D given by (4.70) with $E_c = RE_b$. For $M = 4$, Trumpis [12] has found an optimum constraint length $K = 7$ convolutional code of rate $R = 1$ bit per coded 4-ary symbol whose performance is given by the bound

$$P_b \leq \tfrac{1}{2}[7D^7 + 39D^8 + 104D^9 + 352D^{10} + 1187D^{11} + \cdots]. \tag{4.77}$$

Trumpis also found an optimum convolutional code for alphabet $M = 8$ and constraint length $K = 7$ with rate $R = 1$ bit per 8-ary symbol whose performance is given by the bound

$$P_b \leq \tfrac{1}{2}[D^7 + 4D^8 + 8D^9 + 49D^{10} + 92D^{11} + \cdots]. \tag{4.78}$$

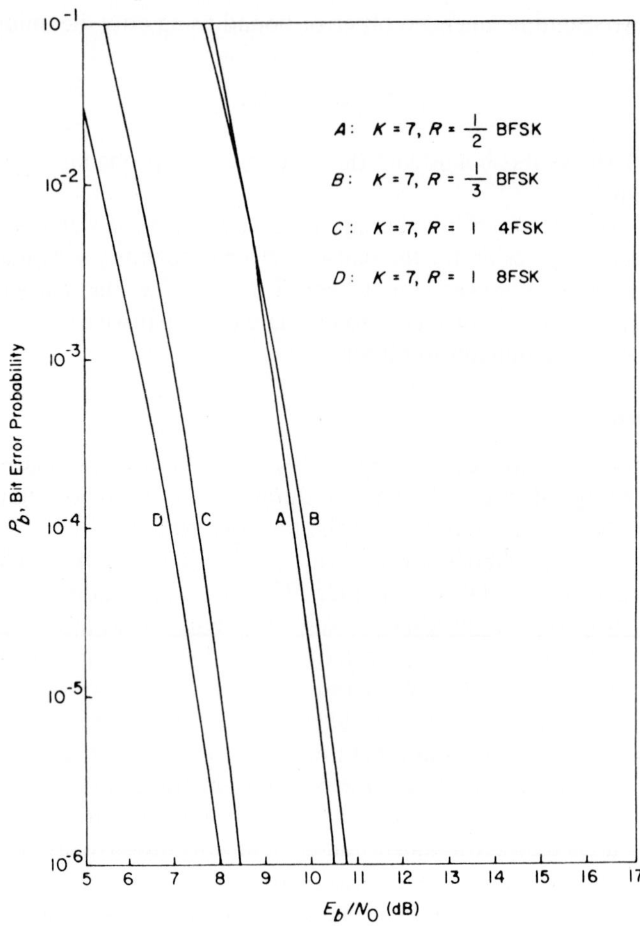

Figure 4.12. Convolutional code bit error bounds—MFSK.

Figure 4.12 shows all these codes for the non-coherent MFSK modulation in the conventional white Gaussian noise channel.

The metric given by (4.62) results in a non-negative real number. Since this metric is not quantized, it is referred to as a soft decision metric analogous to the soft decision metric for coherent BPSK modulation discussed earlier in Section 4.4. Also, the detector of Figure 4.9 is referred to as a soft decision detector since the detector output $y = (e_1, e_2, \ldots, e_M)$ is unquantized. If the detector is forced to make a decision as if there was no coding the result is the hard decision detector with outputs $1, 2, \ldots, M$ where the detector output is the integer i if $e_i > e_j$ for all $j \neq i$.

Essentially the hard decision detector makes the usual uncoded non-coherent MFSK decision and results in a symmetric coding channel shown in Figure 4.13 for $M = 4$ and $M = 8$.

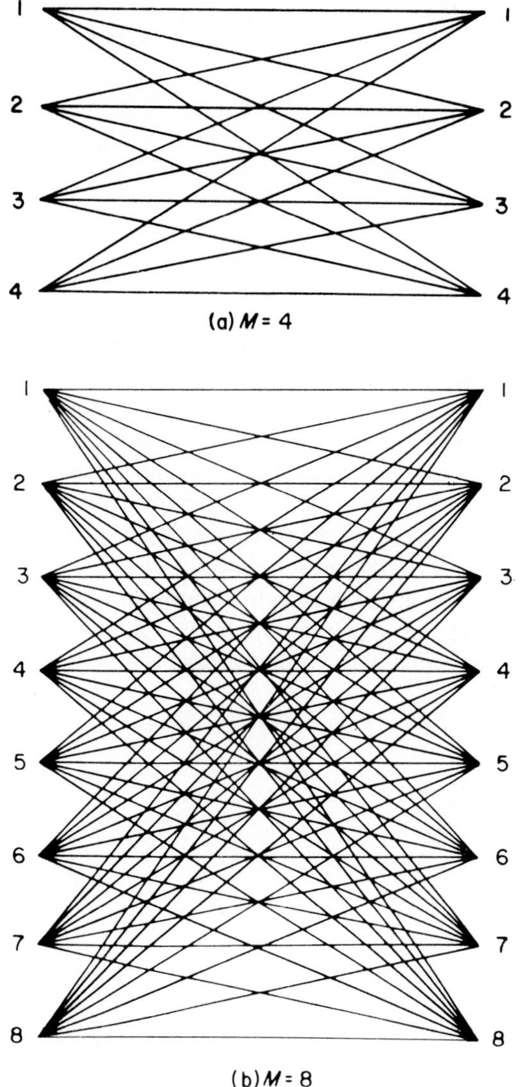

Figure 4.13. Hard decision non-coherent MFSK channels.

If the output of the hard decision detector is given as y, then the hard decision coding channel for fixed M is characterized by

$$p(y|x) = \begin{cases} 1 - P_s, & y = x \\ \dfrac{P_s}{M-1}, & y \neq x \end{cases} \tag{4.79}$$

where P_s is the symbol error probability given by (4.63). For this hard decision channel the maximum-likelihood metric is given by (4.38) and the parameter $D(\lambda)$ is

$$D(\lambda) = E\{e^{\lambda[m(y,\hat{x})-m(y,x)]}|x\}|_{\hat{x}\neq x}$$
$$= (1-P_s)e^{-\lambda} + \frac{P_s}{M-1}e^{\lambda} + \frac{P_s}{M-1}(M-2). \quad (4.80)$$

Thus,

$$D = \sqrt{\frac{4P_s(1-P_s)}{M-1}} + \left(\frac{M-2}{M-1}\right)P_s. \quad (4.81)$$

Note that for $M = 2$, D becomes identical to (4.40) with ε replaced by P_s; i.e., the crossover probability of the BSC.

For both hard and soft decision detectors the cutoff rate is given by (4.27). Figure 4.14 shows the cutoff rates for both the hard and soft decision detectors with the additive white Gaussian noise channel. The coded bit error bounds for the hard decision detector can be obtained for the convolutional codes discussed above by shifting the bit error bounds shown in Figure 4.12 for the soft decision detectors by the amount of difference between hard and soft decision detectors shown in Figure 4.14 for R_0 versus E_s/N_0. This is the basic motivation for evaluating the easy-to-compute cutoff rate R_0 associated with various channels and detectors.

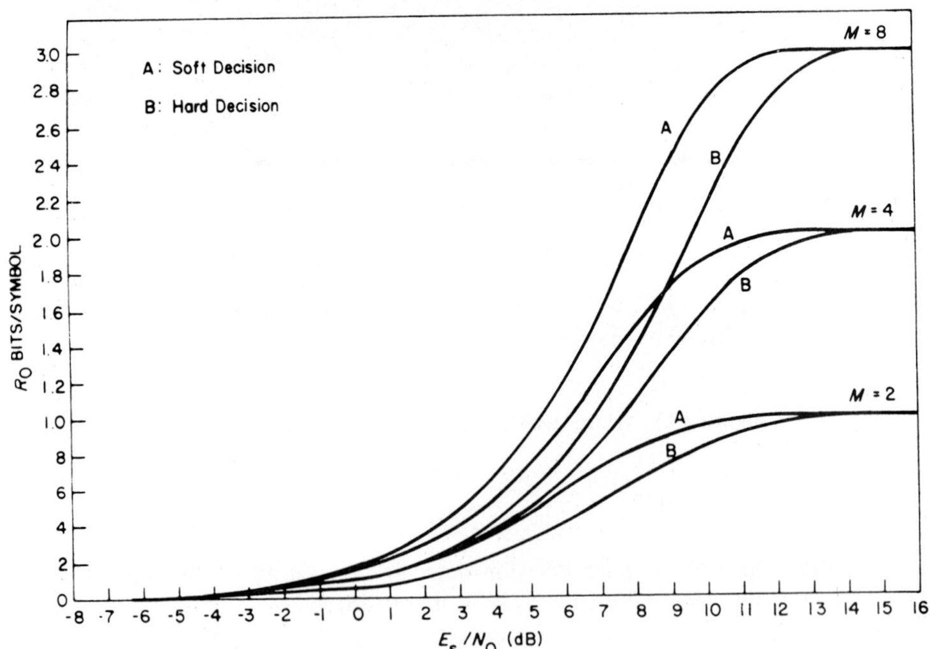

Figure 4.14. Cutoff rates for MFSK.

4.8 FH/MFSK AND PARTIAL-BAND JAMMING

The previous section also applies to FH/MFSK with broadband noise jamming where $N_0 = N_J$ and E_b/N_J is given by (4.3). Here the case of partial-band noise jamming is examined to illustrate our general coded error bound evaluation.

Assume a jammer with power J that transmits Gaussian noise with constant power spectral density over a total bandwidth W_J. This jammed bandwidth is some subset of the total FH/MFSK signal bandwidth W_{ss} and it is assumed that the transmitter and receiver do not know this jammed bandwidth before transmission. Indeed, the jammed subset of total bandwidth W_J may be changed randomly by the jammer to prevent the transmitter and receiver from knowing what frequencies will be jammed. The fraction of the jammed band is denoted

$$\rho = \frac{W_J}{W_{ss}}. \tag{4.82}$$

Thus, defining $N_J = J/W_{ss}$, the true noise power spectral density is

$$N_J' = \frac{N_J}{\rho} = \frac{J}{W_J} \tag{4.83}$$

for W_J Hz and zero for the rest of the spread bandwidth.

Assuming that an MFSK signal is transmitted during the time interval of T_s seconds, the hop time interval is denoted T_h seconds, then

$$T_h = dT_s \tag{4.84}$$

where d is a fraction or a positive integer. Thus, there are d MFSK symbols transmitted during each hop interval.[3] Assume that each hop is independent of other hops and equally likely to be in any part of the total spread-spectrum signal frequency band of W_{ss} Hz. Thus, the probability of transmitting an FH/MFSK symbol in a jammed frequency band is given by ρ.

Throughout this analysis, also assume that

$$\frac{M}{T_s} \ll W_J \tag{4.85}$$

so that during any hop interval the whole set of M possible tones is either totally in the jammed band or not. This ignores the unlikely cases where the M possible tones straddle the edge of the jammed band leaving only some of the M tone positions with jamming noise present. When (4.85) holds, this edge effect can be ignored.

[3]Later in the text, we refer to the case where $d > 1$ as slow frequency hopping (SFH) and $d \leq 1$ as fast frequency hopping (FFH).

As always, ideal interleaving is assumed so that the coding channel is memoryless (see Part 1, Chapter 3, Section 3.8). In this FH/MFSK example, it means that each transmitted M-ary symbol is jammed with probability ρ and not jammed with probability $1-\rho$ independent of other transmitted symbols. As before, define the jammer state random variable Z where

$$P\{Z=1\}=\rho$$

and

$$P\{Z=0\}=1-\rho. \tag{4.86}$$

This is the jammer state information that may be available at the receiver where $Z=1$ indicates that the transmitted symbol hopped into the jammed band while $Z=0$ indicates that it hopped outside the jammed band.

With z available at the receiver, the metric we consider is

$$m(y,x;z)=c(z)e_x \tag{4.87}$$

which is a weighted version of the energy detector output corresponding to input x.

For the above metric the parameter (4.18) has the form

$$\begin{aligned} D(\lambda) &= E\{e^{\lambda c(Z)[e_{\hat{x}}-e_x]}|x\}|_{\hat{x}\neq x} \\ &= \rho E\{e^{\lambda c(1)[e_{\hat{x}}-e_x]}|x, Z=1\}|_{\hat{x}\neq x} \\ &\quad +(1-\rho)E\{e^{\lambda c(0)[e_{\hat{x}}-e_x]}|Z=0\}|_{\hat{x}\neq x}. \end{aligned} \tag{4.88}$$

From (4.67), (4.68), and (4.69) we have

$$E\{e^{\lambda c(1)[e_{\hat{x}}-e_x]}|x, Z=1\}|_{\hat{x}\neq x}=\frac{1}{1-(2\lambda c(1))^2}e^{-2\lambda c(1)\rho(E_s/N_J)/[1+2\lambda c(1)]} \tag{4.89}$$

for $0<2\lambda c(1)<1$ and

$$E\{e^{\lambda c(0)[e_{\hat{x}}-e_x]}|x, Z=0\}|_{\hat{x}\neq x}=e^{-2\lambda c(0)\rho(E_s/N_J)}. \tag{4.90}$$

Thus,

$$\begin{aligned} D(\lambda) &= \frac{\rho}{1-(2\lambda c(1))^2}e^{-2\lambda c(1)\rho(E_s/N_J)/[1+2\lambda c(1)]} \\ &\quad +(1-\rho)e^{-2\lambda c(0)\rho(E_s/N_J)}. \end{aligned} \tag{4.91}$$

When side information is available, the metric can be chosen with $c(0)$ large enough so that the second term in (4.91) is negligible and $c(1)=1/2$ chosen for normalization. Then, the parameter D becomes

$$D=\min_{0\le\lambda\le 1}\left\{\frac{\rho}{1-\lambda^2}e^{-\lambda\rho(E_s/N_J)/(1+\lambda)}\right\}. \tag{4.92}$$

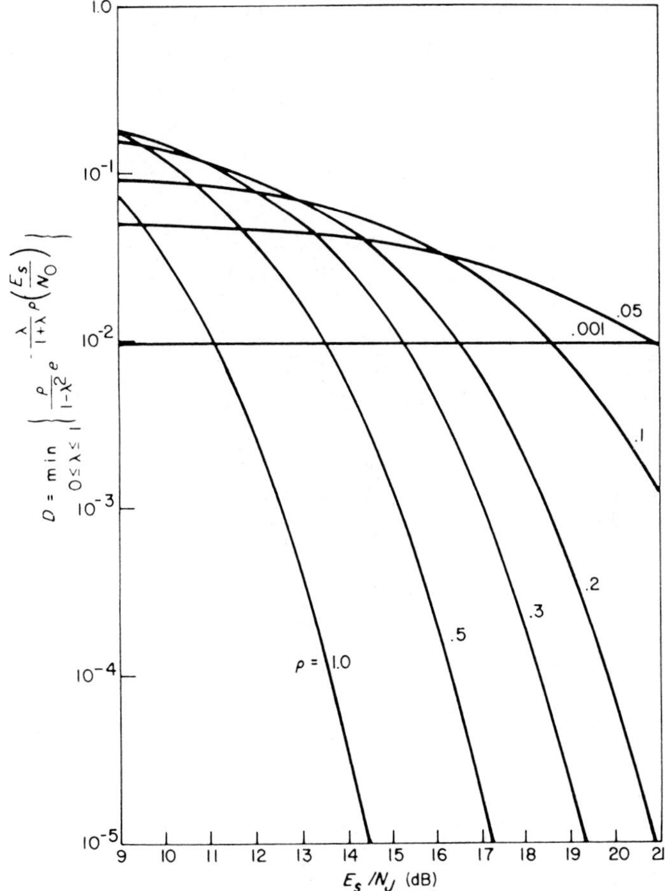

Figure 4.15a. Parameter D for soft decision with jammer state knowledge—FH/MFSK.

With no side information, $c(1) = c(0)$ which can be normalized to $1/2$ to get

$$D = \min_{0 \le \lambda \le 1} \left\{ \frac{\rho}{1-\lambda^2} e^{-\lambda\rho(E_s/N_J)/(1+\lambda)} + (1-\rho)e^{-\lambda\rho(E_s/N_J)} \right\}. \quad (4.93)$$

Figures 4.15a and 4.15b show D given by (4.92) and (4.93), respectively, for various values of ρ. Next, in Figures 4.16 through 4.18, the corresponding cutoff rates given by (4.27) for $M = 2$, 4, and 8 are shown. The special case of $\rho = 1.0$ is the broadband noise jamming case discussed in the previous section.[4] There D is given by (4.70) which is the same as (4.92) and

[4]The broadband noise jammer case is the same as having an additive white Gaussian noise channel with $N_0 = N_J$.

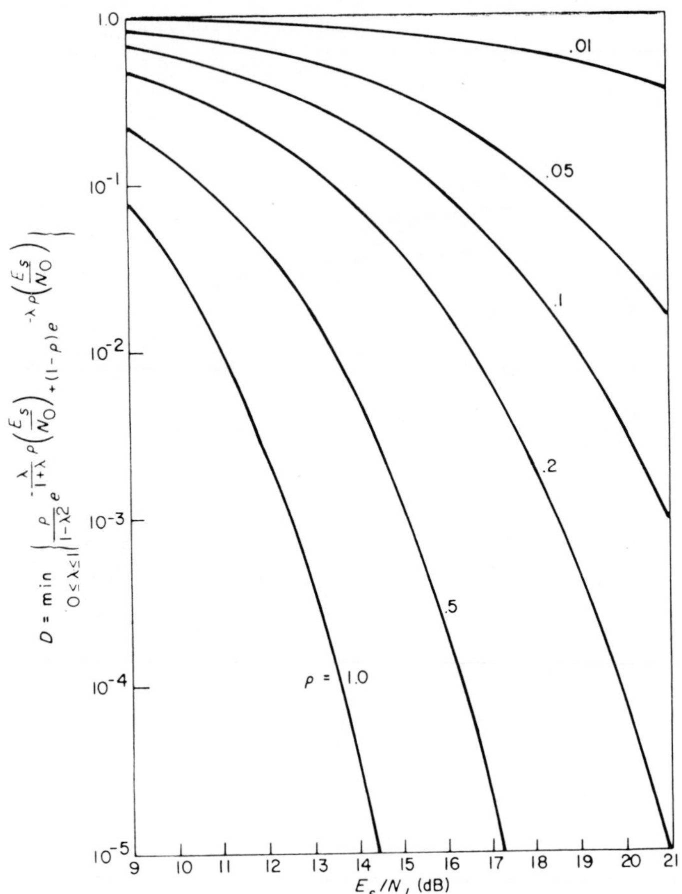

Figure 4.15b. Parameter D for soft decision with no jammer state knowledge—FH/MFSK.

(4.93) for $\rho = 1.0$. Thus, in Figures 4.15 through 4.18, we can compare the broadband noise jammer ($\rho = 1.0$) with various partial-band noise jammers. For any code, the bit error bounds for all these cases can be directly compared using these figures.

As an example, suppose we assume the receiver has no jammer state knowledge and the jammer is a partial-band noise jammer which jams a fraction

$$\rho = .05 \tag{4.94}$$

of the total spread-spectrum band. Assume the conventional non-coherent MFSK metric of (4.62).

With $M = 8$ and using the error bound on the Trumpis code given by (4.78), what is the E_b/N_J given by (4.3) required to achieve 10^{-5} bit error

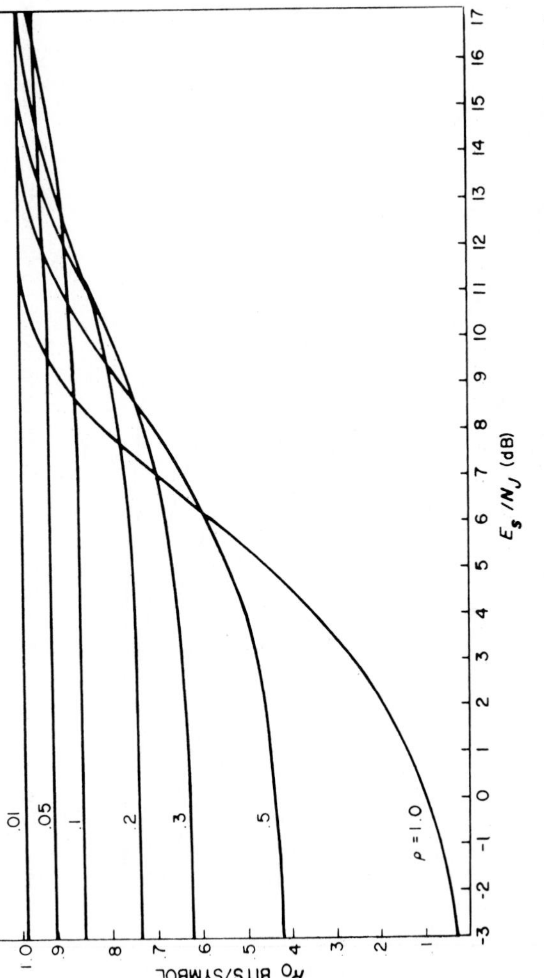

Figure 4.16a. Cutoff rate of FH/BFSK for soft decision with jammer state knowledge.

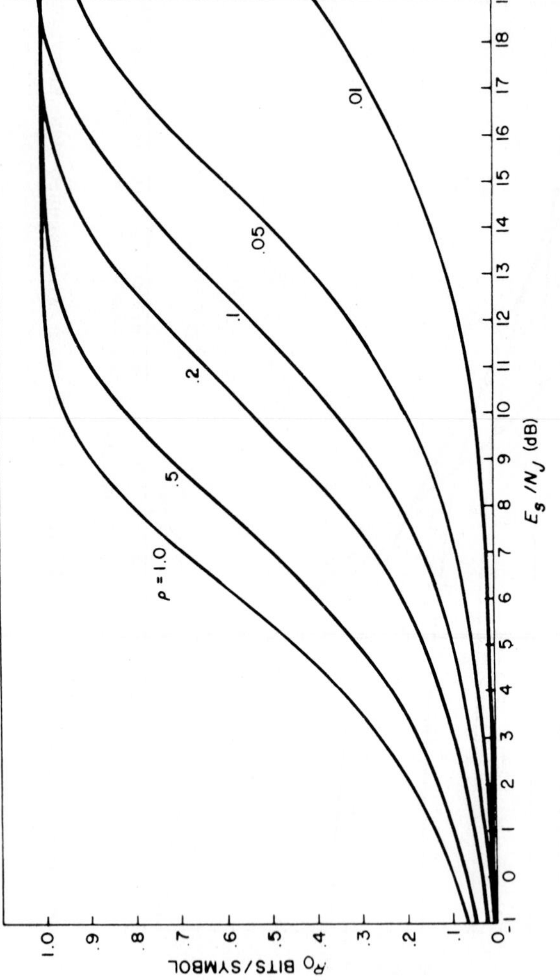

Figure 4.16b. Cutoff rate of FH/BFSK for soft decision with no jammer state knowledge.

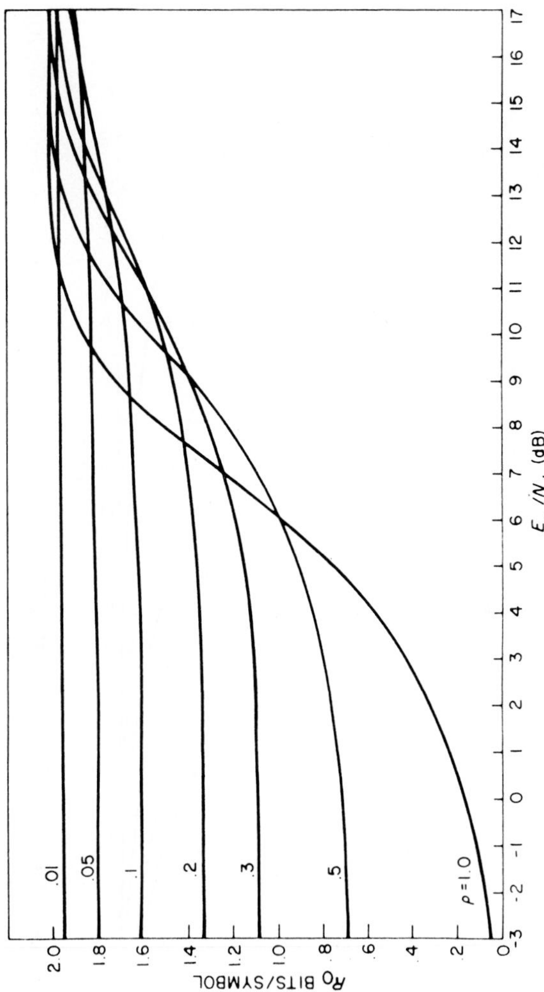

Figure 4.17a. Cutoff rate of FH/4FSK for soft decision with jammer state knowledge.

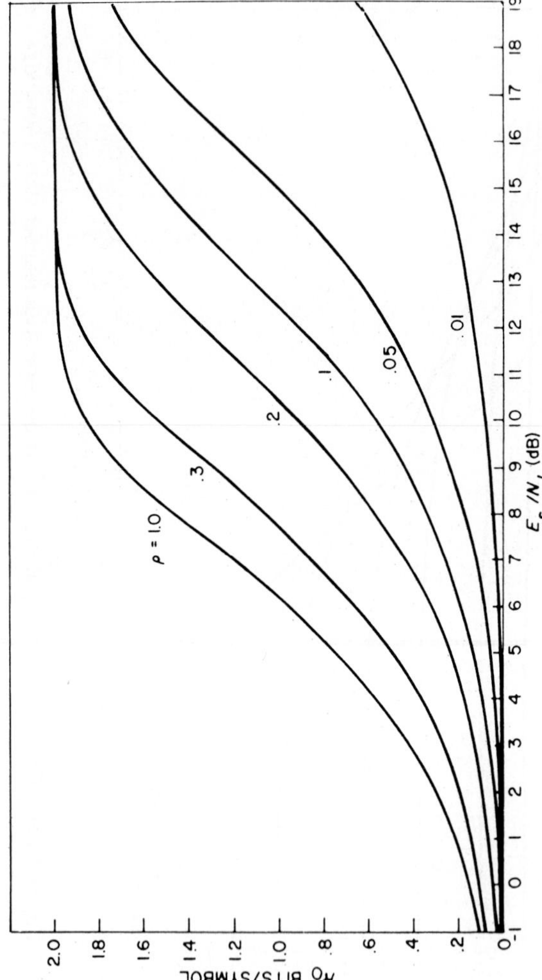

Figure 4.17b. Cutoff rate of FH/4FSK for soft decision with no jammer state knowledge.

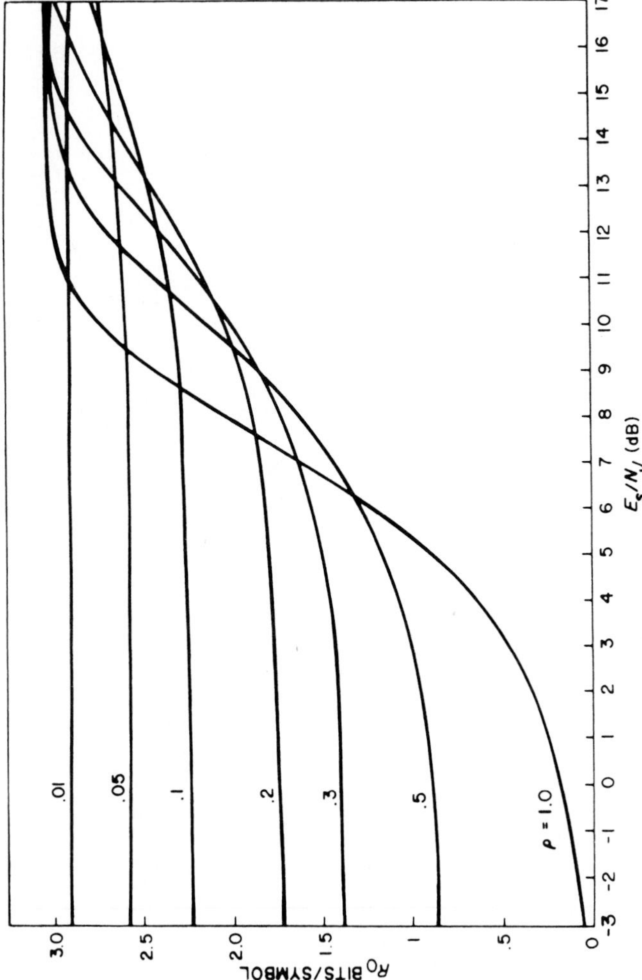

Figure 4.18a. Cutoff rate of FH/8FSK for soft decision with jammer state knowledge.

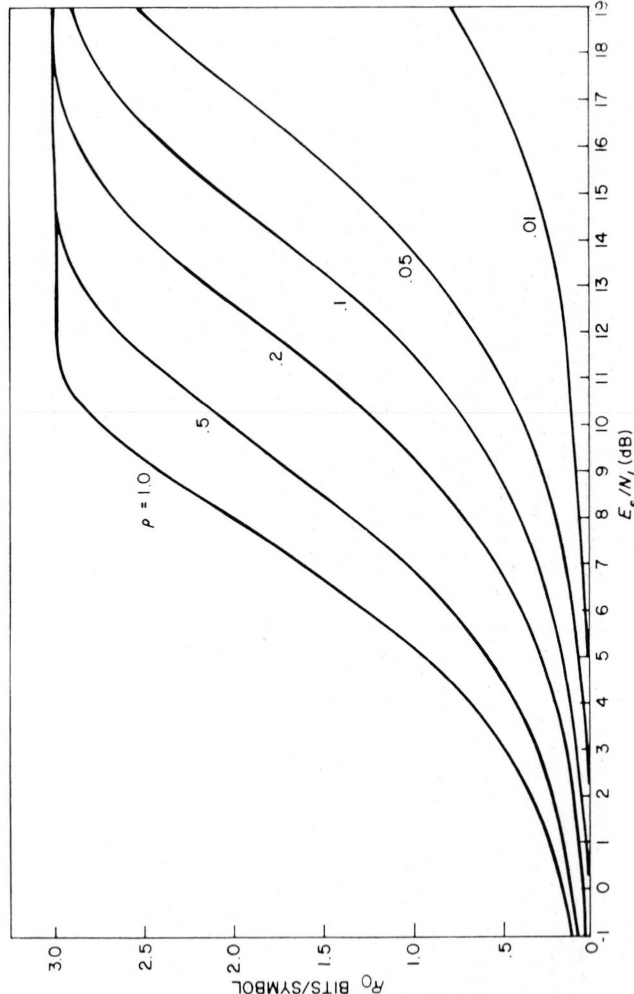

Figure 4.18b. Cutoff rate of FH/8FSK for soft decision with no jammer state knowledge.

probability? From the curve labelled D in Figure 4.12, the required E_b/N_0 for the additive white Gaussian noise channel is

$$E_b/N_0 = 7.5 \text{ dB}. \tag{4.95}$$

Here, since $R = 1$, $E_s = E_b$ so this is also the value of E_s/N_0, the coded symbol energy-to-noise ratio. Figure 4.14 shows that the cutoff rate is

$$R_0 = 1.8 \text{ bits/symbol}. \tag{4.96}$$

This is also shown in the $\rho = 1.0$ curve in Figure 4.18b since broadband noise jamming and the additive white Gaussian noise channels are the same. To achieve the same value of R_0 and, thus, the same 10^{-5} bit error probability for $\rho = 0.05$ we require

$$E_s/N_J = E_b/N_J = 16.8 \text{ dB}. \tag{4.97}$$

This is determined from Figure 4.18b. By repeating this procedure for several values of the bit error probability, the bit error probability curve for the Trumpis code with an additive white Gaussian noise channel can be translated into the corresponding bit error probability curve for a partial-band noise jammer with $\rho = .05$.

4.9 DIVERSITY FOR FH/MFSK

In the FH/MFSK example with partial-band noise jamming for each transmitted M-ary symbol, the channel output signal-to-noise ratio is low with probability ρ and high with probability $1 - \rho$. This is similar to a fading channel except that here there are only two discrete fade levels.[5] Since diversity techniques are useful in fading channels, one would expect that they would be useful against partial-band noise jamming as well. This is indeed true and will be shown next.

Define diversity of order m as the case where each M-ary symbol is transmitted m times over the channels described in the previous sections. Thus, if E_c is the energy for each transmission then each M-ary symbol requires a total energy of

$$E_s = mE_c. \tag{4.98}$$

The transmitted symbol for each single use of the channel is now referred to as a "chip." Thus, with diversity of order m, each M-ary symbol consists of the transmission of m chips.

Each transmitted chip consists of a frequency-hopped MFSK tone over the partial-band noise jammed channel described in the previous section. If symbol $x = i$ is to be transmitted, then the i-th MFSK tone is transmitted

[5] We take the high signal-to-noise ratio to be infinite for one level.

m times where each tone is independently hopped (ideal interleaving assumption is used for slower hop rates) resulting in independent jamming conditions for each chip or transmitted tone. The output corresponding to symbol $x = i$ consists of the m chip outputs

$$y_k = (e_{k1}, e_{k2}, \dots, e_{kM})$$
$$k = 1, 2, \dots, m \tag{4.99}$$

with the channel input $x_k = x$ for $k = 1, 2, \dots, m$ where e_{kj} is the detected energy at the j-th tone frequency during the k-th chip interval or k-th use of the channel. Thus, when symbols $x_k = x$, $k = 1, 2, \dots, m$ are transmitted the m channel outputs are

$$\mathbf{y} = (y_1, y_2, \dots, y_m). \tag{4.100}$$

For the conventional additive white Gaussian noise channel, the natural choice for the metric is

$$m(\mathbf{y}, \mathbf{x}) = e_{1x} + e_{2x} + \cdots + e_{mx} \tag{4.101}$$

for $x = 1, 2, \dots, M$. That is, the decision is based on the non-coherent combining (or sum) of the energies of each of the m chips corresponding to each of the MFSK tones. With the partial-band jammer and jammer state knowledge available a more general metric is

$$m(\mathbf{y}, \mathbf{x}; \mathbf{z}) = c(z_1)e_{1x} + c(z_2)e_{2x} + \cdots + c(z_m)e_{mx} \tag{4.102}$$

where

$$\mathbf{z} = (z_1, z_2, \dots, z_m) \tag{4.103}$$

represents the jammer state information for the m uses of the channel.

A new extended channel is obtained where each input symbol results in m uses of the channel considered in previous sections and where the energy per symbol is m times the energy per chip. To emphasize this we use the notation $D(\lambda; m)$ in place of our earlier parameter $D(\lambda)$. That is, define

$$\begin{aligned} D(\lambda; m) &= E\{e^{\lambda[m(\mathbf{y}, \hat{\mathbf{x}}; \mathbf{Z}) - m(\mathbf{y}, \mathbf{x}; \mathbf{Z})]}|x\}|_{\hat{x} \neq x} \\ &= E\left\{\prod_{j=1}^{m} e^{\lambda c(Z_j)[e_{j\hat{x}} - e_{jx}]}|x\right\}|_{\hat{x} \neq x} \\ &= [D(\lambda)]^m \end{aligned} \tag{4.104}$$

where $D(\lambda)$ is given by (4.91) where E_c replaces E_s. Next, let $c(0)$ be arbitrarily large, normalize $c(1) = 1/2$ and define

$$\begin{aligned} D(m) &= \min_{0 \le \lambda \le 1} D(\lambda; m) \\ &= D^m \end{aligned} \tag{4.105}$$

where D is given by (4.92) with E_c replacing E_s. If jammer state knowledge is not available, then choose $c(0) = c(1) = 1/2$ and D above is given by

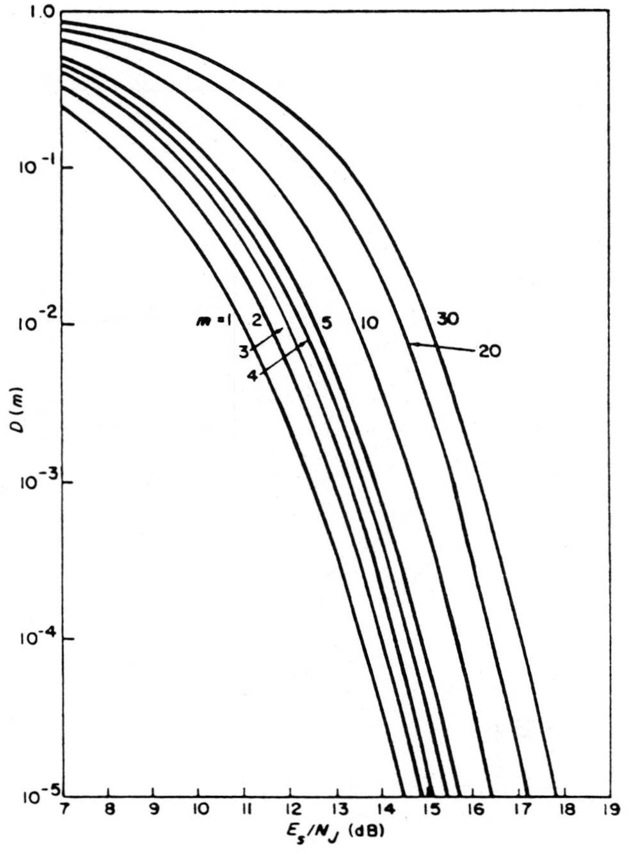

Figure 4.19a. $D(m)$ with jammer state knowledge: $\rho = 1.0$.

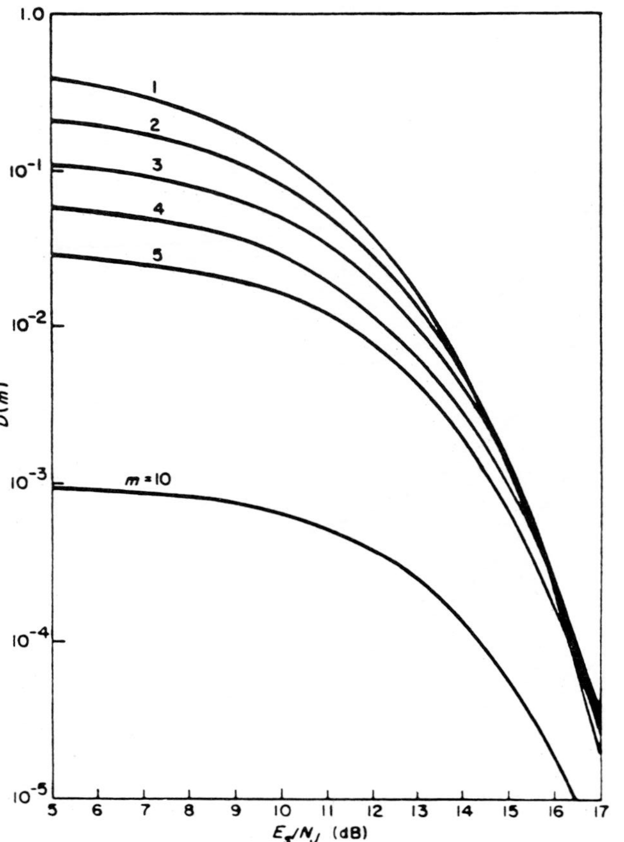

Figure 4.19b. $D(m)$ with jammer state knowledge: $\rho = .5$.

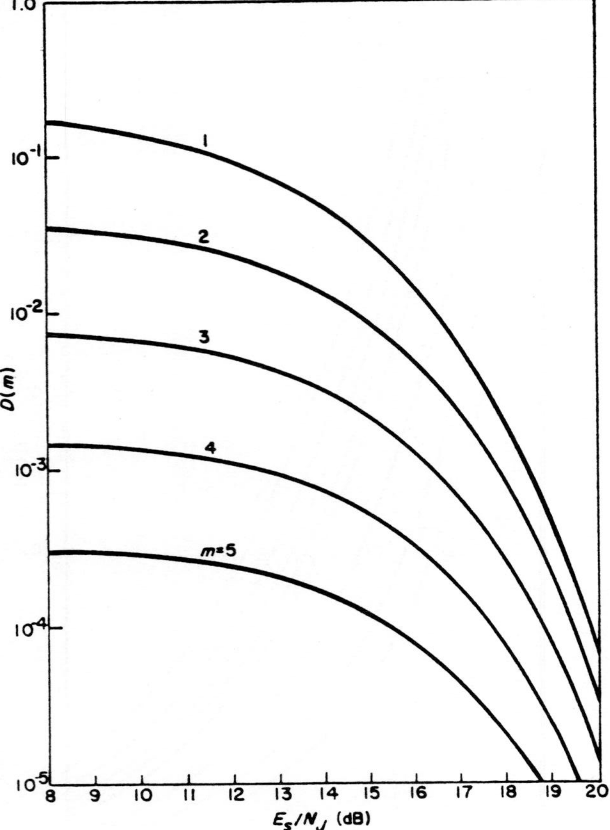

Figure 4.19c. $D(m)$ with jammer state knowledge: $\rho = .2$.

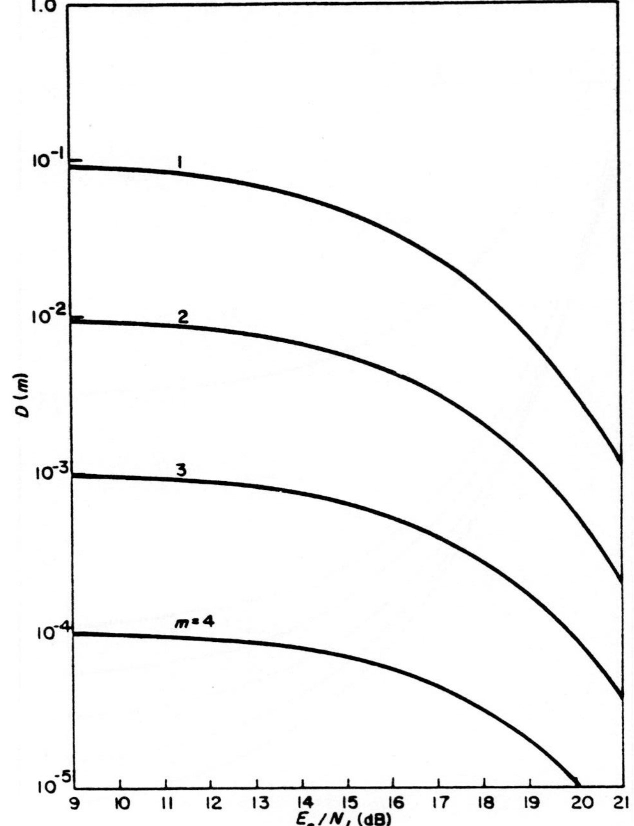

Figure 4.19d. $D(m)$ with jammer state knowledge: $\rho = .1$.

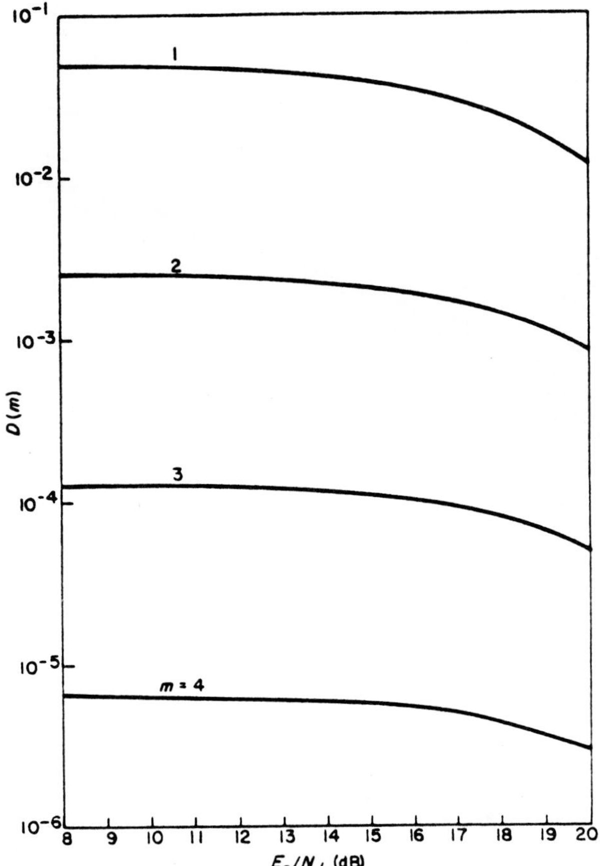

Figure 4.19e. $D(m)$ with jammer state knowledge: $\rho = 0.05$.

(4.93) again with E_c for E_s. Figure 4.19 shows $D(m)$ versus E_s/N_0 for the jammer state knowledge case while Figure 4.20 shows $D(m)$ when there is no jammer state knowledge. The special case of $m = 1$ corresponds to Figure 4.15.

With m diversity, the channel parameter D defined earlier is now replaced by $D(m)$ given in (4.105). The cutoff rate for this extended channel with diversity is denoted by $R_0(m)$ and given by

$$R_0(m) = \log_2 M - \log_2\{1 + (M-1)D(m)\} \text{ bits/symbol.} \tag{4.106}$$

Thus, if an M-ary alphabet code characterized by $G(\cdot)$ or $B(\cdot)$ is used, the coded bit error bound for this code with m diversity of the MFSK signals is given by

$$\begin{aligned} P_b &\le G(D(m)) \\ &= B(R_0(m)). \end{aligned} \tag{4.107}$$

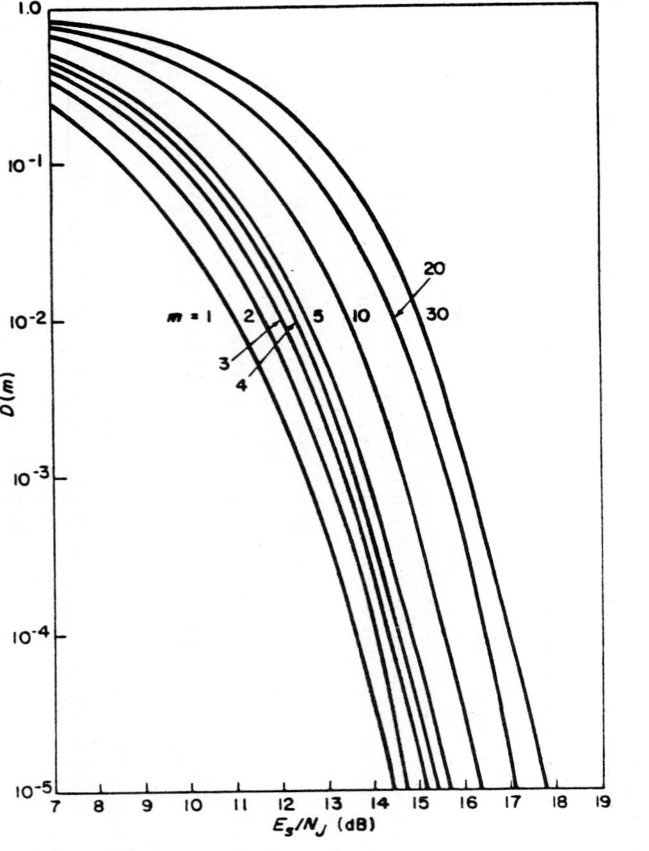

Figure 4.20a. $D(m)$ with no jammer state knowledge: $\rho = 1.0$.

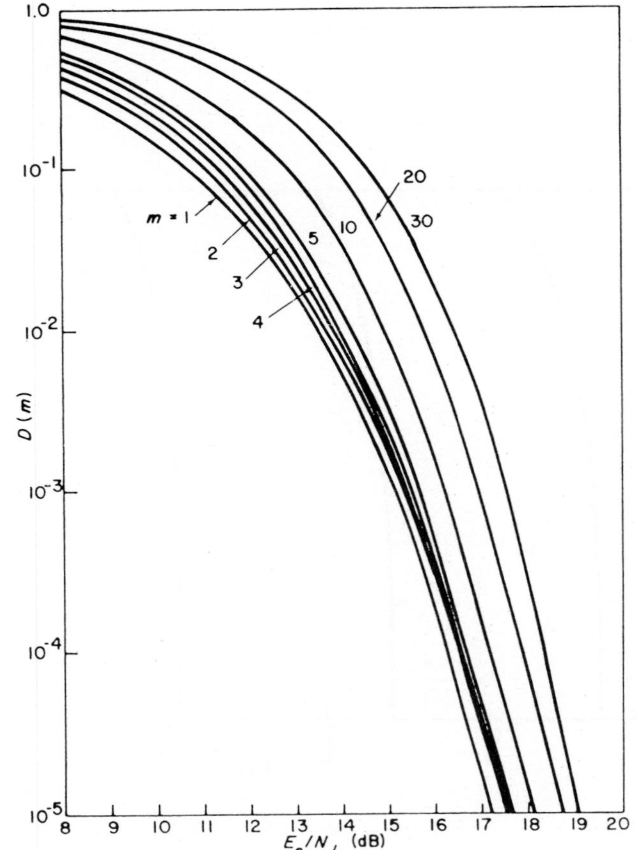

Figure 4.20b. $D(m)$ with no jammer state knowledge: $\rho = .5$.

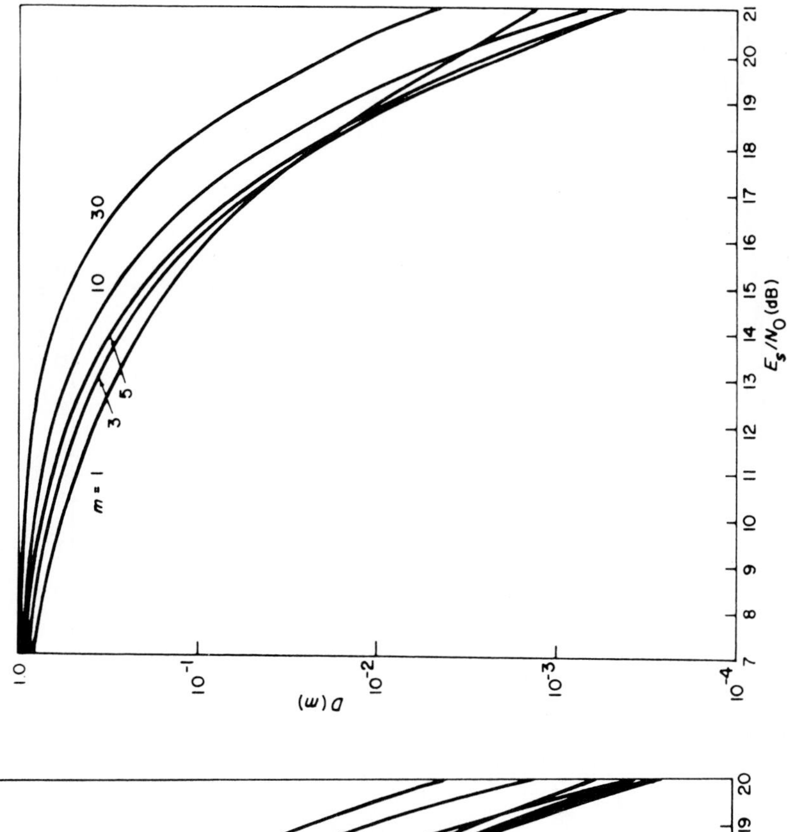

Figure 4.20d. $D(m)$ with no jammer state knowledge: $\rho = .1$.

Figure 4.20c. $D(m)$ with no jammer state knowledge: $\rho = .2$.

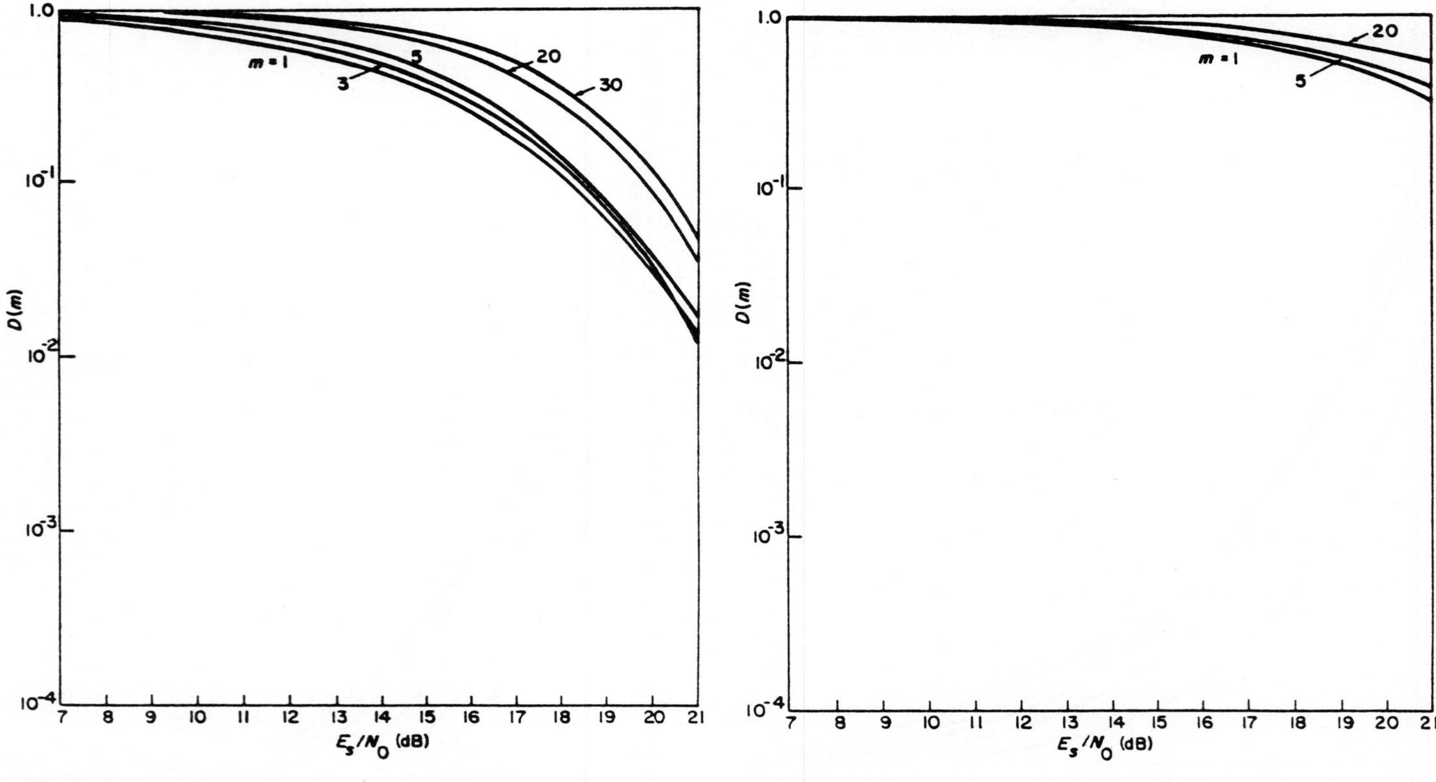

Figure 4.20e. $D(m)$ with no jammer state knowledge: $\rho = .05$.

Figure 4.20f. $D(m)$ with no jammer state knowledge: $\rho = .01$.

The special uncoded case results in the symbol error bound

$$P_s \leq \tfrac{1}{2}(M-1)D(m) \tag{4.108}$$

and the bit error bound

$$P_b \leq \tfrac{1}{4}MD(m) \tag{4.109}$$

where the energy per bit E_b is related to the symbol energy E_s and chip energy E_c by

$$E_s = KE_b = mE_c \tag{4.110}$$

when $M = 2^K$.

Note that diversity of order m can also be viewed as a special case of coding where the code rate is K/m bits per chip. This simple repeat m times code can be quite effective against partial-band jamming as seen in Figure 4.19 where jammer state knowledge is assumed.

4.10 CONCATENATION OF CODES

Although in principle it is possible to achieve arbitrarily small coded bit error probabilities as long as the data rate is less than the channel capacity or cutoff rate, practical applications are limited by the processing complexity and speed required in channel decoding. To achieve small error rates in practice, Forney [13] proposed using a concatenation of codes where two layers of coding are used. This is illustrated in Figure 4.21 where the coding channel is the same as shown enclosed in dotted lines in Figure 4.1. The encoder and decoder of Figure 4.1 now become the "inner" encoder and decoder in Figure 4.21. To create a memoryless super channel interleaving and deinterleaving of the symbols that are encoded and decoded by the inner code is often required.

4.10.1 Binary Super Channel

Typically the inputs to the inner encoder and the inner decoder outputs are binary symbols. With interleaving and deinterleaving, the resulting super channel becomes a memoryless binary symmetric channel (BSC) with crossover probability ε. Here ε is the coded bit error probability for the inner code with the coding channel. Previously examples were presented where this bit error probability has a bound,

$$\varepsilon \leq B(R_0) \tag{4.111}$$

where R_0 is determined by the coding channel (see Figure 4.1) and given as a function of E_c/N_J where now E_c is the energy of each coded symbol of the inner code. If we denote the energy per super channel binary symbol by E_s then

$$E_c = RE_s \tag{4.112}$$

where R is the inner code rate in bits per symbol.

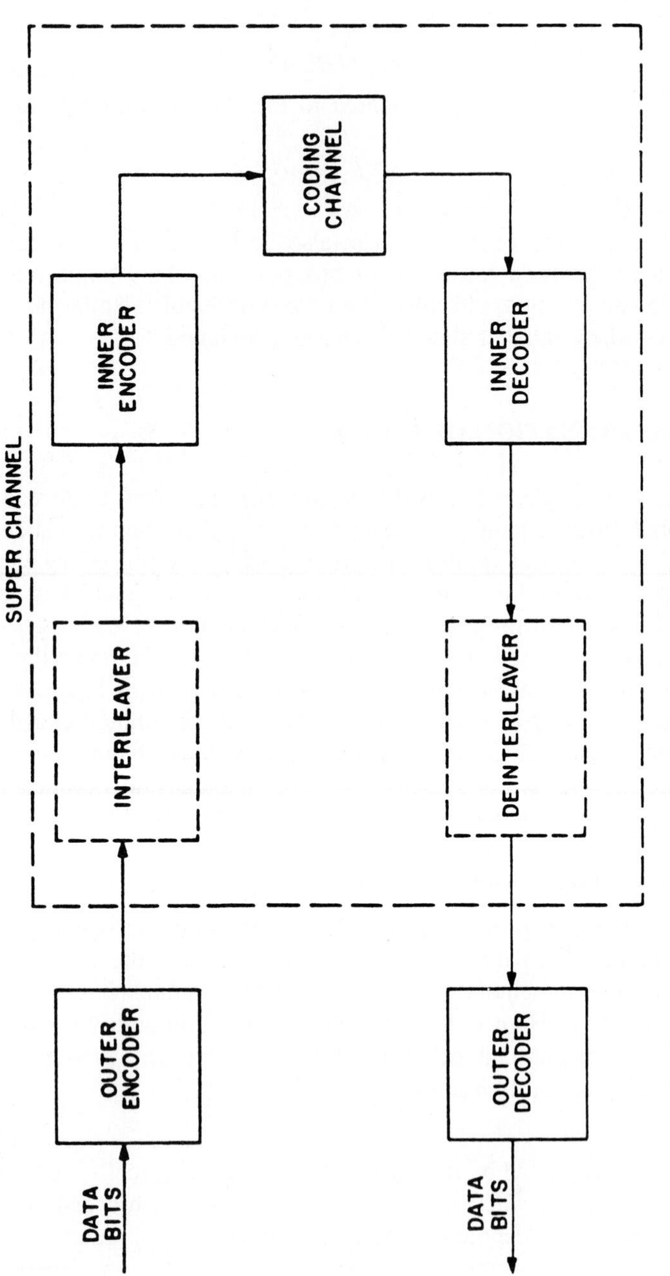

Figure 4.21. Concatenation of codes.

The BSC super channel such as sketched in Figure 4.21 has a parameter like D which is denoted as D_s. Thus,

$$D_s = \sqrt{4\varepsilon(1-\varepsilon)} \tag{4.113}$$

and the cutoff rate is

$$R_s = 1 - \log_2(1 + D_s) \tag{4.114}$$

which is measured in bits per super channel bit. Next, consider an outer code characterized by $B_s(\cdot)$ with the resulting final bit error bound

$$P_b \leq B_s(R_s). \tag{4.115}$$

Note that if R_s is the outer code rate then the overall rate measure in data bits per coding channel symbol is R_sR bits/coding channel symbol and the energy per bit is given by

$$\begin{aligned} E_b &= R_s^{-1}E_s \\ &= (R_sR)^{-1}E_c. \end{aligned} \tag{4.116}$$

As an example, suppose that with 8-ary FSK there is diversity of order $m = 5$. The diversity can be viewed as a special case of a repeat 5 times inner code with the bit error probability which has the bound (see (4.109))

$$\varepsilon \leq \tfrac{1}{4}MD(5) \tag{4.117}$$

where (see (4.105))

$$D(5) = D^5 \tag{4.118}$$

with D given by (4.92) or (4.93). Here the data rate is

$$R = \tfrac{3}{5} \text{ bits/coding channel 8-ary symbol.} \tag{4.119}$$

Suppose the outer code is the optimum rate $R = 1/2$, $K = 7$ binary convolutional code. Then the final bit error bound is (see (4.42))

$$P_b \leq \tfrac{1}{2}\left[36D_s^{10} + 211D_s^{12} + 1404D_s^{14} + 11633D_s^{16} + \cdots\right] \tag{4.120}$$

where

$$D_s = \sqrt{4\varepsilon(1-\varepsilon)} \tag{4.121}$$

with ε bounded by (4.117). Here the concatenation of codes gives an overall code rate of

$$\tfrac{1}{2}\cdot\tfrac{3}{5} = \tfrac{3}{10} \text{ bits/coded channel 8-ary symbol} \tag{4.122}$$

with

$$\frac{E_b}{N_0} = \left(\frac{10}{3}\right)\frac{E_c}{N_0} \tag{4.123}$$

where E_c is the energy per coded 8-ary FSK symbol in the coding channel.

4.10.2 M-ary Super Channel

In the previous example, with the inner code being the diversity or repeat 5 times code, the inputs to the inner encoder are 8-ary symbols. Each 8-ary symbol was taken to be equivalent to three bits each in deriving the bound on the BSC super channel crossover probability given by (4.117). The inputs and outputs of the inner encoder and decoder respectively could also be taken to be 8-ary symbols with the symbol error probability bounded by (4.108).

In general, we can have a super channel with M-ary input and output symbols where in all cases of interest these M-ary channels are symmetric with the super channel probabilities of (4.79) where y and x are now M-ary outputs and inputs respectively of the super channel and P_s is the symbol error probability of the inner code. In this case, parameter D_s is given by (4.81) and

$$R_s = \log_2 M - \log_2 [1 + (M-1) D_s]. \tag{4.124}$$

Thus, for $M = 4$ or $M = 8$ we can have outer codes found by Trumpis with bit error bounds given by (4.77) and (4.78) respectively where the super channel is characterized by D_s and R_s given by (4.81) and (4.124).

Another class of outer codes to consider are the Reed-Solomon codes which are discussed in the next section.

4.10.3 Reed-Solomon Outer Codes

Figure 4.22 shows the most popular form of concatenation of codes. Basically, this approach is to create a super channel as in Figure 4.21, where the super channel begins at the input to a convolutional encoder and ends at the Viterbi decoder output. The convolutional encoder with the Viterbi decoder that forms part of the super channel is the "inner code." The inner code reduces the error probabilities of the first coding channel (see Figure 4.1) which consists of the modulator, radio channel, and demodulator. This then forms a new coding channel for another "outer code" which can further reduce the error rate.

In general, it is difficult to analytically obtain the bit error statistics of the super channel for a specific convolutional code. In the following example, some simulation results assuming an ideal additive white Gaussian noise radio channel [14] are shown. These simulations show that burst lengths out of Viterbi decoders can be modeled by a geometric probability distribution.

Figures 4.23 and 4.24 show how decoded bit errors out of a Viterbi decoder tend to occur in bursts of various lengths with BPSK or QPSK modulation with three bit quantization. Generally, the decoded bits are error free for a while and then when a decoding bit error occurs the errors occur in a burst or string of length L_b with a probability distribution that is geometric [14],

$$\Pr\{L_b = m\} = p(1-p)^{m-1}; \qquad m = 1, 2, \ldots \tag{4.125}$$

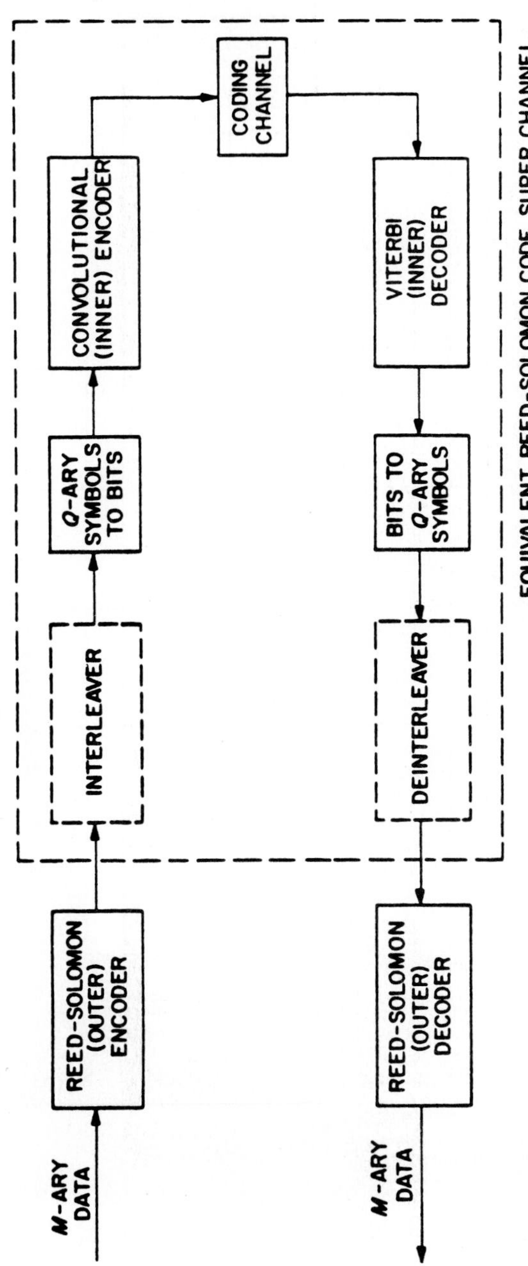

Figure 4.22. Reed-Solomon outer code.

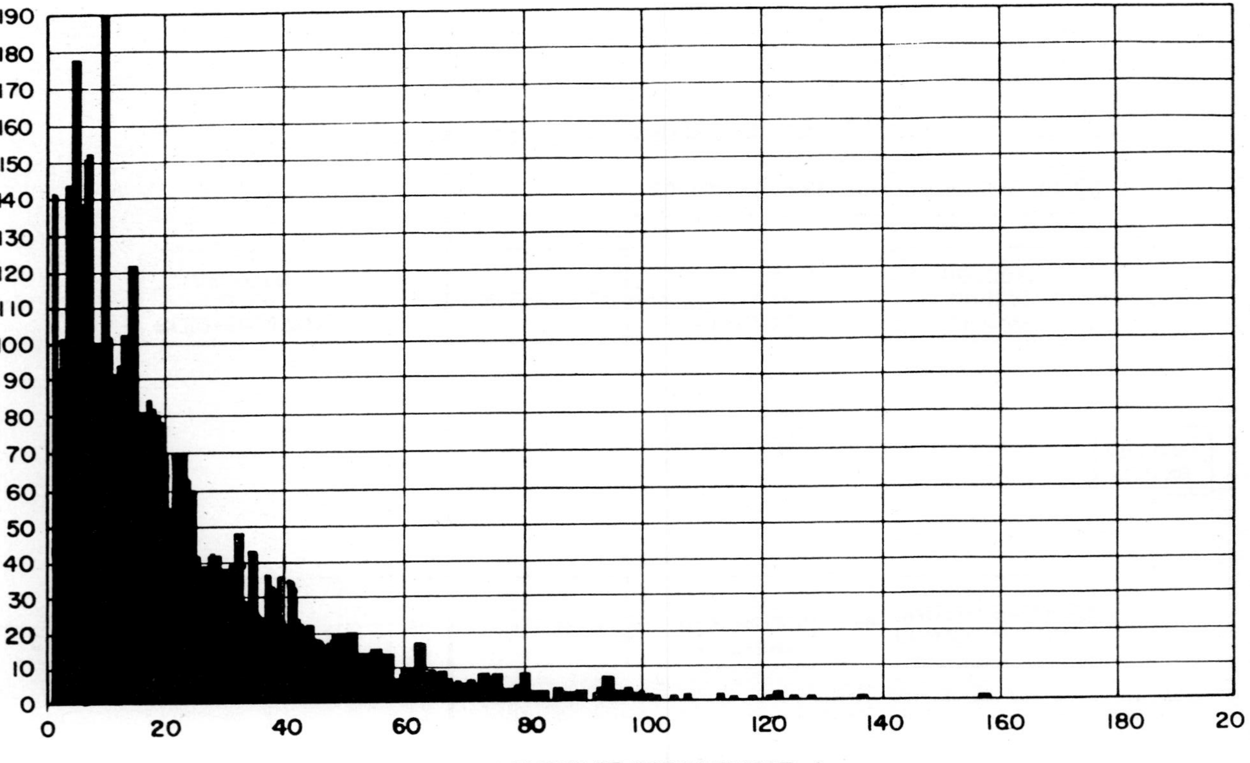

Figure 4.23. Histogram of burst lengths; Viterbi decoded constraint length 7, rate 1/2 convolutional code; $E_b/N_0 = 1.0$ dB (reprinted from [14]).

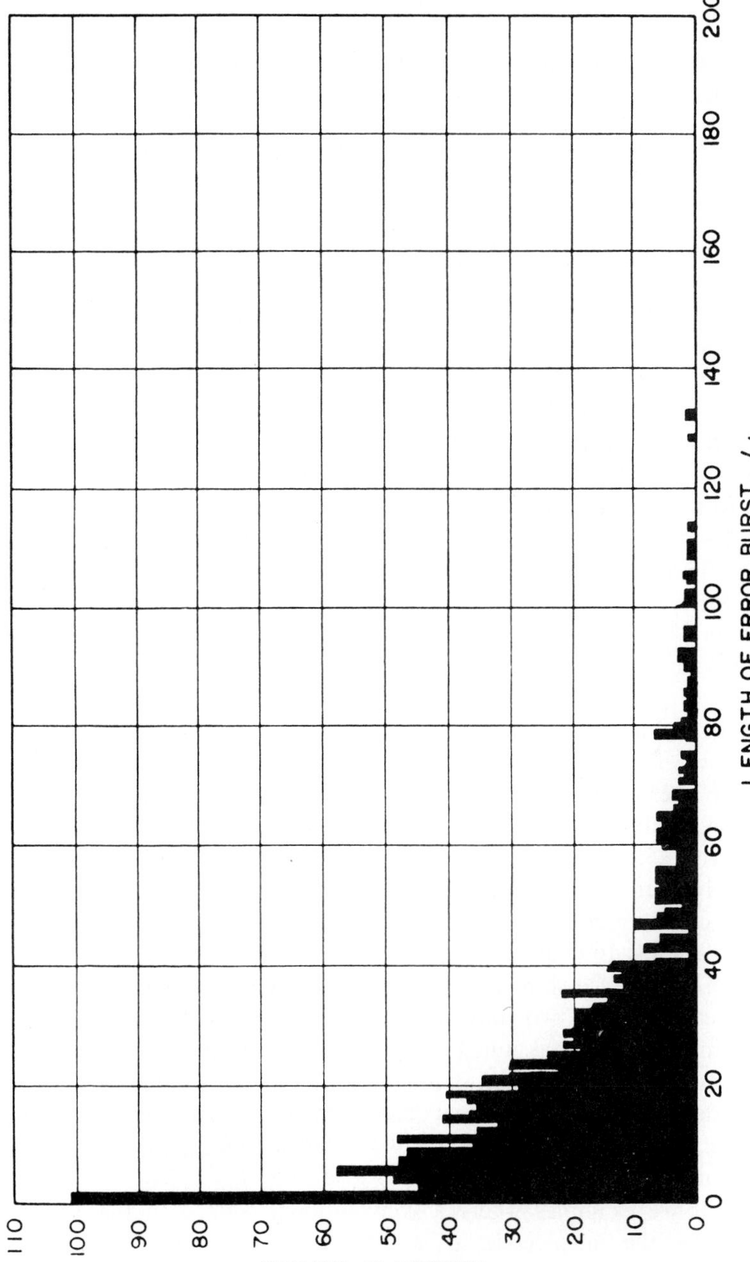

Figure 4.24. Histogram of burst lengths; Viterbi decoded constraint length 10, rate 1/3 convolutional code; $E_b/N_0 = 0.75$ dB (reprinted from [14]).

where

$$p = \frac{1}{\overline{L}_b} \tag{4.126}$$

and $\overline{L}_b$ is the average burst length in data bits. The waiting time, W, between bursts has the empirical distribution

$$\Pr\{W = n\} = q(1-q)^{n-K-1}, \qquad n = K+1, K+2, \ldots \tag{4.127}$$

where

$$q = \frac{1}{\overline{W} - K + 2}. \tag{4.128}$$

In (4.128), $\overline{W}$ is the average waiting time and K is again the convolutional code constraint length.

By choosing a Reed-Solomon (RS) outer code [15], we can take advantage of the bursty nature of the bit errors out of the inner code decoder. RS codes use higher order Q-ary symbols, where typically $Q = 2^m$ for some integer m. In most applications $m = 8$ ($Q = 256$). By taking $m = 8$ bits or 1 byte to form a single Q-ary symbol, a burst of errors in the 8 bits results in only one Q-ary symbol error which tends to reduce the impact of bit error bursts. In Figure 4.22 the conversion from Q-ary symbols to bits and back again for the coding channel of the RS outer code is shown. In addition, to avoid bursts of Q-ary symbol errors interleavers and deinterleavers may be used to provide a memoryless (non-bursty) Q-ary coding channel for the RS code.

As mentioned above, the most commonly employed RS code has $m = 8$ ($Q = 256$) where each symbol is an 8-bit byte and a block length of $N = Q - 1 = 255$ Q-ary symbols. To be able to correct up to $t = 16$ Q-ary symbols the number of data Q-ary symbols must be $K = Q - 1 - 2t = 223$ resulting in a (255, 223) block code using 256-ary symbols that can correct up to $t = 16$ symbols. This is equivalent to a binary (2040, 1784) block code[6] that can correct up to $t = 128$ bits in error as long as these bits are confined to at most 16 Q-ary symbols where $Q = 256$.

Figures 4.25 and 4.26 show the performance of the concatenation system with no interleaving for two convolutional inner codes with Viterbi decoding. Ideal interleaving is assumed in Figure 4.27. These curves show the currently most powerful (non-sequential) coding technique available. Sequential decoding of convolutional codes with large constraint lengths can also achieve similar performance but with the possibility of losing data caused by buffer overflows [1], [2].

For the above examples where a convolutional code with the Viterbi decoder forms the inner code, it is difficult to determine conditional

[6]Each 1784 data bits are encoded into a codeword of 2040 coded bits.

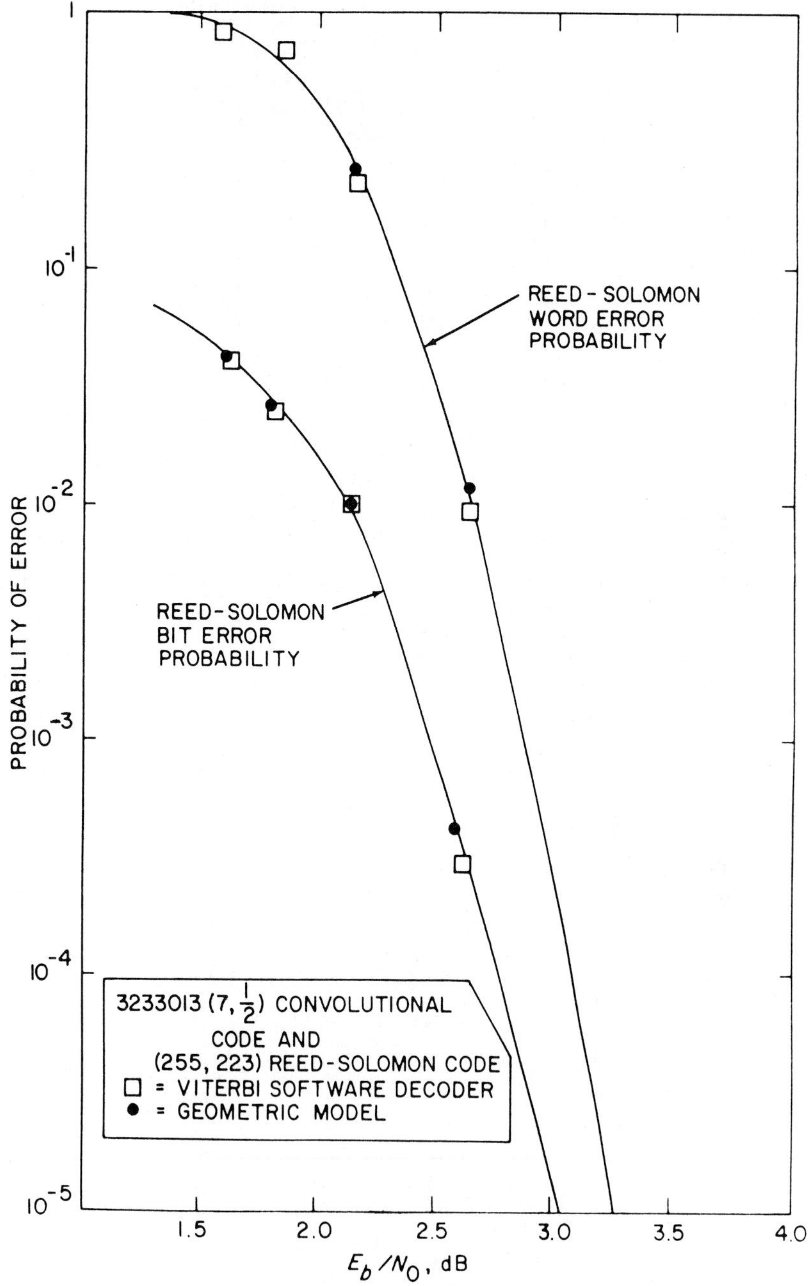

Figure 4.25. Non-interleaved performance statistics for concatenated coding scheme assuming no system losses; (7, 1/2) convolutional code (reprinted from [14]).

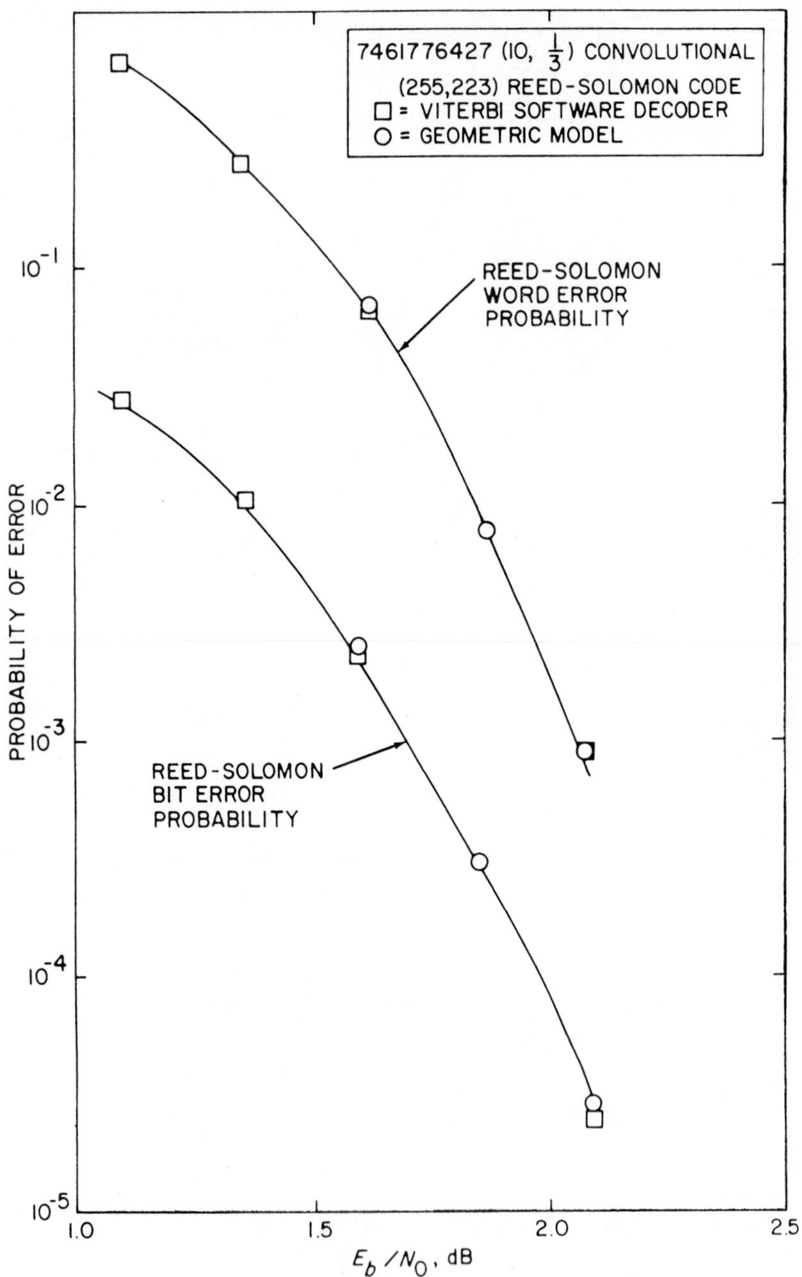

Figure 4.26. Non-interleaved performance statistics for concatenated coding scheme assuming no system losses; (10, 1/3) convolutional code (reprinted from [14]).

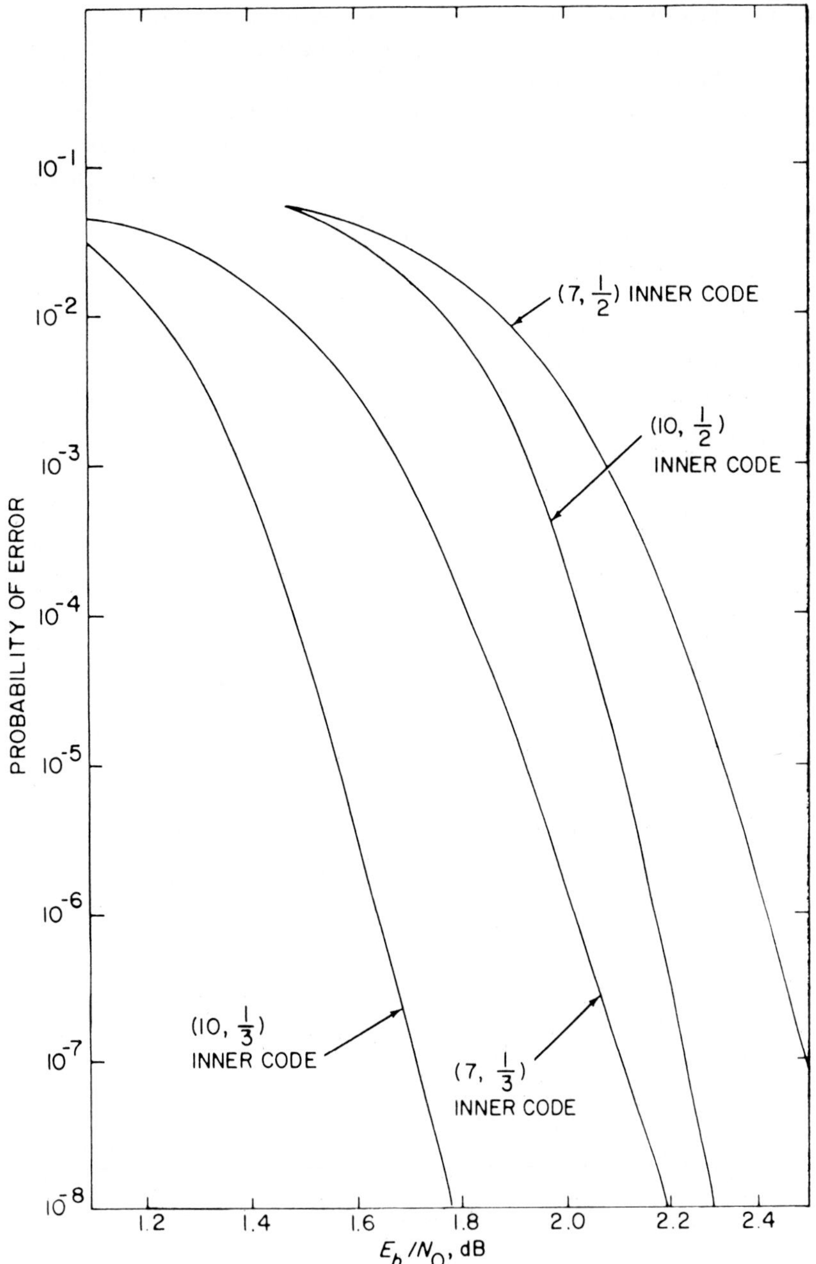

Figure 4.27. Comparison of concatenated channel decoder bit error rates for several convolutional inner codes and a Reed-Solomon (255, 223) outer code with ideal interleaving assuming no system losses (reprinted from [14]).

probabilities of the super channel formed. A natural approximation is to assume a symmetric Q-ary super channel characterized by the single parameter P_s, the symbol error probability. For this model the super channel has conditional probabilities given by (4.79) with parameter D_s given by (4.81) and R_s given by (4.124). This type of symmetric Q-ary super channel occurs for many of the spread-spectrum systems considered earlier. For example, in a symmetric M-ary channel of the type considered earlier, collect L symbols to form Q-ary symbols for the outer channel where

$$M^L = Q. \tag{4.129}$$

For the binary case with $M = 2$, the choice of $L = 8$ gives the $Q = 256$ alphabet for the RS code. Similarly $M = 4$ and $L = 4$ also yields $Q = 256$. For these Q-ary symmetric channels the decoded bit error probability of the RS code P_b is directly a function of the symbol error probability of the inner code denoted P_s. That is,

$$P_b = F(P_s). \tag{4.130}$$

In Appendix 4C, a table showing this relationship for various RS codes is presented.

4.11 SUMMARY OF BIT ERROR BOUNDS

We conclude this chaper with tables of some basic expressions for bit error bounds of direct sequence spread coherent BPSK systems with pulse jamming and frequency-hopped spread non-coherent MFSK systems with partial-band noise jamming. These expressions are based on the discussion in this chapter. There are many other detector types such as detectors with various quantizations, clipping, and rank order lists which have not been included here. The basic analysis approach presented in this chapter, however, can be applied to derive easy to evaluate bit error bounds for these more complex detectors. Some of these will be discussed in Part 2, Chapters 1 and 2.

Recall that regardless of the use of coding the energy per bit-to-jammer noise ratio, E_b/N_J, is defined by (4.3). With time-continuous jamming of DS/BPSK systems, the bit error bound has the same form as for the additive white Gaussian noise channel. Similarly, with broadband noise jamming of FH/MFSK the bit error bound has the same form as for the additive white Gaussian noise channel.

4.11.1 DS/BPSK with Pulse Jamming

Table 4.1 presents the various expressions for the channel parameter D for DS/BPSK systems with pulse jamming. Here ρ is the fraction of time the system is being jammed where continuous jamming is the special case of $\rho = 1$.

Table 4.1.
DS/BPSK with pulse jamming

	Jammer State Information		Metric		$P_b \le G(D)$; $E_c = RE_b$
	Yes	No	Hard	Soft	$R_0 = 1 - \log_2(1 + D)$ bits/symbol
Continuous Jamming	X	X		X	$D = \exp(-E_c/N_J)$
	X	X	X		$D = \sqrt{4\varepsilon(1-\varepsilon)}$; $\varepsilon = Q\left(\sqrt{2E_c/N_J}\right)$
Pulse Jamming	X			X	$D = \rho \exp(-\rho E_c/N_J)$
	X		X		$D = \rho\sqrt{4\varepsilon(1-\varepsilon)}$; $\varepsilon = Q\left(\sqrt{2\rho E_c/N_J}\right)$
		X		X	$D = \min_{\lambda \ge 0}\{\exp(-2\lambda E_c)[\rho \exp(\lambda^2 E_c N_J/\rho) + (1-\rho)]\}$
		X	X		$D = \sqrt{4\varepsilon(1-\varepsilon)}$; $\varepsilon = \rho Q\left(\sqrt{2\rho E_c/N_J}\right)$

For soft decision detectors the metric has the form

$$m(y, x; z) = c(z)yx \tag{4.131}$$

while hard decision detectors have the metric

$$m(y, x; z) = \begin{cases} c(z), & y = x \\ 0, & y \neq x. \end{cases} \tag{4.132}$$

When there is jamming state information

$$c(0) \gg c(1). \tag{4.133}$$

That is, the unjammed metric values are given much more weight than the jammed metric values. With no jammer state information

$$c(0) = c(1). \tag{4.134}$$

With continuous jamming ($\rho = 1$), the jammer always exists and all metrics are weighted the same.

4.11.2 FH / MFSK with Partial-Band Noise Jamming

Table 4.2 gives the expressions for parameter D for FH/MFSK systems with partial-band noise jamming where ρ is the fraction of the spread-spectrum band being jammed. Here $\rho = 1$ corresponds to broadband jamming.

The soft decision metric is

$$m(y, x; z) = c(z)e_x \tag{4.135}$$

while the hard decision metric is

$$m(y, x; z) = \begin{cases} c(z), & y = x \\ 0, & y \neq x. \end{cases} \tag{4.136}$$

As with DS/BPSK $c(z)$ has the form (4.133) when there is jammer state

Table 4.2.
FH/MFSK with partial-band noise jamming

	Jammer State Information		Metric		$P_b \le G(D^m)$; $E_c = RE_b/m$ $R_0 = \log_2 M - \log_2\{1 + (M-1)D^m\}$ bits/symbol
	Yes	No	Hard	Soft	
Broad-band	X	X		X	$D = \min\limits_{0\le\lambda\le1}\left\{\frac{1}{1-\lambda^2}\exp\left[-\frac{\lambda}{1+\lambda}\left(\frac{E_c}{N_J}\right)\right]\right\}$
	X	X	X		$D = \sqrt{\frac{4\varepsilon(1-\varepsilon)}{M-1}} + \left(\frac{M-2}{M-1}\right)\varepsilon;\ \varepsilon = \sum_{l=1}^{M-1}\binom{M-1}{l}\frac{(-1)^{l+1}}{l+1}\exp\left[-\frac{l}{l+1}\left(\frac{E_c}{N_J}\right)\right]$
Partial-band	X			X	$D = \min\limits_{0\le\lambda\le1}\left\{\frac{\rho}{1-\lambda^2}\exp\left[-\frac{\lambda}{1+\lambda}\rho\left(\frac{E_c}{N_J}\right)\right]\right\}$
	X		X		$D = \rho\left[\sqrt{\frac{4\varepsilon(1-\varepsilon)}{M-1}} + \left(\frac{M-2}{M-1}\right)\varepsilon\right];\ \varepsilon = \sum_{l=1}^{M-1}\binom{M-1}{l}\frac{(-1)^{l+1}}{l+1}\exp\left[-\frac{l}{l+1}\rho\left(\frac{E_c}{N_J}\right)\right]$
		X		X	$D = \min\limits_{0\le\lambda\le1}\left\{\frac{\rho}{1-\lambda^2}\exp\left[-\frac{\lambda}{1+\lambda}\rho\left(\frac{E_c}{N_J}\right)\right] + (1-\rho)\exp\left[-\lambda\rho\left(\frac{E_c}{N_J}\right)\right]\right\}$
		X	X		$D = \sqrt{\frac{4\varepsilon(1-\varepsilon)}{M-1}} + \left(\frac{M-2}{M-1}\right)\varepsilon;\ \varepsilon = \rho\sum_{l=1}^{M-1}\binom{M-1}{l}\frac{(-1)^{l+1}}{l+1}\exp\left[-\frac{l}{l+1}\rho\left(\frac{E_c}{N_J}\right)\right]$

Table 4.3.
Code functions.

	M	R	$P_b \le G(D^m)$; $E_c = RE_b/m$
Uncoded	2	1	$G(X) = \frac{1}{2}X$
	M	$\log_2 M$	$G(X) = \frac{1}{4}MX$
$K = 7$ Convolutional Codes	2	$\frac{1}{2}$	$G(X) = \frac{1}{2}[36X^{10} + 211X^{12} + 1404X^{14} + 11633X^{16} + \cdots]$
	2	$\frac{1}{3}$	$G(X) = \frac{1}{2}[7X^{15} + 8X^{16} + 22X^{17} + 44X^{18} + \cdots]$
	4	1	$G(X) = \frac{1}{2}[7X^{7} + 39X^{8} + 104X^{9} + 352X^{10} + 1187X^{11} + \cdots]$
	8	1	$G(X) = \frac{1}{2}[X^{7} + 4X^{8} + 8X^{9} + 49X^{10} + 92X^{11} + \cdots]$

knowledge and (4.134) when there is no jammer state knowledge. Table 4.2 also shows the diversity parameter m.

4.11.3 Coding Functions

Table 4.3 shows some typical coding functions which depend only on the alphabet size M. The $M = 2$ cases apply to both DS/BPSK and FH/BFSK. Diversity $m > 1$ is used only for the FH/MFSK systems. Examples of other codes will be given in Part 2, Chapter 2.

4.12 REFERENCES

[1] R. G. Gallager, *Information Theory and Reliable Communication*, New York: John Wiley, 1968.

[2] A. J. Viterbi and J. K. Omura, *Principles of Digital Communication and Coding*, New York: McGraw-Hill, 1979.

[3] G. C. Clark, Jr., and J. B. Cain, *Error-Correction Coding for Digital Communications*, New York: Plenum Press, 1981.

[4] J. M. Wozencraft and R. S. Kennedy, "Modulation and demodulation for probabilistic coding," *IEEE Trans. Inform. Theory*, IT-12, July 1966, pp. 291–297.

[5] J. L. Massey, "Coding and modulation in digital communications," *Proceedings International Zurich Seminar on Digital Communications*, Switzerland, March 12–15, 1974.

[6] A. J. Viterbi, "Spread-spectrum communications—myths and realities," *IEEE Commun. Soc. Mag.*, vol. 17, no. 3, pp. 11–18, May 1979.

[7] L. Biederman, J. K. Omura, and P. C. Jain, "Decoding with approximate channel statistics for bandlimited nonlinear satellite channels," *IEEE Trans. Inform. Theory*, IT-27, pp. 697–708, November 1981.

[8] I. M. Jacobs, "Probability of error bounds for binary transmission on the slowly fading Rician channel," *IEEE Trans. Inform. Theory*, IT-12, pp. 431–441, October 1966.

[9] M. E. Hellman and J. Raviv, "Probability of error, equivocation, and the Chernoff bound," *IEEE Trans. Inform. Theory*, IT-16, pp. 368–372, July 1970.

[10] J. P. Odenwalder, *Optimum Decoding of Convolutional Codes*, Doctoral Disser-

tation, School of Engineering and Applied Science, University of California, Los Angeles, 1970, p. 64.

[11] W. C. Lindsey and M. K. Simon, *Telecommunication Systems Engineering*, Englewood Cliffs, NJ: Prentice-Hall, 1973.

[12] B. Trumpis, *Convolutional Codes for M-ary Channels*, Doctoral Dissertation, School of Engineering and Applied Science, University of California, Los Angeles, 1975.

[13] G. D. Forney, Jr., *Concatenated Codes*, Cambridge, MA: M.I.T. Press, 1966.

[14] L. J. Deutsch, and R. L. Miller, "Burst statistics of Viterbi decoding," TDA Progress Report 42-64, Jet Propulsion Laboratory, Pasadena, California, pp. 187–193, May-June 1981.

[15] R. Blahut, *Theory and Practice of Error Control Codes*, Reading, MA: Addison-Wesley, 1983.

[16] E. R. Berlekamp, "The technology of error-correcting codes," *Proc. IEEE*, vol. 68, pp. 564–593, May 1980.

APPENDIX 4A. CHERNOFF BOUND

Figure 4A.1 shows two functions

$$u(t) = \begin{cases} 1, & t \geq 0 \\ 0, & t < 0 \end{cases} \tag{4A.1}$$

and

$$e_\lambda(t) = e^{\lambda t} \qquad \text{all } t. \tag{4A.2}$$

For any $\lambda \geq 0$ clearly

$$u(t) \leq e_\lambda(t). \tag{4A.3}$$

Next consider a random variable X with probability density function $p_X(x)$ for all x. Then

$$\begin{aligned} \Pr\{X \geq 0\} &= \int_0^\infty p_X(t)\,dt \\ &= \int_{-\infty}^\infty u(t)\,p_X(t)\,dt \\ &\leq \int_{-\infty}^\infty e_\lambda(t)\,p_X(t)\,dt \\ &= E\{e^{\lambda X}\}. \end{aligned} \tag{4A.4}$$

Hence,

$$\Pr\{X \geq 0\} \leq E\{e^{\lambda X}\} \qquad \text{for any } \lambda \geq 0. \tag{4A.5}$$

This is the Chernoff bound [1].

In the application of the Chernoff bound in this chapter, the random variable X has the form

$$X = \sum_{n=1}^{N} \left[m(y_n, \hat{x}_n; z_n) - m(y_n, x_n; z_n) \right] \tag{4A.6}$$

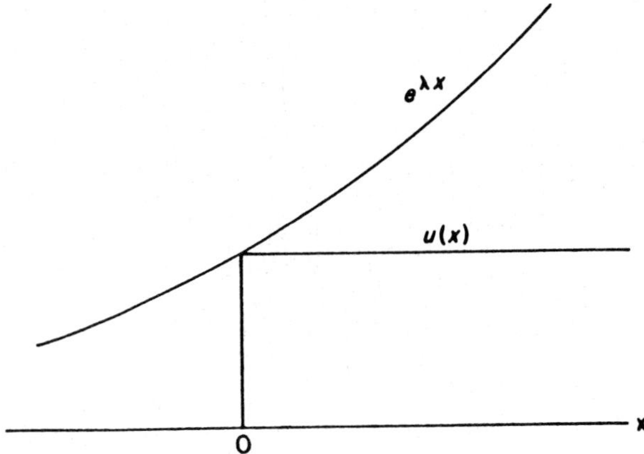

Figure 4A.1. Comparing $u(x)$ and $e^{\lambda x}$.

where the terms in this sum are independent of each other. Thus,

$$\Pr\left\{\sum_{n=1}^{N} m(y_n, \hat{x}_n; z_n) \geq \sum_{n=1}^{N} m(y_n, x_n; z_n)\right\}$$

$$= \Pr\left\{\sum_{n=1}^{N} [m(y_n, \hat{x}_n; z_n) - m(y_n, x_n; z_n)] \geq 0\right\}$$

$$\leq E\left\{\exp\left[\lambda \sum_{n=1}^{N} [m(y_n, \hat{x}_n; z_n) - m(y_n, x_n; z_n)]\right]\right\}$$

$$= \prod_{n=1}^{N} E\{e^{\lambda[m(y_n, \hat{x}_n; z_n) - m(y_n, x_n; z_n)]}\}. \tag{4A.7}$$

This is used as a bound for the pairwise error probability $P(\mathbf{x} \to \hat{\mathbf{x}})$ in Section 4.2.

APPENDIX 4B. FACTOR OF ONE-HALF IN ERROR BOUNDS

Based on the results of Jacobs [8] and Hellman and Raviv [9], general error bounds on the average error probability for cases where there are two hypotheses are derived. Special cases of these bounds result in a factor of one-half times the usual Bhattacharyya bound and the Chernoff bound.

Let Z be a continuous random variable that can have one of two probability densities:

$$\begin{aligned} &H_1: f_1(z), \quad -\infty < z < \infty \\ &H_2: f_2(z), \quad -\infty < z < \infty \end{aligned} \tag{4B.1}$$

where *a priori* probabilities for these two hypotheses are denoted

$$\pi_1 = \Pr\{H_1\} \text{ and } \pi_2 = \Pr\{H_2\}.$$

An arbitrary deterministic decision rule is characterized by the following decision function: given an observed value z of the random variable Z, let

$$u(z) = \begin{cases} 1, & \text{decide } H_1 \\ 0, & \text{decide } H_2. \end{cases} \tag{4B.2}$$

In terms of this decision function define conditional error probabilities

$$\begin{aligned} P_{E_1} &= \Pr\{\text{decide } H_2 | H_1\} \\ &= \int_{-\infty}^{\infty} [1 - u(z)]\, f_1(z)\, dz \end{aligned} \tag{4B.3}$$

and

$$\begin{aligned} P_{E_2} &= \Pr\{\text{decide } H_1 | H_2\} \\ &= \int_{-\infty}^{\infty} u(z) f_2(z)\, dz. \end{aligned} \tag{4B.4}$$

The average error probability is

$$\begin{aligned} P_E &= \pi_1 P_{E_1} + \pi_2 P_{E_2} \\ &= \int_{-\infty}^{\infty} \{\pi_1 f_1(z)[1 - u(z)] + \pi_2 f_2(z) u(z)\}\, dz. \end{aligned} \tag{4B.5}$$

Often error probabilities are difficult to evaluate and so easily computed bounds are sometimes used. In the following Bhattacharyya and Chernoff bounds for various decision rules are examined.

Maximum *A Posteriori* (MAP)

The decision rule that minimizes P_E is the MAP rule,

$$u(z) = \begin{cases} 1, & \pi_1 f_1(z) \geq \pi_2 f_2(z) \\ 0, & \pi_1 f_1(z) < \pi_2 f_2(z) \end{cases} \tag{4B.6}$$

which satisfies the inequalities

$$u(z) \leq \left[\frac{\pi_1 f_1(z)}{\pi_2 f_2(z)}\right]^{\alpha} \tag{4B.7}$$

$$1 - u(z) \leq \left[\frac{\pi_2 f_2(z)}{\pi_1 f_1(z)}\right]^{\beta} \tag{4B.8}$$

for any $\alpha \geq 0$, $\beta \geq 0$. These inequalities are typically used to derive the bounds

$$P_{E_1} \leq \int_{-\infty}^{\infty} \left[\frac{\pi_2 f_2(z)}{\pi_1 f_1(z)}\right]^{\beta} f_1(z)\, dz$$

$$= \left(\frac{\pi_2}{\pi_1}\right)^{\beta} \int_{-\infty}^{\infty} f_1(z)^{1-\beta} f_2(z)^{\beta}\, dz \tag{4B.9}$$

and

$$P_{E_2} \leq \int_{-\infty}^{\infty} \left[\frac{\pi_1 f_1(z)}{\pi_2 f_2(z)}\right]^{\alpha} f_2(z)\, dz$$

$$= \left(\frac{\pi_1}{\pi_2}\right)^{\alpha} \int_{-\infty}^{\infty} f_1(z)^{\alpha} f_2(z)^{1-\alpha}\, dz. \tag{4B.10}$$

Next, define the function

$$B(\alpha) = \int_{-\infty}^{\infty} f_1(z)^{\alpha} f_2(z)^{1-\alpha}\, dz. \tag{4B.11}$$

Then an upper bound on the average error probability is

$$P_E \leq \pi_1^{1-\beta} \pi_2^{\beta} B(1-\beta) + \pi_1^{\alpha} \pi_2^{1-\alpha} B(\alpha) \tag{4B.12}$$

for any $\alpha \geq 0$, $\beta \geq 0$ where in general α and β are chosen to minimize these bounds. The special case where

$$\alpha = \beta = \tfrac{1}{2}$$

results in the Bhattacharyya bound [2]

$$P_E \leq 2\sqrt{\pi_1 \pi_2}\, B\left(\tfrac{1}{2}\right)$$

$$\leq B\left(\tfrac{1}{2}\right)$$

$$= \int_{-\infty}^{\infty} \sqrt{f_1(z) f_2(z)}\, dz \tag{4B.13}$$

since

$$\sqrt{\pi_1 \pi_2} \leq \tfrac{1}{2}. \tag{4B.14}$$

In most cases of interest such as when

$$f_1(z) = f_2(-z) \text{ for all } z \tag{4B.15}$$

$\alpha = 1/2$ minimizes the function $B(\alpha)$. When $f_1(z)$ and $f_2(z)$ are conditional probabilities derived from a communication channel model, this is usually the case.

Let us now re-examine the general form for the average error probability using the MAP decision rule. Note that

$$P_E = \int_{-\infty}^{\infty} \{\pi_1 f_1(z)[1 - u(z)] + \pi_2 f_2(z) u(z)\}\, dz$$
$$= \int_{-\infty}^{\infty} \min\{\pi_1 f_1(z), \pi_2 f_2(z)\}\, dz. \tag{4B.16}$$

Following Hellman and Raviv [9], for any $a \geq 0$, $b \geq 0$ and $0 \leq \alpha \leq 1$

$$\min\{a, b\} \leq a^{\alpha} b^{1-\alpha}. \tag{4B.17}$$

This yields the upper bound on the average error probability

$$P_E \leq \int_{-\infty}^{\infty} [\pi_1 f_1(z)]^{\alpha} [\pi_2 f_2(z)]^{1-\alpha}\, dz$$
$$= \pi_1^{\alpha} \pi_2^{1-\alpha} B(\alpha). \tag{4B.18}$$

If the minimizing choice of α is in the unit interval [0, 1] then this bound is always a factor of one-half smaller than the bound given in (4B.12). In particular, for the Bhattacharyya bound where $\alpha = 1/2$, this bound (Hellman and Raviv) shows that there is always a factor of one-half,

$$P_E \leq \tfrac{1}{2} \int_{-\infty}^{\infty} \sqrt{f_1(z) f_2(z)}\, dz. \tag{4B.19}$$

Thus, the commonly used Bhattacharyya bound (often used in transfer function bit error bounds for convolutional codes) can be tightened by a factor of one-half.

Maximum Likelihood (ML)

The ML decision rule,

$$u(z) = \begin{cases} 1, & f_1(z) \geq f_2(z) \\ 0, & f_1(z) < f_2(z) \end{cases} \tag{4B.20}$$

tends to keep both conditional probabilities closer in value but only minimizes P_E when $\pi_1 = \pi_2 = 1/2$, the equal *a priori* probability case. In general, inequalities

$$u(z) \leq \left[\frac{f_1(z)}{f_2(z)}\right]^{\alpha} \tag{4B.21}$$

and

$$[1 - u(z)] \leq \left[\frac{f_2(z)}{f_1(z)}\right]^{\beta} \tag{4B.22}$$

result in conditional error bounds

$$P_{E_1} \leq B(1 - \beta) \tag{4B.23}$$

and

$$P_{E_2} \leq B(\alpha). \tag{4B.24}$$

The average error probability is simply

$$P_E \leq \pi_1 B(1-\beta) + \pi_2 B(\alpha). \tag{4B.25}$$

The choice $\alpha = \beta = 1/2$ which often minimizes this bound yields the usual Bhattacharyya bound

$$P_E \leq B(\tfrac{1}{2}). \tag{4B.26}$$

Again using the inequality (4B.17) a tighter bound is as follows:

$$\begin{aligned} P_E &= \int_{-\infty}^{\infty} \{\pi_1 f_1(z)[1-u(z)] + \pi_2 f_2(z)u(z)\}\,dz \\ &\leq \max\{\pi_1,\pi_2\}\int_{-\infty}^{\infty}\{f_1(z)[1-u(z)] + f_2(z)u(z)\}\,dz \\ &= \max\{\pi_1,\pi_2\}\int_{-\infty}^{\infty}\min\{f_1(z),f_2(z)\}\,dz \\ &\leq \max\{\pi_1,\pi_2\}\int_{-\infty}^{\infty} f_1(z)^{\alpha} f_2(z)^{1-\alpha}\,dz \\ &= \max\{\pi_1,\pi_2\}B(\alpha) \end{aligned} \tag{4B.27}$$

for $0 \leq \alpha \leq 1$. For the case

$$\pi_1 = \pi_2 = \tfrac{1}{2}$$

and $\alpha = 1/2$, we again have a reduction of the bound by a factor of one-half when compared with (4B.26). Most cases of interest have equal *a priori* probabilities where the MAP and ML decision rules are the same.

Maximum-Likelihood Metric and Chernoff Bounds

Assume that Z is some sort of metric used to make the decision such that when $Z = z$,

$$\begin{aligned} z \geq 0 &\quad \text{choose } H_1 \\ z < 0 &\quad \text{choose } H_2. \end{aligned} \tag{4B.28}$$

The decision function is then

$$u(z) = \begin{cases} 1, & z \geq 0 \\ 0, & z < 0 \end{cases} \tag{4B.29}$$

and the conditional errors are

$$P_{E_1} = \int_{-\infty}^{\infty} [1-u(z)]\, f_1(z)\,dz \tag{4B.30}$$

and

$$P_{E_2} = \int_{-\infty}^{\infty} u(z) f_2(z)\,dz. \tag{4B.31}$$

For any $\alpha \geq 0$ and any $\beta \geq 0$

$$1 - u(z) \leq e^{-\alpha z} \tag{4B.32}$$

and

$$u(z) \leq e^{\beta z} \tag{4B.33}$$

resulting in the Chernoff bounds

$$P_{E_1} \le \int_{-\infty}^{\infty} e^{-\alpha z} f_1(z)\, dz \tag{4B.34}$$

and

$$P_{E_2} \le \int_{-\infty}^{\infty} e^{\beta z} f_2(z)\, dz. \tag{4B.35}$$

Thus, the averaged error probability is

$$P_E \le \pi_1 C_1(\alpha) + \pi_2 C_2(\beta) \tag{4B.36}$$

where

$$C_1(\alpha) = \int_{-\infty}^{\infty} e^{-\alpha z} f_1(z)\, dz \tag{4B.37}$$

and

$$C_2(\beta) = \int_{-\infty}^{\infty} e^{\beta z} f_2(z)\, dz. \tag{4B.38}$$

Jacobs [8] considered the conditions

$$f_1(-z) \ge f_1(z) \quad \text{all } z \le 0 \tag{4B.39a}$$

and

$$f_2(-z) \ge f_2(z) \quad \text{all } z \ge 0. \tag{4B.39b}$$

Then using the inequality

$$\begin{aligned} \frac{e^{\omega} + e^{-\omega}}{2} &= \cosh \omega \\ &\ge 1 \quad \text{all } \omega \end{aligned} \tag{4B.40}$$

and a change of variables of integration, he derived the following inequalities:

$$\begin{aligned} C_1(\alpha) &= \int_{-\infty}^{\infty} e^{-\alpha z} f_1(z)\, dz \\ &= \int_{-\infty}^{0} e^{-\alpha z} f_1(z)\, dz + \int_{0}^{\infty} e^{-\alpha z} f_1(z)\, dz \\ &= \int_{-\infty}^{0} e^{-\alpha z} f_1(z)\, dz + \int_{-\infty}^{0} e^{\alpha z} f_1(-z)\, dz \\ &\ge \int_{-\infty}^{0} e^{-\alpha z} f_1(z)\, dz + \int_{-\infty}^{0} e^{\alpha z} f_1(z)\, dz \\ &= 2\int_{-\infty}^{0} \cosh \alpha z \cdot f_1(z)\, dz \\ &\ge 2\int_{-\infty}^{0} f_1(z)\, dz \end{aligned} \tag{4B.41}$$

or

$$P_{E_1} \le \tfrac{1}{2} C_1(\alpha) \tag{4B.42}$$

and similarly

$$P_{E_2} \le \tfrac{1}{2} C_2(\beta). \tag{4B.43}$$

Thus, the often satisfied conditions given by Jacobs in (4B.39) result in a factor of one-half in the usual Chernoff bounds.

Less restrictive but more difficult to prove conditions are that

$$\int_0^\infty e^{-\alpha^* z} f_1(z)\,dz \ge \int_{-\infty}^0 e^{\alpha^* z} f_1(z)\,dz \tag{4B.44a}$$

and

$$\int_{-\infty}^0 e^{\beta^* z} f_2(z)\,dz \ge \int_0^\infty e^{-\beta^* z} f_2(z)\,dz \tag{4B.44b}$$

where α^* minimizes $C_1(\alpha)$ and β^* minimizes $C_2(\beta)$. Note that for the special case of $\alpha^* = 0$

$$\begin{aligned}\int_0^\infty f_1(z)\,dz &\ge \int_{-\infty}^0 f_1(z)\,dz \\ &= P_{E_1}\end{aligned} \tag{4B.45}$$

which is always satisfied when

$$P_{E_1} < \tfrac{1}{2}. \tag{4B.46}$$

Indeed, conditions (4B.44) are also true for some non-negative range of α values. We assume it is true for the minimizing choices of the Chernoff bound parameters. Note that conditions (4B.44) are less restrictive than those of (4B.39) since (4B.39) implies (4B.44). Now consider the inequalities,

$$\begin{aligned}C_1(\alpha) &\ge C_1(\alpha^*) \\ &= \int_{-\infty}^\infty e^{-\alpha^* z} f_1(z)\,dz \\ &= \int_{-\infty}^0 e^{-\alpha^* z} f_1(z)\,dz + \int_0^\infty e^{-\alpha^* z} f_1(z)\,dz \\ &\ge \int_{-\infty}^0 e^{-\alpha^* z} f_1(z)\,dz + \int_{-\infty}^0 e^{\alpha^* z} f_1(z)\,dz \\ &= 2\int_{-\infty}^0 \cosh \alpha^* z \cdot f_1(z)\,dz \\ &\ge 2\int_{-\infty}^0 f_1(z)\,dz \\ &= 2P_{E_1}\end{aligned} \tag{4B.47}$$

or

$$P_{E_1} \le \tfrac{1}{2} C_1(\alpha) \tag{4B.48}$$

and similarly

$$P_{E_2} \le \tfrac{1}{2} C_2(\beta). \tag{4B.49}$$

Next, for the special case where

$$\pi_1 = \pi_2 = \tfrac{1}{2} \tag{4B.50}$$

and

$$\alpha^* = \beta^* \tag{4B.51}$$

sufficient conditions can be given by

$$\int_0^{\infty} e^{-\alpha^* z} f_1(z)\, dz \geq \int_0^{\infty} e^{-\alpha^* z} f_2(z)\, dz \tag{4B.52a}$$

and

$$\int_{-\infty}^{0} e^{\alpha^* z} f_2(z)\, dz \geq \int_{-\infty}^{0} e^{\alpha^* z} f_1(z)\, dz. \tag{4B.52b}$$

Note that these conditions are always satisfied if our decision rule is a maximum-likelihood decision rule where

$$f_2(z) \leq f_1(z) \quad \text{for all } z \geq 0 \tag{4B.53a}$$

and

$$f_2(z) > f_1(z) \quad \text{for all } z < 0. \tag{4B.53b}$$

Assuming conditions (4B.52)

$$\begin{aligned} C_1(\alpha) + C_2(\beta) &\geq C_1(\alpha^*) + C_2(\alpha^*) \\ &= \int_{-\infty}^{\infty} e^{-\alpha^* z} f_1(z)\, dz + \int_{-\infty}^{\infty} e^{\alpha^* z} f_2(z)\, dz \\ &= \int_{-\infty}^{0} e^{-\alpha^* z} f_1(z)\, dz + \int_0^{\infty} e^{-\alpha^* z} f_1(z)\, dz \\ &\quad + \int_{-\infty}^{0} e^{\alpha^* z} f_2(z)\, dz + \int_0^{\infty} e^{\alpha^* z} f_2(z)\, dz \\ &\geq \int_{-\infty}^{0} e^{-\alpha^* z} f_1(z)\, dz + \int_0^{\infty} e^{-\alpha^* z} f_2(z)\, dz \\ &\quad + \int_{-\infty}^{0} e^{\alpha^* z} f_1(z)\, dz + \int_0^{\infty} e^{\alpha^* z} f_2(z)\, dz \\ &= 2\int_{-\infty}^{0} \cosh \alpha^* z \cdot f_1(z)\, dz \\ &\quad + 2\int_0^{\infty} \cosh \alpha^* z \cdot f_2(z)\, dz \\ &\geq 2P_{E_1} + 2P_{E_2} \end{aligned} \tag{4B.54}$$

or

$$\begin{aligned} P_E &= \tfrac{1}{2} P_{E_1} + \tfrac{1}{2} P_{E_2} \\ &\leq \tfrac{1}{4} C_1(\alpha) + \tfrac{1}{4} C_2(\beta), \end{aligned} \tag{4B.55}$$

which is again a factor of one-half less than the original Chernoff bound on the average error probability (4B.36) for $\pi_1 = \pi_2 = 1/2$.

For the special case where Z happens to be a maximum-likelihood metric

$$Z = \ln\left[\frac{f_1(Z)}{f_2(Z)}\right], \tag{4B.56}$$

then the conditions (4B.52) hold and

$$\begin{aligned} C_1(\alpha) &= \int_{-\infty}^{\infty} e^{-\alpha z} f_1(z)\,dz \\ &= \int_{-\infty}^{\infty}\left[\frac{f_2(z)}{f_1(z)}\right]^{\alpha} f_1(z)\,dz \\ &= \int_{-\infty}^{\infty} f_1(z)^{1-\alpha} f_2(z)^{\alpha}\,dz \\ &= B(1-\alpha) \end{aligned} \tag{4B.57}$$

and

$$\begin{aligned} C_2(\beta) &= \int_{-\infty}^{\infty} e^{\beta z} f_2(z)\,dz \\ &= \int_{-\infty}^{\infty}\left[\frac{f_1(z)}{f_2(z)}\right]^{\beta} f_2(z)\,dz \\ &= \int_{-\infty}^{\infty} f_1(z)^{\beta} f_2(z)^{1-\beta}\,dz \\ &= B(\beta) \end{aligned} \tag{4B.58}$$

where $B(\cdot)$ is given by (4B.11). Recall that $B(1/2)$ is the Bhattacharyya bound.

Applications

In most applications of interest, we consider two sequences of length N,

$$\underline{\mathbf{x}}_1, \underline{\mathbf{x}}_2 \in X^N \tag{4B.59}$$

that can be transmitted over a memoryless channel with input alphabet X and output alphabet Y and conditional probability

$$p(y|x), \quad x \in X, \quad y \in Y. \tag{4B.60}$$

This is shown in the following figure.

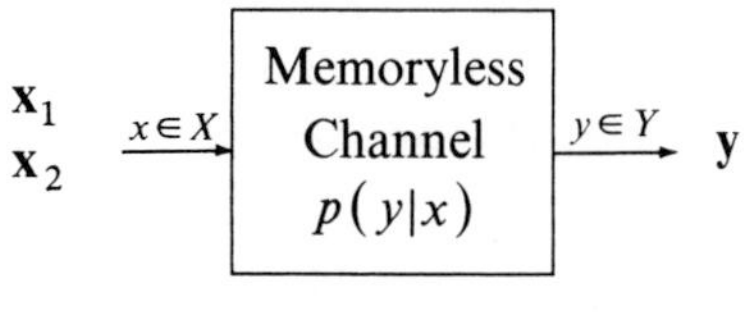

$\mathbf{x}_1$, $\mathbf{x}_2$ —$x \in X$→ [Memoryless Channel $p(y|x)$] —$y \in Y$→ $\mathbf{y}$

$$p_N(\mathbf{y}|\mathbf{x}) = \prod_{n=1}^{N} p(y_n|x_n).$$

The receiver obtains a sequence

$$\mathbf{y} \in Y^N \tag{4B.61}$$

from the channel and must decide between hypotheses

$$\begin{aligned} &H_1: \mathbf{x}_1 \text{ is sent} \\ &H_2: \mathbf{x}_2 \text{ is sent} \end{aligned} \tag{4B.62}$$

which have *a priori* probabilities

$$\pi_1 = \Pr\{H_1\} \quad \text{and} \quad \pi_2 = \Pr\{H_2\}.$$

The receiver will typically use a metric

$$m(y, x) \qquad x \in X, \quad y \in Y \tag{4B.63}$$

and the decision rule of choosing H_1 if and only if

$$\sum_{n=1}^{N} m(y_n, x_{1n}) \geq \sum_{n=1}^{N} m(y_n, x_{2n}). \tag{4B.64}$$

By defining

$$Z = \sum_{n=1}^{N} [m(y_n, x_{1n}) - m(y_n, x_{2n})] \tag{4B.65}$$

we have the case considered in this chapter.

APPENDIX 4C. REED-SOLOMON CODE PERFORMANCE

A Reed-Solomon (RS) code [15] is a block code with an alphabet size of $Q = 2^m$. Its block length is $N = Q - 1$ symbols which can be extended to $N = Q$ and $N = Q + 1$. Here, the performance of only the $N = Q$ block length RS codes is presented since adjacent block lengths are only slightly different.

If an RS code has r redundant symbols, then the minimum Hamming distance between codewords is

$$d = r + 1 \tag{4C.1}$$

and the code is able to correct any pattern of t symbol errors and s symbol erasures for which

$$2t + s < d. \tag{4C.2}$$

Thus, this code can correct up to $t_0 = r/2$ errors when there are no erasures and up to $s_0 = r$ erasures when there are no errors.

Suppose we have a symmetric Q-ary memoryless channel with conditional probabilities

$$p(y|x) = \begin{cases} 1 - P_s, & y = x \\ \dfrac{P_s}{N - 1}, & y \neq x \end{cases} \tag{4C.3}$$

where P_s is the uncoded symbol error probability. The decoded bit error probability is given approximately by

$$P_b = \sum_{i=t_0+1}^{N} \frac{i}{2(N-1)} \binom{N}{i} P_s^i (1-P_s)^{N-i} \tag{4C.4}$$

where t_0 is the number of symbol errors that can be corrected. Table 4C.1 shows values of the uncoded symbol error probabilities needed for each RS code of block length $N = Q = 2^m$ and parameter $t_0 = r/2$ to achieve decoded bit error rates of 10^{-3}, 10^{-5}, 10^{-7}, 10^{-9}, and 10^{-11}. (The last row for each N, however, does not apply here.) Consider, for example, the RS code whose symbols are eight-bit bytes ($m = 8$), whose block length is $N = 256$ symbols and whose redundancy is $r = 32$. This code can correct all symbol error patterns of up to $t_0 = 16$ errors. Suppose this code must attain a decoded bit error rate of $P_b = 10^{-5}$, then from Table 4C.1 the maximum uncoded symbol error probability is $P_s = 0.025$.

Next consider a memoryless erasure channel with conditional probabilities

$$p(y|x) = \begin{cases} 1 - P_E, & y = x \\ P_E, & y = \text{erasure} \end{cases} \tag{4C.5}$$

where P_E is the probability a symbol is erased. The decoded bit error probability is

$$P_b = \sum_{i=s_0+1}^{N} \frac{i}{2(N-1)} \binom{N}{i} P_E^i (1-P_E)^{N-i} \tag{4C.6}$$

where s_0 is the number of erasures that can be corrected. Table 4C.1 also shows values of the erasure probabilities needed for each RS code of blocklength $N = Q = 2^m$ and parameter $s_0 = r$ to achieve decoded bit error rates of 10^{-3}, 10^{-5}, 10^{-7}, 10^{-9}, and 10^{-11}. Again, for the example with $N = 256$ and $r = 32$, up to $s_0 = 32$ erasures can be corrected. For a required decoded bit error rate of $P_b = 10^{-5}$, from Table 4C.1 the maximum erasure probability is $P_E = 0.0651$.

Table 4C.1 is provided courtesy of Dr. Elwyn Berlekamp [16].

Table 4C.1.
Required Probabilities [16]

	$P_b = 10^{-3}$	$P_b = 10^{-5}$	$P_b = 10^{-7}$	$P_b = 10^{-9}$	$P_b = 10^{-11}$
			$N = 8$		
$t_0, s_0 = 2$	4.60E-2	9.51E-3	2.03E-3	4.37E-4	9.41E-5
$= 4$	1.49E-1	5.65E-2	2.21E-2	8.74E-3	3.47E-3
			$N = 16$		
$t_0, s_0 = 2$	2.84E-2	5.73E-3	1.22E-3	2.62E-4	5.63E-5
$= 4$	7.72E-2	2.81E-2	1.09E-2	4.27E-3	1.69E-3
$= 8$	2.23E-1	1.23E-1	7.10E-2	4.17E-2	2.47E-2

Table 4C.1.
Continued

	$p_b = 10^{-3}$	$p_b = 10^{-5}$	$p_b = 10^{-7}$	$p_b = 10^{-9}$	$p_b = 10^{-11}$
			$N = 32$		
$t_0, s_0 = 2$	1.80E-2	3.55E-3	7.51E-4	1.61E-4	3.47E-5
$= 4$	4.36E-2	1.54E-2	5.87E-3	2.30E-3	9.11E-4
$= 8$	1.11E-1	5.88E-2	3.32E-2	1.93E-2	1.13E-2
$= 16$	2.90E-1	2.01E-1	1.45E-1	1.07E-1	7.96E-2
			$N = 64$		
$t_0, s_0 = 2$	1.17E-2	2.23E-3	4.68E-4	1.00E-4	2.16E-5
$= 4$	2.55E-2	8.70E-3	3.29E-3	1.29E-3	5.08E-4
$= 8$	5.96E-2	3.05E-2	1.70E-2	9.78E-3	5.74E-3
$= 16$	1.43E-1	9.50E-2	6.71E-2	4.87E-2	3.59E-2
$= 32$	3.45E-1	2.74E-1	2.25E-1	1.88E-1	1.58E-1
			$N = 128$		
$t_0, s_0 = 2$	7.72E-3	1.41E-3	2.94E-4	6.29E-5	1.35E-5
$= 4$	1.52E-2	5.00E-3	1.87E-3	7.29E-4	2.88E-4
$= 8$	3.30E-2	1.63E-2	8.99E-3	5.15E-3	3.01E-3
$= 16$	7.44E-2	4.81E-2	3.35E-2	2.41E-2	1.76E-2
$= 32$	1.69E-1	1.30E-1	1.05E-1	8.59E-2	7.16E-2
$= 64$	3.88E-1	3.34E-1	2.95E-1	2.64E-1	2.38E-1
			$N = 256$		
$t_0, s_0 = 2$	5.20E-3	8.94E-4	1.85E-4	3.96E-5	8.51E-6
$= 4$	9.29E-3	2.90E-3	1.08E-3	4.17E-4	1.64E-4
$= 8$	1.86E-2	8.89E-3	4.83E-3	2.76E-3	1.61E-3
$= 16$	3.98E-2	2.50E-2	1.72E-2	1.23E-2	8.97E-3
$= 32$	8.68E-2	6.51E-2	5.17E-2	4.21E-2	3.49E-2
$= 64$	1.91E-1	1.60E-1	1.39E-1	1.23E-1	1.10E-1
			$N = 512$		
$t_0, s_0 = 2$	3.62E-3	5.70E-4	1.17E-4	2.49E-5	5.35E-6
$= 4$	5.80E-3	1.70E-3	6.20E-4	2.39E-4	9.41E-5
$= 8$	1.07E-2	4.88E-3	2.62E-3	1.49E-3	8.64E-4
$= 16$	2.16E-2	1.32E-2	8.97E-3	6.37E-3	4.64E-3
$= 32$	4.54E-2	3.33E-2	2.62E-2	2.12E-2	1.75E-2
$= 64$	9.68E-2	7.97E-2	6.85E-2	6.01E-2	5.34E-2
			$N = 1024$		
$t_0, s_0 = 2$	2.65E-3	3.66E-4	7.38E-5	1.57E-5	3.37E-6
$= 4$	3.75E-3	9.95E-4	3.58E-4	1.38E-4	5.40E-5
$= 8$	6.29E-3	2.70E-3	1.43E-3	8.05E-4	4.67E-4
$= 16$	1.19E-2	6.99E-3	4.71E-3	3.33E-3	2.41E-3
$= 32$	2.40E-2	1.72E-2	1.34E-2	1.08E-2	8.90E-3
$= 64$	4.99E-2	4.04E-2	3.45E-2	3.01E-2	2.67E-2

Table 4C.1.
Continued

	$p_b = 10^{-3}$	$p_b = 10^{-5}$	$p_b = 10^{-7}$	$p_b = 10^{-9}$	$p_b = 10^{-11}$
			$N = 2048$		
$t_0, s_0 = 2$	2.14E-3	2.36E-4	4.67E-5	9.89E-6	2.12E-6
$= 4$	2.58E-3	5.88E-4	2.07E-4	7.92E-5	3.10E-5
$= 8$	3.82E-3	1.50E-3	7.81E-4	4.37E-4	2.53E-4
$= 16$	6.68E-3	3.73E-3	2.48E-3	1.74E-3	1.26E-3
$= 32$	1.29E-2	8.95E-3	6.91E-3	5.55E-3	4.55E-3
$= 64$	2.59E-2	2.06E-2	1.75E-2	1.52E-2	1.34E-2
			$N = 4096$		
$t_0, s_0 = 2$	2.00E-3	1.53E-4	2.96E-5	6.24E-6	1.34E-6
$= 4$	2.06E-3	3.49E-4	1.20E-4	4.57E-5	1.78E-5
$= 8$	2.50E-3	8.36E-4	4.28E-4	2.38E-4	1.37E-4
$= 16$	3.87E-3	2.00E-3	1.31E-3	9.17E-4	6.60E-4
$= 32$	6.99E-3	4.67E-3	3.57E-3	2.86E-3	2.34E-3
$= 64$	1.36E-2	1.06E-2	8.92E-3	7.73E-3	6.81E-3

Chapter 5

PSEUDONOISE GENERATORS

5.1 THE STORAGE / GENERATION PROBLEM

Pseudonoise (PN) sequences are used as spectrum-spreading modulations for direct sequence SS designs, as hopping pattern sources in frequency and/or time hopping systems, and as filter section controllers in matched filter SS systems. Ideally, most of the PN sequence design problems would be solved if it were possible to produce a sample of a sequence of independent random variables, uniformly distributed on the available alphabet, for use at the SS transmitter, and an identical sample sequence at the receiver for use in the detection process. This is the SS equivalent of the one-time pad used in cryptographic systems requiring the highest level of security. Unfortunately, the generation, recording, and distribution of these sample sequences at a rate (per information bit to be communicated) equal to the processing gain of the SS system, is generally not feasible.

Once the one-time pad is discarded as a viable approach, the designer must come to grips with the problem of storing/generating a signal which looks random (e.g., like a one-time pad), despite the fact that it must be done with a real system possessing finite storage capacity/generating capability. Let's illustrate the possibilities by considering methods for the generation of a specified binary (0 or 1) sequence $\{b_n,\ n = 1, 2, \ldots, N\}$. If N bits of the random sequence are not sufficient to complete the communication process, the sequence must be reused, i.e.,

$$b_{n+N} = b_n \quad \text{for all } n, \tag{5.1}$$

where N is the period of the extended sequence. Any other method of reusing the stored sequence other than periodic extension as indicated above, will require additional memory to supervise the reuse algorithm.

Two approaches, in which the complete sequence is stored simultaneously within the generator, are shown in Figure 5.1. One is ROM-based, the other a simple cyclic shift register. Both have the property that they work equally well with any desired sequence $\{b_n\}$. Obviously, the price for this versatility is memory: N binary storage elements and supporting hardware are needed.

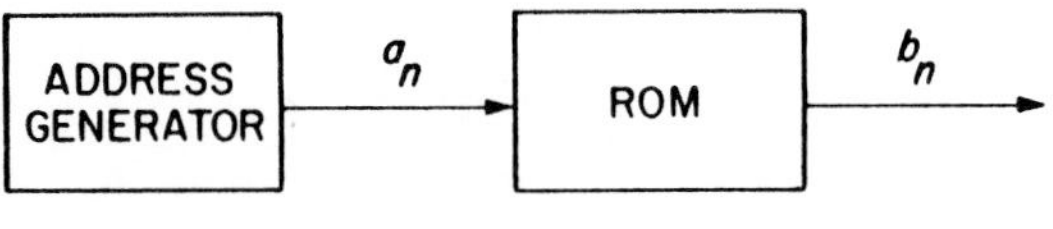

(a) ROM-Based Generator

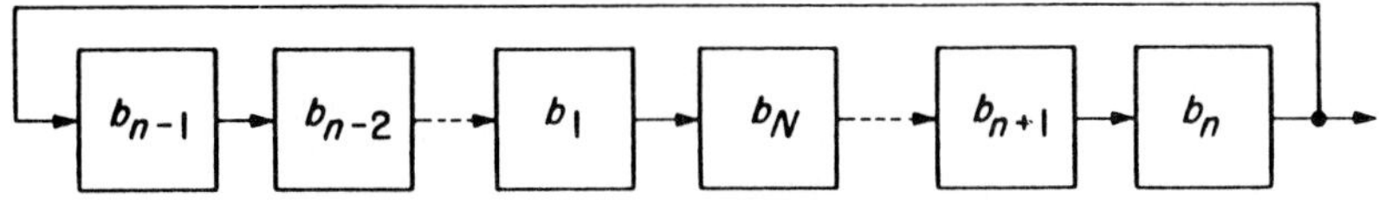

(b) Cyclic-Shift-Register Generator

Figure 5.1. Sequence generators based on complete sequence storage.

The storage requirements indicated by these designs can be reduced by the insertion of Boolean functions at the proper places. The ROM in Figure 5.1(a) can be replaced by a Boolean function which calculates b_n directly from the address a_n. Similarly, all but M of the binary memory elements of the cyclic shift register in Figure 5.1(b) can be eliminated if a Boolean function can be mechanized which, for all n, computes b_{n+M} from the stored values b_{n+j}, $j = 0, 1, \ldots, M-1$. The following two examples illustrate these procedures.

Example 5.1. A ROM-based generator for the sequence

1010110010110010

having period 16 can be specified as follows: For simplicity assume the address generator is a 4-bit binary counter producing consecutive addresses in the range 0 to 15, that is,

$$n = a_n = a_n^{(0)} + a_n^{(1)} \cdot 2 + a_n^{(2)} \cdot 2^2 + a_n^{(3)} \cdot 2^3$$
$$= \left(a_n^{(0)} a_n^{(1)} a_n^{(2)} a_n^{(3)}\right)_2 \tag{5.2}$$

where $(\ldots)_2$ is the binary representation of n. Table 5.1 identifies the mapping which has to be accomplished by the ROM or its replacement function. One possible implementation of this Boolean function is

$$b_n = a_n^{(0)} + a_n^{(1)} \cdot a_n^{(2)} + a_n^{(2)} \cdot a_n^{(3)} \tag{5.3}$$

where + and $\cdot$ represent arithmetic modulo 2, + being the EXCLUSIVE OR and $\cdot$ being the AND logic functions. The resulting PN generator is shown in Figure 5.2.

Table 5.1
Address-to-bit mapping

n	$a_n^{(0)}$	$a_n^{(1)}$	$a_n^{(2)}$	$a_n^{(3)}$	b_n
1	1	0	0	0	1
2	0	1	0	0	0
3	1	1	0	0	1
4	0	0	1	0	0
5	1	0	1	0	1
6	0	1	1	0	1
7	1	1	1	0	0
8	0	0	0	1	0
9	1	0	0	1	1
10	0	1	0	1	0
11	1	1	0	1	1
12	0	0	1	1	1
13	1	0	1	1	0
14	0	1	1	1	0
15	1	1	1	1	1
16	0	0	0	0	0

Notice that the function (5.3) in Example 5.1 is described in terms of two operations, $+$ and $\cdot$ modulo 2, on the pair of elements 0 and 1. This structure has all the mathematical properties of a field, and is usually referred to as the Galois field GF(2) of two elements. Complete mastery of the techniques used to design PN generators will require knowledge of the finite field GF(2) and of the larger finite fields containing GF(2), namely GF(q), where the number q of elements in the field is a power of 2. The

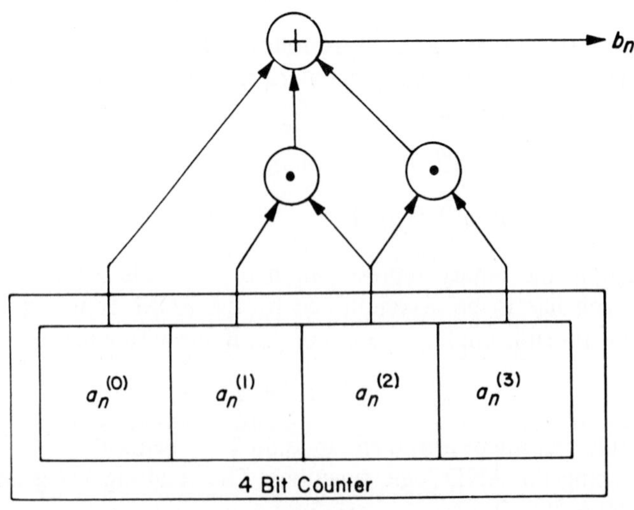

Figure 5.2. Counter-based PN generator.

reader is referred to Appendix 5A for a tutorial description of finite fields and their properties.

A completely specified Boolean function can be determined from tabulated values in at least two ways:

(a) The Quine-McCluskey algorithm [1]–[3], applied to the completely specified Boolean function of Table 5.1, will yield a minimum second-order realization of the function in terms of the logical operations AND, OR, and NEGATION.
(b) The sequences $a_n^{(i)}$, $i = 0, 1, 2, \ldots, k-1$, each of length 2^k, along with the all-ones sequence of length 2^k, are the basis for a first-order Reed-Muller code [4]–[6]. Determination of the function described in Example 5.1 can be viewed as the result of decoding the 16-tuple, viewed as a codeword from a 4-th order Reed-Muller code of word length 16.

On the average, either of these techniques will produce rather complicated logical structures when applied to a random sequence of binary symbols. The expected number of terms in the resultant function determined by the Reed-Muller approach is half the sequence length. Hence, for a k-bit clock used to produce a randomly selected PN sequence of length 2^k, one would expect on the average the necessity of 2^{k-1} multiple input AND gates and an EXCLUSIVE OR capable of handling 2^{k-1} inputs. Being optimal, one would expect the Quine-McCluskey approach to require somewhat fewer operations, but nevertheless, the expected number of operations probably will still be a linear function of the period 2^k.

Although, on the average, the complexity of PN generators using counters is high, could there be a few exceptionally good designs of this type? There are strong reasons to believe that counters are always poor sources for inputs to functions generating PN sequences. First, the individual sequences $\{a_n^{(i)}\}$ have periods which are divisors of the desired period, and do not individually have a "random appearance." Furthermore, very few of the input sequences change value at any one time, i.e., $\{a_n^{(i)}\}$ changes every 2^i-th bit, thereby forcing the use of rather complicated logic to emulate a PN sequence which, on the average, changes every other bit.

Example 5.2. The sequence

001100111010110111110

with period 21 has a particularly simple mechanization based on a shift register with feedback logic. Since all five-tuples $(b_n, b_{n+1}, b_{n+2}, b_{n+3}, b_{n+4})$, $n = 1, 2, \ldots, 21$, are distinct, it follows that b_{n+5} can be determined uniquely from these previous five symbols. Hence, the designer must find a simple Boolean function which mechanizes the mapping shown in Table 5.2. One possible result, employing GF(2) arithmetic, is

$$b_{n+5} = b_n + b_{n+1} \cdot b_{n+2} \tag{5.4}$$

with the corresponding mechanization shown in Figure 5.3.

Table 5.2
Feedback logic function

n	b_n	b_{n+1}	b_{n+2}	b_{n+3}	b_{n+4}	b_{n+5}
1	0	0	1	1	0	0
2	0	1	1	0	0	1
3	1	1	0	0	1	1
4	1	0	0	1	1	1
5	0	0	1	1	1	0
6	0	1	1	1	0	1
7	1	1	1	0	1	0
8	1	1	0	1	0	1
9	1	0	1	0	1	1
10	0	1	0	1	1	0
11	1	0	1	1	0	1
12	0	1	1	0	1	1
13	1	1	0	1	1	1
14	1	0	1	1	1	1
15	0	1	1	1	1	1
16	1	1	1	1	1	0
17	1	1	1	1	0	0
18	1	1	1	0	0	0
19	1	1	0	0	0	1
20	1	0	0	0	1	1
21	0	0	0	1	1	0

The approach to determining the feedback function in Example 5.2 can be identical to that used in Example 5.1. The fact that Table 5.2 is incomplete, i.e., the Boolean function's values are specified for only 21 of the 32 possible input binary 5-tuples, may yield some flexibility in the design process. Obviously, then, knowledge of the desired function in incomplete tabular form is not sufficient for determining the behavior of the PN generator when its register is loaded with a 5-tuple not in the table.

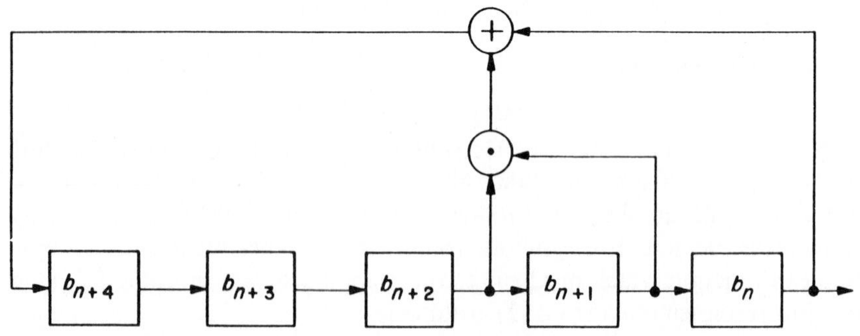

Figure 5.3. A shift-register generator using feedback logic.

Using the implemented function (5.4), it can be seen that the device diagrammed in Figure 5.3 supports three other periodic sequences, namely 0 (period 1), 10000 (period 5), and 01010 (period 5). On the other hand, if the implemented function had the value 1 for each of the ten input 5-tuples missing from Table 5.2, the resulting device would support no other periodic sequences, and regardless of the initial register contents, the output sequence would eventually become the specified period 21 sequence.

Pseudonoise generators are similar to oscillators in the sense that they provide an output signal but are not driven by an input signal, their next memory state being a prescribed function of their present memory state. The period N of the output sequence, therefore, is upper bounded by the number of distinct states, that number being 2^m when the memory is composed of m binary storage elements. Hence, when implemented in binary, the minimum number m of memory elements necessary to support period N operation is given by

$$m = \lceil \log_2(N) \rceil \tag{5.5}$$

where $\lceil x \rceil$ denotes the smallest integer greater than or equal to x. If designing a PN generator for a specified, randomly selected sequence, using a shift register design with feedback logic as in Example 5.2, one can typically expect that the number of binary memory elements needed will be approximately twice the minimum number given by (5.5).

It is worth noting that the period of a sequence should be long enough to preclude the possibility that natural delays caused by multipath or artificial delays created by repeater jamming result in a signal delay of an integral number of periods. Such integral period delays could result in situations in which an SS receiver could not discriminate between the desired SS signal and the multipath or jammer interference. It is possible to size the minimum memory requirements needed to preclude this situation by evaluating (5.5). As indicated by Table 5.3, it clearly is within the realm of possibility to achieve a practically non-repetitive PN generator with a modest investment in memory.

Table 5.3

Memory requirements (measured in binary storage elements) for memory-efficient PN generators operating at 10^6 or 10^9 bits/sec.

Period	Memory Requirement (10^6 bits/sec)	Memory Requirement (10^9 bits/sec)
1 second	20	30
1 minute	26	36
1 hour	32	42
1 day	37	47
1 year	45	55
1 century	52	62

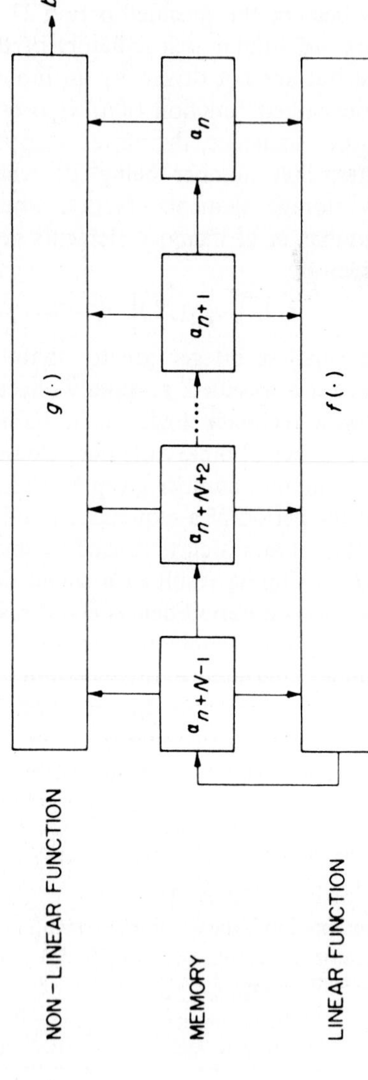

Figure 5.4. A linear feedback shift register with feedforward logic.

There do indeed exist shift registers which, along with a minimal amount of feedback logic, produce binary sequences possessing very large period and excellent pseudo-randomness properties. However, an extreme measure of luck would be necessary to randomly pick a sequence producible by a generator possessing relatively simple structural properties; analytical techniques must be used to determine structures which will serve adequately as PN generators. The PN generators to be explored in this chapter all are variations of a linear-feedback shift register (LFSR) with non-linear feedforward output logic (see Figure 5.4). LFSRs are amenable to analysis, and provide a register through which flows a steady stream of pseudorandom bits. Non-linear feedforward logic is added for several reasons; it suffices to say that the effect of this addition is to make the structure of the shift register difficult to determine rapidly from observations of the output sequence.

5.2 LINEAR RECURSIONS

5.2.1 Fibonacci Generators

A sequence $\{b_n\}$ of elements from a field $\mathscr{F}$ is said to satisfy a *linear recursion* if there exists a relation of the form

$$b_n = -\sum_{i=1}^{M} a_i b_{n-i} \quad \text{for all } n, \tag{5.6}$$

which allows each sequence element to be calculated from the M immediately preceding elements. The coefficients a_i in (5.6) are from the same field $\mathscr{F}$, and, assuming $a_M \neq 0$, M is called the *degree* of the linear recursion. A sequence generator based on (5.6) can be constructed as shown in Figure 5.5. When properly initialized with the first M elements of the desired sequence, this shift register will, without further inputs, produce the remainder of the periodic infinite-length sequence $\{b_n\}$. A generator, structured as shown in Figure 5.5, is often said to be in the *Fibonacci configuration* (after the mathematician who studied linear recursions) to distinguish it from other LFSR forms.

Every periodic sequence $\{b_n\}$ satisfies an infinite number of linear recursions, including the obvious recursions

$$b_n = b_{n+mN} \quad \text{for all integers } m \text{ and } n, \tag{5.7}$$

where N is the period of the sequence. For the case $m = 1$ in (5.7) the Fibonacci-configured LFSR is the cyclic register of Figure 5.1(b). This obvious recursion often is not the minimum-degree recursion satisfied by the sequence.

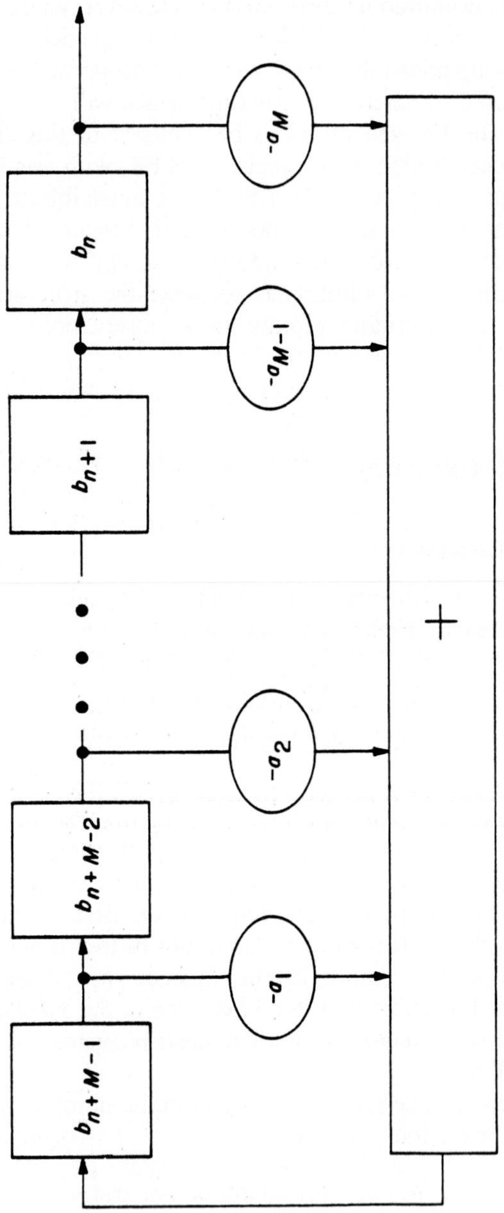

Figure 5.5. An M-stage linear-feedback shift register in Fibonacci form.

Table 5.4
Coefficients of linear recursions (5.6) of degree less than 7, satisfied by the period-7 sequence of Example 5.3.

M	$a_1 a_2 \cdots a_M$
3	011
4	1101
5	00111
5	10001
6	010011
6	000101
6	111111
6	101001

Example 5.3. The binary sequence of period 7, beginning with

$$0010111,$$

satisfies several recursions of degree less than 7 over GF(2) (see Table 5.4).

The minimum number L of memory elements required to build a Fibonacci generator for $\{b_n\}$ is the degree of the minimum-degree recursion which generates $\{b_n\}$. This key number L is called the *linear span* of the sequence $\{b_n\}$, and is often used as an abstract measure of complexity of the sequence structure. In Example 5.3, the linear span L of the period-7 sequence is 3.

5.2.2 Formal Power Series and Characteristic Polynomials

The linear span and corresponding linear recursion for a given periodic sequence can be found theoretically by formal power series manipulations. Let $B(z)$ denote the formal power series having sequence elements as coefficients, i.e.,

$$B(z) = \sum_{n=1}^{\infty} b_n z^{-n}. \tag{5.8}$$

The connection between $B(z)$ and a linear recursion (5.6) satisfied by $\{b_n\}$ can be established in the following manner. Define

$$a_0 = 1, \tag{5.9}$$

multiply (5.6) by z^{-n}, sum over n, and manipulate to arrive at

$$\begin{aligned} 0 &= \sum_{i=0}^{M} a_i z^{-i} \sum_{n=M+1}^{\infty} b_{n-i} z^{-(n-i)} \\ &= A(z)B(z) - D(z), \end{aligned} \tag{5.10}$$

and, hence,

$$B(z) = \frac{D(z)}{A(z)}, \tag{5.11}$$

where

$$A(z) = \sum_{i=0}^{M} a_i z^{M-i}, \tag{5.12}$$

$$D(z) = \sum_{n=1}^{M} d_n z^{M-n}, \tag{5.13a}$$

$$d_n = \sum_{i=0}^{n-1} a_i b_{n-i}, \qquad n = 1, 2, \ldots, M. \tag{5.13b}$$

Thus, the formal power series of every sequence which satisfies a linear recursion can be written as the ratio of two polynomials in z (no negative powers of z are contained in either $A(z)$ or $D(z)$). The denominator polynomial's coefficients are the weights used in the linear recursion, and the numerator polynomial's coefficients are related to the initial elements $b_1, b_2, \ldots, b_M$, by the M independent equations (5.13b).

The following technique can be used to find the linear span and corresponding linear recursion for a sequence $\{b_n\}$, beginning with knowledge of $b_1, b_2, \ldots, b_N$, and the fact that N is the sequence period. By substituting the periodic sequence structure into (5.8), $B(z)$ is identified as a ratio of polynomials.

$$\begin{aligned} B(z) &= \sum_{m=0}^{\infty} \sum_{n=1}^{N} b_n z^{-(mN+n)} \\ &= \frac{1}{1 - z^{-N}} \cdot \sum_{n=1}^{N} b_n z^{-n} \\ &= \frac{\sum_{n=1}^{N} b_n z^{N-n}}{z^N - 1}. \end{aligned} \tag{5.14}$$

The recursion and initial conditions identified with the denominator and numerator polynomials of (5.14) correspond to the cyclic generator structure of Figure 5.1(b). Cancellation of common factors in the numerator and denominator polynomials in (5.14) will yield lower-degree recursions and, hence, mechanizations with lower memory requirements.

Carrying this idea to its logical conclusions, Euclid's algorithm (see Appendix 5A, sections 5A.2 and 5A.3) can be applied to determine the greatest common divisor $G(z)$,

$$G(z) = \gcd\left(\sum_{n=1}^{N} b_n z^{N-n}, z^N - 1 \right), \tag{5.15}$$

of the numerator and denominator polynomials in (5.14). After cancellation of this common factor of highest possible degree, $B(z)$ is of the form

$$B(z) = \frac{P(z)}{Q(z)}, \tag{5.16}$$

where

$$\gcd(P(z), Q(z)) = 1. \tag{5.17}$$

It can be assumed without loss of generality that multiplicative constants have been transferred to the numerator in (5.16), so that the denominator polynomial $Q(z)$ is *monic*, i.e., the coefficient of the highest power of z in $Q(z)$ is unity. Clearly, there is no rational representation of $B(z)$ with a denominator polynomial of lesser degree, and, hence, the linear span L of $\{b_n\}$ is given by

$$L = \deg Q(z), \tag{5.18}$$

and $\{b_n\}$ satisfies the linear recursion

$$b_n = -\sum_{i=1}^{L} q_i b_{n-i}, \tag{5.19}$$

where q_i is the i-th coefficient of $Q(z)$, i.e.,

$$Q(z) = \sum_{i=0}^{L} q_i z^{L-i}. \tag{5.20}$$

The monic denominator polynomial $Q(z)$ in (5.16) achieving this linear span is called the *characteristic polynomial* of the sequence $\{b_n\}$, and the corresponding numerator polynomial $P(z)$ is called the *initial condition polynomial* of $\{b_n\}$. The following theorem is based on the above derivation.

THEOREM 5.1. *Let $\{b_n\}$ be a sequence possessing characteristic polynomial $Q(z)$. Then the period N of $\{b_n\}$ is the smallest integer N such that $Q(z)$ divides $z^N - 1$.*

Clearly then, sequences possessing the same characteristic polynomial have the same period.

5.2.3 Galois Generators

One consequence of the above development is that the sequence $\{b_n\}$ can be generated alternatively by a logic circuit that performs the division of $P(z)$ by $Q(z)$. The first step in this formal long division is shown below:

$$\begin{array}{r|l} & p_1 z^{-1} \\ \hline z^L + q_1 z^{L-1} + \cdots + q_L & p_1 z^{L-1} + p_2 z^{L-2} + \cdots + p_L \\ & p_1 z^{L-1} + q_1 p_1 z^{L-2} + \cdots + q_{L-1} p_1 + q_L p_1 z^{-1} \\ \hline & r_1^{(1)} z^{L-2} + \cdots + r_{L-1}^{(1)} + r_L^{(1)} z^{-1} \end{array}$$

Note that the above formal computation is valid, even if $p_1 = 0$. The first cycle (shown above) in this never-ending long-division process produces a remainder polynomial via the equation

$$P(z) - p_1 z^{-1} Q(z) = z^{-1} R^{(1)}(z), \tag{5.21}$$

with the quotient coefficient p_1 being the first bit b_1 of the formal power series $B(z)$. Each succeeding cycle in the long-division process divides the previous cycle's remainder by $Q(z)$ to produce a quotient corresponding to the next element in $\{b_n\}$, and a new remainder. Specifically, let the n-th formal power series remainder in the division process be represented by

$$z^{-n} R^{(n)}(z) = \sum_{i=1}^{L} r_i^{(n)} z^{L-i-n}, \qquad n = 1, 2, \ldots . \tag{5.22}$$

The long division process imposes the following recursion on these remainders:

$$z^{-n}\left[R^{(n)}(z) - r_1^{(n)} z^{-1} Q(z)\right] = z^{-n-1} R^{(n+1)}(z). \tag{5.23}$$

In summary, the remainder polynomial (no negative powers of z) recursion

$$z R^{(n)}(z) - r_1^{(n)} Q(z) = R^{(n+1)}(z), \qquad n = 1, 2, \ldots, \tag{5.24}$$

initialized by

$$R^{(0)}(z) = P(z), \tag{5.25}$$

produces the desired output sequence through the series of quotient coefficients

$$b_n = r_1^{(n-1)}, \qquad n = 1, 2, \ldots . \tag{5.26}$$

The division of $P(z)$ by $Q(z)$ is embodied in the device, shown in Figure 5.6, which mechanizes the remainder recursion (5.22). This LFSR form is called the *Galois configuration* because it is related to Galois field multiplication (more on this in Section 5.5).

Example 5.4. A binary sequence of period $N = 30$ begins with the following thirty bits, indexed from the left:

000001100010010111110011101101

The formal power series representation (5.7) for this sequence begins

$$B(z) = z^{-6} + z^{-7} + z^{-11} + z^{-14} + z^{-16} + z^{-17} + \ldots, \tag{5.27}$$

and reduces by (5.14)–(5.17) to

$$B(z) = \frac{1}{z^6 + z^5 + z^4 + z^3 + z^2 + 1}. \tag{5.28}$$

The Galois and Fibonacci generators for the above sequence are shown in Figure 5.7.

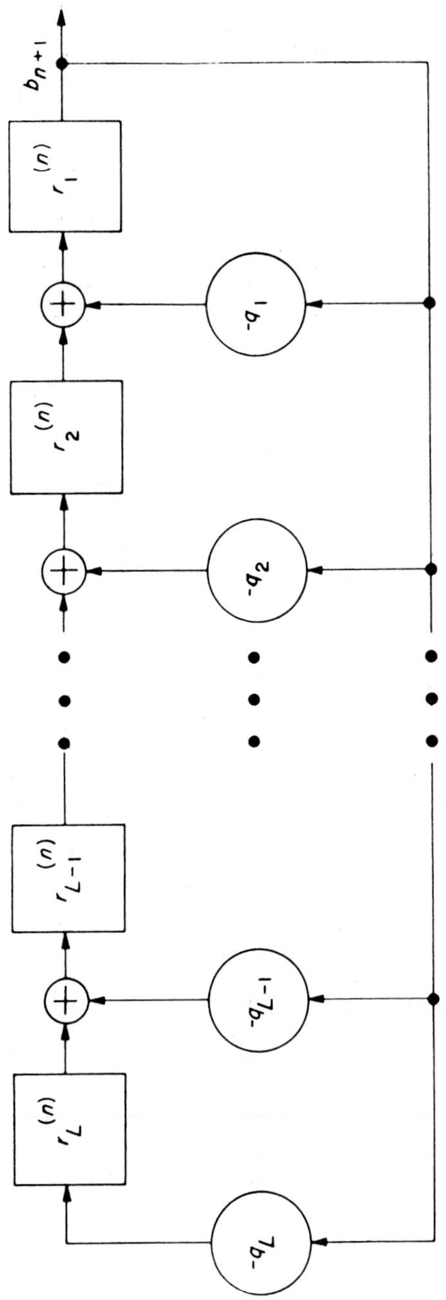

Figure 5.6. A minimum-memory LFSR in the Galois configuration for generating $\{ b_n \}$.

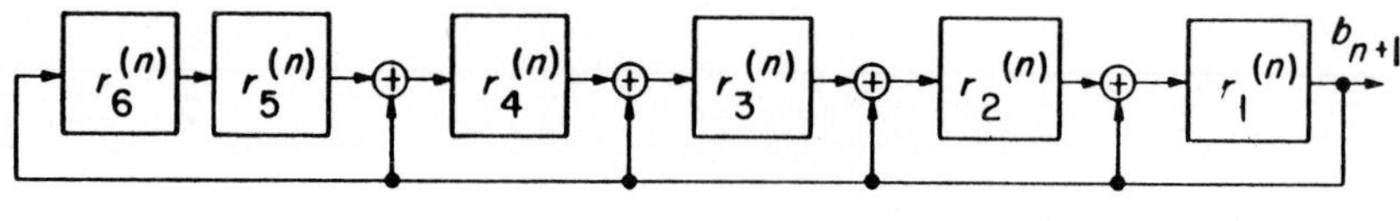

(a) Galois configuration

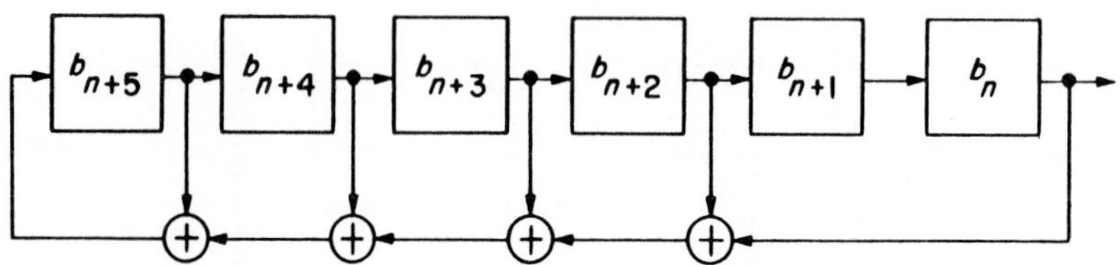

(b) Fibonacci configuration

Figure 5.7. Minimum-memory, linear feedback generators for the sequence represented by $1/(z^6 + z^5 + z^4 + z^3 + z^2 + 1)$.

5.2.4 State Space Viewpoint

The PN generators above can be viewed as autonomous linear sequential circuits, whose state vector s_n corresponds to the register contents, and whose operation is described formally by a state equation

$$\boldsymbol{s}_{n+1} = \boldsymbol{A}\boldsymbol{s}_n, \tag{5.29}$$

and an output equation

$$b_n = \boldsymbol{B}\boldsymbol{s}_n, \tag{5.30}$$

which describe circuit operation for $n = 1, 2, 3, \ldots$. Then it follows that

$$b_n = \boldsymbol{B}\boldsymbol{A}^{n-1}\boldsymbol{s}_1 \tag{5.31}$$

For minimum-memory linear generators, the matrix $\boldsymbol{A}$ is $L \times L$ and the vector $\boldsymbol{B}$ is $1 \times L$. The minimum-memory Fibonacci generator is described in these terms by

$$\boldsymbol{s}_n = \begin{bmatrix} b_n \\ b_{n+1} \\ \vdots \\ b_{n+L-1} \end{bmatrix}, \tag{5.32}$$

$$A = \begin{bmatrix} 0 & 1 & 0 & \cdots & 0 \\ 0 & 0 & 1 & & 0 \\ \vdots & & & & \vdots \\ 0 & 0 & 0 & & 1 \\ -q_L & -q_{L-1} & -q_{L-2} & \cdots & -q_1 \end{bmatrix}, \tag{5.33}$$

$$B = \begin{bmatrix} 1 & 0 & 0 & \cdots & 0 \end{bmatrix}. \tag{5.34}$$

Similarly, the minimum-memory Galois generator is represented by

$$s_n = \begin{bmatrix} r_L^{(n-1)} \\ r_{L-1}^{(n-1)} \\ \vdots \\ r_1^{(n-1)} \end{bmatrix}, \tag{5.35}$$

$$A = \begin{bmatrix} 0 & 0 & \cdots & 0 & -q_L \\ 1 & 0 & & 0 & -q_{L-1} \\ 0 & 1 & & 0 & -q_{L-2} \\ & \vdots & & & \\ 0 & 0 & \cdots & 1 & -q_1 \end{bmatrix}, \tag{5.36a}$$

$$B = \begin{bmatrix} 0 & 0 & \cdots & 0 & 1 \end{bmatrix}. \tag{5.36b}$$

The A matrices in (5.33) and (5.36a), which are transposes of each other, are referred to as *companion matrices* of the monic characteristic polynomial $Q(z)$, where

$$Q(z) = \sum_{i=0}^{L} q_i z^{L-i}. \tag{5.37}$$

Other linear sequential circuits, which generate the same output sequence $\{b_n\}$, can be constructed from transformations of the state space.

Let T be a nonsingular matrix over the sequence element field $\mathscr{F}$, and define a new state vector s'_n,

$$s'_n = Ts_n. \tag{5.38}$$

Then the linear sequential circuit of the new state sequence $\{s'_n\}$ has a state equation governed by the transition matrix

$$A' = TAT^{-1}, \tag{5.39}$$

and an output equation

$$b_n = BT^{-1}s'_n. \tag{5.40}$$

There is no significant difference between these generators when the output sequence is a linear function of the state sequence, as shown in (5.30), and (5.31). Certainly, the memory requirements are identical in each case, although some realizations may use fewer adders than others [50]. On the other hand, when the output b_n is a non-linear function of the circuit state s_n, i.e., non-linear feedforward logic is employed, then attempts to deduce the structure of the generator from a short segment of the output sequence may be complicated by the insertion of $\boldsymbol{T}$.

5.2.5 Determination of Linear Recursions from Sequence Segments

When given a segment $b_1, b_2, \ldots, b_K$, of K symbols from a sequence $\{b_n\}$, it is impossible to determine with absolute certainty the remainder of the sequence. However, if one proceeds on the assumption that K is at least twice the linear span of the sequence, and if that assumption is in fact correct, then a linear generator of the complete sequence can be determined. For the moment, consider the possibility of knowing the linear span L of the sequence *a priori*, in addition to $2L$ consecutive sequence elements. In this case, the fact that (5.6) also is linear in the L unknown coefficients a_i, $i = 1, 2, \ldots, L$, can be used to determine the recursion.

Example 5.5. Suppose that a binary sequence of elements from GF(2) is known to satisfy a linear recursion of degree 5, and, furthermore, a portion of the sequence contains

$$\ldots 1011101100011 \ldots \tag{5.41}$$

where the sequence index is increasing from left to right. Applying (5.6) separately to overlapping blocks of six consecutive symbols from the sequence gives the following set of equations:

$$\begin{aligned}
0 &= a_1 + a_2 + a_3 + \quad\;\; + a_5 \\
1 &= \quad\;\;\, a_2 + a_3 + a_4 \\
1 &= a_1 \qquad\;\; + a_3 + a_4 + a_5 \\
0 &= a_1 + a_2 \qquad\;\; + a_4 + a_5 \\
0 &= \quad\;\;\, a_2 + a_3 \qquad\;\; + a_5.
\end{aligned} \tag{5.42}$$

In constructing these L (in this case five) linearly independent equations, we used $L + 1$ specified sequence elements for the first equation plus one additional (previously unused) element for each additional equation. Hence, knowledge of $2L$ bits from the given sequence was used in the construction of (5.42). In the special case where the element field is GF(2) as it is here, the fact that the degree of the recursion is L and a_L is non-zero implies that a_L must be 1, the only non-zero field element. Therefore, only $L - 1$ equations are needed in the GF(2) case, in this example the first four in (5.42), which can be rewritten as

$$\begin{aligned}
1 &= a_1 + a_2 + a_3 \\
1 &= \quad\;\;\, a_2 + a_3 + a_4 \\
0 &= a_1 \qquad\;\; + a_3 + a_4 \\
1 &= a_1 + a_2 \qquad\;\; + a_4.
\end{aligned} \tag{5.43}$$

Since addition in GF(2) is modulo 2, adding the first three equations directly gives $a_3 = 0$, and adding the last three gives $a_4 = 0$. Substitution of these values gives $a_2 = 1$ and $a_1 = 0$, and, hence, the resulting linear recursion is

$$b_n = b_{n-2} + b_{n-5}. \tag{5.44}$$

When K symbols from the sequence are known but the linear span L is not, one can always guess L and follow the above procedure. If the guess is less than the true linear span, additional data will not be consistent with the deduced (incorrectly) linear generator. On the other hand, if the guess is greater than the true linear span, then multiple solutions will appear in the above procedure, all leading to correct, but usually non-minimal, generators of the complete sequence. Lacking knowledge of L, a more organized approach uses techniques for constructing rational approximations to the sequence's formal power series $B(z)$, when only the first K terms are known. These techniques, suggested by Massey for use in the Berlekamp-Massey decoding algorithm [7], [8], are closely related to continued fraction computations [9], [10], and will produce the characteristic and initial condition polynomials, $Q(z)$ and $P(z)$ of (5.16), whenever the number of available symbols K is at least twice the linear span L. Furthermore, this analysis can be performed in real time, in a manner such that more sequence symbols can be inserted into the computation as they become available.

If the above procedure is perceived as a threat to the objectives of the SS system design, then the designer must take steps to insure that $2L$ sequence elements cannot be observed directly from the transmitted signal. Three possible methods for accomplishing this are:

(a) Ensure that the linear span of the sequence $\{b_n\}$ (presumably used as a SS carrier of some sort) is much larger than the processing gain of the system, so that data modulation effects will, with high probability, preclude direct observation of $2L$ sequence elements.
(b) Insert erroneous symbols in the transmission of $\{b_n\}$ so that error-free observation of $2L$ consecutive sequence elements is virtually impossible. This can be accomplished with very little degradation to system performance when high processing gain is employed.
(c) Transmit in-band noise along with the SS signal based on $\{b_n\}$, to insure that no observer will get a "clean look" at the sequence. The cost of this can be made a small fraction of the processing gain.

Other methods for insuring transmission security against this threat are left to the ingenuity of the reader.

5.3 MEMORY-EFFICIENT LINEAR GENERATORS

5.3.1 Partial Fraction Decompositions

Initial conditions notwithstanding, the basic structural information about a linear generator is contained in its characteristic polynomial, $Q(z)$. Assuming that the generated sequence $\{b_n\}$ consists of elements from GF(q), the polynomial $Q(z)$ will then be over GF(q), i.e., have coefficients in GF(q). However, its roots may not be in GF(q). Let's assume that $Q(z)$ can be factored so that

$$Q(z) = \prod_{j=1}^{J} Q_j^{p_j}(z), \tag{5.45}$$

where each polynomial $Q_j(z)$ is irreducible over GF(q), and the linear span L of $\{b_n\}$ is given by

$$L = \sum_{j=1}^{J} p_j \deg Q_j(z). \tag{5.46}$$

The term *irreducible* over GF(q), when applied to a polynomial $A(z)$ over GF(q), means that $A(z)$ cannot be factored into a product of polynomials over GF(q). Hence, the factorization described in (5.45) is similar to the decomposition of an integer into prime factors.

The factorization (5.45) indicates that the rational representation (5.16) of the formal power series $B(z)$ can be expanded by partial fractions.

$$B(z) = \frac{P(z)}{\prod_{j=1}^{J} Q_j^{p_j}(z)} = \sum_{j=1}^{J} \frac{P_j(z)}{Q_j^{p_j}(z)}. \tag{5.47}$$

Therefore, the sequence represented by $B(z)$ also can be generated by summing the component sequences represented by

$$B_j(z) = \frac{P_j(z)}{Q_j^{p_j}(z)}, \qquad j = 1, 2, \ldots, J, \tag{5.48}$$

the j-th sequence having characteristic polynomial $Q_j^{P_j}(z)$ and initial condition polynomial $P_j(z)$. Let's define the period of the j-th sequence to be N_j. Then the period of the composite sequence $\{b_n\}$ is given by

$$N = \operatorname{lcm}(N_1, N_2, \ldots, N_J), \tag{5.49}$$

where lcm( ) represents the least common multiple of the listed integers.

Example 5.6. The sequence of Example 5.4 was represented by

$$B(z) = \frac{1}{z^6 + z^5 + z^4 + z^3 + z^2 + 1} = \frac{P_1(z)}{(z+1)^2} + \frac{P_2(z)}{z^4 + z^3 + 1}, \tag{5.50}$$

where $P_1(z)$ and $P_2(z)$ are polynomials of degrees at most 1 and 3,

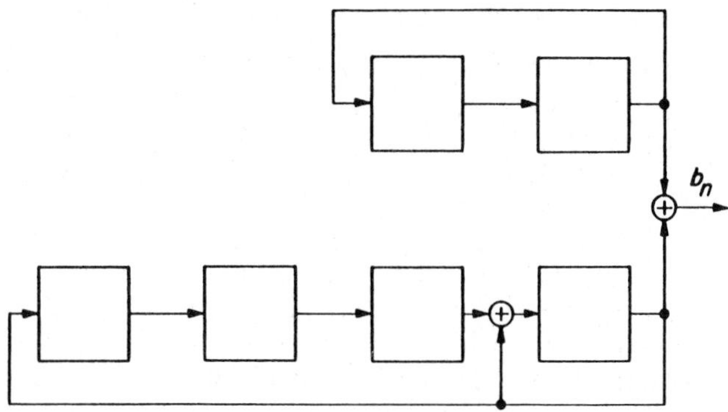

Figure 5.8. An LFSR generator for the sequence of Examples 5.4 and 5.6.

respectively. Solving for these polynomials gives the component generators

$$B_1(z) = \frac{z}{(z+1)^2} \tag{5.51a}$$

$$B_2(z) = \frac{z^3+z^2+z+1}{z^4+z^3+1}. \tag{5.51b}$$

The first generator produces the period 2 sequence

10

while the second generator outputs the period 15 sequence

101011001000111.

Extending these sequences periodically and summing gives the period 30 sequence of Example 5.4. The Galois-configured, component-structured, LFSR shown in Figure 5.8 can be initialized to have an output identical to the generators of Figure 5.7.

5.3.2 Maximization of Period for a Fixed Memory Size

The fundamental memory constraint (5.5) indicates that the maximum period achievable by any q-ary generator with M memory elements is q^M. This maximum period is reduced by 1 if the generator uses linear feedback, because the zero state is self-perpetuating, i.e., an LFSR initialized with zeros produces the uninteresting all-zeros sequence. Thus, the most efficient LFSR generators must cycle through all possible non-zero states before repeating, and the period N of an LFSR's state sequence is bounded by

$$N \leq q^M - 1. \tag{5.52}$$

In Example 5.6, the four-stage component LFSR generator achieved its maximum possible period of 15, while the two-stage generator did not; and the composite generator of six stages produced a period 30 sequence, nowhere near the upper bound of 63 dictated by (5.52).

Assuming a $Q(z)$ of the form (5.45), applying the bound (5.52) to the component sequences, and using (5.49) gives

$$\begin{aligned} N &\leq \prod_{j=1}^{J} N_j \\ &\leq \prod_{j=1}^{J} q^{p_j \deg Q_j(z)} - 1 \\ &\leq q^L - 1. \end{aligned} \tag{5.53}$$

It is clear from (5.53) that the fundamental bound (5.52) on N can be achieved if and only if all the above inequalities hold with equality. Equivalently, considering each inequality in turn, equality holds in (5.53) if and only if

(a) the periods of the component sequences are relatively prime,
(b) each component sequence achieves the bound (5.52) on its period for its memory size, and
(c) the number J of component sequences must be 1.

When the degrees of the component generator polynomials are large, then item (c) is not critical to the efficient use of memory in creating large periods.

5.3.3 Repeated Factors in the Characteristic Polynomial

Consider now the special case in which the characteristic polynomial of a sequence over GF(q) is the q-th power of a polynomial over GF(q). Theorem 5A.10 of Appendix 5A indicates that

$$Q^q(z) = \left(\sum_{i=0}^{d} q_{d-i} z^i \right)^q = \sum_{i=0}^{d} q_{d-i} z^{qi}. \tag{5.54}$$

Hence, the coefficient list of $Q^q(z)$ is simply

$$q_0 0 \ldots 0 q_1 0 \ldots 0 q_2 0 \ldots 0 q_{d-1} 0 \ldots 0 q_d,$$

where $0 \ldots 0$ represents a string of $q - 1$ zeros. A shift register governed by this form of generator polynomial will produce q interleaved sequences. That is, a symbol b_n in the composite output sequence $\{b_n\}$ is linked recursively only to the prior symbols b_{n-mq}, $m = 1, 2, 3, \ldots$.

This line of reasoning can be iterated to yield the following result.

THEOREM 5.2. *Let N be the period of a sequence having characteristic polynomial $Q(z)$ over* GF(q). *Then the period N' of the sequence having characteristic polynomial $Q^p(z)$ is given by*

$$N' = q^I N, \tag{5.55}$$

Table 5.5
Maximum periods N for twenty-stage binary LFSRs with characteristic polynomials of the form $Q^p(z)$ over GF(2), where $Q(z)$ has degree d.

degree	power		period
d	p	I	N
20	1	0	1048575
10	2	1	2046
5	4	2	124
4	5	3	120
2	10	4	48

where the interleaving exponent I is the unique integer satisfying the relation

$$q^{I-1} < p \le q^I. \tag{5.56}$$

Assuming that the period of the sequence generated by $Q(z)$ is maximal, i.e., is $q^d - 1$ where d is the degree of $Q(z)$, it is apparent that interleaving is not an efficient way to achieve sequences with long periods. As an example, the achievable periods for a register of twenty binary storage elements are tabulated in Table 5.5.

5.3.4 *M*-Sequences

Linear-feedback shift registers with L stages which produce the maximum possible period $q^L - 1$ do in fact exist, and the sequences which they produce are called *maximal LFSR sequences* or *m-sequences*. When the connection between shift register sequences over GF(q) and larger finite fields is established in Section 5.5, it will be apparent that irreducible polynomials of degree L over GF(q) generate sequences whose periods must be divisors of $q^L - 1$. Those special irreducible polynomials, which are the characteristic polynomials of m-sequences, are called *primitive polynomials*, and they exist for every degree over every finite field. Appendix 5B contains factorizations of $2^L - 1$ and a table of primitive polynomials over GF(2). Techniques described in Appendix 5A.8 can be applied to find other primitive/irreducible polynomials from those listed in Appendix 5B. It suffices at this point to note:

THEOREM 5.3. *A linear generator of a given memory size produces a sequence of elements from* GF(q), *with the largest possible period if and only if its characteristic polynomial is primitive over* GF(q).

Two sequences $\{b_n\}$ and $\{b'_n\}$, each having period N, are called *cyclically equivalent* if there exists an integer τ such that $b_{n+\tau} = b'_n$ for all n. A pair of

Table 5.6
The number $N_p(L)$ of cyclically distinct m-sequences with linear span L.

L	$N_p(L)$	L	$N_p(L)$
2	1	16	2048
3	2	17	7710
4	2	18	7776
5	6	19	27594
6	6	20	24000
7	18	21	84672
8	16	22	120032
9	48	23	356962
10	60	24	276480
11	176	25	1296000
12	144	26	1719900
13	630	27	4202496
14	756	28	4741632
15	1800	29	18407808

sequences, which are not cyclically equivalent, are termed *cyclically distinct*. Since m-sequences are cyclically distinct if and only if their linear recursions differ, the number of cyclically distinct m-sequences over GF(q) with linear span L is equal to the number $N_p(L)$ of primitive polynomials of degree L over GF(q), and is given by

$$N_p(L) = \frac{q^L - 1}{L} \prod_{i=1}^{J} \frac{p_i - 1}{p_i} \tag{5.57}$$

where the J prime numbers p_i, $i = 1, 2, \ldots, J$ are determined from the prime decomposition of $q^L - 1$, i.e.,

$$q^L - 1 = \prod_{i=1}^{J} p_i^{e_i} \tag{5.58}$$

where e_i, $i = 1, \ldots, J$ are positive integers. Table 5.6 illustrates the exponential nature of $N_p(L)$ for binary m-sequences.

5.4 STATISTICAL PROPERTIES OF *M*-SEQUENCES

Primitive polynomials provide LFSR connections for m-sequence generators which are virtually as efficient as counters in providing state sequences with large periods, the LFSR's state sequence being shorter by one than the counter's period for the same memory size. However, the binary counter did not provide a good basis for a PN generator because the individual memory cells of the counter produced simple "square wave" sequences, thereby requiring significant amounts of logic to produce sequences with the appearance of randomness. As will now be demonstrated, each memory cell of a Fibonacci m-sequence generator produces a sequence with statistical properties far superior, for PN applications, to a counter's cell output.

5.4.1 Event Counts

Since m-sequences over GF(q) with linear span L have period $q^L - 1$ and since the all-zeros sequence is self-perpetuating in a linear generator, it immediately follows that an m-sequence generator must cycle through the $q^L - 1$ non-zero state $L-$ tuples. In particular, a Fibonacci generator cycles through the state L-tuples

$$\mathbf{s}_n = \begin{bmatrix} b_n \\ b_{n+1} \\ \vdots \\ b_{n+L-1} \end{bmatrix}, \qquad n = 1, 2, \ldots, q^L - 1, \tag{5.59}$$

which correspond to L-symbol segments of the m-sequence $\{b_n\}$ (see (5.30)–(5.32)). This viewpoint leads to verification of the following random-appearance properties:

Property R-1.

The number N_b of times that a non-zero symbol b occurs in one period of an m-sequence $\{b_n\}$ exceeds the number N_0 of times 0 occurs in one period, by 1.

$$N_b = N_0 + 1, \quad \text{for all } b \neq 0. \tag{5.60}$$

This property, which states that symbols occur as equally often as possible within one period, is referred to as the *balance property*. Its proof follows directly from counting the number of times that a state L-tuple begins with a specific symbol in one cycle of the state sequence.

Property R-2.

Let $\{b_n\}$ be an m-sequence of elements from GF(q) with linear span L. The number $N_{\boldsymbol{a}}$ of positions within one period of $\{b_n\}$ at which a J-tuple $a_1 a_2 \ldots a_J$ occurs, is given by

$$N_{\boldsymbol{a}} = \begin{cases} q^{L-J}, & \text{for } \boldsymbol{a} \neq \mathbf{0}, \quad 1 \leq J \leq L \\ q^{L-J} - 1, & \text{for } \boldsymbol{a} = \mathbf{0}, \quad 1 \leq J \leq L \\ 0 \text{ or } 1, & L < J. \end{cases} \tag{5.61}$$

This generalization of the balance property also follows from state counting arguments.

The probability of obtaining a particular J-tuple $\boldsymbol{a}$ in J independent trials, each trial having q possible equally likely outcomes, is given by q^{-J}.

Table 5.7
Comparison of binary m-sequence J-tuple statistics with Bernoulli sequence probabilities for $L > J$.

J	Bernoulli J-tuple Probability	m-sequence statistics N_0/N, N_a/N		
		$L = 4$	$L = 6$	$L = 8$
1	.500	.467, .533	.492, .508	.498, .502
2	.250	.200, .267	.238, .254	.247, .251
3	.125	.067, .133	.111, .127	.122, .125

If an m-sequence of GF(q) elements is to have the appearance of such a random process's sample function, it is necessary that the time-average statistic N_a/N of the J-tuple event $\boldsymbol{a}$ be as close to q^{-J} as possible. For $J \leq L$, Property R-2 gives

$$\frac{N_0}{N} = \frac{q^{L-J} - 1}{q^L - 1} \tag{5.62}$$

for the all-zeros J-tuple (the worst case). Clearly N_0/N rapidly approaches q^{-J} as L increases (see Table 5.7).

5.4.2 The Shift-and-Add Property

The next property is the foundation for several important characteristics of m-sequences.

Property R-3.

Let $\{b_n\}$ be an m-sequence over GF(q) with linear span L. Then for any τ, $\tau \neq 0 \bmod q^L - 1$, the difference of the m-sequence $\{b_n\}$ and its τ-shift $\{b_{n+\tau}\}$ is another shift $\{b_{n+\tau'(\tau)}\}$ of the same m-sequence. That is,

$$b_{n+\tau'(\tau)} = b_{n+\tau} - b_n \quad \text{for all } n, \tag{5.63}$$

where $\tau'(\tau)$ is defined for all $\tau \neq 0 \bmod q^L - 1$.

Proof. The m-sequence and its τ-shift both satisfy the linear recursion of degree L determined by its characteristic polynomial $Q(z)$.

$$b_{n+\tau} = -\sum_{i=1}^{L} q_i b_{n+\tau-i} \quad \text{for all } n, \tag{5.64}$$

and the difference of $\{b_{n+\tau}\}$ and $\{b_n\}$ therefore satisfies the same recursion.

$$b_{n+\tau} - b_n = -\sum_{i=1}^{L} q_i (b_{n+\tau-i} - b_{n-i}) \quad \text{for all } n. \tag{5.65}$$

Since $\{s_n\}$ represents the state sequence for a Fibonacci generator producing $\{b_n\}$, then the initial state s'_n for $\{b_{n+\tau} - b_n\}$ is

$$s'_1 = s_{1+\tau} - s_1. \tag{5.66}$$

This initial state s'_1 is non-zero if, and only if, τ is not a multiple of the period $q^L - 1$ of the state sequence $\{s_n\}$. When s'_1 is non-zero, it is a state $s_{1+\tau'(\tau)}$ of the Fibonacci generator of $\{b_n\}$, and, hence, $\{b_{n+\tau'(\tau)}\}$ is the result of the recursion (5.64) operating on this initial state. ■

When the symbol field has characteristic 2 as it does in the case of binary (0 or 1) sequences, subtraction and addition are identical operations, and Property R-3 is usually called the *shift-and-add* (or *cycle-and-add*) property. It also is true that the sum of an m-sequence and its proper cyclic shift is another shift of the m-sequence, but the form (5.63) is more useful in the general results to follow.

5.4.3 Hamming Distance Properties of Derived Real-Integer Sequences

Sometimes an m-sequence generator over GF(q) is used to produce a pseudo-random sequence of integers between 0 and $q^J - 1$ by viewing the n-th J-tuple $(b_n, b_{n+1}, \ldots, b_{n+J-1})$ in the m-sequence $\{b_n\}$ as the base q expansion of the n-th integer i_n in the output integer sequence.

$$i_n = \sum_{j=0}^{J-1} b_{n+j} q^j \tag{5.67}$$

Some applications using integer sequences like $\{i_n\}$ require that the sequence be as distinct from its cyclic shifts as possible. One measure of this quality is the *Hamming metric* which counts the number of positions in which two N-tuples $\boldsymbol{x}$ and $\boldsymbol{y}$ differ. This metric takes the form

$$H(\boldsymbol{x}, \boldsymbol{y}) = \sum_{i=1}^{N} h(x_i, y_i) \tag{5.68}$$

where $h(x, y)$ is zero if x and y are identical, and one otherwise. The following attribute indicates that $\{i_n\}$ behaves much like a random sequence, with symbol matches between it and its cyclic shift occurring at a rate very close to one in every q^J tests.

Property R-4.

Let $\{b_n\}$ be an m-sequence over GF(q) with linear span L, and let $\{i_n\}$ be formed according to (5.67). Let $\boldsymbol{i}_k$ denote one period of the sequence $\{i_n\}$, beginning with the k-th integer. Then for $\tau \neq 0 \bmod q^L - 1$, the Hamming distance between $\boldsymbol{i}_1$ and $\boldsymbol{i}_{1+\tau}$ is given by

$$H(\boldsymbol{i}_1, \boldsymbol{i}_{1+\tau}) = q^L(1 - q^{-J}). \tag{5.69}$$

Proof. The proof of this result follows from Property R-3 which establishes that

$$\begin{aligned} i_n &= i_{n+\tau} \\ \text{iff } (b_n, \ldots, b_{n+J-1}) &= (b_{n+\tau}, \ldots, b_{n+\tau+J-1}) \\ \text{iff } (b_{n+\tau'(\tau)}, \ldots, b_{n+\tau'(\tau)+J-1}) &= \mathbf{0} \end{aligned} \tag{5.70}$$

with a count of the latter event evaluated in Property R-2. ■

Using a variation of Plotkin's bound, developed by Lempel and Greenberger [11], it can be proven that the integer sequence $\{i_n\}$ of (5.67) possesses optimal Hamming distance properties.

THEOREM 5.4. *Let $\{a_n\}$ be a sequence of period N, composed of symbols from an alphabet $\mathscr{A}$, and let $\boldsymbol{a}_j$ denote the N-tuple of consecutive symbols from $\{a_n\}$, beginning at the j-th symbol. Let*

$$H_{\min} = \min_{0<\tau<N} H(\boldsymbol{a}_1, \boldsymbol{a}_{1+\tau}), \tag{5.71}$$

and determine the integers α and β from

$$N = \alpha|\mathscr{A}| + \beta, \qquad 0 \le \beta < |\mathscr{A}|. \tag{5.72}$$

Then

$$H_{\min} \le N - \frac{\alpha}{N-1}(N + \beta - |\mathscr{A}|). \tag{5.73}$$

Proof. Certainly the minimum value $H_{\min}$ of Hamming distance between $\{a_n\}$ and its cyclic shifts must be less than the average value H_{avg} of the same quantities. Now

$$\begin{aligned} H_{\text{avg}} &= \frac{1}{N-1} \sum_{\tau=1}^{N-1} H(\boldsymbol{a}_1, \boldsymbol{a}_{1+\tau}) \\ &= \frac{1}{N-1} \sum_{n=1}^{N} \sum_{\tau=1}^{N-1} h(a_n, a_{n+\tau}). \end{aligned} \tag{5.74}$$

Let N_a denote the number of times that the symbol "a" occurs in one period of $\{a_n\}$. The number of times that $h(a_n, a_{n+\tau})$ is zero as τ varies over its range is simply $N_{a_n} - 1$. Hence,

$$\begin{aligned} H_{\text{avg}} &= \frac{1}{N-1} \sum_{n=1}^{N} (N - N_{a_n}) \\ &= \frac{1}{N-1}\left(N^2 - \sum_{a\in\mathscr{A}} N_a^2\right). \end{aligned} \tag{5.75}$$

Removing the dependence of (5.75) on the set of integers $\{N_a\}$ yields the bound

$$H_{\min} \le H_{\text{avg}} \le \max_{\{N_a\}} \frac{1}{N-1}\left(N^2 - \sum_{a\in\mathscr{A}} N_a^2\right), \tag{5.76}$$

where $\{N_a\}$ is a set of non-negative integers summing to N. It can be verified that the right side of (5.76) is maximized by making the integers N_a as nearly equal as possible. That is, the maximizing choice for $\{N_a\}$ contains the integer $\alpha + 1$ a total of β times and the integer α a total of $|\mathscr{A}| - \beta$ times. Substitution of these values into (5.76) and simplification using (5.72) yields the final result. ∎

Evaluation of the bound (5.73) for the parameters

$$N = q^L - 1, \qquad |\mathscr{A}| = q^J, \tag{5.77}$$

whence

$$\beta = q^J - 1, \qquad \alpha = q^{L-J} - 1, \tag{5.78}$$

gives the bound

$$H_{\min} \le q^L(1 - q^{-J}). \tag{5.79}$$

Property R-4 indicates that $\{i_n\}$ satisfies this bound with equality and, therefore, possesses the desirable attribute of being uniformly maximally distant from its proper cyclic shifts.

5.4.4 Correlation Properties of Derived Complex Roots-of-Unity Sequences

The case in which the field size q is a prime p, usually 2 in practice, deserves added attention. In this case, GF(p) arithmetic is modulo p arithmetic, and the field GF(p) is composed solely of integers $0, 1, \dots, p - 1$. By viewing these integers in GF(p) as being identical to their counterparts in the real numbers, the following mapping from b_n in GF(p) to a complex p-th root of unity can be constructed:

$$a_n = \rho^{b_n}, \tag{5.80}$$

where ρ is a primitive p-th root of unity in the field of complex numbers, e.g.,

$$\rho = \exp(i2\pi/p). \tag{5.81}$$

(In the special case when $p = 2$, then $\rho = -1$ and $b_n \in \mathrm{GF}(2) = \{0, 1\}$ is mapped into $a_n \in \{1, -1\}$.) Consequently, addition modulo p of two elements b_m and b_n from GF(p) in the domain of the mapping (5.80) is isomorphic to complex multiplication of two elements in the range of the mapping, i.e.,

$$a_m a_n = \rho^{b_m + b_n}, \tag{5.82}$$

with addition of integers in the exponent being both real and modulo p since ρ is a p-th root of unity.

An m-sequence $\{b_n\}$ of elements from GF(p), satisfying the linear recursion

$$b_n = -\sum_{i=1}^{L} q_i b_{n-i}, \tag{5.83}$$

can be mapped by (5.80) into a sequence $\{a_n\}$ of complex p-th roots of unity satisfying the multiplicative recursion

$$a_n = \prod_{i=1}^{L} a_{n-i}^{-q_i}. \tag{5.84}$$

Note that $\{a_n\}$ generally does not satisfy a linear recursion of degree L over the complex numbers. However, the resulting complex sequence $\{a_n\}$ often retains the name m-sequence.

Since the m-sequence $\{a_n\}$ consists of complex numbers, it is possible to evaluate its *periodic autocorrelation function* $P_{aa}(\tau)$, defined by

$$P_{aa}(\tau) = \sum_{n=1}^{N} a_{n+\tau} a_n^*, \tag{5.85}$$

where ( )* denotes conjugation. The nearly ideal periodic correlation function of m-sequences is described in the following result.

Property R-5.

Let $\{a_n\}$ be a complex m-sequence of period N, composed of p-th roots of unity. The periodic correlation $P_{aa}(\tau)$ of $\{a_n\}$ has the form

$$P_{aa}(\tau) = \begin{cases} N, & \tau = 0 \bmod N \\ -1, & \tau \neq 0 \bmod N. \end{cases} \tag{5.86}$$

Proof. The case $\tau = 0 \bmod N$ is obvious. Note that $N = p^L - 1$, L being the linear span of the corresponding m-sequence $\{b_n\}$ over GF(p), and by R-2 the number of occurrences of any specified non-zero symbol in one period of $\{b_n\}$ is p^{L-1}. Hence, for $\tau \neq 0 \bmod N$,

$$\begin{aligned} P_{aa}(\tau) &= \sum_{n=1}^{N} \rho^{b_{n+\tau} - b_n} && \text{[by (5.80)]} \\ &= \sum_{n=1}^{N} \rho^{b_{n+\tau'(\tau)}} && \text{[by R-3]} \\ &= -1 + \rho^{L-1} \sum_{j=0}^{p-1} \rho^j && \text{[by R-2]} \\ &= -1. \end{aligned} \tag{5.87}$$

■

When the sequence period N is large compared to the processing gain, as it is in many systems, the full period correlation $P_{aa}(\tau)$ loses some of its value as a design parameter. Correlation calculations in this case typically are carried out over blocks of K symbols, where K may be larger than the linear span L and much smaller than the period N. A more appropriate statistic for study in this case is the *partial-period correlation* defined as

$$P_{aa}(K, n, \tau) = \sum_{j=0}^{K-1} a_{n+j+\tau} a_{n+j}^* \tag{5.88}$$

which computes the cross-correlation between two blocks of K symbols from $\{a_n\}$, one block located τ symbols from the other.

Unlike full-period correlation calculations, partial-period correlation values depend on the initial location n in the sequence where the correlation computation begins. Hence, an explicit description of the function $P_{aa}(K, n, \tau)$ must include values over the range $0 \leq n < N$ of n. Often the size of N precludes direct calculation of all these values, and computable time averages therefore are substituted to give a statistical description of the partial-period correlation function. Denoting the time-average operation by $\langle \cdot \rangle$, the first and second time-average moments of $P_{aa}(K, n, \tau)$ are given by

$$\langle P_{aa}(K, n, \tau)\rangle = \frac{1}{N}\sum_{n=1}^{N} P_{aa}(K, n, \tau) \tag{5.89}$$

$$\langle |P_{aa}(K, n, \tau)|^2\rangle = \frac{1}{N}\sum_{n=1}^{N} |P_{aa}(K, n, \tau)|^2, \tag{5.90}$$

where the parameter over which the average is being computed is n.

Property R-6.

Let $\{a_n\}$ be a complex m-sequence of period N, composed of p-th roots of unity. The time-averaged first and second moments of the partial-period correlation function of $\{a_n\}$ are given by

$$\langle P_{aa}(K, n, \tau)\rangle = \begin{cases} -K/N, & \tau \neq 0 \bmod N \\ K, & \tau = 0 \bmod N \end{cases} \tag{5.91}$$

and

$$\langle |P_{aa}(K, n, \tau)|^2\rangle = \begin{cases} K\left(1 - \dfrac{K-1}{N}\right), & \tau \neq 0 \bmod N \\ K^2, & \tau = 0 \bmod N \end{cases} \tag{5.92}$$

respectively, for $K \leq N$.

Proof. The first moment calculation is straightforward:

$$\begin{aligned}\langle P_{aa}(K, n, \tau)\rangle &= \frac{1}{N}\sum_{n=1}^{N}\sum_{k=0}^{K-1} a_{n+k+\tau}a^*_{n+k} \\ &= \frac{1}{N}\sum_{k=0}^{K-1} P_{aa}(\tau),\end{aligned} \tag{5.93}$$

and (5.91) follows directly from Property R-5.

The derivation of the second moment uses the additional fact that Property R-3 for an m-sequence over GF(p) translates via (5.80) into the property

$$a_{n+\tau}a^*_n = a_{n+\tau'(\tau)}, \quad \text{for all } n, \tag{5.94}$$

when $\tau \neq 0 \bmod N$. Hence,

$$\begin{aligned}\langle |P_{aa}(K,n,\tau)|^2\rangle &= \frac{1}{N}\sum_{n=1}^{N}\sum_{j=0}^{K-1} a_{n+j+\tau}a_{n+j}^{*}\left(\sum_{k=0}^{K-1} a_{n+k+\tau}a_{n+k}^{*}\right)^{*}\\ &= \frac{1}{N}\sum_{n=1}^{N}\sum_{j=0}^{K-1}\sum_{k=0}^{K-1} a_{n+j+\tau'(\tau)}a_{n+k+\tau'(\tau)}^{*}\\ &= \frac{1}{N}\sum_{j=0}^{K-1}\sum_{k=0}^{K-1} P_{aa}(j-k).\end{aligned}\tag{5.95}$$

Noting that there are K terms for which $j = k$, and $K(K-1)$ terms for which $j \neq k$, the final result follows immediately by applying Property R-5 to (5.95). ■

As a check, note that the results of Property R-6 reduce to those of the full period case R-5 when $K = N$.

For comparison, consider a periodic sequence $\{x_n\}$ composed of N independent, identically distributed (i.i.d.) random variables, uniformly distributed over the elements of GF(p), p prime. Furthermore, let $\{z_n\}$ be the corresponding complex sequence determined by the usual mapping (5.80) to p-th roots of unity. Clearly the elements of $\{z_n\}$ are i.i.d. random variables, uniformly distributed on the p-th roots of unity. Both the full-period and partial-period time-average autocorrelation functions of $\{z_n\}$ are random variables whose ensemble-average moments can be evaluated, using the independence assumption and the fact that

$$\mathbf{E}\{z_n\} = 0,\tag{5.96}$$

where $\mathbf{E}$ denotes the ensemble average operator. The first moment of the partial period correlation of $\{z_n\}$ is easily shown to be

$$\mathbf{E}\{P_{zz}(K,n,\tau)\} = \begin{cases} K, & \tau = 0 \bmod N\\ 0, & \tau \neq 0 \bmod N\end{cases}\tag{5.97}$$

Evaluation of the second moment of $P_{zz}(K,n,\tau)$ uses the fourth moment

$$\mathbf{E}\{z_{n+j+\tau}z_{n+j}^{*}z_{n+k+\tau}^{*}z_{n+k}\} = \begin{cases} 1, & \tau = 0 \bmod N\\ 1, & k = j \text{ and } \tau \neq 0 \bmod N\\ 0, & k \neq j \text{ and } \tau \neq 0 \bmod N\end{cases}\tag{5.98}$$

to yield

$$\begin{aligned}\mathbf{E}\{|P_{zz}(K,n,\tau)|^2\} &= \sum_{j=0}^{K-1}\sum_{k=0}^{K-1}\mathbf{E}\{z_{n+j+\tau}z_{n+j}^{*}z_{n+k+\tau}^{*}z_{n+k}\}\\ &= \begin{cases} K^2, & \tau = 0 \bmod N\\ K, & \tau \neq 0 \bmod N.\end{cases}\end{aligned}\tag{5.99}$$

Comparisons of (5.97) and (5.99) for a random sequence with (5.91) and

(5.92) for an m-sequence both indicate that when $K \ll N$, then the time-averaged mean and correlation values of an m-sequence are very close to the corresponding ensemble averages for a randomly chosen sequence. This fact and the balance properties of m-sequences are used to justify their approximation by a random sequence of bits in later analyses of SS system performance.

Both the full-period and partial-period correlation computations have a particularly simple characterization when $\{b_n\}$ is a sequence of elements from GF(2) and $\{a_n\}$ is a sequence of $+1$'s and -1's. In this case when $\tau \neq 0 \bmod N$,

$$\begin{aligned} P_{aa}(K, n, \tau) &= \sum_{j=0}^{K-1} (-1)^{b_{n+j+\tau} - b_{n+j}} \\ &= \sum_{j=0}^{K-1} (-1)^{b_{n+j+\tau'(\tau)}} \\ &= K - wt\big((b_{n+\tau'(\tau)}, \ldots, b_{n+\tau'(\tau)+K-1})\big) \end{aligned} \quad (5.100)$$

where the weight $wt(\boldsymbol{x})$ of a vector $\boldsymbol{x}$ denotes the number of non-zero elements in $\boldsymbol{x}$. Hence, $P_{aa}(K, n, \tau)$ is a simple affine transformation of the weight of a K-tuple from $\{b_n\}$, beginning at element index $n + \tau'(\tau)$. This relation, a direct result of the shift-and-add property, simplifies the tabulation and analysis of partial-period correlation statistics.

While the results of the last three sections appear to present a relatively complete theory and are to a great extent available in [12], the study of partial-period correlation has remained a topic of research interest for many years. Bartee and Wood [13] used an exhaustive search to find the binary m-sequence, of each possible period up to $2^{14} - 1$, which possessed the largest value for the minimum K-tuple weight, D.

$$D = \min_{1 \le n \le N} wt\big((b_n, \ldots, b_{n+K-1})\big) \quad (5.101)$$

Equivalently by (5.101), Bartee and Wood found the m-sequences $\{a_n\}$ which possess the maximum value of $\max_{0 \le n \le N} \max_{0 < \tau < N} P_{aa}(K, n, \tau)$, for fixed linear span L and correlation length K.

Table 5.8 displays characteristic polynomials of m-sequences which possess the largest value of D among all m-sequences of linear span L. These polynomials are specified in octal, i.e., the coefficients of the polynomial are the bits in the binary representation of the octal number. The binary representation of the octal number is determined simply by converting each octal symbol to its equivalent three-bit binary representation. For example,

$$27405 \text{ (octal)} = \underline{010}\,\underline{111}\,\underline{100}\,\underline{000}\,\underline{101} \text{ (binary)} \quad (5.102)$$

represents $z^{13} + z^{11} + z^{10} + z^9 + z^8 + z^2 + 1$. Leading zeros resulting from the octal to binary conversion may be ignored.

Table 5.8

Characteristic polynomials (in octal) of m-sequences with linear span L, having largest value D (in parentheses) of minimum K-tuple weight. The optimum polynomial is not unique. (Abstracted from [13].)

L \ K	10	20	30	40	50	60	70	80	90	100	200
2	(6)	(13)	(20)	7 (26)	7 (33)	7 (40)	7 (46)	7 (53)	7 (60)	7 (66)	(133)
3	(5)	(11)	(16)	13 (22)	13 (28)	13 (33)	13 (40)	13 (45)	13 (51)	13 (56)	(113)
4	(4)	(9)	(16)	23 (20)	23 (25)	23 (32)	23 (36)	23 (41)	23 (48)	23 (52)	(105)
5	(3)	(8)	(15)	75 (19)	45 (24)	45 (30)	75 (34)	45 (39)	45 (45)	75 (50)	(101)
6	(2)	(7)	(12)	155 (17)	103 (22)	103 (29)	147 (33)	147 (38)	147 (42)	155 (47)	(99)
7	(2)	(7)	(12)	367 (17)	367 (21)	313 (26)	211 (31)	345 (36)	345 (41)	211 (46)	(96)
8	(2)	(6)	(10)	703 (15)	703 (20)	747 (25)	747 (30)	703 (34)	453 (39)	703 (44)	(96)
9	(1)	(5)	(10)	1131 (14)	1715 (19)	1715 (24)	1773 (29)	1773 (34)	1423 (38)	1773 (43)	(91)
10		(5)	(9)	2033 (14)	3507 (18)	3507 (22)	3507 (27)	2461 (32)	3525 (37)	3525 (42)	(89)
11		(4)	(8)	4173 (13)	7461 (17)	7655 (22)	7655 (27)	7107 (31)	4055 (36)	5607 (40)	(89)
12		(4)	(8)	17147 (12)	14271 (17)	10605 (21)	17147 (25)	17025 (30)	12727 (35)	17025 (39)	(86)
13		(4)	(7)	34035 (11)	21103 (16)	27405 (20)	31231 (24)	23231 (29)	37335 (33)	32467 (38)	(85)
14				41657 (11)	73071 (15)	65575 (19)	64457 (23)	64167 (28)	61333 (32)	65277 (37)	(83)

Lindholm [14] derived expressions for the first five time-average moments of the partial period correlation values of m-sequences (including those of Property R-6). He noted that only the first two moments were independent of the characteristic polynomial of an m-sequence with specified period. Cooper and Lord [15], following a study of Mattson and Turyn [16], noted that for n in the vicinity of a run of $L-1$ zeros in an m-sequence, $P_{aa}(K, n, \tau)$ had lower correlation values, as τ varied around zero, for m-sequences whose characteristic polynomials contained more non-zero coefficients. Wainberg and Wolf [17] compared the moments of K-tuple weight distributions for m-sequences over GF(2) to the corresponding moments for a purely random sequence, and, extending Lindholm's work, carried this out through the sixth moment with $K \leq 100$ for several sequences.

Fredricsson [18] carried this idea closer to the realm of coding theory by noting that the set of N-tuples consisting of one period of an m-sequence and all its cyclic shifts, and the all-zeros N-tuple, together form a linear code which is the dual of a single-error-correcting Hamming code. Since the set $\{(b_n, \ldots, b_{n+K-1})\colon n = 1, 2, \ldots, N\}$ of K-tuples along with the all-zeros K-tuple form a punctured version of this m-sequence code, the set's dual is a shortened Hamming code. The weight distribution of the shortened Hamming code can be related in turn to the moments of the weight distribution of K-tuples from $\{b_n\}$ by the MacWilliams-Pless identities [19]. Bekir [20] extended this approach by applying moment techniques [21], [22] to generate upper and lower bounds on the distribution function of partial-period correlation values.

5.5 GALOIS FIELD CONNECTIONS

5.5.1 Extension Field Construction

The reader with no prior knowledge of finite field structures is urged at this point to review Appendix 5A, for the connection between certain LFSRs and finite fields will now be clarified. Assume that one has mechanized arithmetic units to carry out addition and multiplication in a finite field GF(q) which we will refer to as the *ground field*. In many practical designs the ground field is GF(2) since modulo 2 arithmetic units are available. Let $m_\alpha(z)$ be an irreducible polynomial of degree d over GF(q), $d > 1$, with a root called α; $m_\alpha(z)$ is termed the *minimum polynomial of* α *over* GF(q). Certainly, α is not a member of GF(q), or else $m_\alpha(z)$ would have a factor $z - \alpha$ over GF(q). Hence, α is a member of a larger field, called an *extension field* of GF(q), which will now be constructed.

Let $\mathscr{S}_d$ be the set of q^d distinct polynomials over GF(q) of degree less than d in an indeterminate z. That is,

$$\mathscr{S}_d = \left\{ X(z)\colon X(z) = \sum_{i=0}^{d-1} x_i z^i, x_i \in \mathrm{GF}(q) \right\}. \tag{5.103}$$

It is well known that the q^d distinct elements of $\mathrm{GF}(q^d)$ correspond to the polynomials of $\mathscr{S}_d$ evaluated at a root of an irreducible polynomial of degree d over $\mathrm{GF}(q)$. Therefore, let the field element x in $\mathrm{GF}(q^d)$ corresponding to the polynomial $X(z)$ in $\mathscr{S}_d$ be given by

$$x = X(\alpha) = \sum_{i=0}^{d-1} x_i \alpha^i. \tag{5.104}$$

The representation (5.104) clearly indicates that $\mathrm{GF}(q^d)$ can be viewed as a vector space of dimension d over a scalar field $\mathrm{GF}(q)$ with $1, \alpha, \alpha^2, \ldots, \alpha^{d-1}$ serving as a basis. While there is also an obvious correspondence between field elements x and polynomials $X(z)$, the field element itself is not a polynomial in an indeterminate z, but rather should be viewed as a "pseudopolynomial" in the basis element α.

Addition of the elements x and y in the extension field, corresponding to the polynomials $X(z)$ and $Y(z)$ in $\mathscr{S}_d$, corresponds to vector addition.

$$x + y = X(\alpha) + Y(\alpha) = \sum_{i=0}^{d-1} (x_i + y_i)\alpha^i. \tag{5.105}$$

More effort is required to express the result of a multiplication operation in the same basis; specifically a polynomial multiplication modulo $m_\alpha(z)$ must first be carried out to determine $R(z)$, i.e.,

$$X(z)Y(z) = W(z)m_\alpha(z) + R(z), \tag{5.106}$$

where $R(z)$ is a member of $\mathscr{S}_d$. Then, since α is a root of $m_\alpha(z)$, it follows that

$$xy = X(\alpha)Y(\alpha) = R(\alpha). \tag{5.107}$$

Hence, computation in $\mathrm{GF}(q^d)$ is often referred to as arithmetic modulo $m_\alpha(z)$.

5.5.2 The LFSR as a Galois Field Multiplier

In Section 5.2.3 the contents of a shift register after n shifts were considered to be coefficients of a polynomial $R^{(n)}(z)$, and successive register contents were related by the polynomial recursion (see (5.24)–(5.26))

$$zR^{(n)}(z) = b_n Q(z) + R^{(n+1)}(z), \tag{5.108}$$

with

$$R^{(0)}(z) = P(z), \tag{5.109}$$

where $P(z)/Q(z)$ is the formal power series representation of $\{b_n\}$. Suppose that

$$Q(z) = m_\alpha(z), \tag{5.110}$$

i.e., the characteristic polynomial of the sequence $\{b_n\}$ produced by a Galois-configured LFSR is irreducible over $\mathrm{GF}(q)$ and has root α. Evaluating (5.108) at $z = \alpha$ gives

$$\alpha R^{(n)}(\alpha) = R^{(n+1)}(\alpha). \tag{5.111}$$

Hence, one shift of a d-element LFSR with connections specified by $m_\alpha(z)$, corresponds to multiplication of a field element $R^{(n)}(\alpha)$ of GF(q^d) by the element α, the register contents before the shift being the coefficients of the representation of $R^{(n)}(\alpha)$ in the basis $1, \alpha, \ldots, \alpha^{d-1}$, and after the shift being the coefficients for $R^{(n+1)}(\alpha)$. Solving the recursion in the finite field indicates that the register contents after n shifts represent

$$R^{(n)}(\alpha) = \alpha^n P(\alpha). \tag{5.112}$$

Certainly, the period of the state sequence ($\mathbf{s}_n$} for this LFSR (see (5.35)) is the same as the smallest value of N such that

$$\alpha^n = 1. \tag{5.113}$$

This smallest value of N satisfying (5.113) is called the *exponent* (or *order*) *of* α, and can be shown to be a divisor of the number of non-zero elements of GF(q^d), namely $q^d - 1$ (see Appendix 5A.6). Furthermore, it has been shown that the multiplicative group of a finite field is cyclic; hence, each Galois field GF(q^d) contains elements whose exponents are exactly $q^d - 1$, these elements being called *primitive elements* of the Galois field's multiplicative group. The minimum polynomials of these primitive elements are the *primitive polynomials* appearing as characteristic polynomials of m-sequences.

5.5.3 Determining the Period of Memory Cell Outputs

While the multiplier viewpoint relates the period of certain LFSR state sequences to field element properties, it is not yet clear that the period of the state sequence $\{\mathbf{s}_n\}$ is identical to the period of the output sequence $\{b_n\}$. Referring to Figure 5.6, let $R_i(z)$ denote the formal power series representation of $\{r_i^{(n-1)}\}$, the sequence of contents of the i-th memory element in an arbitrary Galois-configured LFSR.

$$R_i(z) \triangleq \sum_{n=1}^{\infty} r_i^{(n-1)} z^{-n}. \tag{5.114}$$

The output memory element has index 1 and, therefore,

$$R_1(z) = \frac{P(z)}{Q(z)}, \tag{5.115}$$

where $Q(z)$ is the characteristic polynomial of the output sequence $\{b_n\}$. The series representation of the sequence produced by the second memory element can be related to $R_1(z)$ by noting that the input to the first memory element obeys the relation

$$r_1^{(n)} = r_2^{(n-1)} - q_1 r_1^{(n-1)}, \qquad n = 1, 2, \ldots, \tag{5.116}$$

where q_1 is a coefficient of $Q(z)$ (see (5.20)). Hence, carefully checking initial conditions,

$$R_1(z) = z^{-1}\left[r_1^{(0)} + R_2(z) - q_1 R_1(z)\right], \tag{5.117}$$

whence

$$R_2(z) = (z + q_1)R_1(z) - r_1^{(0)}. \tag{5.118}$$

By iterating this computation and substituting (5.115), it can be shown that the formal power series representation for the sequence generated by the k-th memory cell is

$$R_k(z) = \left(\sum_{i=0}^{k-1} q_i z^{k-1-i}\right)\frac{P(z)}{Q(z)} - \left(\sum_{i=1}^{k-1} r_i^{(0)} z^{k-1-i}\right), \qquad k = 2, 3, \ldots, L. \tag{5.119}$$

where L is the number of memory elements (the degree of $Q(z)$) and also the linear span of $\{b_n\}$. Since $P(z)$ and $Q(z)$ contain no common factors, the following result is now evident.

THEOREM 5.5. *Let $Q(z)$ be the characteristic polynomial for the output of a Galois-configured LFSR. Then (with indexing as shown in Figure 5.6) the sequence generated in the k-th memory element, $k > 1$, has characteristic polynomial given by $Q(z)/\gcd(Q(z), \sum_{i=0}^{k-1} q_i z^{k-1-i})$.*

COROLLARY 5.1. *Let the minimum polynomial $m_\alpha(z)$ over GF(q) be the characteristic polynomial of the output sequence from a Galois-configured LFSR. Then all memory cells in the register produce sequences having characteristic polynomial $m_\alpha(z)$ and possess identical periods equal to the exponent of α.*

Proof. Since $m_\alpha(z)$ is irreducible, all cells have the same characteristic polynomial by Theorem 5.5, and all possess identical periods by Theorem 5.1. ■

Example 5.7. As an aside to illustrate what can happen when $Q(z)$ is composite, consider a Galois LFSR with output sequence possessing the following characteristic polynomial over GF(2).

$$\begin{aligned} Q(z) &= z^8 + z^7 + z^6 + z^4 + z^3 + z + 1 \\ &= (z^3 + z + 1)^2(z^2 + z + 1). \end{aligned} \tag{5.120}$$

Since both $(z^3 + z + 1)$ and $(z^2 + z + 1)$ are primitive with periods 7 and 3, respectively, Theorem 5.2 indicates that the period of the output sequence for a properly initialized register should be $2 \times 3 \times 7$, i.e., 42. Theorem 5.5 predicts that the characteristic polynomial for the sequences of memory cells 3 and 4 is $(z^3 + z + 1)^2$, while that for the sequence of cell 5 is $(z^3 + z + 1)(z^2 + z + 1)$. Hence, cells 3 and 4 will generate period 14 sequences (see Theorem 5.2), while cell 5 will produce a period 21 sequence. The register

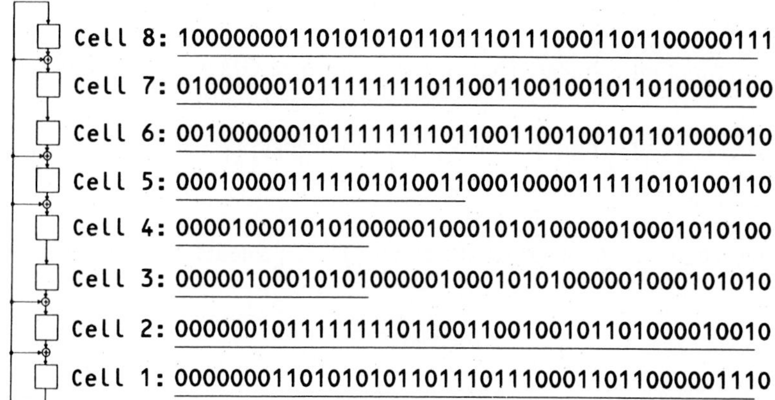

Figure 5.9. A Galois LFSR producing sequences with differing periods. Single periods are underlined.

configuration and memory cell sequences for this example are shown in Figure 5.9.

5.5.4 The Trace Representation of *M*-Sequences

A fundamental mathematical tool used in the further investigation of PN generators is a particular linear mapping from a finite field onto a subfield. This mapping, called the *trace function*, will now be reviewed, and an explicit expression for the elements of an m-sequence will be constructed.

Let GF(q) be any finite field contained within a larger field GF(q^d). Then the *trace polynomial* $\mathrm{Tr}_q^{q^d}(z)$ from GF(q^d) to GF(q) is defined as

$$\mathrm{Tr}_q^{q^d}(z) \triangleq \sum_{i=0}^{d-1} z^{q^i} \tag{5.121}$$

The trace (function) in GF(q) of an element α in GF(q^d) is defined as $\mathrm{Tr}_q^{q^d}(\alpha)$, i.e., the trace polynomial evaluated at α. The values of q and d are often obvious in the context of a particular application, in which case the cumbersome superscript and subscript are dropped from the trace notation.

The trace function has the following useful properties which are proved in Appendix 5A.9.

Property T-1.

When α is in GF(q^d), then $\mathrm{Tr}_q^{q^d}(\alpha)$ is in GF(q).

Property T-2.

All roots of an irreducible polynomial $m_\alpha(z)$ over GF(q), with root α in GF(q^d), have the same trace, i.e.,

$$\mathrm{Tr}_q^{q^d}(\alpha^{q^i}) = \mathrm{Tr}_q^{q^d}(\alpha) \quad \text{for all } i. \tag{5.122}$$

Property T-3.

The trace function is linear. That is, for a and b in GF(q), and α and β in GF(q^d),

$$\mathrm{Tr}_q^{q^d}(a\alpha + b\beta) = a\,\mathrm{Tr}_q^{q^d}(\alpha) + b\,\mathrm{Tr}_q^{q^d}(\beta). \tag{5.123}$$

Property T-4.

For each choice of b in GF(q) there are q^{d-1} elements α in GF(q^d) for which

$$\mathrm{Tr}_q^{q^d}(\alpha) = b. \tag{5.124}$$

Property T-5.

If $\mathrm{GF}(q) \subset \mathrm{GF}(q^k) \subset \mathrm{GF}(q^d)$, then

$$\mathrm{Tr}_q^{q^d}(\alpha) = \mathrm{Tr}_q^{q^k}\big(\mathrm{Tr}_{q^k}^{q^d}(\alpha)\big), \tag{5.125}$$

for all α in GF(q^d).

Those familiar with finite fields will recognize that when the minimum polynomial $m_\alpha(z)$ of α over GF(q) has degree d, then $\alpha, \alpha^q, \alpha^{q^2}, \ldots, \alpha^{q^{d-1}}$ are its distinct roots, $-\mathrm{Tr}_q^{q^d}(\alpha)$ is the coefficient of z^{d-1} in $m_\alpha(z)$, and the trace is therefore in GF(q). However, when $m_\alpha(z)$ has degree k, $k < d$ (k must divide d), then the roots of $m_\alpha(z)$ appear d/k times in (5.121) and $\mathrm{Tr}_q^{q^d}(\alpha)$ is $(d/k)\mathrm{Tr}_q^{q^k}(\alpha)$.

Once a primitive element α has been specified by choosing its minimum polynomial $m_\alpha(z)$ of degree d over GF(q), then the trace of any non-zero element α^k in GF(q) can be evaluated directly.

$$\mathrm{Tr}_q^{q^d}(\alpha^j) = \mathrm{Tr}_q^{q^d}(z^j) \bmod m_\alpha(z). \tag{5.126}$$

The substitution of z^j for z in the trace polynomial allows the evaluation of the trace of α^j by substitution of α, and the reduction of the resulting polynomial $\bmod\, m_\alpha(z)$ eliminates terms which will be zero upon evaluation at α. The result on the right side of (5.126) is an element of $\mathscr{S}_d$ (see (5.103)), while Property T-2 implies that the quantity on the left must be in GF(q). Since the elements of $\mathscr{S}_d$ corresponding to GF(q) elements are in fact those same elements, i.e., only x_0 in (5.104) is non-zero in this case, the substitution of $z = \alpha$ on the right side of (5.126) is not necessary.

Example 5.8. Let α be a root of the primitive polynomial $z^5 + z^2 + 1$. The root α and its conjugates (other roots of the same primitive polynomial), namely α^2, α^4, α^8, and α^{16}, are elements of GF(32). Other elements of GF(32) can also be grouped into root sets. The powers on α corresponding to a root set must be relatively prime to the order of α to insure that the corresponding polynomial is primitive. In this case primitivity is guaranteed

Table 5.9
Cyclotomic cosets and associated trace function values when α is a root of $z^5 + z^2 + 1$ over GF(2).

Cyclotomic coset elements x	$\mathrm{Tr}_2^{32}(\alpha^x)$
1, 2, 4, 8, 16	0
3, 6, 12, 24, 17	1
5, 10, 20, 9, 18	1
7, 14, 28, 25, 19	0
11, 22, 13, 26, 21	1
15, 30, 29, 27, 23	0
0	1

for all degree 5 irreducible polynomials because the order of α, namely 31, is prime. Each set of root powers is called a *cyclotomic coset* (see Appendix 5A.8). Property T-2 indicates that all the roots of the same irreducible polynomial have the same trace value; hence, trace values can be computed by (5.126) and associated with cyclotomic cosets. This is illustrated in Table 5.9 for this example.

The following theorem provides a convenient representation for certain LFSR sequences having irreducible characteristic polynomials. Here, and in discussions to follow, the superscripts and subscripts on the trace function will be omitted when their values are evident.

THEOREM 5.6. *Let* $\mathrm{GF}(q^d)$ *be the smallest field containing the element* α, *and let* $m_\alpha(z)$ *be the degree d minimum polynomial of* α *over* $\mathrm{GF}(q)$. *Then the sequence* $\{\mathrm{Tr}_q^{q^d}(\alpha^n)\}$, *n being the sequence index, has characteristic polynomial* $m_\alpha(z)$.

Proof. Consider a d-cell Galois LFSR producing an output sequence having characteristic polynomial $m_\alpha(z)$. Combining the representation (5.22) for the remainder polynomial in terms of memory contents, with the field element interpretation of (5.112) gives

$$\alpha^n = \beta R^{(n)}(\alpha) = \beta \sum_{i=1}^{L} r_i^{(n)} \alpha^{L-i} \tag{5.127}$$

where

$$\beta = [P(\alpha)]^{-1} \tag{5.128}$$

with α and β in $\mathrm{GF}(q^d)$. Applying the trace function with Property T-3 to both sides of (5.127) and noting that the cell sequences are elements of $\mathrm{GF}(q)$, gives

$$\mathrm{Tr}(\alpha^n) = \sum_{i=1}^{L} \mathrm{Tr}(\beta\alpha^{L-i}) r_i^{(n)}. \tag{5.129}$$

Corollary 5.1 indicates that the L memory cell sequences $\{r_i^{(n)}\}$, $i = 1, \dots, L$, all have the same characteristic polynomial $m_\alpha(z)$; therefore, the linear combination of those sequences specified by (5.129), namely the sequence $\{\mathrm{Tr}(\alpha^n)\}$, has the same characteristic polynomial. ■

The following corollary provides an explicit and compact mathematical representation of the elements of an m-sequence, which will be used in several forthcoming analyses.

COROLLARY 5.2. *If $\{b_n\}$ is an m-sequence over* GF(q) *with the minimum polynomial $m_\alpha(z)$ as its characteristic polynomial, then there exists a non-zero element γ in* GF(q^d) *such that*

$$\{b_n\} = \left\{\mathrm{Tr}_q^{q^d}(\gamma\alpha^n)\right\}. \tag{5.130}$$

Proof. By Theorem 5.6, the same recursion which generates $\{b_n\}$ must also produce $\{\mathrm{Tr}(\alpha^n)\}$, as well as any shift thereof. Since $\{b_n\}$ is an m-sequence, its characteristic polynomial $m_\alpha(z)$ is primitive, and the corresponding LFSR supports only two cyclically distinct state sequences, namely the perpetual zero-state sequence and the state sequence of $\{b_n\}$. Property T-4 indicates that $\mathrm{Tr}(\alpha^n)$ must be non-zero for some n; hence, the state sequence corresponding to the trace sequence cannot be the zero-state sequence. Therefore, the trace sequence or some shift of it must be the m-sequence. That is,

$$\{\mathrm{Tr}(\alpha^{m+n})\} = \{b_n\} \tag{5.131}$$

for some m, and setting $\gamma = \alpha^m$ completes the proof. ■

5.5.5 A Correlation Computation

To illustrate the use of trace representations in the study of periodic correlation properties, consider the calculation of the periodic correlation of $\{a_n\}$, a roots-of-unity m-sequence derived from an m-sequence $\{b_n\}$ over GF(q) via (5.80). Let $m_\alpha(z)$ denote the degree d primitive characteristic polynomial of $\{b_n\}$. Then the periodic correlation function of $\{a_n\}$, defined in (5.85), can be rewritten in terms of the trace function by using Corollary 5.2 and simplifying with Property T-3.

$$P_{aa}(\tau) = \sum_{n=1}^{N} \rho^{\mathrm{Tr}(\gamma\alpha^{n+\tau}) - \mathrm{Tr}(\gamma\alpha^n)}$$

$$= \sum_{n=1}^{N} \rho^{\mathrm{Tr}(\delta\alpha^n)}, \tag{5.132}$$

where

$$\delta = \gamma(\alpha^\tau - 1). \tag{5.133}$$

Since α is primitive, α^n takes on the values of all the non-zero elements in $GF(q^d)$ as n goes from 1 to N, N being the sequence period. Adding the zero element to this list and noting that its trace is zero, yields

$$P_{aa}(\tau) = -1 + \sum_{\beta \in GF(q^d)} \rho^{\delta\beta}. \tag{5.134}$$

As β varies over $GF(q^d)$, so does $\delta\beta$ unless δ is zero, and applying Property T-4, gives

$$P_{aa}(\tau) = \begin{cases} q^d - 1, & \delta = 0 \\ -1, & \delta \neq 0. \end{cases} \tag{5.135}$$

The condition $\delta = 0$ occurs if, and only if, $\alpha^\tau = 1$, and since α is primitive,

$$\delta = 0 \text{ iff } \tau = 0 \bmod q^d - 1. \tag{5.136}$$

While this has been a somewhat more involved proof of randomness Property R-5 than that given in Section 5.4.4, the trace function methodology employed here readily generalizes to several more complicated full-period correlation calculations.

5.5.6 Decimations of Sequences

Let $\{b_n\}$ be an arbitrary sequence of period N, and consider the sequence $\{c_n\}$ defined by

$$c_n = b_{Jn}, \quad \text{for all } n. \tag{5.137}$$

The sequence $\{c_n\}$ is said to be the *decimation by J* of the sequence $\{b_n\}$. If J divides N, then $\{c_n\}$ has period N/J. On the other hand, if J and N are relatively prime, then the smallest multiple of J that is a multiple of N is NJ, and the period of $\{c_n\}$ is N. In general, the decimation by J of a sequence with period N produces a sequence with period $N/\gcd(J, N)$.

It should be clear to the reader that when $\gcd(J, N)$ is 1, the resulting rearrangement of sequence elements does not change the first order statistics of the sequence. A more interesting result indicates that the set of correlation values of real number sequences is preserved under decimation by a number relatively prime to the sequence period.

THEOREM 5.7. *Let $\{a_n\}$ be an arbitrary sequence of complex numbers with period N, and let $\{c_n\}$ be the decimation by J of $\{a_n\}$, where* $\gcd(J, N) = 1$. *Then*

$$P_{cc}(\tau) = P_{aa}(J\tau). \tag{5.138}$$

Proof. Evaluation of the periodic correlation of $\{c_n\}$ gives

$$\begin{aligned} P_{cc}(\tau) &= \sum_{n=1}^{N} a_{J(n+\tau)} a_{Jn}^* \\ &= \sum_{k \in \mathscr{K}} a_{k+J\tau} a_k^*, \end{aligned} \tag{5.139}$$

where

$$\mathscr{K} = \{k\colon Jn = k \bmod N, 1 \le n \le N\}. \tag{5.140}$$

If two distinct choices of n, say n_1 and n_2, in the range 1 to N, yield the same value k in (5.140), then

$$Jn_1 = Jn_2 \bmod N, \tag{5.141}$$

or, assuming $n_1 > n_2$,

$$J(n_1 - n_2) = mN \tag{5.142}$$

where m is integer. However, this is impossible since N has no factors in common with J, and $n_1 - n_2$ is less than N. Therefore, the elements of $\mathscr{K}$ are the N distinct integers from 1 to N. ■

The trace representation gives considerable insight into the effects of decimation on m-sequences. Suppose that by Corollary 5.2 we have constructed the m-sequence

$$\{b_n\} = \mathrm{Tr}_q^{q^d}(\alpha^n), \tag{5.143}$$

and decimation by J of $\{b_n\}$ results in the sequence

$$\{f_n\} = \mathrm{Tr}_q^{q^d}(\alpha^{Jn}). \tag{5.144}$$

When J is relatively prime to the period $q^d - 1$ of $\{b_n\}$, then α^J is another primitive element of GF(q^d) and, thus, $\{f_n\}$ is an m-sequence with the minimum polynomial $m_{\alpha^J}(z)$ for its characteristic polynomial. The results on decimations of m-sequences can now be summarized.

THEOREM 5.8. *Let $\{b_n\}$ denote an m-sequence over* GF(q) *with linear span L. Then:*

(a) *A decimation $\{b_{Jn}\}$ of $\{b_n\}$ is an m-sequence if and only if J is relatively prime to $q^L - 1$.*
(b) *Two sequences $\{b_{Jn}\}$ and $\{b_{Kn}\}$ produced by decimations, with J and K both relatively prime to $q^L - 1$, are cyclically distinct if and only if*

$$J \ne q^k K \bmod q^L - 1, \tag{5.145}$$

for all integers k.
(c) *All m-sequences of period $q^L - 1$ can be constructed by decimations of $\{b_n\}$.*

Example 5.9. Consider the set of m-sequences over GF(2) with period 31. Let α be a root of the primitive polynomial $z^5 + z^2 + 1$. One can construct the m-sequence $\mathrm{Tr}(\alpha^n)$ and its decimations by various values of J simply by

Table 5.10
M-sequences $\mathrm{Tr}(\alpha^{Jn})$, $n = 0, 1, \ldots,$ of period 31 over GF(2), constructed by decimations by J, along with their characteristic polynomials.

J	Sequence	Characteristic Polynomial (in octal)
1	1001011001111100011011101010000	45
3	1111101110001010110100001100100	75
5	1110100010010101100001110011011	67
7	1001001100001011010100011101111	57
11	1110110011100001101010010001011	73
15	1000010101110110001111100110100	51

reading the trace values from Table 5.9. The results of this procedure are shown in Table 5.10. The characteristic polynomials of sequences constructed by the decimation process can be found directly by the techniques of Section 5.2.5, or by calculation of $m_{\alpha^J}(z)$ from $m_\alpha(z)$ as described in Appendix 5A.8.

5.6 NON-LINEAR FEED-FORWARD LOGIC

Two related disadvantages of m-sequences and other LFSR sequences have already been discussed: (1) Simple linear analysis will allow an observer to predict the output of an L-stage LFSR from an observation of $2L$ consecutive output symbols. (2) The shift-and-add property of m-sequences allows an observer to produce different "time-advanced" versions of an m-sequence while observing the sequence, although the amount of shift cannot be predicted without further analysis. In either case, the observer, possessing no *a priori* information about the nature of the SS code generator, has the potential to predict the generator output and use this information to read the message, or to jam or spoof the intended receiver. As will be demonstrated in this section, vulnerability to this type of countermeasure can be significantly reduced by the inclusion of non-linear feed-forward logic (NLFFL) operating on the contents of the m-sequence generator's shift register, to produce an SS code sequence having high linear span.

5.6.1 A Powers-of-α Representation Theorem

The mathematical analysis of NLFFL effects requires use of the representation of a sequence $\{b_n\}$ of GF(q) elements with period $q^M - 1$, in terms of the $q^M - 1$ sequences $\{1\}$ (the all ones sequence), $\{\alpha^n\}, \{\alpha^{2n}\}, \ldots,$ $\{\alpha^{(q^M-2)n}\}$, where α is a primitive element of GF(q^M). Such a representation of $\{b_n\}$ must be unique since the basis sequences in the representation are linearly independent. This can be proven by noting that if there exist coefficients $a_0, \ldots, a_{q^M-2}$, not all zero, such that

$$P(\alpha^n) \triangleq \sum_{i=0}^{q^M-2} a_i \alpha^{in} = 0, \qquad 0 \le n < q^M - 1, \tag{5.146}$$

then the polynomial $P(z)$ has $q^M - 1$ roots and degree at most $q^M - 2$, a contradiction.

The linear span L of a sequence (i.e., the degree of its characteristic polynomial) is related to the sequence's powers-of-α representation in the following result.

THEOREM 5.9. *Let $\{b_n\}$ be a sequence over* GF(q), *and let α be a primitive element of* GF(q^M). *Let $\{b_n\}$ be represented as*

$$b_n = \sum_{\delta \in \Delta} a_\delta \alpha^{\delta n} \tag{5.147}$$

for all n, where Δ is the set of indices of non-zero coefficients in the expansion. Then the linear span L of $\{b_n\}$ is equal to the number of terms in the representation (5.147), *i.e.,*

$$L = |\Delta|. \tag{5.148}$$

Proof. Since b_n is in GF(q) and all elements of that field have multiplicative order dividing $q - 1$, it follows that

$$\begin{aligned} b_n &= b_n^q \\ &= \sum_{\delta \in \Delta} a_\delta^q \alpha^{q\delta n}, \end{aligned} \tag{5.149}$$

for all n, by Theorem 5A.7.1 of Appendix 5A. Since the representation (5.147) is unique, it must be identical to (5.149). Therefore,

$$a_{q\delta} = a_\delta^q \quad \text{for all} \quad \delta \in \Delta. \tag{5.150}$$

This implies that Δ can be decomposed into cyclotomic cosets (see Appendix 5A.8), the terms of (5.147) with indices in the same coset summing to a trace function.

Let Δ' be composed of the coset leaders (single representative elements) of the cyclotomic cosets present in the decomposition of Δ. Then

$$b_n = \sum_{\delta \in \Delta'} \mathrm{Tr}_q^{q^{d(\delta)}}\left(a_\delta \alpha^{\delta n}\right). \tag{5.160}$$

Note that the trace function for the δ-th term is calculated from the smallest field GF($q^{d(\delta)}$) containing α^δ down to GF(q). In the form (5.160), $\{b_n\}$ can be viewed as the sum of $|\Delta'|$ sequences, each over GF(q). Furthermore, the number of terms $d(\delta)$ of (5.147) which are combined to produce the sequence $\{\mathrm{Tr}(a_\delta \alpha^{\delta n})\}$, is identical to the degree of the minimum polynomial

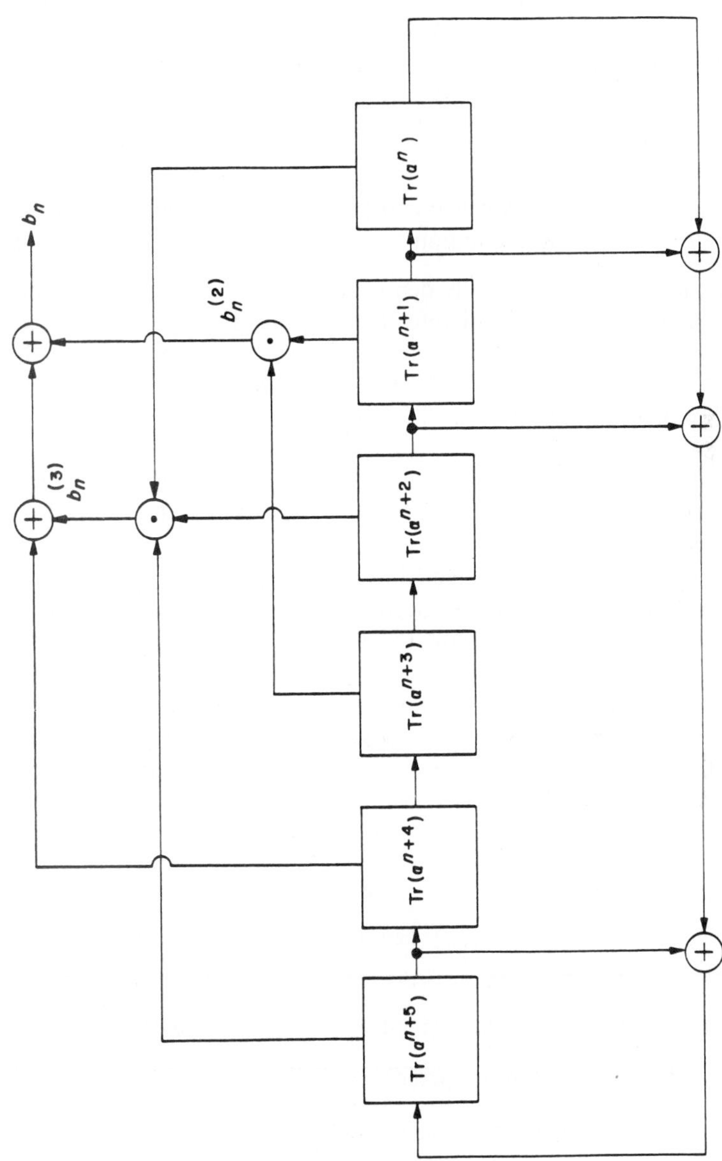

Figure 5.10(a). The LFSR with NLFFL used in Example 5.10. Arithmetic/logic operations are GF(2)/EXCLUSIVE OR and AND.

$m_{\alpha^\delta}(z)$, which by Theorem 5.6 is the characteristic polynomial of that sequence. Therefore, the characteristic polynomial $Q(z)$ of $\{b_n\}$ is given by

$$Q(z) = \prod_{\delta \in \Delta'} m_{\alpha^\delta}(z), \tag{5.161}$$

and has degree L given by

$$L = \sum_{\delta \in \Delta'} d(\delta) = |\Delta|. \tag{5.162}$$

Thus, the linear span of a sequence can be evaluated simply by counting terms in its powers-of-α representation. ■

Since the index n in $\{b_n\}$ usually denotes a discrete time value and since δ multiplies n in (5.147), we will refer to the elements δ of the set Δ in (5.147) as *time coefficients*. Theorem 5.9 can be rephrased to state that the linear span of $\{b_n\}$ is the number of distinct time coefficients in the powers-of-α representation of $\{b_n\}$.

Example 5.10. Consider the binary 6-stage LFSR with primitive characteristic polynomial $z^6 + z^5 + z^2 + z + 1$, to which has been added NLFFL as shown in Figure 5.10(a). By loading the register with $\mathrm{Tr}_2^{64}(\alpha^i)$, $i = 0, \ldots, 5$, i.e., 011111, where α is a root of the LFSR's characteristic polynomial, the sequences in Figure 5.10(b) are produced at different points in the generator. One full period is shown, with the first bit corresponding to index $n = 0$.

The contents of the individual storage elements have been expressed as the trace functions indicated in the above diagram, in accordance with Theorem 5.6. These functions, having domain GF(64) and range GF(2), are defined as

$$\mathrm{Tr}_2^{64}(\alpha^j) = \sum_{i=0}^{5} \alpha^{j2^i}. \tag{5.163}$$

The NLFFL output sequence $\{b_n\}$ can be represented in terms of the

$\mathrm{Tr}(\alpha^n)$:
011111101011100011001110110000011110010010101001101000010001011
$\mathrm{Tr}(\alpha^{n+4})$:
111010111000110011101100000111100100101010011010000100010110111
$b_n^{(2)}$:
111101010100000000010100000000110000000101000001000000000010010
$b_n^{(3)}$:
010100100000000000001000000000001000000000100000000000000001001
b_n:
010011001100110011110000000111011100101111111011000100010101100

Figure 5.10(b). Sequences produced at key locations within the generator of Example 5.10.

storage element sequences by

$$\begin{aligned} b_n &= \mathrm{Tr}(\alpha^{n+4}) + \mathrm{Tr}(\alpha^{n+1})\mathrm{Tr}(\alpha^{n+3}) \\ &\quad + \mathrm{Tr}(\alpha^{n})\mathrm{Tr}(\alpha^{n+2})\mathrm{Tr}(\alpha^{n+5}) \\ &= \mathrm{Tr}_2^{64}(\alpha^{n+17}) + \mathrm{Tr}_2^{64}(\alpha^{3n+28}) \\ &\quad + \mathrm{Tr}_2^{64}(\alpha^{5n+47}) + \mathrm{Tr}_2^{64}(\alpha^{7n+6}) \\ &\quad + \mathrm{Tr}_2^{64}(\alpha^{11n+28}) + \mathrm{Tr}_2^{64}(\alpha^{13n+29}) \\ &\quad + \mathrm{Tr}_2^{4}(\alpha^{21n+21}). \end{aligned} \tag{5.164}$$

Formed by substitution of (5.163) and simplification, the right side of (5.164) contains trace expressions with different domains; hence, domain and range are specified for each term. The above calculation is tedious and, even for this example, is more easily done by computer. By applying Theorem 5.9 and counting the terms in the trace functions of (5.164), namely six functions with six terms and one function with two terms, the linear span L of $\{b_n\}$ is determined to be 38.

The expansion (5.164) indicates that the characteristic polynomial $Q(z)$ of the NLFFL output sequence $\{b_n\}$ is

$$Q(z) = m_{\alpha}(z)m_{\alpha^3}(z)m_{\alpha^5}(z)m_{\alpha^7}(z)m_{\alpha^{11}}(z)m_{\alpha^{13}}(z)m_{\alpha^{21}}(z). \tag{5.165}$$

The factors of $Q(z)$ can be determined from knowledge that $m_{\alpha}(z)$ is $z^6 + z^5 + z^2 + z + 1$, and the techniques of Appendix 5A.8, to give

$$\begin{aligned} Q(z) &= z^{38} + z^{37} + z^{31} + z^{27} + z^{26} + z^{25} \\ &\quad + z^{23} + z^{22} + z^{20} + z^{19} + z^{18} + z^{17} \\ &\quad + z^{16} + z^{15} + z^{8} + z^{7} + z^{4} + z^{3} \\ &\quad + z^{2} + z + 1. \end{aligned} \tag{5.166}$$

As a check, it can be verified that the output sequence shown in Figure 5.10(b) satisfies a recursion based on the characteristic polynomial $Q(z)$.

5.6.2 Key's Bound on Linear Span

Suppose that a binary NLFFL function is put in Reed-Muller canonic form, i.e., described as a sum of products of its inputs. Let's investigate the potential number of terms contributed to the powers-of-α expansion of the logic's output by one product term containing J factors, each factor being the contents of some memory element in an m-sequence generator. Assuming the characteristic polynomial of the m-sequence generator is $m_{\alpha}(z)$, the trace function $\mathrm{Tr}(\gamma_j \alpha^n)$ can be used to represent the j-th factor (sequence) in the product p_n, giving

$$p_n = \prod_{j=1}^{J} \mathrm{Tr}(\gamma_j \alpha^n) = \prod_{j=1}^{J} \sum_{i=0}^{M-1} (\gamma_j \alpha^n)^{2^i}, \tag{5.167}$$

where γ_j, $j = 1, \ldots, J$, and α are elements of GF(2^M), M being the number of memory elements in the m-sequence generator and also the degree of $m_\alpha(z)$. (This representation is valid for a linear m-sequence generator in any configuration.)

Converting the product of sums in (5.167) to a sum of products gives

$$p_n = \sum_{i_1=0}^{M-1} \cdots \sum_{i_J=0}^{M-1} \gamma_i \alpha^{c(i)n} \tag{5.168}$$

where

$$\gamma_i = \prod_{j=1}^{J} \gamma_j^{2^{i_j}}, \tag{5.169}$$

$$c(i) = \sum_{j=1}^{J} 2^{i_j} \bmod 2^M - 1, \tag{5.170}$$

the latter sum being modulo the multiplicative order of the element α. The base 2 representation of $c(i)$, thus, is limited to a binary M-tuple, and (5.170) indicates that at most J of these M symbols can be ones. Since each of the integers i_j in (5.170) ranges independently between zero and $M - 1$, it follows that the number ${}_M N_J$ of distinct values that $c(i)$ can assume is given by the number of binary M-tuples with at most J ones, excluding the all-zeros n-tuple.

$${}_M N_J = \sum_{j=1}^{J} \binom{M}{j}. \tag{5.171}$$

Two different products (AND gates), with distinct sets of J inputs from the memory cells of an m-sequence generator, potentially produce the same set of powers-of-α sequences for their output representations. Furthermore, when one product has J inputs and another has K inputs, $J < K$, the representation of the K-fold product can potentially contain all powers-of-α sequences which occur in the J-fold product, and more. The word "potentially" is used because multiple terms with the same time coefficient $c(i)$ (5.170) are produced, and there is a small likelihood that the coefficients of these terms will add to zero.

The *order D* of an NLFFL function is defined as the largest number of factors in any product from its sum-of-products representation. The following theorem is a consequence of the above arguments.

THEOREM 5.10 (Key's Bound [23]). *The linear span L of a sequence $\{b_n\}$ produced by NLFFL of order D operating on the contents of an M-stage m-sequence generator is bounded by*

$$L \leq {}_M N_D = \sum_{j=1}^{D} \binom{M}{j}. \tag{5.172}$$

Table 5.11
Cyclic equivalence class representatives of non-zero coefficients in the powers-of-α representation in Example 5.11.

coefficients	
base-2	base-10
000001	1
000011	3
000101	5
000111	7
001011	11
001101	13
010101	21

If the logic function includes the possibility of complementation by the use of an additional constant input term "1" in its sum-of-products representation, then the lower limit on the sum in Key's bound (5.172) must be reduced to zero.

Example 5.11. Key's bound on the linear span L for the output of third-order logic operating on a six-stage m-sequence generator is

$$L \leq \binom{6}{1} + \binom{6}{2} + \binom{6}{3} = 41. \tag{5.173}$$

The linear span achieved under these conditions in Example 5.10 is 38. Binary 6-tuple representations of the time coefficients (5.170) occurring in $\{b_n\}$'s powers-of-α expansion in the example include the ones shown in Table 5.11 and their cyclic shifts. This list includes cyclically equivalent representatives of all 6-tuples having weight 3 or less, with the exception of 001001 which in decimal is 9. It can be verified that α^{9n} is produced eight different ways in the product-of-sums to sum-of-products conversion (5.164) in the example, and that the eight corresponding coefficients from GF(64) sum to zero, thereby eliminating $\{\alpha^{9n}\}$ as a component in the representation of $\{b_n\}$. Since α^9 has order 7, it is an element of GF(8) and, therefore, has a three term trace and a degree-three minimum polynomial. Hence, this missing term accounts for the difference of three between Key's bound and the achieved linear span.

It has been pointed out [24] that for cryptographic applications, linear span is only one of several measures that must be considered in selecting a key sequence. This note of caution applies equally well to the selection of spectrum-spreading sequences. For example, the logic imposed on the m-sequence generator of Figure 5.11 produces an output whose linear span is 31, the period of the m-sequence generator. On the other hand, the AND gate output will be a "1" only when the all-ones 5-tuple appears in the register, an event which occurs only once in the 31 bit period of the generator. The output of such a generator can hardly be called pseudo-

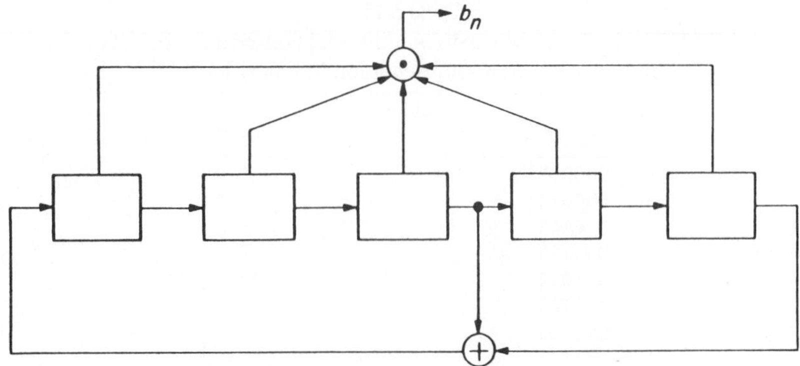

Figure 5.11. A high-linear-span generator.

random, when a prediction that an output bit will be zero is correct 96.7% of the time.

The following result suggests a simple way to guarantee nearly equal numbers of zeros and ones in the output of a generator.

THEOREM 5.11. *Let $s = (r_1, r_2, \ldots, r_M)$ denote the memory state of an m-sequence generator. If the output of NLFFL on the memory state can be represented in the form*

$$b = r_i + f(r_1, \ldots, r_{i-1}, r_{i+1}, \ldots, r_M) \tag{5.174}$$

for some i, where $f(\cdot)$ is any Boolean function independent of r_i, then the NLFFL output sequence will be balanced.

Proof. Since the state M-tuple takes on all possible values except all-zeros during one period of operation, then the states $(r_1, \ldots, r_{i-1}, 0, r_{i+1}, \ldots, r_M)$ and $(r_1, \ldots, r_{i-1}, 1, r_{i+1}, \ldots, r_M)$ each occur once for each choice of the remaining values of the r_j's, $j \neq i$, excluding all-zeros. Each such state pair will contribute one 0 and one 1 in one period of the NLFFL output when (5.174) holds. Therefore, one full period of the output will have either (a) one more 0 than 1, or (b) one more 1 than 0, depending on the output value when the register memory is in the state having $r_j = 0$ for all $j \neq i$, and $r_i = 1$. ■

Figure 5.12, which illustrates a modification of the generator of Figure 5.11, provides a balanced pseudorandom sequence. However, balance and large linear span do not together guarantee the generation of unpredictable sequences.

A preliminary design for the NLFFL to be attached to an M-stage m-sequence generator can be mapped out with the aid of Key's bound, the result being an estimate of the number of multipliers required and the

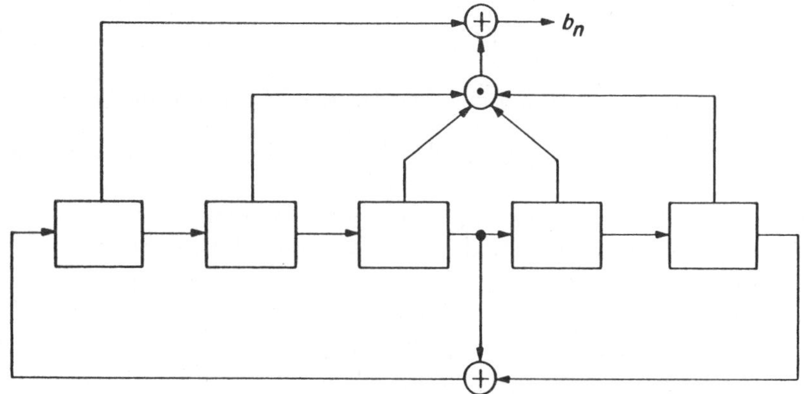

Figure 5.12. A high-linear-span (30) generator with balance.

number of inputs for each multiplier in a sum-of-products form. To complete the design, one must choose the connections between multiplier inputs and shift register memory elements, and then determine, on a case by case basis, whether or not the other statistics (e.g., correlation properties, run-length statistics, etc.) constitute a satisfactory design. Very little has appeared in the open literature on this problem, although it was stated in [24], in the context of quadratic NLFFL and on the basis of experimental results, that each memory element should connect to at most one multiplier, and that the spacing between memory elements connected to one multiplier should differ from the spacing between connections to any other multiplier. These suggestions may serve as initial guidelines in selecting an NLFFL design which will generate a sequence with good statistical properties.

5.6.3 Difference Set Designs

A v, k, λ *cyclic difference set* [26] is a collection $\mathscr{D} = \{d_1, d_2, \ldots, d_k\}$ of k integers modulo v ($0 \leq d_i < v$ for all i) such that for every choice of the integer $\beta, 0 < \beta < v$, the equation

$$d_i - d_j = \beta \bmod v \tag{5.175}$$

has exactly λ solution pairs (d_i, d_j) with d_i and d_j being distinct elements of $\mathscr{D}$. Since there are exactly $k(k-1)$ non-zero differences between the k elements of $\mathscr{D}$, and since these must assume each of $v - 1$ values exactly λ times, the parameters v, k, λ are constrained by the relation

$$k(k-1) = \lambda(v-1). \tag{5.176}$$

It is easily verified that modulo v addition of a constant to each element of a difference set yields a new difference set with the same parameters. The complement $\{0, 1, \ldots, v-1\} - \mathscr{D}$ of a v, k, λ difference set $\mathscr{D}$ is a v^*, k^*, λ^*

difference set $\mathscr{D}^*$ with

$$v^* = v, \quad k^* = v - k, \quad \lambda^* = v - 2k + \lambda. \tag{5.177}$$

The incidence vector $\boldsymbol{b}$ of a difference set has elements defined by

$$b_n = \begin{cases} 0, & n \notin \mathscr{D} \\ 1, & n \in \mathscr{D}, \end{cases} \tag{5.178}$$

for $0 \leq n < v$. The sequence $\{b_n\}$ constructed by extending the incidence vector periodically with period v has a two-level periodic correlation function $P_{bb}(\tau)$ given by

$$\begin{aligned} P_{bb}(\tau) &= \sum_{n=0}^{v-1} b_{n+\tau} b_n \\ &= \begin{cases} k, & \tau = 0 \bmod v \\ \lambda, & \tau \neq 0 \bmod v. \end{cases} \end{aligned} \tag{5.179}$$

Conversely, if a periodic binary (0 or 1) sequence $\{b_n\}$ has two-level periodic correlation function, then one period of $\{b_n\}$ is the index vector of a difference set.

A binary roots-of-unity sequence $\{a_n\}$, based on the difference set $\mathscr{D}$, can be constructed via the relation

$$a_n = (-1)^{b_n} = 1 - 2b_n, \tag{5.180}$$

b_n being 0 or 1. The periodic correlation function $P_{aa}(\tau)$ of the sequence $\{a_n\}$ also is two valued, being

$$\begin{aligned} P_{aa}(\tau) &= \sum_{n=0}^{v-1} a_{n+\tau} a_n \\ &= v - 4k + 4P_{bb}(\tau) \\ &= \begin{cases} v, & \tau = 0 \bmod v \\ v - 4k + 4\lambda, & \tau \neq 0 \bmod v. \end{cases} \end{aligned} \tag{5.181}$$

Any binary ($+1$ or -1) sequence with two-level periodic correlation can be related to the incidence matrix of a difference set by (5.180).

One period of an m-sequence, generated by an M-stage shift register, is the incidence vector for a difference set with parameters

$$v = 2^M - 1, \quad k = 2^{M-1}, \quad \lambda = 2^{M-2}, \tag{5.182}$$

and, complementing this set gives another difference set with parameters

$$v^* = 2^M - 1, \quad k^* = 2^{M-1} - 1, \quad \lambda^* = 2^{M-2} - 1. \tag{5.183}$$

These difference sets, corresponding to m-sequences, are called *Singer sets*, and were developed as a result of work in finite projective geometry [27].

Turyn [68] and Baumert [26] survey the known difference set designs. Decimation of any of the resulting sequences may produce a class of potentially interesting pseudorandom sequences. The sequences to be discussed next are one such class which has many nice attributes.

5.6.4 GMW Sequences

Gordon, Mills, and Welch (GMW) [28] have generalized the structure of Singer sets, thereby creating a larger collection of difference sets possessing the same parameters as displayed in (5.182). More precisely, when the integer M in (5.182) is composite, i.e.,

$$M = JK, \tag{5.184}$$

then some of the difference sets created by the GMW construction do not correspond to Singer sets. The binary sequences, called GMW sequences, derived from GMW difference sets, have correlation properties identical to those of m-sequences, but possess larger linear span than m-sequences.

Some of the difference sets in the GMW construction have incidence vectors whose elements, considered here as being in GF(2), can be specified as

$$b_n = \mathrm{Tr}_2^{2^J}\left(\left[\mathrm{Tr}_{2^J}^{2^M}(\alpha^n)\right]^r\right) \tag{5.185}$$

where α is a primitive element of GF(2^M), and r is any integer relatively prime to $2^J - 1$, r in the range $0 < r < 2^J - 1$. When $r = 1$, then (5.185) reduces by (5.125) to the trace representation of an m-sequence. Notice also that the interior trace function in (5.185) is an m-sequence over GF(2^J), and has the following property.

LEMMA 5.1. *Let an m-sequence over* GF(q), $q \geq 2$, *be defined by*

$$b'_n = \mathrm{Tr}_q^{q^K}(\alpha^n), \tag{5.186}$$

where α *is a primitive element of* GF(q^K), *and let*

$$T = \frac{q^K - 1}{q - 1}. \tag{5.187}$$

Then every segment of T *consecutive symbols from* $\{b'_n\}$ *contains exactly* $(q^{K-1} - 1)/(q - 1)$ *zeros.*

Proof. The field element α^T has order $q - 1$ and, hence, belongs to the ground field GF(q). Therefore, by the linearity property (5.123) of the trace function, it follows that for any integer k,

$$\mathrm{Tr}_q^{q^K}(\alpha^n) = \alpha^{-kT}\mathrm{Tr}(\alpha^{n+kT}). \tag{5.188}$$

Since α^{-kT} is not zero, it follows that when one trace in (5.188) is zero, so is the other; thus, the zero locations in $\{b'_n\}$ are subject to a T periodicity. Consequently, every segment of T symbols from $\{b'_n\}$ contains the same number of zeros, that number being easily evaluated from the fact that $q^{K-1} - 1$ zeroes occur in one period, $q^K - 1$ symbols, of $\{b'_n\}$. ■

It will now be verified directly that the GMW sequences of (5.185) have the same autocorrelation properties as m-sequences.

THEOREM 5.12. *Let $\{a_n\}$ be a GMW sequence whose elements are given by*

$$a_n = (-1)^{\mathrm{Tr}_2^{2^J}([\mathrm{Tr}_{2^J}^{2^M}(\alpha^n)]^r)}, \tag{5.189}$$

where α is a primitive element of GF(2^M), and $r, 0 < r < 2^J - 1$, is relatively prime to $2^J - 1$. Then the periodic autocorrelation function $P_{aa}(\tau)$ of $\{a_n\}$ is given by

$$P_{aa}(\tau) \triangleq \sum_{n=0}^{2^M-2} a_{n+\tau} a_n$$

$$= \begin{cases} 2^M - 1, & \tau = 0 \bmod 2^M - 1 \\ -1, & \tau \neq 0 \bmod 2^M - 1. \end{cases} \tag{5.190}$$

Proof. It follows immediately from trace function linearity that

$$P_{aa}(\tau) = \sum_{n=0}^{2^M-2} (-1)^{\mathrm{Tr}_2^{2^J}([\mathrm{Tr}_{2^J}^{2^M}(\alpha^{n+\tau})]^r + [\mathrm{Tr}_{2^J}^{2^M}(\alpha^n)]^r)} \tag{5.191}$$

Let T be the smallest power of α yielding an element of GF(2^J), i.e.,

$$T = \frac{2^M - 1}{2^J - 1}, \tag{5.192}$$

and express the index n in (5.191) as

$$n = n_0 + n_1 T, \tag{5.193}$$

where $0 \leq n_0 < T$ and $0 \leq n_1 \leq 2^J - 1$. Using the linearity of the inner traces in (5.191) gives

$$P_{aa}(\tau) = \sum_{n_0=0}^{T-1} \sum_{n_1=0}^{2^J-2} (-1)^{\mathrm{Tr}_2^{2^J}(\alpha^{rTn_1}\delta(\tau, n_0))}, \tag{5.194}$$

where

$$\delta(\tau, n_0) = \left[\mathrm{Tr}_{2^J}^{2^M}(\alpha^{\tau+n_0})\right]^r + \left[\mathrm{Tr}_{2^J}^{2^M}(\alpha^{n_0})\right]^r. \tag{5.195}$$

Since r is relatively prime to $2^J - 1$, it follows that α^{rT} is a primitive element of GF(2^J), and α^{rTn_1} takes on the values of all non-zero elements of that field as n_1 varies over its range. Hence, by including the zero element of GF(2^J) in the sum of (5.194), one arrives at

$$P_{aa}(\tau) = -T + \sum_{n_0=0}^{T-1} \sum_{\beta \in \mathrm{GF}(2^J)} (-1)^{\mathrm{Tr}_2^{2^J}(\beta\delta(\tau, n_0))}. \tag{5.196}$$

When $\delta(\tau, n_0)$ is not zero, the inner sum vanishes because half the exponents are zero and half one, by trace Property T-4. Let $N_0(\tau)$ denote the number of values of n_0 in the range $0 \leq n_0 < T$ for which $\delta(\tau, n_0)$ is zero. Then (5.196) reduces to

$$P_{aa}(\tau) = -T + 2^J N_0(\tau). \tag{5.197}$$

Since r is relatively prime to $2^J - 1$ and therefore has an inverse modulo $2^J - 1$, it follows that

$$\delta(\tau, n_0) = 0 \Leftrightarrow \mathrm{Tr}_{2^J}^{2^M}(\alpha^{\tau+n_0}) = \mathrm{Tr}_{2^J}^{2^M}(\alpha^{n_0})$$
$$\Leftrightarrow \mathrm{Tr}_{2^J}^{2^M}((\alpha^\tau - 1)\alpha^{n_0}) = 0. \qquad (5.198)$$

When $\alpha^\tau - 1$ is zero, the right-hand equation in (5.198) is satisfied for all n_0. If $\alpha^\tau - 1$ is not zero, then Lemma 5.1 can be applied with (5.198) to determine $N_0(\tau)$. Thus,

$$N_0(\tau) = \begin{cases} T, & \tau = 0 \bmod 2^M - 1 \\ \dfrac{2^{M-J} - 1}{2^J - 1}, & \tau \neq 0 \bmod 2^M - 1. \end{cases} \qquad (5.199)$$

and the result follows by substitution of (5.199) and (5.192) into (5.197). ■

The linear span of a GMW sequence can be evaluated exactly by finding the number of terms in its powers-of-α representation and applying Theorem 5.9.

THEOREM 5.13. *Let $\{b_n\}$ be a GMW sequence whose elements are given by*

$$b_n = \mathrm{Tr}_2^{2^J}\left(\left[\mathrm{Tr}_{2^J}^{2^M}(\alpha^n)\right]^r\right), \qquad (5.200)$$

where α is a primitive element of $\mathrm{GF}(2^M)$ and r, $0 < r < 2^J - 1$, is relatively prime to $2^J - 1$. Then the linear span L of $\{b_n\}$ is given by

$$L = J(M/J)^w, \qquad (5.201)$$

where w is the number of ones in the base-2 representation of r.

Proof. The exponent r can be written as

$$r = \sum_{i=1}^{w} 2^{j_i}, \qquad (5.202)$$

where the j_i's are distinct integers in the range $0 \le j_i < J$ for all i. Hence,

$$b_n = \mathrm{Tr}_2^{2^J}\left(\prod_{i=1}^{w}\left[\mathrm{Tr}_{2^J}^{2^M}(\alpha^n)\right]^{2^{j_i}}\right). \qquad (5.203)$$

Since the inner trace is a sum of elements from a field of characteristic 2, all cross-product terms disappear when the trace is squared and (5.203) reduces to

$$b_n = \mathrm{Tr}_2^{2^J}\left(\prod_{i=1}^{w}\sum_{k=0}^{K-1}\alpha^{n2^{Jk+j_i}}\right)$$
$$= \mathrm{Tr}_2^{2^J}\left(\sum_{k_1=0}^{K-1}\cdots\sum_{k_w=0}^{K-1}\alpha^{nc(\boldsymbol{k},r)}\right), \qquad (5.204)$$

where K is defined by (5.184) and

$$c(\boldsymbol{k}, r) = \sum_{i=1}^{w} 2^{Jk_i + j_i}. \tag{5.205}$$

The time coefficients $c(\boldsymbol{k}, r)$ for the representation of the nonlinear sequence over GF(2^J), as expressed in (5.205), are all less than $2^M - 1$ (the order of α). Since the exponents of 2 in (5.205) are distinct modulo J, it is easily verified that no two distinct $\boldsymbol{k}$ vectors produce the same time coefficient, $c(\boldsymbol{k}, r)$ and, therefore, no terms in the w-fold sum in (5.204) can be combined.

When expanding the outer trace function in (5.204), cross-product terms again must disappear, and

$$b_n = \sum_{m=0}^{J-1} \sum_{k_1=0}^{K-1} \cdots \sum_{k_w=0}^{K-1} \alpha^{nc(\boldsymbol{k}, r)2^m}. \tag{5.206}$$

Therefore, the time coefficients in the powers-of-α representation of $\{b_n\}$ are simply $c(\boldsymbol{k}, r)2^m$. To determine whether or not these coefficients are distinct modulo the order of α, solutions $\boldsymbol{k}_1, \boldsymbol{k}_2, m_1, m_2$ to the equation

$$c(\boldsymbol{k}_1, r)2^{m_1} = c(\boldsymbol{k}_2, r)2^{m_2} \bmod 2^M - 1, \tag{5.207}$$

must be sought. Since $2^J - 1$ divides $2^M - 1$, any solution to (5.207) must also satisfy the same equation modulo $2^J - 1$. But $c(\boldsymbol{k}, r)$ modulo $2^J - 1$ is simply r, and (5.207) modulo $2^J - 1$ can be rewritten as

$$r(2^{m_1} - 2^{m_2}) = 0 \bmod 2^J - 1. \tag{5.208}$$

However, r is relatively prime to $2^J - 1$ and, hence, in the allowed range of m_1 and m_2, (5.208) exhibits only the solution $m_1 = m_2$. Therefore, the only solution to (5.207) is the identity $\boldsymbol{k}_1 = \boldsymbol{k}_2$ and $m_1 = m_2$, and all time coefficients in (5.206) are distinct. Application of Theorem 5.9 and counting the terms in (5.206) yields the final result. ■

Example 5.12. A GMW sequence of period 63 is defined by

$$b_n = \mathrm{Tr}_2^8\left(\left[\mathrm{Tr}_8^{64}(\alpha^n)\right]^3\right), \tag{5.209}$$

where $z^6 + z^5 + z^2 + z + 1$ is the minimum polynomial of α over GF(2). One simple plan for mechanizing a generator for $\{b_n\}$ is to construct a generator for the m-sequence $\mathrm{Tr}_8^{64}(\alpha^n)$ and use a ROM to complete the mapping to GF(2). The elements of GF(8) are 0 and α^{9i}, $i = 0, 1, \ldots, 6$, and the minimum polynomial of α over GF(8) is easily determined (see Appendix 5A.8) to be $z^2 + \alpha^{54}z + \alpha^9$. A block diagram of the generator employing GF(8) arithmetic is shown in Figure 5.13.

The actual mechanization takes advantage of the fact that GF(8) is a three-dimensional vector space over GF(2) with basis $1, \alpha^9, \alpha^{18}$. That is, an element from GF(8) can be written as

$$\gamma = \gamma_0 \cdot 1 + \gamma_1\alpha^9 + \gamma_2\alpha^{18}, \tag{5.210}$$

Table 5.12
A representation for GF(8) elements, and the ROM mapping for Example 5.12.

γ	γ_0	γ_1	γ_2	$\mathrm{Tr}_2^8(\gamma^3)$
0	0	0	0	0
1	1	0	0	1
α^9	0	1	0	1
α^{18}	0	0	1	1
α^{27}	1	1	0	0
α^{36}	0	1	1	1
α^{45}	1	1	1	0
α^{54}	1	0	1	0

with $\gamma_0, \gamma_1, \gamma_2$ in GF(2). Table 5.12 lists this representation along with the ROM mapping, $\mathrm{Tr}_2^8(\gamma^3)$. The multiplications required in the generator of Figure 5.13 are easily mechanized in this representation.

$$\begin{aligned}\alpha^{54}\gamma &= \alpha^{54}\gamma_0 + \gamma_1 + \alpha^9\gamma_2\\ &= (\alpha^{18}+1)\gamma_0 + \gamma_1 + \alpha^9\gamma_2\\ &= (\gamma_0+\gamma_1)1 + \gamma_2\alpha^9 + \gamma_0\alpha^{18}.\end{aligned} \tag{5.211}$$

Similarly,

$$\alpha^9\gamma = \gamma_2\cdot 1 + (\gamma_0+\gamma_2)\alpha^9 + \gamma_1\alpha^{18}. \tag{5.212}$$

This results in the mechanization of Figure 5.14(a). One period of each of the sequences produced in this generator is shown in Figure 5.14(b). Notice the periodically recurring zeros in the GF(8) sequences (T is 9 in this example), this demonstrating the structure exploited in the proof of Theorem 5.12.

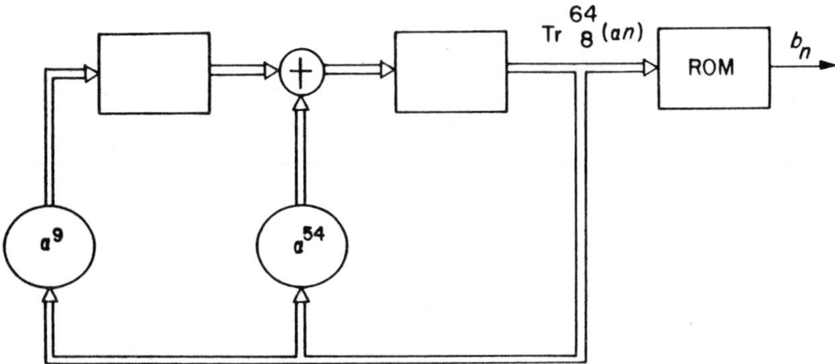

Figure 5.13. A GMW sequence generator in the Galois configuration with elements in GF(8).

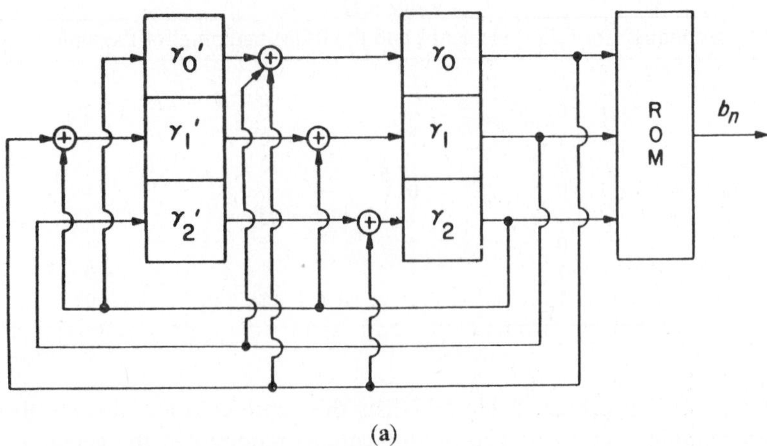

(a)

γ_0: 0111000110011101100000011110010010101001101000010001011011111101
γ_1: 000011110010010101001101000010001011011111101011100011001110110
γ_2: 0011101100000011110010010101001101000010001011011111101011100011

γ_0': 1001110110000001111001001010100110100001000101101111110101110001
γ_1': 0010010101001101000010001011011111101011100011001110110000001111
γ_2': 000001111001001010100110100001000101101111110101110001100111011

b_n: 01001110101110100101110001100111111001001011100111010000001010

(b)

Figure 5.14. **(a)** A GF(2) mechanization of the GMW sequence generator in Example 5.12. **(b)** Sequences produced in this generator.

Since r is 3, the base-2 expansion of r has weight 2, and Theorem 5.13 states that the linear span in this example is 12. The time coefficients $c(\boldsymbol{k}, 3)$ in the powers-of-α expansion of the cubed GF(8) sequence are given in Table 5.13. When the final trace operation to GF(2) is carried out, the remaining cyclic shifts of the binary time coefficients listed in Table 5.12 are added to give twelve distinct coefficients in all. It is obvious from the cyclotomic coset representatives in this table that the characteristic polynomial of $Q(z)$ of $\{b_n\}$ is

$$Q(z) = m_{\alpha^3}(z) m_{\alpha^5}(z)$$
$$= z^{12} + z^8 + z^7 + z^6 + z^5 + z^3 + 1. \tag{5.213}$$

This can be verified directly as specifying the recursion satisfied by the output sequence.

The k-tuple statistics of the output sequence in this example are shown in Table 5.14. As indicated by this data, the k-tuple statistics of a GMW

Table 5.13
Time coefficients $c(\boldsymbol{k}, 3)$ of the sequence $[\mathrm{Tr}_8^{64}(\alpha^n)]^3$.

Time Coefficients	
base-2	base-10
110000	3
100010	17
010100	10
000110	24

sequence are not uniformly distributed for all k less than the number of memory elements used, as they are for m-sequences by Property R-2 (5.61).

A uniform distribution on k-tuple occurrences is achieved in GMW sequences for a restricted range of k, as stated in the following theorem.

THEOREM 5.14. *Let $\{b_n\}$ be the GMW sequence defined by* (5.200). *Then the number N_a of positions within one period of $\{b_n\}$ at which the k-tuple $a_1 a_2 \ldots a_k$ occurs, is given by*

$$N_a = \begin{cases} 2^{M-k}, & \text{for } \boldsymbol{a} \neq \boldsymbol{0}, \quad 1 \le k \le \dfrac{M}{J} \\ 2^{M-k} - 1, & \text{for } \boldsymbol{a} = \boldsymbol{0}, \quad 1 \le k \le \dfrac{M}{J} \end{cases}. \tag{5.214}$$

Proof. The intermediate field sequence $\mathrm{Tr}_{2^J}^{2^M}(\alpha^n)$ is an m-sequence with linear span M/J, and hence k-tuples $a'_1 \ldots a'_k$ from this sequence occur $N'_{a'}$ times in one period according to the count specified in (5.61):

$$N'_{a'} = \begin{cases} 2^{J(M/J-k)}, & \text{for } \boldsymbol{a}' \neq \boldsymbol{0}, \quad 1 \le k \le \dfrac{M}{J} \\ 2^{J(M/J-k)} - 1, & \text{for } \boldsymbol{a}' = \boldsymbol{0}, \quad 1 \le k \le \dfrac{M}{J} \end{cases}. \tag{5.215}$$

Since r is relatively prime to $2^J - 1$, the r-th power mapping of the intermediate field onto itself is one-to-one, and the above count $N'_{a'}$ also applies to the sequence $\{[\mathrm{Tr}_{2^J}^{2^M}(\alpha^n)]^r\}$.

Table 5.14
K-tuple statistics for the GMW sequence of length 63.

k	(k-tuple: Occurrences per period)
1	(0:31), (1:32)
2	(00:15), (01:16), (10:16), (11:16)
3	(000:6), (100:9), (010:9), (001:9)
	(110:7), (101:7), (011:7), (111:9)
4	(0000:4), (1000:2), (0100:5), (0010:5)
	(0001:2), (1100:4), (0110:1), (0011:4)
	(1001:7), (1010:4), (0101:4), (1110:6)
	(0111:6), (1011:3), (1101:3), (1111:3)

Let $\mathscr{A}_{\boldsymbol{a}}$ be the set of k-tuples $\boldsymbol{a}'$ over GF(2^J) which map into $\boldsymbol{a}$ under the trace mapping

$$a_i = \mathrm{Tr}_2^{2^J}(a_i'), \qquad \text{for } i = 1, \ldots, k. \tag{5.216}$$

Note that the all-zeros k-tuple maps into itself. Then the number of occurrences of $\boldsymbol{a}$ in one period of $\{b_n\}$ is given by

$$N_{\boldsymbol{a}} = \sum_{\boldsymbol{a}' \in \mathscr{A}_{\boldsymbol{a}}} N'_{\boldsymbol{a}'}. \tag{5.217}$$

Since the number of elements in GF(2^J) which map into zero by (5.216) is 2^{J-1} (trace property T-4), it is easily verified that

$$|\mathscr{A}_{\boldsymbol{a}}| = (2^{J-1})^k, \quad \text{for all } k\text{-tuples } \boldsymbol{a}. \tag{5.218}$$

Therefore, when $\boldsymbol{a} \neq \mathbf{0}$ and hence $\mathbf{0} \notin \mathscr{A}_{\boldsymbol{a}}$, then all the terms in (5.217) are identical by (5.215), and

$$N_{\boldsymbol{a}} = |\mathscr{A}_{\boldsymbol{a}}| \cdot 2^{J(M/J-k)} = 2^{M-k}, \quad \text{for } \boldsymbol{a} \neq \mathbf{0}. \tag{5.219}$$

A similar computation for $\boldsymbol{a} = \mathbf{0}$ completes the proof. ■

The next result indicates that all proper decimations and allowable choices of the exponent r yield distinct GMW sequences.

THEOREM 5.15. *Let $\{b_n\}$ and $\{c_n\}$ be GMW sequences whose elements are given by*

$$b_n = \mathrm{Tr}_2^{2^J}\left(\left[\mathrm{Tr}_{2^J}^{2^M}(\alpha^n)\right]^r\right) \tag{5.220}$$

$$c_n = \mathrm{Tr}_2^{2^J}\left(\left[\mathrm{Tr}_{2^J}^{2^M}(\alpha^{an})\right]^s\right), \tag{5.221}$$

where r and s are integers relatively prime to $2^J - 1$ and less than $2^J - 1$, a is relatively prime to $2^M - 1$, and α is a primitive element of GF(2^M). Then $\{b_n\}$ and $\{c_n\}$ are cyclically equivalent if and only if

$$r = 2^j s \bmod 2^J - 1 \quad \textit{for some} \quad 0 \le j < J \tag{5.222}$$

and

$$a = 2^m \quad \textit{for some} \quad 0 \le m < M. \tag{5.223}$$

Proof. Define T, n_0, and n_1 as in (5.192) and (5.193). Let $\beta = \alpha^\tau$ and $\gamma = \alpha^T$ (a primitive element of GF(2^J)). Then the linearity property of the trace gives

$$\{b_n\} = \{c_{n+\tau}\}$$
$$\Leftrightarrow \mathrm{Tr}_2^{2^J}(\gamma^{rn_1}k_1) = \mathrm{Tr}_2^{2^J}(\gamma^{asn_1}k_2) \tag{5.224}$$

where

$$k_1 = \left[\mathrm{Tr}_{2^J}^{2^M}(\alpha^{n_0})\right]^r \tag{5.225}$$

$$k_2 = \left[\mathrm{Tr}_{2^J}^{2^M}(\beta\alpha^{an_0})\right]^s. \tag{5.226}$$

The trace functions in (5.224) represent two m-sequences over GF(2), each with element index n_1. These sequences are identical for some β if and only if γ^r and γ^{as} have the same minimum polynomial over GF(2); hence, equality requires

$$r = 2^j as \bmod 2^J - 1, \quad \text{for some} \quad 0 \le j < J \tag{5.227}$$

(see Theorem 5A.14 in Appendix 5A).

Assuming (5.227) is satisfied, the fact that conjugate elements have the same trace (see 5.122) can be used to show that

$$\begin{aligned} \mathrm{Tr}_2^{2^J}(\gamma^{rn_1}k_1) &= \mathrm{Tr}_2^{2^J}\left(\gamma^{2^j asn_1}k_1\right) \\ &= \mathrm{Tr}_2^{2^J}\left(\gamma^{asn_1}k_1^{2^{J-j}}\right), \end{aligned} \tag{5.228}$$

and, hence, equality holds in (5.224) when k_2 is identical to $k_1^{2^{J-j}}$, i.e., when

$$\left[\mathrm{Tr}_{2^J}^{2^M}(\alpha^{n_0})\right]^{2^{J-j}r} = \left[\mathrm{Tr}_{2^J}^{2^M}(\beta\alpha^{an_0})\right]^s. \tag{5.229}$$

Substitution of (5.227) into (5.229) and raising each side of the result to a power equal to the multiplicative inverse of s modulo $2^J - 1$ yields the result

$$\left[\mathrm{Tr}_{2^J}^{2^M}(\alpha^{n_0})\right]^a = \mathrm{Tr}_{2^J}^{2^M}(\beta\alpha^{an_0}). \tag{5.230}$$

If the two sequences over GF(2^J), whose elements with index n_0 are given by the right and left sides of (5.230), are cyclically equivalent, then their linear spans must be equal. It can be shown via the techniques of Theorem 5.13, that the sequence defined by the left side of (5.230) has linear span $(M/J)^w$, where w is the number of ones in the binary representation of $a \bmod 2^J - 1$. The linear span of the sequence represented by the right side of (5.230) is M/J, since α^a is also a primitive element of GF(2^M). Hence, equality requires that w be 1 and, therefore, (5.223) is necessary. Substitution of (5.223) into (5.227) results in (5.222) as a necessary requirement. It is easily verified that these necessary conditions are also sufficient. ■

Hence, the number N_{GMW} of cyclically distinct GMW sequences, which can be constructed by this method for a fixed M and J, is given by

$$N_{\mathrm{GMW}} = N_p(M)N_p(J), \tag{5.231}$$

where $N_p(d)$ denotes the number of primitive polynomials of degree d over GF(2), or equivalently the number of cyclically distinct m-sequences of linear span d over GF(2) (see Section 5.3.4).

Example 5.13. Consider a design in which the ROM size constrains J to be 7. Since $2^7 - 1$ is the prime number 127, all binary 7-tuples, except 0000000 and 1111111, are radix-2 representations of numbers relatively prime to 127. One set of acceptable choices of r, with cyclically inequivalent radix-2

Table 5.15
Design parameter tradeoffs for GMW sequences with a constraint $J = 7$.

w	$\binom{J}{w}/J$	r values	$M = 14$		$M = 28$	
			$N_{\text{GMW}}(w)$	L	$N_{\text{GMW}}(w)$	L
1	1	1	756	14	4741632	28
2	3	3, 5, 9	2268	28	14224896	112
3	5	7, 11, 13, 19, 21	3780	56	23708160	448
4	5	15, 23, 27, 29, 43	3780	112	23708160	1792
5	3	31, 47, 55	2268	224	14224896	7168
6	1	63	756	448	4741632	28672

representations, is shown in Table 5.15, which contains a total of $N_p(7)$ entries, with $\binom{J}{w}/J$ entries for each value of w. This table also indicates the number $N_{\text{GMW}}(w)$ of GMW sequences constructed with weight-w values of r, along with their linear span L, for two possible values of memory size M.

5.7 DIRECT-SEQUENCE MULTIPLE-ACCESS DESIGNS

5.7.1 A Design Criterion

In many situations, more than one SS code generator is required to operate simultaneously within the same locale and bandwidth, i.e., in a multiple-access (MA) environment. The distinguishability of different SS signals by receivers participating in the SSMA scheme depends on many factors, including the SS sequences, modulation formats, and the receiver's detector structure. This section will explore one tractable criterion for DS-SSMA signal design, namely minimization of the absolute value of periodic correlation between signals.

Consider a set of J sequences, each with period N, denoted by $\{a_n^{(j)}\}$, $j = 1, \dots, J$. The periodic cross-correlation $P_{jk}(\tau)$ at shift τ between sequences from this collection is defined as

$$P_{jk}(\tau) = \sum_{n=1}^{N} a_{n+\tau}^{(j)} \left(a_n^{(k)}\right)^*. \tag{5.232}$$

The maximum out-of-phase periodic autocorrelation magnitude P_A for this signal set is defined as

$$P_A = \max_j \max_{0<\tau<N} |P_{jj}(\tau)|, \tag{5.233}$$

and the maximum cross-correlation magnitude P_C between signals in this set is given by

$$P_C = \max_{j \neq k} \max_{0 \leq \tau < N} |P_{jk}(\tau)|. \tag{5.234}$$

The signal sets to be discussed here all are designed to minimize

$$P_{\max} = \max(P_A, P_C). \tag{5.235}$$

This criterion for sequence selection may not correspond to any DS-SSMA network performance measure, but it can be argued that a signal set which optimizes network performance probably has a small value of $P_{\max}$; hence, one should find good signal sets among those with small $P_{\max}$. Furthermore, from an analytic viewpoint, no other design criteria have proven tractable in choosing long-period sequences.

In situations in which a capability against repeater jamming is not a requirement, the code period N may be relatively short, its value in most instances being underbounded by the multipath time-spread of the channel. Hence, in some multiple access designs which require no AJ provisions, correlations may be calculated over full periods. Conversely, when intelligent jamming is a possible threat, then the SS direct sequence must possess a large period and large linear span; shortening the DS period in this situation for the sake of somewhat improved multiple access capability would allow the possibility of catastrophic consequences.

5.7.2 Welch's Inner Product Bound

The correlation computation of (5.232) can be viewed as an inner product between the N-tuples $(a_{1+\tau}^{(j)}, \ldots, a_{N+\tau}^{(j)})$ and $(a_1^{(k)}, \ldots, a_N^{(k)})$. This connection will be exploited in applying the following theorem to determine a bound on $P_{\max}$.

THEOREM 5.16 (Welch's Bound [29]). *Let* $(c_1^{(\nu)}, \ldots, c_L^{(\nu)})$, $\nu = 1, \ldots, M$, *represent L-tuples of complex numbers, and define the inner product*

$$R_{\nu\lambda} = \sum_{n=1}^{L} c_n^{(\nu)} \left(c_n^{(\lambda)}\right)^*. \tag{5.236}$$

Assume that each L-tuple has unit length, i.e., $R_{\nu\nu} = 1$ *for all* ν, *and define*

$$R_{\max} = \max_{\nu \neq \lambda} |R_{\nu\lambda}|. \tag{5.237}$$

Then

$$R_{\max}^2 \geq \frac{M - L}{(M - 1)L}. \tag{5.238}$$

Proof. Beginning with the definition of $R_{\max}$ and the fact that the vectors are unit length, it is easily verified that

$$\begin{aligned}
M(M-1)R_{\max}^2 + M &\geq \sum_{\nu=1}^{M}\sum_{\lambda=1}^{M}|R_{\nu\lambda}|^2 \\
&= \sum_{\nu=1}^{M}\sum_{\lambda=1}^{M}\sum_{i=1}^{L}\sum_{j=1}^{L} c_i^{(\nu)}\left(c_i^{(\lambda)}\right)^*\left(c_j^{(\nu)}\right)^* c_j^{(\lambda)} \\
&\overset{(1)}{=} \sum_{i=1}^{L}\sum_{j=1}^{L}\left|\sum_{\nu=1}^{M} c_i^{(\nu)}\left(c_j^{(\nu)}\right)^*\right|^2 \\
&\overset{(2)}{\geq} \sum_{i=1}^{L}\left|\sum_{\nu=1}^{M}|c_i^{(\nu)}|^2\right|^2 \\
&\overset{(3)}{\geq} \frac{1}{L}\left|\sum_{i=1}^{L}\sum_{\nu=1}^{M}|c_i^{(\nu)}|^2\right|^2 \overset{(4)}{=} \frac{M^2}{L}.
\end{aligned} \tag{5.239}$$

Here equality (1) follows from changing the order of summation, inequality (2) is achieved by neglecting terms with $i \neq j$, (3) is Cauchy's inequality for sums of squares, or equivalently is a result of the convexity of the quadratic function, and (4) simply uses the fact that the L-tuples are unit length. Solving the derived inequality (5.239) for $R_{\max}^2$ gives the final result. ■

Welch's inner-product bound can be applied to a variety of signal design situations. Here we apply it to the maximum absolute value of correlation for a set of roots-of-unity sequences. Let

$$\left(c_1^{(\nu)}, \ldots, c_L^{(\nu)}\right) = N^{-1/2}\left(a_{1+\tau}^{(j)}, \ldots, a_{N+\tau}^{(j)}\right) \tag{5.240}$$

for $0 \leq \tau < N$ and $1 \leq j \leq J$, the $N^{-1/2}$ being required to make the N-tuple unit length. Here one may think of ν as ranging over JN values corresponding to the distinct pairs (j, τ); hence, the required parameter substitution in Welch's bound is $L = N$ and $M = JN$. The quantity $R_{\max}$ can be shown to correspond to $P_{\max}/N$, giving the following result.

COROLLARY 5.3. *The maximum absolute value $P_{\max}$ of the out-of-phase periodic autocorrelation and of the periodic cross-correlation for a set of J roots-of-unity sequences with period N is lower bounded by*

$$\left(\frac{P_{\max}}{N}\right)^2 \geq \frac{J-1}{JN-1}. \tag{5.241}$$

When the number J of sequences is even moderately large, then (5.241) indicates that $P_{\max}$ must be at least on the order of $\sqrt{N}$.

When the set of sequences $\{a_n^{(j)}\}$, $1 \leq j \leq J$, of period N, are composed of ± 1 strings, a correspondence with a code $\mathscr{C}$ containing JN binary code words $\boldsymbol{b}_{j,m}$, $1 \le j \le J$, $0 \le m < N$, of length N over GF(2), can be established through the relation

$$a_n^{(j)} = (-1)^{b_n^{(j)}}, \quad \boldsymbol{b}_{j,m} = \left(b_{m+1}^{(j)}, \ldots, b_{m+N}^{(j)}\right). \tag{5.242}$$

Note that the n code words $\boldsymbol{b}_{j,m}$, $0 \le m < N$, are cyclically equivalent for each value of j; therefore, the code $\mathscr{C}$ is called a *cyclic code*. A bound on periodic cross-correlation magnitude for the ± 1 sequence set can be rewritten in terms of Hamming distance for the corresponding cyclic code over GF(2), as

$$\begin{aligned} P_{\max} \ge |P_{jk}(\tau)| &= \left| \sum_{n=1}^{N} (-1)^{b_{n+\tau}^{(j)} - b_n^{(k)}} \right| \\ &= |N - 2H(\boldsymbol{b}_{j,\tau}, \boldsymbol{b}_{k,0})|, \end{aligned} \tag{5.243}$$

whence,

$$(N - P_{\max})/2 \le H(\boldsymbol{b}_{j,\tau}, \boldsymbol{b}_{k,0}) \le (N + P_{\max})/2 \tag{5.244}$$

for all j, k, and τ. Thus, the design of a set of J, period N, binary, roots-of-unity sequences to have small correlation, is equivalent to the design of a cyclic error-control code $\mathscr{C}$ containing NJ words of length N with the Hamming distance between all pairs of code words close to $N/2$. This link with error-control coding makes many of the design techniques in the well-developed theory of coding available for DS-SSMA signal design.

Two well-known SSMA signal designs, namely Gold sequences [35], [36] and the small set of Kasami sequences [30], [31], are a direct result of design techniques for cyclic error-control codes. The Kasami sequences are among several known sets of sequences which nearly meet the Welch bound on $P_{\max}$, including bent sequences [32], and the prime-period group-character sequences [33]. The Kasami and bent sequence designs are both binary and possess identical numbers, periods, and periodic correlation properties, but the bent sequences have considerably longer linear span. The group-character sequences are non-binary but each design contains one binary sequence, namely the quadratic residue (or Legendre) sequence (e.g., see [12], Chapter 3, Section 5.6). Gold sequence sets, although not meeting the Welch bound, are larger than the Kasami and bent sets, and achieve a more restricted bound of Sidelnikov [39], which states that for any N binary (± 1) sequences of period N,

$$P_{\max} > (2N - 2)^{1/2}. \tag{5.245}$$

The Gold, Kasami, and bent designs will be developed later in this section.

5.7.3 Cross-Correlation of Binary *M*-Sequences

It is clear from Table 5.6 that for reasonable register lengths, e.g., 20 to 30 stages, there exist large numbers of cyclically distinct m-sequences. Therefore, it is reasonable to determine whether or not several m-sequences can be used together as a DS-SSMA signal set. We approach this question by considering the cross-correlation between a roots-of-unity m-sequence $\{a_n\}$ and its r-th decimation $\{a_{rn}\}$, the latter being another m-sequence whenever r is relatively prime to the period of $\{a_n\}$.

Let $\{\mathrm{Tr}_2^{2^L}(\alpha^n)\}$ denote a binary m-sequence, α being a primitive element of GF(2^L), and let $\{a_n\}$ be the corresponding roots-of-unity m-sequence. The periodic cross-correlation between $\{a_n\}$ and its r-th decimation $\{a'_n\}$, $a'_n = a_{rn}$ for all n, is given by

$$P_{aa'}(\tau) = \sum_{n=1}^{2^L-1} (-1)^{\mathrm{Tr}(\alpha^{n+\tau})+\mathrm{Tr}(\alpha^{rn})}. \tag{5.246}$$

Since α is primitive, α^n scans through the non-zero elements of GF(2^L) as n varies in (5.246), and, after compensating for the insertion of the zero element into the calculation, (5.246) leads to

$$\Delta_r(y) \triangleq 1 + P_{aa'}(\tau) = \sum_{x\in \mathrm{GF}(2^L)} (-1)^{\mathrm{Tr}(xy+x^r)}, \tag{5.247}$$

where $y = \alpha^\tau$. Analytical simplifications of (5.247) have been achieved only for certain values of r. A comprehensive survey of these results, including tabulations of computer searches is given in [37].

One particularly good result will be derived from the following lemmas.

LEMMA 5.2. *Let*

$$r = 2^k + 1, \qquad e = \gcd(2k, L), \tag{5.248}$$

and assume e divides k. Then $\Delta_r(y)$ takes on three values: 0, $2^{(L+e)/2}$, *and* $-2^{(L+e)/2}$, *with* 0 *occurring for* $2^L - 2^{L-e}$ *different values of* y.

Proof. Squaring and simplifying (5.247) gives

$$\begin{aligned}[\Delta_r(y)]^2 &= \sum\sum_{x,z\in \mathrm{GF}(2^L)} (-1)^{\mathrm{Tr}[y(x+z)+x^r+z^r]} \\ &\overset{(1)}{=} \sum\sum_{x,w\in \mathrm{GF}(2^L)} (-1)^{\mathrm{Tr}[yw+x^r+(w+x)(w^{2^k}+x^{2^k})]} \\ &\overset{(2)}{=} \sum_{w\in \mathrm{GF}(2^L)} (-1)^{\mathrm{Tr}(yw+w^r)} \sum_{x\in \mathrm{GF}(2^L)} (-1)^{\mathrm{Tr}[x(w^{2^k}+w^{2^{L-k}})]}\end{aligned} \tag{5.249}$$

Equality (1) results from the substitution of $z = w + x$ and the form of r, and equality (2) employs trace linearity and the fact that wx^{2^k} and $xw^{2^{L-k}}$ have the same trace since they are conjugates.

As x varies over GF(2^L), the trace in the inner sum is 0 and 1 equally often (see trace Property T-4) provided that $w^{2^k} + w^{2^{L-k}}$ is not zero. Hence, the sum on x is 0 or 2^L, and (5.249) reduces to

$$[\Delta_r(y)]^2 = 2^L \sum_{w \in \Omega} (-1)^{\mathrm{Tr}(yw + w^r)}, \tag{5.250}$$

where

$$\begin{aligned} \Omega &= \left\{ w\colon w^{2^k} + w^{2^{L-k}} = 0,\ w \in \mathrm{GF}(2^L) \right\} \\ &= \left\{ w\colon w^{2^{2k}} = w,\ w \in \mathrm{GF}(2^L) \right\} \\ &= \left\{ w\colon w \in \mathrm{GF}(2^{2k}),\ w \in \mathrm{GF}(2^L) \right\}. \end{aligned} \tag{5.251}$$

The intersection of $\mathrm{GF}(2^{2k})$ and $\mathrm{GF}(2^L)$ is $\mathrm{GF}(2^e)$, where e is the gcd $(2k, L)$.

The order of every w in $\mathrm{GF}(2^e)$ divides $2^e - 1$, and, therefore, assuming e divides k,

$$w^r = w^{(2^e)^c} \cdot w = w^2, \tag{5.252}$$

where c is an integer. Since the traces of w and w^2 are identical, (5.250) reduces to

$$[\Delta_r(y)]^2 = 2^L \sum_{w \in \mathrm{GF}(2^e)} (-1)^{\mathrm{Tr}_2^{2^e}\{[\mathrm{Tr}_{2^e}^{2^L}(y) + \mathrm{Tr}_{2^e}^{2^L}(1)]w\}} \tag{5.253}$$

by (5.125). Since $\mathrm{Tr}_{2^e}^{2^L}(y+1)$ is zero for 2^{L-e} values of y by trace property T-4,

$$[\Delta_r(y)]^2 = 2^{L+e} \quad \text{for } 2^{L-e} \text{ values of } y. \tag{5.254}$$

When $\mathrm{Tr}_{2^e}^{2^L}(y+1)$ is non-zero, the outer trace in (5.253) is zero and one equally often as w scans through $\mathrm{GF}(2^e)$ and, therefore,

$$[\Delta_r(y)]^2 = 0 \quad \text{for } 2^L - 2^{L-e} \text{ values of } y. \tag{5.255}$$

■

Lemma 5.2 provides the mathematical background for computing the periodic cross-correlation between an m-sequence and its r-th decimation, when r is of the form $2^k + 1$. The application of this result to the cross-correlation of m-sequences requires the following lemma to determine when the r-th decimation of an m-sequence is itself an m-sequence.

LEMMA 5.3. *For all integers m and n,*

$$\gcd(2^m - 1, 2^n - 1) = 2^{\gcd(m,n)} - 1 \tag{5.256}$$

$$\gcd(2^m + 1, 2^n - 1) = 1 \text{ iff } n/\gcd(m,n) \text{ is odd.} \tag{5.257}$$

Proof. By Euclidean division,

$$m = an + r, \quad 0 \le r < n, \tag{5.258}$$

and, using binary representations of $2^m - 1$ and $2^n - 1$ as m- and n-tuples of ones, Euclidean division of $2^m - 1$ by $2^n - 1$ gives

$$(2^m - 1) = b(2^n - 1) + (2^r - 1), \quad 0 \le 2^r - 1 < 2^n - 1, \quad (5.259)$$

for some integer b. Hence, there is a correspondence between terms in Euclid's algorithm (see Appendix 5A.2) for determining $\gcd(m, n)$ and that for finding $\gcd(2^m - 1, 2^n - 1)$, which easily yields a proof of (5.256).

A proof of (5.257) begins by applying (5.256) to give

$$\gcd((2^m - 1)(2^m + 1), 2^n - 1) = 2^{\gcd(2m, n)} - 1, \qquad (5.260)$$

and noting that

$$\gcd(2^m - 1, 2^m + 1) = 1, \qquad (5.261)$$

since these numbers differ by two and are odd. Therefore,

$$\begin{aligned} \gcd(2^m + 1, 2^n - 1) = 1 & \\ & \Leftrightarrow \gcd(2m, n) | m \\ & \Leftrightarrow n/\gcd(m, n) \text{ is odd.} \end{aligned} \qquad (5.262)$$

■

When the decimation coefficient r is relatively prime to $2^L - 1$, Theorem 5.8 indicates that the resulting decimation of an m-sequence is also an m-sequence. Placing Lemma 5.2 in correlation terms and restricting the decimation by r to produce an m-sequence, gives the following theorem.

THEOREM 5.17. *Let $\{a_n\}$ be a roots-of-unity m-sequence with period $2^L - 1$, and let $P_{aa'}(\tau)$ be the periodic cross-correlation of $\{a_n\}$ with $\{a'_n\}$, its decimation by r. Let r and e be defined by* (5.248), *with $L/\gcd(k, L)$ odd. Then*

$$P_{aa'}(\tau) = \begin{cases} -1 & \text{for } 2^L - 2^{L-e} - 1 \text{ values of } \tau, \\ -1 + 2^{(L+e)/2} & \text{for } 2^{L-e-1} + 2^{(L-e-2)/2} \text{ values of } \tau, \\ -1 - 2^{(L+e)/2} & \text{for } 2^{L-e-1} - 2^{(L-e-2)/2} \text{ values of } \tau \end{cases} \qquad (5.263)$$

where $0 \le \tau < 2^L - 1$.

Final determination of the counts shown in this theorem can be made after showing that $\Sigma_\tau P_{aa'}(\tau) = 1$.

Information concerning other pairs of m-sequences with good periodic cross-correlation is given in Table 5.16. It is assumed in this listing that r is relatively prime to $2^L - 1$, and e is the greatest common divisor of L and $2k$. Note that while Welch's proof of the second listed result is unpublished, it is the $m = 3$ case of the third listed result. Each of the entries in Table 5.16 gives rise to peak cross-correlation magnitudes on the order of $2^{(L+1)/2}$ when L is odd, and $2^{(L+2)/2}$ when L is even. However, this table does not list all such cases.

Table 5.16
Maximum absolute value of the cross-correlation between m-sequences with characteristic polynomials $m_\alpha(z)$ and $m_\alpha^r(z)$, α a primitive element of GF(2^L).

r	$\max\lvert P_{aa'}(\tau)\rvert$	Comments
$2^k + 1$	$2^{(L+e)/2} + 1$	[30]
$2^{2k} - 2^k + 1$	$2^{(L+e)/2} + 1$	(Welch, unpublished)
$(2^{mk} + 1)/(2^k + 1)$	$2^{(L+e)/2} + 1$	m odd, [37]
$2^{(L+2)/2} - 1$	$2^{(L+2)/2} - 1$	$L = 0 \bmod 4$, [37]
$2^{L-1} - 1$	$\leq 2^{(L+2)/2}$	[38]

Periodic cross-correlation calculations can be carried out analytically on m-sequences of differing periods, sometimes with good results. This is illustrated in the following theorem and proof.

THEOREM 5.18. *Let α be a primitive element of* GF(2^L), *L even, and let*

$$r = 2^{L/2} + 1, \tag{5.264}$$

α^r being a primitive element of GF($2^{L/2}$). *Then the roots-of-unity m-sequences of periods $2^L - 1$ and $2^{L/2} - 1$, with elements defined by*

$$a_n = (-1)^{\mathrm{Tr}_2^{2^L}(\alpha^n)} \tag{5.265}$$

and

$$a'_n = (-1)^{\mathrm{Tr}_2^{2^{L/2}}(\alpha^{rn})} \tag{5.266}$$

respectively, have periodic cross-correlation (over $2^L - 1$ sequence elements) values $-1 \pm 2^{L/2}$ at all shifts.

Proof. The cross-correlation between $\{a_n\}$ and $\{a'_n\}$ at shift τ is given by

$$P_{aa'}(\tau) = \sum_{n=1}^{2^L-1} (-1)^{\mathrm{Tr}_2^{2^L}(\alpha^{n+\tau}) + \mathrm{Tr}_2^{2^{L/2}}(\alpha^{rn})}$$

$$= -1 + \sum_{x \in \mathrm{GF}(2^L)} (-1)^{\mathrm{Tr}_2^{2^L}(yx) + \mathrm{Tr}_2^{2^{L/2}}(x^r)} \tag{5.267}$$

where $x = \alpha^n$, $y = \alpha^\tau$, and the field element 0 has been added to the sum range. The elements of GF(2^L) can be represented in the form

$$x = u\beta + v \tag{5.268}$$

where u and v are elements of GF($2^{L/2}$) and β is the root of an irreducible quadratic polynomial over GF($2^{L/2}$) (see Appendix 5A.5, Theorem 5A.9).

Then, using trace properties (5.123) and (5.125) on (5.268) gives

$$\begin{aligned} P_{aa'}(\tau) &= -1 + \sum_{u,v \in \mathrm{GF}(2^{L/2})}\sum (-1)^{\mathrm{Tr}_2^{2^{L/2}}[u\,\mathrm{Tr}_{2^{L/2}}^{2^L}(y\beta) + v\,\mathrm{Tr}_{2^{L/2}}^{2^L}(y) + (u\beta+v)(u\beta^{2^{L/2}}+v)]} \\ &= -1 + \sum_{u \in \mathrm{GF}(2^{L/2})} (-1)^{\mathrm{Tr}_2^{2^{L/2}}[\mathrm{Tr}_{2^{L/2}}^{2^L}(y\beta)u + \beta^r u^2]} \\ &\quad \times \sum_{v \in \mathrm{GF}(2^{L/2})} (-1)^{\mathrm{Tr}_2^{2^{L/2}}[(\mathrm{Tr}_{2^{L/2}}^{2^L}(y) + u\,\mathrm{Tr}_{2^{L/2}}^{2^L}(\beta)+1)v]}, \end{aligned} \tag{5.269}$$

the latter step using the fact that v and v^2 have the same trace. The interior sum over v in (5.269) is zero by trace property T-4 unless the coefficient of v is zero, in which case the sum is $2^{L/2}$. Furthermore, the coefficient of v in (5.265) is zero for exactly one value of u, namely

$$u_y = \left[\mathrm{Tr}_{2^{L/2}}^{2^L}(\beta)\right]^{-1}\left[1 + \mathrm{Tr}_{2^{L/2}}^{2^L}(y)\right], \tag{5.270}$$

and it follows that

$$P_{aa'}(\tau) = -1 + 2^{L/2}(-1)^{\mathrm{Tr}_2^{2^L}(y\beta u_y) + \mathrm{Tr}_2^{2^{L/2}}(\beta^r u_y^2)}. \tag{5.271}$$

■

Theorems 5.17 and 5.18 will now be applied to the design of large sets of sequences with good periodic correlation properties.

5.7.4 Linear Designs

Two roots-of-unity m-sequences, $\{a_n\}$ and $\{a'_n\}$, with corresponding sequences $\{b_n\}$ over GF(p) and $\{b'_n\}$ over GF(p'), possessing known cross-correlation properties, can be used to construct a larger set of sequences with easily determined correlation properties. In this general situation, the periodic cross-correlation of the roots-of-unity m-sequences is defined as

$$P_{aa'}(\tau) = \sum_{n=1}^{N_m} \rho^{b_{n+\tau}} \rho'^{-b'_n}, \tag{5.272}$$

where ρ and ρ' are primitive complex p-th and p'-th roots of unity respectively, and

$$N_m = \mathrm{lcm}(p^L - 1, p'^{L'} - 1), \tag{5.273}$$

L and L' being the linear spans of the corresponding m-sequences. The following theorem relates the cross-correlation properties defined in (5.272) to those of a larger collection of sequences.

THEOREM 5.19. *Let* $\{b_n\}$ *and* $\{b'_n\}$ *be the m-sequences described above and let*

$$a_n^{(j)} = \rho^{b_{n+j}} \rho'^{-b'_n}. \tag{5.274}$$

Then the set of N_d sequences, namely $\{a_n^{(0)}\}, \{a_n^{(1)}\}, \ldots, \{a_n^{(N_d-1)}\}$, where

$$N_d = \gcd(p^L - 1, p'^{L'} - 1), \tag{5.275}$$

have periodic cross-correlation (over N_m symbols) taking on values $-N_m/(p'^{L'} - 1)$, $-N_m/(p^L - 1)$, and the cross-correlation values calculated in (5.272).

Proof. The cross-correlation of $\{a_n^{(j)}\}$ and $\{a_n^{(k)}\}$ can be simplified immediately, using the shift-and-add property of m-sequences.

$$P_{jk}(\tau) = \sum_{n=1}^{N_m} \rho^{b_{n+\tau+j} - b_{n+k}} \rho'^{-b'_{n+\tau} + b'_n}. \tag{5.276}$$

Case (a): Assume $\tau + j - k \neq 0 \bmod p^L - 1$, and $\tau \neq 0 \bmod p'^{L'} - 1$. Then from (5.63),

$$\begin{aligned} P_{jk}(\tau) &= \sum_{n=1}^{N_m} \rho^{b_{n+k+\tau'(\tau+j-k)}} \rho'^{-b'_{n+\tau''(\tau)}} \\ &= P_{aa'}(k + \tau'(\tau + j - k) - \tau''(\tau)). \end{aligned} \tag{5.277}$$

Case (b): Assume $\tau + j - k \neq 0 \bmod p^L - 1$, and $\tau = 0 \bmod p'^{L'} - 1$. In this case, b'_n cancels in the exponent of (5.276) and

$$P_{jk}(\tau) = \sum_{n=1}^{N_m} \rho^{b_{n+k+\tau'(\tau+j-k)}} = -N_m/(p^L - 1). \tag{5.278}$$

Case (c): Assume $\tau + j - k = 0 \bmod p^L - 1$, and $\tau \neq 0 \bmod p'^{L'} - 1$. As in case (c), (5.276) reduces to

$$P_{jk}(\tau) = \sum_{n=1}^{N_m} \rho'^{-b_{n+\tau''(\tau)}} = -N_m/(p'^{L'} - 1). \tag{5.279}$$

Case (d): Assume $\tau + j - k = 0 \bmod p^L - 1$, and $\tau = 0 \bmod p'^{L'} - 1$. Then

$$P_{jk}(\tau) = N_m. \tag{5.280}$$

This last case can occur only if

$$\tau = C_1(p'^{L'} - 1), \quad \tau + j - k = C_2(p^L - 1), \tag{5.281}$$

whence

$$j - k = C_2(p^L - 1) - C_1(p'^{L'} - 1). \tag{5.282}$$

Since the right side of (5.282) is a multiple of N_d, the allowed range of j and k excludes the occurrence of case (d), except when $j = k$ and $\tau = 0$. ■

When $p = p'$, there is a common mathematical structure available for describing the sequences in Theorem 5.19. The characteristic polynomial of

$\{b_n\}$ is a minimum polynomial $m_\alpha(z)$ of degree L over GF(p) with α a primitive element of GF(p^L).

$$m_\alpha(z) = z^L + \sum_{j=1}^{L} q_j z^{L-j}. \tag{5.283}$$

Likewise, $m_\beta(z)$ of degree L' over GF(p) is the characteristic polynomial of $\{b'_n\}$, where β is a primitive element of GF$(p^{L'})$, and we assume that $m_\alpha(z) \neq m_\beta(z)$.

$$m_\beta(z) = z^{L'} + \sum_{j=1}^{L'} s_j z^{L'-j}. \tag{5.284}$$

The generator for a sequence $\{a_n^{(j)}\}$ can be organized with p-ary shift registers as shown in Figure 5.15. This generator form is equivalent to a single $L + L'$ stage shift-register generator producing a sequence over GF(p) with characteristic polynomial $m_\alpha(z)m_\beta(z)$.

Let $\boldsymbol{b}_k$ denote an L-tuple of $\{b_n\}$ beginning at the k-th symbol, and similarly denote an L'-tuple from $\{b'_n\}$, beginning at the k-th symbol, by $\boldsymbol{b}'_k$. Hence, the states of the two Fibonacci generators in Figure 5.15 can be specified by one such L-tuple and one such L'-tuple from the component sequences, provided the registers are not loaded with all-zeroes vectors 0. The results of various register initializations on the generator's GF(p) output sequence $\{c_n\}$ are shown in Table 5.17. The notation $\{b_n^{(j)}\}$ has been used here to describe the GF(p) form of the output sequence, and, hence, when neither register is initialized with a zero vector,

$$a_n^{(j)} = a_{n+j}a'_n = \rho^{b_{n+j} - b'_n} = \rho^{b_n^{(j)}} \tag{5.285}$$

for all j and n where ρ is a complex primitive p-th root of unity.

The set of sequences $\{c_n\}$ for all i and k, enumerated in Table 5.17 forms a linear space. Specifically, if $\{c_n\}$ and $\{c'_n\}$ both satisfy the linear recursion having characteristic polynomial $m_\alpha(z)m_\beta(z)$, then so do sequences of the form $\{dc_n + ec'_n\}$ for any choice of d, e GF(p). Since Table 5.17 enumerates the $p^{L+L'}$ distinct sequences which satisfy such a recursion, the sequence $\{dc_n + ec'_n\}$ must correspond to one of the tabulated sequences. Hence, the initial N_m-tuples of the GF(p) sequences $\{c_n\}$ listed in Table 5.17 and generated by the structure in Figure 5.15, form a *linear cyclic code* [6], [7], [40], [41], [48] and we shall refer to the sequence set as a *linear design*.

By proper initialization of the register contents, the generator of Figure 5.15 can be used to produce any of the N_d possible sequences $\{a_n^{(j)}\}$, $j = 0, \ldots, N_d - 1$, the component sequences $\{a_n\}$ and $\{a'_n\}$, and the all-ones sequence. The latter sequence, definitely not pseudorandom in nature, is simply avoided by not initializing both registers with all zeroes. A purely random non-zero initialization of the registers is equally likely to produce any one of the sequences of interest. To load the registers for the production

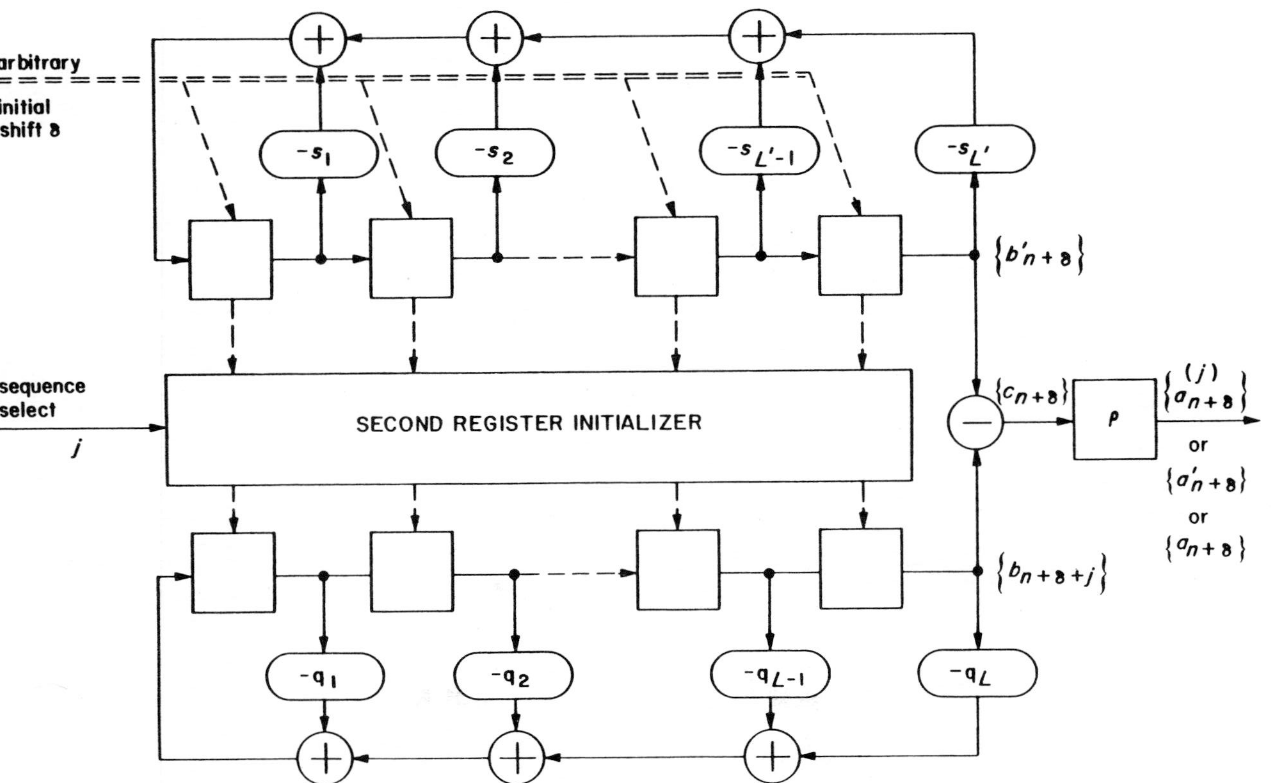

Figure 5.15. Fibonacci form of a linear generator structure for $\{a_n^{(j)}\}$ when both $\{b_n\}$ and $\{b'_n\}$ are over GF(p).

Table 5.17

Initialization data for the linear generator structure of Figure 5.15.

Register Initializations Lower	Register Initializations Upper	Output $\{c_n\}$	Size of Index Set	Output Linear Span
$\boldsymbol{b}_k$	$\boldsymbol{b}'_i$	$\{\boldsymbol{b}_{n+i-1}^{(k-i)}\}$	$(p^L - 1)(p^{L'} - 1)$	$L + L'$
$\mathbf{0}$	$\boldsymbol{b}'_i$	$\{\boldsymbol{b}'_{n+i-1}\}$	$p^{L'} - 1$	L'
$\boldsymbol{b}_k$	$\mathbf{0}$	$\{\boldsymbol{b}_{n+k-1}\}$	$p^L - 1$	L
$\mathbf{0}$	$\mathbf{0}$	$\{0\}$	1	1

of $\{a_{n+\delta}^{(j)}\}$ for a particular j at a random shift δ, one register of the sequence generator in Figure 5.15 may be initialized randomly with non-zero contents, and then the allowed choice(s) for the initial contents of the other register must be determined mathematically. This calculation could be done off line, thereby complicating the use of the system by requiring that operators have tables of allowed register contents, or it could be mechanized in hardware, as suggested in Figure 5.15.

If the second register initialization is mechanized in hardware and the computation can be carried out in a fraction of the registers' clock time with a unique answer, then the second register can be eliminated and the initializing hardware can be used to calculate the second register's output symbol for each successive contents of the first register. This calculating hardware, and the adder which combines the two component sequences, form an NLFFL function of the contents of the first register to produce the output sequence over GF(p). Note that the structure of this NLFFL is dependent on the sequence to be generated, i.e., the index j, and is generally rather complex.

Insight into the balance properties of a sequence $\{b_n^{(j)}\}$ in a linear design can be obtained by relating balance to correlation. Let N_b be the number of occurrences of the symbol b in one period of $\{b_n^{(j)}\}$, and note that

$$\sum_{b \in \mathrm{GF}(p)} N_b \rho^b = \sum_{n=1}^{N_m} \rho^{b_n^{(j)}} = \sum_{n=1}^{N_m} \rho^{b_{n+j} - b'_n} = P_{aa'}(j). \qquad (5.286)$$

Knowledge of the periodic cross-correlation values on the left side of (5.286) imposes constraints on the possible values of N_b, and vice versa. The clearest example of this relation occurs when $p = 2$, and is summarized in the following.

THEOREM 5.20. *Let* $\{b_n^{(j)}\}$, $j = 0, 1, \ldots, N_d - 1$, *be the compound sequences of a binary linear design, based on component m-sequences* $\{b_n\}$ *and* $\{b'_n\}$ *with corresponding roots-of-unity m-sequences* $\{a_n\}$ *and* $\{a'_n\}$ *respectively. Then the number of compound sequences in the binary linear design, having* N_1 *ones in one period, is given by the number of shifts* j,

$0 \le j < N$, for which

$$P_{aa'}(j) = N_m - 2N_1,$$

where N_m and N_1 are defined in (5.273) and (5.275) with $p = p' = 2$, and L and L' are the linear spans of the component m-sequences.

Note that $N_m - 2N_1$ is the number of zeroes in the binary sequence $\{b_n^{(j)}\}$ minus the number of ones, and, hence, $P_{aa'}(j)$ can be interpreted as the imbalance in $\{b_n^{(j)}\}$.

Example 5.14 (Gold sequences). In a 1967 paper [35], Gold suggested combining two binary m-sequences with identical periods to produce a set of SSMA codes with good periodic correlation properties. Gold considered a linear design in which two component sequences, each with linear span L, were employed, one with characteristic polynomial $m_\alpha(z)$, and the other with characteristic polynomial $m_{\alpha^r}(z)$, where

$$r = 2^{\lfloor (L+2)/2 \rfloor} + 1, \tag{5.287}$$

with $\lfloor x \rfloor$ denoting the integer part of x. This choice of r satisfies the conditions of the cross-correlation Theorem 5.17 with $e = 1$ for L odd and $e = 2$ for L even. The combining process of Theorem 5.19, in this case with $p = p' = 2$ and $N_m = N_d = 2^L - 1$, yields a binary linear design with all cross-correlation and out-of-phase autocorrelation values taken from the set $-1, -1 + 2^{\lfloor (L+2)/2 \rfloor}, -1 - 2^{\lfloor (L+2)/2 \rfloor}$.

Including the component sequences, Gold's design contains $2^L + 1$ sequences, a sufficient number for Sidelnikov's bound (5.245) to apply. Specializing the bound to this case gives

$$P_{\max} > \left[2(2^L - 1) - 2\right]^{1/2} = (2^{L+1} - 4)^{1/2}. \tag{5.288}$$

where $P_{\max}$ is defined in (5.232)–(5.235). For $L \ge 3$, this implies that $P_{\max}$ is greater than $-1 + 2^{(L+1)/2}$, and, since the binary sequence set's period is odd, $P_{\max}$ must be odd, yielding

$$P_{\max} \ge 1 + 2^{(L+1)/2}. \tag{5.289}$$

Gold sequences with L odd have $P_{\max}$ satisfying this bound with equality, and, hence, are an optimal design from the viewpoint of minimizing the absolute periodic correlation parameter $P_{\max}$.

Theorem 5.20 indicates that only $2^L - 2^{L-e} - 1$ of the compound sequences in the Gold set are balanced, with the imbalance in the remaining 2^{L-e} sequences being on the order of $2^{\lfloor (L+2)/2 \rfloor}$.

Example 5.15 (the small set of Kasami sequences). Kasami [30] in 1966 reported results on the enumeration of weights of linear cyclic codes over GF(2). He noted that this problem is equivalent (as in Theorem 5.20) to the evaluation of cross-correlation or out-of-phase autocorrelation between two binary (± 1) sequences, and produced forms of the results described in Theorems 5.16 and 5.18.

The small set of Kasami sequences is a binary linear design whose component sequences are (1) an m-sequence with period $2^L - 1$, L even, and characteristic polynomial $m_\alpha(z)$, $\alpha \in \mathrm{GF}(2^L)$, and (2) an m-sequence with shorter period $2^{L/2} - 1$ and characteristic polynomial $m_{\alpha^r}(z)$, where

$$r = 2^{L/2} + 1, \tag{5.290}$$

α^r being an element of $\mathrm{GF}(2^{L/2})$. The period of the latter m-sequence divides the longer period of the first m-sequence (see Lemma 5.3), and Theorem 5.18 states that the periodic cross-correlation of these two m-sequences, over the longer period, is $-1 \pm 2^{L/2}$ at all relative phase shifts.

Application of Theorem 5.19 to these m-sequences, with $p = p' = 2$, $N_m = 2^L - 1$, and $N_d = 2^{L/2} - 1$, yields a binary linear design now referred to as the small set of Kasami sequences, with all cross-correlation and out-of-phase autocorrelation values from the set -1, $-1 + 2^{L/2}$, and $-1 - 2^{L/2}$. Adding the long-period m-sequence to this set gives $2^{L/2}$ sequences with a $P_{\max}$ of $1 + 2^{L/2}$.

Evaluation of the Welch bound (5.241) at $J = 2^{L/2}$ and $N = 2^L - 1$, gives

$$\begin{aligned} P_{\max} &\geq \left(\frac{N^2(J-1)}{NJ-1} \right)^{1/2} = (2^L - 2^{L/2} - 1 + r)^{1/2} \\ &> (2^L - 2 \cdot 2^{L/2} + 1)^{1/2} = 2^{L/2} - 1 \end{aligned} \tag{5.291a}$$

for some r, $0 < r < 1$. Since the inequality is strict and since $P_{\max}$ must be odd for binary sequences with odd periods, the Welch bound for this binary case reduces to

$$P_{\max} \geq 2^{L/2} + 1. \tag{5.291b}$$

The small set of Kasami sequences achieves this bound with equality, and, therefore, is optimal in the sense of minimizing the maximum absolute correlation parameter $P_{\max}$.

Theorem 5.20 can be used to verify that none of the compound sequences in the Kasami set is balanced.

5.7.5 A Transform-Domain Design Philosophy

The linear designs of the previous section have excellent periodic correlation properties, but short linear spans. A transform domain design approach will now be described which results in a NLFFL design producing balanced binary sequences with optimal correlation properties and longer linear span [32], [42].

Consider two functions, $r(x)$ and $s(x)$, mapping the elements of $\mathrm{GF}(2^d)$ into $+1$ and -1. These functions can be viewed as representing NLFFL functions operating on a Galois m-sequence generator with characteristic polynomial $m_\alpha(z)$, whose d-stage register contents $r_1^{(n)}, \ldots, r_d^{(n)}$ represent α^n (see (5.127)). The resulting binary ($+1$ and -1) sequences, $\{r(\alpha^n)\}$ and $\{s(\alpha^n)\}$, have periodic cross-correlation at shift τ given by

$$R_{rs}(\tau) = \sum_{n=1}^{2^d-1} r(\alpha^{n+\tau})s(\alpha^n)$$
$$= -r(0)s(0) + \sum_{x \in \mathrm{GF}(2^d)} r(yx)s(x). \tag{5.292}$$

where $y = \alpha^\tau$.

The inner product of $r(yx)$ and $s(x)$ over $x \in \mathrm{GF}(2^d)$ in (5.292) can be studied in a transform domain using any inner product-preserving transform. Two closely related transforms will be considered for this purpose, the first being the *trace transform* which is defined as

$$\hat{r}(\lambda) = \frac{1}{2^{d/2}} \sum_{x \in \mathrm{GF}(2^d)} r(x)(-1)^{\mathrm{Tr}(\lambda x)} \tag{5.293}$$

for all $\lambda \in \mathrm{GF}(2^d)$. The following properties of the trace transform can be verified:

(a) Inversion theorem:

$$r(x) = \frac{1}{2^{d/2}} \sum_{\lambda \in \mathrm{GF}(2^d)} \hat{r}(\lambda)(-1)^{\mathrm{Tr}(\lambda x)}. \tag{5.294}$$

(b) Multiplicative shifting theorem: For $y \neq 0$,

$$s(x) = r(yx) \text{ for all } x \text{ iff } \hat{s}(\lambda) = \hat{r}(y^{-1}\lambda) \text{ for all } \lambda. \tag{5.295}$$

(c) Parseval's relation:

$$\sum_{x \in \mathrm{GF}(2^d)} r(x)s(x) = \sum_{\lambda \in \mathrm{GF}(2^d)} \hat{r}(\lambda)\hat{s}(\lambda). \tag{5.296}$$

(d) Additive shifting theorem:

$$s(x) = r(x+y) \text{ for all } x \text{ iff } \hat{s}(\lambda) = \hat{r}(\lambda)(-1)^{\mathrm{Tr}(\lambda y)} \text{ for all } \lambda, \tag{5.297}$$

$$\hat{s}(\lambda) = \hat{r}(\lambda + y) \text{ for all } \lambda \text{ iff } s(x) = r(x)(-1)^{\mathrm{Tr}(xy)} \text{ for all } x. \tag{5.298}$$

Another equivalent inner-product-preserving transform is defined after a one-to-one linear mapping of $\mathrm{GF}(2^d)$ onto the space $\mathscr{V}_d$ of d-tuples with elements in GF(2). Specifically, let $\beta_1, \ldots, \beta_d$ be an arbitrary basis for $\mathrm{GF}(2^d)$, and let $\gamma_1, \ldots, \gamma_d$ be another basis for $\mathrm{GF}(2^d)$ with the property that

$$\mathrm{Tr}(\beta_i \gamma_j) = \begin{cases} 1, & i = j \\ 0, & i \neq j. \end{cases} \tag{5.299}$$

Two bases satisfying (5.299) are called *complementary*. It can be verified [42] that every basis for GF(2^d) has a complementary basis. Let x and λ be arbitrary elements of GF(2^d), represented in complementary bases by

$$x = \sum_{i=1}^{d} x_i \beta_i, \qquad \lambda = \sum_{i=1}^{d} \lambda_i \gamma_i. \tag{5.300}$$

Coordinate values can be determined by applying (5.299) and trace linearity to (5.301) to yield

$$x_i = \mathrm{Tr}(\gamma_i x), \qquad \lambda_i = \mathrm{Tr}(\beta_i \lambda) \tag{5.301}$$

for all i. These same relations allow $\mathrm{Tr}(\lambda x)$ to be interpreted as an inner product of vectors of coefficients from the expansions (5.300).

$$\mathrm{Tr}(\lambda x) = \boldsymbol{x}^t \boldsymbol{\lambda}. \tag{5.302}$$

The mapping from $x \in$ GF(2^d) to $\boldsymbol{x} \in \mathscr{V}_d$, can be used to define

$$R(\boldsymbol{x}) \triangleq r(x) \tag{5.303}$$

for all x in GF(2^d), substitution of (5.302) and (5.303) into the trace transform definition (5.293) gives

$$\hat{r}(\lambda) = \frac{1}{2^{d/2}} \sum_{\boldsymbol{x} \in \mathscr{V}_d} R(\boldsymbol{x})(-1)^{\boldsymbol{\lambda}^t \boldsymbol{x}} \triangleq \tilde{R}(\boldsymbol{\lambda}). \tag{5.304}$$

The right side of (5.304) defines the *Fourier transform* $\tilde{R}(\boldsymbol{\lambda})$ of the function $R(\boldsymbol{x})$. The inversion theorem, Parseval's relation, and additive shifting theorem for the Fourier transform are easily derived from the corresponding results for trace transforms, in view of (5.304). Both transforms will be used in the design approach to follow.

Returning to the periodic cross-correlation computation of (5.292), we now develop a bound on cross-correlation. Applying Parseval's relation (5.296) gives

$$R_{rs}(\tau) = -r(0)s(0) + \sum_{\lambda \in \mathrm{GF}(2^d)} \hat{r}(y^{-1}\lambda)\hat{s}(\lambda). \tag{5.305}$$

Therefore,

$$|R_{rs}(\tau)| \le 1 + \sum_{\lambda \in y\mathscr{S}_r \cap \mathscr{S}_s} |\hat{r}(y^{-1}\lambda)||\hat{s}(\lambda)|, \tag{5.306}$$

where the sum over λ in (5.306) has been limited to those λ for which the corresponding term is non-zero, i.e.,

$$\mathscr{S}_s \triangleq \{\lambda \colon \hat{s}(\lambda) \neq 0\} \tag{5.307}$$

and

$$y\mathscr{S}_r = \{\lambda \colon \hat{r}(y^{-1}\lambda) \neq 0\} = \{\lambda y \colon \lambda \in \mathscr{S}_r\}. \tag{5.308}$$

Parseval's relation also implies that

$$\sum_{\lambda \in \mathscr{S}_r} |\hat{r}(\lambda)|^2 = \sum_{\lambda \in \mathrm{GF}(2^d)} |\hat{r}(\lambda)|^2 = \sum_{x \in \mathrm{GF}(2^d)} |r(x)|^2 = 2^d, \tag{5.309}$$

which yields a bound on the trace transform, namely

$$B_r \triangleq \max_{\lambda} |\hat{r}(\lambda)|^2 \geq \frac{2^d}{|\mathcal{S}_r|}. \tag{5.310}$$

Applying the definition on the left side of (5.310) to (5.306) gives a general bound on correlation magnitude.

$$|R_{rs}(\tau)| \leq 1 + \sqrt{B_r B_s}\,|y\mathcal{S}_r \cap \mathcal{S}_s|. \tag{5.311}$$

The above development suggests the following procedure for designing a set $\mathcal{B}$ of distinct NLFFL functions operating on identical m-sequence shift registers, to produce sequences with good periodic auto- and cross-correlation properties:

Property P-1.

Assume that the transforms of all functions in $\mathcal{B}$ are non-zero on the same subset $\mathcal{S}$ of GF(2^d) and are all zero outside $\mathcal{S}$. Notice that

$$0 \notin \mathcal{S} \Leftrightarrow \hat{r}(0) = 0 = \sum_{x \in \mathrm{GF}(2^d)} r(x) \Leftrightarrow \{r(\alpha^n)\} \text{ is balanced,} \tag{5.312}$$

for all $r \in \mathcal{B}$. Hence, a set of balanced sequences will be achieved in this design if and only if 0 is not in $\mathcal{S}$.

Property P-2.

Choose the set $\mathcal{S}$ (with $0 \notin \mathcal{S}$) so that $y\mathcal{S} \cap \mathcal{S}$ is as small as possible for all non-integer y in GF(2^d). To calculate the average size of the intersection, let $a_i = 1$ for each i for which $\alpha^i \in \mathcal{S}$, and let $a_i = 0$ otherwise. Then for $y = \alpha^\tau$, we have

$$|y\mathcal{S} \cap \mathcal{S}| = \sum_{i=0}^{2^d-2} a_{i+\tau} a_i, \tag{5.313}$$

and bounding the maximum intersection by the average intersection gives

$$\begin{aligned} \max_{\substack{y \in \mathrm{GF}(2^d) \\ y \notin \mathrm{GF}(2)}} |y\mathcal{S} \cap \mathcal{S}| &\geq \frac{1}{2^d - 2} \sum_{\tau=1}^{2^d-2} \sum_{i=0}^{2^d-2} a_{i+\tau} a_i \\ &\geq \frac{|\mathcal{S}|(|\mathcal{S}| - 1)}{2^d - 2}. \end{aligned} \tag{5.314}$$

Property P-3.

Design the set $\mathcal{B}$ of functions so that for each r and s in $\mathcal{B}$, $r \neq s$,

$$\sum_{x \in \mathrm{GF}(2^d)} r(x)s(x) = 0 = \sum_{\lambda \in \mathrm{GF}(2^d)} \hat{r}(\lambda)\hat{s}(\lambda). \tag{5.315}$$

This orthogonality guarantees that $|R_{rs}(0)|$ is 1. Since in the transform domain $\hat{r}(\lambda)$ can be viewed as a $|\mathscr{S}|$-tuple, the achievable size of $\mathscr{B}$ is limited by $|\mathscr{S}|$, i.e.,

$$|\mathscr{B}| \leq |\mathscr{S}|. \tag{5.316}$$

Property P-4.

Design each function in $\mathscr{B}$ so that its trace transform has constant magnitude, namely $2^d/|\mathscr{S}|$ on $\mathscr{S}$ by (5.309). If this objective can be achieved and if the bounds (5.314) and (5.316) can be achieved with equality, then by (5.311) it is possible to find orthogonal NLFFL functions such that

$$|R_{rs}(\tau)| \leq 1 + \frac{2^d|\mathscr{S}|}{2^d - 2}, \tag{5.317}$$

for all $\tau \neq 0 \bmod 2^d - 1$.

The final parameter, namely $|\mathscr{S}|$, can be chosen with the aid of the Welch bound, which states that $|R_{rs}(\tau)|$ must be on the order of $2^{d/2}$ when $|\mathscr{B}|$ is large. Assuming that (5.317) is valid and tight, the Welch bound (5.241) indicates that $|\mathscr{S}|$ should be on the order of $2^{d/2}$, with larger values of $|\mathscr{S}|$ resulting in designs which cannot meet that bound with equality. The above design approach, with $|\mathscr{S}| = 2^{d/2}$, will be successfully demonstrated in the next section.

5.7.6 Bent Sequences

Rothaus [43] defined a function $f(\boldsymbol{x})$ mapping the space $\mathscr{V}_k$ of binary k-tuples over GF(2) into $\mathscr{V}_1$ (GF(2)) to be *bent* if the Fourier transform of $(-1)^{f(\boldsymbol{x})}$, namely

$$\tilde{F}(\boldsymbol{\lambda}) \triangleq \frac{1}{2^{k/2}} \sum_{\boldsymbol{x} \in \mathscr{V}_k} (-1)^{f(\boldsymbol{x}) + \boldsymbol{x}'\boldsymbol{\lambda}}, \tag{5.318}$$

is ± 1 for all $\boldsymbol{\lambda}$ in $\mathscr{V}_k$. Although there are many families of bent functions [43]–[45], only one bent function form will be described here.

THEOREM 5.21 (Rothaus [43]). *Let*

$$\boldsymbol{x} = \begin{bmatrix} \boldsymbol{x}_1 \\ \boldsymbol{x}_2 \end{bmatrix}, \quad \boldsymbol{x}_1, \boldsymbol{x}_2 \in \mathscr{V}_j. \tag{5.319}$$

Let the function $f_z(\boldsymbol{x})$, mapping $\mathscr{V}_{2j}$ onto $\mathscr{V}_1$, be defined as

$$f_z(\boldsymbol{x}) = \boldsymbol{x}_1'\boldsymbol{x}_2 + g(\boldsymbol{x}_2) + \boldsymbol{z}'\boldsymbol{x}, \tag{5.320}$$

where $g(\boldsymbol{x}_2)$ is an arbitrary function mapping $\mathscr{V}_j$ into $\mathscr{V}_1$. Then $f_z(\boldsymbol{x})$ is bent for every $\boldsymbol{z}$ in $\mathscr{V}_{2j}$.

Proof. The Fourier transform of $f_z(\boldsymbol{x})$ is given by

$$\tilde{F}_z(\lambda) = 2^{-j} \sum\sum_{\boldsymbol{x}_1, \boldsymbol{x}_2 \in \mathscr{V}_j} (-1)^{\boldsymbol{x}_1^t \boldsymbol{x}_2 + g(\boldsymbol{x}_2) + \boldsymbol{x}^t z + \boldsymbol{x}^t \lambda}$$

$$= 2^{-j} \sum_{\boldsymbol{x}_2 \in \mathscr{V}_j} (-1)^{g(\boldsymbol{x}_2) + \boldsymbol{x}_2^t (z_2 + \lambda_2)}$$

$$\times \sum_{\boldsymbol{x}_1 \in \mathscr{V}_j} (-1)^{\boldsymbol{x}_1^t (\boldsymbol{x}_2 + z_1 + \lambda_1)}, \tag{5.321}$$

where, in the latter step, z and λ have been appropriately partitioned into vectors of dimension j. The sum over $\boldsymbol{x}_1$ in (5.321) is zero if and only if $\boldsymbol{x}_2 + z_1 + \lambda_1$ is not zero, its alternative value being 2^j. Hence,

$$\tilde{F}_z(\lambda) = (-1)^{g(z_1 + \lambda_1) + (z_1 + \lambda_1)^t (z_2 + \lambda_2)}. \tag{5.322}$$

■

With regard to dimensionality, this design will now fix

$$d = 2k = 4j, \tag{5.323}$$

with $g(\cdot)$ an arbitrary function from $\mathscr{V}_j$ to $\mathscr{V}_1$, and $f_z(\cdot)$ a bent function mapping $\mathscr{V}_k$ into $\mathscr{V}_1$. Let $\boldsymbol{L}(x)$ define a linear mapping from GF(2^d) to $\mathscr{V}_k$. The set $\mathscr{B}$ of NLFFL functions used to produce bent sequences is now defined to contain all functions of the form

$$r_z(x) = (-1)^{f_z(\boldsymbol{L}(x)) + \mathrm{Tr}(\sigma x)}, \tag{5.324}$$

where σ is fixed and $z \in \mathscr{V}_k$.

The trace transform of $r_z(x)$ is given by

$$\hat{r}_z(\lambda) = 2^{-k} \sum_{x \in \mathrm{GF}(2^d)} (-1)^{f_z(\boldsymbol{L}(x)) + \mathrm{Tr}(\sigma x) + \mathrm{Tr}(\lambda x)}. \tag{5.325}$$

Representing $(-1)^{f_z}$ in terms of its inverse transform on $\mathscr{V}_k$ gives

$$\hat{r}_z(\lambda) = 2^{-k} \sum_{x \in \mathrm{GF}(2^d)} (-1)^{\mathrm{Tr}((\sigma + \lambda)x)} 2^{-j} \sum_{\lambda' \in \mathscr{V}_k} \tilde{F}_z(\lambda')(-1)^{\lambda'^t \boldsymbol{L}(x)}. \tag{5.326}$$

The linear mapping $\boldsymbol{L}(x)$ can be represented as

$$\boldsymbol{L}(x) = \boldsymbol{M}\boldsymbol{x} = \boldsymbol{M} \begin{bmatrix} \mathrm{Tr}(\gamma_1 x) \\ \vdots \\ \mathrm{Tr}(\gamma_d x) \end{bmatrix}, \tag{5.327}$$

where $\boldsymbol{M}$ is a $k \times d$ matrix over GF(2), of rank k, and $\boldsymbol{x}$ is the vector representation of the GF(2^d) element x (see (5.300)–(5.301)). The inner product $\lambda'^t \boldsymbol{L}(x)$ in (5.326) can be rewritten using (5.327) and the linearity of the trace function, so that

$$\lambda'^t \boldsymbol{L}(x) = \mathrm{Tr}(\ell(\lambda')x), \tag{5.328}$$

where the *adjoint* $\ell(\lambda')$ of $L(x)$ is

$$\ell(\lambda') = \lambda'' M\gamma, \tag{5.329}$$

and γ is the vector of basis elements $\gamma_1, \dots, \gamma_d$. Since the rank of M is k, $\ell(\lambda')$ is a one-to-one mapping from $\mathscr{V}_k$ onto a k-dimensional linear subspace of GF(2^d) with basis $M\gamma$.

Substituting (5.328) into (5.326) and interchanging the order of summation gives

$$\hat{r}_z(\lambda) = 2^{-j} \sum_{\lambda' \in \mathscr{V}_k} \tilde{F}_z(\lambda') \cdot 2^{-k} \sum_{x \in \mathrm{GF}(2^d)} (-1)^{\mathrm{Tr}\{[\sigma+\lambda+\ell(\lambda')]x\}} \tag{5.330}$$

The sum over x is non-zero if and only if the coefficient of x (in the trace function) is zero. Hence, $\hat{r}_z(\lambda)$ is non-zero if and only if $\sigma + \lambda$ is in the range of $\ell(\cdot)$. Denoting the inverse of ℓ on the range of ℓ by ℓ^{-1}, it follows that

$$\hat{r}_z(\lambda) = \begin{cases} 2^j \tilde{F}_z(\ell^{-1}(\sigma + \lambda)), & \text{for } \sigma + \lambda \in \text{range}(\ell) \\ 0, & \text{otherwise.} \end{cases} \tag{5.331}$$

Since $\tilde{F}_z$ is the transform of a bent function, $|\hat{r}_z(\lambda)|$ takes on two values, 0 and 2^j, as λ varies over GF(2^d), thereby satisfying design properties P-1 and P-4 of the previous section. One purpose of the added term Tr(σx) in the design of $f_z(x)$ now is apparent: The element σ can be chosen to make $\hat{r}_z(0) = 0$, thereby guaranteeing that the bent sequences are balanced.

Two applications of Parseval's relation can be used to verify the orthogonality of functions in $\mathscr{B}$.

$$\begin{aligned} \sum_{\lambda \in \mathrm{GF}(2^d)} \hat{r}_z(\lambda)\hat{r}_{w'}(\lambda) &= 2^k \sum_{\lambda \in \mathscr{V}_k} \tilde{F}_z(\lambda)\tilde{F}_{w'}(\lambda) \\ &= 2^k \sum_{x \in \mathscr{V}_k} (-1)^{(z-w)'x} \\ &= 0 \text{ for } z \neq w. \end{aligned} \tag{5.332}$$

Thus, design objective (Property P-3) is satisfied, guaranteeing good "in-phase" cross-correlation properties of bent sequences.

All requirements of the design procedure (Properties P-1 to P-4) have been satisfied except Property P-2, i.e., the minimization of $|y\mathscr{S} \cap \mathscr{S}|$. In this design, the set $\mathscr{S}$ is defined from (5.331) as

$$\mathscr{S} = \{\lambda\colon \sigma + \lambda \in \text{range}(\ell)\}. \tag{5.333}$$

Since σ is a constant and the range of ℓ contains 2^k points, $\mathscr{S}$ contains 2^k points, and (5.314) indicates that a good design may at best achieve

$$|y\mathscr{S} \cap \mathscr{S}| \leq 1 \quad \text{for all } y \notin \mathrm{GF}(2). \tag{5.334}$$

The final design step is performed by choosing an appropriate basis for the range of $\ell(\cdot)$ so that (5.334) is satisfied. Let

$$\text{range}(\ell) = \{\delta\varepsilon_0 \colon \delta \in \text{GF}(2^k)\}, \tag{5.335}$$

where ε_0 is any element of GF(2^d) that is not contained in a smaller field. Then $\mathscr{S}$ in (5.333) may be represented as

$$\begin{aligned}\mathscr{S} &= \{\lambda \colon \sigma + \lambda = \delta\varepsilon_0, \delta \in \text{GF}(2^k)\}\\ &= \{\delta\varepsilon_0 + \sigma \colon \delta \in \text{GF}(2^k)\}.\end{aligned} \tag{5.336}$$

We will now demonstrate that (5.334) is satisfied. Viewing GF(2^d) as an extension field of GF(2^k) which can be represented as a two-dimensional vector space over GF(2^k) (see Appendix 5A.4), an arbitrary element y of GF(2^d) can be represented as

$$y = y_1\varepsilon_0 + y_0, \tag{5.337}$$

where the basis for the vector space is 1 and ε_0, and the coefficients y_1 and y_0 are in GF(2^k). Then a point in the intersection of $y\mathscr{S}$ and $\mathscr{S}$ corresponds to a solution of the equation

$$(y_1\varepsilon_0 + y_0)(\delta\varepsilon_0 + \sigma) = \delta'\varepsilon_0 + \sigma \tag{5.338}$$

for the unknowns δ and δ' in GF(2^k). The element ε_0^2 can also be represented as $e_1\varepsilon_0 + e_0$, where e_1 and e_0 are in GF(2^k) and e_0 is not 0. A similar representation may be used for the element σ. This reduces the solution of (5.338) to the solution of a pair of linear equations over GF(2^k), by setting the coefficients of the basis elements ε_0 and 1 to zero, giving

$$\begin{aligned}(y_1e_1 + y_0)\delta + \delta' &= (y_0 + y_1e_1 + 1)\sigma_1 + y_1\sigma_0\\ y_1e_0\delta &= y_1e_0\sigma_1 + (y_0 + 1)\sigma_0.\end{aligned} \tag{5.339}$$

These equations are linearly independent and have a unique solution, except when $y_1 = 0$ and $y_0 = 1$, corresponding to the uninteresting case when $y = 1$. Therefore, (5.334) is satisfied, there being a single point in the intersection $y\mathscr{S} \cap \mathscr{S}$ when $y \notin \text{GF}(2)$, and hence, design objective P-2 has been achieved. The choice of σ can now be made so that $\hat{r}_z(0)$ is zero, by requiring that σ not be of the form $\delta\varepsilon_0$ for any δ in GF(2^k), i.e., by requiring that σ not be in range (ℓ).

The specification of range (ℓ) in (5.335) may be used to determine a suitable choice for $\boldsymbol{M}$. Let $\phi_1, \ldots, \phi_k$ be a basis for GF(2^k), and let ϕ be the vector composed of these basis elements. Then, equating

$$\varepsilon_0\phi = \boldsymbol{M}\gamma \tag{5.340}$$

guarantees by (5.329) that range (ℓ) matches the designed range specified in (5.335). Multiplying the i-th entry of the vector in (5.340) by β_j, taking the trace of the result, and using the fact that γ is a vector of elements from a complementary basis for (β_j: $j = 1, \ldots, d$}, gives the ij-th element of $\boldsymbol{M}$ to be

$$m_{ij} = \text{Tr}(\varepsilon_0\phi_i\beta_j). \tag{5.341}$$

Thus, the elements of $\boldsymbol{M}$ can be determined by trace calculations. The design can be completed by choosing a vector $\boldsymbol{s}$ so that

$$\mathrm{Tr}(\sigma x) = \boldsymbol{s}^t \boldsymbol{x}, \tag{5.342}$$

the requirement that σ not be in the range (ℓ) corresponding to $\boldsymbol{s}^t$ not being in the row space of $\boldsymbol{M}$.

It is worth noting that both transforms were useful at certain points in the derivation, but neither transform need be mechanized. Furthermore, completion of a design does not require the determination of a complementary basis. A compact description of the preceding development is given in the following result.

THEOREM 5.22. *Let α be a primitive element of* GF(2^d), *d divisible by* 4, *and let $\boldsymbol{x}$ represent the contents of a Galois-configured m-sequence generator having the minimum polynomial of α over* GF(2) *as its characteristic polynomial, i.e.,*

$$x = \sum_{i=0}^{d-1} x_i \alpha^i. \tag{5.343a}$$

Let ε_0 be any element of GF(2^d) *that is not contained in a smaller field, and let $\{\phi_1, \ldots, \phi_{d/2}\}$ be a basis for* GF$(2^{d/2})$ *over* GF(2). *Let $\boldsymbol{M}$ be a $d/2 \times d$ matrix whose i, j-th entry m_{ij} is given by*

$$m_{ij} = \mathrm{Tr}_2^{2^d}\left(\varepsilon_0 \phi_i \alpha^{j-1}\right) \tag{5.343b}$$

and let $\boldsymbol{s}^t$ be any d-dimensional vector not contained in the linear subspace spanned by the rows of $\boldsymbol{M}$. Then the $2^{d/2}$ NLFFL functions of the form

$$r_z(x) = (-1)^{f_z(\boldsymbol{Mx}) + \boldsymbol{s}^t \boldsymbol{x}} \tag{5.343c}$$

indexed by $z \in \mathscr{V}_{d/2}$, where $f_z(\cdot)$ is a bent function of the form (5.320), *produce balanced sequences with periodic cross-correlation and out-of-phase autocorrelation bounded in magnitude by* $1 + 2^{d/2}$.

Example 5.16. Consider a primitive polynomial $z^{12} + z^6 + z^4 + z + 1$ with root α in GF(4096), which serves as the characteristic polynomial of a Galois LFSR. This register's state sequence has period 4095, and its contents $\boldsymbol{x}$ represent the field element x in the basis $\{\alpha^i\colon i = 0, 1, \ldots, 11\}$ as indicated in (5.343). In this notation, the set $(\alpha^{65i}\colon i = 0, 1, \ldots, 5\}$ is composed of elements having order dividing 63, α^{65} being primitive in GF(64), and, hence, these elements form a basis for the subfield GF(64). One possible choice for the element ε_0, which must be outside GF(64), is α. With the choices just stated, the 6×12 basis reduction matrix M has ij-th entry

$$m_{ij} = \mathrm{Tr}_2^{4096}\left(\alpha^{65(i-1)+(j-1)+1}\right), \tag{5.344}$$

resulting in the matrix

$$M = \begin{bmatrix} 000000000010 \\ 001100010111 \\ 100001110000 \\ 101001100100 \\ 110010100001 \\ 011001001001 \end{bmatrix} \tag{5.345}$$

A suitable choice for the vector s^t, which must be outside the row space of M, is

$$s^t = (000000000001). \tag{5.346}$$

Employing a bent function of the form described in Theorem 5.21, operating on Mx, with the arbitrary function $g(\ )$ being a three-input AND gate, one bent-sequence generator design is shown in Figure. 5.16. The set of bent sequences produced by this generator has an absolute correlation measure P_{max} of 65.

The linear span L of a bent sequence can be bounded by Key's technique (5.172) to give

$$L \le \sum_{i=1}^{D} \binom{d}{i} \tag{5.347}$$

where D is the order of the nonlinearity employed in a d-stage register design, D presumably taking on the maximum allowed value $d/4$ (when $d \ge 8$) as determined by the choice of arbitrary nonlinearity $g(\cdot)$ (see (5.320)). Key's bound is not tight in this case, the intuitive reason for this being the fact that the nonlinearity is imposed on a lower dimensional subspace. The following theorem provides upper and lower bounds on the linear span of a well-designed bent sequence.

THEOREM 5.23 [46]. *Let L denote the maximum-achievable linear span of bent sequences produced by maximal-order* $(d/4)$ NLFFL *functions operating on a d-stage* LFSR *with d at least* 8 *and divisible by* 4. *Then L can be upper- and lower-bounded as follows*:

$$L \le \sum_{i=1}^{\frac{d}{4}-1} \binom{d}{i} + \binom{d/2}{d/4} 2^{d/4} - \sum_{i=1}^{\left\lfloor \frac{\frac{d}{4}-1}{2} \right\rfloor} \binom{d/2}{i}, \tag{5.348a}$$

$$L \ge \begin{cases} 20, & d = 8 \\ \binom{d/2}{d/4} 2^{d/4} + d + \frac{1}{2} \sum_{i=2}^{\frac{d}{4}-1} \binom{d/2}{i} 2^i, & d > 8. \end{cases} \tag{5.348b}$$

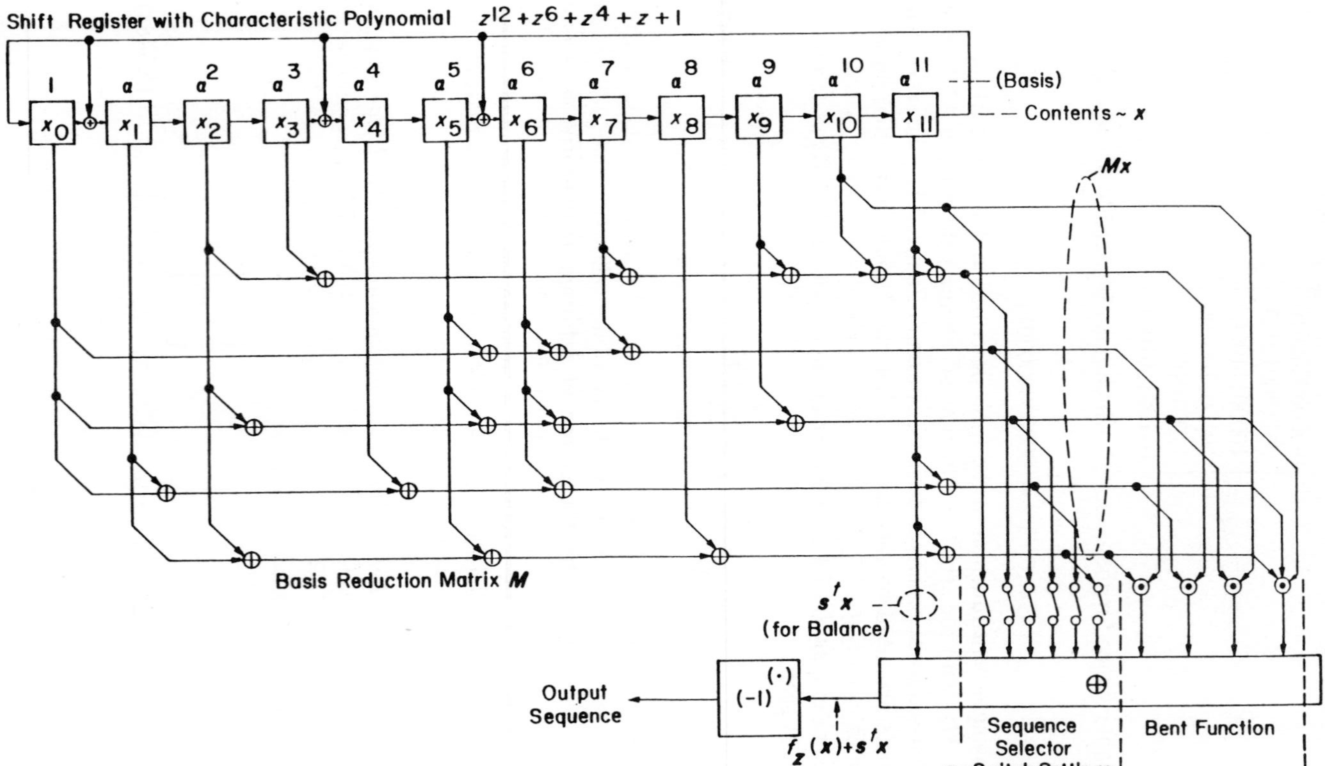

Figure 5.16. Typical bent sequence generator. Connections correspond to Example 5.16.

Table 5.18
Bounds on the maximum linear span of bent function sequences employing d-stage generators.

d	lower bound	upper bound
8	20	32
12	202	232
16	1416	1808
20	10334	14204
24	76804	114512
28	577098	938004

The term $\binom{d/2}{d/4} 2^{d/4}$ tends to dominate the lower bound and, therefore, may be used as a conservative estimate of the achievable linear span. These bounds on the linear span of bent sequences are evaluated in Table 5.18 for several values of register length d. A comparison of the properties of various DS-SSMA signal sets is shown in Table 5.19.

In summary, bent sequences and their generators have several desirable features:

(a) optimal periodic cross-correlation properties for multiple access uses (although the choice of short periods is limited).
(b) Large linear span and balance for AJ applications.
(c) Easy sequence selection in hardware.
(d) Efficient use of memory in the receiver.

Thus, these sequences have potential applications in both the multiple access and jamming environments.

Table 5.19
Properties of sequence sets with period $2^d - 1$.

Family	d	size	P_{max}	maximum achievable linear span	maximum achievable linear span for $d \leq 20$
Gold	odd	$2^d + 1$	$1 + 2^{(d+1)/2}$	$2d$	38
Gold	2 (mod 4)	$2^d + 1$	$1 + 2^{(d+2)/2}$	$2d$	36
Kasami (small set)	even	$2^{d/2}$	$1 + 2^{d/2}$	$3d/2$	30
Kasami (large set)	even	$2^{d/2}(2^d + 1)$	$1 + 2^{(d+2)/2}$	$5d/2$	50
Bent Sequences	0 (mod 4)	$2^{d/2}$	$1 + 2^{d/2}$	$\geq \binom{d/2}{d/4} 2^{d/4}$	≥ 8064

5.8 FREQUENCY-HOPPING MULTIPLE-ACCESS DESIGNS

5.8.1 Design Criteria

The design of PN sequences to be used in frequency-hopping multiple-access (FHMA) systems differs from DSMA design in several ways:

1. The sequences' alphabet size is larger in an FHMA design, with one alphabetical character for each synthesizable frequency. In the DSMA case, that alphabet size usually corresponds to the number of carrier phase shifts used to modulate the sequence, the number typically being two (BPSK) or four (QPSK).
2. Interference occurs in a FHMA system when two distinct transmitters use the same frequency simultaneously. Hence, the Hamming distance between the FH sequences being used by the transmitters is a measure of the quality of the sequence design, the ideal design possessing the maximum possible distance between FH sequences. In the DSMA case, optimal designs were based on minimum absolute correlation between sequences, which corresponded, in the binary case under ideal conditions, to a design in which all Hamming distances between sequences were equal to half the number of symbols over which the distances were being calculated.
3. The one-to-one mapping of a PN generator's output symbols into frequencies in a FHMA system is arbitrary and preserves Hamming distance. If this mapping can be changed by the system operators, e.g., used as a code-of-the-day, this may make the system less susceptible to jammers attempting to predict the hopping pattern, but should not be relied upon, as a substitute for large linear span, to baffle intelligent jammers. The predetermined mapping of PN generator output to signal phase (or amplitude), required in a DSMA system to preserve the correlation properties designed into the PN generator outputs, allows the intelligent jammer to observe the PN generator output directly; hence, design characteristics such as linear span are, to some extent, more important in the DSMA case.

The Hamming distance design criterion for FHMA schemes will now be formalized.

Let $\{f_n^{(k)}\}$ represent the k-th in a set of K periodic sequences of symbols, each symbol being in one-to-one correspondence with a transmitted frequency, and denote the common period by N. Then the maximum self-interference which a sequence in this set can encounter corresponds to the minimum Hamming distance H_A defined by

$$H_A = \min_{k} \min_{0<\tau<N} H(\boldsymbol{f}_{k,\tau}, \boldsymbol{f}_{k,0}), \tag{5.349}$$

where $H(\boldsymbol{x}, \boldsymbol{y})$ denotes the Hamming distance between the vectors $\boldsymbol{x}$ and $\boldsymbol{y}$, and $\boldsymbol{f}_{k,t}$ denotes the vector of N consecutive symbols from the sequence

$\{f_n^{(k)}\}$, beginning with the t-th symbol. Similarly the maximum interference between a pair of FH signals in the design corresponds to the minimum Hamming distance H_C, given by

$$H_C = \min_{i \neq k} \min_{0 \le \tau < N} H(f_{i,\tau}, f_{k,0}), \tag{5.350}$$

and, therefore, a reasonable design criterion for FHMA PN generators consists of minimizing

$$H_{\min} = \min(H_A, H_C). \tag{5.351}$$

This criterion corresponds to designing cyclic codes (over large alphabets) with large minimum distance between code words.

5.8.2 A Bound on Hamming Distance

Theorem 5.4 provides an upper bound on H which depends only on the sequence period and alphabet size. The approach used in deriving Theorem 5.4 can be modified to give the following bound on H_C.

THEOREM 5.24 [11]. *Let $\{f_n^{(1)}\}$ and $\{f_n^{(2)}\}$ denote sequences of period N over an alphabet $\mathscr{A}$, and let $f_{i,n}$ denote the N-tuple of consecutive elements from $\{f_n^{(i)}\}$ beginning at element n. Let*

$$H_C = \min_{0 \le \tau < N} H(f_{1,\tau}, f_{2,0}) \tag{5.352}$$

and determine α and β from

$$N = \alpha|\mathscr{A}| + \beta, \qquad 0 \le \beta < |\mathscr{A}|. \tag{5.353}$$

Then

$$H_C \le N - \frac{\alpha + 1}{N}(N + \beta - |\mathscr{A}|). \tag{5.354}$$

Proof. Following the approach of Theorem 5.4, it is easily verified that

$$H_C \le \max_{\{N_{1,a}\},\{N_{2,a}\}} \frac{1}{N}\left(N^2 - \sum_{a \in \mathscr{A}} N_{1,a}N_{2,a}\right), \tag{5.355}$$

where $N_{i,a}$ is the number of occurrences of the symbol a in one period of $\{f_n^{(i)}\}$. Assuming for simplicity that $\mathscr{A}$ is the set of integers, $\{1, 2, \ldots, |\mathscr{A}|\}$, the maximizing choices for the symbol counts are

$$N_{1,a} = \begin{cases} \alpha + 1, & a = 1, 2, \ldots, \beta \\ \alpha, & a = \beta + 1, \ldots, |\mathscr{A}| \end{cases} \tag{5.356}$$

$$N_{2,a} = \begin{cases} \alpha, & a = 1, 2, \ldots, |\mathscr{A}| - \beta \\ \alpha + 1, & a = |\mathscr{A}| - \beta + 1, \ldots, |\mathscr{A}|. \end{cases} \tag{5.357}$$

Note that these maximizing counts correspond to balanced sequences. Substitution of (5.356) and (5.357) into (5.355) yields the final result. ■

This bound on H_C for a two-sequence set also must apply for larger sets of sequences. Surprisingly, significantly larger sets can achieve this two-sequence bound with equality.

This section includes two well-known FHMA PN generator designs which achieve the bound of Theorem 5.24 with equality. One approach, analyzed by Lempel and Greenberger [11], adapts an m-sequence generator for FH purposes. The second approach described here is based on the use of Reed-Solomon code words as hopping patterns [47]. (Further material on the structure of Reed-Solomon codes is available in most major texts on error-correcting codes [6], [7], [40], [41], [48].)

5.8.3 An FHMA Design Employing an M-Sequence Generator

Let $\{b_n\}$ denote an m-sequence of period $q^L - 1$ with elements in GF(q), and let $\boldsymbol{b}_n$ denote a J-tuple of consecutive elements from $\{b_n\}$, beginning with the n-th element. Furthermore let $s(\boldsymbol{x})$ denote an arbitrary one-to-one mapping of J-tuples over GF(q) onto a set of q frequencies. A set of q^J sequences $\{f_n^{(\boldsymbol{v})}\}$ of frequencies, the set indexed by the J-tuple $\boldsymbol{v}$ of elements from GF(q), can now be defined by the relation

$$f_n^{(\boldsymbol{v})} = s(\boldsymbol{b}_n + \boldsymbol{v}). \tag{5.358}$$

One possible generator mechanization is shown in Figure 5.17. Notice that indexing into a particular sequence is easily accommodated in this generator mechanization, and is independent of shift register initialization.

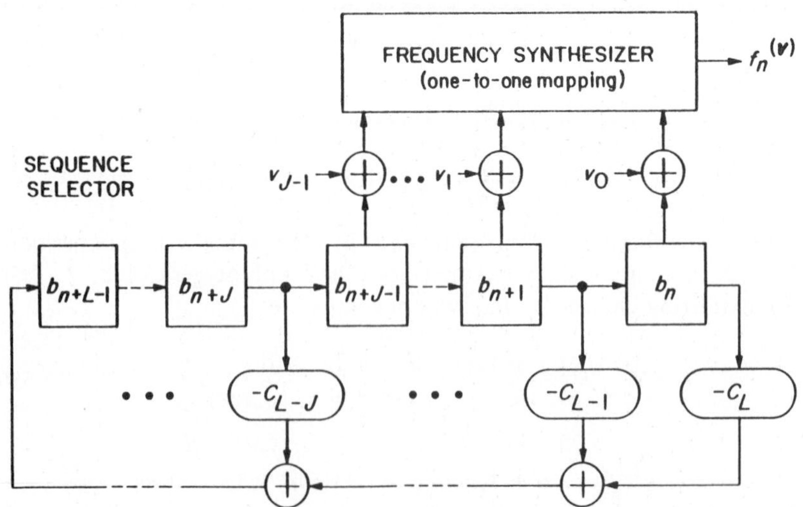

Figure 5.17. FH pseudonoise generator for SSMA use, based on an m-sequence design employing a q-ary shift register. All operations are in GF(q).

The Hamming distance between two of the sequences defined by (5.358) and calculated over a full period at a relative shift τ, can be derived as follows:

$$
\begin{aligned}
H(f_{v,\tau}, f_{w,0}) &= \sum_{n=1}^{q^L-1} h(s(b_{n+\tau} + v), s(b_n + w)) \\
&\overset{(1)}{=} \sum_{n=1}^{q^L-1} h'(b_{n+\tau} + v, b_n + w) \\
&\overset{(2)}{=} \sum_{n=1}^{q^L-1} h'(b_{n+\tau'(\tau)}, w - v) \\
&\overset{(3)}{=} \begin{cases} q^L - 1 - q^{L-J}, & w \neq v \\ q^L - q^{L-J}, & w = v \end{cases}
\end{aligned}
\tag{5.359}
$$

Both $h(\ ,\ )$ and $h'(\ ,\ )$ are zero if their two arguments (scalars and vectors respectively) are equal, and are one otherwise. At (1) in (5.359), the Hamming distance-preserving property of one-to-one mappings is used; (2) is based on the shift-and-add property (5.63) of m-sequences; and (3) results from the balance property (5.61) of m-sequences.

The minimum Hamming distance $H_{\min}$ for this design is $q^L - 1 - q^{L-J}$, indicating that at most q^{L-J} matching frequencies appear in a comparison of two sequences over one period, at any relative shift. The quantities β and α of (5.353) are $q^J - 1$ and $q^{L-J} - 1$ respectively, and, hence, using the fact that H_A and H_C must be integer, it can be verified that these Hamming measures for this design satisfy the bounds of Theorem 5.4 and Theorem 5.24 with equality.

5.8.4 Reed-Solomon Sequences

This algebraic design is based on mechanizing calculations in GF(q), and employing a one-to-one mapping $s(\cdot)$ from elements of GF(q) to a set of q output frequency values. Let γ denote a primitive element of GF(q), and define the polynomial $P_c(z)$ of degree $t-1$, $t > 1$, over GF(q) to be

$$P_c(z) = \sum_{i=0}^{t-1} c_i z^i. \tag{5.360}$$

Elements of the sequences in this set are defined by

$$f_n^{(c)} = s(P_c(\gamma^n)) \tag{5.361}$$

for all n, where c is any coefficient vector $(c_0, \ldots, c_{t-1})$ over GF(q) with $c_1 = 1$. Hence, there are q^{t-1} sequences in this set. Each of these sequences has period $q-1$, the multiplicative order of γ.

Two sequences, $\{f_n^{(c)}\}$ and $\{f_n^{(d)}\}$, are cyclically distinct if

$$P_c(\gamma^{n+\tau}) \neq P_d(\gamma^n) \tag{5.362}$$

for some value of n at each possible value of τ. This condition (5.362) reduces by (5.360) to

$$\sum_{i=0}^{t-1} (c_i\gamma^{\tau i})\gamma^{ni} = \sum_{i=0}^{t-1} c_i\gamma^{(\tau+n)i} \neq \sum_{i=0}^{t-1} d_i\gamma^{ni}. \tag{5.363}$$

Since the t sequences $\{\gamma^{ni}\}$, $i = 0, 1, \ldots, t-1$, are linearly independent, the condition (5.363) can be satisfied if and only if $c_i\gamma^{\tau i} \neq d_i$ for some i at each value of τ. Fixing $c_1 = d_1 = 1$ for all sequences guarantees that this inequality is satisfied for $i = 1$ at all $\tau \neq 0 \bmod q-1$. When $\tau = 0 \bmod q-1$, the condition (5.363) reduces to $\mathbf{c} \neq \mathbf{d}$. Hence, the set of sequences with $c_1 = 1$ are cyclically distinct.

Let $e_i = c_i\gamma^{\tau i}$ and denote the vector $(e_0, \ldots, e_{t-1})$ by $\mathbf{e}$. Based on the left side of (5.363),

$$P_c(\gamma^{n+\tau}) = P_e(\gamma^n). \tag{5.364}$$

The Hamming distance over one period between $\{f_n^{(c)}\}$ and $\{f_n^{(d)}\}$ at relative shift τ is given by

$$\begin{aligned} H(f_{c,\tau}, f_{d,0}) &= \sum_{n=1}^{q-1} h(P_c(\gamma^{n+\tau}), P_d(\gamma^n)) \\ &= \sum_{n=1}^{q-1} h(P_e(\gamma^n), P_d(\gamma^n)). \end{aligned} \tag{5.365}$$

Notice that

$$\begin{aligned} P_e(\gamma^n) &= P_d(\gamma^n) \\ &\Leftrightarrow P_{e-d}(\gamma^n) = 0 \\ &\Leftrightarrow \gamma^n \text{ is a root of } P_{e-d}(z). \end{aligned} \tag{5.366}$$

The number of roots in GF(q) of such a polynomial is bounded by $t-1$, its maximum possible degree. Use of this fact in (5.365) leads to the distance bound for Reed-Solomon sequences, namely

$$H_{\min} \geq q - t. \tag{5.367}$$

Since the sequences' alphabet size is q and their period is $q-1$, the bound on $H_{\min}$ based on Theorem 5.24 is

$$H_{\min} \leq q - 2. \tag{5.368}$$

In view of (5.367) and (5.368), the Reed-Solomon design with $t = 2$ produces a set of q sequences over GF(q) with $H_{\min} = q - 2$, indicating that in a comparison of two sequences, at any relative shift τ, the $t = 2$ design guarantees at most one frequency match.

A conceptual block diagram of a $t = 3$ Reed-Solomon sequence generator is shown in Figure 5.18. In this form, a squaring device is required to randomly initialize this generator within a particular sequence. Another configuration can be obtained by combining the two single-stage q-ary LFSRs into a single two-stage LFSR. Still another possibility is to square the contents γ^n of the first single-stage q-ary register to directly determine the input to the c_2 multiplier, thereby eliminating the second register and the need for a squarer during initialization. Notice that the generator for a $t = 2$ design is contained within that shown in Figure 5.18, and is de-

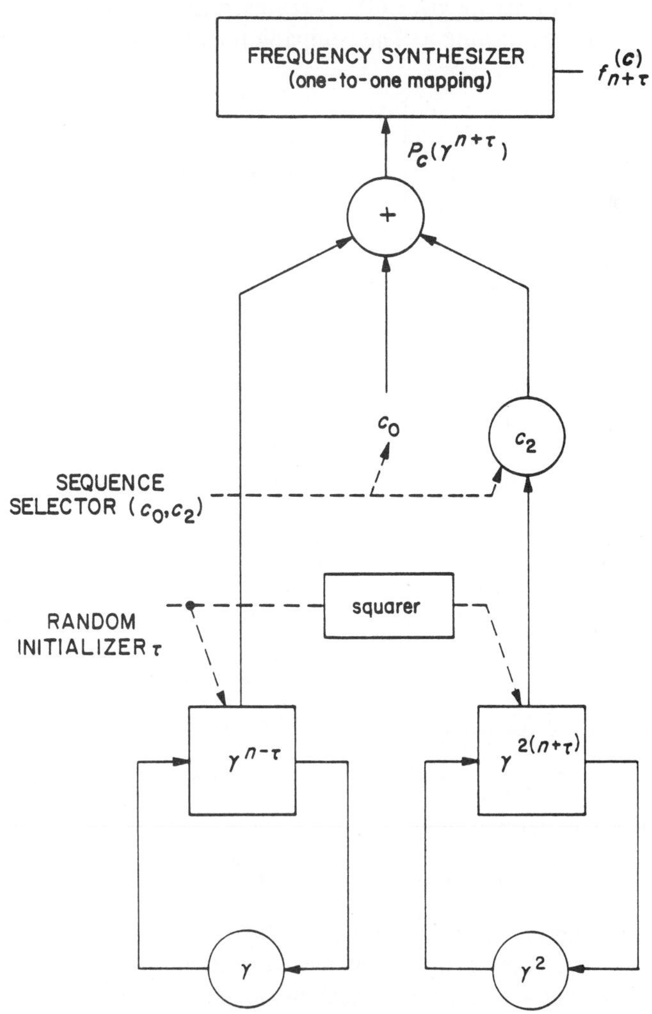

Figure 5.18. Mathematical block diagram of a Reed-Solomon FH PN generator. All arithmetic operations are in GF(q).

termined by setting c_2 to zero permanently, thereby eliminating the need for the right-hand (γ^2) shift register.

Example 5.17. A Reed-Solomon design with q being a power of 2 results in a relatively simple implementation. In this example let $q = 32$, $t = 3$, and let γ be a root of the primitive polynomial $z^5 + z^2 + 1$ over GF(2). Then γ^n can be generated by a Galois-configured, binary LFSR having characteristic polynomial $z^5 + z^2 + 1$, as noted in Section 5.5. Hence, let

$$\boldsymbol{\gamma}^t = (1, \gamma, \gamma^2, \gamma^3, \gamma^4), \quad \gamma^n = \boldsymbol{\gamma}^t \boldsymbol{s}_n \tag{5.369}$$

where $\boldsymbol{s}_n$ is a state vector over GF(2) representing the contents of the five stages of the LFSR at time n. The companion matrix for this register is (see (5.36))

$$\boldsymbol{A} = \begin{bmatrix} 0 & 0 & 0 & 0 & 1 \\ 1 & 0 & 0 & 0 & 0 \\ 0 & 1 & 0 & 0 & 1 \\ 0 & 0 & 1 & 0 & 0 \\ 0 & 0 & 0 & 1 & 0 \end{bmatrix} \tag{5.370a}$$

and from the development of Section 5.8.2,

$$\boldsymbol{s}_{n+1} = \boldsymbol{A}\boldsymbol{s}_n. \tag{5.370b}$$

Squaring γ^n as represented in (5.369) and using the fact that $\gamma^5 = \gamma^2 + 1$ to reduce the resultant powers of γ, gives

$$\boldsymbol{s}_{2n} = \boldsymbol{S}\boldsymbol{s}_n \tag{5.371}$$

where

$$\boldsymbol{S} = \begin{bmatrix} 1 & 0 & 0 & 0 & 1 \\ 0 & 0 & 0 & 1 & 0 \\ 0 & 1 & 0 & 1 & 0 \\ 0 & 0 & 0 & 1 & 1 \\ 0 & 0 & 1 & 0 & 0 \end{bmatrix}. \tag{5.372}$$

Let $\boldsymbol{y}_n$ and $\boldsymbol{k}_i$ be coefficient vectors for the representations

$$P_c(\gamma^n) = \boldsymbol{\gamma}^t \boldsymbol{y}_n, \quad c_i = \boldsymbol{\gamma}^t \boldsymbol{k}_i. \tag{5.373}$$

Then it is easily verified that

$$\boldsymbol{y}_n = \boldsymbol{k}_0 + \left[\boldsymbol{I} + \left(k_{20}\boldsymbol{I} + k_{21}\boldsymbol{A} + k_{22}\boldsymbol{A}^2 + k_{23}\boldsymbol{A}^3 + k_{24}\boldsymbol{A}^4\right)\boldsymbol{S}\right]\boldsymbol{s}_n.$$

A block diagram of the generator in matrix/vector terms is shown in Figure 5.19. The complexity of this mechanization comes from the requirement that the value of $\boldsymbol{k}_2$ be changeable, as part of the sequence selection process. Were it not for this specification, the quantity in brackets in (5.374) could be reduced to a single binary matrix, making the generator structure quite simple.

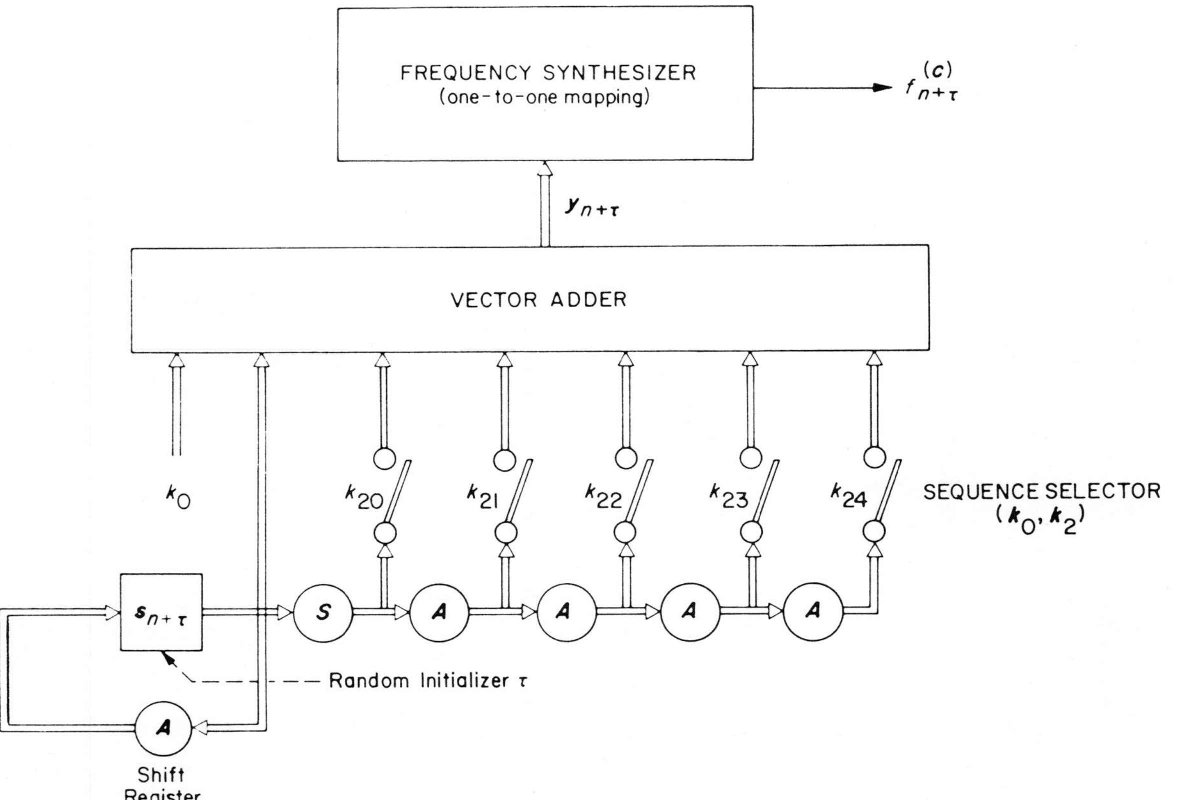

Figure 5.19. Matrix/vector description of a Reed-Solomon FH SSMA PN generator for Example 5.17. All arithmetic operations are in GF(2).

There is a simple tradeoff in the design shown in Figure 5.19, involving generator complexity and the size of the sequence set. If the switches $k_{20}, \ldots, k_{24}$ are left permanently open, thereby eliminating the need for five matrix multipliers, then the input to the vector adder is $\boldsymbol{k}_0 + \boldsymbol{s}_{n+\tau}$, the thirty-two possible choices of $\boldsymbol{k}_0$ corresponding to the thirty-two period-31 sequences of a $t = 2$ Reed-Solomon design with $H_{\min} = 30$. If instead $\boldsymbol{k}_0$ and only the k_{21} switch are enabled, then the matrix multiply $\boldsymbol{S}$ is required, and there are sixty-four possible sequences that can be generated, a subset of the $H_{\min} = 29$, $t = 3$ design. Each additional multiplication by $\boldsymbol{A}$ and k_{2i} switch enablement doubles the number of possible FH sequences, and maintains $H_{\min}$ at 29. When the full generator in Figure 5.19 is employed, any of a set of 1024 period-31 sequences can be generated.

The FHMA design of Lempel and Greenberger, based on an m-sequence generator, is in fact a $t = 2$ Reed-Solomon sequence generator with several elements of the vector adder output disabled. Or equivalently, the Lempel-Greenberger design with $J = L$ is a $t = 2$ Reed-Solomon sequence generator. In making this comparison, the reader should note that the definitions of q differ in the discussions of these two designs.

Both of the sequence sets discussed in this section are generated linearly; hence, the sequences driving the frequency synthesizers have short linear span. Therefore, these designs, while optimal for FHMA applications, are potentially weak when the threat of intelligent jamming exists.

5.9 A LOOK AT THE LITERATURE

While we have covered considerable ground in this chapter and presented the fundamentals of PN generator design, much more is available in the open literature. As starting points for literature searches, we refer the reader to Golomb's comprehensive bibliography (406 references) in the revised edition of [12], to the "Cumulative Index 1953–1981," of the *IEEE Transactions on Information Theory* published with the September 1982 issue (especially papers listed under the headings: sequences, shift register sequences, shift registers, and pseudonoise sequences), and to Sarwate and Pursley's survey article [31] (136 references) on pseudonoise sequences. Also of interest may be Levine's book [51] on cryptographic patents, many being SS related.

Additional references on bent sequences [52], spectral analysis of sequences [53], [54], [55], correlation bounds [56], [70], [71], [72], frequency hopping designs [57], [58], [59], [67], [73], [74], [75], [76], balanced sequence sets [92], sequences with large linear span [87], [88], [89], and linear span bounds [60], [61] are given in Section 5.10. A special DSMA PN sequence design criterion, which takes into account the effects of data modulation on sequence cross-correlations, has been studied in [31], [62], [63], [64], [90] and is useful in short period designs.

Table 5.20.
Additional multiple-access sequence set designs (Table 5.19 contains comparable information for the designs discussed in this book). Here N is the period of each sequence, p represents a prime number, and d is an integer.

Family	Restriction on length N	Alphabet Size	Family Size	P_{max}
Alltop (difference set) [65]*	$2N + 1$ prime	$2N + 1$	2	$\sqrt{\frac{N+1}{2}}$
Sarwate (FZC seq.) [64]*	Prime	$2N$	$N - 1$	$\sqrt{N}$
Blake and Mark [77]	$N + 1$ Prime	$N + 1$	$(N + 1)^k$	$\leq 1 + (k + 1)\sqrt{N + 1}$
McGree [78]	Prime	N	N^k	$\leq k\sqrt{N}$
Alltop (cubic phase) [65]*	Prime	N	N	$\sqrt{N}$
Alltop (quad. phase) [65]*	Prime	N	$N - 1$	$\sqrt{N}$
Scholtz and Welch (grp. char.) [33]*	Prime	N	$N - 2$	$\leq \sqrt{N}\frac{N}{N+1}$
H. Trachtenberg [66]	$N = p^d - 1$, d odd	p	$N + 2$	$1 + \sqrt{p(N + 1)}$
T. Helleseth [79]	$N = p^d - 1$, $p^{d/2} \neq 2 \bmod 3$	p	$N + 2$	$1 + 2\sqrt{N + 1}$
Sidelnikov [80]*	$N = p^d - 1$	p	$N + 1$	$\leq 1 + \sqrt{N + 1}$
Kumar and Moreno [81]*	$N = p^d - 1$	p	$N + 1$	$\leq 1 + \sqrt{N + 1}$
Kumar, Scholtz, and Welch [82]*	$N = p^d - 1$, d even	p	$\sqrt{N + 1}$	$1 + \sqrt{N + 1}$
Suehiro and Hatori [83]*	$N = p^2$	p	$\sqrt{N} - 1$	$\sqrt{N}$
Krone and Sarwate [84]	$N = p^d - 1$, $p^d \equiv 1 \bmod 4$	4	$2N + 4$	$5 + 3\sqrt{N + 1}$
P. Solé [85], Boztaş et al. (type $\mathscr{A}$) [86] also Udaya and Siddiqi [91]*	$N = 2^d - 1$	4	$N + 2$	$\leq 1 + \sqrt{N + 1}$
Boztaş et al. (type $\mathscr{B}$) [86]*	$N = 2(2^d - 1)$	4	$\frac{N + 2}{4}$	$\leq 2 + \sqrt{N + 2}$
Boztaş and Kumar [89]*	$N = 2^d - 1$, d odd	2	$N + 2$	$1 + \sqrt{2(N + 1)}$
No and Kumar [87]*	$N = 2^{2d} - 1$	2	$\sqrt{N + 1}$	$1 + \sqrt{N + 1}$

*Sequence sets that are asymptotically optimal because they meet known correlation bounds as N goes to infinity.

Recent applications of DSMA techniques to commercial communications has renewed interest in the design of sequence families with good correlation properties. Table 5.20 gives the parameters of several designs not covered in this chapter, along with source references. The table is given in order of decreasing alphabet size with the sequences near the end of the list possessing a considerable implementation advantage.

The core material of this chapter has been based solely on the LFSR which provides a long state sequence from which the output sequence is derived. The design of DeBruijn sequences, i.e., sequences of period 2^m generated by m-stage binary registers with nonlinear feedback, are surveyed in [69].

5.10 REFERENCES

[1] W. V. Quine, "The problem of simplifying truth functions," *Am. Math. Monthly*, vol. 59, no. 8, pp. 521–531, October 1952.

[2] E. J. McCluskey, "Minimization of Boolean functions," *Bell Syst. Tech. J.*, vol. 35, no. 5, pp. 1417–1444, November 1956.

[3] F. J. Hill and G. R. Peterson, *Introduction to Switching Theory and Logical Design*, New York: John Wiley, 1968.

[4] I. S. Reed, "A class of multiple error-correcting codes and the decoding scheme," *IRE Trans. Inform. Theory*, vol. 4, pp. 38–49, 1954.

[5] D. E. Muller, "Application of Boolean algebra to switching circuit design and to error correction," *IRE Trans. Electron. Comput.*, vol. 3, pp. 6–12, 1954.

[6] W. W. Peterson and E. J. Weldon, Jr., *Error-Correcting Codes*, 2nd ed., Cambridge, MA: M.I.T. Press, 1972.

[7] E. R. Berlekamp, *Algebraic Coding Theory*, New York: McGraw-Hill, 1968.

[8] J. L. Massey, "Shift register synthesis and BCH decoding," *IEEE Trans. Inform. Theory*, IT-15, pp. 122–127, January 1969.

[9] W. H. Mills, "Continued fractions and linear recurrences," *Math. Comput.*, vol. 29, pp. 173–180, January 1975.

[10] R. A. Scholtz and L. R. Welch, "Continued fractions and Berlekamp's Algorithm," *IEEE Trans. Inform. Theory*, IT-25, no. 1, pp. 19–27, January 1979.

[11] A. Lempel and H. Greenberger, "Families of sequences with optimal Hamming correlation properties," *IEEE Trans. Inform. Theory*, IT-15, pp. 90–94, January 1974.

[12] S. W. Golomb, *Shift Register Sequences*, San Francisco, CA: Holden-Day, 1967; revised edition, Aegean Park Press, Laguna Hills, CA, 1982.

[13] T. C. Bartee and P. W. Wood, "Coding for Tracking Radar Ranging," M.I.T. Lincoln Lab., Lexington, MA, Tech. Rept. 318, 1963.

[14] J. H. Lindholm, "An analysis of the pseudo-randomness properties of subsequences of long m-sequences," *IEEE Trans. Inform. Theory*, IT-14, pp. 569–576, July 1968.

[15] A. B. Cooper and P. H. Lord, "Subsequence Correlation Analysis," Research and Technology Div., Rome Air Development Center, USAF Systems Command, Griffiss AFB, Rome, NY, Tech. Rept. RADC-TR-67-591, Dec. 1967.

[16] H. F. Mattson, Jr., and R. J. Turyn, "On correlation by subsequences," Sylvania Applied Research Lab., Sylvania Electronic Systems, Waltham, MA, Res. Note 692, Feb. 1967.

[17] S. Wainberg and J. K. Wolf, "Subsequences of pseudo-random sequences," *IEEE Trans. Commun. Tech.*, COM-18, pp. 606–612, October 1970.

[18] S. A. Fredricsson, "Pseudo-randomness properties of binary shift register sequences," *IEEE Trans. Inform. Theory*, pp. 115–120, January 1975.

[19] V. Pless, "Power moment identities on weight distributions in error correcting codes," *Inform. Contr.*, vol. 6, pp. 147–152, 1963.

[20] N. E. Bekir, "Bounds on the Distribution of Partial Correlation for PN and Gold Sequences," Ph.D. Dissertation, Electrical Engineering Dept., Univ. of Southern California, Los Angeles, CA, Jan. 1978.

[21] N. I. Akhiezer, *The Classical Moment Problem*, New York: Hafner, 1965.

[22] J. A. Shohat and J. D. Tamarkin, *The Problems of Moments*, New York: American Math. Society, 1943.

[23] E. L. Key, "An analysis of the structure and complexity of nonlinear binary sequence generators," *IEEE Trans. Inform. Theory*, IT-22, pp. 732–736, November 1976.

[24] W. Diffie and M. E. Hellman, "Privacy and authentication: an introduction to cryptography," *Proc. IEEE*, vol. 67, pp. 397–427, March 1979.

[25] E. J. Groth, "Generation of binary sequences with controllable complexity," *IEEE Trans. Inform. Theory*, IT-17, pp. 288–296, May 1971.

[26] L. D. Baumert, *Cyclic Difference Sets*, Lecture Notes in Math. No. 182, New York: Springer Verlag, 1971.

[27] J. Singer, "A theorem in finite projective geometry and some applications to number theory," *Trans. Amer. Math. Soc.*, vol. 43, pp. 377–385, 1938.

[28] B. Gordon, W. H. Mills, and L. R. Welch, "Some new difference sets," *Canad. J. Math.*, vol. 14, pp. 614–625, 1962.

[29] L. R. Welch, "Lower bounds on the maximum cross correlation of signals," *IEEE Trans. Inform. Theory*, IT-20, pp. 397–399, May 1974.

[30] T. Kasami, "Weight distribution formula for some class of cyclic codes," Coordinated Science Lab., Univ. Illinois, Urbana. Tech. Rep. R-285, April 1966 (AD 632574).

[31] D. V. Sarwate and M. B. Pursley, "Crosscorrelation properties of pseudorandom and related sequences," *Proc. IEEE*, vol. 68, pp. 593–619, May 1980.

[32] J. D. Olsen, R. A. Scholtz, and L. R. Welch, "Bent-function sequences," *IEEE Trans. Inform. Theory*, IT-28, pp. 858–864, November, 1982.

[33] R. A. Scholtz and L. R. Welch, "Group characters: sequences with good correlation properties," *IEEE Trans. Inform. Theory*, IT-24, pp. 537–545, September 1978.

[34] R. A. Scholtz, "Optimal CDMA codes," *IEEE National Telecommunications Conference Record*, November 1979, pp. 54.2.1–54.2.4.

[35] R. Gold, "Optimum binary sequences for spread spectrum multiplexing," *IEEE Trans. Inform. Theory*, IT-13, pp. 619–621, October 1967.

[36] R. Gold, "Maximal recursive sequences with 3-valued recursive cross-correlation functions," *IEEE Trans. Inform. Theory*, IT-14, pp. 154–156, January 1968.

[37] Y. Niho, "Multi-valued Cross-correlation Functions between Two Maximal Linear Recursive Sequences," Ph.D. dissertation, Electrical Engineering De-

partment, Univ. Southern California, 1972.

[38] T. A. Dowling and R. J. McEliece, "Cross-correlation of reverse maximal-length shift-register sequences," JPL Space Programs Summary 37-53, vol. 3, pp. 192–193, 1968.

[39] V. M. Sidelnikov, "On the mutual correlation of sequences," *Soviet Math. Dokl.*, vol. 12, pp. 197–201, 1971.

[40] F. J. MacWilliams and N. J. A. Sloane, *The Theory of Error-Correcting Codes*, New York: North Holland Publishing Co., 1977.

[41] S. Lin and D. J. Costello, Jr., *Error Control Coding: Fundamentals and Applications*, Englewood Cliffs, NJ: Prentice-Hall, 1983.

[42] J. D. Olsen, "Nonlinear Binary Sequences with Asymptotically Optimum Periodic Cross-Correlation," Ph.D. dissertation, Electrical Engineering Department, Univ. Southern California, December 1977.

[43] O. S. Rothaus, "On 'bent' functions," *J. Comb. Theory*, Series A20, pp. 300–305, 1976.

[44] J. F. Dillon, "Elementary Hadamard Difference Sets," Ph.D. dissertation, University of Maryland, 1974.

[45] J. F. Dillon, "Elementary Hadamard difference sets," *Proc. 6th S.E. Conf. Combinatorics, Graph Theory, and Computing* (Utilitas Math., Winnepeg, 1975), pp. 237–249.

[46] P. V. Kumar and R. A. Scholtz, "Bounds on the linear span of bent sequences," *IEEE Trans. Inform. Theory*, IT-29, pp. 854–862, November 1983.

[47] G. Solomon, "Optimal frequency hopping for multiple access," *Proc. of the 1977 Symposium on Spread Spectrum Communications*, Naval Electronics Laboratory Center, San Diego, CA, 13–16 March 1973, pp. 33–35.

[48] R. E. Blahut, *Theory and Practice of Error Control Codes*, Reading, MA: Addison-Wesley, 1983.

[49] R. A. Scholtz and L. R. Welch, "GMW sequences," *IEEE Trans. Inform. Theory*, IT-30, pp. 548–553, May 1984.

[50] P. H. R. Scholefield, "Shift registers generating maximum-length sequences," *Electronic Technology*, vol. 37, pp. 389–394, October 1960.

[51] J. Levine, *United States Cryptographic Patents 1861–1981*. Terre Haute, IN: Cryptologia, Inc., February 1983.

[52] A. Lempel and M. Cohn, "Maximal families of bent sequences," *IEEE Trans. Inform. Theory*, IT-28, pp. 865–868, November 1982.

[53] R. A. Scholtz, "The spread spectrum concept," *IEEE Trans. Commun.*, COM-25, pp. 748–755, August 1977.

[54] S. G. Glisic, "Power density spectrum of the product of two time displaced versions of a maximum length binary pseudonoise signal," *IEEE Trans. Commun.*, COM-31, pp. 281–286, February 1983.

[55] R. C. Titsworth and L. R. Welch, "Modulation by Random and Pseudorandom Sequences," JPL Laboratory Report No. 20-387, 1959.

[56] J. E. Mazo, "Some theoretical observations on spread-spectrum communications," *Bell Syst. Tech. J.*, vol. 58, pp. 2013–2023, 1979.

[57] R. M. Marsareau and T. S. Seay, "Multiple access frequency hopping patterns with low ambiguity," *IEEE Trans. Aerosp. Electron. Syst.*, AES-17, pp. 571–578, July 1981.

[58] G. Einarsson, "Address assignment for a time-frequency-coded spread spectrum system," *Bell Syst. Tech. J.*, vol. 59, pp. 1241–1255, September 1980.

[59] R. C. Singleton, "Maximum distance *q*-nary codes," *IEEE Trans. Inform. Theory*, IT-10, pp. 116–118, April 1964.

[60] M. P. Ristenbatt and J. L. Daws, Jr., "Performance criteria for spread spectrum communications," *IEEE Trans. Commun.*, COM-25, pp. 756–763, August 1977.

[61] R. A. Games and A. H. Chan, "A fast algorithm for determining the complexity of a binary sequence with period 2^n," *IEEE Trans. Inform. Theory*, IT-29, pp. 144–146, January 1983.

[62] J. L. Massey and J. J. Urhan, Jr., "Sub-baud decoding," *Proc. 13th Annu. Allerton Conf. Circuit and System Theory*, pp. 539–547, 1975.

[63] M. B. Pursley and D. V. Sarwate, "Evaluation of correlation parameters for periodic sequences," *IEEE Trans. Inform. Theory*, IT-23, pp. 508–513, July 1977.

[64] D. V. Sarwate, "Bounds on crosscorrelation and autocorrelation of sequences," *IEEE Trans. Inform. Theory*, IT-25, pp. 720–724, November 1979.

[65] W. O. Alltop, "Complex sequences with low periodic correlations," *IEEE Trans. Inform. Theory*, IT-26, pp. 350–354, May 1980.

[66] H. M. Trachtenberg, "On the cross-correlation functions of maximal recurring sequences," Ph.D. dissertation, Univ. of Southern California, Los Angeles, CA, 1970.

[67] D. V. Sarwate and M. B. Pursley, "Hopping patterns for frequency-hopped multiple-access communication," *IEEE Int. Conf. Commun.*, June 1978, pp. 7.4.1–7.4.3.

[68] R. Turyn, "Sequences with small correlation," *Error Correcting Codes*, H. B. Mann, ed., New York: John Wiley, 1968.

[69] H. Fredricksen, "A survey of full length nonlinear shift register cycle algorithms," *SIAM Review*, vol. 24, pp. 195–221, April 1982.

[70] V. I. Levenshtein, "Bounds on the maximum cardinality of a code with bounded modules of the inner product," *Soviet Math. Dokl.*, 25, pp. 526–531, 1982.

[71] P. V. Kumar and C. M. Liu, "Lower bounds on the maximum correlation of complex roots-of-unity sequences," *IEEE Trans. Inform. Theory*, IT-36, pp. 633–640, May 1990.

[72] A. Tietäväinen, "On the cardinality of sets of sequences with a given maximum correlation," *Discrete Mathematics*, 106/107, pp. 471–477, 1992.

[73] P. V. Kumar, "Frequency hopping code designs having large linear span," *IEEE Trans. Inform. Theory*, IT-34, pp. 146–151, January 1988.

[74] P. V. Kumar and R. A. Scholtz, "Generalized GMW sequences and applications to frequency hopping," *Cryptologic Quarterly*, 3, Spring-Summer, 1984.

[75] P. Udaya and M. U. Siddiqi, "Slow frequency hopping patterns derived from polynomial residue class rings," *Proc. 1993 IEEE International Symposium on Inform. Theory*, San Antonio, TX, January 17–22, 1993, p. 258.

[76] I. Vadja, "Code sequences for FH-CDMA channels," *Proc. IEEE Second International Symposium on Spread Spectrum Techniques*, Yokohama, Japan, Nov. 29–Dec. 2, 1992, pp. 192–195.

[77] I. F. Blake and J. Mark, "A note on complex sequences with low correlations," *IEEE Trans. Inform. Theory*, IT-28, pp. 814–816, September 1982.

[78] T. P. McGree, "Arbitrarily large sets of complex sequences with bounded

periodic correlation functions," preprint, 1984.

[79] T. Helleseth, "Some results about the cross-correlation function between two maximal linear sequences," *Discrete Math.*, vol. 16, pp. 209–232, 1976.

[80] V. M. Sidelnikov, "On mutual correlation of sequences," *Soviet Math. Dokl.*, 12(1), pp. 197–201, 1971.

[81] P. V. Kumar and O. Moreno, "Prime-phase sequences with periodic correlation properties better than binary sequences," *IEEE Trans. Inform. Theory*, IT-37, pp. 603–616, May 1991.

[82] P. V. Kumar, R. A. Scholtz, and L. R. Welch, "Generalized bent functions and their properties," *J. Combinat. Theory*, Series A, vol. 40, no. 1, pp. 90–107, September, 1985.

[83] N. Suehiro and M. Hatori, "Modulatable orthogonal sequences and their application to SSMA systems," *IEEE Trans. Inform. Theory*, IT-34, pp. 93–100, January 1988.

[84] S. M. Krone and D. V. Sarwate, "Quadriphase sequences for spread-spectrum multiple access communications," *IEEE Trans. Inform. Theory*, IT-30, pp. 520–529, May 1984.

[85] P. Solé, "A quaternary cyclic code and a family of quadriphase sequences with low correlation properties," in *Coding Theory and Applications*, Lecture Notes in Computer Science. New York: Springer Verlag, vol. 388, 1989.

[86] S. Boztaş, R. Hammons, and P. V. Kumar, "4-Phase sequences with near-optimum correlation properties," *IEEE Trans. Inform. Theory*, IT-38, pp. 1101–1113, May 1992.

[87] J. S. No and P. V. Kumar, "A new family of binary pseudorandom sequences having optimal correlation properties and large linear span," *IEEE Trans. Inform. Theory*, IT-35, pp. 371–379, March 1989.

[88] M. Antweiler and L. Bömer, "Complex sequences over GF(p^m) with a two-level autocorrelation function and large linear span," *IEEE Trans. Inform. Theory*, IT-38, pp. 120–130, January 1992.

[89] S. Boztaş, and P. V. Kumar, "Binary sequences with Gold-like correlation but large linear span," *IEEE Trans. Inform. Theory* (to appear).

[90] H. Fukumasa, R. Kohno, and H. Imai, "Design of pseudonoise sequences with good odd and even correlation properties," *Proc. IEEE Second International Symposium on Spread Spectrum Techniques*, Yokohama, Japan, Nov. 29–Dec. 2, 1992, pp. 139–142.

[91] P. Udaya and M. U. Siddiqi, "Large linear complexity sequences over Z_4 for quadriphase modulated communication systems having good correlation properties," *Proc. 1993 IEEE International Symposium on Inform. Theory*, Budapest, Hungary, June 24–28, 1991, p. 386.

[92] T. Moriuchi and K. Imamura, "Balanced polyphase sequences with good periodic correlation properties obtained from Kumar-Moreno sequences," *Proc. 1993 IEEE International Symposium on Inform. Theory*, Budapest, Hungary, June 24–28, 1991, p. 382.

APPENDIX 5A. FINITE FIELD ARITHMETIC

5A.1. COMMUTATIVE GROUPS

DEFINITION 5A.1. *A* commutative (Abelian) group *is a collection* $\mathcal{G}$ *of elements and a rule of combination*, &, *satisfying the following axioms*:

1. *Closure*: *If* $g_1 \in \mathcal{G}$ *and* $g_2 \in \mathcal{G}$, *then* $g_1 \& g_2 \in \mathcal{G}$.
2. *Associative law*: *For any* g_1, g_2, *and* g_3 *in* $\mathcal{G}$, $(g_1 \& g_2) \& g_3 = g_1 \& (g_2 \& g_3)$.
3. *Identity*: *There exists an element* e *in* $\mathcal{G}$ *such that for all* $g \in \mathcal{G}$, $g \& e = e \& g = g$.
4. *Inverse*: *For each element* $g \in \mathcal{G}$ *there exists an element* $\bar{g}$ *such that* $g \& \bar{g} = e = \bar{g} \& g$.
5. *Commutative law*: *If* $g_1 \in \mathcal{G}$ *and* $g_2 \in \mathcal{G}$, *then* $g_1 \& g_2 = g_2 \& g_1$.

It can be verified that the identity element e is unique as is each element's inverse. The identity element is its own inverse; if $\bar{h}$ is the inverse of g, then $\bar{g}$ is the inverse of h.

Obviously the integers under ordinary addition are a simple example of a commutative group. All N-dimensional vectors of real numbers form a commutative group under addition. All complex numbers of unit magnitude form a commutative group under multiplication.

DEFINITION 5A.2. *A* subgroup $\mathcal{S}$ of the group $\mathcal{G}$ *is a collection of elements from* $\mathcal{G}$ *which form a group. A subgroup* $\mathcal{S}$ *of* $\mathcal{G}$, *which is not equal to* $\mathcal{G}$, *is called a* proper *subgroup*.

The identification of a subgroup $\mathcal{S}$ within $\mathcal{G}$ permits the following procedure to be performed.

Coset Construction Algorithm:

(a) Let $\mathcal{C}_0 = \mathcal{S}$. $n = 0$.
(b) Construct $\mathcal{A}_{n+1} = \mathcal{G} - \bigcup_{i=0}^{n} \mathcal{C}_i$
(c) If $\mathcal{A}_{n+1}$ is empty, then STOP.
(d) Increase n by 1.
(e) Select an element g_n from $\mathcal{A}_n$.
(f) Construct $\mathcal{C}_n = \{g : g = g_n \& s,\ s \in \mathcal{S}\}$
(g) Go to (b).

The sets $\mathcal{C}_i$, $i > 0$, are called *cosets* of the subgroup $\mathcal{S}$. It can be shown that

(a) Two elements g and g' are in the same coset if and only if $g \& \bar{g}' \in \mathcal{S}$.

(b) There is a one-to-one correspondence between the elements of $\mathcal{S}$ and the elements of each coset.

(c) $\mathcal{C}_i$ and $\mathcal{C}_j$ are disjoint for $i \neq j$, and unique, and hence, when $\mathcal{G}$ is finite,

$$|\mathcal{G}| = N|\mathcal{S}|, \tag{5A.1}$$

where $|\mathcal{A}|$ denotes the number of elements in $\mathcal{A}$, and $N - 1$ is the number of cosets generated in the above construction algorithm. The number $|\mathcal{G}|$ of elements in a group $\mathcal{G}$ is called the *order* of $\mathcal{G}$. If the order of $\mathcal{G}$ is prime, then by (5A.1), $\mathcal{G}$ contains no proper subgroups.

Example 5A.1. The integers $0, 1, \dots, 11$ under addition modulo 12 form a group $\mathcal{G}$ (The term "modulo" is described in Section 5A.2 for those not familiar with it.) One proper subgroup $\mathcal{S}$ of $\mathcal{G}$ is

$$\mathcal{S} = \{0, 3, 6, 9\},$$

and the cosets of this subgroup are

$$\{1, 4, 7, 10\} \text{ and } \{2, 5, 8, 11\}.$$

Suppose that g is an element of a finite-order commutative group. An element g^m can be constructed by combining m of the elements g according to the rule of combination used in $\mathcal{G}$. Thus,

$$\begin{aligned} g^1 &= g \\ g^2 &= g \,\&\, g \\ g^3 &= g \,\&\, g \,\&\, g, \text{ etc.} \end{aligned}$$

DEFINITION 5A.3. *Let e be the identity element of $\mathcal{G}$ and let $g \in \mathcal{G}$. Then the smallest positive integer k such that*

$$g^k = e \tag{5A.2}$$

is called the exponent *of g.*

It can be shown that:

(a) The collection of elements defined by

$$\mathcal{S}_g = \{g^j : 1 \leq j \leq k\} \tag{5A.3}$$

is a subgroup of $\mathcal{G}$. $\mathcal{S}_g$ is called the *cyclic group generated by g*. If there exists a $g \in \mathcal{G}$ such that $\mathcal{S}_g = \mathcal{G}$, then $\mathcal{G}$ is cyclic and g is called a *primitive element* of $\mathcal{G}$.

(b) The exponent of g is the order of $\mathcal{S}_g$. (This has led to the interchangeable use of exponent and order in describing an element g.)

(c) The exponent of g divides the order of $\mathcal{G}$, i.e.,

$$|\mathcal{S}_g| \,\big|\, |\mathcal{G}|. \tag{5A.4}$$

(The vertical bar between two quantities should be read "divides.")

Example 5A.2. Consider the integers relatively prime to 9 under multiplication mod 9. (The term "relatively prime" is defined in Section 2 for those not familiar with it.) The elements of this collection are 1, 2, 4, 5, 7, and 8. This group has the operation table:

×	1	2	4	5	7	8
1	1	2	4	5	7	8
2	2	4	8	1	5	7
4	4	8	7	2	1	5
5	5	1	2	7	8	4
7	7	5	1	8	4	2
8	8	7	5	4	2	1

A tabulation of the cyclic subgroup generated by each element gives

$$\mathcal{S}_1 = \{1\}$$
$$\mathcal{S}_2 = \{1,2,4,8,7,5\}$$
$$\mathcal{S}_4 = \{1,4,7\}$$
$$\mathcal{S}_5 = \{1,5,7,8,4,2\}$$
$$\mathcal{S}_7 = \{1,7,4\}$$
$$\mathcal{S}_8 = \{1,8\}.$$

Clearly this six element group is cyclic, the elements 2 and 5 are primitive, 7 and 4 have exponent 3, and 8 has exponent 2.

A cyclic group $\mathcal{G}$ of order k is *isomorphic* to the integers $0,1,\ldots,k-1$ under addition modulo k. Specifically, using the convention $g^0 = e$ and assuming g generates $\mathcal{G}$, the correspondence

$$g^m \leftrightarrow m, \qquad m = 0,1,\ldots,k-1, \tag{5A.5}$$

implies that the group operation tables for $\mathcal{G}$ and for modulo k addition are identical. That is,

$$g^m g^n = g^h \text{ if and only if } h = (m+n) \bmod k,$$

for all m and n. This isomorphism can be used to find the exponent of each element of $\mathcal{G}$. Let k_m denote the order of g^m. Then k_m is by definition the smallest integer such that

$$g^{mk_m} = e, \tag{5A.6}$$

or, under the isomorphism, the smallest integer k_m such that mk_m is a multiple of k. Thus, k_m can be determined directly from k and m as

$$mk_m = \text{lcm}(k,m), \tag{5A.7}$$

where lcm( ) denotes the *least common (integer) multiple* of the integers in parentheses.

Example 5A.3. The cyclic group of Example 5A.2 has six elements and has primitive element 2. Solving (5A.7) leads to the following table, and verifies the calculations of Example 5A.2.

m	element 2^m	exponent k_m
1	2	. 6
2	4	3
3	8	2
4	7	3
5	5	6
6	1	1

5A.2. RINGS AND FIELDS

In the real number system we have learned to think in terms of two fundamental operations: addition and multiplication. The abstract description of this is a field.

DEFINITION 5A.4. *A* field *is a non-empty collection $\mathscr{F}$ of elements which has the following properties*:

1. *$\mathscr{F}$ is a commutative group under an operation,* + *(addition), with the identity element under* + *denoted by* 0.
2. *Excluding* 0, *the remaining elements of $\mathscr{F}$ are a commutative group under a second operation,* · *(multiplication), with the identity element under denoted by* 1.
3. *Distributive law*: *If f_1, f_2 and f_3 are in $\mathscr{F}$, then*

$$f_1 \cdot (f_2 + f_3) = (f_1 \cdot f_2) + (f_1 \cdot f_3)$$
$$(f_2 + f_3) \cdot f_1 = (f_2 \cdot f_1) + (f_3 \cdot f_1).$$

Additive and multiplicative inverses of a field element will be denoted by $-f$ and f^{-1}, respectively.

Many algebraic structures have all but one or two of the properties of a field. Two structures, the integers under addition and multiplication, and the polynomials under addition and multiplication, have all but one of these properties; neither has multiplicative inverses for its elements. These are examples of structures, with addition and multiplication operations, which are called *commutative rings*. A commutative ring is an Abelian group under addition, is closed, associative, and commutative under multiplication, and satisfies the distributive law.

Two properties of rings and fields are the following:

Property R1. Let r be an element of a ring $\mathscr{R}$ with additive identity 0. Then

$$r \cdot 0 = 0 \cdot r = 0 \quad \text{for all } r \in \mathscr{R}.$$

Property R2. Let r_1 and r_2 be elements of a ring $\mathscr{R}$. Then

$$(-r_1) \cdot r_2 = r_1 \cdot (-r_2) = -(r_1 \cdot r_2) = (-1) \cdot (r_1 \cdot r_2) \quad \text{for all } r_1, r_2 \in \mathscr{R}.$$

Henceforth, the following notational simplifications will be observed:

$$r_1 \cdot r_2 = r_1 r_2, \tag{5A.8}$$

$$r_1 + (-r_2) = r_1 - r_2 \tag{5A.9}$$

Lack of multiplicative inverses precludes use of the cancellation law. That is, if r_1 is a ring element which does not have a multiplicative inverse, then $r_1 r_2 = r_1 r_3$ does *not* imply $r_2 = r_3$.

Example 5A.4. The ring of integers $0, 1, \dots, 7$ under addition and multiplication mod 8 exhibits the following relation:

$$4 \cdot 1 = 4 \cdot 3 = 4 \cdot 5 = 4 \cdot 7.$$

Yet 1, 3, 5, and 7 are distinct elements of the ring.

In the ring of integers it is possible to define a process called *division*, which is akin to multiplication by a multiplicative inverse. The result of the *Euclidean division algorithm* is: If n_1 and n_2 are any two real integers, $n_2 \neq 0$, then n_1 can be represented by

$$n_1 = q n_2 + r, \tag{5A.10}$$

where q and r are integers and $0 \le r < |n_2|$. If $r = 0$, we say that n_2 divides n_1, and denote this by $n_2 | n_1$. The *remainder* r is often called (the value of) n_1 *modulo* n_2, or in abbreviated fashion $n_1 \bmod n_2$.

The *greatest common divisor* $\gcd(m, n)$ of two integers m and n, defined as the largest integer dividing both m and n, can be determined by repeated application of the Euclidean division algorithm. Furthermore, it can be shown that

$$\gcd(m, n) = am + bn \tag{5A.11}$$

where a and b are also elements of the ring of integers. If $\gcd(m, n) = 1$, then m and n are said to be *relatively prime*.

The relation (5A.11) is extremely important in the sections to follow so we will review it here and indicate an algorithm for determining it. Reviewing briefly, Euclid's division algorithm states that

$$m_i = a_i n_i + r_i, \quad 0 \le r_i < |n_i|. \tag{5A.12}$$

From this relation, it follows that if g divides any two of the three quantities, m_i, $a_i n_i$, and r_i, then it divides the third also. Hence,

$$\gcd(m_i, n_i) = \gcd(n_i, r_i). \tag{5A.13}$$

Let's suppose we wish to compute $\gcd(m, n)$, $m > n$. Then the algorithm's structure is as follows.

Euclid's Greatest Common Divisor Algorithm

(a) Let $m_1 = m$, $n_1 = n$, $i = 1$.
(b) Compute r_i.
(c) If $r_i = 0$ then [$\gcd(m, n) = n_i$, STOP].
(d) If $r_i \neq 0$, set $m_{i+1} = n_i$, $n_{i+1} = r_i$.
(e) Increase i by one and go to (b).

Suppose that we also wish to determine the integer coefficients a and b which are used to combine m and n to give the $\gcd(m, n)$. This can be done by keeping track of how m_i and n_i can be written in terms of m and n as the algorithm progresses. Let's define

$$\boldsymbol{A}^{(i)} = \begin{bmatrix} A_1^{(i)} \\ A_2^{(i)} \end{bmatrix} \quad \text{where } m_i = A_1^{(i)} m + A_2^{(i)} n. \tag{5A.14}$$

$$\boldsymbol{B}^{(i)} = \begin{bmatrix} B_1^{(i)} \\ B_2^{(i)} \end{bmatrix} \quad \text{where } n_i = B_1^{(i)} m + B_2^{(i)} n \tag{5A.15}$$

As the algorithm is set up,

$$\boldsymbol{A}^{(1)} = \begin{bmatrix} 1 \\ 0 \end{bmatrix}, \quad \boldsymbol{B}^{(1)} = \begin{bmatrix} 0 \\ 1 \end{bmatrix}, \tag{5A.16}$$

and since $m_{i+1} = n_i$, it follows that

$$\boldsymbol{A}^{(i+1)} = \boldsymbol{B}^{(i)} \tag{5A.17}$$

A recursion for $\boldsymbol{B}^{(i+1)}$ can also be determined, using the fact that

$$n_{i+1} = r_i = m_i - a_i n_i. \tag{5A.18}$$

Hence,

$$\boldsymbol{B}^{(i+1)} = \boldsymbol{A}^{(i)} - a_i \boldsymbol{B}^{(i)}. \tag{5A.19}$$

Hence, the modified algorithm for determining $\gcd(m, n)$, $m > n$, is:

Revised GCD Algorithm:

(a) Let $m_1 = m$, $n_1 = n$, $i = 1$, $\boldsymbol{A}^{(i)} = \begin{bmatrix} 1 \\ 0 \end{bmatrix}$, $\boldsymbol{B}^{(1)} = \begin{bmatrix} 0 \\ 1 \end{bmatrix}$.

(b) Compute a_i and r_i by Euclid's Division Algorithm.
(c) If $r_i = 0$, the [gcd$(m, n) = n_i = B_1^{(i)}m + B_2^{(i)}n$. STOP].
(d) If $r_i \neq 0$, then compute m_{i+1}, n_{i+1}, $\boldsymbol{A}^{(i+1)}$ and $\boldsymbol{B}^{(i+1)}$, using the proper recursions.
(e) Increase i by 1 and go to (b).

Further insight into this algorithm can be seen by comparing it to continued fraction computations.

Example 5A.5. Find the gcd(46410, 36310300).

i	m_i	n_i	a_i	r_i	$(\boldsymbol{A}^{(i)})^t$	$(\boldsymbol{B}^{(i)})^t$
1	36310300	46410	782	17680	(1,0)	(0,1)
2	46410	17680	2	11050	(0,1)	(1, −782)
3	17680	11050	1	6630	(1, −782)	(−2, 1565)
4	11050	6630	1	4420	(−2, 1565)	(3, −2347)
5	6630	4420	1	2210	(3, −2347)	(−5, 3912)
6	4420	2210	2	0	(−5, 3912)	(8, −6259)

Therefore gcd(46410, 36310300) = 2210.

Check: $46410 = 21 \cdot 2210$

$36310300 = 6430 \cdot 2210$

$2210 = 8 \cdot 36310300 - 6259 \cdot 46410$

5A.3. POLYNOMIALS

A *polynomial* $P(z)$ of *degree* n over a commutative ring $\mathscr{R}$ (i.e., with coefficients in $\mathscr{R}$) can be written as

$$P(z) = \sum_{i=0}^{n} r_i z^i, \quad r_n \neq 0. \tag{5A.20}$$

The coefficients, r_i, $i = 0, \ldots, n$, of the polynomial are elements of $\mathscr{R}$. The *indeterminate* z obeys all the properties of a commutative ring element with respect to the coefficients; hence z can be thought of as an element in $\mathscr{R}$ or a larger ring containing $\mathscr{R}$. The collection of all polynomials over a ring is itself a ring $\mathscr{R}_P$. Our main interest in polynomial rings is restricted to the case where the coefficients come from a field.

A Euclidean division algorithm also exists for polynomials: If $P_1(z)$ and $P_2(z)$ are polynomials over a field $\mathscr{F}$ (or over a ring $\mathscr{R}$ with the highest degree coefficient r_n of $P_2(z)$ being the multiplicative identity of $\mathscr{R}$), then there exists polynomials $Q(z)$ and $R(z)$ over $\mathscr{F}$ such that

$$P_1(z) = Q(z)P_2(z) + R(z), \tag{5A.21}$$

where $0 \leq \deg R(z) < \deg P_2(z)$. The polynomial $R(z)$ is often referred to as the value of $P_1(z)$ *modulo* $P_2(z)$ or simply $P_1(z) \bmod P_2(z)$. Again, if $R(z) = 0$, we say that $P_2(z)$ divides $P_1(z)$. We can also define the *greatest common divisor* of two polynomials $P_1(z)$ and $P_2(z)$ over a field $\mathscr{F}$ as the highest degree polynomial dividing both $P_1(z)$ and $P_2(z)$. By an algorithm identical to that used in the ring of integers (see Section 5A.2), the $\gcd(P_1(z), P_2(z))$ can be found and shown to be of the form

$$\gcd(P_1(z), P_2(z)) = C_1(z)P_1(z) + C_2(z)P_2(z) \tag{5A.22}$$

where $C_1(z)$ and $C_2(z)$ are polynomials over the same field as $P_1(z)$ and $P_2(z)$.

Example 5A.6. Find $\gcd(z^{16} + z^{15} + z^{14} + z^{13} + z^{12} + z^{11} + z^{10} + z^9 + z^7 + z^4 + z + 1, z^{13} + z^{12} + z^{11} + z^9 + z^7 + z^3 + z)$. These polynomials are over GF(2) and only polynomial coefficients are listed in the following table. The notation is identical to that used for integers earlier.

	m_i	n_i	a_i	r_i	$(B^{(i)})^t$
1	(11111111010010011)	(11101010001010)	(1001)	(1000001001001)	(0,1)
2	(11101010001010)	(1000001001001)	(11)	(101001010001)	(1,1001)
3	(1000001001001)	(101001010001)	(10)	(10011101011)	(11,11010)
4	(101001010001)	(10011101011)	(10)	(1110000111)	(111,11101)
5	(10011101011)	(1110000111)	(11)	(1100010)	(1101,1100000)
6	(1110000111)	(1100010)	(1011)	(110001)	(100000,10011101)
7	(1100010)	(110001)	(10)	---	(10111101,10100101111)

gcd $= z^5 + z^4 + 1$

Check: $z^{16} + z^{15} + z^{14} + z^{13} + z^{12} + z^{11} + z^{10} + z^9 + z^7 + z^4 + z + 1 = (z^5 + z^4 + 1)$
$\times (z^{11} + z^9 + z^7 + z^6 + z + 1)$

$z^{13} + z^{12} + z^{11} + z^9 + z^7 + z^3 + z = (z^5 + z^4 + 1)(z^8 + z^6 + z^5 + z^3 + z)$

$(z^5 + z^4 + 1) = (z^{16} + z^{15} + z^{14} + z^{13} + z^{12} + z^{11} + z^{10} + z^9 + z^7 + z^4 + z + 1)$
$\times (z^7 + z^5 + z^4 + z^3 + z^2 + 1) + (z^{13} + z^{12} + z^{11} + z^9 + z^7 + z^3 + z)$
$\times (z^{10} + z^8 + z^5 + z^3 + z^2 + z + 1)$

Suppose α is an element of a ring which contains the ring $\mathscr{R}$ of polynomial coefficients. We say that α is *root of multiplicity* K, of the polynomial $P(z)$ if $(z - \alpha)^K$ divides $P(z)$. To determine if α is a root of $P(z)$, long division can be used, generally resulting in

$$P(z) = (z - \alpha)Q(z) + P(\alpha), \tag{5A.23}$$

where the polynomial $Q(z)$ has degree one less than $P(z)$. Hence, we have the following theorem:

THEOREM 5A.1 (Factorization Theorem). *The element α is a root of $P(z)$ if and only if $P(\alpha) = 0$. If $P(\alpha) = 0$, we can determine if $(z - \alpha)^2$ divides*

$P(z)$ by determining if $(z - \alpha)$ divides $Q(z)$. This operation can be iterated until the number of $(z - \alpha)$ factors of $P(z)$ is determined.

The student should observe that "strange" things can happen in the factorization of polynomials *over rings*: (a) The number of roots of a polynomial over a ring, which are in the ring, may possibly be greater than or less than the degree of the polynomial. (b) Factorizations of polynomials over rings are not unique.

Example 5A.7. Consider the following polynomials over the ring of integers $0, 1, \ldots, 7$ under addition and multiplication modulo 8.

(a) $z^2 + 7$ has four roots in the ring, namely $1, 3, 5, 7$.
(b) $z^2 + z + 1$ has no roots in the ring.
(c) z^2 has two roots in the ring, namely 0 and 4, each of multiplicity 2.
(d) Furthermore with an excess of roots available, factorization is certainly not unique.

$$z^2 + 7 = (z + 1)(z + 7) = (z + 5)(z + 3)$$

$$z^2 = (z)(z) = (z + 4)(z + 4)$$

(e) There can be more factors on one side of an equality than the degree of the other side:

$$(4z + 2)(2z + 4) = 4z.$$

These unusual properties disappear when we require that the polynomial be over a field.

Polynomials over any field satisfy certain basic factorization properties. These properties are most easily described in terms of a special kind of polynomial.

DEFINITION 5A.5. *A polynomial of degree n in an indeterminate z is said to be* monic *if the (non-zero) coefficient of z^n is* 1.

The reader can easily verify that if a polynomial has coefficients in a *field*, then the following are true:

(a) Every polynomial over a finite field can be uniquely written as a monic polynomial times an element of the coefficient field.
(b) The product of two monic polynomials of degrees m and n is a monic polynomial of degree $m + n$.
(c) If a monic polynomial is the product of two polynomials, then it is the product of two monic polynomials.

(d) If $F(z)$ and $H(z)$ are two polynomials over a field, which have greatest common divisor 1, then $F(z)|H(z)J(z)$ implies $F(z)|J(z)$.
(e) A monic polynomial over a field $\mathscr{F}$ can always be uniquely factored into a product of irreducible monic polynomials over $\mathscr{F}$.
(f) Let $P(z)$ be a polynomial of degree d over a field $\mathscr{F}$, and let $a_1, \dots, a_n$ be the distinct roots of $P(z)$ in $\mathscr{F}$ with multiplicities $m_1, \dots, m_n$, respectively. Then

$$\sum_{i=1}^{n} m_i \leq d. \tag{5A.24}$$

If a polynomial $P(z)$ over a field $\mathscr{F}$ can be written as a product of two or more polynomials (each with degree greater than 0) over the same field $\mathscr{F}$, we say that $P(z)$ is *factorable over* $\mathscr{F}$. On the other hand, if $P(z)$ cannot be factored in this manner, $P(z)$ is said to be *irreducible over* $\mathscr{F}$. In specifying whether a polynomial is irreducible or factorable, the coefficient field be specified. Notice that the greatest common divisor of an irreducible polynomial $F(z)$ and any other polynomial $G(z)$ over the same field must be 1 or $F(z)$.

Example 5A.8. $z^2 + 1$ is irreducible over the real numbers. It is factorable over the complex numbers since

$$z^2 + 1 = (z + i)(z - i)$$

where i is a name for a root of the polynomial $z^2 + 1$ over the real numbers.

5A.4. ANALYZING THE STRUCTURE OF GALOIS FIELDS

A field with a finite number of elements q is called a Galois field, and is denoted by GF(q). The addition and multiplication tables of GF(16) are shown in Figure 5A.1, as are the tables for GF(2) (i.e., $\{0,1\}$) and GF(4) ($\{0, 1, a, b\}$). The reader may want to refer to GF(16) as a typical example of the abstract fields in the discussions to follow.

Assuming that the addition and multiplication tables of a finite field GF(q) exist, let's explore the structures which GF(q) must contain. Suppose that the cyclic subgroup, $\mathscr{I}$, generated by 1 under addition has p elements,

$$\mathscr{I} = \{0, 1, \dots, p - 1\}. \tag{5A.25}$$

$\mathscr{I}$ is the set of *integers* of GF(q), and it can be verified that addition and multiplication of elements of $\mathscr{I}$ corresponds to arithmetic modulo p.

It can be shown that subsets of an arbitrary field GF(q), which are closed under addition and multiplication and contain the identities 0 and 1, are in fact fields in their own right. Hence, the following can be verified:

THEOREM 5A.2. *The integers* $0, 1, 2, \ldots, p-1$, *of a finite field form a subfield under addition and multiplication modulo p where p is the number of distinct integer elements of the field.*

Example 5A.9. In the addition and multiplication tables of GF(16) (see Figure 5A.1), $1 + 1 = 0$ and hence $\{0, 1\} = \mathrm{GF}(2)$.

Now consider the case in which a subfield $\mathrm{GF}(q)$ (not necessarily an integer subfield) exists within a larger field, e.g., as GF(2) or GF(4) exist within GF(16) in Figure 5A.1. Let x be a field element in the larger field but *not* in $\mathrm{GF}(q)$. Find all elements in the larger field which are equal to linear combinations of powers of x with coefficients in $\mathrm{GF}(q)$, i.e., elements of the form

$$v_{\boldsymbol{a}} = \sum_{i=0}^{d-1} a_i x^i, \tag{5A.26}$$

where $\boldsymbol{a} = (a_0, a_1, \ldots, a_{d-1})$ is a coefficient vector of elements from $\mathrm{GF}(q)$. The right side above will be referred to as a *pseudopolynomial* in x, since x is not an indeterminate and the sum is simply a field element. For a given value of d, the number of possible coefficient vectors $\boldsymbol{a}$ is q^d. If the larger finite field contains n elements, we shall choose d so that $q^d > n$. This means that

$$v_{\boldsymbol{a}} = v_{\boldsymbol{b}} \tag{5A.27}$$

for some $\boldsymbol{a} \neq \boldsymbol{b}$. Hence,

$$\sum_{i=0}^{d-1} a_i x^i = \sum_{i=0}^{d-1} b_i x^i \tag{5A.28}$$

or

$$\sum_{i=0}^{d-1} (a_i - b_i) x^i = 0 \tag{5A.29}$$

and the coefficients $(a_i - b_i)$ cannot all be zero, though the non-zero coefficient with largest subscript need not be $(a_{d-1} - b_{d-1})$. Replacing x by an indeterminate z above, it is apparent that the set of polynomials over $\mathrm{GF}(q)$ which has x as a root, is not empty.

One polynomial totally characterizes the properties of x and the way it interacts with elements of $\mathrm{GF}(q)$.

DEFINITION 5A.6. *The monic polynomial* $m_x(z)$ *over* $\mathrm{GF}(q)$, *of minimum degree* d_m *with respect to all polynomials over* $\mathrm{GF}(q)$ *having x as a root, is called the* minimum polynomial $m_x(z)$ of x over $\mathrm{GF}(q)$.

+	0	1	*a*	*b*	*c*	*d*	*e*	*f*	*g*	*h*	*j*	*k*	*m*	*n*	*p*	*q*
0	0	1	*a*	*b*	*c*	*d*	*e*	*f*	*g*	*h*	*j*	*k*	*m*	*n*	*p*	*q*
1	1	0	*b*	*a*	*f*	*j*	*q*	*c*	*p*	*k*	*d*	*h*	*n*	*m*	*g*	*e*
a	*a*	*b*	0	1	*d*	*c*	*m*	*j*	*k*	*p*	*f*	*g*	*e*	*q*	*h*	*n*
b	*b*	*a*	1	0	*j*	*f*	*n*	*d*	*h*	*g*	*c*	*p*	*q*	*e*	*k*	*m*
c	*c*	*f*	*d*	*j*	0	*a*	*k*	1	*m*	*q*	*b*	*e*	*g*	*p*	*n*	*h*
d	*d*	*j*	*c*	*f*	*a*	0	*g*	*b*	*e*	*n*	1	*m*	*k*	*h*	*q*	*p*
e	*e*	*q*	*m*	*n*	*k*	*g*	0	*h*	*d*	*f*	*p*	*c*	*a*	*b*	*j*	1
f	*f*	*c*	*j*	*d*	1	*b*	*h*	0	*n*	*e*	*a*	*q*	*p*	*g*	*m*	*k*
g	*g*	*p*	*k*	*h*	*m*	*e*	*d*	*n*	0	*b*	*q*	*a*	*c*	*f*	1	*j*
h	*h*	*k*	*p*	*g*	*q*	*n*	*f*	*e*	*b*	0	*m*	1	*j*	*d*	*a*	*c*
j	*j*	*d*	*f*	*c*	*b*	1	*p*	*a*	*q*	*m*	0	*n*	*h*	*k*	*e*	*g*
k	*k*	*h*	*g*	*p*	*e*	*m*	*c*	*q*	*a*	1	*n*	0	*d*	*j*	*b*	*f*
m	*m*	*n*	*e*	*q*	*g*	*k*	*a*	*p*	*c*	*j*	*h*	*d*	0	1	*f*	*b*
n	*n*	*m*	*q*	*e*	*p*	*h*	*b*	*g*	*f*	*d*	*k*	*j*	1	0	*c*	*a*
p	*p*	*g*	*h*	*k*	*n*	*q*	*j*	*m*	1	*a*	*e*	*b*	*f*	*c*	0	*d*
q	*q*	*e*	*n*	*m*	*h*	*p*	1	*k*	*j*	*c*	*g*	*f*	*b*	*a*	*d*	0

·	0	1	*a*	*b*	*c*	*d*	*e*	*f*	*g*	*h*	*j*	*k*	*m*	*n*	*p*	*q*
0	0	0	0	0	0	0	0	0	0	0	0	0	0	0	0	0
1	0	1	*a*	*b*	*c*	*d*	*e*	*f*	*g*	*h*	*j*	*k*	*m*	*n*	*p*	*q*
a	0	*a*	*b*	1	*g*	*h*	*j*	*k*	*m*	*n*	*p*	*q*	*c*	*d*	*e*	*f*
b	0	*b*	1	*a*	*m*	*n*	*p*	*q*	*c*	*d*	*e*	*f*	*g*	*h*	*j*	*k*
c	0	*c*	*g*	*m*	*d*	*e*	*f*	*a*	*h*	*j*	*k*	*b*	*n*	*p*	*q*	1
d	0	*d*	*h*	*n*	*e*	*f*	*a*	*g*	*j*	*k*	*b*	*m*	*p*	*q*	1	*c*
e	0	*e*	*j*	*p*	*f*	*a*	*g*	*h*	*k*	*b*	*m*	*n*	*q*	1	*c*	*d*
f	0	*f*	*k*	*q*	*a*	*g*	*h*	*j*	*b*	*m*	*n*	*p*	1	*c*	*d*	*e*
g	0	*g*	*m*	*c*	*h*	*j*	*k*	*b*	*n*	*p*	*q*	1	*d*	*e*	*f*	*a*
h	0	*h*	*n*	*d*	*j*	*k*	*b*	*m*	*p*	*q*	1	*c*	*e*	*f*	*a*	*g*
j	0	*j*	*p*	*e*	*k*	*b*	*m*	*n*	*q*	1	*c*	*d*	*f*	*a*	*g*	*h*
k	0	*k*	*q*	*f*	*b*	*m*	*n*	*p*	1	*c*	*d*	*e*	*a*	*g*	*h*	*j*
m	0	*m*	*c*	*g*	*n*	*p*	*q*	1	*d*	*e*	*f*	*a*	*h*	*j*	*k*	*b*
n	0	*n*	*d*	*h*	*p*	*q*	1	*c*	*e*	*f*	*a*	*g*	*j*	*k*	*b*	*m*
p	0	*p*	*e*	*j*	*q*	1	*c*	*d*	*f*	*a*	*g*	*h*	*k*	*b*	*m*	*n*
q	0	*q*	*f*	*k*	1	*c*	*d*	*e*	*a*	*g*	*h*	*j*	*b*	*m*	*n*	*p*

Figure 5A.1. Addition and multiplication in GF(16).

The minimum polynomial of a field element x over a subfield GF(q) must exist since it has already been demonstrated that at least one polynomial over GF(q) having x as a root, exists. It can also be shown that the minimum polynomial of x is unique and irreducible over GF(q).

Suppose we now investigate the collection $\mathscr{V}$ of all elements of the form

$$v_a = \sum_{i=0}^{d_m - 1} a_i x^i \tag{5A.30}$$

$$\boldsymbol{a} = (a_0, a_1, \ldots, a_{d_m - 1}). \tag{5A.31}$$

where the coefficients a_i are in GF(q), x is a field element not in GF(q), and d_m is the degree of the minimum polynomial of x over GF(q).

(a) For two distinct vectors $\boldsymbol{a}$ and $\boldsymbol{b}$ of dimensions d_m,

$$v_{\boldsymbol{a}} \neq v_{\boldsymbol{b}}.$$

Proof. Assume $v_{\boldsymbol{a}} = v_{\boldsymbol{b}}$. Then $v_{\mathbf{a}-\mathbf{b}}$ is a pseudopolynomial of degree $d_m - 1$ or less in x with coefficients in GF(q) which is equal to 0. But the minimum polynomial of x has degree d_m, and, hence, $v_{\boldsymbol{a}} \neq v_{\boldsymbol{b}}$. ■

(b) $\mathscr{V}$ is closed under addition.

Proof.

$$v_{\boldsymbol{a}} + v_{\boldsymbol{b}} = v_{\boldsymbol{a}+\boldsymbol{b}} \tag{5A.32}$$

■

(c) $\mathscr{V}$ is closed under multiplication.

Proof.

$$\begin{aligned} v_{\boldsymbol{a}} v_{\boldsymbol{b}} &= \left(\sum_{i=0}^{d_m - 1} a_i x^i \right) \left(\sum_{i=0}^{d_m - 1} b_i x^i \right) \\ &= \sum_{i=0}^{2(d_m - 1)} c_i x^i = C(x) \end{aligned} \tag{5A.33}$$

where c_i is in GF(q). By the Euclidean division algorithm for polynomials in an indeterminate, $C(z) = Q(z)m_x(z) + R(z)$, $\deg R(z) < \deg m_x(z) = d_m$. Now since $m_x(x) = 0$, substitution of x for z gives $C(x) = R(x)$, a pseudopolynomial in the field element x of degree less than d_m with coefficients in GF(q). ■

Since this subset $\mathscr{V}$ of the field is closed under addition and multiplication, we have the following result:

THEOREM 5A.3. *Let GF(q) be a subfield of a larger field and let x be a field element not in GF(q), the minimum polynomial $m_x(z)$ of x over GF(q) having degree d_m. Then the pseudopolynomials in x over GF(q), having degree less than d_m, are the distinct elements of a field GF(q^{d_m}).*

Example 5A.10. Consider the addition and multiplication tables of GF(16) shown in figure 5A.1. Forming pseudopolynomials in a over GF(2), and evaluating them using Figure 5A.1 gives

$$a + 1 = b,\ a^2 = b,\ a^2 + 1 = a,\ a^2 + a = 1,\ a^2 + a + 1 = 0.$$

Hence, $a^2 + a + 1$ is the lowest degree pseudopolynomial in a which is zero, and the minimum polynomial of a is

$$m_a(z) = z^2 + z + 1.$$

The smallest subfield containing a is GF(4), whose elements are represented as

element	a-representation
0	0
1	1
a	a
b	$a + 1$

and whose addition and multiplication tables are characterized completely by the GF(2) addition and multiplication tables and the fact that $a^2 + a + 1 = 0$.

The element c of Figure 5A.1 is not in GF(4). To determine the minimum polynomial of c over GF(4), evaluate the monic pseudopolynomials in c over GF(4).

$$c + 1 = f,\ c + a = d,\ c + b = j,\ c^2 = d.$$

Note that

$$c + a = d = c^2 \Rightarrow c^2 + c + a = 0.$$

(Addition and subtraction are identical operations in fields containing GF(2).) Hence,

$$m_c(z) = z^2 + z + a \text{ (over GF(4))}.$$

If instead the minimum polynomial of c over GF(2) had been determined, it would be seen that

$$m_c(z) = z^4 + z + 1 \text{ (over GF(2))}.$$

Representations of GF(16) elements as pseudopolynomials in c over GF(4) and GF(2) are shown in Table 5A.1. It is obvious from the above pseudopolynomial representations that the elements of GF(16) may be viewed as a 2-dimensional vector space over GF(4) or a 4-dimensional vector space over GF(2). In either case, vector addition corresponds to field element addition. For example, the field element h can be viewed as the vector (a, b) of pseudopolynomial coefficients over GF(4), or as $(1, 0, 1, 1)$ over GF(2).

Using the c-representations over GF(4) of GF(16) elements, only the GF(4) arithmetic tables and the fact that $c^2 + c + a = 0$ are necessary to do calculations. For example:

$$
\begin{aligned}
e(m+k) &= (bc+a)((bc)+(ac+a)) && \text{(representation)}\\
&= (bc+a)(c+a) && \text{(addition in GF(4))}\\
&= bc^2+(a+ab)c+a^2 && \text{(distributive law)}\\
&= b(c+a)+(a+ab)c+a^2 && (c^2=c+a)\\
&= a && \text{(GF(4) arithmetic)}
\end{aligned}
$$

The same calculations using c-representations over GF(2) along with the fact that $c^4 + c + 1 = 0$ is:

$$
\begin{aligned}
e(m+k) &= c^3((c^3+c^2+c)+(c^3+c)) && \text{(representation)}\\
&= c^5 && \text{(GF(2) arithmetic)}\\
&= c(c+1) && (c^4=c+1)\\
&= c^2+c && \text{(distributive law)}\\
&= a && \text{(representation)}
\end{aligned}
$$

The above agree with the direct calculation

$$e(m + k) = ed = a$$

from Figure 5A.1.

Clearly the cumbersome tables of Figure 5A.1 can be totally eliminated, and the elements of GF(16) viewed as the pseudopolynomials in c of degree

Table 5A.1

Representations of elements in GF(16) as pseudopolynomials in c over GF(4) and GF(2).

element	c-representation over GF(4)	c-representation over GF(2)
0	0	0
1	1	1
a	a	$c^2 + c$
b	b	$c^2 + c + 1$
c	c	c
d	$c + a$	c^2
e	$bc + a$	c^3
f	$c + 1$	$c + 1$
g	ac	$c^3 + c^2$
h	$ac + b$	$c^3 + c + 1$
j	$c + b$	$c^2 + 1$
k	$ac + a$	$c^3 + c$
m	bc	$c^3 + c^2 + c$
n	$bc + 1$	$c^3 + c^2 + c + 1$
p	$ac + 1$	$c^3 + c^2 + 1$
q	$bc + b$	$c^3 + 1$

three or less. The structure of GF(16) arithmetic then is dictated by GF(2) arithmetic and the fact that $c^4 + c + 1 = 0$.

5A.5. THE CONSTRUCTION OF FINITE FIELDS

Using the structures uncovered in the previous section, it now is possible to construct finite fields. To first construct the integer subfield, note that the integers $0, 1, \ldots, p - 1$ are a commutative ring under addition and multiplication modulo p. Hence, $0, 1, 2, \ldots, p - 1$ form a field under addition and multiplication mod p if the integers $1, 2, \ldots, p - 1$ have inverses under multiplication mod p.

THEOREM 5A.4. *If p is prime, then $1, 2, \ldots, p - 1$ all have inverses under multiplication* mod p.

Proof. Suppose $1 \leq j < p$. Then, since p is prime, the greatest common divisor of j and p is 1. Hence, there exist integers n_1 and n_2 such that

$$1 = \gcd(j, p) = n_1 j + n_2 p. \tag{5A.34}$$

Reducing both sides of the equation mod p gives

$$1 = ((n_1 \bmod p) j) \bmod p \tag{5A.35}$$

Hence, $n_1 \bmod p$ is the inverse of j. ■

THEOREM 5A.5. *If p is not prime, then at least one element in the collection $1, 2, \ldots, p - 1$ does not have an inverse under multiplication mod p, and the collection is not closed under multiplication mod p.*

Proof. The integer p not prime means $p = p_1 p_2$ for some p_1 and p_2 in the range $1 < p_1 < p$, $1 < p_2 < p$. Hence, under multiplication mod p

$$0 = p_1 p_2 \bmod p. \tag{5A.36}$$

If p_2 had an inverse under multiplication mod p, the above equation would imply

$$0 = p_1 \bmod p. \tag{5A.37}$$

Since p_1 is a non-zero element of the ring, p_2 cannot have an inverse under multiplication. ■

Summarizing these results gives:

THEOREM 5A.6. *The integers $0, 1, \ldots, p - 1$ form a field under addition and multiplication* mod p *if and only if p is a prime number.*

The next step in the field synthesis problem is to assume the existence of a field GF(q), and attempt to construct a larger field containing it. Emulating the structures of the previous section, let $P(z)$ be a polynomial of degree d_m over GF(q) in an indeterminate z. It is easily demonstrated that the collection of pseudopolynomials in x of degree $d_m - 1$ or less forms a commutative ring under multiplication modulo $P(x)$. Again, the question of field existence resolves to determining when multiplicative inverses exist.

THEOREM 5A.7. *If $P(z)$ is an irreducible polynomial over* GF(q), *having x as a root, then the nonzero pseudopolynomials in x over* GF(q) *of degree less than the degree of $P(z)$ all have multiplicative inverses under multiplication* mod $P(x)$.

Proof. Let $J(z)$ be a polynomial in $z, 1 \leq \deg J(z) < \deg P(z)$. Since $P(z)$ is irreducible, the greatest common divisor of $J(z)$ and $P(z)$ is 1. Hence, there exist polynomials $N_1(z)$ and $N_2(z)$ such that

$$1 = \gcd(J(z), P(z)) = N_1(z)J(z) + N_2(z)P(z) \qquad (5A.38)$$

Reducing this equation mod $P(z)$ gives

$$1 = ((N_1(z) \bmod P(z))J(z)) \bmod P(z) \qquad (5A.39)$$

Hence, by setting the indeterminate z equal to x, it follows that $N_1(x)$ mod $P(x)$ is the inverse of $J(x)$ under multiplication mod $P(x)$. ∎

By now the reader should recognize the similarity of the roles played by the prime numbers within the ring of integers and the irreducible polynomials within the ring of polynomials. The proof of the following theorem follows exactly the proof of the equivalent theorem for the integers.

THEOREM 5A.8. *If $P(z)$ is not irreducible over the field* GF(q) *then at least one non-zero pseudopolynomial in x over* GF(q) *with degree less than the degree of $P(x)$ does not have an inverse under multiplication* mod $P(x)$.

With the background developed thus far, it is possible to conclude the following:

THEOREM 5A.9. *Let* GF(q) *be a known field. A larger field* GF(q^m) *containing* GF(q) *exists if, and only if, a polynomial $P(z)$ of degree m over* GF(q), *irreducible over* GF(q), *exists. The distinct members of* GF(q^m) *are all pseudopolynomials in x of degree less than m over* GF(q), *and addition and multiplication in* GF(q^m) *is polynomial addition and multiplication* mod $P(x)$, *where x is a root of $P(z)$.*

In the method of construction just outlined, GF(q) is called the *ground field* and GF(q^m) is termed the (algebraic) *extension field* of GF(q). The term "extension field of GF(q)" may be used to describe any larger field containing GF(q); the modifier "algebraic" refers to the method of construction by which the field GF(q) is augmented with the root of an algebraic expression to construct the larger field.

Since each finite field contains an integer field having a prime number of elements, and since any field containing the integer subfield can be constructed by the method stated in the above theorem, a finite field GF(q) containing q elements cannot exist unless q is a power of a prime number p. The prime p is called the *characteristic* of the field GF(q) when $q = p^n$. Hence, finite fields containing 6, 10, 12, 14, 15, 18, (etc.) elements do not exist. The existence of fields containing 2, 3, 5, 7, 11, 13, 17, (etc.) elements has already been demonstrated, since these are prime fields (integer fields mod p). The existence of fields containing 4, 8, 9, 16, 25, 27, 32 (etc.) elements can be demonstrated; this is equivalent to showing the existence of an irreducible polynomial of the appropriate degree over the appropriate integer fields.

The number $N_I(d)$ of irreducible polynomials over GF(q) of degree d can be shown to be

$$N_I(d) = \frac{1}{d} \sum_{m|d} \mu\left(\frac{d}{m}\right) q^m, \tag{5A.40}$$

where the sum is over all integer divisors of the degree d and $\mu(\ )$ is the Möbius function:

$$\mu(k) = \begin{cases} 1 & k = 1 \\ (-1)^j & k = \text{product of } j \text{ distinct primes} \\ 0 & k \text{ divisible by a square.} \end{cases} \tag{5A.41}$$

It is easily verified that $N_I(d)$ is a positive integer for all degrees d.

5A.6. PRIMITIVE ELEMENTS

The non-zero elements of a Galois field GF(q) form a multiplicative group of order $q - 1$; hence, the exponent e of the non-zero elements of GF(q) under multiplication must divide $q - 1$ (see Section 5A.1). If the exponent e of an element x equals the order $q - 1$ of the multiplicative group of GF(q), then x is termed a *primitive* field element. (It can be shown that the multiplicative group of a finite field is cyclic.)

Example 5A.11. In the Galois field of sixteen elements shown in Figure 5A.1, the element c is primitive. This can be verified from Table 5A.2.

The addition and multiplication tables for GF(16), shown in Figure 5A.1, were constructed from Table 5A.2 in the following manner. An irreducible polynomial over GF(2) of degree 4, namely $z^4 + z + 1$ was known to have a primitive element as its root, which we named c. The powers of c were reduced to pseudopolynomials of degree 3 or less in c, since $c^4 + c + 1$

Table 5A.2
Representations of GF(16)

Element name	Representations	
	Power of c	Pseudopolynomial in c
1	c^0	1
c	c^1	c
d	c^2	c^2
e	c^3	c^3
f	c^4	$1 + c$
a	c^5	$c + c^2$
g	c^6	$c^2 + c^3$
h	c^7	$1 + c + c^3$
j	c^8	$1 + c^2$
k	c^9	$c + c^3$
b	c^{10}	$1 + c + c^2$
m	c^{11}	$c + c^2 + c^3$
n	c^{12}	$1 + c + c^2 + c^3$
p	c^{13}	$1 + c^2 + c^3$
q	c^{14}	$1 + c^3$

= 0, giving the representation columns in the table. Names were assigned as in the first column. The addition table of Figure 5A.1 was constructed using the pseudopolynomial representations and coefficient addition in GF(2); the multiplication table was constructed using the power representations and the fact that $c^{15} = 1$. Obviously the table embodies the additive and multiplicative properties of the field.

The representation columns of the table can be generated by shift registers storing the coefficients of c. Suppose a binary shift register is constructed as shown below, with the coefficient of c^i shifting into the coefficient of c^{i+1}.

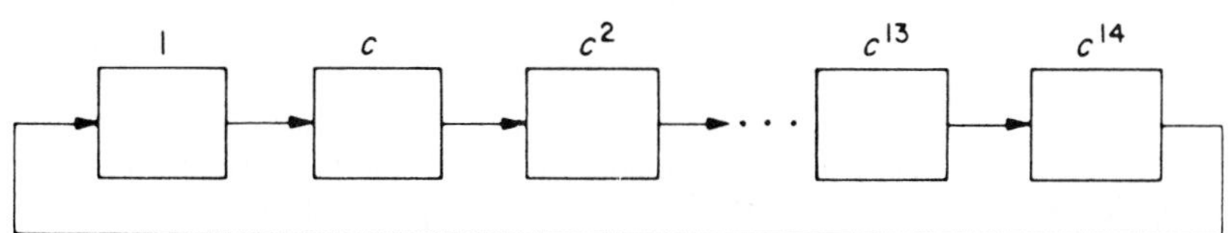

If 011010110000001 is present in the register, this represents $c + c^2 + c^4 + c^6 + c^7 + c^{14}$. A single shift of the contents of the register corresponds to a multiplication by c. Hence, in the above example, 101101011000000 represents $c(c + c^2 + c^4 + c^6 + c^7 + c^{14}) = 1 + c^2 + c^3 + c^5 + c^7 + c^8$. If we had started the register with 100000000000000, the successive contents of the register would have represented $1, c, c^2, c^3, c^4, \ldots, c^{14}, c^{15}, c^{16}, \ldots$. The above representation for multiplication by c only uses the fact that c has order 15. A similar shift register using the additional fact that $c^4 = c + 1$, is shown below.

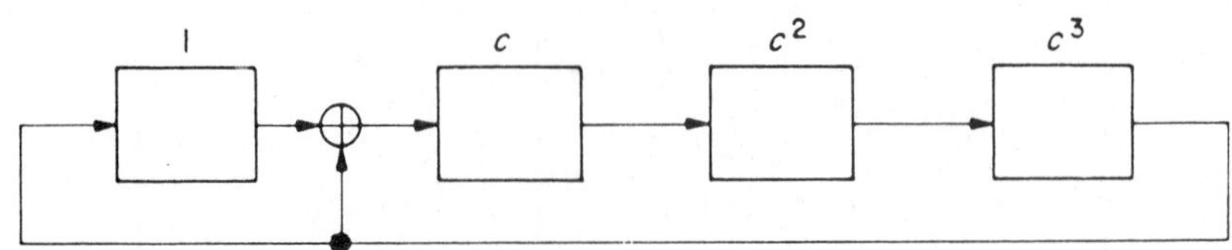

A shift (multiplication by c) of the c^3 coefficient results in $c^4 = c + 1$ being added to the contents of the register. If this register is started with 1000, the register contents after each shift will represent $1, c, c^2, \ldots, c^{13}, c^{14}, c^{15}, c^{16}, \ldots$. The representations will be pseudopolynomials of degree 3 or less in c, i.e., the pseudopolynomials in Table 5A.2.

The multiplicative order of each element in a field GF(q^d) can be determined from the representation table. To determine the order of c^i where c is primitive, we first compute the gcd $(i, q^d - 1)$. Then the smallest number e for which e is a multiple of $q^d - 1$ is

$$e = \frac{lcm(i, q^d - 1)}{i} = \frac{q^d - 1}{\gcd(i, q^d - 1)}. \tag{5A.42}$$

Hence, e is the order of c^i.

It can be shown that all the roots of an irreducible polynomial have the same order. Hence, an irreducible polynomial can be labelled with the order of its roots. An irreducible polynomial with a primitive field element as its root is called a *primitive polynomial.* The number of primitive polynomials $N_p(d)$ of degree d over GF(q) is given by

$$N_p(d) = \frac{q^d - 1}{d} \prod_{i=1}^{J} \frac{p_i - 1}{p_i} \tag{5A.43}$$

where p_i, $i = 1, \ldots, J$ are the distinct primes which divide $q^d - 1$. Certainly $N_p(d)$ is greater than zero for all powers of a prime as represented by q, and all degrees d. As a result every finite field can be constructed using a primitive irreducible polynomial.

Example 5A.12. In GF(16) the orders of the elements are as follows:

1	has order 1
c^5, c^{10}	have order 3
c^3, c^6, c^9, c^{12}	have order 5
$c, c^2, c^4, c^7, c^8, c^{11}, c^{13}, c^{14}$	have order 15.

Excluding the elements of GF(4), namely 0, 1, c^5, and c^{10}, any of the remaining twelve elements could be used to generate GF(16) as c did in Section 5A.5, and, hence, all must be roots of irreducible polynomials of degree 4. From the previous section, the number $N_I(4)$ irreducible polynomials of degree 4 over GF(2) is

$$N_I(4) = \tfrac{1}{4}\left[\mu(1)2^4 + \mu(2)2^2 + \mu(4)2\right]$$
$$= \tfrac{1}{4}[2^4 - 2^2] = 3,$$

while the number $N_p(4)$ of primitive irreducible polynomials of degree 4 over GF(2) is

$$N_p(4) = \frac{2^4 - 1}{4}\left(\frac{5-1}{5}\right)\left(\frac{3-1}{3}\right) = 2$$

Hence, the nonprimitive elements c^3, c^6, c^9, and c^{12} must be roots of the same irreducible degree-4 polynomial. The eight elements of order 15 must be roots of the two degree-4 primitive polynomials.

5A.7. FINDING IRREDUCIBLE AND PRIMITIVE POLYNOMIALS

Some fundamental ideas are necessary before further progress can be made. The following are stated without proof:

(a) A finite field of specified size is unique. This means that different irreducible polynomials of the same degree over the same ground field must lead to the same extension field structure.
(b) $GF(q^{d'}) \subset GF(q^d) \Leftrightarrow d'|d$. This is a dimensionality constraint that comes from viewing $GF(q^d)$ as the result of a construction employing a polynomial of degree d/d' over $GF(q^{d'})$.
(c) All roots of an irreducible polynomial lie in the same field. If this were not the case, the construction of Section 5 might yield different extension fields using the same polynomial.
(d) The elements of $GF(q^d)$ are the roots of the polynomial $z^{q^d} - z$. A proof of this fact follows directly from noting that the non-zero elements of $GF(q^d)$ have order dividing $q^d - 1$ and, therefore, are roots of $z^{q^d - 1} - 1$.

As a result of (a)–(d), it follows that the polynomial containing all elements of $GF(q^d)$ as roots can be factored as follows:

$$z^{q^d} - z = \prod_{d'|d} \prod_{m(z) \in P_{d'}} m(z) \tag{5A.44}$$

where P_d denotes the set of all monic irreducible polynomials of degree d over GF(q).

Let $A(z)$ be a polynomial of degree d over GF(q). The following algorithm can be used to determine if $A(z)$ is irreducible.

Irreducibility Test:

(a) $d' = 1$.
(b) $N_{d'}(z) = \gcd(A(z), z^{q^{d'}} - z)$.
(c) If $N_{d'}(z) \neq 1$, then [$A(z)$ has a factor $N_{d'}(z)$, STOP].
(d) If $d' < \lfloor d/2 \rfloor$, then [$d' = d' + 1$, Go to (b)].
(e) $A(z)$ is irreducible. STOP.

Step (b) will recover any polynomial factors over GF(q) that are common to $A(z)$ and $z^{q^{d'}} - z$. If the test runs its full course for all d' in the range $1 \leq d' \leq d/2$, $A(z)$ will have been checked for all possible irreducible factors of degree at most $d/2$. Since if $A(z)$ is factorable, it must have a factor in this degree range, the test shows $A(z)$ to be irreducible if and only if no factors are uncovered.

Euclid's algorithm of Section 5A.2 can be mechanized to determine the greatest common divisor in step (b). However, the first part of this calculation may be difficult since the degree $q^{d'}$ may be a very large number. The solution to this problem is to note that the first step in Euclid's algorithm will be to evaluate $z^{q^{d'}} - z \bmod A(z)$. This can be done with the following routine.

Evaluation of $R(z) = z^{q^d} - z$ mod $A(z)$

(a) $R_0(z) = z$, $e = 1$.
(b) $R_e(z) = [R_{e-1}(z)]^q \bmod A(z)$.
(c) If $e < d$, then [$e = e + 1$, Go to (b)].
(d) $R(z) = [R_d(z) - z] \bmod A(z)$. STOP.

The degrees of the polynomials in the calculation never exceed qd, because of the judicious insertions of mod $A(z)$ reductions into the calculations.

The operation of raising a polynomial $R(z)$ over GF(q) to the q-th power is a simple procedure as indicated by the following theorem.

THEOREM 5A.10. *Let $R(z)$ be a polynomial over* GF(q). *Then*

$$(R(z))^q = R(z^q) \tag{5A.45}$$

Proof. Consider a polynomial $R(z)$ with coefficients in the ground field GF(q), where $q = p^n$, p being a prime number.

$$R(z) = \sum_{i=0}^{d} a_i z^i, \quad a_i \in \mathrm{GF}(q). \tag{5A.46}$$

If we raise $R(z)$ to a power equal to the characteristic of the field GF(q) we get

$$(R(z))^p = \sum_{j=0}^{p} \binom{p}{j} (a_d z^d)^j \left(\sum_{i=0}^{d-1} a_i z^i \right)^{p-j} \tag{5A.47}$$

Here we have used the binomial expansion treating the d-th term as one element and the sum of the remaining terms as the other element in the expansion. The binomial coefficient $\binom{p}{j}$ counts the number of times a term appears and, hence, can be considered to be the element of GF(q) corresponding to the sun of $\binom{p}{j}$ unit elements. In GF(q), integer elements are added mod p. Since p is prime, $\binom{p}{j}$ is divisible by p unless $j = p$ or $j = 0$. Hence,

$$\binom{p}{j} \bmod p = \begin{cases} 1 & \text{if } j = p \text{ or } j = 0 \\ 0 & \text{otherwise.} \end{cases} \tag{5A.48}$$

Thus,

$$(R(z))^p = (a_d z^d)^p + \left(\sum_{i=0}^{d-1} a_i z^i \right)^p, \tag{5A.49}$$

and iterating this result on the remaining polynomial of degree $(d-1)p$ gives

$$(R(z))^p = \sum_{i=0}^{d} (a_i)^p (z^p)^i. \tag{5A.50}$$

If this procedure is repeated n times we have

$$(R(z))^{p^n} = \sum_{i=0}^{d} (a_i)^{p^n} (z^{p^n})^i. \tag{5A.51}$$

Now a_i is in GF(q) where $q = p^n$. Hence, the order of a_i divides $q - 1$ and $a_i^q = a_i$. Therefore,

$$(R(z))^q = \sum_{i=0}^{d} a_i z^{qi} = R(z^q). \tag{5A.52}$$

■

This theorem makes the computation of $R(z)$ equivalent to simply changing the powers of z in the polynomial. Hence, the evaluation algorithm for $z^{q^{d'}} - z \bmod A(z)$ is extremely efficient numerically.

Highly structured sieve methods which employ efficient exhaustive search techniques could be used to construct a table of irreducible polynomials. However, this approach bogs down at a relatively low degree, since a large number of polynomials is involved. A much faster approach for finding a single irreducible polynomial of high degree is simply to select a polynomial $A(z)$ of degree d over GF(q) at random, and apply the irreducibility test outlined above. The probability of success on any given test is $N_I(d)/q^d$, a quantity which generally decreases as $1/d$.

The random selection process by which a trial polynomial $A(z)$ is selected can be improved by not choosing polynomials which are easily shown to be factorable. For example, when $q = 2$, note the following guidelines.

(a) $A(z)$ has a factor z if the coefficient of 1 in the polynomial $A(z)$ is zero. (This obviously works for all q.)
(b) $A(z)$ has a root 1 if $A(z)$ has an even number of non-zero coefficients.

Observance of these facts by selecting trial polynomials, which do not have roots in GF(2), has the effect of improving the probability of test success by approximately a factor of 4. Many other results, e.g., Theorem 5A.10, can be used to further eliminate poor choices.

After determining that a polynomial $A(z)$ is irreducible, it is also possible to determine the order of its roots. For example, if one wishes to test an irreducible polynomial $A(z)$ of degree d over GF(q) to see if it is primitive, first determine the prime decomposition of $q^d - 1$.

$$q^d - 1 = \prod_{i=1}^{J} p_i^{e_i}$$

where p_i, $i = 1, \ldots, J$ are distinct primes. Then carry out the following algorithm.

Primitivity Test

(a) $i = 1$.
(b) $N_i(z) = z^{(q^d - 1)/p_i} \bmod A(z)$.
(c) If $N_i(z) = 1$, then [$A(z)$ is not primitive. STOP].
(d) If $i < J$, then [$i = i + 1$, Go to (b)].
(e) $A(z)$ is primitive. STOP.

Step (b) in this test checks to see if the exponent of $A(z)$ lacks the prime factor p_i, which, if this is the case, results in $N_i(z) = 1$. The difficult part of this test is to determine the prime decomposition of $q^d - 1$. A decomposition table for the case $q = 2$, for $1 < d \leq 120$ is included in Appendix 5B. A selected table of primitive polynomials over this range of parameters is also included in Appendix 5B, along with references to more extensive listings.

5A.8. PROPERTIES OF MINIMUM POLYNOMIALS

Once a primitive polynomial $m_x(z)$ of degree d over GF(q) has been determined, the elements of GF(q^d) (excluding zero), can be represented as pseudopolynomials in x or as powers of x and addition and multiplication operations defined. The minimum polynomials of the remaining field elements of GF(q^d) can be calculated directly.

Suppose that y is another element of GF(q^d) and its minimum polynomial is desired. Knowledge of y as a power of x allows the exponent of y

to be determined as in Section 5A.6. This provides the following additional information.

THEOREM 5A.11. *Let y be an element of exponent e in an extension field of* GF(q). *Then the following are equivalent statements*:

(*a*) *d is the smallest integer for which $e|q^d - 1$.*
(*b*) GF(q^d) *is the smallest field containing y.*
(*c*) *d is the degree of the minimum polynomial of y over* GF(q).

Proof. Let a be the smallest integer such that $e|q^a - 1$; let b be the smallest integer such that $y \in \mathrm{GF}(q^b)$; let c be the degree of the minimum polynomial of y over GF(q). The results of previous sections justify the following relations:

(a) $e|q^a - 1 \Rightarrow y$ is a root of $z^{q^a} - z \Rightarrow y \in \mathrm{GF}(q^a) \Rightarrow b \leq a$.
(b) $y \in \mathrm{GF}(q^b) \Rightarrow y$ is a root of $z^{q^b} - z \Rightarrow c \leq b$.
(c) $m_y(z)$ irreducible of degree $c \Rightarrow m_y(z)|z^{q^c} - z \Rightarrow y^{q^c} = y \Rightarrow e|q^c - 1 \Rightarrow a \leq c$.
(d) Since $a \leq c \leq b \leq a$, $a = b = c$. ■

It is now possible to find the minimum polynomial over GF(q) of a field element y.

Linear Equation Algorithm for Determining $m_y(z)$ over GF(q)

(a) Determine the exponent of y.
(b) Determine the degree d' of $m_y(z)$ over GF(q).
(c) Represent y^i as a pseudopolynomial over GF(q) in x, x being a primitive element of the field GF(q^d) containing y, and the minimum polynomial of x being known. Hence, determine a_{ij} in GF(q) such that

$$y^i = \sum_{j=0}^{d-1} a_{ij}x^j, \quad i = 0, 1, \ldots, d'. \tag{5A.53}$$

(d) Find the coefficients $b_0, \ldots, b_{d'-1}$ in the minimum polynomial $m_y(z)$, such that

$$m_y(y) = \sum_{i=0}^{d'-1} b_i y^i + y^{d'} = 0, \tag{5A.54}$$

or equivalently, solve the following equations in GF(q) for $b_0, \ldots, b_{d'-1}$:

$$\sum_{i=0}^{d'-1} b_i a_{ij} = -a_{d'j}, \quad j = 0, 1, \ldots, d-1. \tag{5A.55}$$

(e) The minimum polynomial of y over GF(q) is

$$m_y(z) = z^{d'} + b_{d'-1}z^{d'-1} + \cdots + b_1 z + b_0. \tag{5A.56}$$

We shall illustrate this algorithm with an example using the description of GF(16) in Section 5A.6.

Example 5A.13. Consider the element h in GF(16).

(a) $h = c^7$, c primitive, so the order of h is $15/\gcd(7, 15) = 15$
(b) $m_h(z)$ over GF(2) has degree $d_m = 4$ since

$$15 \text{ does not divide } (2 - 1)$$
$$15 \text{ does not divide } (2^2 - 1)$$
$$15 \text{ does not divide } (2^3 - 1)$$
$$15 \text{ divides } (2^4 - 1).$$

(c) $h^0 = 1 = 1$
$h^1 = c^7 = 1 + c + c^3$
$h^2 = c^{14} = 1 + c^3$
$h^3 = c^6 = c^2 + c^3$
$h^4 = c^{13} = 1 + c^2 + c^3$

(d) $h^4 + b_3 h^3 + b_2 h^2 + b_1 h + b_0 = 0$
gives for the coefficients of c^i:
$i = 0$: $1 + b_2 + b_1 + b_0 = 0$
$i = 1$: $b_1 = 0$
$i = 2$: $1 + b_3 = 0$
$i = 3$: $1 + b_3 + b_2 + b_1 = 0$
which are easily solved over GF(2) to give $b_0 = b_3 = 1$, $b_1 = b_2 = 0$.

(e) The minimum polynomial of h over GF(2) is $z^4 + z^3 + 1$.

Instead of specifying a monic polynomial by its coefficients, it can be described by listing its roots.

DEFINITION 5A.7. *The* q-conjugates *of x are the $d - 1$ roots of the minimum polynomial $m_x(z)$ of x over* GF(q), *after x has been excluded, d being the degree of $m_x(z)$.*

The q-conjugates of x are easily derived from x via the following theorem.

THEOREM 5A.12. *Let $m_x(z)$, the minimum polynomial of x over* GF(q), *have degree d. Then $x, x^q, x^{q^2}, \ldots, x^{q^{d-1}}$, are all distinct and are the d roots of $m_x(z)$.*

Proof. Using Theorem 5A.10, we have that

$$m_x(z) = 0 \Rightarrow [m_x(z)]^q = 0 \Rightarrow m_x(z^q) = 0.$$

Hence, if x is a non-zero root of a polynomial over GF(q), then so is x^q. Iterating this line of reason we see that $x, x^q, x^{q^2}, x^{q^3}, \ldots,$ must all be roots of $m_x(z)$.

We now show that $x, x^q, x^{q^2}, \ldots, x^{q^{d-1}}$ are all distinct. Suppose $x^{q^j} = x^{q^i}$ for $0 \leq i < j$. Multiplying both sides of this equation by the inverse of x^{q^i} in GF(q^d) gives

$$x^{q^j - q^i} = 1 \tag{5A.57}$$

which implies that the order e of x divides $q^j - q^i$. Hence,

$$e | q^i \left(q^{j-i} - 1\right).$$

Since $e | q^d - 1$, it follows that $\gcd(e, q) = 1$,

$$e | \left(q^{j-i} - 1\right),$$

and, therefore, by Theorem 5A.11, $d \leq j - i$. Since j and i are both non-negative integers, $x, x^2, \ldots, x^{q^{d-1}}$ are all distinct. Because a polynomial over a field can have no more roots than its degree, these elements are all the roots of $m_x(z)$. ■

We now have an alternative algorithm for determining the roots of $m_y(z)$ over GF(q) whenever the arithmetic for any extension field of GF(q), containing y, is specified.

***q*-Conjugate Algorithm for Determining $m_y(z)$ over GF(*q*).**

(a) Compute $y, y^q, y^{q^2}, \ldots,$ until an integer d is reached for which $y^{q^d} = y$.
(b) Form the polynomial

$$m_y(z) = \prod_{i=0}^{d-1} \left(z - y^{q^i}\right) \tag{5A.58}$$

(c) Evaluate the coefficients of $m_y(z)$ in (b) using the arithmetic specified for the field.

We shall again provide an example from GF(16). This time, for the sake of variety, we shall use the notation of the addition and multiplication tables of Figure 5A.1.

Example 5A.14. As a check, let us again consider the element h of GF(16), and try to find $m_h(z)$ over GF(2) using the q-conjugate method.

(a) $h^{2^0} = h$
$h^{2^1} = h^2 = q$
$h^{2^2} = q^2 = p$
$h^{2^3} = p^2 = m$
$h^{2^4} = m^2 = h$

(b) $m_h(z) = (z-h)(z-h^2)(z-h^4)(z-h^8)$

$$\begin{aligned} m_h(z) &= (z-h)(z-q)(z-p)(z-m) \\ &= (z^2 - cz + g)(z^2 - fz + k) \\ &= z^4 - (c+f)z^3 + (k+q+fc)z^2 - (ck+fg)z + gk \\ &= z^4 + z^3 + 1 \text{ (over GF(2))} \end{aligned}$$

(c) This is a check on the previous computation.

Using Theorem 5A.12, the entire collection of non-zero elements of $\mathrm{GF}(q^d)$ can be separated into disjoint sets, each set containing all the roots of a single irreducible polynomial over $\mathrm{GF}(q)$. Suppose that each field element in this construction is represented as a power of a primitive element x of $\mathrm{GF}(q^d)$, and to simplify notation, represent x^i by its base-x logarithm i. Hence, one logarithm set in the construction will be

$$\mathscr{S}_1 = \{1, q, q^2, \ldots, q^{d-1}\}, \tag{5A.59}$$

representing the roots $x, x^q, x^{q^2}, \ldots, x^{q^{d-1}}$ of $m_x(z)$. Another set in the construction, representing the minimum polynomial $m_{x^e}(z)$ of degree d', is

$$S_e = \{e, eq, eq^2, \ldots, eq^{d'-1}\}. \tag{5A.60}$$

The logarithms in S_e may be calculated by a coset-like construction. In fact, if e is relatively prime to $q^d - 1$, then $\mathscr{S}_e$ is a coset of the subgroup $\mathscr{S}_1$ in the group of integers relatively prime to $q^d - 1$ under multiplication modulo $q^d - 1$, and represents the roots of another primitive polynomial. If e is not relatively prime to $q^d - 1$, then $\mathscr{S}_e$ is not the result of a formal coset construction; however, all the distinct sets $\mathscr{S}_e$ are called *cyclotomic cosets*. Note that the d symbol, base q expansion of e and eq^i modulo $q^d - 1$ are related for all i by a cyclic shift, making the determination of the sets $\mathscr{S}_e$ a simple matter in a base q number system.

Example 5A.15. In GF(16), the root logarithm sets are given by $\mathscr{S}_1$, $\mathscr{S}_3$, $\mathscr{S}_5$, and $\mathscr{S}_7$, with $\mathscr{S}_1$ being the basic subgroup, $\mathscr{S}_7$ representing the one formal coset of $\mathscr{S}_1$, and $\mathscr{S}_3$ and $\mathscr{S}_5$ representing the remaining cyclotomic cosets. Using the element c of Table 5A.2 as the primitive element, the q-conjugate algorithm can be used to construct the polynomials corresponding to the above sets:

$$\mathscr{S}_1 = \{1, 2, 4, 8\} \to z^4 + z + 1$$

$$\mathscr{S}_3 = \{3, 6, 12, 9\} \to z^4 + z^3 + z^2 + z + 1$$

$$\mathscr{S}_5 = \{5, 10\} \to z^2 + z + 1$$

$$\mathscr{S}_7 = \{7, 14, 13, 11\} \to z^4 + z^3 + 1$$

$$\mathscr{S}_0 = \{0\} \to z + 1$$

The following relation reduces the amount of work necessary to evaluate the irreducible polynomials associated with the root sets. Let

$$A(z) = \sum_{i=0}^{d} a_i z^i = \prod_{i=1}^{d} (z - r_i) \tag{5A.61}$$

be an irreducible polynomial whose roots have exponent e. Then the corresponding *reciprocal polynomial*, defined by

$$\begin{aligned} B(z) &= a_0^{-1} z^d A\left(\frac{1}{z}\right) \\ &= \sum_{i=0}^{d} a_0^{-1} a_{d-i} z^i = \prod_{i=1}^{d} (z - r_i^{-1}), \end{aligned} \tag{5A.62}$$

is easily determined by reversing the coefficient order (and scaling if necessary). The roots of $B(z)$ are the reciprocals of the roots of $A(z)$ and have the same order. Hence, in Example 5A.15, knowing that c and c^{14} are reciprocals and that $m_c(z)$ is $z^4 + z + 1$ is enough to conclude directly that $m_{c^{14}}(z)$ is $z^4 + z^3 + 1$.

5A.9. THE TRACE FUNCTION

The *trace polynomial* from $\text{GF}(q^n)$ to $\text{GF}(q)$ is defined as

$$\text{Tr}_q^{q^n}(z) = \sum_{j=0}^{n-1} z^{q^j}, \tag{5A.63}$$

where the superscript and subscript on Tr have been added to clarify the fields under consideration. The *trace* in $\text{GF}(q)$ of an element α in $\text{GF}(q^n)$ is then defined as $\text{Tr}_q^{q^n}(\alpha)$, i.e., the trace polynomial evaluated at α. For a given element α which is in several fields, $\text{Tr}_q^{q^n}(\alpha)$ will vary as the choice of q and/or q^n varies. We shall drop the superscripts and subscripts on $\text{Tr}_q^{q^n}(\alpha)$ only when n and q are obvious in the context of the discussion.

Example 5A.16. In GF(16) model of Figure 5A.1,

$$\text{Tr}_2^{16}(a) = a + a^2 + a^4 + a^8 = a + a^2 + a + a^2 = 0$$

Since a is in GF(4), we may also compute

$$\text{Tr}_2^{4}(a) = a + a^2 = 1.$$

Notice that the variations of trace value with the parameter n are possible. To illustrate variations with the range field of the trace function, consider the element e in GF(16),

$$\begin{aligned} \text{Tr}_{16}^{16}(e) &= e \\ \text{Tr}_{4}^{16}(e) &= e + e^4 = b \\ \text{Tr}_{2}^{16}(e) &= e + e^2 + e^4 + e^8 = 1 \end{aligned}$$

We now will prove useful properties of the trace function.

Property 1. When α is in $\mathrm{GF}(q^n)$, $\mathrm{Tr}_q^{q^n}(\alpha)$ has values in $\mathrm{GF}(q)$.

Proof.

$$\left[\mathrm{Tr}_q^{q^n}(\alpha)\right]^q = \left(\sum_{j=0}^{n-1} \alpha^{q^j}\right)^q \qquad \text{(Definition)}$$

$$= \sum_{j=0}^{n-1} \alpha^{q^{j+1}} \qquad \text{(Theorem 5A.10)}$$

$$= \sum_{j=1}^{n-1} \alpha^{q^j} + \alpha \qquad \left(\alpha \in \mathrm{GF}(q^n) \Rightarrow \alpha^{q^n} = \alpha\right)$$

$$= \mathrm{Tr}_q^{q^n}(\alpha). \qquad \text{(Definition)}$$

Therefore, $\mathrm{Tr}_q^{q^n}(\alpha)$ is a field element whose q-th power equals itself. Only elements of $\mathrm{GF}(q)$ have this property. ■

Property 2. Conjugate field elements have the same trace, i.e.,

$$\mathrm{Tr}_q^{q^n}(\alpha^q) = \mathrm{Tr}_q^{q^n}(\alpha) \text{ for } \alpha \in \mathrm{GF}(q^n). \qquad (5A.64)$$

The proof of this property follows from the previous property and the fact (Theorem 5A.10) that $P(z^q) = [P(z)]^q$.

Property 3. The trace is linear: for $a, b \in \mathrm{GF}(q)$ and $\alpha, \beta \in \mathrm{GF}(q^n)$,

$$\mathrm{Tr}_q^{q^n}(a\alpha + b\beta) = a\,\mathrm{Tr}_q^{q^n}(\alpha) + b\,\mathrm{Tr}_q^{q^n}(\beta) \qquad (5A.65)$$

Proof.

$$\mathrm{Tr}(a\alpha + b\beta) = \sum_{j=0}^{n-1} (a\alpha + b\beta)^{q^j} \qquad \text{(Definition)}$$

$$= \sum_{j=0}^{n-1} \left(a^{q^j}\alpha^{q^j} + b^{q^j}\beta^{q^j}\right) \qquad \text{(Theorem 5A.10)}$$

$$= \sum_{j=0}^{n-1} a\alpha^{q^j} + b\beta^{q^j} \qquad (a \in \mathrm{GF}(q) \Rightarrow a^q = a)$$

$$= a\,\mathrm{Tr}_q^{q^n}(\alpha) + b\,\mathrm{Tr}_q^{q^n}(\beta) \qquad \text{(Definition)}$$

■

Property 4. There are q^{n-1} elements in $\mathrm{GF}(q^n)$ which have trace value a for each a in $\mathrm{GF}(q)$.

Proof. An element α in GF(q^n) has

$$\mathrm{Tr}_q^{q^n}(\alpha) = a \tag{5A.66}$$

if and only if α is a root of the trace equation

$$z + z^q + z^{q^2} + \cdots + z^{q^{n-1}} - a = 0,\ a \in \mathrm{GF}(q).$$

Every element of GF(q^n) must be the root of exactly one such equation, and each of the q equations has exactly q^{n-1} roots. Since all roots of the trace equations are accounted for by elements of GF(q^n), there must be exactly q^{n-1} elements of GF(q^n) with trace a in GF(q). ■

Property 5. If GF(q) ⊂ GF(q^k) ⊂ GF(q^d), then

$$\mathrm{Tr}_q^{q^d}(\alpha) = \mathrm{Tr}_q^{q^k}\left(\mathrm{Tr}_{q^k}^{q^d}(\alpha)\right). \tag{5A.67}$$

Proof. Consider the nested trace-polynomial expression:

$$\mathrm{Tr}_q^{q^k}\left(\mathrm{Tr}_{q^k}^{q^d}(z)\right) = \sum_{j=0}^{k-1}\left(\sum_{i=0}^{\frac{d}{k}-1} z^{q^{ki}}\right)^{q^j} \qquad \text{(Definitions)}$$

$$= \sum_{j=0}^{k-1}\sum_{i=0}^{\frac{d}{k}-1} z^{q^{ki+j}} \qquad \text{(Theorem 5A.10)}$$

$$= \sum_{n=0}^{d-1} z^{q^n} \qquad (n = ki + j)$$

$$= \mathrm{Tr}_q^{q^d}(z) \qquad \text{(Definition)}$$

Evaluating the above polynomial relation at $z = \alpha$, α in GF(q^d), gives the final result. ■

Property 6. Let GF(q^d) be the smallest field containing α, and let the minimum polynomial of $m_\alpha(z)$ be denoted by

$$m_\alpha(z) = \sum_{i=0}^{d} a_i z^{d-i}. \tag{5A.68}$$

Then

$$a_1 = -\mathrm{Tr}_q^{q^d}(\alpha). \tag{5A.69}$$

Proof. This property follows directly from Theorem 5A.12, whence

$$m_\alpha(z) = \prod_{i=0}^{d-1}(z - \alpha^{q^i}). \tag{5A.70}$$

■

APPENDIX 5B. FACTORIZATIONS OF $2^n - 1$ AND SELECTED PRIMITIVE POLYNOMIALS

The table in this appendix contains prime factorizations of numbers of the form $2^n - 1$, and a listing of selected primitive polynomials of degree n over GF(2). For further information on factorizations of $2^n - 1$, see Reisel [1] and Brillhart et al. [9]. Useful tables of primitive polynomials have been published by Peterson and Weldon [2], Watson [3], Stahnke [4], Zierler and Brillhart [5, 6], Zierler [7], and Lidl and Niederreiter [8].

In certain listings the notation $F(n)$ will be used to represent the factorization of $2^n - 1$. For example, since

$$2^{40} - 1 = (2^{20} - 1)(2^{20} + 1),$$

the factorization of $2^{40} - 1$ reads $F(20) \times 17 \times 61681$, indicating that the factorization of $2^{20} - 1$ should be inserted. Clearly 17×61681 must be the factorization of $2^{20} + 1$.

The primitive polynomials in this table all have a small number of nonzero terms, and therefore will be represented by the set $\mathscr{I}_n$ of intermediate powers of z present in the polynomial. For example, the primitive polynomial $z^{24} + z^4 + z^3 + z + 1$ is represented by $\mathscr{I}_{24} = (4, 3, 1)$, i.e.,

$$z^{24} + z^4 + z^3 + z + 1 = z^{24} + \left(\sum_{i \in \mathscr{I}_{24}} z^i \right) + 1.$$

n	$F(n)$	$\mathscr{I}_n$
2	3	(1)
3	7	(1)
4	3×5	(1)
5	31	(2)
6	$3^2 \times 7$	(1)
7	127	(1), (3)
8	$3 \times 5 \times 17$	(4, 3, 2), (6, 5, 1)
9	7×73	(4)
10	$3 \times 11 \times 31$	(3)
11	23×89	(2)
12	$3^2 \times 5 \times 7 \times 13$	(6, 4, 1), (7, 4, 3)
13	8191	(4, 3, 1)
14	$3 \times 43 \times 127$	(5, 3, 1), (12, 11, 1)
15	$7 \times 31 \times 151$	(1), (4), (7)
16	$3 \times 5 \times 17 \times 257$	(5, 3, 2), (12, 3, 1)
17	131071	(3), (5), (6)
18	$3^3 \times 7 \times 19 \times 73$	(7), (9), (5, 2, 1)
19	524287	(5, 2, 1), (6, 5, 1)
20	$3 \times 5^2 \times 11 \times 31 \times 41$	(3)
21	$7^2 \times 127 \times 337$	(2)
22	$3 \times 23 \times 89 \times 683$	(1)

23	47×178481	(5), (9)
24	$3^2 \times 5 \times 7 \times 13 \times 17 \times 241$	(7, 2, 1), (4, 3, 1)
25	$31 \times 601 \times 1801$	(3), (7)
26	$3 \times 2731 \times 8191$	(6, 2, 1), (8, 7, 1)
27	$7 \times 73 \times 262657$	(5, 2, 1), (8, 7, 1)
28	$3 \times 5 \times 29 \times 43 \times 113 \times 127$	(3), (9), (13)
29	$233 \times 1103 \times 2089$	(2)
30	$3^2 \times 7 \times 11 \times 31 \times 151 \times 331$	(6, 4, 1), (16, 15, 1)
31	2147483647	(3), (6), (7), (13)
32	$3 \times 5 \times 17 \times 257 \times 65537$	(22, 2, 1), (28, 27, 1)
33	$7 \times 23 \times 89 \times 599479$	(13), (6, 4, 1)
34	$3 \times 43691 \times 131071$	(15, 14, 1), (27, 2, 1)
35	$31 \times 71 \times 127 \times 122921$	(2)
36	$F(18) \times 5 \times 13 \times 37 \times 109$	(11), (6, 5, 4, 2, 1)
37	223×616318177	(12, 10, 2), (6, 4, 1)
38	$F(19) \times 3 \times 174763$	(6, 5, 1)
39	$7 \times 79 \times 8191 \times 121369$	(4), (8), (14)
40	$F(20) \times 17 \times 61681$	(5, 4, 3), (21, 19, 2)
41	13367×164511353	(3), (20)
42	$F(21) \times 3^2 \times 43 \times 5419$	(23, 22, 1), (7, 4, 3)
43	$431 \times 9719 \times 2099863$	(6, 4, 3), (6, 5, 1)
44	$F(22) \times 5 \times 397 \times 2113$	(6, 5, 2), (27, 26, 1)
45	$7 \times 31 \times 73 \times 151 \times 631 \times 23311$	(4, 3, 1)
46	$F(23) \times 3 \times 2796203$	(21, 20, 1), (8, 5, 3, 2, 1)
47	$2351 \times 4513 \times 13264529$	(5), (14), (20), (21)
48	$F(24) \times 97 \times 257 \times 673$	(28, 27, 1), (7, 5, 4, 2, 1)
49	127×4432676798593	(9), (12), (15), (22)
50	$F(25) \times 3 \times 11 \times 251 \times 4051$	(4, 3, 2), (27, 26, 1)
51	$7 \times 103 \times 2143 \times 11119 \times 131071$	(6, 3, 1), (16, 15, 1)
52	$F(26) \times 5 \times 53 \times 157 \times 1613$	(3), (19), (21)
53	$6361 \times 69431 \times 20394401$	(6, 2, 1), (16, 15, 1)
54	$F(27) \times 3^4 \times 19 \times 87211$	(37, 36, 1), (6, 5, 4, 3, 2)
55	$23 \times 31 \times 89 \times 881 \times 3191 \times 201961$	(24), (6, 2, 1)
56	$F(28) \times 17 \times 15790321$	(7, 4, 2), (22, 21, 1)
57	$7 \times 32377 \times 524287 \times 1212847$	(7), (22), (5, 3, 2)
58	$F(29) \times 3 \times 59 \times 3033169$	(19), (6, 5, 1)
59	$179951 \times 3203431780337$	(22, 21, 1), (6, 5, 4, 3, 1)
60	$F(30) \times 5^2 \times 13 \times 41 \times 61 \times 1321$	(1), (11)
61	2305843009213693951	(5, 2, 1), (16, 15, 1)
62	$F(31) \times 3 \times 715827883$	(6, 5, 3), (57, 56, 1)
63	$F(21) \times 73 \times 92737 \times 649657$	(1), (5), (31)
64	$F(32) \times 641 \times 6700417$	(4, 3, 1)
65	$31 \times 8191 \times 145295143558111$	(18), (32), (4, 3, 1)
66	$F(33) \times 3^2 \times 67 \times 683 \times 20857$	(10, 9, 1), (8, 6, 5, 3, 2)
67	$193707721 \times 761838257287$	(5, 2, 1), (10, 9, 1)
68	$F(34) \times 5 \times 137 \times 953 \times 26317$	(9), (33), (7, 5, 1)
69	$F(23) \times 7 \times 10052678938039$	(6, 5, 2), (29, 27, 2)
70	$F(35) \times 3 \times 11 \times 43 \times 281 \times 86171$	(5, 3, 1), (16, 15, 1)

71	$228479 \times 48544121 \times 212885833$	(6), (9), (18), (20), (35)
72	$F(36) \times 17 \times 241 \times 433 \times 38737$	(53, 47, 6), (6, 4, 3, 2, 1)
73	$439 \times 2298041 \times 9361973132609$	(25), (28), (31), (4, 3, 2)
74	$F(37) \times 3 \times 1777 \times 25781083$	(7, 4, 3), (16, 15, 1)
75	$F(25) \times 7 \times 151 \times 100801 \times 10567201$	(6, 3, 1), (11, 10, 1)
76	$F(38) \times 5 \times 229 \times 457 \times 525313$	(5, 4, 2), (36, 35, 1)
77	$23 \times 89 \times 127 \times 581283643249112959$	(6, 5, 2), (31, 30, 1)
78	$F(39) \times 3^2 \times 2731 \times 22366891$	(7, 2, 1), (20, 19, 1)
79	$2687 \times 202029703 \times 1113491139767$	(9), (19), (4, 3, 2)
80	$F(40) \times 257 \times 4278255361$	(38, 37, 1), (7, 5, 3, 2, 1)
81	$F(27) \times 2593 \times 71119 \times 97685839$	(4), (16), (35)
82	$F(41) \times 3 \times 83 \times 8831418697$	(38, 35, 3), (8, 7, 6, 4, 1)
83	$167 \times 57912614113275649087721$	(7, 4, 2), (46, 45, 1)
84	$F(42) \times 5 \times 13 \times 29 \times 113 \times 1429 \times 14449$	(13), (8, 7, 5, 3, 1)
85	$31 \times 131071 \times 9520972806333758431$	(8, 2, 1), (28, 27, 1)
86	$F(43) \times 3 \times 2932031007403$	(6, 5, 2), (13, 12, 1)
87	$F(29) \times 7 \times 4177 \times 9857737155463$	(13), (7, 5, 1)
88	$F(44) \times 17 \times 353 \times 2931542417$	(72, 71, 1), (8, 5, 4, 3, 1)
89	$618970019642690137449562111$	(38), (6, 5, 3)
90	$F(45) \times 3^3 \times 11 \times 19 \times 331 \times 18837001$	(5, 3, 2), (19, 18, 1)
91	$127 \times 911 \times 8191 \times 112901153 \times 23140471537$	(84, 83, 1), (7, 6, 5, 3, 2)
92	$F(46) \times 5 \times 277 \times 1013 \times 1657 \times 30269$	(6, 5, 2), (13, 12, 1)
93	$F(31) \times 7 \times 658812288653553079$	(2)
94	$F(47) \times 3 \times 283 \times 165768537521$	(21), (6, 5, 1)
95	$31 \times 191 \times 524287 \times 420778751 \times 30327152671$	(11), (17), (6, 5, 4, 2, 1)
96	$F(48) \times 193 \times 65537 \times 22253377$	(49, 47, 2), (7, 6, 4, 3, 2)
97	$11447 \times 13842607235828485645766393$	(6), (12), (33), (34)
98	$F(49) \times 3 \times 43 \times 4363953127297$	(11), (27), (7, 4, 3, 2, 1)
99	$F(33) \times 73 \times 199 \times 153649 \times 33057806959$	(7, 5, 4), (47, 45, 2)
100	$F(50) \times 5^3 \times 41 \times 101 \times 8101 \times 268501$	(37), (8, 7, 2)
101	$7432339208719 \times 341117531003194129$	(7, 6, 1)
102	$F(51) \times 3^2 \times 307 \times 2857 \times 6529 \times 43691$	(77, 76, 1)
103	$2550183799 \times 3976656429941438590393$	(9), (13), (30), (31)
104	$F(52) \times 17 \times 858001 \times 308761441$	(11, 10, 1)
105	$F(35) \times 7^2 \times 151 \times 337 \times 29191 \times 106681 \times 152041$	(16), (17), (37), (43), (52)
106	$F(53) \times 3 \times 107 \times 28059810762433$	(15)
107	$162259276829213363391578010288127$	(65, 63, 2), (7, 5, 3, 2, 1)
108	$F(54) \times 5 \times 13 \times 37 \times 109 \times 246241 \times 279073$	(31)
109	$745988807 \times 870035986098720987332873$	(7, 6, 1)
110	$F(55) \times 3 \times 11^2 \times 683 \times 2971 \times 48912491$	(13, 12, 1)
111	$F(37) \times 7 \times 321679 \times 26295457 \times 319020217$	(10), (49)
112	$F(56) \times 257 \times 5153 \times 54410972897$	(45, 43, 2)
113	$3391 \times 23279 \times 65993 \times 1868569 \times 1066818132868207$	(9), (15), (30)
114	$F(57) \times 3^2 \times 571 \times 174763 \times 160465489$	(82, 81, 1)
115	$31 \times 47 \times 14951 \times 178481 \times 4036961 \times 2646507710984041$	(15, 14, 1)
116	$F(58) \times 5 \times 107367629 \times 536903681$	(71, 70, 1)
117	$F(39) \times 73 \times 937 \times 6553 \times 86113 \times 7830118297$	(20, 18, 2)
118	$F(59) \times 3 \times 2833 \times 37171 \times 1824726041$	(33), (45)
119	$127 \times 239 \times 20231 \times 131071 \times 62983048367 \times 131105292137$	(8), (38)
120	$F(60) \times 17 \times 241 \times 61681 \times 4562284561$	(118, 111, 7)

REFERENCES

[1] H. Reisel, *En bok om primtal*, Odense, Denmark: Studentlitteratur, 1968.

[2] W. Peterson and E. Weldon, *Error-Correcting Codes*. Cambridge, MA: MIT Press, 1972.

[3] E. Watson, "Primitive polynomials (mod 2)," *Math. Comp.*, vol. 16, 1962, pp. 368–369.

[4] W. Stahnke, "Primitive binary polynomials," *Math. Comp.*, vol. 27, Oct. 1973, pp 977–980.

[5] N. Zierler and J. Brillhart, "On primitive trinomials (mod 2)," *Inform. Contr.*, vol. 13, Dec. 1968, pp. 541–554.

[6] N. Zierler and J. Brillhart, "On primitive trinomials (mod 2), II," *Inform. Contr.*, vol. 14, June 1969, pp. 566–569.

[7] N. Zierler, "Primitive trinomials whose degree is a Mersenne exponent," *Inform. Contr.*, vol. 15, July 1969, pp. 67–69.

[8] R. Lidl and H. Niederreiter, *Finite Fields*, Reading, MA: Addison-Wesley, 1983.

[9] J. Brillhart, D. Lehmer, J. Selfridge, B. Tuckerman, and S. Wagstaff, Jr., *Factorizations of* $b^n \pm 1$. Providence, RI: American Mathematical Society, volume 22 in Contemporary Mathematics Series, 1983.

Part 2

CLASSICAL SPREAD-SPECTRUM COMMUNICATIONS

Chapter 1

COHERENT DIRECT-SEQUENCE SYSTEMS

In its most general form a direct-sequence spread anti-jam communication system takes a binary data sequence and multiplies it by a higher rate pseudorandom (PN) binary sequence. The result is a binary sequence at the PN binary sequence rate which is then modulated. Compared to the usual modulation of the data, the data multiplied by the PN sequence causes the modulated signal spectrum to spread by a factor of N, the ratio of the PN sequence bit rate to the data bit rate. Such systems have been discussed in recent books and proceedings on spread-spectrum communications [1]–[11] and in tutorial papers [12]–[19]. Clark and Cain [9] provide the most complete discussion.

Figure 1.1 illustrates the general direct-sequence spread modulation. The data waveform is given by

$$\begin{aligned} d(t) &= d_n, \qquad nT_b \le t < (n+1)T_b \\ d_n &\in \{-1, 1\} \\ n &= \text{integer} \end{aligned} \tag{1.1}$$

where $\{d_n\}$ is the data sequence. The PN binary waveform is

$$\begin{aligned} c(t) &= c_k, \qquad kT_c \le t < (k+1)T_c \\ c_k &\in \{-1, 1\} \\ k &= \text{integer} \end{aligned} \tag{1.2}$$

where $\{c_k\}$ is the PN sequence. Here,

$$N = \frac{T_b}{T_c} \tag{1.3}$$

is the signal spectrum-spreading factor. Typically, N is on the order of 1000 or more. T_b is the bit time and T_c is referred to as the "chip" time interval.

In the above multiplication of the data and the PN binary sequence, it is important that the data clock and the PN sequence clock are coincident [12]. That is, the data transition times must be at the transition time of a PN

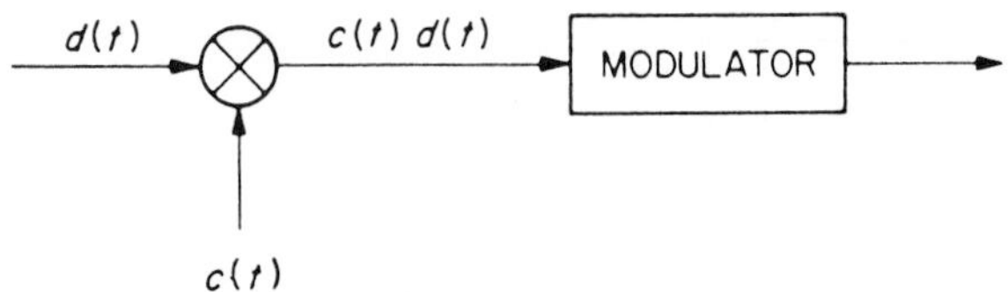

Figure 1.1. Direct-sequence modulation.

sequence binary symbol. Figure 1.2 shows examples of data multiplied by a PN sequence for $N = 10$ where in (a) we do not have coincidence of the two sequence clocks. The problem here is that it may be possible for anyone to read the data directly from a clean copy of the multiplied binary sequence even when the PN sequence is unknown. One can first estimate the PN sequence clock (see (c)) and then determine unscheduled transitions (solid arrows in Figure 1.2(a)) in the sequence which must be due to the data. In (b) we show coincident data and PN sequence clocks where it is impossible to read the data without knowledge of the PN sequence. In (c) we show the clock times for the PN sequence.

In this book it is assumed that the data clock is divided down from the PN sequence clock so that possible transition times in the data line up with transition times of the PN sequence and no unscheduled transitions occur. Systems which have coincident data and PN sequence clocks are often said to have a data "privacy" feature since the data is hidden by the PN sequence.

The most common data modulation is coherent binary phase-shift-keying (BPSK) for direct-sequence spread systems. This coherent direct-sequence

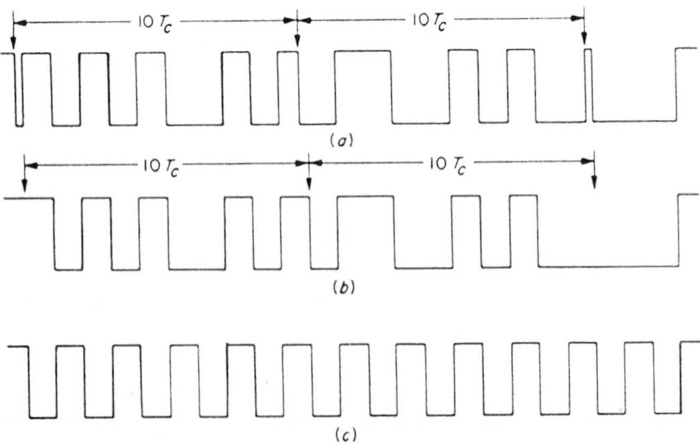

Figure 1.2. Data times PN sequence with (a) no coincident, (b) coincident, and (c) PN clocks.

system is the one considered in this chapter. At the receiver ideal chip and phase synchronization is assumed. Acquisition and synchronization techniques are considered in Part 4.

1.1 DIRECT-SEQUENCE SPREAD COHERENT BINARY PHASE-SHIFT-KEYING

The simplest form of direct-sequence spread-spectrum communication systems uses coherent binary phase-shift-keying (BPSK) data modulation and binary PN modulation. However, the most common form employs BPSK data modulation and quaternary phase-shift-keying (QPSK) PN modulation. This has some potential advantage against a single tone jammer at the transmitted signal carrier frequency. It forces the jammer power to be evenly distributed over the cosine and sine signal coordinates.

Section 3.4 of Chapter 3, Part 1, describes the uncoded direct-sequence spread binary phase-shift-keying (DS/BPSK) signal which is given by

$$\begin{aligned} x(t) &= c(t)\,d(t)\sqrt{2S}\cos\omega_0 t \\ &= c(t)s(t) \end{aligned} \tag{1.4}$$

where

$$s(t) = d(t)\sqrt{2S}\cos\omega_0 t \tag{1.5}$$

is the unspread BPSK signal. Defining T_b as the data bit time interval and T_c as the PN sequence bit time interval, $s(t)$ has a $\sin^2 x/x^2$ spectrum of bandwidth roughly $1/T_b$ while the spread-spectrum signal $x(t)$ has a similar-shaped spectrum but of bandwidth roughly

$$W_{ss} = 1/T_c. \tag{1.6}$$

The processing gain is

$$\begin{aligned} \text{PG} &= \frac{W_{ss}}{R_b} \\ &= \frac{T_b}{T_c} \\ &= N. \end{aligned} \tag{1.7}$$

The jamming signal is represented by $J(t)$ and in the absence of noise (assume the jammer limits performance) the signal at the receiver is

$$x(t) + J(t). \tag{1.8}$$

The receiver multiplies this by the PN waveform to obtain the signal[1]

$$\begin{aligned} r(t) &= c(t)[x(t) + J(t)] \\ &= s(t) + c(t)J(t) \end{aligned} \tag{1.9}$$

---

[1] Perfect chip synchronization is assumed for the intended receiver. Chip sequence acquisition and synchronization techniques are presented in Chapters 1 and 2, Part 4.

since

$$c^2(t) = 1. \tag{1.10}$$

Here $c(t)J(t)$ is the effective noise waveform due to jamming.

The conventional BPSK detector (see Figure 3.6 of Chapter 3, Part 1) output is thus

$$r = d\sqrt{E_b} + n \tag{1.11}$$

where d is the data bit for the T_b second interval, $E_b = ST_b$ is the bit energy, and n is the equivalent noise component given by

$$n = \sqrt{\frac{2}{T_b}} \int_0^{T_b} c(t)J(t)\cos\omega_0 t\,dt. \tag{1.12}$$

For QPSK modulation the inphase and quadrature data waveforms are denoted $d_c(t)$ and $d_s(t)$, respectively, and corresponding PN binary waveforms are $c_c(t)$ and $c_s(t)$. These form a QPSK signal

$$x(t) = c_c(t)d_c(t)\sqrt{S}\cos\omega_0 t + c_s(t)d_s(t)\sqrt{S}\sin\omega_0 t \tag{1.13}$$

where each QPSK pulse is of duration $T_s = 2T_b$. The channel output waveform given by (1.8) is multiplied by $\sqrt{2/T_s}\,c_c(t)\cos\omega_0 t$ and integrated over T_s seconds to obtain the inphase component

$$r_c = d_c\sqrt{E_b} + n_c \tag{1.14}$$

where

$$n_c = \sqrt{\frac{2}{T_s}} \int_0^{T_s} c_c(t)J(t)\cos\omega_0 t\,dt. \tag{1.15}$$

Here we assume that[2]

$$\int_\tau^{\tau+T_c} \cos\omega_0 t\sin\omega_0 t\,dt = 0 \tag{1.16}$$

for all τ where T_c is the "chip" time interval for both PN sequences. Similar results hold for the quadrature component

$$r_s = d_s\sqrt{E_b} + n_s \tag{1.17}$$

where

$$n_s = \sqrt{\frac{2}{T_s}} \int_0^{T_s} c_s(t)J(t)\sin\omega_0 t\,dt. \tag{1.18}$$

Thus, as in the conventional case, QPSK modulation can be viewed as two independent BPSK modulations each at half the data rate.

---

[2] This is the usual assumption that inphase and quadrature signal components are orthogonal. Perfect phase synchronization is assumed for the receiver. Orthogonality is approximately true for the weaker condition $W_{ss} < f_0 = \omega_0/2\pi$.

1.2 UNCODED BIT ERROR PROBABILITY FOR ARBITRARY JAMMER WAVEFORMS

Without coding, the BPSK detector decision rule is to decide $\hat{d}$ is the data bit where

$$\hat{d} = \begin{cases} 1, & \text{if } r \geq 0 \\ -1, & \text{if } r < 0 \end{cases} \tag{1.19}$$

The bit error probability is thus

$$\begin{aligned} P_b &= \Pr\{r \geq 0 | d = -1\} \\ &= \Pr\left\{n \geq \sqrt{E_b}\right\}. \end{aligned} \tag{1.20}$$

Naturally, this bit error probability depends on the random variable n given by (1.12). For QPSK the same decision rule (1.19) can be applied to r_c and r_s to obtain $\hat{d}_c$ and $\hat{d}_s$. This results in the same bit error probability expression (1.20) with n_c and n_s replacing n.

For BPSK modulation the noise component given by (1.12) has the form

$$\begin{aligned} n &= \sqrt{\frac{2}{T_b}} \sum_{k=0}^{N-1} \int_{kT_c}^{(k+1)T_c} c(t) J(t) \cos \omega_0 t \, dt \\ &= \sqrt{\frac{2}{T_b}} \sum_{k=0}^{N-1} c_k \int_{kT_c}^{(k+1)T_c} J(t) \cos \omega_0 t \, dt \end{aligned} \tag{1.21}$$

where $c_0, c_1, \ldots, c_{N-1}$ are the N PN bits occurring during the data bit time interval. Defining the jamming component

$$J_k = \sqrt{\frac{2}{T_c}} \int_{kT_c}^{(k+1)T_c} J(t) \cos \omega_0 t \, dt \tag{1.22}$$

we have

$$n = \sqrt{\frac{1}{N}} \sum_{k=0}^{N-1} c_k J_k \tag{1.23}$$

as the final form for the noise component.

The PN sequence is approximated as an independent identically distributed binary sequence where

$$\Pr\{c_k = 1\} = \Pr\{c_k = -1\} = \tfrac{1}{2}. \tag{1.24}$$

Then for any fixed jammer sequence

$$\boldsymbol{J} = (J_0, J_1, \ldots, J_{N-1}) \tag{1.25}$$

the noise component given by (1.23) is a sum of independent random variables. We next examine ways of evaluating the conditional bit error probability

$$P_b(\boldsymbol{J}) = \Pr\left\{n \geq \sqrt{E_b} \middle| \boldsymbol{J}\right\} \tag{1.26}$$

for given jammer components $\boldsymbol{J}$. The final bit error probability may be in terms of a parameter set characterizing a deterministic jammer model or a statistical characterization of the jammer with evaluation of the overall average bit error probability by

$$P_b = E\{P_b(\boldsymbol{J})\} \tag{1.27}$$

where the expectation is over the jammer statistics.

1.2.1 Chernoff Bound

For a given jammer coordinate sequence $\boldsymbol{J}$ fixed consider the Chernoff bound to the bit error probability of (1.26) as follows:

$$\begin{aligned}
P_b(\boldsymbol{J}) &= \Pr\left\{n \geq \sqrt{E_b} \middle| \boldsymbol{J}\right\} \\
&= \Pr\left\{n - \sqrt{E_b} \geq 0 \middle| \boldsymbol{J}\right\} \\
&\leq E\left\{e^{\lambda[n-\sqrt{E_b}]} \middle| \boldsymbol{J}\right\} \\
&= e^{-\lambda\sqrt{E_b}} E\left\{\exp\left[\lambda\sqrt{\frac{1}{N}} \sum_{k=0}^{N-1} c_k J_k\right] \middle| \boldsymbol{J}\right\} \\
&= e^{-\lambda\sqrt{E_b}} \prod_{k=0}^{N-1} E\left\{\exp\left[\lambda\sqrt{\frac{1}{N}} c_k J_k\right] \middle| J_k\right\} \\
&= e^{-\lambda\sqrt{E_b}} \prod_{k=0}^{N-1} \left\{\tfrac{1}{2}e^{\lambda\sqrt{1/N}J_k} + \tfrac{1}{2}e^{-\lambda\sqrt{1/N}J_k}\right\} \\
&= e^{-\lambda\sqrt{E_b}} \prod_{k=0}^{N-1} \cosh\left(\frac{\lambda J_k}{\sqrt{N}}\right)
\end{aligned} \tag{1.28}$$

for any $\lambda \geq 0$. Next, following the approach of Kullstam [20], [21], use the inequality

$$\cosh x \leq e^{x^2/2} \tag{1.29}$$

to obtain the form

$$P_b(\boldsymbol{J}) \leq e^{-\lambda\sqrt{E_b}} e^{(\lambda^2/2N)\sum_{k=0}^{N-1} J_k^2}. \tag{1.30}$$

The $\lambda \geq 0$ that minimizes this Chernoff bound is

$$\lambda^* = \sqrt{E_b} \bigg/ \left(\frac{1}{N} \sum_{k=0}^{N-1} J_k^2\right) \tag{1.31}$$

giving the result

$$P_b(\boldsymbol{J}) \leq \exp\left\{-E_b \bigg/ \left(\frac{2}{N} \sum_{k=0}^{N-1} J_k^2\right)\right\}. \tag{1.32}$$

In addition, note that a factor of 1/2 can be applied[3] to the above Chernoff bound (see Appendix 4B, Chapter 4, Part 1). The final Chernoff bound is then

$$P_b(\boldsymbol{J}) \le \frac{1}{2}\exp\left\{-E_b\bigg/\left(\frac{2}{N}\sum_{k=0}^{N-1} J_k^2\right)\right\}. \tag{1.33}$$

This bound applies for all N and $\boldsymbol{J}$ and only assumes the PN sequence $\{c_k\}$ is an i.i.d sequence of binary symbols equally likely to be 1 or -1.

1.2.2 Gaussian Assumption

The Central Limit Theorem [22] states that the normalized sum of independent random variables approaches (in distribution) a Gaussian random variable as the number of terms increases. This basically applies to cases where the variances of the terms are more or less evenly distributed over some bounded range. For fixed $\boldsymbol{J}$ the Gaussian assumption means n is a Gaussian random variable with zero mean since for each k

$$\begin{aligned} E\{c_k J_k | J_k\} &= \tfrac{1}{2}J_k - \tfrac{1}{2}J_k \\ &= 0, \end{aligned} \tag{1.34}$$

and variance given by

$$\mathrm{Var}\{n|\boldsymbol{J}\} = \frac{1}{N}\sum_{k=0}^{N-1} J_k^2. \tag{1.35}$$

The conditional bit error probability is then

$$P_b(\boldsymbol{J}) = Q\left(\sqrt{E_b\bigg/\left(\frac{1}{N}\sum_{k=0}^{N-1} J_k^2\right)}\right). \tag{1.36}$$

This approximation to the conditional bit error probability applies for large values of N, which is typically the case with direct-sequence spread systems.

Using the inequality

$$Q(x) \le \frac{1}{2}e^{-x^2/2}, \qquad x \ge 0 \tag{1.37}$$

we have

$$P_b(\boldsymbol{J}) \le \frac{1}{2}\exp\left\{-E_b\bigg/\left(\frac{2}{N}\sum_{k=0}^{N-1} J_k^2\right)\right\}. \tag{1.38}$$

This inequality shows that in applying the Chernoff bound *assuming* n is a Gaussian random variable, we obtain exactly the same result as the general Chernoff bound derived in the previous section where no Gaussian assump-

[3]Although this factor of 1/2 does not always apply in theory, it is a realistic approximation for all practical cases of interest.

tions were made. *Thus, the Gaussian assumption results in a bit error probability that is appropriate for direct-sequence spread systems for any spread factor N.*

1.3 UNCODED BIT ERROR PROBABILITY FOR SPECIFIC JAMMER WAVEFORMS

Consider the set of orthonormal basis

$$\phi_k(t) = \begin{cases} \sqrt{\dfrac{2}{T_c}} \cos \omega_0 t, & kT_c \le t < (k+1)T_c \\ 0, & \text{elsewhere} \end{cases}$$

$$\tilde{\phi}_k(t) = \begin{cases} \sqrt{\dfrac{2}{T_c}} \sin \omega_0 t, & kT_c \le t < (k+1)T_c \\ 0, & \text{elsewhere} \end{cases}$$

$$k = 0, 1, \ldots, N-1. \tag{1.39}$$

The transmitted direct-sequence spread BPSK signal during the data bit time interval $[0, T_b]$ has the form

$$\begin{aligned} x(t) &= c(t)\, d(t) \sqrt{2S} \cos \omega_0 t \\ &= d \sqrt{ST_c} \sum_{k=0}^{N-1} c_k \phi_k(t) \\ &\qquad 0 \le t \le T_b. \end{aligned} \tag{1.40}$$

The jammer would like to place all of its signal energy into the same signal space as the transmitted signal, otherwise its power would be wasted. It, however, can only know the signal bandwidth and not the signal phase. Thus, in general it has the form

$$J(t) = \sum_{k=0}^{N-1} J_k \phi_k(t) + \sum_{k=0}^{N-1} \tilde{J}_k \tilde{\phi}_k(t) \tag{1.41}$$

where recall $\boldsymbol{J} = (J_0, J_1, \ldots, J_{N-1})$ consists of the cosine components. Note that only these cosine components enter into the bit error probability bound. The total jammer signal energy during the data bit time is

$$\begin{aligned} JT_b &= \int_0^{T_b} J^2(t)\, dt \\ &= \sum_{k=0}^{N-1} J_k^2 + \sum_{k=0}^{N-1} \tilde{J}_k^2 \end{aligned} \tag{1.42}$$

or

$$N_J = \frac{1}{N} \sum_{k=0}^{N-1} J_k^2 + \frac{1}{N} \sum_{k=0}^{N-1} \tilde{J}_k^2. \tag{1.43}$$

The worst case jammer is one that places all its energy in the cosine coordinates so that

$$\sum_{k=0}^{N-1} J_k^2 = JT_b. \tag{1.44}$$

Normally, however, the jammer can only place equal energy in the cosine and sine coordinates with the result that

$$\sum_{k=0}^{N-1} J_k^2 = \frac{JT_b}{2}. \tag{1.45}$$

Figure 1.3 shows the bit error probability for the Gaussian assumption and

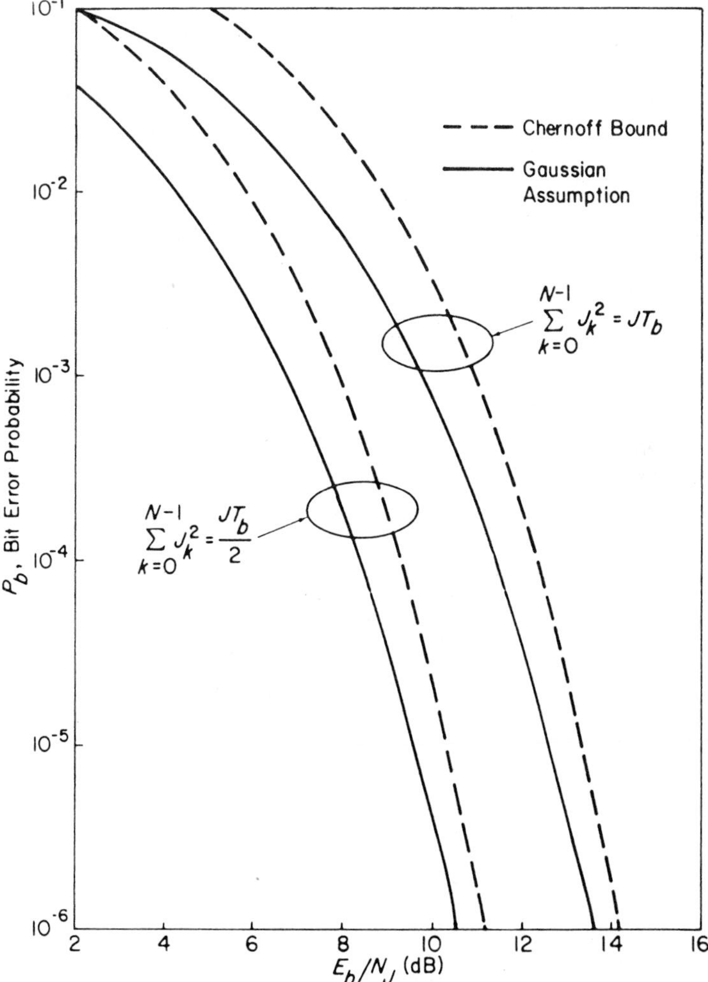

Figure 1.3. Gaussian assumption and Chernoff bound.

the general Chernoff bound for these two cases. Note that there is only about a one dB difference for fixed bit error rates. This suggests that the Gaussian assumption is reasonable for all N.

The impact of jamming signals by characterizing two types of jammers will now be illustrated. The first model assumes a deterministic jammer waveform that is characterized by a set of parameters $\boldsymbol{\theta}$. The second model assumes the jammer is a stationary random process with statistical characterizations. In both cases the jammer is assumed to be transmitting continuously with constant power J. In the next section pulse jamming will be examined along with its generalization where the jammer power can be varied in time while maintaining a time-averaged power J.

1.3.1 CW Jammer

The most harmful jammer waveform is one that maximizes J_k given by (1.22) for each value of k. Since the jammer does not know the PN sequence $\{c_k\}$ this means the jammer should place as much energy as possible in the cosine coordinate which is achieved with a CW signal. Generally, the jammer may not know the transmitted signal carrier phase so consider the deterministic jammer waveform model

$$J(t) = \sqrt{2J}\cos[\omega_0 t + \theta] \tag{1.46}$$

which is characterized by the phase parameter θ. Thus

$$J_k = \sqrt{JT_c}\cos\theta, \quad \text{all } k \tag{1.47}$$

which is maximized when $\theta = 0$.

For this CW jammer the conditional variance of n given in (1.35) is

$$\mathrm{Var}\{n|\boldsymbol{J}\} = JT_c\cos^2\theta. \tag{1.48}$$

For the Gaussian approximation (Central Limit Theorem applied for large $N = T_b/T_c$) the conditional bit error probability is

$$\begin{aligned} P_b(\theta) &= P_b(\boldsymbol{J}) \\ &= Q\left(\sqrt{\frac{E_b}{JT_c\cos^2\theta}}\right). \end{aligned} \tag{1.49}$$

Using $JT_c = N_J$ this becomes

$$P_b(\theta) = Q\left(\sqrt{\frac{E_b}{N_J\cos^2\theta}}\right) \tag{1.50}$$

for the CW jammer. The choice of $\theta = 0$ maximizes $P_b(\theta)$ yielding the bound

$$P_b(\theta) \le Q\left(\sqrt{\frac{E_b}{N_J}}\right). \tag{1.51}$$

This upper bound is the same as that for binary orthogonal signals in an additive white Gaussian noise channel of single-sided spectral density N_J. For a jammer with constant power J this is the worst performance of the direct-sequence spread BPSK system.

Against a CW jammer an effective technique is to use BPSK data modulation with QPSK PN spreading. This is a DS/BPSK signal of the form

$$x(t) = d(t)\sqrt{S}\left[c_c(t)\cos\omega_0 t + c_s(t)\sin\omega_0 t\right] \tag{1.52}$$

where $c_c(t)$ and $c_s(t)$ are PN waveforms. This is the special case of $d_c = d_s = d$ in the QPSK modulation given in (1.13) where the QPSK symbol energy is also the bit energy (one bit per QPSK signal). For this case (1.14) and (1.17) have the form

$$r_c = d\sqrt{E_b/2} + n_c \tag{1.53}$$

and

$$r_s = d\sqrt{E_b/2} + n_s \tag{1.54}$$

where n_c and n_s are zero mean independent with conditional variances

$$\mathrm{Var}\{n_c|\theta\} = JT_c\cos^2\theta \tag{1.55}$$

and

$$\mathrm{Var}\{n_s|\theta\} = JT_c\sin^2\theta. \tag{1.56}$$

Next use

$$r = \frac{r_c + r_s}{2} = d\sqrt{E_b/2} + \frac{n_c + n_s}{2} \tag{1.57}$$

as the statistic for the decision rule given in (1.19). Since

$$\begin{aligned}\mathrm{Var}\left\{\left.\frac{n_c + n_s}{2}\right|\theta\right\} &= \frac{1}{4}\{JT_c\cos^2\theta + JT_c\sin^2\theta\} \\ &= \frac{JT_c}{4},\end{aligned} \tag{1.58}$$

the bit error probability for the Gaussian approximation is

$$P_b(\theta) = Q\left(\sqrt{\frac{2E_b}{N_J}}\right). \tag{1.59}$$

This is independent of θ and is a 3 dB improvement over the worst case ($\theta = 0$) BPSK PN spreading system. Thus, to minimize the maximum possible degradation due to a CW jammer, one should use QPSK modulation with the same data in both inphase and quadrature coordinates. (For further discussion on this see Kullstam [20].)

1.3.2 Random Jammer

Consider next characterizing the jammer as a stationary random process with autocorrelation

$$R_J(\tau) = E\{J(t+\tau)J(t)\} \tag{1.60}$$

and power spectral density

$$S_J(f) = \int_{-\infty}^{\infty} R_J(\tau)e^{-j2\pi f\tau}\,d\tau \tag{1.61}$$

where

$$\int_{-\infty}^{\infty} S_J(f)\,df = J, \tag{1.62}$$

the constant power of the jammer.

The PN waveform $c(t)$ is also stationary (introduce a uniformly distributed time shift) with autocorrelation

$$R_c(\tau) = E\{c(t+\tau)c(t)\} = \begin{cases} 1 - \dfrac{|\tau|}{T_c}, & |\tau| \le T_c \\ 0, & |\tau| > T_c \end{cases} \tag{1.63}$$

and power spectral density

$$S_c(f) = \int_{-\infty}^{\infty} R_c(\tau)e^{-j2\pi f\tau}\,d\tau. \tag{1.64}$$

Naturally, $J(t)$ and $c(t)$ are independent of each other.

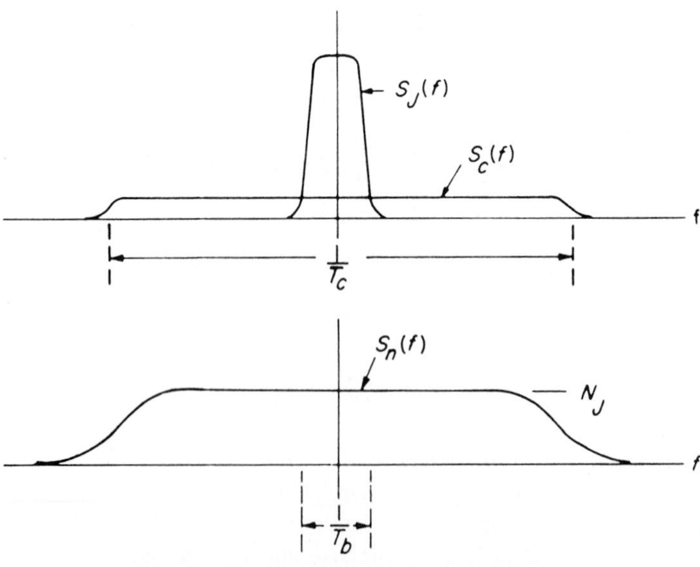

Figure 1.4. Power spectral densities.

Recall from (1.9) that when received waveform $x(t) + J(t)$ is multiplied by the PN waveform $c(t)$, the resulting noise term is

$$n(t) = c(t)J(t). \tag{1.65}$$

Since $J(t)$ and $c(t)$ are independent, the autocorrelation of $n(t)$ is

$$\begin{aligned} R_n(\tau) &= E\{n(t+\tau)n(t)\} \\ &= E\{c(t+\tau)c(t)\}E\{J(t+\tau)J(t)\} \\ &= R_c(\tau)R_J(\tau), \end{aligned} \tag{1.66}$$

which has the power spectral density

$$S_n(f) = S_c(f) * S_J(f) \tag{1.67}$$

where $*$ indicates the convolution operation.

Figure 1.4 illustrates the power spectra of $c(t)$, $J(t)$, and the product $n(t) = c(t)J(t)$. Here $S_J(f)$ is arbitrary and $S_c(f)$ is a broad $\sin^2 x/x^2$ spectrum of bandwidth roughly $1/T_c$. The resulting noise spectrum $S_n(f)$ has value at $f = 0$ given by

$$\begin{aligned} S_n(0) &= \int_{-\infty}^{\infty} S_c(f)S_J(f)\,df \\ &\le S_c(0)\int_{-\infty}^{\infty} S_J(f)\,df \\ &= S_c(0)J \end{aligned} \tag{1.68}$$

since

$$S_c(f) \le S_c(0) \tag{1.69}$$

and J is the total jammer power given by (1.62). There is equality in (1.68) when $J(t)$ has a narrow power density spectrum compared to the PN waveform $c(t)$. In addition

$$\begin{aligned} S_c(0) &= \int_{-\infty}^{\infty} R_c(\tau)\,d\tau \\ &= \int_{-T_c}^{T_c}\left(1 - \frac{|\tau|}{T_c}\right)d\tau \\ &= T_c. \end{aligned} \tag{1.70}$$

Thus

$$\begin{aligned} S_n(0) &\le JT_c \\ &= N_J \end{aligned} \tag{1.71}$$

where W_{ss} is given by (1.6) and N_J is our usual definition given as J/W_{ss}.

Note that the equivalent noise of power spectral density bounded by N_J represents the total interference power. If we were to divide this power equally between the sine and cosine coordinates of the narrowband (unspread) signal, then each coordinate would have a noise component of variance less than or equal to $N_J/2$. With BPSK data modulation and QPSK PN spreading, equal distribution of the jammer power is guaranteed. In this case the jammer appears as white noise of power spectral density bounded by $N_J/2$.

Multiplying the channel output signal by the PN waveform results in the narrowband signal $s(t)$ in broadband noise $n(t)$. Here $s(t)$ has bandwidth $1/T_b$ while $n(t)$ has bandwidth greater than $W_{ss} = 1/T_c = N/T_b$ which is N times wider than the signal bandwidth. Since $S_n(f)$ is essentially flat over the narrowband signal bandwidth, the detection problem reduces to demodulation of a BPSK signal in white noise of double-sided power spectral density less than or equal to $N_J/2$. Thus, making the Gaussian approximation, the uncoded bit error probability is bounded by

$$P_b \leq Q\left(\sqrt{\frac{2E_b}{N_J}}\right). \tag{1.72}$$

Here equality is achieved for narrowband jamming signals. This gives the same result as with a CW jammer and QPSK modulation where the same data is entered in both the inphase and quadrature components (BPSK data modulation with QPSK PN spreading). It also is the baseline performance where the jammer simply transmits broadband Gaussian noise.

Based on these results for CW and random jammers, we would expect the direct-sequence BPSK anti-jam systems to be robust and insensitive to all jammers that produce waveforms which are independent of the transmission. They appear to always give as good a performance as the baseline jammer case and that is all one can expect from a good anti-jam communication system. This, however, is true only for constant power jammers.

1.4 PULSE JAMMING

Now consider the impact of pulse jamming and its generalization where the jammer can arbitrarily distribute its energy in time under a long time average power constraint. The worst time distribution of energy by the jammer is the two-level jammer corresponding to pulse jamming. This distribution results in considerable degradation to the uncoded DS/BPSK system.

1.4.1 Arbitrary Time Distribution

Consider an arbitrary continuous time distribution of the jammer power which is approximated as having L discrete levels $\hat{J}_1, \hat{J}_2, \ldots, \hat{J}_L$ with corresponding fraction of time occurrences given by $\rho_1, \rho_2, \ldots, \rho_L$. Thus, assume that at any given time the jammer power is $\hat{J}_l$ with probability ρ_l for

$l = 1, 2, \ldots, L$ where

$$J = \sum_{l=1}^{L} \rho_l \hat{J}_l \tag{1.73}$$

is the average power constraint. Also during the transmission time of a data bit, T_b, the jammer power is assumed to be constant with value equal to one of the L levels. Thus compared to T_b, the jammer power is slowly varying. Even with faster jammer power time variations this assumption is reasonable, since the receiver correlates or integrates the received channel output signal over every T_b seconds.

It is convenient to define

$$\gamma_l = \rho_l \frac{\hat{J}_l}{J}; \quad l = 1, 2, \ldots, L \tag{1.74}$$

where the average power constraint (1.73) becomes

$$\sum_{l=1}^{L} \gamma_l = 1. \tag{1.75}$$

For a DS/BPSK system when the jammer is transmitting with power $\hat{J}_l$ the uncoded bit error bound is analogous to (1.36)

$$\begin{aligned} P_b(\hat{J}_l) &\le Q\left(\sqrt{\frac{2E_b W_{ss}}{\hat{J}_l}}\right) \\ &= Q\left(\sqrt{\frac{2\rho_l E_b}{\gamma_l N_J}}\right). \end{aligned} \tag{1.76}$$

For CW jamming assume the same data is sent in both the inphase and quadrature components of a direct-sequence spread QPSK system. Next, using the inequality (1.37) we obtain

$$P_b(\hat{J}_l) \le \tfrac{1}{2} e^{-\rho_l E_b/(\gamma_l N_J)} \tag{1.77}$$

and the average uncoded bit error rate bound

$$\begin{aligned} P_b &= \sum_{l=1}^{L} \rho_l P_b(\hat{J}_l) \\ &\le \tfrac{1}{2} \sum_{l=1}^{L} \rho_l e^{-\rho_l E_b/(\gamma_l N_J)}. \end{aligned} \tag{1.78}$$

Using the inequality

$$\rho e^{-\rho A} \le \max_{\rho'} \rho' e^{-\rho' A} = \frac{e^{-1}}{A} \tag{1.79}$$

(1.78) is further bounded by

$$P_b \le \frac{1}{2} \sum_{l=1}^{L} \gamma_l \frac{e^{-1}}{(E_b/N_J)} \tag{1.80}$$

or

$$P_b \leq \frac{e^{-1}}{2(E_b/N_J)} \tag{1.81}$$

when constraint (1.75) is imposed.

The upper bound (1.81) can be achieved with two jammer power levels ($L = 2$) given by

$$\begin{aligned} \hat{J}_1 &= 0 \\ \hat{J}_2 &= J/\rho \end{aligned} \tag{1.82}$$

where

$$\begin{aligned} \rho_1 &= 1 - \rho \\ \rho_2 &= \rho \end{aligned} \tag{1.83}$$

and

$$\rho = \frac{1}{(E_b/N_J)} \tag{1.84}$$

provided

$$E_b/N_J > 1. \tag{1.85}$$

When (1.85) is not satisfied we have the special case of constant jammer power, i.e., $\rho = 1$.

1.4.2 Worst Case Jammer

The jammer time distribution of power that maximizes the bound on the uncoded bit error probability is the pulse jammer with peak power

$$J_{\text{peak}} = J(E_b/N_J) \tag{1.86}$$

for a fraction ρ of the time where ρ is given by (1.84). This is not necessarily the jammer that maximizes the true bit error probability. Assuming a narrowband pulse jammer (or CW pulse jammer at the carrier frequency) which is on a fraction ρ of the time, the exact uncoded bit error probability is

$$P_b(\rho) = \rho Q\left(\sqrt{2\rho(E_b/N_J)}\right). \tag{1.87}$$

The choice of ρ that maximizes (1.87) is

$$\rho^* = \begin{cases} \dfrac{0.709}{E_b/N_J}, & E_b/N_J > 0.709 \\ 1, & E_b/N_J \leq 0.709 \end{cases} \tag{1.88}$$

resulting in the bit error probability

$$P_b(\rho^*) = \begin{cases} \dfrac{0.083}{E_b/N_J}, & E_b/N_J > 0.709 \\ Q\left(\sqrt{\dfrac{2E_b}{N_J}}\right), & E_b/N_J \leq 0.709. \end{cases} \tag{1.89}$$

The worst jammer time distribution of power will result in a bit error probability P_b^* which satisfies

$$P_b(\rho^*) \le P_b^* \le \begin{cases} \dfrac{e^{-1}}{2(E_b/N_J)}, & E_b/N_J > 1 \\ \frac{1}{2}e^{-E_b/N_J}, & E_b/N_J \le 1. \end{cases} \tag{1.90}$$

Figure 1.5 shows the constant power bit error probability $Q(\sqrt{2E_b/N_J})$, its bound $(1/2)e^{-(E_b/N_J)}$, $P_b(\rho^*)$, and the bound given in (1.90). The cross-hatched region indicates the unknown bit error probability P_b^* of the worst case jammer with average power J. It is clear that pulse jamming can degrade the performance of uncoded DS/BPSK systems to a considerable

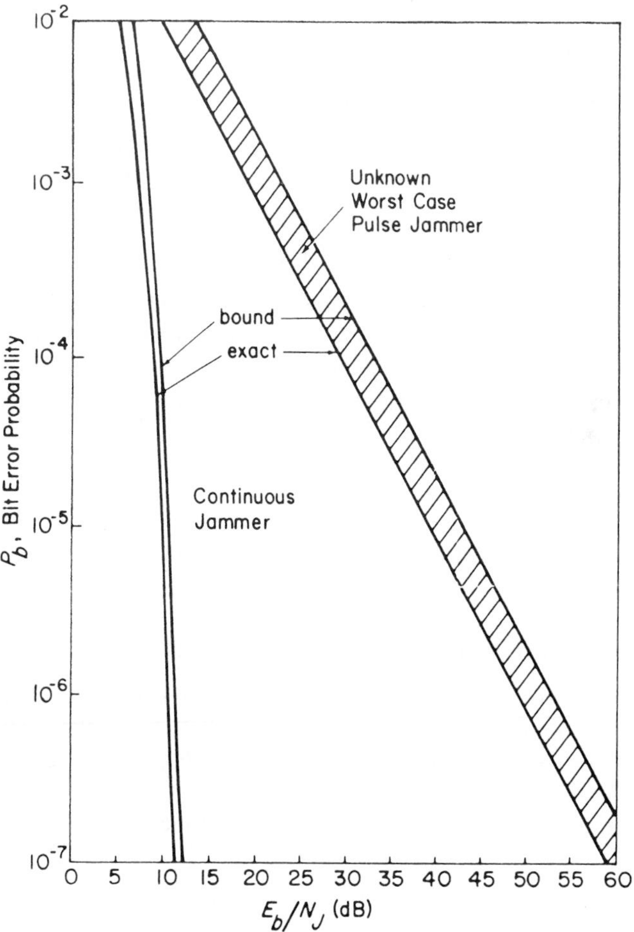

Figure 1.5. Pulse jamming DS/BPSK.

degree compared to the baseline jammer. At bit error probability of 10^{-6} there is approximately a 40 dB degradation due to pulse jamming. These jammers, however, can be effectively neutralized with coding and interleaving.

1.5 STANDARD CODES AND CUTOFF RATES

In Chapter 3, Part 1, the point was made that the use of coding with spread-spectrum systems does not require any reduction in data rate or increase in the spread-spectrum signal bandwidth. Even with simple repeat codes, the large degradation due to pulse jamming in DS/BPSK systems can be neutralized. With more powerful codes the pulse jammer neutralization plus additional coding gain can be achieved.

Recall that in the general coding analysis in Chapter 4, Part 1, the coded bit error bound was given in the form

$$P_b \le G(D) = B(R_0) \tag{1.91}$$

where $G(\cdot)$ and $B(\cdot)$ are functions specified by the particular code, while D and R_0 are parameters of the channel. For DS/BPSK systems, D and R_0 have the relationship

$$R_0 = 1 - \log_2(1 + D) \quad \text{bits/symbol} \tag{1.92}$$

where Figure 1.6 shows the general system block diagram. The system enclosed in dotted lines represents an equivalent binary input channel for which D and R_0 can be evaluated. In this case, a symbol entering the equivalent channel is a coded bit and the energy per coded bit (channel symbol) E_s is related to the energy per bit E_b by

$$E_s = RE_b \tag{1.93}$$

where R is the code rate in bits per channel symbol. Parameter D, and hence parameter R_0, depend on E_s/N_J, the symbol energy to equivalent jammer noise ratio.

1.5.1 The Additive White Gaussian Noise Channel

This section summarizes well-known results for standard coherent BPSK and QPSK modulations with some binary codes and the additive white Gaussian noise channel model. These results will serve as a reference for the DS/BPSK system with jamming.

For the additive white Gaussian noise channel R_0 is given by (1.92) where

$$D = e^{-E_s/N_0} \tag{1.94}$$

and N_0 is the single-sided noise spectral density. Coded bit error bounds of the form given by (1.91) are shown in Figure 1.7 for several binary codes.

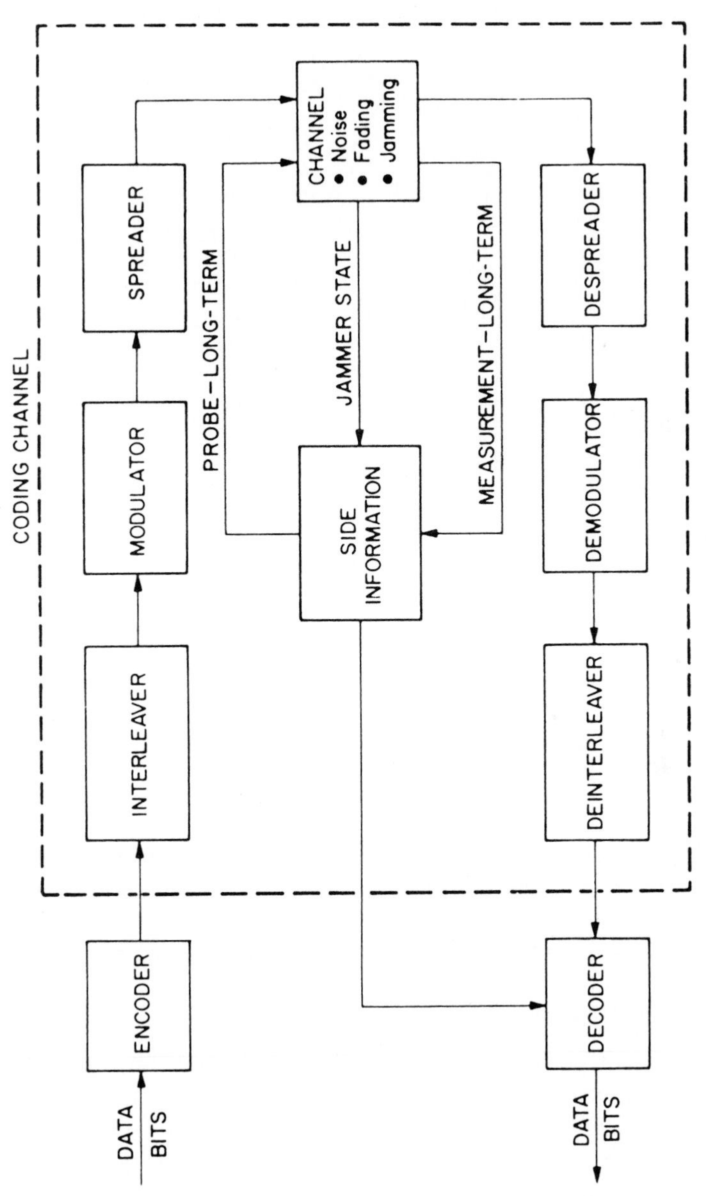

Figure 1.6. AJ system overview.

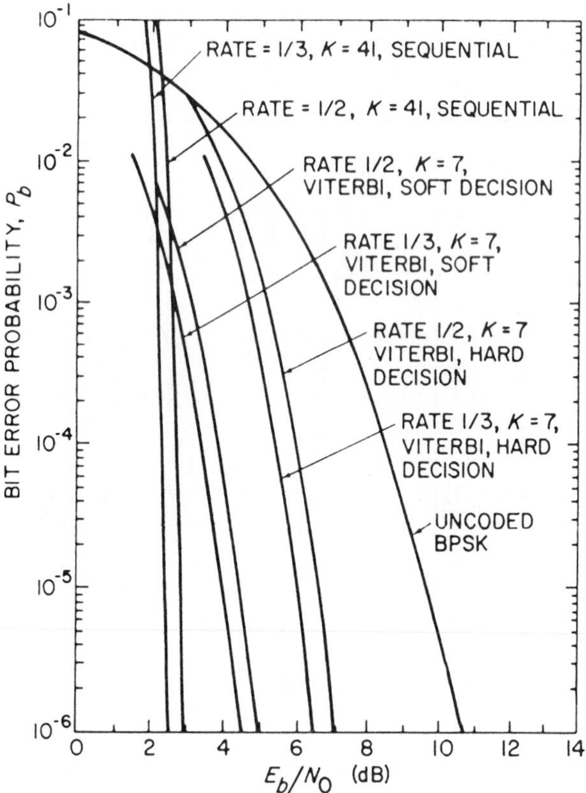

Figure 1.7. A comparison of the bit error probability performances of rate 1/2 and 1/3, hard and soft decision Viterbi and sequential decoders.

These curves serve as basic reference coded bit error probabilities from which we can derive coded performance for all other jamming channels. The only difference in the various jamming cases will be in the value of D and R_0 for each coded symbol to equivalent jammer noise ratio, E_b/N_J.

1.5.2 Jamming Channels

For the constant power jammer, regardless of the waveform used by the jammer, the bit error probability was bounded by the bit error probability of coherent BPSK modulation with the additive white Gaussian noise channel where $N_0 = N_J$, the equivalent jammer noise density. This assumes the Central Limit Theorem applies and in the case of CW jammers the system uses the same data in the inphase and quadrature coordinates of a direct-sequence spread QPSK modulation. In this case, the results for the additive white Gaussian noise channel shown in Figure 1.7 apply where E_b/N_0 is replaced by E_b/N_J.

The only remaining case of interest is when there is a pulse jammer that transmits pulses with power J/ρ for ρ fraction of the time. When the pulse is on, assume the jammer waveform is equivalent to additive white Gaussian noise with single-sided spectral density $N_0 = N_J/\rho$.

For pulse jamming, values of D are shown in Table 4.1 of Chapter 4, Part 1, for various cases of hard and soft decision metrics, which may or may not include jammer state information. These are all shown as a function of ρ. If for each of the four possible cases in Table 4.1, Part 1, the worst value of ρ that maximizes D is chosen, then the resulting values of the cutoff rates as a function of E_s/N_J are shown in Figure 1.8. Also shown here is the additive white Gaussian noise channel reference. For each case the worst case value of ρ is given in Figure 1.9.

To obtain the bit error bounds from standard error rate curves such as those shown in Figure 1.7 when there are worst case pulse jammers consider the constraint length $K = 7$, rate $R = 1/2$ convolutional code shown in Figure 1.7 for the additive white Gaussian noise channel with soft decision decoding. Suppose we wanted the bit error bound for this code with a hard decision decoder operating with no jammer state information and where the jammer is a worst case pulse jammer for this coded DS/BPSK system.

At 10^{-5} bit error probability, the $K = 7$, $R = 1/2$ convolutional code shown in Figure 1.7 requires

$$E_b/N_0 = 4.5 \text{ dB} \tag{1.95}$$

or since there is a rate $R = 1/2$ code, it requires

$$E_s/N_0 = 1.5 \text{ dB}. \tag{1.96}$$

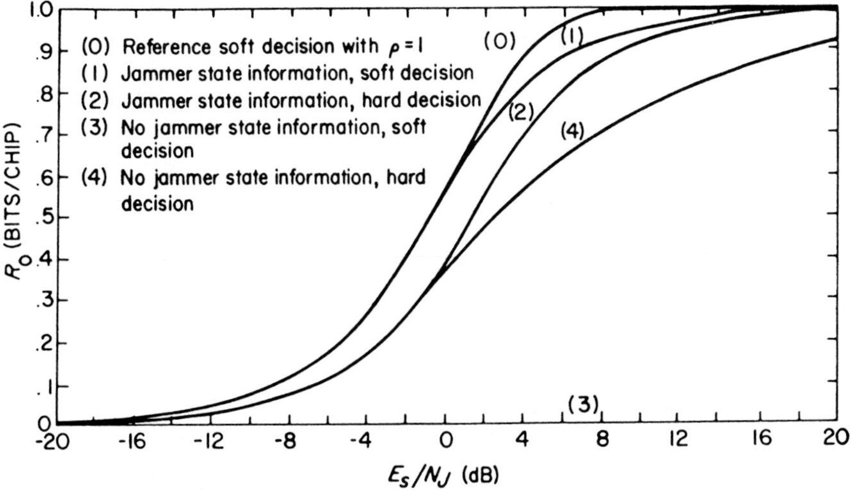

Figure 1.8. R_0 for DS/BPSK examples.

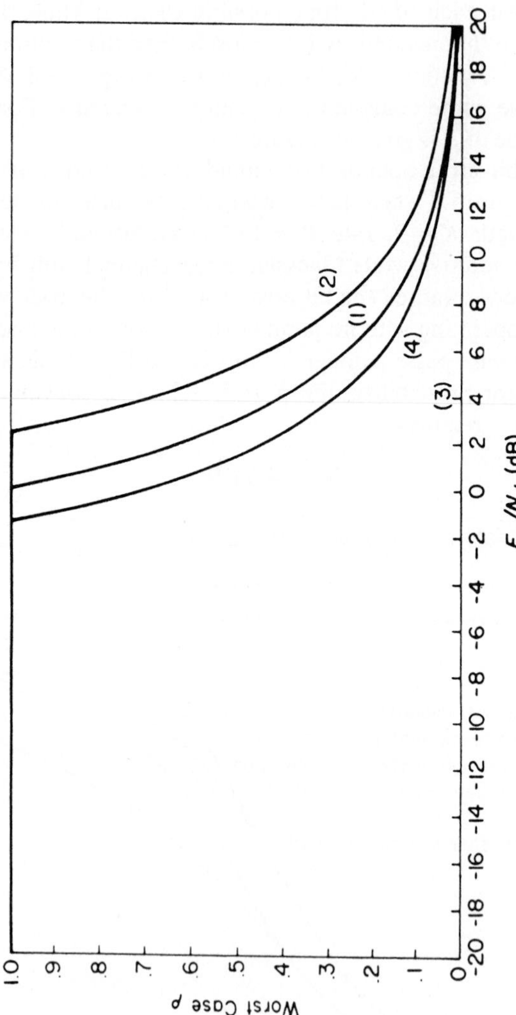

Figure 1.9. Worst case ρ for DS/BPSK examples.

From Figure 1.8 this choice of E_s/N_0 gives the cutoff rate

$$R_0 = 0.7 \tag{1.97}$$

on the reference cutoff rate corresponding to the additive white Gaussian noise channel with soft decision decoding. This gives the value of R_0 required to achieve 10^{-5} bit error probabilities regardless of the channel. For this choice of R_0, the worst case pulse jamming channel with hard decision and no jamming state information requires (see curve labelled (4))

$$E_s/N_J = 8.0 \text{ dB} \tag{1.98}$$

or

$$E_b/N_J = 11.0 \text{ dB}. \tag{1.99}$$

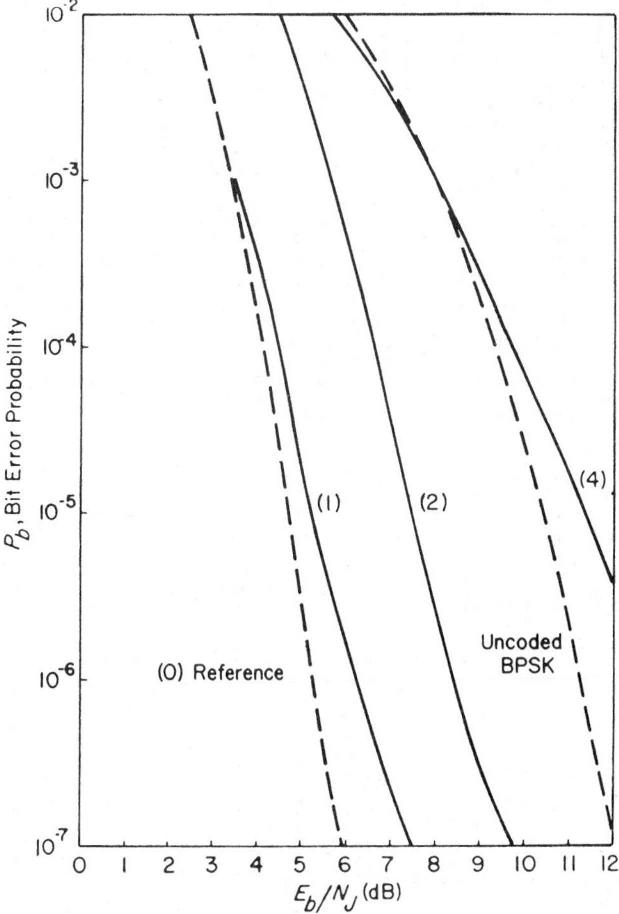

Figure 1.10. Worst pulse jamming: $K = 7$, $R = 1/2$ code.

This is the energy per bit required for this case to achieve 10^{-5} bit error probability with this code.

The above procedure repeated for various choices of the bit error probability results in the bit error bounds shown in Figure 1.10 for the reference case and three worst case pulse jammer examples. Note that the bit error probability curves shown here are shifted by exactly the same shift shown in Figure 1.8 for the cutoff rates. This is simply because for any given code, the coded bit error bound depends only on the value of R_0. Similar bit error bounds can be found for other codes by shifting the standard bit error probability curves by the same amount.

Figure 1.10 also illustrates the effectiveness of coding and interleaving in combatting pulse jamming. Comparing the coded bit error probabilities of Figure 1.10 with the uncoded case of Figure 1.5, we see that most of the large degradation due to pulse jamming has been neutralized and additional coding gain achieved. At 10^{-6} bit error probability, for example, there is about a 45 dB coding gain for the soft decision known jammer state decoder for this $K = 7$ convolutional code compared to no coding. These are against the worst case pulse jammer for each point on the bit error probability curves.

1.6 SLOW FREQUENCY NON-SELECTIVE FADING CHANNELS

Here we examine the performance of DS/BPSK systems in a fading channel [23]–[32]. The fading is assumed to be constant across the total spread spectrum bandwidth, W_{ss}, and varies slowly in time such that during any data bit time interval, T_b, the fading is assumed to be constant. This slowly varying frequency non-selective fading is sometimes referred to as flat-flat fading [23]. Although our analysis allows for arbitrary fade statistics, the examples will assume the commonly used Rayleigh fading amplitude statistics which models the case where there are many similar scatterers causing the fading [33].

1.6.1 Continuous Jammer with No Coding

Suppose the received signal amplitude is A. Then the energy per bit is

$$E_b = \frac{A^2 T_b}{2}. \tag{1.100}$$

Assuming the maximum-likelihood demodulator for the AWGN channel, then the uncoded bit error probability is bounded by (see (1.37) and (1.72))

$$P_b(A) = Q\left(\sqrt{\frac{A^2 T_b}{N_J}}\right) \leq \frac{1}{2} e^{-A^2 T_b/(2N_J)} \tag{1.101}$$

where as before N_J is given by J/W_{ss} for the continuous jammer of average power J.

For a fading channel A is a random variable with some probability density function $p_A(\cdot)$ and the average uncoded bit error probability is bounded by

$$P_b = \int_0^\infty Q\left(\sqrt{\frac{a^2 T_b}{N_J}}\right) p_A(a)\, da$$

$$\leq \tfrac{1}{2}\int_0^\infty e^{-a^2 T_b/(2N_J)} p_A(a)\, da. \tag{1.102}$$

For Rayleigh statistics where

$$p_A(a) = \frac{a}{\sigma^2} e^{-a^2/(2\sigma^2)}, \qquad a \geq 0 \tag{1.103}$$

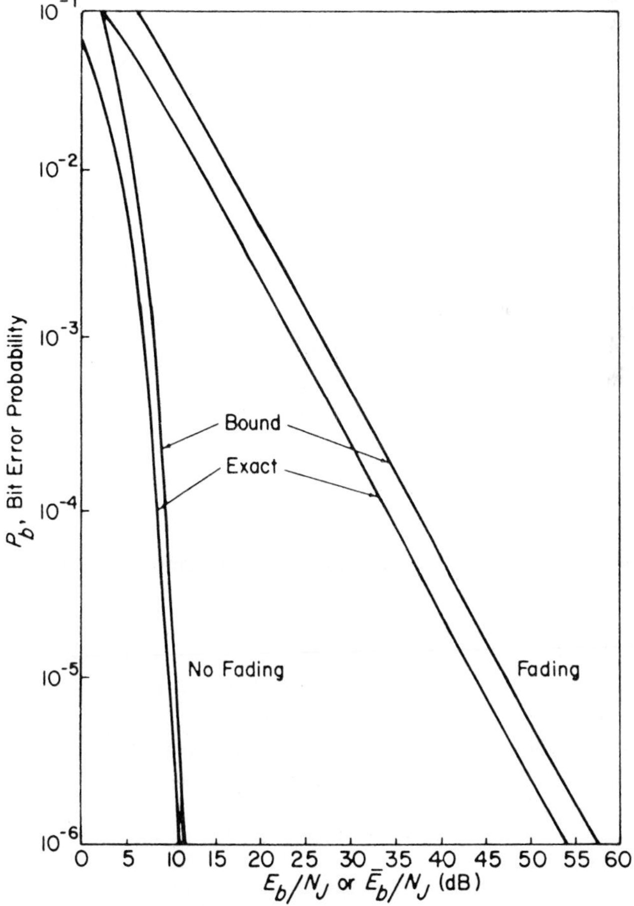

Figure 1.11. Uncoded bit error probability.

and the received signal energy has average value

$$\bar{E}_b \triangleq \frac{T_b}{2} \int_0^\infty a^2 p_A(a)\, da = \sigma^2 T_b, \tag{1.104}$$

the exact uncoded bit error probability is

$$\begin{aligned} P_b &= \int_0^\infty Q\left(\sqrt{\frac{a^2 T_b}{N_J}}\right) \frac{a}{\sigma^2} e^{-a^2/(2\sigma^2)}\, da \\ &= \frac{1}{2}\left\{1 - \sqrt{\frac{\bar{E}_b/N_J}{1 + \bar{E}_b/N_J}}\right\}. \end{aligned} \tag{1.105}$$

The bound in (1.102) is

$$P_b \le \frac{1}{2}\left\{\frac{1}{1 + \bar{E}_b/N_J}\right\}. \tag{1.106}$$

Figure 1.11 shows the uncoded bit error probabilities and their bounds with no fading versus E_b/N_J and with Rayleigh fading versus $\bar{E}_b/N_J$. Note that the effects of Rayleigh fading are like the worst case pulse jammer shown in Figure 1.5.

1.6.2 Continuous Jammer with Coding—No Fading Estimate

With coding, assume ideal interleaving where each coded symbol is assumed to have an independent fading term. Consider two binary sequences of length N denoted

$$\boldsymbol{x} = (x_1, x_2, \ldots, x_N) \tag{1.107}$$

and

$$\hat{\boldsymbol{x}} = (\hat{x}_1, \hat{x}_2, \ldots, \hat{x}_N)$$

where

$$x, \hat{x} \in \{-1, 1\}. \tag{1.108}$$

Let the Hamming weight be $H(\boldsymbol{x}, \hat{\boldsymbol{x}}) = d$ and assume the fading amplitude sequence is

$$\boldsymbol{A} = (A_1, A_2, \ldots, A_N) \tag{1.109}$$

where $\{A_n\}$ are independent identically distributed random variables with common probability density function $p_A(\cdot)$.

For the equivalent white Gaussian noise channel due to the constant power jammer, the unquantized channel outputs are

$$r_k = x_k A_k \sqrt{T_s/2} + n_k; \qquad k = 1, 2, \ldots, N \tag{1.110}$$

where T_s is the coded symbol time and n_k is zero mean with variance $N_J/2$. Assuming the soft decision metric $m(r, x) = rx$, the pairwise error probability that the receiver chooses $\hat{\boldsymbol{x}}$ when $\boldsymbol{x}$ is sent is Chernoff bounded by

$$
\begin{aligned}
\Pr(\boldsymbol{x} \to \hat{\boldsymbol{x}}) &= \Pr\left\{ \sum_{k=1}^{N} r_k \hat{x}_k \geq \sum_{k=1}^{N} r_k x_k \middle| \boldsymbol{x} \right\} \\
&= \Pr\left\{ \sum_{k=1}^{N} r_k(\hat{x}_k - x_k) \geq 0 \middle| \boldsymbol{x} \right\} \\
&\leq E\left\{ \exp\left[\lambda \sum_{k=1}^{N} r_k(\hat{x}_k - x_k) \right] \middle| \boldsymbol{x} \right\} \\
&= \prod_{k=1}^{N} E\{ e^{\lambda r_k(\hat{x}_k - x_k)} | x_k \}
\end{aligned}
\tag{1.111}
$$

for all $\lambda \geq 0$. Note that here

$$
E\{ e^{\lambda r_k(\hat{x}_k - x_k)} | A_k, x_k \} = \begin{cases} 1, & \hat{x}_k = x_k \\ e^{\lambda^2 N_J} e^{-\lambda A_k \sqrt{2T_s}}, & \hat{x}_k \neq x_k \end{cases}
\tag{1.112}
$$

and

$$
E\{ e^{\lambda r_k(\hat{x}_k - x_k)} | x_k \} = \begin{cases} 1, & \hat{x}_k = x_k \\ e^{\lambda^2 N_J} \int_0^{\infty} e^{-\lambda a \sqrt{2T_s}} p_A(a)\, da, & \hat{x}_k \neq x_k. \end{cases}
\tag{1.113}
$$

Defining

$$
D = \min_{\lambda \geq 0} e^{\lambda^2 N_J} \int_0^{\infty} e^{-\lambda a \sqrt{2T_s}} p_A(a)\, da
\tag{1.114}
$$

the pairwise error bound has the form

$$
\Pr\{ \boldsymbol{x} \to \hat{\boldsymbol{x}} \} \leq D^d
\tag{1.115}
$$

and a general coded error bound of the form

$$
P_b \leq \sum_k a_k D^k.
\tag{1.116}
$$

For the simple repeat m code described in Chapters 3 and 4, Volume I, the bit error bound is

$$
P_b \leq \tfrac{1}{2} D^m
\tag{1.117}
$$

where D is given by (1.114). For the constraint length $K = 7$, rate $R = 1/2$ convolutional code the bit error bound is given by

$$
P_b \leq \tfrac{1}{2}[36D^{10} + 211d^{12} + 1404D^{14} + 11633D^{16} + \cdots]
\tag{1.118}
$$

for the same D where T_s is the coded symbol time.

For the case of Rayleigh fading D is given by

$$D = \min_{\lambda \geq 0} e^{(1/2)\lambda^2(\bar{E}_s/N_J)}\left[1 - \sqrt{2\pi}\lambda(\bar{E}_s/N_J)e^{(1/2)\lambda^2(\bar{E}_s/N_J)}Q(\lambda(\bar{E}_s/N_J))\right] \tag{1.119}$$

where $\bar{E}_s = \sigma^2 T_s$ is the average coded symbol energy. Figure 1.12 shows coded bit error bounds for several repeat codes and the $K = 7$, $R = 1/2$ convolutional code when there is Rayleigh fading. Here $\bar{E}_s = R\bar{E}_b$ where R is the code rate in bits per coded symbol. Note that coding with interleaving

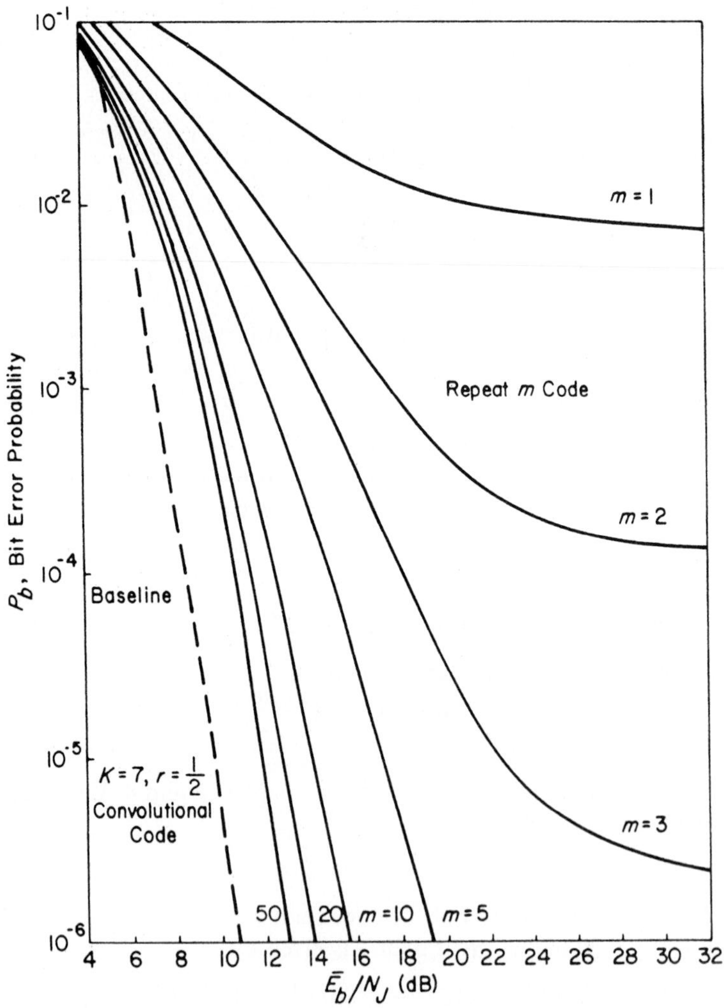

Figure 1.12. Coded bit error probability—soft decision.

combats fading much like it did for the worst case pulse jammer. Indeed, pulse jamming is similar to a fading channel where the signal-to-noise ratio can change in time.

The results illustrated above assume the soft decision metric

$$m(r, x) = rx \tag{1.120}$$

as implied in (1.111). A hard decision channel with ideal interleaving results in a binary symmetric channel where the crossover probability would depend on the specific amplitude term A. Here the crossover probability is

$$\varepsilon(A) = Q\left(\sqrt{\frac{A^2 T_s}{N_J}}\right) \tag{1.121}$$

which is the same as (1.101) with T_b replaced by T_s, the coded symbol time.

Now consider the fading channel with ideal interleaving and the usual hard decision metric when there are only two binary sequences of length N as shown in (1.107). Assuming $\boldsymbol{x}$ is transmitted and the channel output binary sequence is $\boldsymbol{y} = (y_1, y_2, \ldots, y_N)$, the probability that the decoder incorrectly chooses $\hat{\boldsymbol{x}}$ is the probability that

$$w(\boldsymbol{y}, \boldsymbol{x}) \geq w(\boldsymbol{y}, \hat{\boldsymbol{x}}). \tag{1.122}$$

The hard decision pairwise probability of error is thus Chernoff bounded by

$$\begin{aligned}
P(\boldsymbol{x} \to \hat{\boldsymbol{x}}) &= \Pr\{w(\boldsymbol{y}, \boldsymbol{x}) \geq w(\boldsymbol{y}, \hat{\boldsymbol{x}}) | \boldsymbol{x}\} \\
&= \Pr\{w(\boldsymbol{y}, \boldsymbol{x}) - w(\boldsymbol{y}, \hat{\boldsymbol{x}}) \geq 0 | \boldsymbol{x}\} \\
&= \Pr\left\{\sum_{n=1}^{N} [w(y_n, x_n) - w(y_n, \hat{x}_n)] \geq 0 | \boldsymbol{x}\right\} \\
&\leq E\left\{\exp \lambda \sum_{n=1}^{N} [w(y_n, x_n) - w(y_n, \hat{x}_n)] | \boldsymbol{x}\right\} \\
&= \prod_{n=1}^{N} E\{e^{\lambda[w(y_n, x_n) - w(y_n, \hat{x}_n)]} | x_n\}
\end{aligned} \tag{1.123}$$

where $\lambda \geq 0$ and the Hamming distance between two elements is a special case of the Hamming distance between two vectors,

$$w(y, x) = \begin{cases} 1, & y \neq x \\ 0, & y = x. \end{cases} \tag{1.124}$$

Thus

$$w(\boldsymbol{y}, \boldsymbol{x}) = w(y_1, x_1) + w(y_2, x_2) + \cdots + w(y_N, x_N). \tag{1.125}$$

Note that

$$y_n = \begin{cases} x_n, & \text{with probability } 1 - \varepsilon(A_n) \\ \hat{x}_n, & \text{with probability } \varepsilon(A_n) \end{cases} \tag{1.126}$$

for those d components where $\hat{x}_n \neq x_n$. Thus,

$$E\left\{ e^{\lambda[w(y_n, x_n) - w(y_n, \hat{x}_n)]} \middle| x_n, A_n \right\} = \begin{cases} 1, & \hat{x}_n = x_n \\ (1 - \varepsilon(A_n))e^{-\lambda} + \varepsilon(A_n)e^{\lambda}, & \hat{x}_n \neq x_n \end{cases} \tag{1.127}$$

and

$$E\left\{ e^{\lambda[w(y_n, x_n) - w(y_n, \hat{x}_n)]} \middle| x_n \right\} = \begin{cases} 1, & \hat{x}_n = x_n \\ (1 - \bar{\varepsilon})e^{-\lambda} + \bar{\varepsilon}e^{\lambda}, & \hat{x}_n \neq x_n \end{cases} \tag{1.128}$$

where

$$\bar{\varepsilon} = \int_0^\infty \varepsilon(a) p_A(a)\, da \tag{1.129}$$

is the averaged crossover probability. Defining

$$D(\lambda) = (1 - \bar{\varepsilon})e^{-\lambda} + \bar{\varepsilon}e^{\lambda} \tag{1.130}$$

we have

$$P(\mathbf{x} \to \hat{\mathbf{x}}) \leq [D(\lambda)]^{w(\mathbf{x}, \hat{\mathbf{x}})}, \qquad \text{all } \lambda \geq 0. \tag{1.131}$$

The choice of λ that minimizes $D(\lambda)$ satisfies

$$e^{\lambda} = \sqrt{\frac{1 - \bar{\varepsilon}}{\bar{\varepsilon}}} \tag{1.132}$$

giving the parameter

$$D = \min_{\lambda \geq 0} D(\lambda) = \sqrt{4\bar{\varepsilon}(1 - \bar{\varepsilon})} \tag{1.133}$$

The Rayleigh fading amplitude statistics has

$$\bar{\varepsilon} = \frac{1}{2}\left\{1 - \sqrt{\frac{\bar{E}_s/N_J}{1 + \bar{E}_s/N_J}}\right\}. \tag{1.134}$$

For the repeat m code with the bit error bound given by (1.117) and the constraint length $K = 7$, rate $R = 1/2$ convolutional code with the bit error bound (1.118) where D is given above by (1.133), the coded bit error probabilities are shown in Figure 1.13. Again note that coding can overcome the degradation due to fading.

In practice quantized amplitude histograms of a fading channel may be available through measurements. Suppose, for example, the measured quantized amplitude values are $\alpha_1, \alpha_2, \ldots, \alpha_L$ with measured probabilities

$$p_l = \Pr\{A = \alpha_l\}; \qquad l = 1, 2, \ldots, L. \tag{1.135}$$

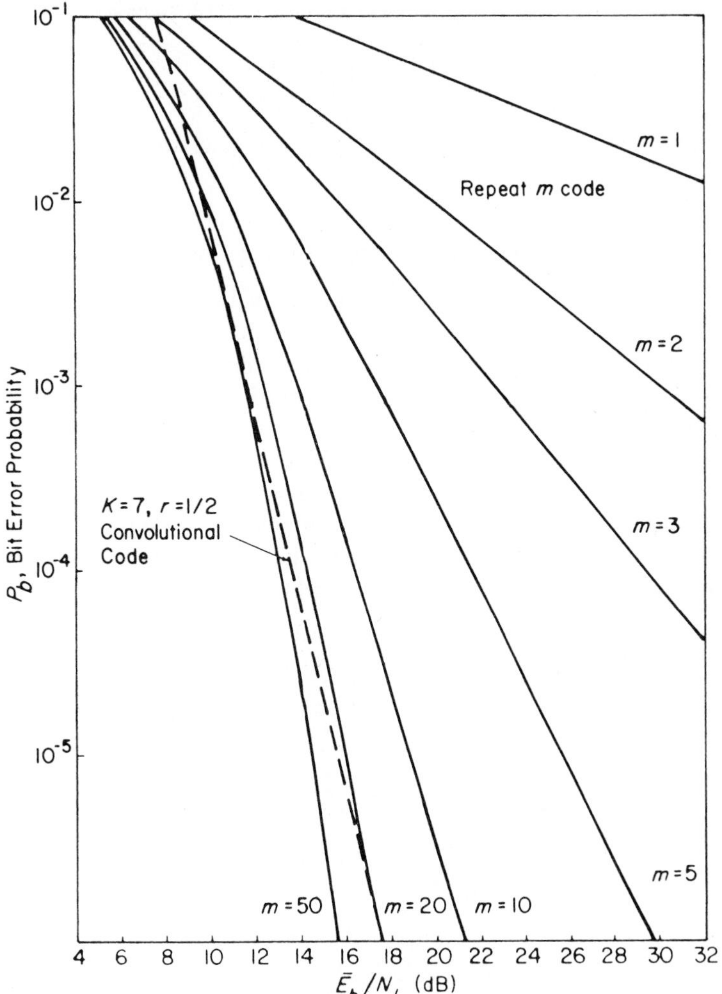

Figure 1.13. Coded bit error probability—hard decision.

For this channel the uncoded bit error probability is

$$P_b = \int_0^\infty Q\left(\sqrt{\frac{a^2 T_b}{N_J}}\right) p_A(a)\, da$$

$$= \sum_{l=1}^{L} p_l Q\left(\sqrt{\frac{\alpha_l^2 T_b}{N_J}}\right). \tag{1.136}$$

For soft decision decoding (1.114) becomes

$$D = \min_{\lambda \geq 0} e^{\lambda^2 N_J} \sum_{l=1}^{L} p_l e^{-\lambda \alpha_l \sqrt{2T_s}} \tag{1.137}$$

while for hard decision decoding D is given by (1.133) where

$$\bar{\varepsilon} = \sum_{l=1}^{L} p_l Q\left(\sqrt{\frac{\alpha_l^2 T_s}{N_J}}\right). \tag{1.138}$$

With this empirically measured fading, the impact of coding with ideal interleaving can be computed.

1.6.3 Continuous Jammer with Coding—Fading Estimate

With no coding, the optimum demodulator with a fading channel is the same as that for the non-fading channel. Thus, for the uncoded case in Section 1.6.1 knowledge of the fade term A does not change the performance. This is not true, however, for coded DS/BPSK systems with fading (see Proakis [33]).

Consider the same coding case described in Section 1.6.2 except that we now assume ideal estimates[4] for the fade values $A_1, A_2, \ldots, A_N$. That is, during any coded symbol transmission, complete knowledge of the random fade amplitude is assumed. In this case the maximum-likelihood decision rule obtained by comparing $p_N(\boldsymbol{r}|\boldsymbol{x}, \boldsymbol{A})$ with $p_N(\boldsymbol{r}|\hat{\boldsymbol{x}}, \boldsymbol{A})$ results in metric

$$m(r_k, x_k|A_k) = A_k r_k x_k. \tag{1.139}$$

Without loss of generality take the first d places of $\boldsymbol{x}$ and $\hat{\boldsymbol{x}}$ to be different and obtain the conditional pairwise error bound

$$\begin{aligned}
P(\boldsymbol{x} \to \hat{\boldsymbol{x}}|\boldsymbol{A}) &= \Pr\left\{ \sum_{k=1}^{N} A_k r_k \hat{x}_k \geq \sum_{k=1}^{N} A_k r_k x_k \,\middle|\, \boldsymbol{x}, \boldsymbol{A} \right\} \\
&= \Pr\left\{ \sum_{k=1}^{N} A_k r_k (\hat{x}_k - x_k) \geq 0 \,\middle|\, \boldsymbol{x}, \boldsymbol{A} \right\} \\
&= \Pr\left\{ \sum_{k=1}^{N} A_k \left(x_k A_k \sqrt{T_s/2} + n_k\right)(\hat{x}_k - x_k) \geq 0 \,\middle|\, \boldsymbol{x}, \boldsymbol{A} \right\} \\
&= \Pr\left\{ \sum_{k=1}^{d} A_k n_k \geq \sum_{k=1}^{d} A_k^2 \sqrt{T_s/2} \,\middle|\, \boldsymbol{x}, \boldsymbol{A} \right\} \\
&= Q\left(\sqrt{\left(\sum_{k=1}^{d} A_k^2 \right)(T_s/N_J)} \right) \\
&\leq e^{-(\sum_{k=1}^{d} A_k^2) T_s/(2N_J)} \\
&= \prod_{k=1}^{d} e^{-A_k^2 T_s/(2N_J)}.
\end{aligned} \tag{1.140}$$

[4] This is reasonable for slowly varying fading channels where these estimates must also be deinterleaved.

Averaging this bound over the common fading density function $p_A(\cdot)$ gives

$$P(x \to \hat{x}) \le \left\{ \int_0^\infty e^{-a^2 T_s/(2N_J)} p_A(a)\, da \right\}^d$$
$$= D^d \tag{1.141}$$

where

$$D = \int_0^\infty e^{-a^2 T_s/(2N_J)} p_A(a)\, da. \tag{1.142}$$

This can be compared with (1.114) for the case with no fading estimate.

When the fades are i.i.d. Rayleigh random variables

$$D = \frac{1}{1 + \bar{E}_s/N_J}. \tag{1.143}$$

This result can be compared with (1.119) where there is no fading estimate. In Figure 1.14, the cutoff rates of these two cases using R_0 given by (1.92) are shown. Note that for small values of $\bar{E}_s/N_J$ there is about a 1.25 dB difference for the same value of R_0.

An exact expression can be obtained for the pairwise error probability for the Rayleigh fading case where

$$Z = \sum_{k=1}^{d} A_k^2 (T_s/N_J) \tag{1.144}$$

is a chi-square random variable with $2d$ degrees of freedom having the probability density function

$$p_z(z) = \frac{z^{d-1} e^{-z/(\bar{E}_s/N_J)}}{(d-1)!(\bar{E}_s/N_J)^d}, \qquad z \ge 0. \tag{1.145}$$

Averaging the exact expression in (1.140) over this probability density function results in the closed form solution

$$P(x \to \hat{x}) = \int_0^\infty Q(\sqrt{z})\, p_z(z)\, dz$$
$$= \left(\frac{1-\gamma}{2}\right)^d \sum_{k=0}^{d-1} \binom{d-1+k}{k} \left(\frac{1+\gamma}{2}\right)^k \tag{1.146}$$

where

$$\gamma = \sqrt{\frac{\bar{E}_s/N_J}{1 + \bar{E}_s/N_J}}. \tag{1.147}$$

In Figure 1.15, the exact bit error probability is compared with the Chernoff bound for repeat codes having diversity $m = 1$, 2, and 4. There is about a 1.5 dB to 3 dB difference between the exact bit error probability and the Chernoff bound. As in earlier examples, the Chernoff bound is looser for

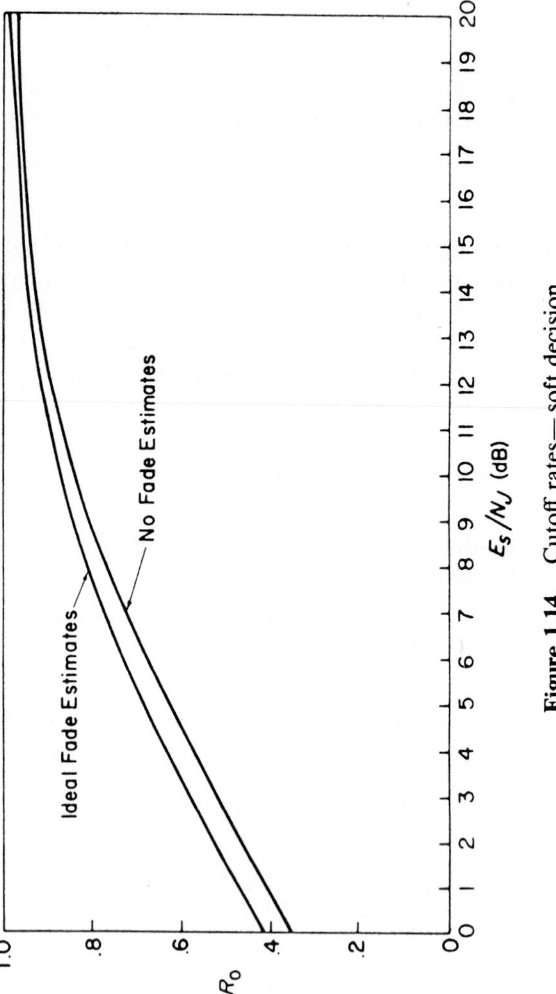

Figure 1.14. Cutoff rates—soft decision.

cases when the error probabilities fall off more slowly with signal-to-noise ratio.

In Figure 1.15 the impact of having ideal fade estimates and using the optimum metric (1.139) compared to the suboptimum metric (1.120) where no fade estimates are used can be seen. Using the Chernoff bounds for these two cases and assuming repeat codes with diversity m, we have the results shown in Figure 1.16. For smaller values of signal-to-noise ratio, there is approximately a 1.25 dB difference between these two metrics. At higher signal-to-jammer noise ratios, however, there is a much greater difference.

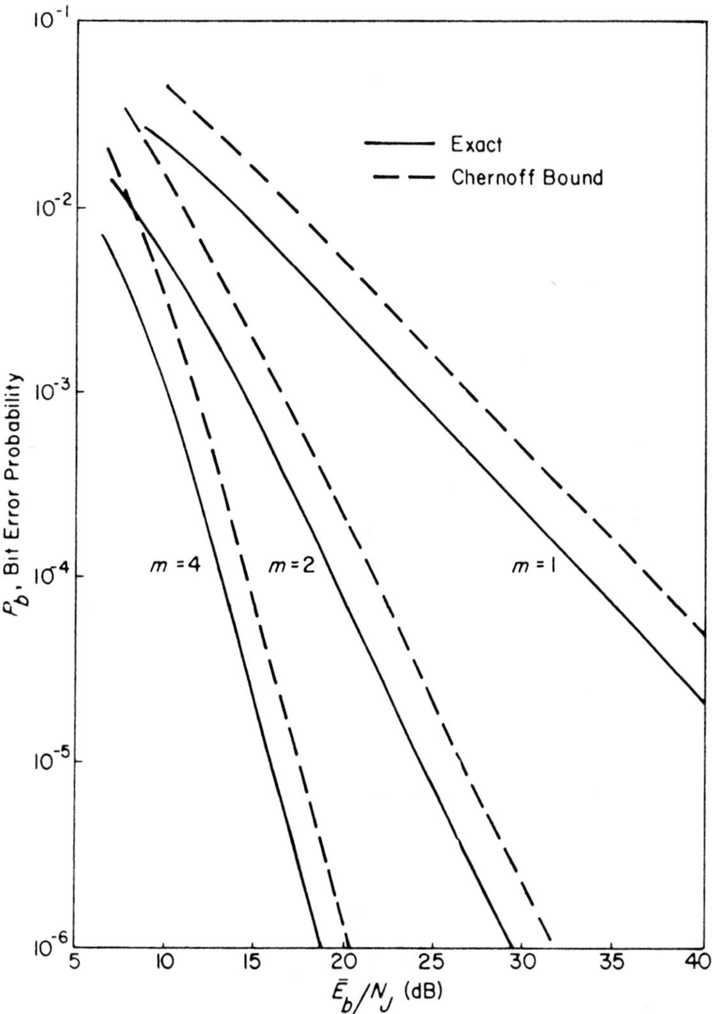

Figure 1.15. Repeat code— soft decision with ideal fade estimate.

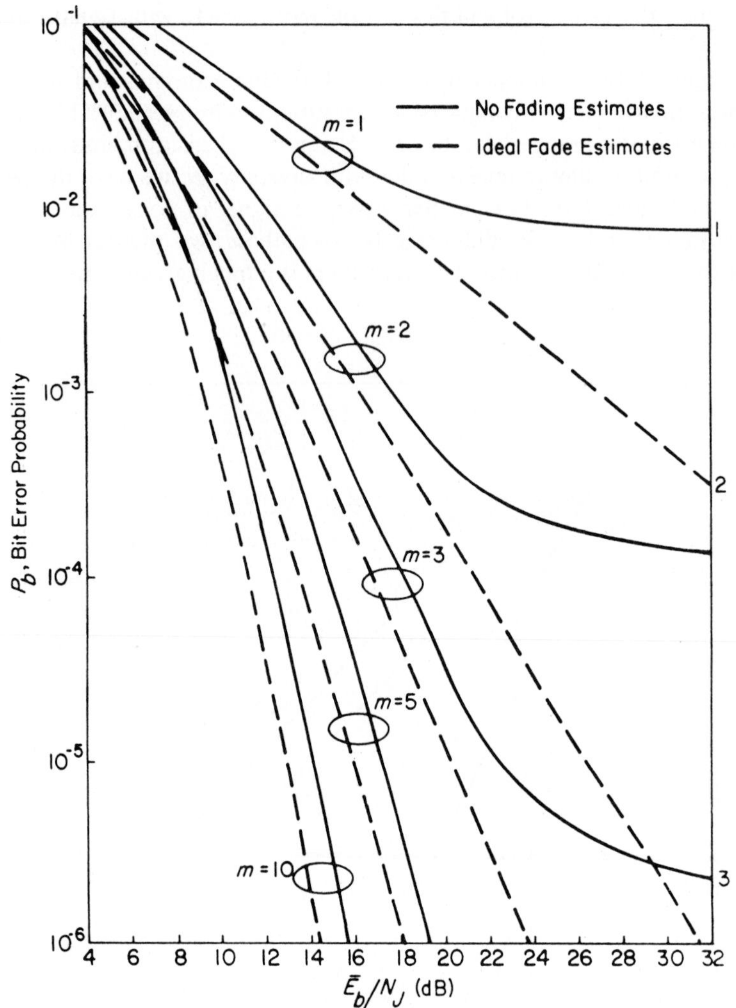

Figure 1.16. Repeat code Chernoff bounds— soft decision.

For the hard decision channel with ideal fade estimates the conditional probability of $\boldsymbol{y}$ given $\boldsymbol{x}$ and $\boldsymbol{A}$ is

$$p_N(\boldsymbol{y}|\boldsymbol{x}, \boldsymbol{A}) = \prod_{k=1}^{N} (1 - \varepsilon(A_k))^{1 - w(y_k, x_k)} \varepsilon(A_k)^{w(y_k, x_k)}$$

$$= \prod_{k=1}^{N} \left(\frac{\varepsilon(A_k)}{1 - \varepsilon(A_k)} \right)^{w(y_k, x_k)} \cdot \prod_{n=1}^{N} (1 - \varepsilon(A_n)) \tag{1.148}$$

where $\varepsilon(A)$ is given by (1.121). Here the maximum-likelihood metric is

$$m(y_k, x_k|A_k) = w(y_k, x_k)\log\left[\frac{\varepsilon(A_k)}{1-\varepsilon(A_k)}\right]. \tag{1.149}$$

Assuming this optimum metric, the Chernoff bound for the conditional pairwise error probability is the Bhattacharyya bound

$$\begin{aligned} P(\boldsymbol{x} \to \hat{\boldsymbol{x}}|\boldsymbol{A}) &\le \sum_{\boldsymbol{y}} \sqrt{p_N(\boldsymbol{y}|\boldsymbol{x}, \boldsymbol{A})\, p_N(\boldsymbol{y}|\hat{\boldsymbol{x}}, \boldsymbol{A})} \\ &= \prod_{k=1}^{N} \left\{ \sum_{y} \sqrt{p(y|x_k, A_k)\, p(y|\hat{x}_k, A_k)} \right\} \\ &= \prod_{k=1}^{d} \sqrt{4\varepsilon(A_k)(1-\varepsilon(A_k))} \end{aligned} \tag{1.150}$$

where, without loss of generality, only the first d places in $\boldsymbol{x}$ and $\hat{\boldsymbol{x}}$ are assumed to differ. The pairwise error probability is thus

$$P(\boldsymbol{x} \to \hat{\boldsymbol{x}}) \le \left[\int_0^\infty \sqrt{4\varepsilon(a)(1-\varepsilon(a))}\, p_A(a)\, da\right]^d. \tag{1.151}$$

Here

$$D = \int_0^\infty \sqrt{4\varepsilon(a)(1-\varepsilon(a))}\, p_A(a)\, da. \tag{1.152}$$

For the suboptimum hard decision metric with no fade estimates, D is given by (1.133) where $\bar{\varepsilon}$ is given by (1.134). Since the function

$$f(x) = \sqrt{4x(1-x)} \tag{1.153}$$

is concave for $0 \le x \le 1$, using Jensen's inequality [22],

$$E\{f(X)\} \le f(E\{X\}), \tag{1.154}$$

for the random variable X,

$$\int_0^\infty \sqrt{4\varepsilon(a)(1-\varepsilon(a))}\, p_A(a)\, da \le \sqrt{4\bar{\varepsilon}(1-\bar{\varepsilon})} \tag{1.155}$$

as expected.

1.6.4 Pulse Jammer with No Coding

Now consider the case of a fading channel together with a pulse jammer with average power J and jamming with power J/ρ for a fraction ρ of the time. Again assuming that when there is no jammer pulse the bit error probability is negligible, then the average uncoded bit error probability is

$$P_b = \rho \int_0^\infty Q\left(\sqrt{\frac{a^2 T_b}{N_J}\rho}\right) p_A(a)\, da. \tag{1.156}$$

For the case of Rayleigh fading, this has the form

$$P_b = \tfrac{1}{2}\rho\left\{1 - \sqrt{\frac{\rho(\bar{E}_b/N_J)}{1+\rho(\bar{E}_b/N_J)}}\right\}. \tag{1.157}$$

The choice of jammer pulse parameter ρ that maximizes the bit error probability for Rayleigh fading channels is $\rho = 1$ for all $\bar{E}_b/N_J$. Thus *the constant power jammer is the worst jammer in a Rayleigh fading channel.* This is primarily due to the fact that Rayleigh fading has already created the same impact as that of a worst case pulse jammer with a resulting uncoded bit error bound that changes slowly with increasing values of $\bar{E}_b/N_J$. Changes in the signal-to-noise ratio caused by a pulse jammer no longer result in large changes in the uncoded bit error probability and the constant power jammer turns out to be the worst case. Coding and interleaving still showed dramatic improvements but this time to overcome the effects of Rayleigh fading. For other fading statistics it is not clear what is the worst pulse jammer parameter. Each case would have to be analyzed separately.

1.7 SLOW FADING MULTIPATH CHANNELS

In many radio channels signals reflect off the surface of water, buildings, trees, etc., causing multiple signal terms at the receiver. The atmosphere also causes reflections where sometimes the reflected signals are used as the primary means of sending signals from transmitters to receivers. Examples include shortwave ionospheric radio communication at HF (3 MHz to 30 MHz), tropospheric scatter radio communication at UHF (300 MHz to 3000 MHz) and SHF (3000 MHz to 30,000 MHz), and ionospheric forward scatter radio communication at VHF (30 MHz to 300 MHz). These fading multipath channels are usually modeled as having a randomly time-varying filter together with noise and interference [33].

Examination of the DS/BPSK system in a fading multipath channel begins by defining the DS/BPSK signal in (1.4) with an arbitrary phase term θ, i.e.,

$$x(t;\theta) = c(t)\,d(t)\sqrt{2S}\cos[\omega_0 t + \theta]. \tag{1.158}$$

The simplest multipath example is where there is an unfaded direct path signal and one reflected path signal. The received signal has the form

$$y(t) = x(t;0) + \alpha x(t-\tau;\theta) + J(t). \tag{1.159}$$

Here α is the reflected signal amplitude term, τ is its delay relative to the direct signal, and θ is its phase relative to the direct signal. Here $x(t) = c(t)s(t)$ is the DS/BPSK signal with no fading and $J(t)$ is the jamming signal.

The usual DS/BPSK receiver would multiply $y(t)$ with the PN waveform $c(t)$ and then compute the cosine component of the carrier,

$$r_0 = \int_0^{T_b} r(t)\phi_c(t)\,dt \tag{1.160}$$

where

$$\begin{aligned} r(t) &= c(t)y(t) \\ &= s(t) + c(t)\alpha x(t-\tau;\theta) + c(t)J(t) \end{aligned} \tag{1.161}$$

and

$$\phi_c(t) = \sqrt{\frac{2}{T_b}}\cos\omega_0 t$$
$$0 \le t \le T_b. \tag{1.162}$$

Evaluating (1.160) using (1.161) and (1.162) gives

$$r_0 = d_0\sqrt{E_b} + n_0' + n_0 \tag{1.163}$$

where

$$n_0 = \int_0^{T_b} c(t)J(t)\phi_c(t)\,dt \tag{1.164}$$

is a Gaussian random variable with variance $N_J/2$ and

$$\begin{aligned} n_0' &= \int_0^{T_b} c(t)\alpha x(t-\tau;\theta)\phi_c(t)\,dt \\ &= \alpha d_0\sqrt{2S}\int_\tau^{T_b} c(t)c(t-\tau)\cos[\omega_0(t-\tau)+\theta]\phi_c(t)\,dt \end{aligned} \tag{1.165}$$

where d_0 is the value of the data signal $d(t)$ during the interval $(0, T_b)$.

Suppose in (1.159) the multipath delay τ satisfies

$$\tau \ge T_c \tag{1.166}$$

where T_c is the PN chip time. Then for each t, $c(t)$ and $c(t-\tau)$ are independent and n' is a sum of independent random variables which can be approximated as a Gaussian random variable with variance no greater than $\alpha^2 S/(2W_{ss})$. Since typically $S \ll J$ is assumed, for all realistic values of α, this multipath noise term n_0' is negligible compared to the noise term n_0 which is due to jamming. Thus we have the approximation

$$r_0 \cong d_0\sqrt{E_b} + n_0 \tag{1.167}$$

for multipath delay τ satisfying (1.166).

When the multipath delay τ is greater than the chip time T_c, there is negligible degradation due to multipath. This also applies when the direct path experiences slowly varying frequency non-selective fading as discussed in the previous section. In general, however, it is possible to do better. Assuming the channel is slowly varying so that the multipath parameters α,

τ, and θ are known to the receiver, the receiver can multiply $y(t)$ with $c(t-\tau)$ and find the cosine component corresponding to the coordinate

$$\phi_c(t-\tau;\theta) = \sqrt{\frac{2}{T_b}}\cos[\omega_0(t-\tau)+\theta]$$
$$\tau \le t \le T_b + \tau. \tag{1.168}$$

This results in the cosine component relative to the multipath signal of the form (ignoring the direct path noise term)

$$r_1 \cong d_0\alpha\sqrt{E_b} + n_1 \tag{1.169}$$

where

$$n_1 = \int_\tau^{T_b+\tau} c(t-\tau)J(t)\phi_c(t-\tau;\theta)\,dt \tag{1.170}$$

is a Gaussian random variable with variance $N_J/2$. Thus there are two outputs of the channel given by r_0 and r_1.

Except for some unrealistic waveforms for the jammer, the correlation between n_0 and n_1 is zero and thus these are independent Gaussian random variables. The optimum decision rule[5] based on r_0 and r_1 is to compare

$$\begin{aligned} r &= r_0 + \alpha r_1 \\ &= d_0(1+\alpha^2)\sqrt{E_b} + n_0 + \alpha n_1 \end{aligned} \tag{1.171}$$

with zero as in (1.19). The bit error probability is thus

$$P_b = Q\left(\sqrt{\frac{(1+\alpha^2)2E_b}{N_J}}\right). \tag{1.172}$$

This bit error probability is better than using a conventional DS/BPSK receiver which only uses r_0 in its decision.

Condition (1.166) for multipath delay results in a diversity system where two independent channel outputs are available. Thus DS/BPSK spread-spectrum signals not only provide protection against jamming but also can resolve multipath and take advantage of the natural diversity available.

For a multipath channel with L paths and a resulting channel output

$$y(t) = \sum_{l=1}^{L} \alpha_l x(t-\tau_l;\theta_l) + J(t) \tag{1.173}$$

it is possible to compute at the receiver the L outputs

$$r_l = \int_{\tau_l}^{T_b+\tau_l} c(t-\tau_l)y(t)\phi_c(t-\tau_l;\theta_l)\,dt \tag{1.174}$$

where $\phi_c(t-\tau;\theta)$ is given in (1.168). This assumes the receiver has complete knowledge of the multipath statistics which include amplitudes $\{\alpha_l\}$,

[5] This can be obtained by using the maximum-likelihood rule of comparing $p(r_0, r_1|d=-1)$ with $p(r_0, r_1|d=1)$.

delays $\{\tau_l\}$, and carrier phases $\{\theta_l\}$. If now

$$|\tau_i - \tau_j| \geq T_c \quad \text{for all } i \neq j \tag{1.175}$$

then we have the approximation

$$r_l \cong d_0 \alpha_l \sqrt{E_b} + n_l$$
$$l = 1, 2, \ldots, L \tag{1.176}$$

where $\{n_l\}$ are independent Gaussian random variables with variance $N_J/2$. Here the optimum decision rule is given by (1.19) with

$$r = \sum_{l=1}^{L} \alpha_l r_l \tag{1.177}$$

and the bit error probability is

$$P_b = Q\left(\sqrt{\frac{\left(\sum_{l=1}^{L} \alpha_l^2\right) 2E_b}{N_J}}\right) \tag{1.178}$$

where E_b is the energy of any single multipath signal when the amplitude term is unity ($\alpha = 1$). The energy due to all multipath terms is

$$E_T = \left(\sum_{l=1}^{L} \alpha_l^2\right) E_b \tag{1.179}$$

and (1.178) can be rewritten as

$$P_b = Q\left(\sqrt{\frac{2E_T}{N_J}}\right). \tag{1.180}$$

Next suppose that each multipath signal has a slowly varying independent fade. The L receiver outputs are then given by

$$r_l \cong d_0 A_l \sqrt{E_b} + n_l$$
$$l = 1, 2, \ldots, L \tag{1.181}$$

where $\{A_l\}$ are independent fade random variables. Conditioned on

$$\boldsymbol{A} = (A_1, A_2, \ldots, A_L) \tag{1.182}$$

the bit error probability and its Chernoff bound are given by

$$P_b(\boldsymbol{A}) = Q\left(\sqrt{\frac{\left(\sum_{l=1}^{L} A_l^2\right) 2E_b}{N_J}}\right)$$
$$\leq \tfrac{1}{2} e^{-\left(\sum_{l=1}^{L} A_l^2\right) E_b/N_J}$$
$$= \frac{1}{2} \prod_{l=1}^{L} e^{-A_l^2 E_b/N_J}. \tag{1.183}$$

Assuming A_l has probability density function $p_l(\cdot)$ for each $l = 1, 2, \ldots, L$ the average bit error bound is

$$P_b \leq \frac{1}{2} \prod_{l=1}^{L} \left\{ \int_0^{\infty} e^{-a^2 E_b / N_J} p_l(a)\, da \right\} \tag{1.184}$$

which for Rayleigh amplitudes with

$$\sigma_l^2 = \int_0^{\infty} a^2 p_l(a)\, da; \qquad l = 1, 2, \ldots, L \tag{1.185}$$

becomes

$$P_b \leq \frac{1}{2} \prod_{l=1}^{L} \left(\frac{1}{1 + \overline{E}_l / N_J} \right) \tag{1.186}$$

where $\overline{E}_l$ is the average signal energy in the l-th multipath signal given by

$$\overline{E}_l = \sigma_l^2 E_b; \qquad l = 1, 2, \ldots, L. \tag{1.187}$$

Note that when all the multipath energy terms are identical the exact expression for P_b is given by (1.146) with $d = L$. The general exact expression will be shown in (1.201).

In many channels, such as the tropospheric scatter channel, it is more appropriate to view the received signal as consisting of a continuum of multipath components. Such channels are usually characterized with channel output (see Proakis [33]),

$$y(t) = \int_{-\infty}^{\infty} H(\tau; t) x(t - \tau; (t \leftrightarrow \theta)(t - \tau))\, d\tau + J(t) \tag{1.188}$$

where $H(\tau; t)$ is a randomly time-varying filter.

Associated with the randomly time-varying filter $H(\tau; t)$ are two basic parameters; T_m denotes the total multipath delay spread of the channel and B_d denotes the Doppler spread of the channel. From these define

$$\Delta f_c = \frac{1}{T_m} \tag{1.189}$$

as the "coherence bandwidth" and

$$\Delta t_c = \frac{1}{B_d} \tag{1.190}$$

as the "coherence time" of the channel. Roughly, if two CW signals of frequency separation greater than Δf_c were transmitted through the channel, then the output signals at the two carrier frequencies would have independent channel disturbances (phase and envelope). Similarly, when a single CW signal is transmitted through the channel, its output sampled at time separations greater than Δt_c would have independent channel disturbances at the sample times.

For the uncoded DS/BPSK signal one data bit is transmitted every T_b seconds. Assume

$$T_b \gg T_m \tag{1.191}$$

so that intersymbol interference between data bits can be ignored. Also assume the channel is slowly varying so that

$$T_b \ll \Delta t_c. \tag{1.192}$$

Thus the channel disturbance is almost constant during a data bit time T_b. Finally, since our signal is a wideband signal of bandwidth W_{ss} assume

$$W_{ss} \gg \Delta f_c. \tag{1.193}$$

This model assumes many independent scatters are causing the continuum of multipath components. Thus the resulting channel output signal term is the sum of many independent scatters which justifies assuming it is a Gaussian random process. At any time it has a Rayleigh envelope probability distribution and an independent phase uniformly distributed over $[0, 2\pi]$. Skywave propagation where an HF signal is reflected off the ionosphere is an example where this model applies. If, however, there also exists a strong unfaded signal component such as a groundwave at HF, which appears in shorter ranges between transmitter and receivers, the signal out of the channel is assumed to have Rician fading statistics. In the following assume Rayleigh fading only.

Since the transmitted signal $x(t)$ has bandwidth W_{ss} centered at carrier frequency ω_0 radians, it can be represented in terms of samples of the inphase and quadrature components of the signal at sample times $\{n/W_{ss}: n = \dots, -1, 0, 1, 2, \dots\}$. Thus the channel output can be modelled as

$$y(t) = \sum_{n=-\infty}^{\infty} A_n(t) x\left(t - \frac{n}{W_{ss}}; \theta_n(t)\right) + J(t) \tag{1.194}$$

where at any time t the envelope terms are independent Rayleigh random variables and all phase terms are independent and uniformly distributed over $[0, 2\pi]$. Also, since the total multipath spread is T_m, for all practical purposes we can truncate the number of terms to

$$L = W_{ss} T_m + 1. \tag{1.195}$$

The assumption regarding the slowly varying nature of the channel where (1.192) holds means that $A_n(t)$ and $\theta_n(t)$ are constant during the bit time T_b. Thus

$$y(t) = \sum_{n=1}^{L} A_n x\left(t - \frac{n}{W_{ss}}; \theta_n\right) + J(t) \tag{1.196}$$

and the same situation as before with the finite number of distinct multipath components shown in (1.173) occurs here.

For this case the receiver can compute outputs for individual multipath signals as follows,

$$r_n = \int_{n/W_{ss}}^{T_b + n/W_{ss}} c\left(t - \frac{n}{W_{ss}}\right) y(t) \phi_c\left(t - \frac{n}{W_{ss}}; \theta_n\right) dt;$$

$$n = 1, 2, \ldots, L \tag{1.197}$$

provided the phase terms $\{\theta_n\}$ are known at the receiver. Also assuming envelopes $\{A_n\}$ are known, the optimum receiver compares

$$r = \sum_{n=1}^{L} A_n r_n \tag{1.198}$$

to zero to make the binary decision $\hat{d}$.

Next examine the optimum receiver structure implied by (1.197) and (1.198). Note that (1.197) can be rewritten as

$$r_n = \int_0^{T_b} y\left(t + \frac{n}{W_{ss}}\right) c(t) \phi_c(t; \theta_n)\, dt$$

$$n = 1, 2, \ldots, L \tag{1.199}$$

and so (1.198) becomes

$$r = \int_0^{T_b} \left[\sum_{n=1}^{L} y\left(t + \frac{n}{W_{ss}}\right) A_n c(t) \phi_c(t; \theta_n) \right] dt. \tag{1.200}$$

Figure 1.17 shows a block diagram for the optimum demodulator.

The ideal tapped delay line receiver of Figure 1.17 attempts to collect coherently the signal energy from all the received signal paths that fall within the span of the delay line and carry the same information. Because its actions act like a garden rake this has been coined the "Rake receiver" [23].

The bit error bound using the ideal Rake receiver is given by (1.186). An exact expression is given by (see Proakis [3], Chapter 7)

$$P_b = \frac{1}{2} \sum_{l=1}^{L} \pi_l \left[1 - \sqrt{\frac{\bar{E}_l / N_J}{1 + \bar{E}_l / N_J}} \right] \tag{1.201}$$

where

$$\pi_l = \prod_{\substack{k=1 \\ k \neq l}}^{L} \left(\frac{\bar{E}_l}{\bar{E}_l - \bar{E}_k} \right)$$

$$l = 1, 2, \ldots, L. \tag{1.202}$$

The ideal Rake receiver assumes complete knowledge of the phase and envelope terms which appear in the correlation functions $\{A_n c(t) \phi_c(t; \theta_n)\}$. When the fading is slow this estimate is quite good.

A simpler form of the optimum receiver can be obtained using complex baseband representations for the radio signals on a carrier frequency of ω_0 radians. In general, the radio signal $f(t)$ with a carrier frequency ω_0 has representation

$$f(t) = g(t)\cos[\omega_0 t + \eta(t)]$$
$$= \mathrm{Re}\{\mathscr{F}(t)e^{j\omega_0 t}\} \tag{1.203}$$

where $g(t)$ and $\eta(t)$ are real-valued functions and

$$\mathscr{F}(t) = g(t)e^{j\eta(t)} \tag{1.204}$$

is the complex baseband signal representing the radio signal $f(t)$. Using script letters to represent complex baseband signals

$$\begin{aligned} x(t;\theta) &= \mathrm{Re}\{\mathscr{X}(t;\theta)e^{j\omega_0 t}\}, \\ \phi(t;\theta) &= \mathrm{Re}\{\Phi(t;\theta)e^{j\omega_0 t}\}, \\ J(t) &= \mathrm{Re}\{\mathscr{J}(t)e^{j\omega_0 t}\}, \\ y(t) &= \mathrm{Re}\{\mathscr{Y}(t)e^{j\omega_0 t}\} \end{aligned} \tag{1.205}$$

where

$$\begin{aligned} \mathscr{X}(t;\theta) &= c(t)\,d(t)\sqrt{2S}\,e^{j\theta}, \\ \Phi(t;\theta) &= \sqrt{\frac{2}{T_b}}\,e^{j\theta}, \\ \mathscr{Y}(t) &= \sum_{n=1}^{L} A_n c\left(t - \frac{n}{W_{ss}}\right) d\left(t - \frac{n}{W_{ss}}\right)\sqrt{2S}\,e^{j\theta} + \mathscr{J}(t). \end{aligned} \tag{1.206}$$

Assuming the carrier frequency is much greater than the signal bandwidth, the form for r in (1.200) is given by

$$\begin{aligned} r &= \mathrm{Re}\left\{\int_0^{T_b}\left[\sum_{n=1}^{L}\mathscr{Y}\left(t + \frac{n}{W_{ss}}\right)A_n c(t)\Phi^*(t;\theta_n)\right]dt\right\} \\ &= \mathrm{Re}\left\{\int_0^{T_b}\left[\sum_{n=1}^{L}\sqrt{\frac{2}{T_b}}\,\mathscr{Y}\left(t + \frac{n}{W_{ss}}\right)A_n e^{-j\theta_n}c(t)\right]dt\right\}. \end{aligned} \tag{1.207}$$

The receiver structure of Figure 1.17 can implement this complex form of the optimum receiver by replacing $y(t)$ by $\mathscr{Y}(t)$ and $A_n c(t)\Phi(t;\theta_n)$ by $A_n e^{-j\theta_n}c(t)$ for each n.

We now examine a way of estimating $A_n e^{-j\theta_n}$ which is required in a practical Rake receiver. Note that

$$\begin{aligned} \mathscr{Y}\left(t + \frac{l}{W_{ss}}\right)c(t) &= c(t)\sum_{n=1}^{L} A_n c\left(t - \frac{n-l}{W_{ss}}\right) d\left(t - \frac{n-l}{W_{ss}}\right)\sqrt{2S}\,e^{j\theta_n} \\ &\quad + c(t)\mathscr{J}(t) \\ &= A_l e^{j\theta_l}\sqrt{2S}\,d(t) + c(t)\mathscr{J}(t) \\ &\quad + \sum_{\substack{n=1 \\ n\neq l}}^{L} A_n c(t) c\left(t - \frac{n-l}{W_{ss}}\right) d\left(t - \frac{n-l}{W_{ss}}\right)\sqrt{2S}\,e^{j\theta_n}. \end{aligned} \tag{1.208}$$

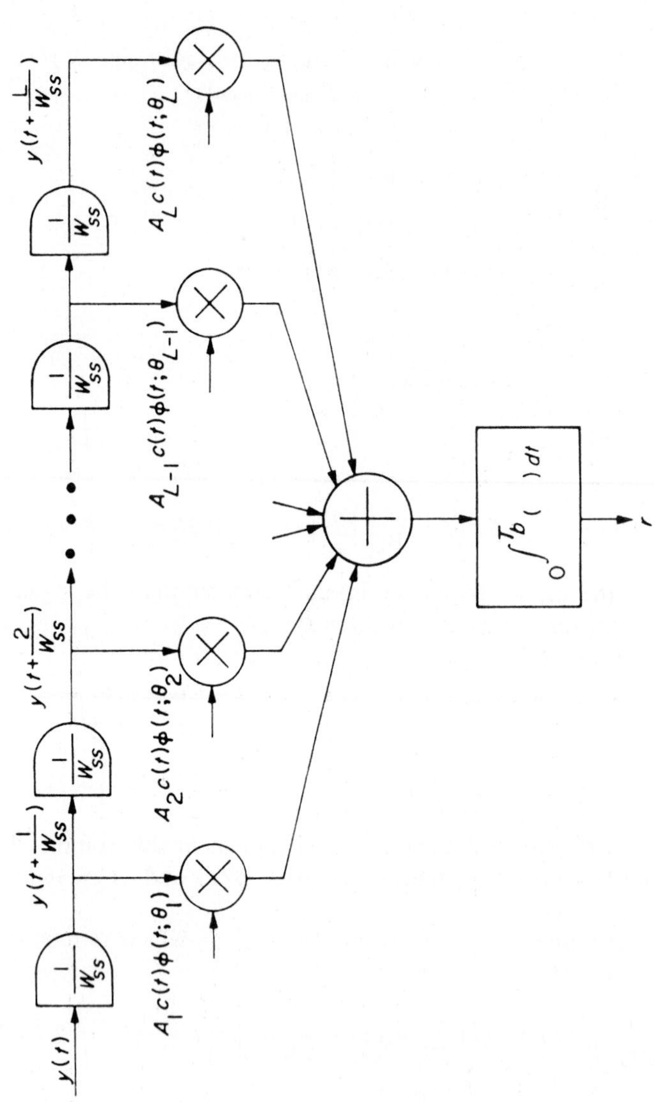

Figure 1.17. Ideal Rake receiver.

Recall that $c(t)$ is independent of $c(t-(n-l)/W_{ss})$ for each value of t when $n \neq l$ and thus,

$$\int_0^{T_b} \mathcal{Y}\left(t+\frac{l}{W_{ss}}\right) c(t)\,dt = A_l e^{j\theta_l}\sqrt{2S}\,d_0 \cdot T_b + n_l \qquad (1.209)$$

where d_0 is the data bit in $(0, T_b)$ and n_l is a Gaussian random variable. This suggests that the estimate for $A_n e^{-j\theta_n}$ be given by the conjugate of (1.209). This estimate, however, includes the data bit d_0. Assuming $A_n e^{-j\theta_n}$ remains unchanged over $2T_b$ seconds, an estimate can be based on the previous T_b second channel output signal. This estimate is shown in the complex form of the Rake receiver illustrated in Figure 1.18.

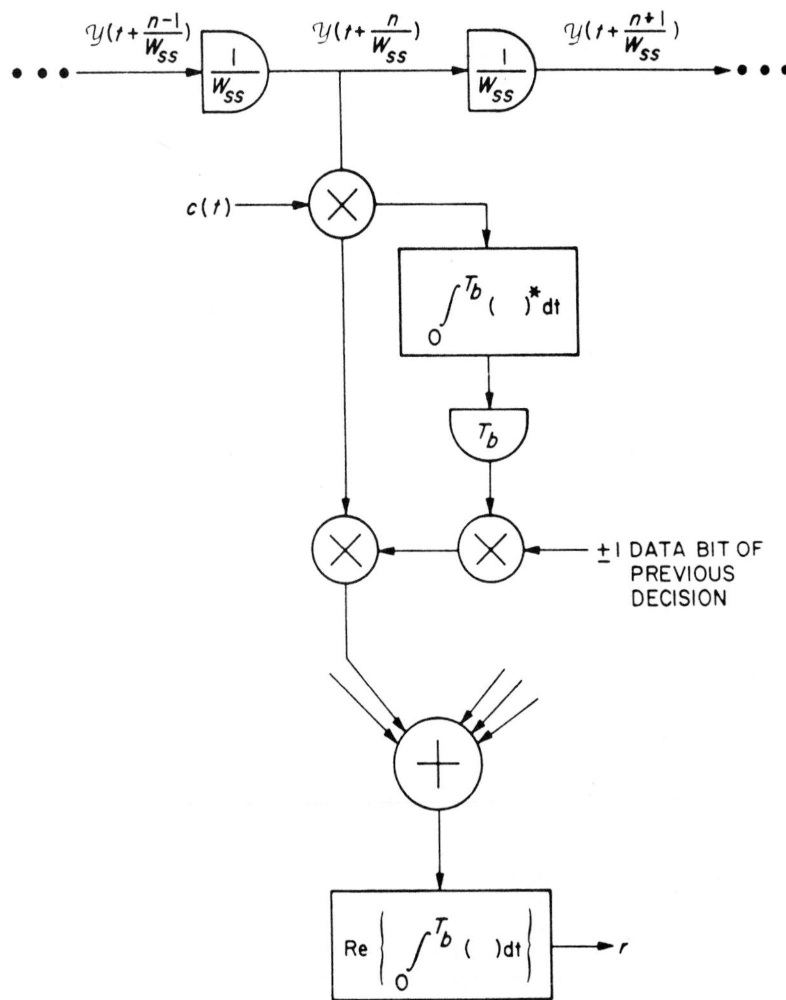

Figure 1.18. Rake with estimates.

Thus far the results in this section have applied only to uncoded DS/BPSK signals in slow fading multipath channels. With coding and ideal interleavers and deinterleavers the channel disturbance can be assumed to be independent for each transmitted coded bit. Assuming the soft decision metric of (1.120) where r is given by (1.207) and $x \in \{-1, 1\}$ the pairwise error bound for two sequences $\boldsymbol{x}$ and $\hat{\boldsymbol{x}}$ is given by (1.131) where

$$D(\lambda) = E\{e^{\lambda r(\hat{x}-x)}|x\}, \quad \hat{x} \neq x. \tag{1.210}$$

From (1.181) and (1.198)

$$\begin{aligned} r &= \sum_{l=1}^{L} A_l r_l \\ &= \sum_{l=1}^{L} \left(d_0 A_l^2 \sqrt{E_s} + A_l n_l\right) \end{aligned} \tag{1.211}$$

where $\{n_l\}$ are i.i.d. zero-mean Gaussian random variables with variance $N_J/2$. Thus

$$\begin{aligned} D(\lambda) &= \prod_{l=1}^{L} E\{e^{-2\lambda[A_l^2\sqrt{E_s}+A_l n_l]}\} \\ &= \prod_{l=1}^{L} E\left\{E\left\{e^{-2\lambda[A_l^2\sqrt{E_s}+A_l n_l]}\middle|A_l\right\}\right\} \\ &= \prod_{l=1}^{L} E\left\{e^{-2\lambda A_l^2\sqrt{E_s}}E\left\{e^{-2\lambda A_l n_l}\middle|A_l\right\}\right\} \\ &= \prod_{l=1}^{L} E\left\{e^{-A_l^2(2\lambda\sqrt{E_s}-\lambda^2 N_J)}\right\} \\ &= \prod_{l=1}^{L}\left(\frac{1}{1+2\sigma_l^2\left(2\lambda\sqrt{E_s}-\lambda^2 N_J\right)}\right) \end{aligned} \tag{1.212}$$

where the amplitudes $\{A_l\}$ are again assumed Rayleigh distributed with variance as in (1.185). Then, define parameter

$$\begin{aligned} D &= \min_{\lambda \geq 0} \prod_{l=1}^{L}\left(\frac{1}{1+2\sigma_l^2\left(2\lambda\sqrt{E_s}-\lambda^2 N_J\right)}\right) \\ &= \min_{s \geq 0} \prod_{l=1}^{L}\left(\frac{1}{1+2(\overline{E}_l/N_0)(2s-s^2)}\right) \end{aligned} \tag{1.213}$$

where $\overline{E}_l$ is given by (1.187) with E_b replaced by E_s.

Suppose $\overline{E}_T$ is the total average energy and each multipath energy term is the same. That is,

$$\overline{E}_l = \frac{\overline{E}_T}{L} \qquad l = 1, 2, \ldots, L. \tag{1.214}$$

Then $s = 1$ minimizes the bound and

$$D = \left[\frac{L}{L + \bar{E}_T/N_J}\right]^L \tag{1.215}$$

For the hard decision channel with the usual unweighted metric we have simply

$$D = \sqrt{4\varepsilon(1 - \varepsilon)} \tag{1.216}$$

where now $\varepsilon = P_b$ given by (1.201) and (1.202).

1.8 OTHER CODING METRICS FOR PULSE JAMMING

In the previous section, the ideal Rake receiver was approximated by a receiver that estimated the slowly varying multipath fading envelopes. Earlier, we had examined a similar ideal case in Section 1.4 where we considered various decoding metrics for DS/BPSK signals against pulse jamming. The ideal metric for this case is the soft decision metric with jammer state information given by

$$m(y, x; Z) = c(Z)yx \tag{1.217}$$

where Z is the jammer state random variable with probabilities

$$\begin{aligned} \Pr\{Z = 1\} &= \rho \\ \Pr\{Z = 0\} &= 1 - \rho \end{aligned} \tag{1.218}$$

and $c(Z)$ is a weighting function such that $c(0)$ is chosen as large as possible and $c(1) = 1$. Under these conditions, it was previously shown in Chapter 4, Part 1, that the channel parameter for this case is given by

$$\begin{aligned} D &= \min_{\lambda \geq 0} \rho \exp\{-2\lambda E_s + \lambda^2 E_s N_J/\rho\} \\ &= \rho e^{-\rho E_s/N_J} \end{aligned} \tag{1.219}$$

which when translated to its equivalent computational cutoff rate R_0 via (1.92) is illustrated as curve (1) in Figure 1.8.

When using the same soft decision metric, i.e., (1.217) without jammer state information, we observed in Chapter 4, Part 1, that the appropriate metric weighting then becomes $c(0) = c(1) = 1$. For this case, we obtain (see Chapter 4, Volume I)

$$D = \min_{\lambda \geq 0} e^{-2\lambda E_s}\left[\rho e^{\lambda^2 E_s N_J/\rho} + 1 - \rho\right] \tag{1.220}$$

which has the equivalent computational cutoff rate $R_0 = 0$ *for all* E_s/N_0 as illustrated by curve (3) in Figure 1.8. The implication of this result is that the soft decision metric without jammer state information has no protection against a jammer who concentrates his available power in a very narrow pulse. Stated another way, a receiver that uses a soft decision metric with no jammer state information has, in the presence of an optimized pulse jammer, an unbounded probability of error. One way of getting around this intolerable degradation in the absence of jammer state information is to use hard decision decoding. This was shown, however, to result in a relatively poor performance, as can be witnessed by examining curve (4) in Figure 1.8.

In this section, we first examine other metrics that allow soft decision decoding to be used with an optimized pulse jammer and no jammer state information. Following this, we reexamine the behavior of soft decision decoding with jammer state information and the necessary modifications to the metric when, indeed, the estimate of the jammer state Z is not perfect, e.g., in the presence of background noise.

Perhaps the simplest modification of the soft decision receiver to allow operation in the presence of a pulse jammer is to *clamp* the input to the decoder at either a fixed or variable level, the latter case requiring an intelligent controller in the decoder. Clamping the decoder input level provides a means for limiting the potentially large excursions in this level caused by narrow pulse jammers and as such prevents the decoder's decision metric from being dominated by these extreme signal level swings when the jammer is present. Mathematically speaking, the operation of clamping is equivalent to first passing the decoder input y through a zero mean non-linearity with transfer function

$$y' = \begin{cases} k\sqrt{E_s}\,; & y > k\sqrt{E_s} \\ y; & |y| \le k\sqrt{E_s} \\ -k\sqrt{E_s}\,; & y < -k\sqrt{E_s} \end{cases} \tag{1.221}$$

where y' now represents the actual decoder input and $k \ge 0$ is a parameter which is either fixed or is allowed to vary with E_s/N_J and the pulse jammer's strategy, i.e., ρ.

In the absence of jammer state information, El-Wailly [34] has shown that using the normalized maximum-likelihood metric $m(y', x) = y'x/N_J$, the channel parameter D is given by

$$\begin{aligned} D = \min_{\lambda \ge 0} e^{-\lambda 2E_s/N_J}\Big[(1-\rho) + \rho\Big\{ & Q\Big[\sqrt{2\rho E_s/N_J}\,(k-1)\Big]e^{2\lambda(1-k)E_s/N_J} \\ & + Q\Big[\sqrt{2\rho E_s/N_J}\,(k+1)\Big]e^{2\lambda(1+k)E_s/N_J} \\ & + e^{\lambda^2 E_s/(\rho N_J)}\big[Q(A) - Q(B)\big]\Big\}\Big], \end{aligned} \tag{1.222}$$

where $Q(x)$ is again the Gaussian probability integral and

$$\begin{aligned} A &= (1-k)\sqrt{2\rho E_s/N_J} - \lambda\sqrt{2E_s/(\rho N_J)}\,, \\ B &= (1+k)\sqrt{2\rho E_s/N_J} - \lambda\sqrt{2E_s/(\rho N_J)}\,. \end{aligned} \tag{1.223}$$

Intuitively, one would expect that a clamped (fixed or variable) soft decision receiver characterized by (1.221) would outperform a hard decision decoding metric and at the same time not be totally vulnerable to the optimum pulse jammer as is the unclamped soft decision metric (i.e., $k = \infty$). The degree to which this observation is true is demonstrated by the following illustrations and discussion.

Figure 1.19 is an illustration of D as computed from (1.222) versus E_s/N_J for a fixed clamping level of $k = 1$ and the worst case jammer who chooses his ρ to maximize D for each value of E_s/N_J. Also illustrated for purposes of comparison is the corresponding result for the hard decision decoding metric (with no jammer state information) which from Chapter 4, Volume I, is given by

$$D = \sqrt{4\varepsilon(1-\varepsilon)}\,; \quad \varepsilon = \rho Q\left(\sqrt{2\rho E_s/N_J}\right). \tag{1.224}$$

As a reminder, the curve for the unclamped soft decision decoder (with no jamming state information) for worst case pulse jamming would simply be a horizontal line corresponding to $D = 1$ for all E_s/N_J.

When the clamping level is allowed to vary, then assuming that the receiver contains an intelligent controller that can choose the value of k so as to minimize D for each value of ρ, Figure 1.20 illustrates the corresponding performance in terms of a three-dimensional plot of D versus E_s/N_J and ρ. Alternately, suppose it is assumed that the receiver has no intelli-

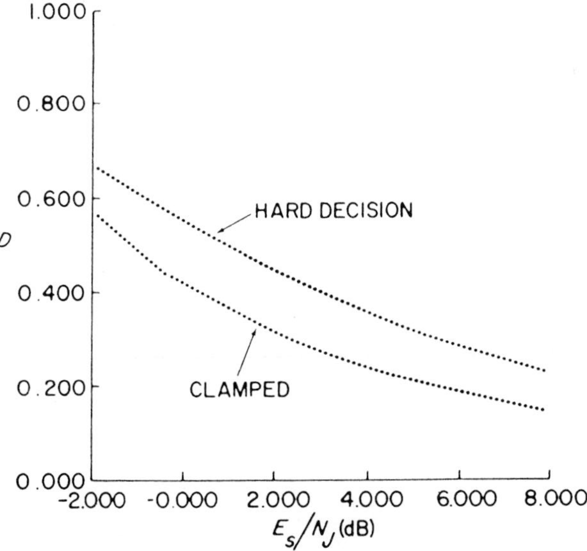

Figure 1.19. Channel parameter versus signal-to-noise ratio for worst case jammer (no jammer state information). (Reprinted from [35].)

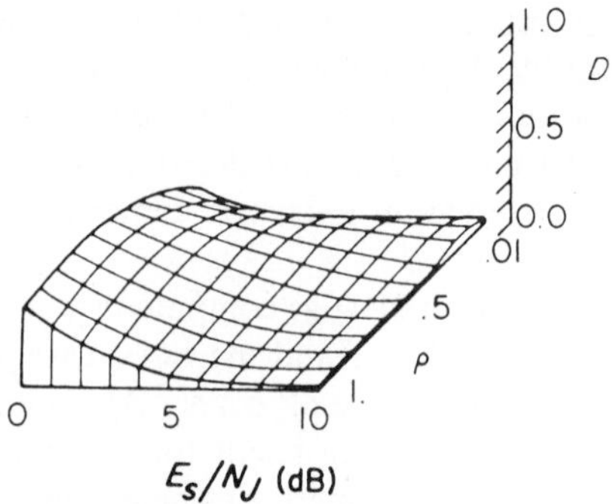

Figure 1.20. Channel parameter versus ρ and signal-to-noise ratio for best clamping level. (Reprinted from [35].)

gence, i.e., it fixes k at some value between .01 and 1.0, but the jammer, on the other hand, is intelligent and assumed to know k, in which case, he chooses ρ to maximize D. For this scenario, Figure 1.21 illustrates D versus E_s/N_J and k. Clearly, much larger values of D result for this case as compared with those in Figure 1.20.

We now return to a consideration of soft decision decoding metrics with jammer state information that derive their benefit from the fact that the contribution to the metric in those time intervals where the jammer is absent is very heavily weighted compared to that in the intervals where the jammer is known to be present. Up until now, we have assumed that knowledge of the presence or absence of the jammer during a given time interval was perfect. With, for example, additive background noise, the estimation of Z, the jammer state parameter, will not be perfect. We now examine how to suitably modify the soft decision decoding metric and the impact on its performance as a result of having imperfect jammer state information.

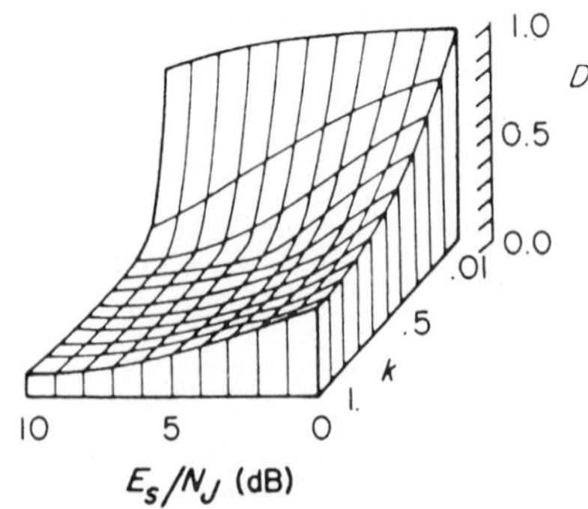

Figure 1.21. Channel parameter versus signal-to-noise ratio and clamping level for worst case jammer. (Reprinted from [35].)

DS/BPSK transmission over a channel with background additive white Gaussian noise of power spectral density N_0 and a pulse jammer with parameters $N_J = J/W$ and ρ, is equivalent to sending a BPSK signal over an additive white Gaussian noise channel with noise spectral density

$$N_{0e} = \begin{cases} N_0; & \text{if } Z = 0 \\ N_0' \triangleq N_0 + \dfrac{N_J}{\rho}; & \text{if } Z = 1 \end{cases} \tag{1.225}$$

where Z is again the jammer state parameter with probabilities as in (1.218). If perfect jammer state information were possible, then the metric of (1.217) would be used with

$$c(0) = \frac{1}{N_0}$$

$$c(1) = \frac{1}{N_0'}. \tag{1.226}$$

Since, as mentioned above, the background noise perfect jammer state information is not possible, then the metric of (1.217) is still appropriate except that now Z is replaced by an estimate $\hat{Z}$ of the jammer state. The manner in which the estimate $\hat{Z}$ is obtained and its statistics are the subject of the following discussion.

As in the Rake receiver illustrated in Figure 1.18, an estimate $\hat{Z}$ of the jammer state might be based on the previous BPSK transmission.[6] Another approach would be to base the estimate on the amplitude of the received signal in the current interval as follows:

$$\hat{Z} = \begin{cases} 0; & \text{if } |y| \le \beta\sqrt{E_s} \\ 1; & \text{if } |y| > \beta\sqrt{E_s}. \end{cases} \tag{1.227}$$

Basically, this receiver assumes that when the channel output y is close to one of the two signal terms, $\sqrt{E_s}$ or $-\sqrt{E_s}$, then the channel contains only background noise. Substituting (1.226) in (1.217) then gives the metric examined by El-Wailly and Costello [35]:

$$m(y, x; \hat{Z}) = \begin{cases} \dfrac{yx}{N_0}; & \text{if } \hat{Z} = 0 \\ \dfrac{yx}{N_0'}; & \text{if } \hat{Z} = 1. \end{cases} \tag{1.228}$$

It should be noted that the metric of (1.228) can also be regarded as one that assumes no jammer state information since indeed the jammer state information comes directly from measurements on the observable (i.e., the channel output) rather than from an external source. Thus, combining

[6] This estimate can be done before deinterleaving at the receiver to make the channel memoryless.

(1.227) and (1.228), we get the alternate form

$$m(y, x; \hat{Z}) = \begin{cases} \dfrac{yx}{N_0}; & \text{if } |y| \leq \beta\sqrt{E_s} \\ \dfrac{yx}{N_0'}; & \text{if } |y| > \beta\sqrt{E_s} \end{cases} \tag{1.229}$$

For the metric of (1.229), El-Wailly and Costello [35] have shown that the channel parameter D is given by

$$\begin{aligned} D = \min_{\lambda \geq 0} (1 - \rho)\Big\{ & I\big[-\infty, (1 - \beta)\sqrt{E_s}, N_0', N_0\big] \\ & + I\big[(1 - \beta)\sqrt{E_s}, (1 + \beta)\sqrt{E_s}, N_0, N_0\big] \\ & + I\big[(1 + \beta)\sqrt{E_s}, +\infty, N_0', N_0\big]\Big\} \\ & + \rho\Big\{I\big[-\infty, (1 - \beta)\sqrt{E_s}, N_0', N_0'\big] \\ & + I\big[(1 - \beta)\sqrt{E_s}, (1 + \beta)\sqrt{E_s}, N_0, N_0'\big] \\ & + I\big[(1 + \beta)\sqrt{E_s}, +\infty, N_0', N_0'\big]\Big\}, \end{aligned} \tag{1.230}$$

where

$$I[L, H, \hat{N}, N] = e^{-(E_s/\hat{N})[2\lambda - (N/\hat{N})\lambda^2]}[F(L) - F(H)], \tag{1.231}$$

and

$$F(t) = Q\Big[t\sqrt{2/N} - \lambda\sqrt{(2E_s/\hat{N})(N/\hat{N})}\Big]. \tag{1.232}$$

Figure 1.22 illustrates the performance of a receiver using the metric of (1.229) in terms of D versus ρ with β as a parameter for $E_s/N_J = 5$ dB and a background-to-jammer-noise-spectral-density ratio $N_0/N_J = 1.0$. Also shown for comparison are the corresponding results for the ideal soft decision metric with unknown and perfectly known jamming state information. We observe that the performance corresponding to (1.230) is much improved over that of the unknown jammer state case but not as good as when the jammer state is perfectly known. Also, a value of $\beta = 2$ seems to give best performance.

Suppose that we again use the metric of (1.228) but now the jammer state estimate is provided by means external to the decoder. In particular, assume that the probability of error in Z is described by the false alarm and missed detection probabilities

$$\begin{aligned} P_{FA} &= \Pr\{\hat{Z} \neq Z\} \text{ when } Z = 0 \\ P_{MD} &= \Pr\{\hat{Z} \neq Z\} \text{ when } Z = 1 \end{aligned} \tag{1.233}$$

i.e., the probability of estimating the state of the jammer depends on the state of the jammer. Typically, we would want to choose $P_{MD} \ll P_{FA}$ since

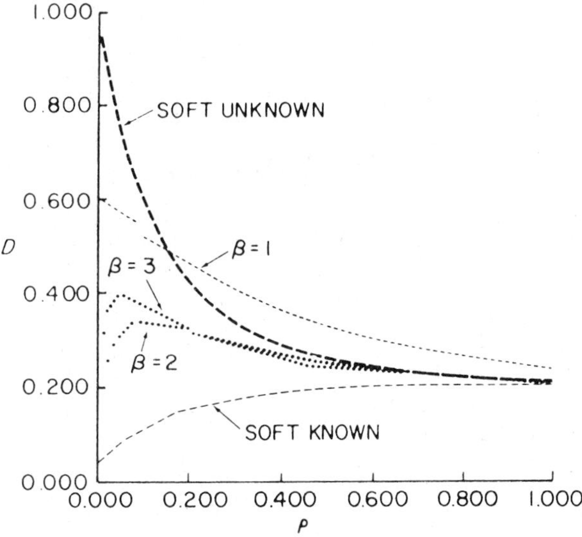

Figure 1.22. Channel parameter vs. ρ for system with estimate based on signal level and with $E_s/N_J = 5$ dB and $N_0/N_J = 1.0$. (Reprinted from [35].)

the effect on the metric of missing a jammed channel symbol is much more severe than that produced by assuming the jammer is present when indeed he is not. For this scenario, the channel parameter D has been shown to be given by [35]

$$\begin{aligned} D = \min_{\lambda \geq 0} & (1-\rho)(1-P_{FA})e^{-[2\lambda-\lambda^2]E_s/N_0} \\ & + (1-\rho)P_{FA}e^{-[2\lambda-(N_0/N_0')\lambda^2]E_s/N_0'} \\ & + \rho(1-P_{MD})e^{-[2\lambda-\lambda^2]E_s/N_0'} \\ & + \rho P_{MD}e^{-[2\lambda-(N_0'/N_0)\lambda^2]E_s/N_0}. \end{aligned} \tag{1.234}$$

which is illustrated in Figure 1.23 versus ρ and P_{FA} for $P_{MD} = 10^{-8}$, $E_s/N_J = 5$ dB, and $N_0/N_J = 1.0$.

Finally, it should be obvious that one could employ a metric that combines the advantages of clamping the decoder input level with a jammer state estimate provided by external means. Such metrics have been considered in [35] and their performance analyzed by the general analysis techniques of Chapter 4, Part 1.

In conclusion, we leave the reader with the thought that while many other metrics for the pulse jamming channel with additive background noise are theoretically possible, from a practical standpoint, one wants to select a metric that is easy to implement and robust in the sense that the worst case

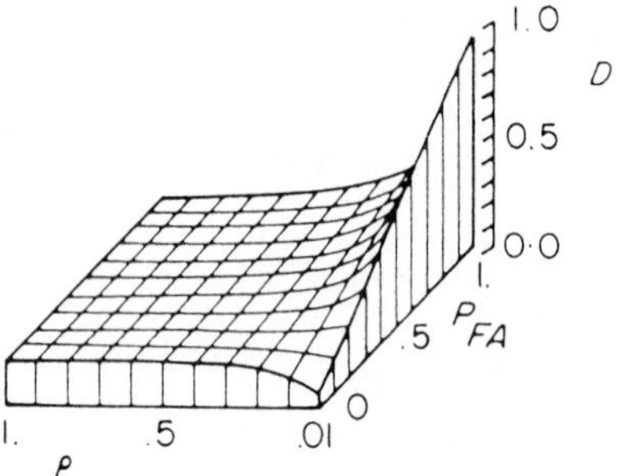

Figure 1.23. Channel parameter versus ρ and P_{FA} for $P_{MD} = 10^{-8}$, $E_s/N_J = 5$ dB, and $N_0/N_J = 1.0$. (Reprinted from [35].)

jammer does not do much more harm than the baseline constant power jammer.

1.9 DISCUSSION

With DS/BPSK signals we have shown that any jammer signal, after despreading at the receiver, can be approximated as additive Gaussian noise. Thus there is an equivalent Gaussian noise channel with BPSK data modulation. For uncoded BPSK data modulation with BPSK PN spreading, however, it was possible for the jammer power in the BPSK signal coordinate (cosine) to be as much as 3 dB more than expected with natural noise of the same power. To combat this potential degradation BPSK data modulation with QPSK PN spreading can be used. In this case the uncoded bit error probability is (see (1.59) and (1.72))

$$P_b = Q\left(\sqrt{\frac{E_b}{\sigma^2}}\right) \tag{1.235}$$

where

$$\sigma^2 = N_J/2 \tag{1.236}$$

is the equivalent two-sided jammer noise spectral density.

Although the jammer statistics can be approximated as Gaussian regardless of the waveform used by the jammer, its power may be varied in time. This results in a Gaussian noise channel where the noise variance varies in time. Denote this variance sequence as $\{\sigma_n^2\}$ where σ_n^2 is the noise variance during the n-th BPSK modulated data symbol.

By concentrating its power on a few uncoded data bits, the jammer can dramatically increase the average bit error probability for the same time-averaged power level. To combat this jammer strategy some form of coding is required. For a sequence of L-coded symbols $x_1, x_2, \ldots, x_L$ where $x_n \in \{1, -1\}$ the ideal decoder metric is (see [33])

$$m(y, x) = \sum_{n=1}^{L} \frac{y_n x_n}{\sigma_n^2} \tag{1.237}$$

where $y_1, y_2, \ldots, y_L$ is the sampled BPSK correlator output. With this type of decoder metric the degradation due to time-varying jammer power (pulse jamming) can be effectively neutralized.

The ideal soft decision metric (1.237) assumes complete knowledge of the jammer power level during each coded BPSK modulation symbol time. That is, it assumes knowledge of the noise variances $\{\sigma_n^2\}$. Section 1.7 examined various alternative metrics where this jammer state information is not available or only partially available or estimated. Various quantized forms of this metric have also been considered in this chapter.

DS/BPSK waveforms can also be used effectively in fading channels where a more complex receiver structure is required. Here, too, decision and decoding metrics are used that require complete or estimated information regarding the channel.

The discussion of this chapter focussed on BPSK data modulation where coding consists of transmitting a constrained sequence of binary (± 1) symbols each modulated on a BPSK waveform. In some applications it is useful to use orthogonal binary sequences. In particular, $M = 2^L$ orthogonal binary sequences of L bit length can be generated by defining a sequence of $m \times m$ binary matrices $\{H_m\}$ as,

$$H_{m+1} = \begin{bmatrix} H_m & H_m \\ H_m & -H_m \end{bmatrix} \tag{1.238}$$

where

$$H_1 = \begin{bmatrix} 1 & 1 \\ 1 & -1 \end{bmatrix}. \tag{1.239}$$

The $M = 2^L$ rows of H_L are L bit length orthogonal binary sequences.

Orthogonal binary sequences can be viewed as an orthogonal code. Alternatively the entire L bit sequence of BPSK waveforms can be considered to be a single M-ary waveform. The set of waveforms form M orthogonal signals which can be demodulated coherently or non-coherently. These M-ary waveforms can be regarded as basic signals for an M-ary input modulation. In some applications DS/BPSK spread-spectrum signals are converted to these M-ary modulations where demodulation is done non-coherently.

In the next chapter we examine M-ary orthogonal signals that are non-coherently demodulated. There the orthogonal signals consist of CW carriers of different frequencies referred to as frequency-shift-keying (FSK) modulation. Many of the results there apply to the M-ary waveforms described above which consist of orthogonal binary sequences modulated onto BPSK waveforms.

1.10 REFERENCES

[1] *Proceedings of the 1973 Symposium on Spread Spectrum Communications*, Naval Electronics Laboratory Center, San Diego, CA, March 13–16, 1973.

[2] *Spread Spectrum Communications*, Lecture Series No. 58, Advisory Group for Aerospace Research and Development, North Atlantic Treaty Organization, July 1973 (AD 766914).

[3] R. C. Dixon, ed., *Spread Spectrum Techniques*, New York: IEEE Press, 1976.

[4] R. C. Dixon, *Spread Spectrum Systems*, New York: John Wiley, 1976.

[5] L. A. Gerhardt and R. C. Dixon, Special Issue on Spread Spectrum Communications, *IEEE Trans. Commun.*, COM-25, August 1977.

[6] D. J. Torrieri, *Principles of Military Communication Systems*, Dedham, MA: Artech House, 1981.

[7] C. E. Cook, F. W. Ellersick, L. B. Milstein, and D. L. Schilling, eds., Special Issue on Spread Spectrum Communications, *IEEE Trans. Commun.*, COM-30, May 1982.

[8] J. K. Holmes, *Coherent Spread Spectrum Systems*, New York: John Wiley, 1982.

[9] G. C. Clark, Jr., and J. B. Cain, *Error-Correction Coding for Digital Communications*, New York: Plenum Press, 1981.

[10] *MILCOM Conference Record*, 1982 IEEE Military Communications Conference, Boston, MA, October 17–20, 1982.

[11] Proceedings of the *1983* Spread Spectrum Symposium, *Long Island, NY. Sponsored by the Long Island Chapter of the IEEE Commun. Soc.*, 807 *Grundy Ave., Holbrook, NY.*

[12] R. A. Scholtz, "The spread spectrum concept," *IEEE Trans. Commun.*, COM-25, pp. 748-755, August 1977.

[13] M. P. Ristenbatt and J. L. Daws, Jr., "Performance criteria for spread spectrum communications," *IEEE Trans. Commun.*, COM-25, pp. 756–763, August 1977.

[14] C. L. Cuccia, "Spread spectrum techniques are revolutionizing communications," *MSN*, pp. 37–49, September 1977.

[15] R. E. Kahn, S. A. Gronemeyer, J. Burchfield, and R. C. Kunzelman, "Advances in packet radio technology," *Proc. IEEE*, vol. 66, pp. 1468–1496, November 1978.

[16] A. J. Viterbi, "Spread spectrum communications—Myths and realities," *IEEE Commun. Mag.*, vol. 17, pp. 11–18, May 1979.

[17] R. L. Pickholtz, D. L. Schilling, and L. B. Milstein, "Theory of spread spectrum communications—A tutorial," *IEEE Trans. Commun.*, COM-30, pp. 855–884, May 1982.

[18] C. E. Cook and H. S. Marsh, "An introduction to spread spectrum," *IEEE Commun. Mag.*, vol. 21, pp. 8–16, March 1983.

[19] M. Spellman, "A comparison between frequency hopping and direct sequence PN as antijam techniques," *IEEE Commun. Mag.*, vol. 21, pp. 37–51, March 1983.

[20] P. A. Kullstam, "A Theoretical Investigation of Spread Spectrum Modulation Concepts and Performance," Ph.D. Thesis, Catholic University of America, May 1977.

[21] P. A. Kullstam, "Spread spectrum performance analysis in arbitrary interference," *IEEE Trans. Commun.*, COM-25, pp. 848–853, August 1977.

[22] W. Feller, *An Introduction to Probability Theory and Its Applications, Vol. II*, New York: John Wiley, 1966.

[23] R. Price, "The detection of signals perturbed by scatter and noise," *IRE Trans. Inform. Theory*, PGIT-4, pp. 163–170, September 1954.

[24] R. Price and P. E. Green, Jr., "A communication technique for multipath channels," *Proc. IRE*, vol. 46, pp. 555–570, March 1958.

[25] R. Price and P. E. Green, Jr., "Signal processing in radar astronomy—Communication via fluctuating multipath media," MIT Lincoln Laboratory, Lexington, Mass., Tech. Report No. 234, October 1960.

[26] T. Kailath, "Correlation detection of signals perturbed by a random channel," *IRE Trans. Inform. Theory*, IT-6, pp. 361–366, June 1960.

[27] T. Kailath, "Channel characterization: Time-variant dispersive channels," Chap. 6, in *Lectures on Communication System Theory*, E. Baghdady, ed., New York: McGraw-Hill, 1961.

[28] G. L. Turin, "On optimal diversity reception," *IRE Trans. Inform. Theory*, IT-7, pp. 154–166, July 1961.

[29] G. L. Turin, "On optimal diversity reception II," *IRE Trans. Commun. Systems*, vol. CS-12, pp. 22–31, March 1962.

[30] R. Price, "Error probabilities for adaptive multichannel reception of binary signals," *IRE Trans. Inform. Theory*, IT-8, pp. 305–316, September 1962.

[31] D. Chase, "Digital signal design concepts for a time-varying Rician channel," *IEEE Trans. Commun.*, COM-24, pp. 164–172, February 1976.

[32] J. F. Pieper, J. G. Proakis, R. R. Reed, and J. K. Wolf., "Design of efficient coding and modulation for a Rayleigh fading channel," *IEEE Trans. Inform. Theory*, IT-24, pp. 457–468, July 1978.

[33] J. G. Proakis, *Digital Communications*, New York: McGraw-Hill, 1983.

[34] F. El-Wailly, "Convolutional Code Performance Analysis of Jammed Spread Spectrum Channels Without Side Information," Ph.D. dissertation, Illinois Institute of Technology, 1982.

[35] F. El-Wailly, and D. J. Costello, "Analysis of coded spread spectrum soft decision receivers: Part I – Direct sequence modulation with pulse jamming, Part II–Frequency hopped modualtion with partial band jamming," submitted to *IEEE Trans. Inform. Theory*.

Chapter 2

NON-COHERENT FREQUENCY-HOPPED SYSTEMS

In Chapter 1 we considered direct-sequence (DS) spread-spectrum (SS) communication systems with coherent phase-shift-keyed (PSK) modulation. These systems use a pseudonoise (PN) sequence to directly spread the data-modulated carrier, producing a continuous $(\sin x/x)^2$ power spectrum (assuming the usual rectangular modulation pulse shape) with bandwidth W_{ss}. Because of practical considerations (it is difficult to synchronize the PN generator in the receiver to sub-nanosecond accuracy), current DS systems typically operate with PN rates of 100 Mchips/sec or less, implying that W_{ss} is limited to several hundred MHz.

We will now analyze the other principal category of SS systems, namely, frequency hopping (FH) with non-coherent M-ary frequency-shift-keyed (MFSK) modulation. This is essentially a conventional MFSK scheme in which the carrier frequency is pseudorandomly hopped over W_{ss} under the control of a PN sequence. Specifically, as illustrated in Figure 2.1, successive (not necessarily disjoint) k-chip segments of the PN sequence drive a frequency synthesizer which hops the carrier over 2^k frequencies. On a given hop, the signal bandwidth is identical to conventional MFSK, which is typically much smaller than W_{ss}; however, averaged over many hops, the FH/MFSK spectrum occupies the entire SS bandwidth. Current technology permits FH bandwidths of the order of several GHz, which is an order of magnitude larger than implementable DS bandwidths. Because they must operate over such wide bandwidths, FH synthesizers generally do not maintain phase coherence over successive hops: consequently, coherent data demodulation techniques are possible only within each hop. As mentioned above and shown in Figure 2.1, this chapter will consider only non-coherent energy detection.

In other publications, the term "fast frequency hopping" (FFH) has occasionally been used to denote systems with relatively high hop rates, independent of the data rate. However, synthesizer technology is progress-

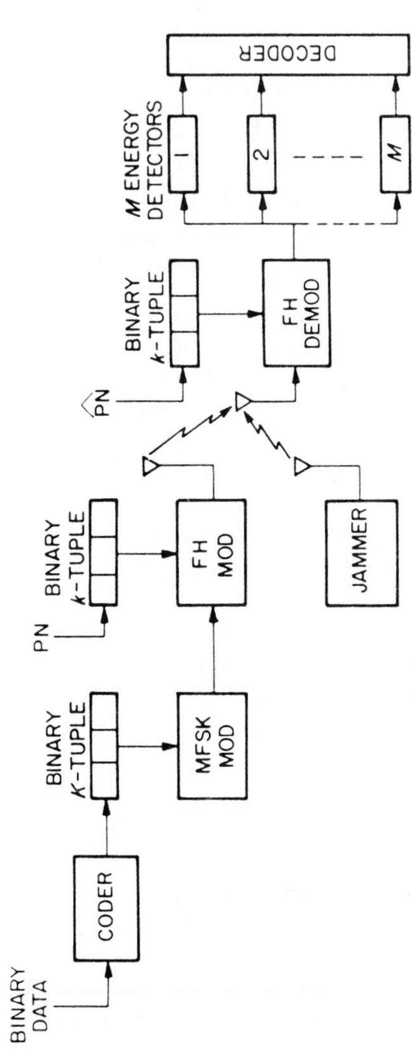

Figure 2.1. Functional block diagram of FH/MFSK system perturbed by jamming. Transmit one of $M = 2^K$ tones; carrier is hopped to one of 2^k frequencies determined by k-chip segments of PN code; dehopping requires derived PN reference ($\widehat{PN}$); non-coherent detection.

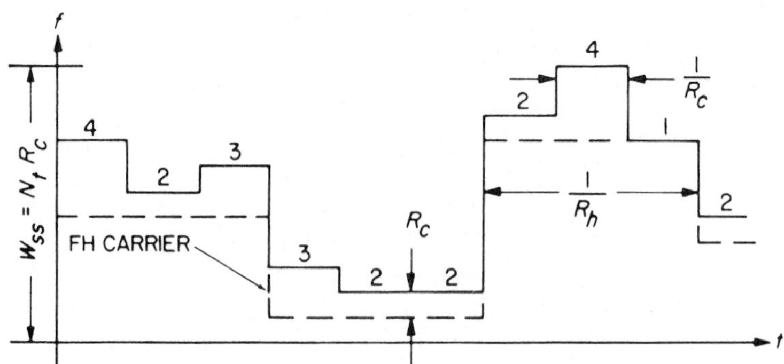

Figure 2.2. Example of SFH/MFSK signal, with $K = 2$ or $M = 4$ symbols $(1, 2, 3, 4)$, $R_c = R_s = R_b/2 = 3R_h$, and N_t equally spaced FH tone frequencies.

ing so rapidly that today's FFH system will invariably become tomorrow's slow frequency-hopped (SFH) system under this terminology. For example, in the recent past it was common for FH systems to operate at several hundred hops/sec, and 10–20 Khops/sec was considered to be state-of-the-art. Yet prototype synthesizer implementations have now been developed that deliver several hundred Khops/sec, and rates greater than 1 Mhop/sec should be realizable in the near term. To avoid technology-dependent terminology, we will define an FFH system to be one in which the hop rate R_h is an integer multiple of the MFSK symbol rate R_s, while the term SFH denotes the reverse condition.

Another terminological ambiguity is the widespread use of the word "chip" to refer to an individual FH/MFSK tone of shortest duration, which should not be confused with the PN chips that drive the frequency synthesizer. In an FFH system where there are multiple hops per M-ary symbol, each hop is a chip, whereas, in an SFH system as shown in Figure 2.2, a chip denotes an M-ary symbol. The chip rate $R_c = \max(R_h, R_s)$ is the highest FH system clock rate; the energy detectors in Figure 2.1 generate outputs at this rate. In the FFH mode, the M-ary symbol metrics are usually formed by linearly combining the R_h/R_s detected chip energies for each symbol, resulting in a non-coherent combining loss that will be discussed in detail later.

With non-coherent detection, the MFSK tones on a given hop must be separated in frequency by an integer multiple of R_c to provide orthogonality. This implies that a transmitted symbol will not produce any crosstalk in the other $M - 1$ energy detectors, and, if the M-ary band contains additive white Gaussian noise (AWGN), the components of that noise in each detector output will be uncorrelated. Figure 2.3(a) depicts a common implementation in which the entire SS band is partitioned into $N_t = W_{ss}/R_c$ equally spaced FH tones; these are then grouped into $N_b = N_t/M$ adjacent,

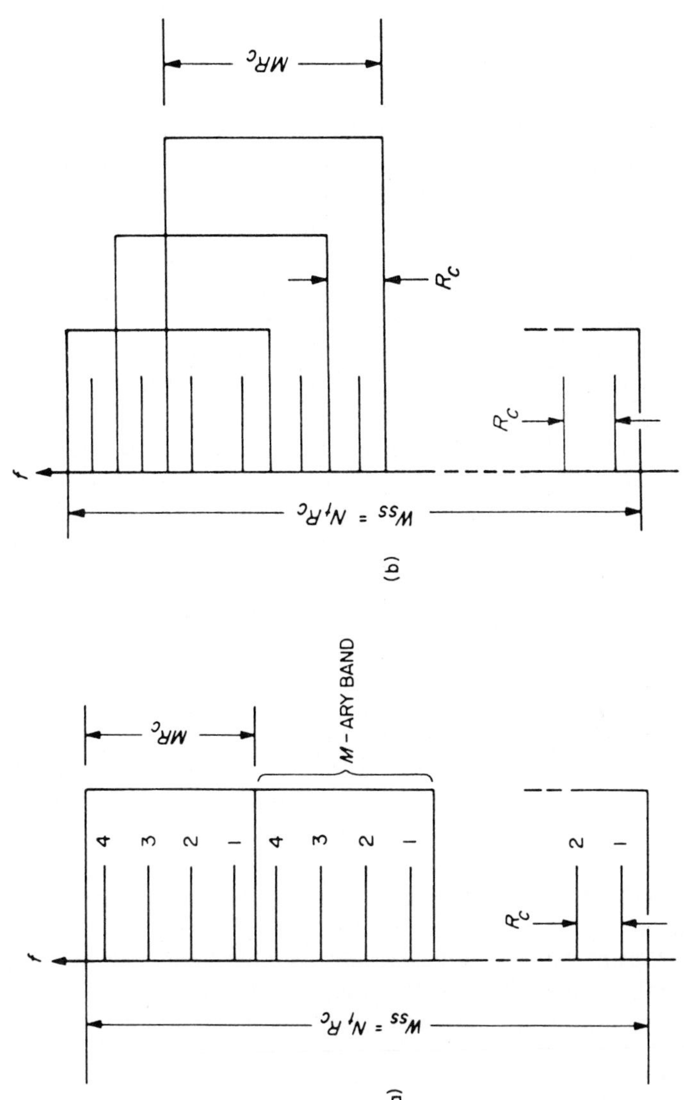

Figure 2.3. Frequency structures for FH/MFSK systems with N_t tones equally separated by R_c: in (a), M-ary bands are contiguous and non-overlapping, whereas in (b), these bands are shifted by R_c, which scrambles the FH tone/M-ary symbol mapping ($M = 4$ here).

non-overlapping M-ary bands, each with bandwidth MR_c. Under this arrangement, the PN binary k-tuples direct the frequency synthesizer to any of $N_b = 2^k$ carrier frequencies, and each FH tone is assigned to a specific, hop-invariant M-ary symbol. It is conceivable that a sophisticated jammer could exploit this fixed assignment scheme. One method of scrambling the FH tone/M-ary symbol mapping from hop to hop is to allow the synthesizer to hop the carrier over all but $M - 1$ of the N_t available frequencies so that adjacent M-ary bands are only shifted by R_c as shown in Figure 2.3(b). A more jam-resistant (and more expensive) approach is to use M distinct frequency synthesizers to individually hop the M-ary symbols, destroying the contiguous nature of an M-ary band.

There are situations in which it is desirable to avoid certain regions of the radio frequency (RF) band (e.g., fading or narrowband jamming), and here FH enjoys a distinct advantage over DS systems. The synthesizer algorithm which maps the k-chip PN segments into specific carrier frequencies can be modified to eliminate these undesirable bands, resulting in a discontinuous spectrum.

In addition to its anti-jam (AJ) capability, an SS signal is generally difficult to detect and even harder to decipher by an unauthorized receiver: this characteristic is usually referred to as a low probability of intercept (LPI). Most interceptors operate as energy detectors, and they have to monitor the received signal long enough to achieve a sufficiently high signal-to-noise ratio (SNR) for reliable detection in the presence of background noise. The LPI advantage of an SS signal is that its power is spread over a bandwidth considerably larger than conventional transmissions, significantly increasing the noise in a receiver that is not privy to the despreading sequence. In the past, when implementable FH systems operated at low hop rates, their transmissions could conceivably be detected by narrowband monitors capable of following the pseudorandom frequency variations (these so-called "frequency followers" could be used to drive repeat-back jammers which could effectively defeat the AJ capability of FH systems). Now, with hop rates of 100 KHz or more, the current generation of FH systems no longer has this vulnerability: an FH interceptor must detect multiple hops of the transmitted signal with a front end wide enough to accommodate the entire SS bandwidth. And, since FH signals can occupy much larger SS bandwidths than DS signals, they have a corresponding LPI advantage.

As with all SS systems, an FH receiver must derive a synchronized replica of the received spreading sequence to perform properly. And the despreading operation, in which the received signal is despread by this SS reference, simultaneously spreads any accompanying interference over W_{ss} or more, so that most of the interfering power can be eliminated by a narrowband filter matched to the data modulation bandwidth. As noted in Part 1, this AJ capability of an SS system is often measured by its processing gain (PG), a term which has been saddled with several conflicting definitions in the literature. For example, in his pioneering text on SS systems, Dixon at one point defines PG as the ratio of the SNR's at the output and input of the despreader [1, p. 8]; elsewhere (e.g., [1, p. 7]), he uses the definition we prefer, PG $= W_{ss}/R_b$ ((3.4) in Chapter 3, Part 1), which has the advantage that it does not depend on the particular choice of modulation or coding. Adding to this confusion, for FH systems, Dixon defines PG to be "the number of available frequency choices" [1, p. 29], which could refer to either N_t or N_b in our notation. This last definition is actually consistent with (3.4) in Part 1 under certain constraints: the FH/MFSK scheme described earlier has $N_t = W_{ss}/R_c$ equally spaced tones so that PG $= N_t R_c/R_b$. For the special case of SFH with uncoded binary FSK (BFSK, or MFSK with $M = 2$), $R_c = R_b$ so that PG reduces to N_t; this holds even if the SS bandwidth is not contiguous.

Although our definition of PG is universally valid for all SS systems, the interpretation of W_{ss} is not always obvious. An instructive case in point is a generalization of the FH/MFSK implementation of Figure 2.3. Consider the structure of Figure 2.4, where each M-ary band again has tones with uniform spacing R_c, but the bands themselves are now uniformly separated by an arbitrary amount ΔW, which is algebraically negative if the bands overlap. For clarification, $\Delta W = 0$ in Figure 2.3(a), while $\Delta W = -(M-1)R_c$ in Figure 2.3(b). In the overlapping band case, with $-MR_c < \Delta W < 0$, the spectrum averaged over many hops is approximately rectangular with

$$W_{ss} = N_b M R_c - (N_b - 1)|\Delta W|. \tag{2.1}$$

However, when $\Delta W > 0$, there are unused gaps in the multihop spectrum so that the occupied SS bandwidth that contributes to the PG is given by

$$W_{ss} = N_b M R_c \tag{2.2}$$

under the simplified approximation of a piecewise rectangular spectrum.

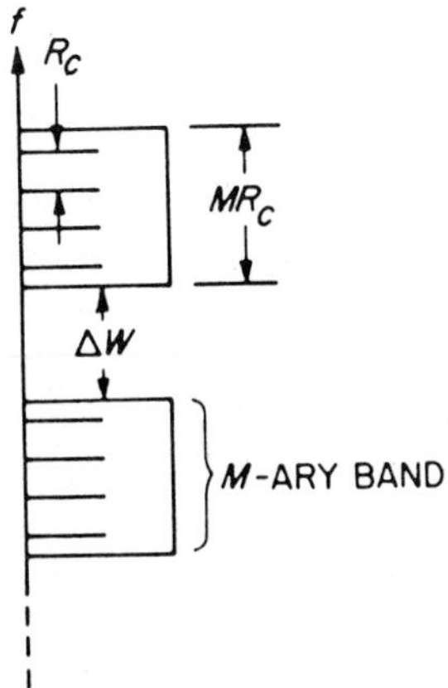

Figure 2.4. A generalization of frequency structure of FH/MFSK systems (shown for $M = 4$) in Figure 2.3: each M-ary band contains tones with uniform separation R_c, but adjacent bands are spaced ΔW apart.

All of this underscores our contention that while PG is a gross measure of the SS advantage relative to conventional modulation techniques, it is more accurate and meaningful to quantitatively characterize the performance of a specific system over a particular jamming channel by the bit error probability (P_b) as a function of the received SNR (see (3.3), Part 1). The remainder of this chapter is devoted to this type of characterization for non-coherent FH/MFSK systems. Where possible, exact closed form performance expressions will be derived; however, in most cases involving coded communication links, exponentially tight upperbounds on P_b will be computed in the interest of mathematical expediency. Exact analyses of coded systems generally prove to be intractable, necessitating the use of computer simulations or numerical integrations. While these approaches can generate more accurate results than bounding techniques, they are inconvenient, requiring a new computer calculation whenever even a single system parameter is changed. Furthermore, the functional dependence of a closed form P_b bound on the various system parameters can provide useful insights into system sensitivity to variations in these parameters. Of course, where simulation results are available, comparisons will be made to indicate the accuracy of our bounds.

Our examination of the performance of non-coherent FH/MFSK communications begins with uncoded signals received over the familiar additive white Gaussian noise (AWGN) channel. This could represent the situation in which a relatively unsophisticated jammer injects spectrally flat noise over the entire SS bandwidth into the FH receiver, and will be used as a benchmark against which more intelligent jammers and FH countermeasures can be compared.

As in the DS case, we will conservatively adopt the worst case perspective that the jammer has *a priori* knowledge of all relevant signalling parameters, with the critical exception of real time PN spreading sequence synchronization. Specifically, a smart jammer is assumed to have the ability to optimize its strategy to exploit information about W_{ss}, M, N_t, N_b, R_b, R_h, the location of the FH tones and the M-ary bands, the channel code and decoding algorithm, the detection metric, the signal power, and the nominal P_b. Also, reflecting realistic jamming scenarios, we will neglect the received thermal or non-hostile background noise in deference to the typically dominant jamming power.

We will consider the two principal types of intelligent but non-adaptive FH jamming threats, namely, partial-band noise and multitone interference. It will be shown that when such jammers optimize their system parameters based on their assumed knowledge of the FH/MFSK target, the resulting performance degradation can be severe, particularly at low error probabilities. To counteract this threat, the FH system must incorporate some coding redundancy which allows the received data decisions to be based on multiple hops. One particularly simple coding scheme that we will consider is time diversity or repetition coding, which can also be used in a concatenation structure to augment the effectiveness of the more powerful block and convolutional codes.

In analyzing these coded systems, we will focus on a detection metric that assumes that the receiver can determine with certainty whether a given hop is jammed. This is the so-called perfect jamming state knowledge or side-information case discussed in Chapters 3 and 4, Part 1, and it is a common assumption in many published articles on pulsed jamming of DS systems and the dual case of partial-band jamming of FH systems (e.g., [2, p. 288]). However, we should caution that in practice a receiver's derived jamming state side information is subject to error, and such a metric is non-robust in the sense that it depends on the received signal, thermal noise, and jamming power levels. While a few other, more robust metrics are considered at the end of this chapter, our main intent here is not to exhaustively consider all possible detection metrics, but rather to use the principal selected metric to illustrate techniques for analyzing the performance of a variety of coded FH/MFSK systems in the presence of different jamming strategies.

We will also not consider the class of adaptive jammers known as repeat-back or frequency-follower jammers. As technology moves to higher hop rates, this threat becomes less viable since it requires that the jammer intercept the FH signal, detect the frequency of the M-ary band, and synthesize an appropriate narrowband signal, all within each hop dwell time.

2.1 BROADBAND NOISE JAMMING

Consider a non-coherent FH/MFSK communication link with received power S transmitting data at a bit rate R_b: the received energy per bit is

$$E_b = S/R_b. \tag{2.3}$$

Suppose this signal is jammed by Gaussian noise with received power J and an approximately rectangular spectrum which coincides with the FH bandwidth W_{ss}. This is equivalent to an AWGN channel, with an effective noise power spectral density

$$N_J = J/W_{ss}. \tag{2.4}$$

The SS system can therefore be characterized by the SNR

$$E_b/N_J = (S/J)(W_{ss}/R_b). \tag{2.5}$$

Identifying PG $= W_{ss}/R_b$, S/J as the signal-to-jamming power ratio prior to despreading, and E_b/N_J as the despread SNR in the information bandwidth, we see that this particular example agrees with Dixon's definition of PG as the ratio of the despread-to-spread SNR's.

We will initially restrict our attention to uncoded SFH systems with an alphabet of $M = 2^K$ orthogonal signals, each containing K bits of information. The chip, M-ary symbol, bit, and hop rates satisfy

$$R_c = R_s = R_b/K \geq R_h. \tag{2.6}$$

The received symbol energy is then

$$E_s = S/R_s = KE_b. \tag{2.7}$$

Without loss of generality, assume that symbol 1 is sent on a given data transmission. Referring to the block diagram of Figure 2.1, the output e_1 of the first energy detector, normalized for convenience by $1/N_J$, is a non-central chi-square random variable with 2 degrees of freedom, whose probability density function is given by

$$p(e_1) = \begin{cases} \exp(-e_1 - E_s/N_J)I_0\left(2\sqrt{e_1 E_s/N_J}\right); \; e_1 \geq 0 \\ 0; \; e_1 < 0 \end{cases} \tag{2.8}$$

where $I_0(\cdot)$ is the zeroeth-order modified Bessel function of the first kind. Since the symbols are separated in frequency by the symbol rate R_s, the other $M - 1$ energy detectors contain no signal components. Their outputs are identically distributed central chi-square random variables with 2 degrees of freedom:

$$p(e_i) = \begin{cases} \exp(-e_i); \; e_i \geq 0 \\ 0; \; e_i < 0 \end{cases} \qquad (i = 2, \ldots, M). \tag{2.9}$$

Because the M signals are orthogonal, the e_i's are all statistically independent.

The system performance in this example is the same as for non-coherent detection of conventional (unhopped) M-ary orthogonal signals in AWGN. The derivation of this performance has been widely documented (e.g., [3, Section 8.10]): however, it is reviewed here for the sake of completeness. The M-ary symbol error probability (P_s) is given by

$$P_s = \Pr\left\{ \bigcup_{i=2}^{M} (e_i \geq e_1) \right\} \tag{2.10a}$$

$$\begin{aligned} &= 1 - \Pr\left\{ \bigcap_{i=2}^{M} (e_i < e_1) \right\} \\ &= 1 - \int_0^\infty de_1 \, p(e_1) \left[\int_0^{e_1} de_2 \, p(e_2) \right]^{M-1} \\ &= 1 - e^{-E_s/N_J} \int_0^\infty du \, u \, e^{-u^2/2} I_0\left(u\sqrt{\frac{2E_s}{N_J}} \right) \left[\int_0^u dv \, v \, e^{-v^2/2} \right]^{M-1} \end{aligned} \tag{2.10b}$$

where (2.8) and (2.9) were used with the change of variables $u = \sqrt{2e_1}$ and $v = \sqrt{2e_2}$. But

$$\left[\int_0^u dv\, v\, e^{-v^2/2}\right]^{M-1} = \left(1 - e^{-u^2/2}\right)^{M-1} = \sum_{j=0}^{M-1} (-1)^j \binom{M-1}{j} e^{-ju^2/2} \tag{2.11}$$

so that (2.10b) reduces to

$$P_s = 1 - e^{-E_s/N_J} \sum_{j=0}^{M-1} (-1)^j \binom{M-1}{j} \times \underbrace{\int_0^\infty du\, u\, e^{-(j+1)u^2/2} I_0\left(u\sqrt{\frac{2E_s}{N_J}}\right)}_{\left(\frac{1}{j+1}\right) e^{E_s/(j+1)N_J}}. \tag{2.12}$$

The elimination of the integral in (2.12) is based on the identity

$$\int_0^\infty de_1\, p(e_1) = 1 \tag{2.13}$$

with appropriate parameter changes. Letting $i = j + 1$, (2.12) becomes

$$P_s = 1 - \frac{1}{M} \sum_{i=1}^{M} (-1)^{i-1} \binom{M}{i} e^{-(E_s/N_J)(1-1/i)} = \frac{1}{M} \sum_{i=2}^{M} (-1)^i \binom{M}{i} e^{-(E_s/N_J)(1-1/i)}. \tag{2.14}$$

For larger values of K (i.e., K's of the order of 5 or more), the summation of (2.14) involves an exponentially large number of terms with alternating signs, each of which is composed of the product of a factor $\binom{M}{i}$ which can be very large in the neighborhood $i \sim M/2$, and a very small factor, $\exp[-(E_s/N_J)(1 - 1/i)]$. Consequently, evaluation of this expression on a digital computer often yields unsatisfactory results. A more practical approach is to apply numerical integration techniques to the integral of (2.10b) and (2.11):

$$P_s = 1 - e^{-E_s/N_J} \int_0^\infty du\, u\, e^{-u^2/2}\left(1 - e^{-u^2/2}\right)^{M-1} I_0\left(u\sqrt{\frac{2E_s}{N_J}}\right). \tag{2.15}$$

However, for large values of E_s/N_J (i.e., small P_s), the value of the integral is close to 1, and the expression is again inherently inaccurate. To reduce the computational burden, make the variable change $x = u^2/2$:

$$P_s = 1 - e^{-E_s/N_J} \int_0^\infty dx\, e^{-x}(1 - e^{-x})^{M-1} I_0\left(2\sqrt{\frac{xE_s}{N_J}}\right). \tag{2.16}$$

Now, integrating (2.16) by parts, and introducing the Marcum Q-function [4] defined by

$$Q_M(\sqrt{2\gamma}, \sqrt{2x}) = \int_x^\infty du\, e^{-(u+\gamma)} I_0(2\sqrt{u\gamma}) \tag{2.17}$$

with

$$Q_M(\sqrt{2\gamma}, 0) = 1$$

we can write

$$P_s = (M-1)\int_0^\infty dx \left[1 - Q_M\left(\sqrt{\frac{2E_s}{N_J}}, \sqrt{2x}\right)\right] e^{-x}(1-e^{-x})^{M-2}. \tag{2.18}$$

In practice, (2.18) can be evaluated accurately by using about 300 equally spaced increments for x between 0 and 30; iterative formulas exist for computing $Q_M(\cdot, \cdot)$.

As an alternative to computing P_s exactly using the techniques discussed above, it is often more convenient and insightful to evaluate the simple, closed form expression for its union upperbound: from (2.10a),

$$\begin{aligned} P_s &\le (M-1)\Pr\{e_2 \ge e_1\} \\ &= \left(\frac{M-1}{2}\right)\exp(-E_s/2N_J) \end{aligned} \tag{2.19}$$

where we have applied (2.14) with $M = 2$. Note that the upperbound in (2.19) is the leading (i.e., $i = 2$) term in the summation of (2.14), and is satisfied with equality for $M = 2$.

When a symbol error occurs, the decision is equally likely to favor any of the $M - 1$ incorrect orthogonal symbols. Since $M/2$ of these incorrect binary K-tuples will produce an error in a given bit, the probability of a bit error is given by [3, (8.14)]

$$P_b = \frac{M}{2(M-1)} P_s \tag{2.20a}$$

$$= \frac{1}{2(M-1)} \sum_{i=2}^{M} (-1)^i \binom{M}{i} e^{-(KE_b/N_J)(1-1/i)} \tag{2.20b}$$

$$\le 2^{K-2} e^{-KE_b/2N_J} \tag{2.20c}$$

where (2.20c) is satisfied with equality when $K = 1$.

The performance results above are illustrated in Figure 2.5. It is evident that as E_b/N_J becomes large enough for a given K or M, the union bound approaches arbitrarily close to the exact bit error probability, reflecting the dominance of the leading term in the summation of (2.20b). Also, the performance improves as K increases, which is to be expected since MFSK modulation is equivalent to using an (M, K) binary block orthogonal code (i.e., a code which maps blocks of K bits into $M = 2^K$ symbol codewords).

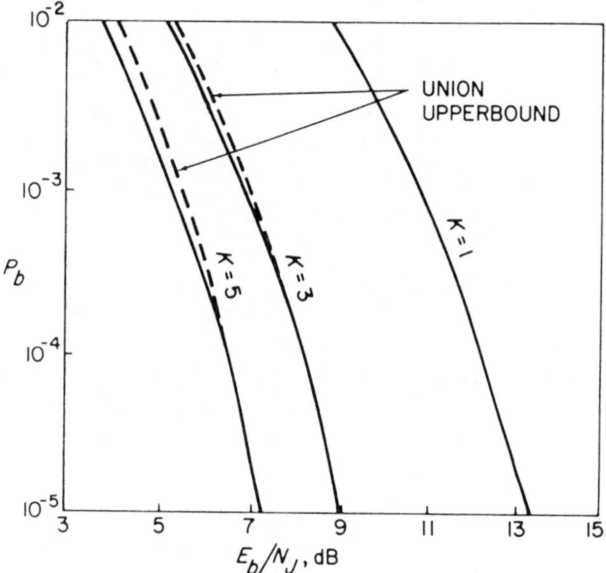

Figure 2.5. Performance of conventional MFSK ($M = 2^K$) system over AWGN channel, with bit energy E_b and noise power density N_J.

The broadband noise jamming results of (2.20) will be used as a reference point for comparing the performance of more sophisticated jammers and FH schemes in the sections that follow.

2.2 WORST CASE JAMMING

In this section we will examine the degradation in performance of uncoded SFH/MFSK systems that occurs when a smart jammer has *a priori* knowledge of all FH system parameters except for the PN code (the jammer can even know which PN code is being used provided that it cannot achieve real time PN synchronization), and devises an optimum strategy to exploit this. We will consider the two most effective jamming strategies against FH systems: partial-band noise and multitone jamming. In the multitone category, we will analyze several distinct approaches, and identify the best of these.

Much of the credit for the initial work in this area belongs to Houston [5], and we will refer frequently to his results below.

2.2.1 Partial-Band Noise Jamming

Suppose a Gaussian noise jammer chooses to restrict its total power J (referenced to the FH receiver input) to a fraction ρ ($0 < \rho \leq 1$) of the full SS bandwidth W_{ss}. As shown in Figure 2.6, the jamming noise power is

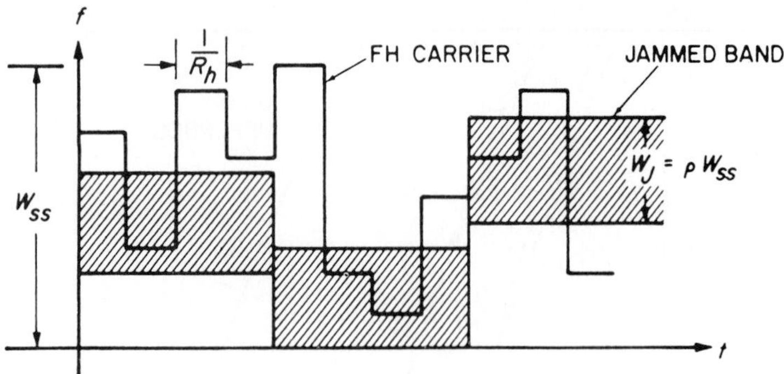

Figure 2.6. Partial-band noise jamming of FH system: jammer concentrates power in fraction $\rho \in (0,1]$ of SS bandwidth, and hops noise band to prevent FH band avoidance countermeasure.

spread uniformly over $W_J = \rho W_{ss}$, resulting in an increased power density

$$N_J' = \frac{J}{W_J} = \frac{J}{\rho W_{ss}} = \frac{N_J}{\rho}, \tag{2.21}$$

and a correspondingly degraded SNR level

$$\frac{E_b}{N_J'} = \frac{\rho E_b}{N_J} \tag{2.22}$$

in the jammed band, where N_J is still defined by (1.4).

Recall that an FH system can in principle avoid certain frequency bands that it determines are particularly noisy. Consequently, we assume as in Figure 2.6 that the jammer hops the jammed band over W_{ss}, slowly relative to the FH dwell time $1/R_h$, but often enough to deny the FH system the opportunity to detect that it is being jammed in a specific portion of W_{ss} and take remedial action. Also, to simplify the analysis, we will assume that shifts in the jammed band coincide with carrier hop transitions, so that the channel is stationary over each hop. Furthermore, we will assume that on a given hop, each M-ary band lies entirely inside or outside W_J. This last restriction is common to most analytical treatments of partial-band FH jamming and the dual case of pulsed DS jamming. (Since the FH carrier hops in and out of W_J, partial-band jamming can be regarded as pulsed jamming with non-uniformly spaced pulses of duration $1/R_h$, under the simplifying assumptions made above.) The performance computed based on these assumptions is actually somewhat pessimistic, as Viterbi has noted [6, p. 14]: on a given M-ary symbol transmission, if only part of the M-ary band is jammed, and/or if it is only jammed over part of the symbol band, less noise is intercepted by the energy detectors, thereby reducing the probability of error. We should add that it does not matter whether the jammed band W_J is a single contiguous region as suggested by Figure 2.6: the analysis below is transparent to partitions of W_J so long as each of them satisfies the assumptions above.

Because of the pseudorandom hopping, it is reasonable to model the FH/MFSK system in partial-band noise as a two-state channel, independent from hop to hop. With probability ρ, an M-ary transmission is jammed and the conditional P_b is determined by the SNR ratio of (2.22); but, since we are neglecting thermal noise, with probability $(1 - \rho)$, the transmission is noiseless and an error-free decision is made. Then the average error rate is simply

$$P_b = \rho P_b\left(\frac{\rho E_b}{N_J}\right), \tag{2.23}$$

where the term on the right denotes the expression of (2.20b) with E_b/N_J replaced by $\rho E_b/N_J$.

What (2.23) tells us is that if ρ is reduced, the probability that an M-ary transmission is jammed is decreased, but jammed signals suffer a higher conditional error rate: the net effect may degrade the average FH/MFSK performance, depending on the values of M and E_b/N_J. The utility of jamming only part of the RF band is illustrated in Figure 2.7 for $M = 2$. Suppose S, J, W_{ss}, and R_b combine to make $E_b/N_J = 10.9$ dB. In broadband noise ($\rho = 1$), the resulting $P_b = 10^{-3}$.

If the jammer concentrates the same noise power over half the SS band ($\rho = 1/2$), only half the transmissions are jammed, but these have a

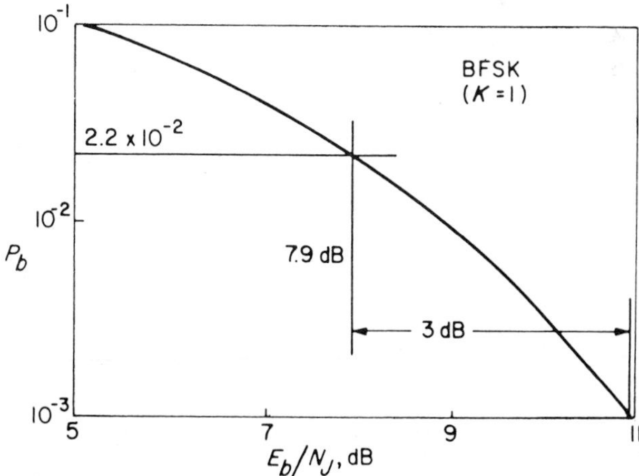

Figure 2.7. Illustration of partial-band jamming advantage against FH/MFSK systems. Referring to (2.20b) and (2.23), if $M = 2$ and $E_b/N_J = 10.9$ dB, when $\rho = 1$ then $P_b = 10^{-3}$; however, if $\rho = 1/2$, then conditional SNR ratio in jammed band is 7.9 dB, so that conditional $P_b = 2.2 \times 10^{-2}$, resulting in average $P_b = 1.1 \times 10^{-2}$.

conditional $P_b = 2.2 \times 10^{-2}$, which results in an average $P_b = 1.1 \times 10^{-2}$ according to (2.23). So in this example, reducing ρ to 1/2 degrades the performance more than an order of magnitude because of the steepness of the P_b curve in the selected region. (The results below indicate that the worst performance for these parameters occurs at $\rho = .16$, for which $P_b = 3.0 \times 10^{-2}$.)

Figure 2.8 illustrates the performance of an FH/BFSK system in partial-band noise for several partial-band jamming factors ρ. For small enough E_b/N_J, it is evident that broadband noise jamming ($\rho = 1$) is the most effective. In general, for any value of E_b/N_J, there is an optimum value of $\rho \in (0, 1]$ from the jammer's viewpoint which maximizes P_b, and this is denoted by ρ_{wc} (for worst case jamming). The performance in worst case partial-band noise is the upper envelope (or supremum) of the family of P_b curves for fixed values of ρ: as shown in Figure 2.8, when E_b/N_J exceeds a threshold level, $\rho_{wc} < 1$ indicating a partial-band jamming advantage, and the performance curve is a straight line. Of course, in practice, it may be difficult for the jammer to match ρ to the actual E_b/N_J.

The worst case partial-band noise jammer chooses ρ to maximize the P_b for a given M and E_b/N_J. From (2.20b) and (2.23), the resulting average

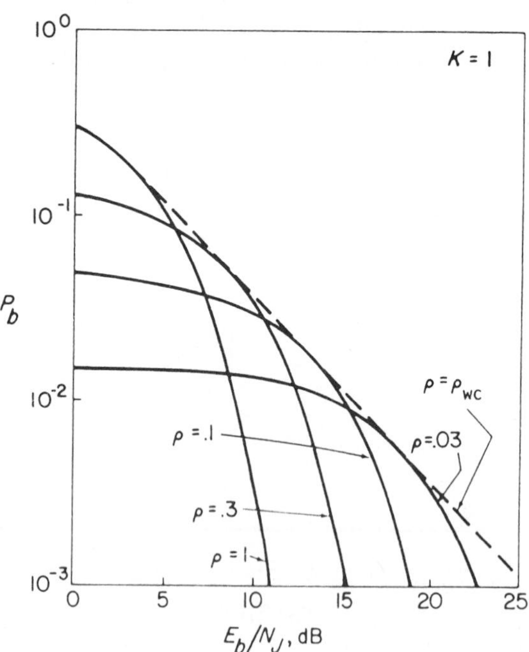

Figure 2.8. Performance of FH/BFSK system in partial-band noise for several fixed values of ρ. The performance in worst case partial-band noise is realized when the jammer chooses $\rho = \rho_{wc}$ to maximize P_b for a given E_b/N_J. Note that ρ_{wc} decreases as E_b/N_J gets larger.

performance can be expressed as

$$P_b = \max_{0<\rho\leq 1}\left[\frac{\rho}{2(M-1)}\sum_{i=2}^{M}(-1)^i\binom{M}{i}e^{-(\rho K E_b/N_J)(1-1/i)}\right]. \quad (2.24)$$

For $M = 2$, this maximization is a simple mathematical calculation; for larger values of M, it must be evaluated numerically. The results have the form [5, (15) and (16)]

$$P_b = \begin{cases} \dfrac{1}{2(M-1)}\displaystyle\sum_{i=2}^{M}(-1)^i\binom{M}{i}e^{-(KE_b/N_J)(1-1/i)}, \\ \qquad \text{and } \rho_{\text{wc}} = 1;\ \dfrac{E_b}{N_J} \leq \gamma \\ \dfrac{\beta}{E_b/N_J},\ \text{and } \rho_{\text{wc}} = \dfrac{\gamma}{E_b/N_J};\ \dfrac{E_b}{N_J} \geq \gamma \end{cases} \quad (2.25)$$

where the parameters β and γ are tabulated for $1 \leq K \leq S$ below and ρ_{wc} denotes the jammer's optimum ρ.

(2.25) demonstrates that so long as E_b/N_J is not unusually small, worst case partial-band jamming converts the exponential relationship between P_b and E_b/N_J in (2.20) into an inverse linear dependence. As shown in Figure 2.9, the resulting degradation can be severe for small P_b's: for example, the loss is 14.7 dB at $P_b = 10^{-3}$ for $K = 1$, and increases with K. At P_b's of 10^{-5} and lower, this gap exceeds 30 dB for any K, illustrating the effectiveness of worst case partial-band noise jamming against uncoded FH/MFSK signals at typical operating points.

(2.25) indicates that ρ_{wc} becomes very small for large E_b/N_J's; that is, a worst case noise jammer concentrates its power in a small portion of W_{ss} at low P_b's. The signals do not get jammed most of the time, but those that do are likely to result in errors. This is an indication that some form of coding redundancy that causes data decisions to depend on multiple symbol transmissions can reduce the effectiveness of partial-band jamming; the degree to which this statement is true will become evident in Section 1.3.

Table 2.1

Parameters associated with performance of uncoded FH/MFSK signals in worst case partial-band noise, as defined in (2.25).

K	β	γ, dB
1	e^{-1} = .3679	3.01
2	.2329	.76
3	.1954	− .33
4	.1812	− .59
5	.1759	−1.41

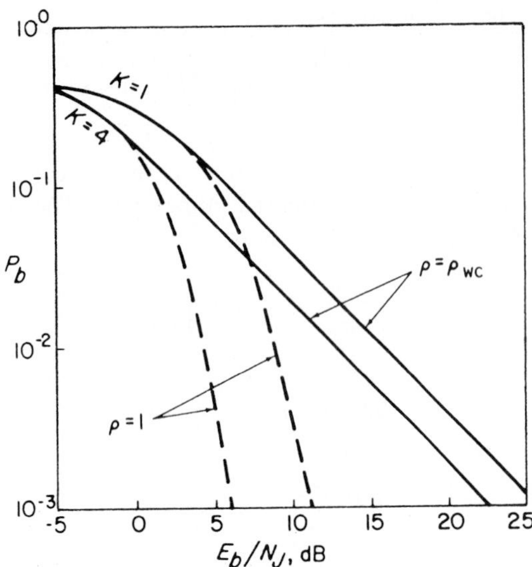

Figure 2.9. Degradation in FH/MFSK ($M = 2^K$) performance due to worst case ($\rho = \rho_{wc} \leq 1$) partial-band noise relative to broadband ($\rho = 1$) noise jamming.

2.2.2 Multitone Jamming

A second, sometimes more effective, class of intelligent FH jamming than partial-band noise is multitone or multiple CW tone interference. In this category, the jammer divides its total received power J into Q distinct, equal power, random phase CW tones. These are distributed over the spread-spectrum bandwidth W_{ss} according to one of several strategies illustrated in Figure 2.10 and discussed in detail below. One of the reasons that multitone jamming can be more effective against FH/MFSK signals than partial-band noise is that CW tones are the most efficient way for a jammer to inject energy into the non-coherent detectors.

The analysis below involves several simplifying assumptions to allow us to focus on the issues of interest. We continue to neglect receiver thermal noise under the assumption that it is dominated by the jamming interference. As shown in Figure 2.10, we assume that each jamming tone coincides exactly in frequency with one of the N_t available FH slots, with at most one tone per slot. Furthermore, while the multitone jammer may periodically rearrange the location of its tones to thwart any FH avoidance measures, it is assumed that such changes coincide with hop transitions. While these artificial constraints could never be achieved in practice, like the earlier partial-band jamming assumptions, they simplify the analysis and yield somewhat pessimistic performance results. For example, if a jamming tone is offset in frequency from an FH slot, less energy gets into the adjacent MFSK detector reducing the jamming effectiveness, and the performance must be averaged over the frequency offset distribution.

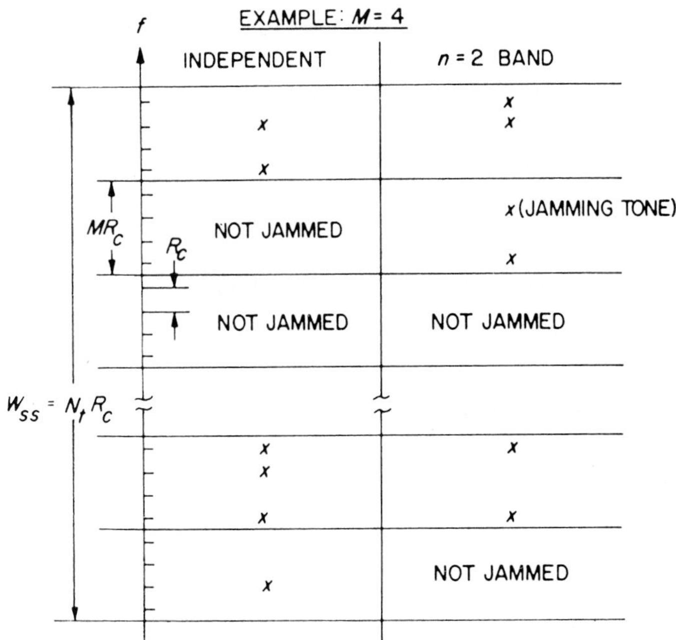

Figure 2.10. Multitone jamming strategies: independent multitone jamming distributes the tones pseudorandomly over all N_t FH frequencies; band multitone jamming places $n \in [1, M]$ tones in each jammed M-ary band.

We denote the fraction of the FH slots jammed by

$$\rho \equiv \frac{Q}{N_t} \tag{2.26}$$

analogous to the fraction of the SS bandwidth jammed in the partial-band noise case. However, there was a uniformity in the partial-band jamming scheme that does not generally carry over to the multitone case. In the former, an entire M-ary band was assumed to be evenly degraded by Gaussian noise if it was jammed at all. Under the various multitone scenarios, the number of symbols in an M-ary band that can be hit by jamming tones can range anywhere between zero and all M. A single jamming tone hitting any of the $M - 1$ untransmitted symbols can produce an error, provided that the jamming tone power J/Q is slightly greater than the signal power S, in the absence of additive noise. Since the jammer is presumed to not know the hopping sequence, it is to its advantage to place its tones in as many M-ary bands as possible, even if most of these jammed bands contain a single jamming tone. Consequently, with regard to multitone jamming, a more significant parameter than ρ is

$$\mu \equiv \Pr\{\text{any symbol in an } M\text{-ary band is jammed}\} \tag{2.27}$$

Note that $\mu = \rho$ in the partial-band noise case.

If in fact it can be shown that the best multitone strategy is to maximize μ, the jammer should leave at least $M - 1$ unjammed FH slots between each of its Q available tones (assuming $Q \leq N_t/M$) so that no M-ary band can contain more than one jamming tone. Of course, this assumes that the FH system adopts the distinct M-ary band structure of Figure 2.3(a) or (b), with all MFSK symbols occupying adjacent FH slots. Without loss of generality, the multitone analysis below assumes the non-overlapping band structure of Figure 2.3(a) for conceptual convenience, although the results would be unchanged for the arrangement of Figure 2.3(b).

The "band multitone" strategy of Figure 2.10 is a generalization of these arguments in which a jammed band contains exactly n jamming tones, under the implied assumption that Q/n is an integer. If the jammed bands are selected pseudorandomly, we have

$$\mu = \frac{QM}{nN_t} = \frac{M}{n}\rho. \tag{2.28}$$

In previous publications, multitone jamming analyses of non-coherent FH/MFSK systems have restricted the jamming tones to be contiguous in the frequency domain, with uniform spacing R_c or MR_c [5, p. 53] and [7]. Indeed, Trumpis refers to this structure as "partial-band multitone jamming" by analogy to the noise jamming case. In our notation, these two schemes fall into the band multitone jamming category with $n = 1$ or M. If a large μ is desirable, $n = M$ band multitone jamming should prove to be relatively ineffective since it does not judiciously allocate its available power to the largest number of bands.

A simpler strategy that bypasses the assumptions that permit the band multitone implementation is to pseudorandomly distribute the Q jamming tones uniformly over the N_t available FH slots. Under this so-called "independent multitone" scheme shown in Figure 2.10, a given FH slot is jammed with probability ρ, and we assume that other slots are independently jammed with the same probability. In fact, the independence assumption is not always justified. Conditioned on one FH slot being jammed, another given slot is jammed with probability $(Q - 1)/(N_t - 1)$, which is essentially equal to ρ in (2.26) implying independent, equally likely jamming of both slots provided $N_t \geq Q \gg 1$. Since our performance analysis focusses on the dehopped M-ary band containing the transmitted data symbol, we can assume that each of the M slots in that band is independently tone jammed with probability ρ by extending the provision above to

$$N_t \geq Q \gg M - 1. \tag{2.29}$$

Under this assumption,

$$\mu = 1 - (1 - \rho)^M \tag{2.30}$$

which reduces to the value of μ for $n = 1$ band multitone jamming when ρ is small; this suggests that these two strategies may be equally effective for $\rho \ll 1$.

2.2.2.1 Random Jamming Tone Phase

For all of the multitone strategies under consideration, there is the possibility that a given MFSK received signal will itself be jammed. When this occurs, the relative phase of the data and jamming tones impacts the energy detector output for that frequency, a factor first analyzed by Trumpis [7, pp. 15–16]. We have already assumed that there is no frequency offset between the data and jamming tones. We now additionally assume that the phase difference ϕ is uniformly distributed over $[0, 2\pi)$.

The received signal power is S: denote the received power in each jamming tone by

$$\frac{J}{Q} = \frac{S}{\alpha}, \tag{2.31}$$

where α is a parameter to be optimized by the jammer. Then a received data signal which has been tone jammed has the composite form

$$\sqrt{2S}\sin\omega_0 t + \sqrt{\frac{2S}{\alpha}}\sin(\omega_0 t + \phi) = \sqrt{2S'}\sin(\omega_0 t + \phi'), \tag{2.32}$$

where the phasor representation of (2.32) in Figure 2.11 indicates that the total resultant power is

$$\begin{aligned} S' &= S\left[\left(1 + \frac{1}{\sqrt{\alpha}}\cos\phi\right)^2 + \left(\frac{1}{\sqrt{\alpha}}\sin\phi\right)^2\right] \\ &= S\left(1 + \frac{2}{\sqrt{\alpha}}\cos\phi + \frac{1}{\alpha}\right). \end{aligned} \tag{2.33}$$

The energy detector output for that M-ary symbol (or chip, in the uncoded case) is

$$\frac{S'}{R_c} = E_c\left(1 + \frac{2}{\sqrt{\alpha}}\cos\phi + \frac{1}{\alpha}\right), \tag{2.34}$$

where the symbol (chip) energy $E_c = S/R_c = S/R_s$. Table 2.2 extends (2.34) to the other three cases required to determine the system performance with multitone jamming in the absence of thermal noise.

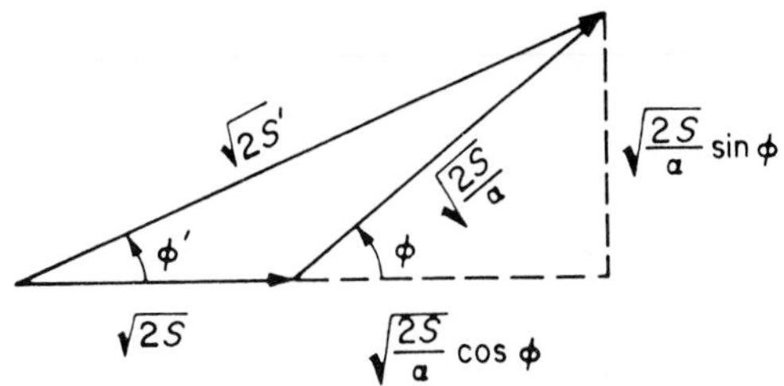

Figure 2.11. Phasor representation of tone jammed MFSK data signal.

Table 2.2
Normalized energy detector outputs.

	If tone jammed	If not jammed
Transmitted M-ary symbol	$1 + \frac{2}{\sqrt{\alpha}} \cos\phi + \frac{1}{\alpha}$	1
Any of the $(M-1)$ other symbols	$\frac{1}{\alpha}$	0

The table reveals the range of α for which symbol errors can occur. If none of the M dehopped symbols is jammed, there can be no error. If the data symbol is not jammed and *any* of the other symbols is hit with a jamming tone, an error will *always* be made if $\alpha < 1$, and *never* for $\alpha > 1$ (ties that occur when $\alpha = 1$ can be resolved with an M-sided coin flip, or simply assigned to the error side of the ledger). Note that in the uncoded case, with hard decisions made on each symbol, there is no advantage to hitting more than one of the untransmitted symbols. If only the data symbol is hit, its energy detector output is greater than zero except for a singular value of ϕ depending on α; since that singular point occurs with probability zero, an error cannot occur. Finally, if the transmitted symbol and any of the other symbols are simultaneously jammed, an error can occur with probability

$$\Pr\left\{\cos\phi < -\frac{\sqrt{\alpha}}{2}\right\} = \frac{1}{\pi}\cos^{-1}\left(\frac{\sqrt{\alpha}}{2}\right), \tag{2.35}$$

which is non-zero for $0 \le \alpha < 4$. This is a surprising result. Most multitone jamming analyses simply assume axiomatically that the jammer should set $\alpha = 1_-$, so that each jamming tone has power slightly in excess of S. Houston pointed out that the jammer could do better by optimizing α, but he neglected the impact of the random jammer phase and restricted α to the range (0, 1) [5, pp. 53–54]. Only Trumpis [7, p. 16] recognized that an error could still occur even when the power in each jamming tone was up to 6 dB *below* the received signal power. It remains to be seen whether in fact a worst case jammer would ever select $\alpha > 1$ for any of the multitone strategies, and this will be resolved in the next two sections.

2.2.2.2 Band Multitone Jamming

The simplest scheme to analyze is $n = 1$ band multitone jamming. The random jamming phase has no effect on the system performance, and it demonstrates the basic approach to determining the worst case α for the other multitone strategies.

From Table 2.2 and the discussion above, a symbol error can only occur if the M-ary band containing the transmitted data is jammed, and then only if the data symbol itself is not hit and $\alpha < 1$:

$$P_s = \mu\left(\frac{M-1}{M}\right). \tag{2.36}$$

Since we know that

$$N_t = \frac{W_{ss}}{R_s} = \frac{KW_{ss}}{R_b} \tag{2.37}$$

(2.3), (2.4), (2.28), and (2.31) allow us to rewrite μ in the form

$$\mu = \frac{\alpha M}{nKE_b/N_J} \tag{2.38}$$

for multitone band jamming with arbitrary n.

Recalling the relation between P_s and P_b (see (2.20a)), and setting $n = 1$, the performance for a given α is specified by

$$P_b = \frac{\alpha M}{2KE_b/N_J} \tag{2.39}$$

The worst case performance is achieved by maximizing α. But, in addition to the constraint $\alpha < 1$, there is the requirement that the number of jamming tones not exceed the number of M-ary bands, i.e., $\mu \leq 1$. Therefore, the worst case $n = 1$ band multitone jammer sets α equal to

$$\alpha_{\mathrm{wc}} = \begin{cases} \dfrac{K}{M}\left(\dfrac{E_b}{N_J}\right); & \dfrac{E_b}{N_J} < \dfrac{M}{K} \\ 1_-; & \dfrac{E_b}{N_J} \geq \dfrac{M}{K} \end{cases} \tag{2.40}$$

for which (2.39) reduces to

$$P_b = \begin{cases} \dfrac{1}{2}; & \dfrac{E_b}{N_J} \leq \dfrac{2^K}{K} \\ \dfrac{2^{K-1}}{KE_b/N_J}; & \dfrac{E_b}{N_J} \geq \dfrac{2^K}{K} \end{cases} \tag{2.41}$$

since $M = 2^K$.

Under the worst case partial-band noise scenario, the relationship between P_b and E_b/N_J became inverse linear for P_b's below a threshold that depended on K (see (2.25)); here that same type of relationship arises *for all* $P_b < 1/2$, independent of K. Both worst case jammers are significantly more effective than broadband noise against uncoded FH/MFSK signals with non-coherent detection, especially for large E_b/N_J, as shown in Figure 2.12. However, of the two, it is clear that the multitone structure is a better

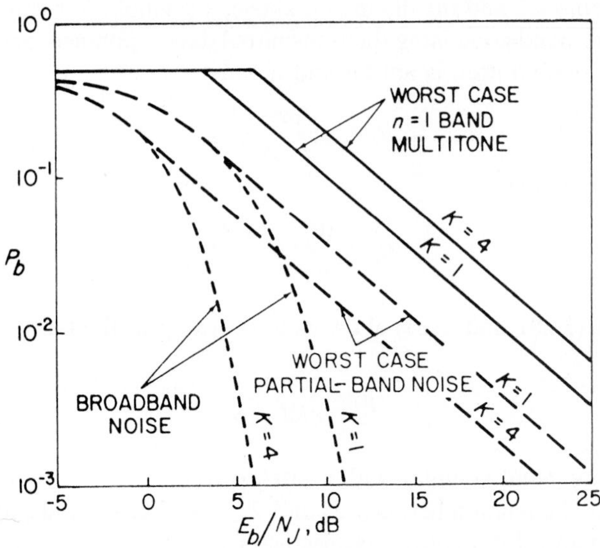

Figure 2.12. Advantage of $n = 1$ band multitone strategy over partial-band noise and broadband noise jamming of uncoded FH/MFSK signals.

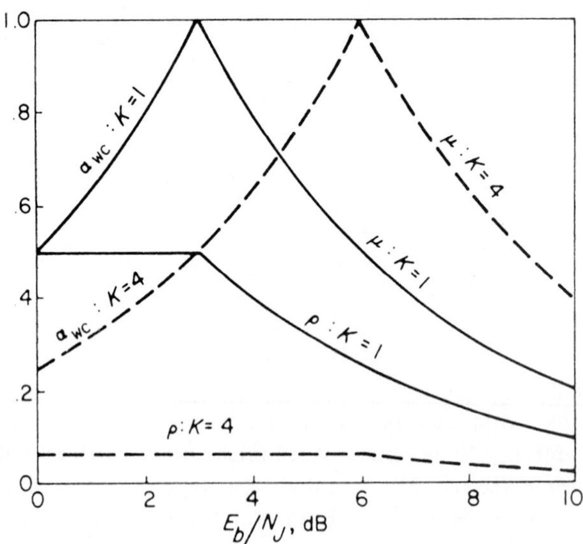

Figure 2.13. Parameters characterizing worst case $n = 1$ band multitone jamming of uncoded FH/MFSK signals.

jamming strategy, particularly for larger values of K. The performance in additive noise improves with K due to the block orthogonal coding gain implicit in the MFSK modulation; *for multitone jamming the performance degrades with* K since the critical parameter μ is proportional to $2^K/K$. In the inverse linear performance regions, the advantage of worst case $n = 1$ band multitone jamming over partial-band noise is ((2.25) and (2.41))

$$\Delta(E_b/N_J) = 10\log_{10}\left(\frac{2^{K-1}}{K\beta}\right) \text{ dB} \tag{2.42}$$

where β has been computed by Houston [5, (16); or see our corrected Table 2.1 above]. In particular, $\Delta(E_b/N_0) = 4.3$ dB at $K = 1$, and 10.5 dB at $K = 4$. Since β decreases monotonically with K, the effectiveness of the worst case partial-band noise and $n = 1$ band multitone jamming schemes continues to diverge as K increases.

Figure 2.13 illustrates that for a given value of K, when E_b/N_J falls below the threshold specified in (2.40), the entire SS bandwidth is saturated with one jamming tone per M-ary band. In this saturation region, $\mu = 1$ and $\rho = 1/M$ (refer to (2.28) and (2.38)), and the jamming tone power rises above S. For large values of E_b/N_J, $\alpha_{wc} = 1$ and μ and ρ asymptotically approach zero.

We now turn to the general class of band multitone jamming with $n > 1$ tones per jammed band. Because a jammed band will contain at least two interfering tones, there is now the possibility of simultaneously hitting the data symbol and at least one other M-ary symbol in the dehopped band. Consequently, the random jamming phase arguments summarized in Table 2.2 are applicable here.

The band containing a transmitted data symbol will be jammed with probability μ defined in (2.38). Conditioned on this event, the probability that one of the n jamming tones hits the data symbol is

$$\frac{\binom{M-1}{n-1}}{\binom{M}{n}} = \frac{n}{M}. \tag{2.43}$$

As discussed in Section 2.2.2.1, a symbol error occurs only if (i) the data symbol is not jammed, any of the other symbols is hit, and $\alpha < 1$, or (ii) the data symbol is jammed along with any of the other symbols, the random jamming phase lies in the range defined by (2.35), and $\alpha < 4$:

$$P_s = \mu\left[\left(1 - \frac{n}{M}\right)u_{-1}(1-\alpha) + \frac{n}{M\pi}\cos^{-1}\left(\frac{\sqrt{\alpha}}{2}\right)\right] \tag{2.44}$$

where $u_{-1}(\cdot)$ is the unit step function. Invoking (2.38) and constraining

$\mu \leq 1$, we find that the worst case performance is given by

$$P_b = \frac{M^2}{2nK(M-1)E_b/N_J} \times \max_{0<\alpha \leq \min\left(4, \frac{nKE_b/N_J}{M}\right)} \left\{ \alpha\left[\left(1 - \frac{n}{M}\right)u_{-1}(1-\alpha) + \frac{n}{M\pi}\cos^{-1}\left(\frac{\sqrt{\alpha}}{2}\right)\right]\right\}. \tag{2.45}$$

Before performing the maximization over α in (2.45), it is instructive to determine the behavior of the term $\alpha\cos^{-1}(\sqrt{\alpha}/2)$ over the range $0 < \alpha \leq 4$. As shown in Figure 2.14, it has a single maximum at $\alpha = 2.52$, and decreases monotonically on either side of that peak. The other term that must be maximized in (2.45), $\alpha u_{-1}(1-\alpha)$, increases monotonically with α over its range $(0, 1)$.

Depending on the range of E_b/N_J and n/M, the worst case performance is specified by

(i) $\dfrac{E_b}{N_J} \leq \dfrac{M}{nK}$

$$\alpha_{\text{wc}} = \left(\frac{nK}{M}\right)\frac{E_b}{N_J} \Rightarrow \mu = 1,\ \rho = \frac{n}{M}$$
$$\leq 1$$

$$P_b = \frac{M}{2(M-1)}\left\{1 - \frac{n}{M}\left[1 - \frac{1}{\pi}\cos^{-1}\left(\frac{\sqrt{\alpha_{\text{wc}}}}{2}\right)\right]\right\} \tag{2.46a}$$

(ii) $\dfrac{E_b}{N_J} \geq \dfrac{M}{nK}$

Because the function being maximized in (2.45) is discontinuous at $\alpha = 1$, it is easier to maximize it separately over the ranges $0 < \alpha < 1$ and $1 \leq \alpha \leq (nK/M)(E_b/N_J)$, and then to determine the larger of these two maxima for the given ratio n/M. Since $(\alpha/\pi)\cos^{-1}(\sqrt{\alpha}/2)$ peaks at .525 when $\alpha = 2.52$, (2.45) reduces to

$$P_b = \frac{M^2}{2nK(M-1)E_b/N_J}\max\left(1 - \frac{2n}{3M}, \frac{\beta n}{M}\right) \tag{2.46b}$$

where

$$\beta \equiv \begin{cases} \dfrac{nKE_b/N_J}{M\pi}\cos^{-1}\left(\dfrac{1}{2}\sqrt{\dfrac{nKE_b/N_J}{M}}\right); & \dfrac{E_b}{N_J} \leq 2.52\dfrac{M}{nK} \\ .525; & \dfrac{E_b}{N_J} \geq 2.52\dfrac{M}{nK}. \end{cases}$$

Defining

$$\gamma \equiv \left(\beta + \tfrac{2}{3}\right)^{-1} \in [.839, 1] \tag{2.46c}$$

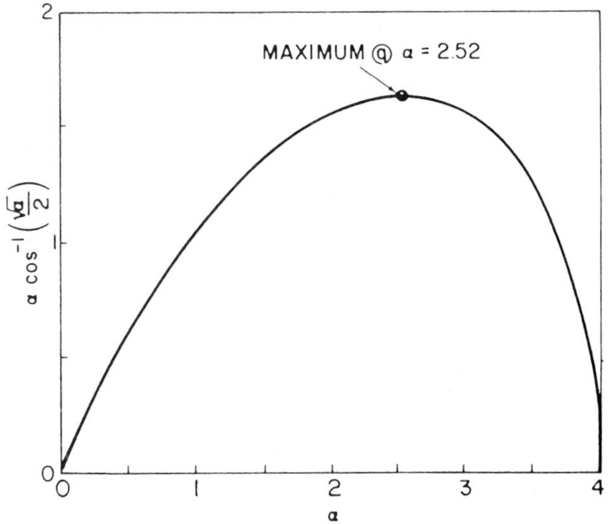

Figure 2.14. The behavior of one of the terms involved in the maximization of P_b in (2.45).

we must consider two ranges of n/M for the given range of E_b/N_J:

(*a*) $n \leq \gamma M$

$$\alpha_{wc} = 1_{-} \Rightarrow \mu = \frac{M}{nKE_b/N_J}, \; \rho = \frac{1}{KE_b/N_J}$$

$$P_b = \frac{M(M - \frac{2}{3}n)}{2nK(M-1)E_b/N_J}. \tag{2.46d}$$

(*b*) $\gamma M \leq n \leq M$

$$\alpha_{wc} = \min\left(2.52, \frac{nKE_b/N_J}{M}\right) \geq 1$$

$$\mu = \min\left(1, \frac{2.52M}{nKE_b/N_J}\right)$$

$$\rho = \min\left(\frac{n}{M}, \frac{2.52}{KE_b/N_J}\right)$$

$$P_b = \frac{M\beta}{2K(M-1)E_b/N_J}. \tag{2.46e}$$

One of the most interesting conclusions presented by (2.46a–e) is that there exist conditions for which it is in fact advantageous to allocate less power to each jamming tone than the received signal power. This occurs only for sufficiently large values of E_b/N_J and $n \sim M$.

In particular, consider the special case of $n = M$. Here we know with certainty that all M symbols of a jammed band will be hit, so that the only error mechanism is the random jamming phase effect. This is reinforced by (2.44), which reduces to

$$P_s = \frac{\alpha \cos^{-1}(\sqrt{\alpha}/2)}{\pi K E_b/N_J}. \tag{2.47}$$

We have already seen in Figure 2.14 that this function of α peaks at $\alpha = 2.52$. So we are not surprised that α_{wc} can exceed 1, nor that it saturates at 2.52 for $E_b/N_J \geq 2.52/K$ as shown in Figure 2.15. The impact of allowing α_{wc} to exceed 1 is to increase the likelihood μ that a band is jammed (see Figure 2.16), even though the larger value of α decreases the range of jamming phase ϕ for which an error can occur (refer to (2.35)). Figure 2.17 shows that the resulting uncoded FH/MFSK performance is 2 dB worse in the inverse linear region than the same jammer with $\alpha_{wc} = 1_-$.

The advantage of using $\alpha > 1$ does not only apply to the limiting case of $n = M$ band multitone jamming where all errors are attributed to the random phase effect. (2.46e) shows that α_{wc} peaks at 2.52 for large enough E_b/N_J whenever $n \geq .84M$: interestingly, in this region, the asymptotic P_b is independent of n. By contrast, had we restricted α to be less than 1, the worst case asymptotic P_b would have been that of (2.46d). The jamming advantage realized by permitting $\alpha_{wc} \geq 1$ is the ratio of these two P_b expressions

$$\frac{.525\dfrac{n}{M}}{1 - \dfrac{2n}{3M}}; \qquad \frac{n}{M} \geq .84. \tag{2.48}$$

For example, at $M = 16$ that advantage is 0.4 dB at $n = 14$ and 1.2 dB at $n = 15$, as well as the previously mentioned 2.0 dB at $n = M = 16$.

A final observation from Figure 2.17 is that unlike $n = 1$ band multitone jamming (refer to Figure 2.12), when $n = M$ the performance improves with increasing K or M, just as it does for broadband or worst case partial-band noise. Actually, (2.46e) shows that this effect occurs over the range $.84M \leq n \leq M$ for large enough E_b/N_J, since $M/K(M-1)$ increases with $K \geq 1$.

For $K = 1$ and 4, Figure 2.18 illustrates the relative effectiveness of band multitone jamming for $n = 2$ and M. Figure 2.19 shows the variation in performance with n for $K = 4$. The implication of these two graphs is that the performance improves with n for fixed K, and degrades with K for fixed n. In fact, these conclusions are essentially correct. Consider the large E_b/N_J asymptotic expressions for P_b in (2.41), (2.46d), and (2.46e): these all have the form

$$P_b = \left(\frac{M}{2K}\right)\frac{\zeta}{E_b/N_J} \tag{2.49}$$

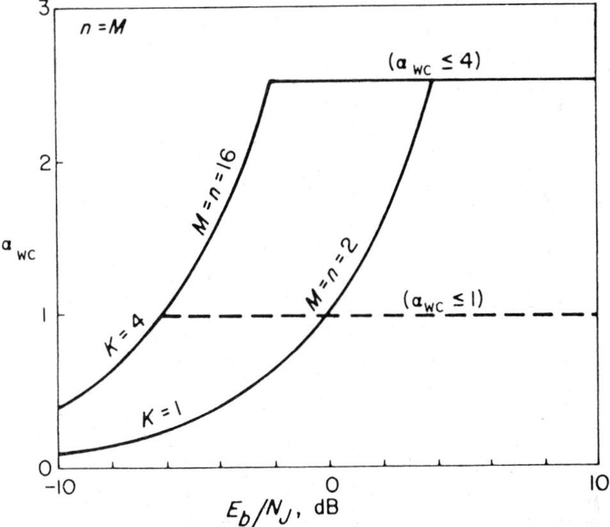

Figure 2.15. Optimum power allocation for $n = M$ band multitone jammer.

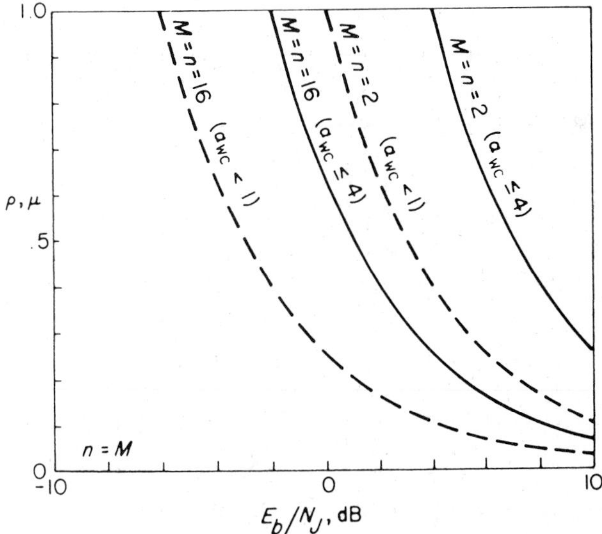

Figure 2.16. The probability ρ that a given FH slot is jammed, and the probability μ that a given M-ary band is jammed, for worst case $n = M$ band multitone jamming.

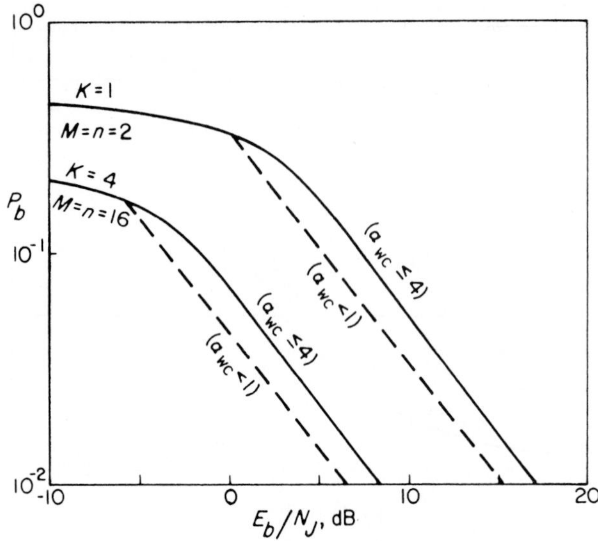

Figure 2.17. Performance of uncoded FH/MFSK system with $n = M$ band multitone interference when jamming tone powers are optimized (solid lines), or are constrained to always exceed the received signal power (dotted lines).

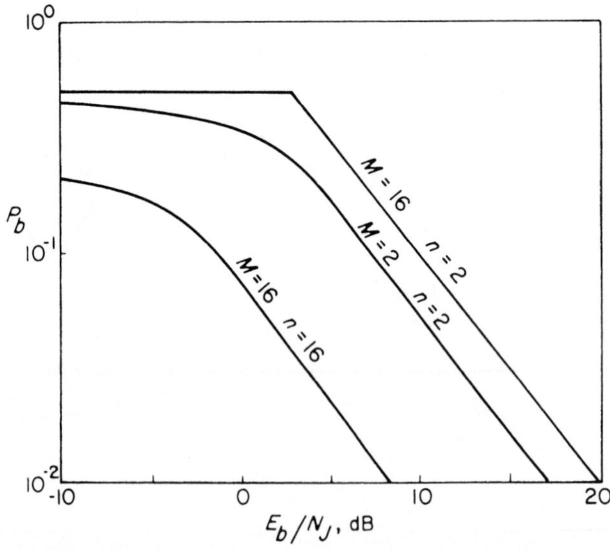

Figure 2.18. Relative effectiveness of band multitone jamming for several values of M and n.

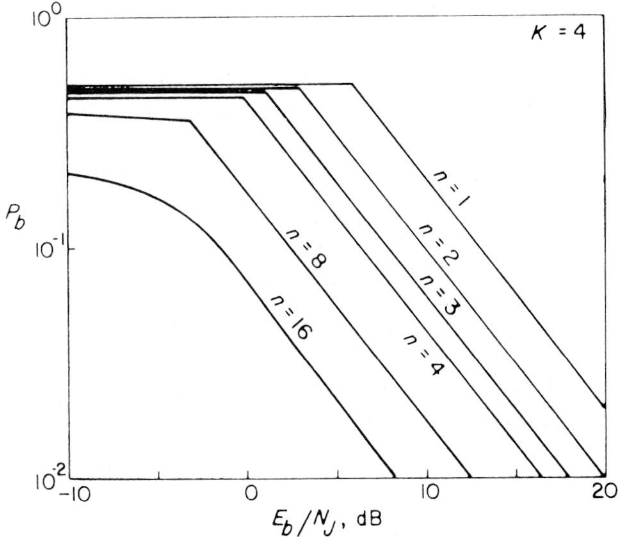

Figure 2.19. Performance improves with n for band multitone jamming, for a given K.

where ζ is given by

$$\zeta = \begin{cases} 1; & n = 1 \\ \dfrac{\left(\dfrac{M}{n} - \dfrac{2}{3}\right)}{M-1}; & 2 \le n \le .84M \text{ (provided } K \ge 2) \\ \dfrac{.525}{M-1}; & .84M \le n \le M. \end{cases} \tag{2.50}$$

(2.49) and (2.50) reveal a singular exception to our premature conjectures: for $n = 2$ the asymptotic P_b is minimized at $K = 2$. With this one anomaly, the relative effectiveness of band multitone jamming for large E_b/N_J can be summarized as follows:

(i) for a given K, the performance improves with n;
(ii) for a given n, the performance degrades with K;
(iii) for a given $n/m \ge .84$, the performance improves with K.

From the jammer's point of view, the $n = 1$ band multitone strategy is preferred, while the $n = M$ case is relatively ineffective.

2.2.2.3 Independent Multitone Jamming

As we noted in our introduction to multitone jamming, the particular appeal of the so-called independent category is its simplicity. Its effectiveness is not contingent on the jammer knowing the location of the tone frequencies in each M-ary band, which could be independently hopped over the entire spread-spectrum bandwidth, and there is no need to regulate the number of jamming tones on each band. Utilizing a seemingly inelegant strategy, the Q jamming tones are distributed uniformly over the N_t available frequencies. If $Q \gg M - 1$ (see (2.29)), each of the FH slots that comprise a given M-ary band are independently jammed with probability ρ, which reduces to

$$\rho = \frac{\alpha}{KE_b/N_J} \tag{2.51}$$

based on (2.5), (2.26), (2.31), and (2.37). We will now analyze the effectiveness of independent multitone jamming, and compare it with the other jamming schemes.

Referring to Table 2.1, a symbol error can occur only if at least one of the $M - 1$ untransmitted symbols in the M-ary band containing the data is jammed. Then, conditioned on this event, a symbol error is made if the data tone is not jammed and $\alpha < 1$, or the data tone is jammed but the relative jamming tone phase ϕ satisfies (2.35) with $\alpha < 4$. By the assumptions implicit in the independent multitone strategy, the likelihood of the data tone being jammed is independent of the prerequisite that one or more of the other untransmitted tones is jammed:

$$P_s = \left[1 - (1 - \rho)^{M-1}\right]\left[(1 - \rho)u_{-1}(1 - \alpha) + \frac{\rho}{\pi}\cos^{-1}\left(\frac{\sqrt{\alpha}}{2}\right)u_{-1}(4 - \alpha)\right] \tag{2.52}$$

Applying (2.20a) and (2.51), with the restriction that $\rho \leq 1$, the bit error rate in worst case jamming is specified by

$$P_b = \frac{M}{2(M-1)} \max_{0 < \alpha < \min(4, KE_b/N_J)} \left[1 - (1 - \rho)^{M-1}\right] \times \left[(1 - \rho)u_{-1}(1 - \alpha) + \frac{\rho}{\pi}\cos^{-1}\left(\frac{\sqrt{\alpha}}{2}\right)\right] \tag{2.53}$$

where ρ is a function of α defined by (2.51).

For $E_b/N_J < \gamma$ (tabulated below), Figure 2.20 shows that $\alpha_{wc} < 1$, but the maximization in (2.53) must be computed separately for each combination of K and E_b/N_J. However, Table 2.3 shows that this computationally difficult region corresponds to $P_b > .37$ for any K, so it is not of practical interest. When $E_b/N_J \geq \gamma$, $\alpha_{wc} = 1_-$, $\rho \leq 1/K\gamma \equiv \rho_0 < 1 \; \forall K$, and (2.53) reduces to

$$P_b = \frac{M}{2(M-1)}\left(1 - \frac{2}{3}\rho\right)\left[1 - (1 - \rho)^{M-1}\right]. \tag{2.54}$$

Note that when $\alpha = \alpha_{wc} = 1_-$ and $KE_b/N_J \gg 1$, (2.51) says that $\rho \ll 1$ (see Figure 2.20 as well): then (2.54) reduces to

$$P_b \cong \frac{M\rho}{2} = \frac{2^{K-1}}{KE_b/N_J} \tag{2.55}$$

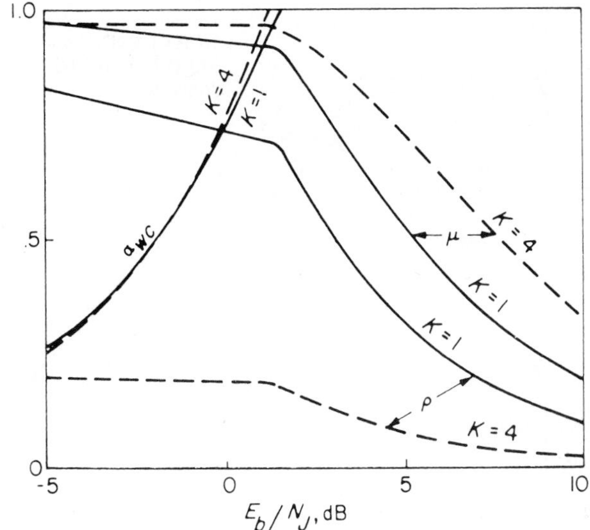

Figure 2.20. Worst case independent multitone jamming parameters: α_{wc} is ratio of signal-to-jamming tone powers, ρ is probability that a given FH slot is jammed, and μ is probability that at least one slot in an M-ary band is jammed.

which is identical to (2.41) for $n = 1$ band multitone jamming. So, as illustrated in Figure 2.21, for the low error rates that typify most practical communication systems, these two jamming strategies are equally effective against uncoded non-coherent FH/MFSK signals. Recall that we suggested this hypothesis at the beginning of this section based on identical expressions for μ when ρ is small (refer to (2.30) and the discussion that follows).

A summary of the relative effectiveness of all of the worst case partial-band noise and multitone jammers is shown in Figure 2.22 for $K = 4$. The $n = 1$ band and independent multitone strategies are the most effective in the absence of coding; partial-band noise is as effective as band multitone jamming for $n \sim M/2$; and $n = M$ band multitone jamming is the least

Table 2.3
Parameters associated with performance of uncoded FH/MFSK signals in worst case independent multitone jamming.

K	γ, dB	$\rho_0 \equiv \dfrac{1}{K\gamma}$	$P_b\rvert_{\rho=\rho_0}$
1	1.54	.70	.37
2	.45	.45	.39
3	.54	.29	.42
4	1.26	.19	.45

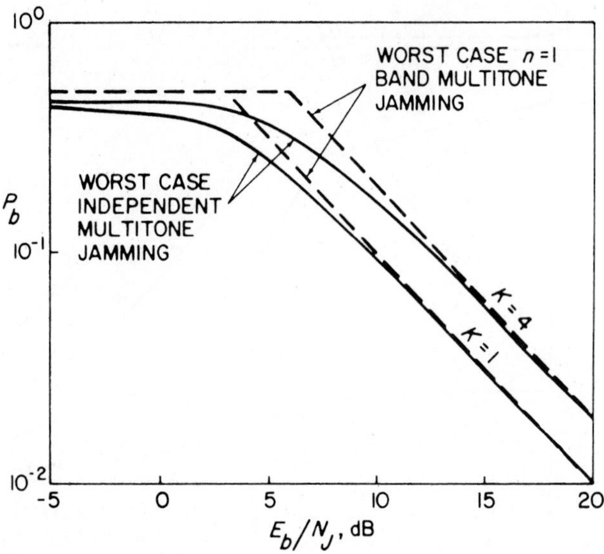

Figure 2.21. Worst case independent and $n = 1$ band multitone jammers are equally effective against uncoded FH/MFSK signals for low P_b's.

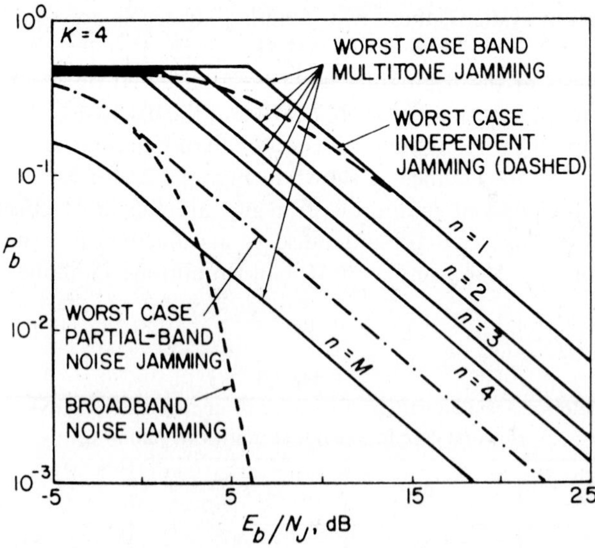

Figure 2.22. Comparison of relative effectiveness of various worst case jamming strategies against uncoded, non-coherently detected FH/16-ary FSK signals.

effective (even worse than broadband noise for low E_b/N_J). Furthermore, all of the worst case jammers result in the inverse linear performance characteristic for large enough E_b/N_J.

2.3 CODING COUNTERMEASURES

Up to this point, each M-ary symbol was sent entirely on a single hop. And we have seen that sophisticated non-adaptive (i.e., non-repeat back) jammers can severely degrade the performance of such systems. These jammers all concentrate their available power over portions of the total spread-spectrum bandwidth W_{ss}; although only a small fraction of the data may be hit, those data suffer a relatively high conditional error rate.

An effective countermeasure against this form of concentrated jamming is to introduce coding redundancy, so that if a given hop is jammed other hopefully more reliable received data can be used to resolve the contaminated data. By basing data decisions on multiple hops, the jammer will have to deconcentrate its power so as to hit a larger fraction of the transmitted data. The ultimate goal is to force the jammer to retreat back towards the original broadband (unconcentrated) noise jamming strategy. In this manner, we would expect to recover the desired exponential performance characteristic.

In computing the performance of a coded system for which each data decision depends on multiple uses of a noisy channel, it is generally impractical to derive closed form exact error rate expressions. Such computations typically involve the integrals of special functions which are at best cumbersome or must be evaluated numerically. Furthermore, these calculations must often be repeated when a single system parameter is changed. Consequently, it is more expedient to use Chernoff upperbounding techniques which involve the statistics of a single channel use. This approach often yields closed form expressions which can produce useful insights. Furthermore, these bounds are exponentially accurate in the region of greatest interest, namely, small P_b's. Our analysis will be based extensively on such bounds; where exact results have been documented, they will be used to determine the accuracy of our bounds.

2.3.1 Time Diversity

One of the simplest yet effective coding techniques is to subdivide each information symbol into equal energy subsymbols which are then transmitted over independent channel states. This is referred to as diversity transmission or a repetition code.

In the context of the FH/MFSK structure, each M-ary symbol is partitioned into m subsymbols or "chips" (not to be confused with the PN spreading code chips) with energy $E_c = KE_b/m$. As illustrated in Figure

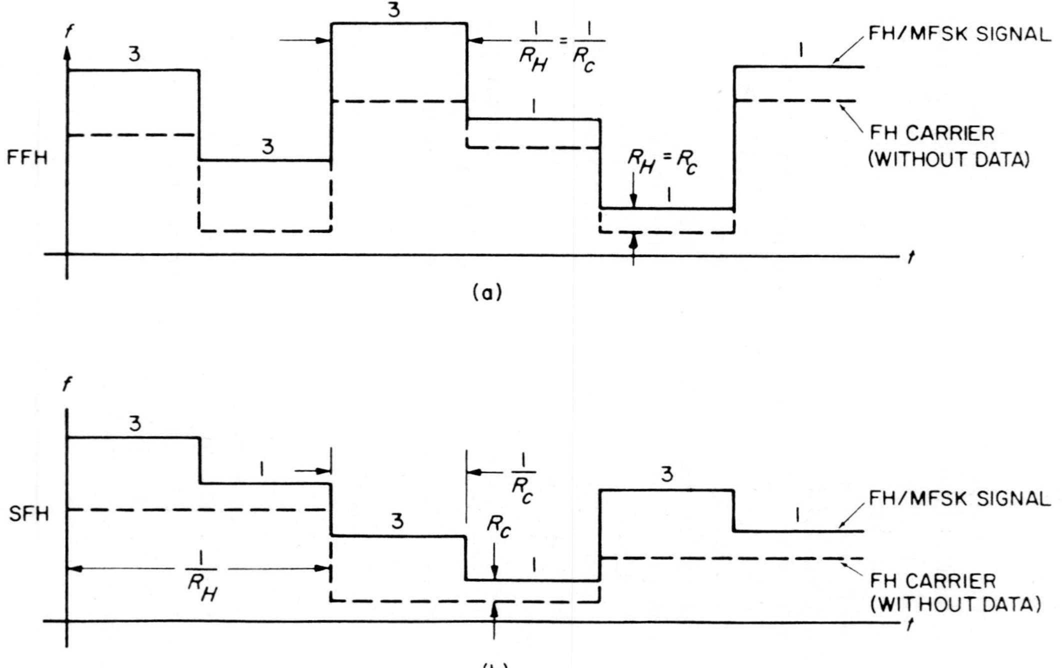

Figure 2.23. Two ways to achieve FH/MFSK diversity. For example, suppose $M = 4$, $m = 3$ chips/4-ary symbol, $R_b = 10$ Kb/s ($R_s = R_b/K = 5$ Ks/s; $R_c = mR_s = 15$ Kchips/s), and we want to send the 4-ary symbol 3 followed by 1. In (a), $R_h = R_c = 15$ Khops/s; in (b), $R_h = 7.5$ Khops/s and interleaving of depth $d = R_c/R_h = 2$ is required (the message is that a slow FH synthesizer hop rate does not preclude the use of diversity).

2.23, each chip is transmitted on a different hop using fast frequency hopping (FFH) or slow frequency hopping (SFH) with pseudorandom interleaving. The intention is that each chip comprising an M-ary symbol will have an independent chance of being jammed. Because these chips are distributed in time, this technique is often termed "time diversity," although "jamming-state diversity" would be an equally descriptive label. The resulting chip rate $R_c = mR_b/K$; recall that we use the term FFH to denote the condition $R_c = R_h$ (the hop rate), whereas SFH implies $R_c > R_h$.

For each received M-ary chip, after the FH carrier has been demodulated, the received signal is input to M non-coherent detectors which measure the energy at each of the possible tone frequencies over the chip duration $1/R_c$ (refer to Figure 2.1). To ensure that none of the signal energy is detected by the $M - 1$ energy detectors at the untransmitted frequencies, the spacing between adjacent FH slots (within an M-ary band) must be an integer multiple of R_c; if the minimum separation is used, then the number of available frequencies

$$N_t = \frac{W_{ss}}{R_c} = \frac{KW_{ss}}{mR_b} \tag{2.56}$$

decreases with the amount of diversity m per M-ary symbol[1] (see Figure 2.3). In addition to the M detected energies per chip, the receiver may have some channel state side information available to aid the data decision process [8]. We will assume that *the receiver knows with certainty whether each hop is jammed or not*. One way to derive this information in practice is to implement automatic gain control (AGC) in the receiver, which may be monitored to determine whether jamming power is corrupting a given hop [2, p. 288]. However, we will instead use an approach suggested by Trumpis [7]: since only one of the energy detector outputs will be high[2] on a given chip transmission in the absence of jamming, we will *declare a chip to be jammed when two or more energy detector outputs are high*.

Since the channel statistics can change at the pleasure of the jammer, any decision metric will be suboptimum for some form of jamming. For simplicity, we will use the following procedure based on the soft decision energy detector outputs for the M tones and m diversity transmissions relevant to a given M-ary symbol, along with the corresponding jamming state side information. If *any* of the m chips is not jammed, an error-free M-ary decision can be made; otherwise, select the largest of the metrics

$$\left\{ \Lambda_i \equiv \sum_{j=1}^{m} e_{ij};\ 1 \le i \le M \right\} \tag{2.57}$$

[1] Viterbi and Jacobs [2] and others prefer the parameter $L = m/K$, which is the diversity per bit.

[2] Actually, since we are neglecting receiver thermal noise, the other $M - 1$ detected energies will be identically zero.

where e_{ij} is the energy detector output for the i-th M-ary symbol on the j-th diversity transmission. The linear sum metric of (2.57) is maximum likelihood for a Rayleigh fading channel [9, pp. 533–540], and it is asymptotically optimum for the additive white Gaussian noise channel in the limit of large E_b/N_J. However, in general it is suboptimum, and we will later see that there is a signal-to-noise ratio reduction as a result of the non-coherent energy combining implicit in the Λ_i's.

2.3.1.1 Partial-Band Noise Jamming

We will now analyze the performance of the FH/MFSK system with diversity utilizing the soft decision metric with side information in a worst case partial-band noise environment (refer back to Section 2.2.1). Suppose symbol 1 is sent: conditioned on the j-th chip being jammed, e_{1j} is a non-central chi-square random variable while the remaining $M-1$ e_{ij}'s are central chi-square random variables, each with two degrees of freedom. The probability density functions of the e_{ij}'s have the form of (2.8) and (2.9), with E_s/N_J replaced by $E_c/N_J' = \rho K E_b/m N_J$ (see (2.21)).

Let H_j denote the event that the j-th chip is hit by partial-band noise, with $\boldsymbol{H} \equiv (H_1, H_2, \dots, H_m)$ representing the event that all m diversity transmissions are jammed; since the H_j's are independent,

$$\Pr\{\boldsymbol{H}\} = \rho^m. \tag{2.58}$$

With perfect side information, an M-ary symbol error requires that $\boldsymbol{H}$ occur:

$$P_s = \rho^m \Pr\left\{ \bigcup_{i=2}^{M} (\Lambda_i \geq \Lambda_1) \middle| \boldsymbol{H} \right\}. \tag{2.59}$$

Adopting the bounding approach of [2], the M-ary problem of (2.59) is first reduced to a binary problem by applying the union bounding technique and noting that the Λ_i's are identically distributed for $i \neq 1$:

$$P_s \leq (M-1)\rho^m \Pr\{\Lambda_2 \geq \Lambda_1 | \boldsymbol{H}\}. \tag{2.60}$$

This expression is then reduced to the statistics of a single diversity transmission by using (2.57) and the Chernoff bound [2, (9), with $L = m$ and E_b replaced by $E_s = KE_b$]:

$$\begin{aligned}
\Pr\{\Lambda_2 \geq \Lambda_1 | \boldsymbol{H}\} &= \Pr\left\{ \sum_{j=1}^{m} (e_{2j} - e_{ij}) \geq 0 \middle| \boldsymbol{H} \right\} \\
&\leq \frac{1}{2}\left[\overline{e^{\lambda(e_{2j} - e_{1j})}|H_j}\right]^m; \qquad \lambda \geq 0 \\
&= \frac{1}{2}\left[\frac{e^{-(\lambda/1+\lambda)(\rho K E_b/m N_J)}}{1-\lambda^2}\right]^m; \quad 0 \leq \lambda < 1 \qquad (2.61)
\end{aligned}$$

which should be minimized over the Chernoff parameter λ. The factor of $1/2$ in the Chernoff bound is justified under certain conditions [10] which are satisfied for partial-band noise jamming (see Appendix 2A). Using (2.20a) and optimizing over λ and ρ for worst case jamming,

$$P_b \le \frac{M}{4} \max_{0<\rho\le 1} \min_{0\le\lambda<1} \left[\left(\frac{\rho}{1-\lambda^2}\right) e^{-(\lambda/1+\lambda)(\rho K E_b/m N_J)}\right]^m \tag{2.62}$$

for arbitrary K, E_b/N_J, and m. Computing the joint extrema over ρ and λ, there are two distinct solutions:

(i) $m \ge KE_b/3N_J$

$$P_b \le \frac{M}{4}\left[\left(\frac{1}{1-\lambda^2}\right) e^{-2\beta(\lambda/1+\lambda)}\right]^m \tag{2.63}$$

where

$$\rho_{\mathrm{wc}} = 1,\ \beta \equiv \frac{KE_b}{2mN_J},$$

and

$$2\lambda = \sqrt{1+6\beta+\beta^2} - (1+\beta)$$

(ii) $1 \le m \le KE_b/3N_J$

$$P_b \le \frac{M}{4}\left(\frac{4mN_J}{eKE_b}\right)^m \quad \text{and} \quad \rho_{\mathrm{wc}} = \frac{3m}{KE_b/N_J}. \tag{2.64}$$

Note that as m increases for a given KE_b/N_J, the jammer's need to hit all m diversity transmissions forces it to broaden the jammed frequency band;

Table 2.4

Parameters derived by Trumpis [7] for exact performance of FH/MFSK signals with diversity m in worst case partial-band noise (see (2.65)).

	$K=1$		$K=2$		$K=3$		$K=4$		$K=5$	
m	β	γ, dB	β	γ, dB	β	γ, dB	β	γ, dB	β	γ, dB
2	.4168	6.7	.5959	4.2	.8575	2.8	1.0796	2.0	1.3659	1.4
3	.5210	8.8	.8265	6.1	1.2565	4.6	1.8198	3.7	2.5937	3.0
4	.6797	10.2	1.1401	7.4	1.8320	5.9	2.8251	4.8	4.1493	4.1
6	1.2392	12.1	2.2245	9.2	3.8464	7.6	6.4370	6.5	10.3502	5.7
8	2.3584	13.5	4.4101	10.5	8.0165	8.9	14.0997	7.7	24.0142	6.8
10	4.6110	14.5	8.8385	11.5	16.5774	9.8	30.2829	8.7	61.6169	7.8

when $m > KE_b/3N_J$, the worst case partial-band noise jammer is simply the broadband noise jammer with $\rho = 1$.

The accuracy of these upperbounds can be investigated by comparing them with exact expressions derived by Trumpis [7], involving the optimization of a sum of generalized Laguerre polynomials over ρ, which must be performed by a computer for each combination of K and m (the computation is lengthy for larger values of K and m since the number of terms in the summation is $(M-1)[\frac{1}{2}M(m-1)+1] \sim m2^{2K-1}$). For small E_b/N_J, $\rho_{wc} = 1$ and P_b must be computed numerically for each value of E_b/N_J; however, in the region of interest where P_b is low, Trumpis showed that

$$P_b = \beta\left(\frac{mN_J}{KE_b}\right)^m \quad \text{and} \quad \rho_{wc} = \frac{\gamma}{E_b/N_J} \tag{2.65}$$

$$\text{provided} \quad E_b/N_J \geq \gamma$$

where β and γ are given in Table 2.4.

The accuracy of the upperbounds for several values of K and m is illustrated in Figures 2.24–2.26. For large enough E_b/N_J, it is seen that the separation between the bounds and the exact performance approaches an asymptotic limit. We can compute this asymptotic difference analytically using (2.64) and (2.65) for large E_b/N_J. For a given K and m, (2.64)

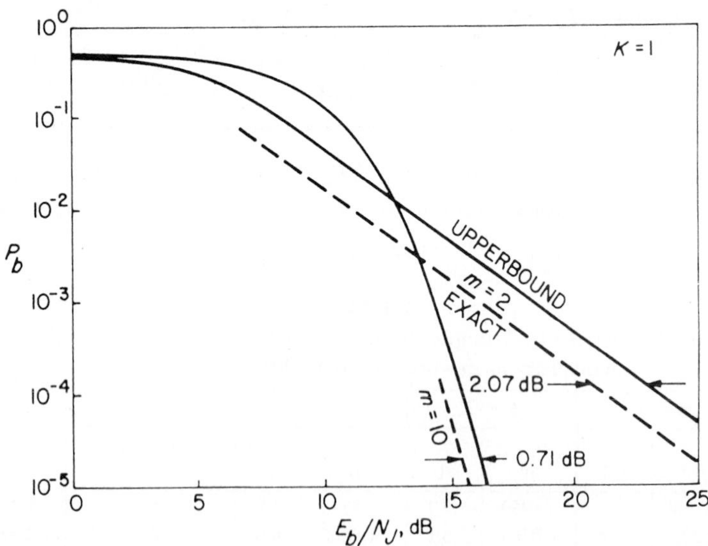

Figure 2.24. Comparison of upperbounds on performance of FH/BFSK ($K = 1$) signals with diversity m chips/bit in worst case partial-band noise against exact P_b (dashed curves).

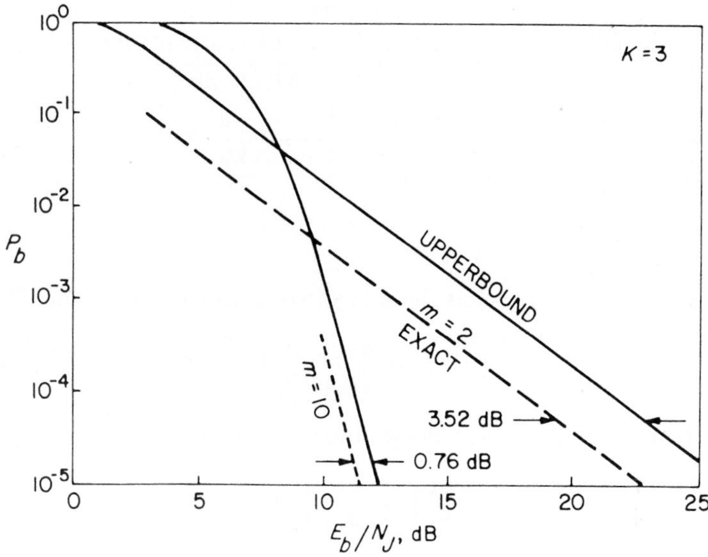

Figure 2.25. Same as Figure 2.24, except FH/MFSK signals with $K = 3$ or $M = 8$, and m chips/8-ary symbol.

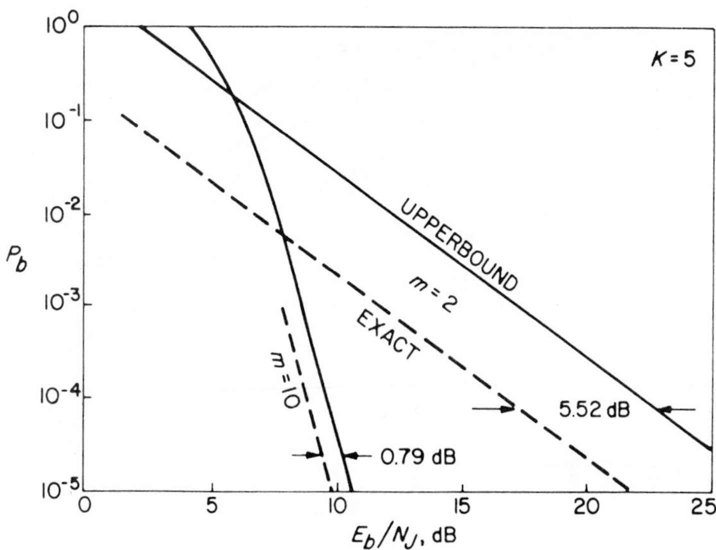

Figure 2.26. Same as Figures 2.24 and 2.25, except $K = 5$ or $M = 32$ with m diversity chips/32-ary symbol.

Table 2.5
Asymptotic accuracy of performance upperbound in (2.64) for low P_b

m	$\Delta E_b/N_J$, dB		
	$K = 1$	$K = 3$	$K = 5$
2	2.07	3.52	5.52
10	.71	.76	.79

overbounds the signal-to-noise level required to achieve a particular P_b:

$$\left(\frac{E_b}{N_J}\right)_1 \equiv \frac{4m}{eK}\left(\frac{M}{4P_b}\right)^{1/m}. \tag{2.66}$$

The actual required signal-to-noise ratio is given by (2.65):

$$\left(\frac{E_b}{N_J}\right)_2 = \frac{m}{K}\left(\frac{\beta}{P_b}\right)^{1/m} \tag{2.67}$$

The bound accuracy may be specified by the ratio

$$\Delta E_b/N_J \equiv \left(\frac{E_b}{N_J}\right)_1 \Bigg/ \left(\frac{E_b}{N_J}\right)_2 = \frac{4}{e}\left(\frac{M}{4\beta}\right)^{1/m} \tag{2.68}$$

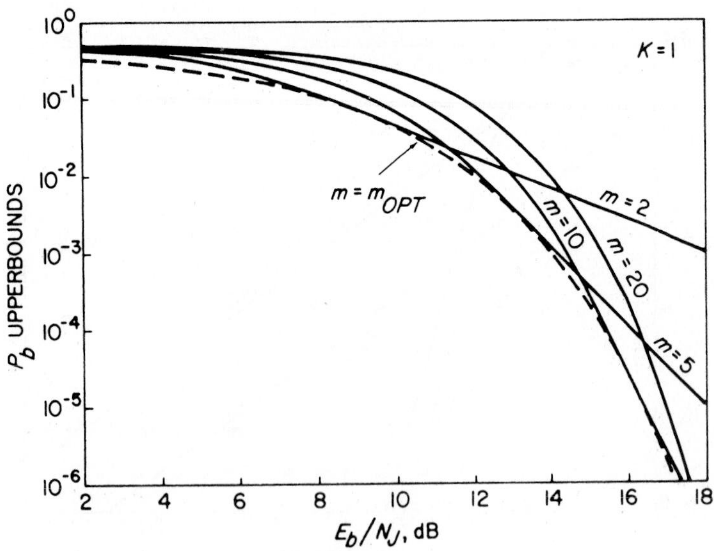

Figure 2.27. Variation in performance upperbounds for FH/BFSK signals in worst case partial-band noise with diversity m chips/bit; optimum diversity (m_{opt}) performance is lower envelope, shown as dotted curve.

which is given in Table 2.5 for selected values of K and m. We see that the bound is quite accurate for larger values of m; for example, it is only 3/4 dB above the exact result for $m = 10$, with minor variation over K. However, for small m the bound is pessimistic by several dB, and the accuracy degrades with increasing K.

Returning to the upperbounds now, (2.63) and (2.64) are used to illustrate the variation in performance with diversity m for a given K in Figures 2.27–2.29. Notice that the curves cross each other, so that for fixed K and E_b/N_J, the performance actually degrades if m is too large due to non-coherent combining of the detected chip energies in the metric of (2.57). For example, consider the performance curves for $K = 3$ in Figure 2.28: if $E_b/N_J = 12$ dB, P_b is lower at $m = 10$ than at $m = 5$ or 20. The existence of an optimum amount of diversity for a given K and E_b/N_J is further illustrated in Figure 2.30. (Although the diversity m is treated like a continuous variable, it should be remembered that it only has meaning for integer values. Since the minima in Figure 2.30 are quite broad, there is essentially no loss in performance when the continuous value of m_{opt}, defined below in (2.70), is truncated to the nearest integer.) The loss in performance for $m > m_{\text{opt}}$ due to non-coherent combining is clearly evident in Figure 2.30.

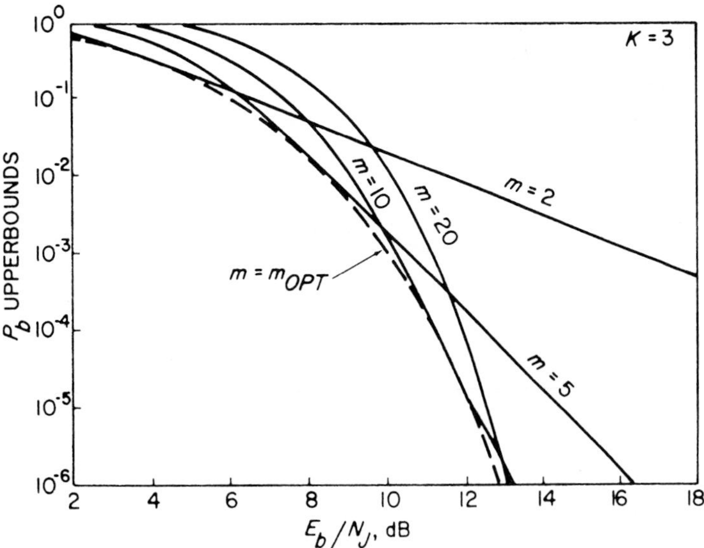

Figure 2.28. Same as Figure 2.27, except FH/MFSK signals with $K = 3$ or $M = 8$, and m diversity chips/8-ary symbol.

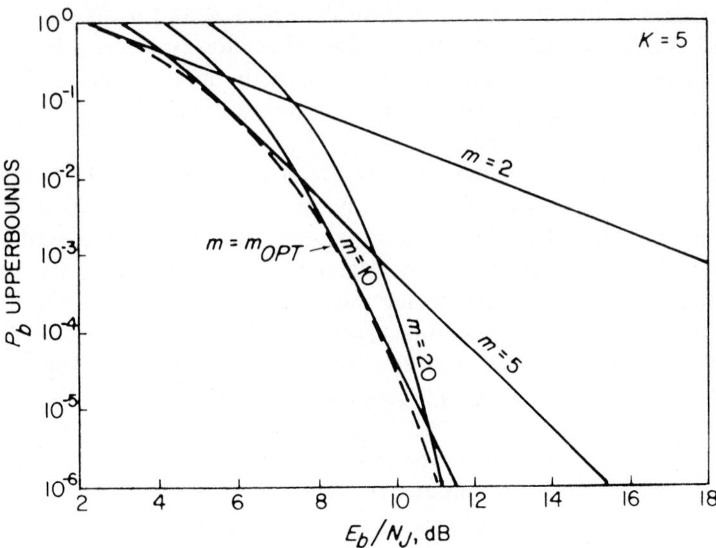

Figure 2.29. Same as Figures 2.27 and 2.28, except that $K = 5$ or $M = 32$ and m diversity chips/32-ary symbol.

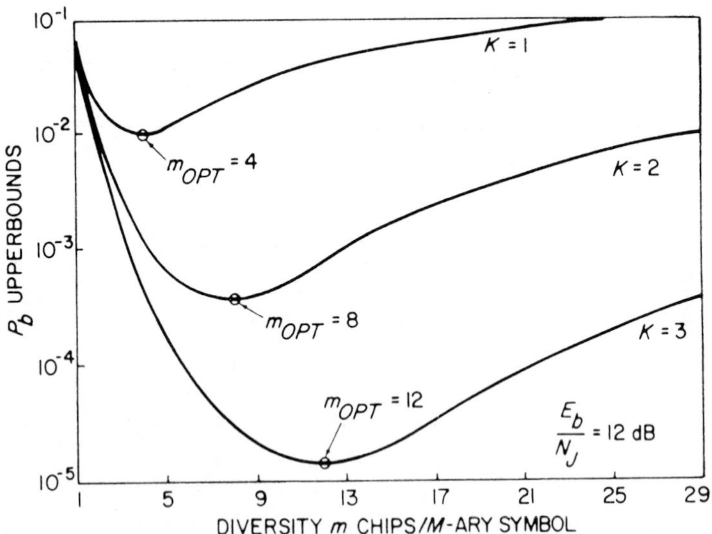

Figure 2.30. Variation in performance of FH/MFSK signals in worst case partial-band noise with amount of diversity for $E_b/N_J = 12$ dB. The P_b upperbound is minimized at $m = m_{\text{opt}}$, and the performance degrades for larger values of m due to non-coherent combining of the diversity chip energies.

Referring again to Figures 2.27–2.29, the performance in worst case jamming with optimized diversity is the lower envelope of the set of curves with parameter m, shown as a dotted curve in each graph. Analytically, we are looking for the solution

$$P_b \le \frac{M}{4} \min_{m\ge 1} \max_{0<\rho\le 1} \min_{0\le\lambda<1} \left[\left(\frac{\rho}{1-\lambda^2}\right) e^{-(\lambda/1+\lambda)(\rho K E_b/mN_J)}\right]^m \tag{2.69}$$

which implies that we want the smaller of the minima of (2.63) and (2.64) over $m \ge 1$. We find that the desired solution derives from (2.64), provided E_b/N_J is large enough:

$$\left.\begin{aligned} P_b &\le 2^{K-2} e^{-KE_b/4N_J} \\ m_{\text{opt}} &= \frac{KE_b}{4N_J} \\ \rho_{\text{wc}} &= \tfrac{3}{4} \end{aligned}\right\} \quad \text{provided} \quad \frac{E_b}{N_J} \ge \frac{4}{K}. \tag{2.70}$$

The constraint in (2.70) simply guarantees that $m_{\text{opt}} \ge 1$; for smaller values of E_b/N_J, $m_{\text{opt}} = 1$ and (2.25) yields the exact P_b (which is obviously discontinuous from the upperbound of (2.70) at its lower limit on E_b/N_J).

The result of (2.70) was first documented in [2], where the extrema m_{opt} and ρ_{wc} were termed "quasi-optimum" since they are based on an upperbound. It is plotted in Figure 2.31 for $1 \le K \le 5$, which shows that the performance with optimum diversity in worst case partial-band noise im-

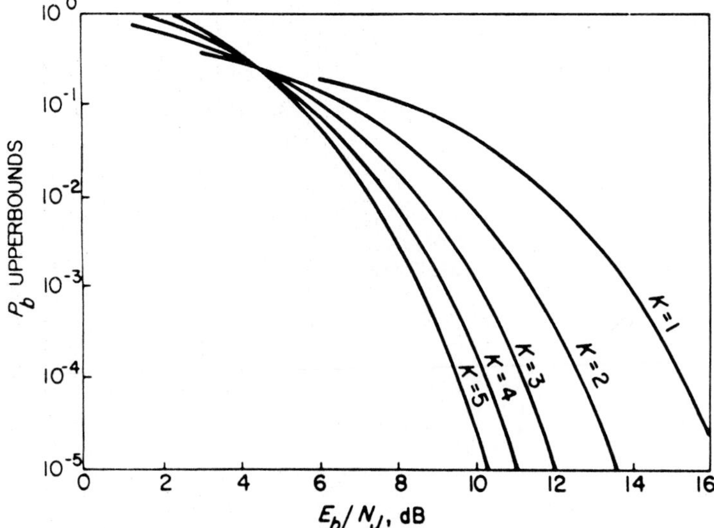

Figure 2.31. Performance of FH/MFSK signals with optimum diversity in worst case partial-band noise ($\rho_{\text{wc}} = 3/4$, $\forall K$ and $E_b/N_J \ge 4/K$).

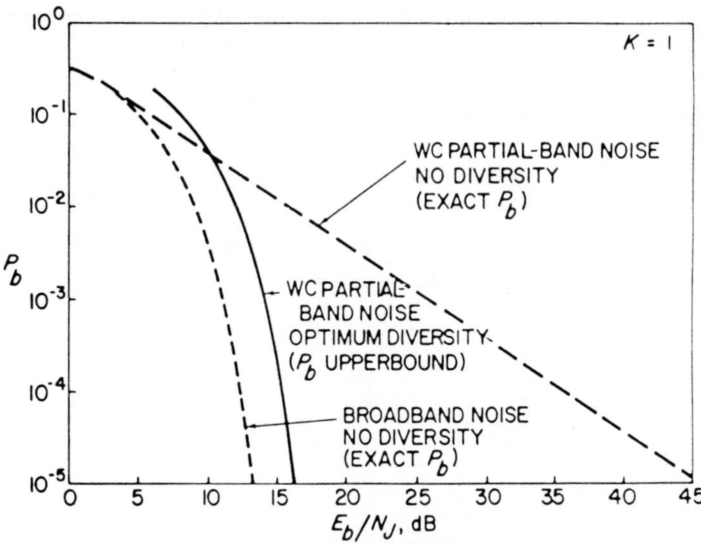

Figure 2.32. Improvement in performance of FH/BFSK signals in worst case (WC) partial-band noise due to optimum diversity; recovery from no diversity case (dashed curve) is significant at low P_b's (e.g., better than 29 dB at $P_b = 10^{-5}$), and performance is within 3 dB of broadband noise (dotted curve).

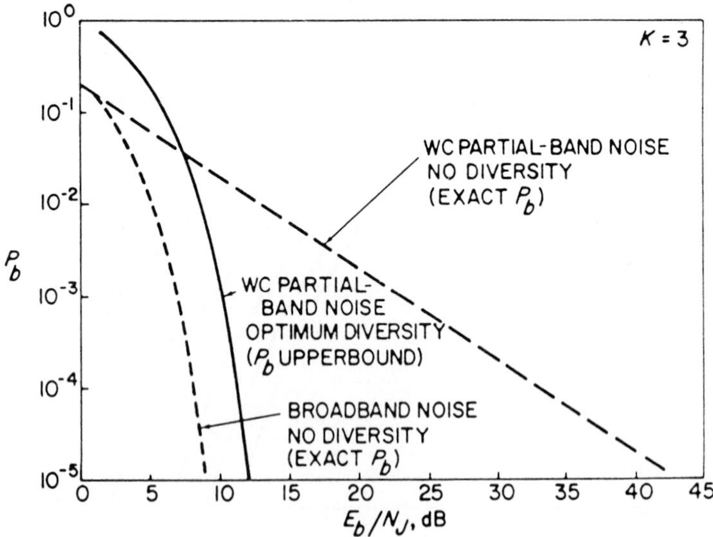

Figure 2.33. Same as Figure 2.32, except FH/MFSK signals with $K = 3$ ($M = 8$); optimum diversity recovers about 31 dB relative to no diversity case at $P_b = 10^{-5}$ (benchmark).

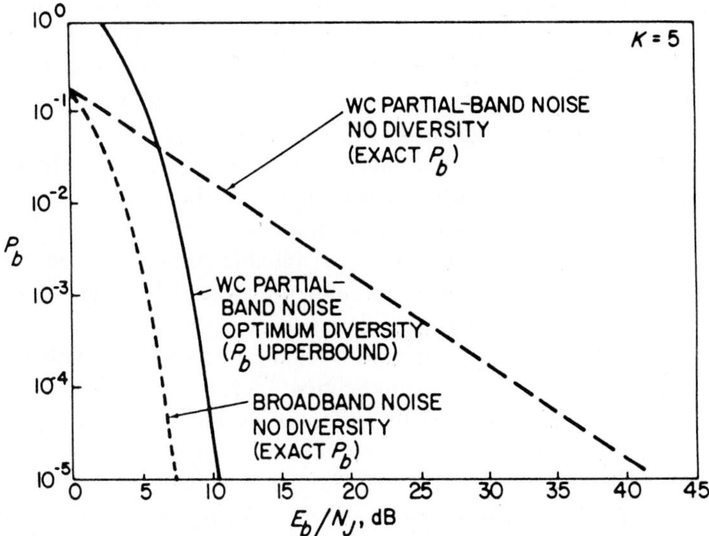

Figure 2.34. Same as Figures 2.32 and 2.33, except $K = 5$ ($M = 32$); optimum diversity recovers over 32 dB relative to no diversity case at $P_b = 10^{-5}$.

proves with K, as it did with no diversity in worst case partial-band and broadband noise (see Figure 2.9). Most important, we see in (2.70) that optimum diversity restores the desired exponential performance behavior characteristic of brute force broadband noise jamming. As shown in Figures 2.32–2.34, optimum diversity recovers most of the advantage that a worst case partial-band noise jammer enjoys against uncoded FH/MFSK signals. For example, Table 2.6 contrasts the performance with no diversity and optimum diversity at the benchmark $P_b = 10^{-5}$, based on the exact expressions of 2.25 and the upperbound of (2.70):

Table 2.6

Effectiveness of diversity against worst case partial-band noise: $\Delta E_b/N_J$ is improvement with optimum diversity at $P_b = 10^{-5}$.

	$P_b = 10^{-5}$				
	$m = 1$		$m = m_{\text{opt}}$		
K	E_b/N_J, dB (Exact)	ρ_{wc}	E_b/N_J, dB (Upperbound)	ρ_{wc}	$\Delta E_b/N_J$, dB (Lowerbound)
1	45.66	5.43×10^{-5}	16.36	.75	29.30
2	43.67	5.12×10^{-5}	13.62	.75	30.05
3	42.91	4.74×10^{-5}	12.12	.75	30.79
4	42.56	4.84×10^{-5}	11.11	.75	31.45
5	42.42	4.57×10^{-5}	10.36	.75	32.06

In particular, Table 2.6 demonstrates that optimum diversity recovers more than 29 dB at $K = 1$ (even more for larger K) at $P_b = 10^{-5}$. Furthermore, comparing the upperbounds of (2.20c) and (2.70), we see that the performance with optimum diversity in worst case partial-band noise is only about 3 dB worse than with no diversity in broadband noise.

(2.70) shows that the desired amount of diversity m_{opt} can become large for sufficiently low P_b's, especially for larger alphabet sizes M, under worst case partial-band noise jamming conditions (e.g., $m_{\text{opt}} = 20$ at $P_b = 10^{-5}$ when $K = 5$). This is an indication that reliable communication over such channels demands a substantial amount of coding redundancy. Since time diversity corresponds to a primitive repetition code, it is conceivable that more powerful codes may achieve the required redundancy with improved efficiency; this will be examined in Section 2.3.2.

A surprising result is that with optimum diversity, $\rho_{\text{wc}} = \frac{3}{4}$ independent of K and E_b/N_J, provided that the constraint in (2.70) is satisfied. This invariance can probably be attributed to the form of the P_b upperbound in (2.69); an exact joint determination of m_{opt} and ρ_{wc} would in all likelihood exhibit some complex variation with K and E_b/N_J. Table 2.6 reminds us that in the absence of diversity, at low P_b's, an effective partial-band noise jammer concentrates its available power over a small fraction of W_{ss} (e.g., $\rho_{\text{wc}} \sim 5 \times 10^{-5}$ at $P_b = 10^{-5}$ for $1 \leq K \leq 5$). Optimum diversity forces the jammer to retreat back towards the broadband ($\rho = 1$) strategy, with the resultant loss of most of its prior advantage (see Figures 2.32–2.34).

It should be noted that the solution to the joint optimization of the P_b bound in (2.69) over m and ρ is *not a saddlepoint*; that is, if we reverse the order of that optimization and consider instead the expression

$$P_b \leq \frac{M}{4} \max_{0<\rho\leq 1} \min_{m\geq 1} \min_{0\leq\lambda<1} \left[\left(\frac{\rho}{1-\lambda^2}\right) e^{-(\lambda/1+\lambda)(\rho K E_b/m N_J)}\right]^m \tag{2.71}$$

the result would differ from (2.70) [11]. Let us consider the implications of (2.69). The underlying assumption is that the three extrema are computed for arbitrary but fixed values of K (or M) and E_b/N_J. The first minimization over λ simply guarantees the tightest Chernoff upperbound, and the optimum λ is in general a function of m and ρ:

$$\lambda = \tfrac{1}{2}\left[\sqrt{1 + 6\beta + \beta^2} - (1 + \beta)\right] \tag{2.72}$$

where

$$\beta \equiv \frac{\rho K E_b}{2 m N_J}$$

which is a variation of (2.63). Next, the P_b bound with λ given by (2.72) is maximized over ρ for any m, and the optimum ρ depends on m, as does λ above. In particular, if $E_b/N_J \geq 3m/K$ so that $\rho_{\text{wc}} \leq 1$, the solution is (2.64) with the optimum λ in (2.72) reducing to $1/2$; for smaller E_b/N_J,

$\rho_{wc} = 1$ and (2.72) reduces to (2.63). The implication is that no matter which value of m is selected by the communicator, the jammer is privy to that parameter, either through surveillance or espionage, and can *subsequently* choose ρ_{wc} accordingly. Since the communicator must reveal his strategy first while the jammer gets the last move in this game of electronic countermeasure (ECM) and counter-countermeasure (ECCM), the jammer realizes an advantage in principle. Under these playing rules, the best strategy for the communicator is to choose m according to (2.70), provided $E_b/N_J \geq 4/K$ so that $m_{\text{opt}} \geq 1$; then ρ_{wc} in (2.64) reduces to $3/4$.

Suppose instead that the jammer must declare his choice of ρ first, and the communicator can subsequently select m knowing ρ. Under this reversal of the game rules to the detriment of the jammer, the optimized performance is given by (2.71), with λ still defined by (2.72). The solution is then $m_{\text{opt}} = \rho_{wc} = 1$, corresponding to the performance of an uncoded FH/MFSK system in broadband Gaussian noise [11]. The performance improvement is illustrated in Figures 2.32–2.34.

This introduces some game theoretic considerations regarding the selection of m and ρ. The arguments are easier to follow in the context of a specific example, so suppose we want to achieve a P_b of 10^{-5} with $K = 4$. Based on (2.70), the communicator would design for $E_b/N_J = 11.11$ dB with $m = 13$. For these values of K, E_b/N_J, and m, (2.64) (or (2.70)) shows that the jammer will maximize the P_b upperbound at 10^{-5} if he uses $\rho = 3/4$; any other choice of ρ would result in a lower P_b upperbound. So the advantage to the communicator of designing his system parameters based on (2.70) is that it guarantees a minimum performance level for any partial-band noise jammer.

Suppose the communicator anticipates that the jammer will use $\rho = 3/4$, or discovers this by monitoring the interference or utilizing covert methods. He may elect to simplify his system implementation by eliminating the diversity ($m = 1$): then, the exact performance is given by ((2.24) without the maximization over ρ)

$$P_b = \frac{\rho}{2(M-1)} \sum_{i=2}^{M} (-1)^i \binom{M}{i} e^{-(\rho K E_b/N_J)(1-1/i)} \tag{2.73}$$

with $K = 4$, $M = 16$, and $\rho = 3/4$. The desired P_b of 10^{-5} can now be realized with E_b/N_J reduced to 9.23 dB, representing a savings of about 1.9 dB (remember that we are comparing an exact result with an upperbound) over the $m = 13$ case. The risk in such a strategy is that the jammer may somehow discover that the communicator is not using diversity and retaliate by reducing ρ to about 5×10^{-5}, which would require $E_b/N_J = 42.56$ dB to achieve the desired P_b. So, in electing to use $m = 1$, the communicator could save less than 1.9 dB at the cost of a possible degradation of more than 31.5 dB. The prudent approach is to accept the guaranteed performance of (2.70).

2.3.1.2 Band Multitone Jamming

We now turn to the performance of FH/MFSK signals with m-diversity in a band multitone jamming environment. Recall from Section 2.22, and particularly Figure 2.10, that this a highly structured jamming strategy in which an M-ary band is jammed with probability μ (refer to (2.28)), and a jammed band contains exactly n jamming tones, each with power S/α (see (2.31)), where α is a parameter to be optimized by the jammer. With m-diversity, the expression for μ in (2.38) has the modified form

$$\mu = \frac{\alpha m M}{nKE_b/N_J} \tag{2.74}$$

since $R_s = mR_b/K$ in (2.37).

For the special case of $n = 1$ and $K = 1$, we can readily compute the exact performance. An error will occur whenever the m diversity transmissions are all jammed, the untransmitted symbol is hit each time, and $\alpha < 1$ ((2.36) raised to the m-th power):

$$P_b = \left(\frac{\mu}{2}\right)^m = \left(\frac{\alpha m}{E_b/N_J}\right)^m. \tag{2.75}$$

This is maximized at $\alpha = 1_-$ provided E_b/N_J is large enough so that $\mu \leq 1$; therefore the performance of FH/BFSK signals with diversity m in worst case $n = 1$ band multitone jamming is exactly specified by

$$P_b = \begin{cases} \left(\dfrac{m}{E_b/N_J}\right)^m \text{ and } \alpha_{\text{wc}} = 1_-; & \dfrac{E_b}{N_J} \geq 2m \\ 2^{-m} \text{ and } \alpha_{\text{wc}} = \dfrac{E_b/N_J}{2m}; & \dfrac{E_b}{N_J} < 2m. \end{cases} \tag{2.76}$$

This is plotted in Figure 2.35 for various values of m, including the uncoded $m = 1$ case. Note that (2.76) is valid $\forall m \geq 1$, and is identical to (2.40) and (2.41) for $K = m = 1$.

The slope discontinuity in these curves is characteristic of band multitone jamming because of the constraint that each jammed M-ary band contain *exactly n* jamming tones (recall Figures 2.12, 2.18, and 2.19). The horizontal portion of each curve in Figure 2.35 is the "saturation region" where $\mu = 1$; that is, each binary ($M = 2$) band contains its quota of one jamming tone. In this region, the power in each jamming tone exceeds S and continues to rise (α_{wc} falls in (2.76)) as E_b/N_J decreases.

There is somewhat of a paradox here. The $n = 1$ band multitone scenario is highly structured. It concedes the jammer knowledge of the location of the M-ary bands, information that is used to undermine the receiver's awareness of which hops are jammed by distributing the jamming power so as to hit the maximum number of hops. Yet, unlike the less structured partial-band noise behavior illustrated in Figure 2.30, the constraint im-

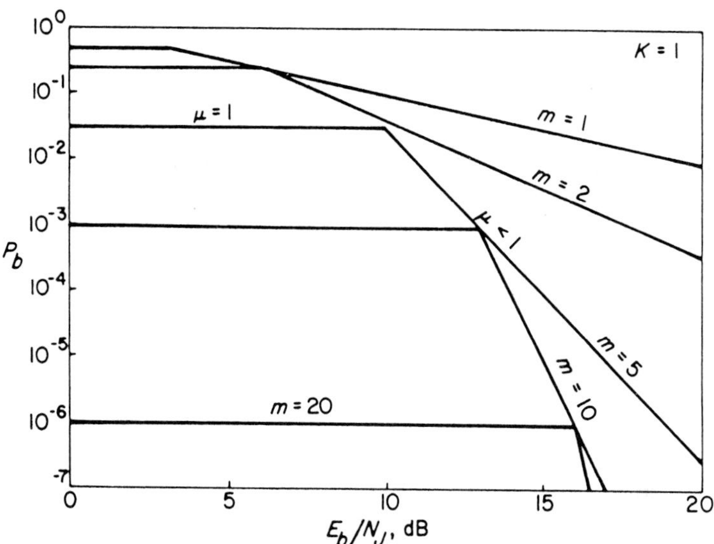

Figure 2.35. Performance of FH/BFSK signals with diversity m chips/bit in worst case $n = 1$ band multitone jamming. In the horizontal regions, the probability μ that a binary band is jammed is 1.

posed by $n = 1$ band multitone jamming ultimately leads to error-free performance as m becomes large. For small values of m, each jamming tone contains the same power as the signal tones, and the $Q = J/S$ jamming tones are less than the number of M-ary bands. However, as m increases so does the chip rate R_c, which causes the number of M-ary bands to decrease (refer to Figure 2.10). Eventually, the number of M-ary bands equals J/S, and the saturation condition $\mu = 1$ is reached. In this region, under the assumption of perfect receiver jamming state side information, P_b is simply the probability 2^{-m} that the incorrect binary symbol is hit on all m diversity transmissions.

This surprising behavior is better illustrated in Figure 2.36, which demonstrates the variation in performance with diversity for several SNR's. There is an initial minimum P_b in the region $\mu < 1$ or $m < E_b/2N_J$; from (2.76), this occurs at

$$m = m_{\text{opt}} = \frac{E_b/N_J}{e} < \frac{E_b/N_J}{2}$$

where

$$P_b = e^{-e^{-1}E_b/N_J} \tag{2.77}$$

and

$$\alpha_{\text{wc}} = 1_-$$

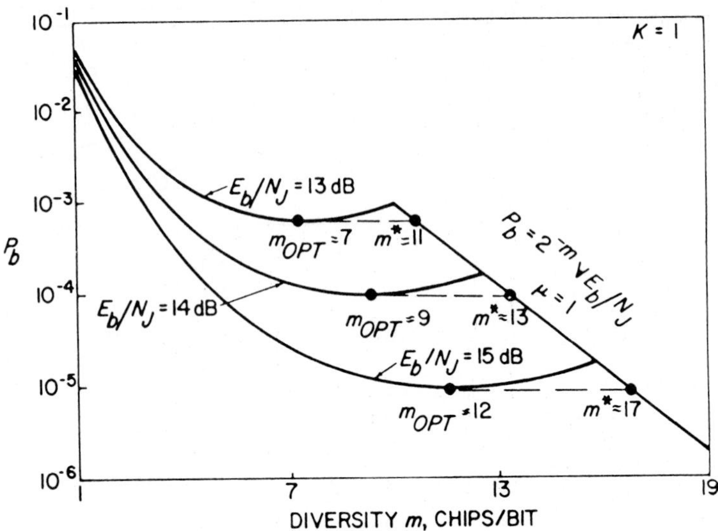

Figure 2.36. Variation in performance of FH/BFSK signals in worst case $n = 1$ band multitone jamming with diversity. Note that P_b decreases as 2^{-m} for large m, independent of E_b/N_J. For fixed E_b/N_J, the initial minimum occurs at $m = m_{\text{opt}}$; however, lower P_b's are later achieved for $m > m^*$ (refer to (2.79)).

provided

$$E_b/N_J \geq e \Rightarrow m_{\text{opt}} \geq 1.$$

For smaller values of E_b/N_J, $m_{\text{opt}} = 1$ and the performance is given by (2.40) and (2.41):

$$P_b = \begin{cases} \dfrac{1}{E_b/N_J} \text{ and } \alpha_{\text{wc}} = 1_-; & 2 \leq \dfrac{E_b}{N_J} \leq e \\ \dfrac{1}{2} \text{ and } \alpha_{\text{wc}} = \dfrac{E_b}{2N_J}; & \dfrac{E_b}{N_J} \leq 2. \end{cases} \tag{2.78}$$

However, in the saturation region, P_b falls below that defined in (2.77) for $m > m^*$, where

$$m^* \equiv \frac{E_b/N_J}{e \ln 2} = \frac{m_{\text{opt}}}{\ln 2} = 1.44 m_{\text{opt}} \tag{2.79}$$

and P_b becomes arbitrarily small for larger values of m. If it is important to use minimal diversity, m_{opt} is a good choice. However, since m^* is only moderately larger, better performance can be achieved without resorting to impractically large amounts of diversity.

Figure 2.37 illustrates the extreme effectiveness of diversity for FH/BFSK signals in worst case $n = 1$ band multitone jamming. Even at the local

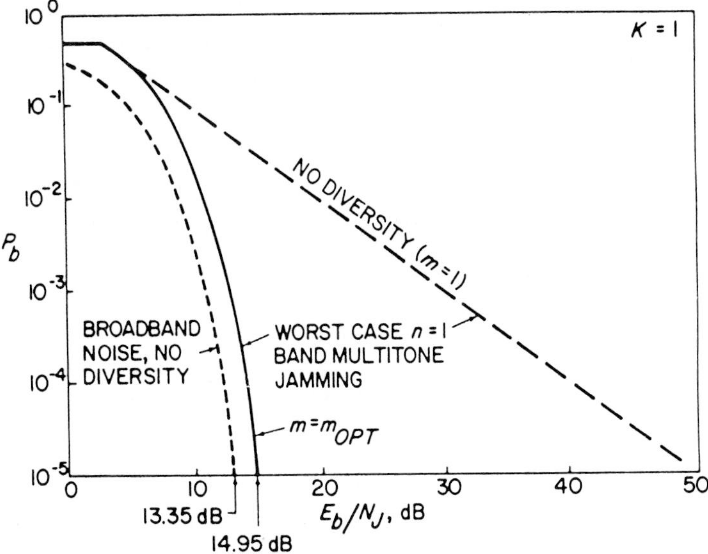

Figure 2.37. Effectiveness of diversity against worst case $n = 1$ band multitone jamming for FH/BFSK signalling. Improvement is 35 dB relative to $m = 1$ system, and performance is only 1.6 dB worse than in broadband noise, with $m = m_{\text{opt}}$ at $P_b = 10^{-5}$.

minimum, $m = m_{\text{opt}}$, the improvement relative to $m = 1$ is 35 dB at $P_b = 10^{-5}$, and the performance at that P_b is only 1.6 dB worse than in broadband noise. And for $m > m^*$, the performance is even better; in fact, for large enough values of m, P_b is lower than in broadband noise (it is not plotted since P_b becomes arbitrarily small for large m). If the $m = m_{\text{opt}}$ performance here is compared with the worst case partial-band noise/optimum diversity curve in Figure 2.32, which was 3 dB worse than the broadband noise case for small P_b's, recall that the latter curve is an upperbound while the former is exact.

Turning now to larger size alphabets ($K > 1$) but still considering only $n = 1$ band multitone interference, the performance with m-diversity and the suboptimum linear sum metric with perfect side information will now be analyzed using the union/Chernoff bounding techniques of Section 2.3.1.1. Because of the side information, it is convenient to introduce the event H_j that the j-th chip is jammed, as in the partial-band noise case. Adopting the convention of Section 2.3.1 which declares that a particular chip is jammed when two or more energy detector outputs are high on a given transmission, for $n = 1$ band multitone jamming,

$$\Pr\{H_j\} = \left(\frac{M-1}{M}\right)\mu. \tag{2.80}$$

Under the assumption that the receiver has error-free information about which of the m diversity transmissions are jammed, an M-ary symbol error requires the occurrence of $\boldsymbol{H} \equiv (H_1, H_2, \ldots, H_m)$, where

$$\Pr\{\boldsymbol{H}\} = \left[\left(\frac{M-1}{M}\right)\mu\right]^m = \left[\frac{(M-1)\alpha m}{KE_b/N_J}\right]^m \tag{2.81}$$

using (2.74).

Let e_{ij} denote the energy detected for the i-th M-ary symbol on the j-th diversity transmission, normalized by the chip signal energy E_c, and suppose symbol 1 is sent. Then, as in (2.60) and (2.61), the M-ary detection problem is reduced to a binary one by employing the union bound:

$$P_s \le (M-1)\Pr\{\boldsymbol{H}\}\Pr\left\{\sum_{j=1}^{m}(e_{2j}-e_{1j}) \ge 0 \,\middle|\, \boldsymbol{H}\right\}. \tag{2.82}$$

Next, the m-ary statistics are simplified to those for a single chip transmission by applying the Chernoff bound:

$$\Pr\left\{\sum_{j=1}^{m}(e_{2j}-e_{1j}) \ge 0 \,\middle|\, \boldsymbol{H}\right\} \le \left\{\overline{e^{\lambda(e_{2j}-e_{1j})}}^{|H_j}\right\}^m; \qquad \lambda \ge 0. \tag{2.83}$$

The factor of $1/2$ that appeared in the partial-band noise bound of (2.61) is absent here because the discrete-valued e_{ij}'s do not satisfy the sufficient condition specified in [10] and Appendix 2A. Conditioned on H_j, e_{1j} and e_{2j} have the following probability distributions:

$$\Pr\{e_{1j} = 1|H_j\} = 1$$

$$\Pr\{e_{2j} = \beta|H_j\} = \begin{cases} \dfrac{1}{M-1}; & \beta = \dfrac{1}{\alpha} \\[2ex] \dfrac{M-2}{M-1}; & \beta = 0 \end{cases} \tag{2.84}$$

so that

$$\Pr\{(e_{2j}-e_{1j}) = \beta|H_j\} = \begin{cases} \dfrac{1}{M-1}; & \beta = \dfrac{1}{\alpha} - 1 \\[2ex] \dfrac{M-2}{M-1}; & \beta = -1 \end{cases} \tag{2.85}$$

Since (2.83) (or common sense) says that $(e_{2j} - e_{1j})$ must have a non-zero probability of being greater than zero for a symbol error to occur, (2.85) shows that this requires that $\alpha < 1$. Using the familiar relationship of (2.20a) between bit and symbol error rates, and combining (2.81)–(2.83) and (2.85), we have, for arbitrary m and α,

$$P_b \le \frac{M}{2}F^m \tag{2.86}$$

where

$$F \equiv \min_{\lambda \geq 0} \left[\frac{\alpha m e^{-\lambda}}{KE_b/N_J} \left(M - 2 + e^{\lambda/\alpha} \right) \right].$$

Performing the minimization by setting $\partial F / \partial \lambda$ to zero yields

$$F = \frac{m}{KE_b/N_J} \left[\frac{\alpha(M-2)}{1-\alpha} \right]^{1-\alpha} \tag{2.87}$$

provided $M > 2$, and $\alpha \geq 1/(M-1)$ so that $\lambda \geq 0$.

For worst case jamming, we want to choose $\alpha \in (0,1)$ to maximize F. Although it is not immediately obvious from the form of (2.87), Figure 2.38 demonstrates that F has a unique maximum for each value of $K \geq 2$ over this range of α. Denote the maximizing value of α by α_0, and define

$$\beta \equiv \left(\frac{E_b}{mN_J} \right) F \bigg|_{\alpha = \alpha_0} = \frac{1}{K} \left[\frac{\alpha_0 (M-2)}{1-\alpha_0} \right]^{1-\alpha_0} \tag{2.88}$$

where β and α_0 are given in Table 2.7 below. The constraint $\mu \leq 1$ must also be satisfied: using (2.74) with $n = 1$, this translates into

$$\alpha \leq \frac{K}{mM} \left(\frac{E_b}{N_J} \right). \tag{2.89}$$

Consequently, the performance in worst case $n = 1$ band multitone jam-

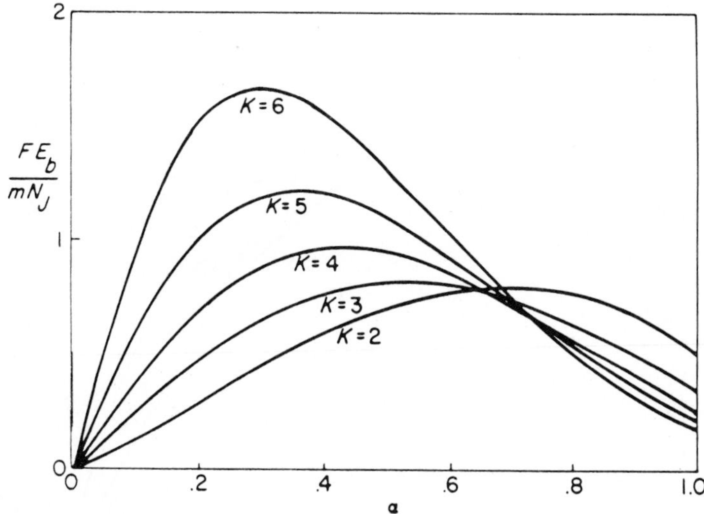

Figure 2.38. Demonstration that P_b bound for FH/MFSK signals with arbitrary diversity m and SNR E_b/N_J in $n = 1$ band multitone jamming has unique maximum over jammer parameter α (refer to (2.86)–(2.88)).

ming with diversity m is upperbounded by

$$P_b \le \begin{cases} \dfrac{M}{2}\left(\dfrac{\beta m}{E_b/N_J}\right)^m \text{ and } \alpha_{wc} = \alpha_0; & \dfrac{E_B}{N_J} \ge \zeta m \\ \dfrac{M}{2}\left(\dfrac{1}{\alpha_{wc} M}\left[\dfrac{\alpha_{wc}(M-2)}{1-\alpha_{wc}}\right]^{1-\alpha_{wc}}\right)^m & \\ \text{and } \alpha_{wc} = \dfrac{K}{mM}\left(\dfrac{E_b}{N_J}\right); & \dfrac{mM}{K(M-1)} \le \dfrac{E_b}{N_J} \le \zeta m \end{cases} \tag{2.90}$$

where $\zeta \equiv \alpha_0 M/K$ is also computed in Table 2.7.

Although (2.90) is an upperbound, it is relatively simple and easy to evaluate, and many behavioral performance characteristics can be deduced from it. It is plotted in two different formats for several values of $K \ge 2$ in Figures 2.39–2.41. Unlike the $K = 1$ curves in Figure 2.35, the P_b upperbounds for fixed m in Figures 2.39 and 2.40 have no slope discontinuities; this does not rule out such behavior in the exact bit error rate. The arguments in Section 2.3.1.2 discussing the saturation effect imposed by the constraints of band multitone jamming are valid for all values of K, so we should not be surprised that the $K = 2$ performance in Figure 2.41 improves for larger values of m. (This effect would be evident for other values of K in Figure 2.41 if we had gone beyond $m = 30$.) Mathematically, for large values of m in the saturation region of (2.90),

$$\alpha_{wc} \ll 1 \Rightarrow P_b \le \frac{M}{2}\left(\frac{M-2}{M}\right)^m \underset{m\to\infty}{\longrightarrow} 0. \tag{2.91}$$

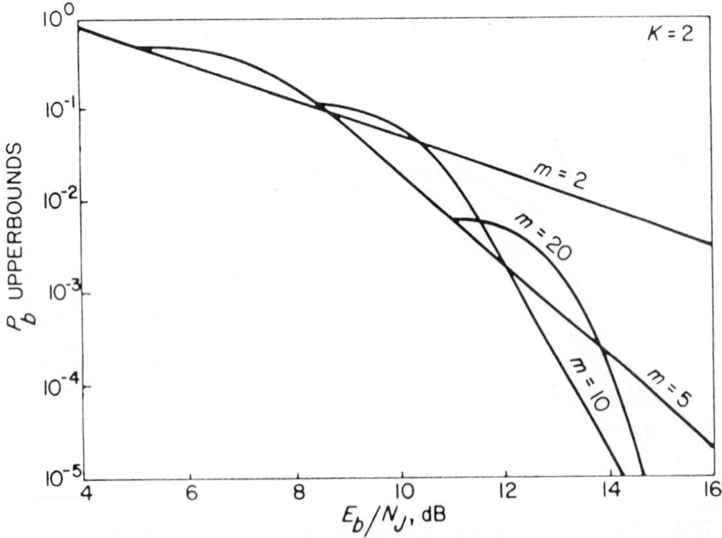

Figure 2.39. Performance upperbounds for FH/4-ary FSK signals with diversity m chips per 4-ary symbol in worst case $n = 1$ band multitone jamming.

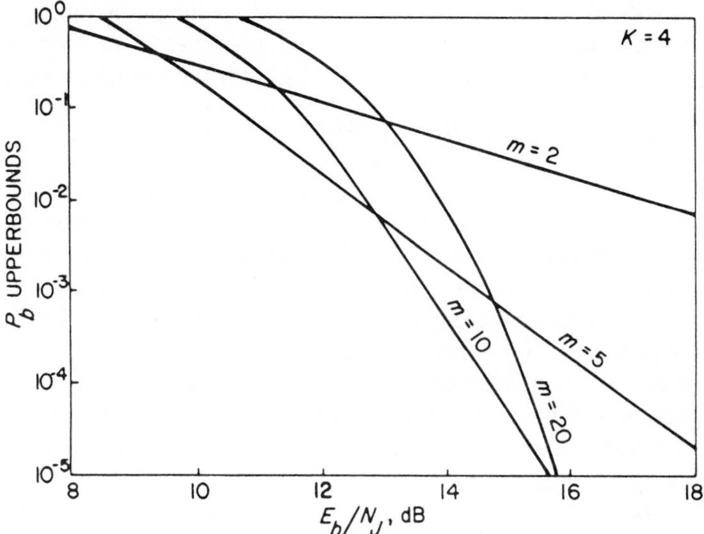

Figure 2.40. Same as Figure 2.39, except $K = 4$.

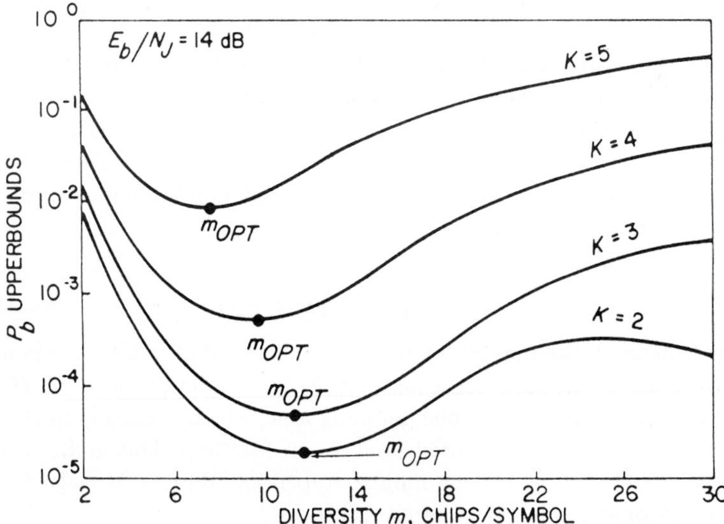

Figure 2.41. Behavior of performance upperbounds for FH/MFSK signals in worst case $n = 1$ band multitone jamming as a function of diversity m. Note that performance improves for large m in the $K = 2$ curve, and the performance degrades as K increases.

Another way of seeing this is to recall that under the perfect side information assumption, an M-ary symbol error requires that all m diversity chips be jammed, denoted by the event $\boldsymbol{H}$ in (2.81). In the saturation region,

$$\Pr\{\boldsymbol{H}\} = \left(\frac{M-1}{M}\right)^m \xrightarrow[m \to \infty]{} 0 \tag{2.92}$$

and the error rate must fall accordingly for large amounts of diversity. However, unlike the $K = 1$ case where it was possible to achieve P_b's less than the first local minimum at $m = m_{\text{opt}}$ (see Figure 2.36) with moderately larger values of m, such is not the case for $K \geq 2$. Figure 2.41 clearly implies that for practical implementations with non-binary alphabets, the best design tradeoff is to use $m = m_{\text{opt}}$. Finally, Figure 2.41 demonstrates that for $K \geq 2$, the performance with diversity degrades as K increases in worst case $n = 1$ band multitone jamming, in contrast to the behavior in worst case partial-band noise; this echoes our earlier observations for $m = 1$ signalling (e.g., refer to Figure 2.12).

With diversity transmission, where received data decisions involve multiple channel uses, it is generally difficult and cumbersome to compute the exact performance. We circumvent this problem by evaluating exponentially tight upperbounds. Still, the accuracy of these bounds remains a source of concern and raises issues of credibility. In the partial-band noise case we were able to use some exact calculations derived by Trumpis as a benchmark (recall Figures 2.25 and 2.26). Here, for $n = 1$ band multitone jamming and a soft decision non-coherent combining metric with perfect jamming state information, we can use combinatorial techniques to again compute the exact performance. However, the results are much more complex, particularly for large amounts of diversity, and they do not yield insights as readily as the closed form expression of (2.90).

Suppose symbol 1 is sent and event $\boldsymbol{H}$ occurs, which is a necessary condition for a symbol error in the perfect side information case. Then, for a given jammer parameter α, the normalized conditional soft decision symbol metrics of (2.57) are

$$\begin{aligned} \Lambda_1 &= m \\ \Lambda_i &= l_i/\alpha; \qquad 2 \leq i \leq M \end{aligned} \tag{2.93}$$

where l_i denotes the number of times the i-th symbol is hit by a jamming tone over the m diversity transmissions. Note that conditioned on $\boldsymbol{H}$, each of the m hops contains only one jamming tone, which is equally likely to hit any of the $M - 1$ untransmitted symbols on that hop. This is the situation pictured in the grid at the beginning of Appendix 2B ($I \to M - 1$, $J \to m$). The conditional symbol error rate is given by

$$\begin{aligned} P_s|^{\boldsymbol{H}} &= \Pr\left\{ \bigcup_{i=2}^{M} (\Lambda_i \geq \Lambda_1) \middle| \boldsymbol{H} \right\} \\ &= \Pr\{ l_{\max} \geq m\alpha | \boldsymbol{H} \} \end{aligned} \tag{2.94}$$

where

$$l_{\max} \equiv \max_{2 \le i \le M} \{l_i\}. \tag{2.95}$$

The probability of any particular pattern of m jamming tones conditioned on $\boldsymbol{H}$ is $(M-1)^{-m}$. Appendix 2B computes the number of these patterns satisfying the constraint on $l_{\max}$ in (2.94); in the notation of Appendix 2B,

$$P_s|^{H} = (M-1)^{-m} S_{M-1,m}(k); \qquad k \equiv \lceil m\alpha \tag{2.96}$$

where $\lceil x$ is the smallest integer greater than or equal to x. Using (2.81) and (2B.8), we have

$$\begin{aligned} P_b &= \frac{M}{2(M-1)} \Pr\{\boldsymbol{H}\} P_s|^{H} = \frac{M}{2}\left(\frac{\alpha m}{KE_b/N_J}\right)^m \\ &\times \left\{ \sum_{i=k}^{m} \binom{m}{i} (M-2)^{m-i} - \left(\frac{M-2}{2}\right) \sum_{i=k}^{\lfloor m/2} \binom{m}{i}\binom{m-i}{i} (M-3)^{m-2i} \right. \\ &\left. - (M-2) \sum_{i=k}^{\lfloor m/2} \binom{m}{i} \sum_{j=i+1}^{m-i} \binom{m-i}{j} (M-3)^{m-i-j} \right\}; \\ &\qquad \text{where } k-1 < m\alpha \le k, \quad \text{and} \\ &\qquad \text{provided } \frac{m}{3} < k \le m \end{aligned} \tag{2.97}$$

where $\lfloor x$ denotes the integer part of x, and we are adopting the convention that $\sum_{i=a}^{b} c_i = 0$ if $a > b$. For the special case of $k = 1$ or 2, (2B.6) and (2B.7) yield simpler expressions for P_b:

$$P_b = \frac{M}{2(M-1)} \left[\frac{\alpha m(M-1)}{KE_b/N_J}\right]^m; \qquad k = 1 \quad \text{and} \quad 0 < m\alpha \le 1 \tag{2.98}$$

$$P_b = \frac{M}{2}\left(\frac{\alpha m}{KE_b/N_J}\right)^m \times \begin{cases} (M-1)^{m-1} - \dfrac{(M-2)!}{(M-m-1)!}; & m \le M-1 \\ (M-1)^{m-1}; & m > M-1 \end{cases}$$

$$\text{provided } k = 2 \quad \text{and} \quad 1 < m\alpha \le 2. \tag{2.99}$$

So for $m \le 8$, we can compute the exact performance for any $k \in [1, m]$; for larger m, there is a computational gap for $3 \le k \le \lfloor m/3$. We could extend (2.97) to smaller values of k, but the result would be even more complex. As it is, compare (2.97) with the simplicity of the P_b bound of (2.90). And we still have to maximize these exact expressions over $\alpha < 1$ to establish the worst case jamming condition. If we treat k rather than α as the maximizing variable, it is clear from (2.97)–(2.99) that P_b is maximized over α for a given k by selecting

$$m\alpha = k. \tag{2.100}$$

Then why did we not replace $m\alpha$ by k in (2.97)–(2.99) and be done with it? The reason is that we must also satisfy the constraint $\mu \leq 1$, which implies that

$$m\alpha \leq \frac{KE_b}{MN_J}. \tag{2.101}$$

In the singular cases for which KE_b/MN_J is precisely integer, $k \leq KE_b/MN_J$ and (2.100) is valid for all k in this range. In general, when KE_b/MN_J is non-integer, we have

$$m\alpha = \begin{cases} k; & k \leq \left\lfloor \dfrac{KE_b}{MN_J} \right\rfloor \\[2ex] \dfrac{KE_b}{MN_J}; & k = \left\lceil \dfrac{KE_b}{MN_J} \right\rceil = \left\lfloor \dfrac{KE_b}{MN_J} \right\rfloor + 1. \end{cases} \tag{2.102}$$

The worst case jamming condition is now established by maximizing the expressions for P_b in (2.97)–(2.99) over the range $1 \leq k \leq \min\left(m, \lceil KE_b/MN_J \rceil\right)$; this operation must be performed using a computer for each combination of K, E_b/N_J, and m, further emphasizing the practical utility of the P_b upperbound. Note that since (2.97) can be evaluated only if $k = \lceil m\alpha \rceil > m/3$, (2.101) limits us to the range

$$m \lessapprox \frac{3KE_b}{MN_J}. \tag{2.103}$$

These exact results are first used to assess the accuracy of the upperbounds plotted in Figures 2.39–2.41. As we observed in the partial-band noise case of Figures 2.24–2.26, for worst case $n = 1$ band multitone jamming, Figures 2.42 and 2.43 demonstrate that the bounds are pessimistic by several dB for small $m \sim 2$, but are accurate to within about 1/2 dB of the exact performance for moderate $m \gtrsim 10$. Actually, the asymptotic accuracy is about 30% better for the band multitone case relative to the partial-band noise curves. Note that for the values of m selected, we could not plot exact P_b's for SNR's that were too small to satisfy the constraint of (2.103). Figure 2.44 gives a different perspective on the accuracy of the P_b bounds. In the $K = 2$ case, we see that the exact P_b does indeed decrease for sufficiently large m, so this characteristic is not simply a bound anomaly. The piecewise linear nature of the exact curves is due to the real world constraint that m and the maximizing parameter k take on only integer values, so the worst case performance variation with diversity is not as smooth as the bounds suggest. As a matter of interest, the exact performance for $K = 1$ is superimposed on Figure 2.44. Before the saturation condition $\mu = 1$ is reached, for the selected SNR, we see that the $K = 1$ performance is only marginally better than for $K = 4$ and worse than for $K = 2$ (or $K = 3$, which was not plotted). However, because the $K = 1$

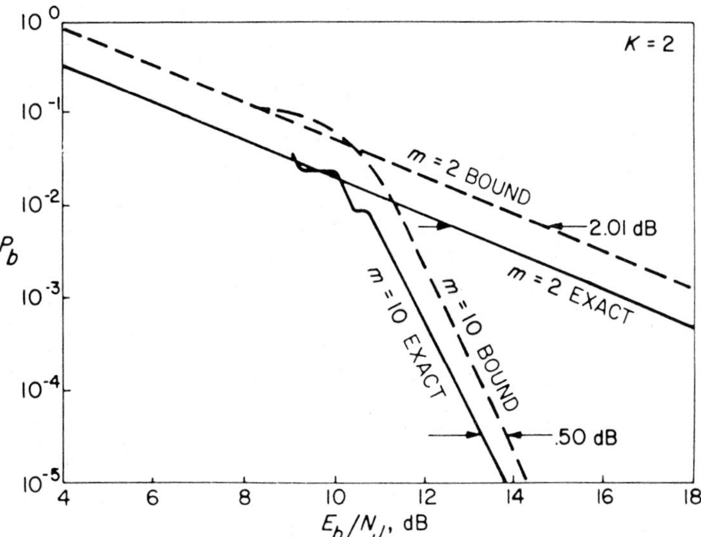

Figure 2.42. Comparison of exact and upperbound P_b formulas for FH/4-ary FSK signalling with diversity m chips per symbol in worst case $n = 1$ band multitone jamming. Accuracy of bound improves with m, and is moderately tighter than for worst case partial-band noise (Figures 2.24 and 2.25).

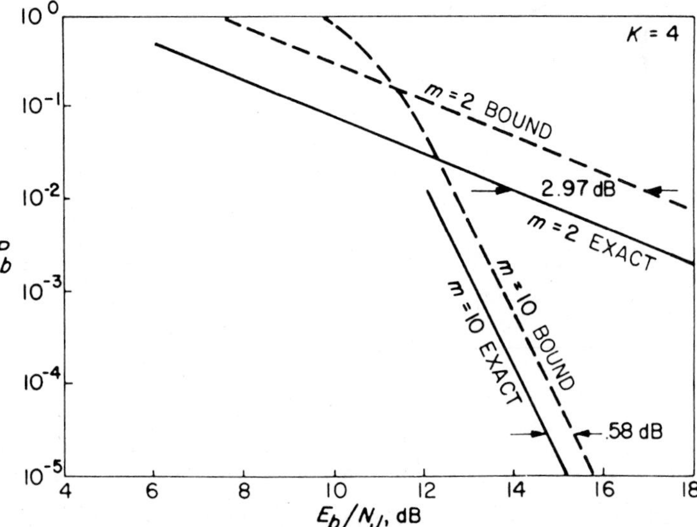

Figure 2.43. Same as Figure 2.42, except $K = 4$. Accuracy degrades significantly with K for small $m \sim 2$, but increases only slightly with K for large $m \gtrsim 10$.

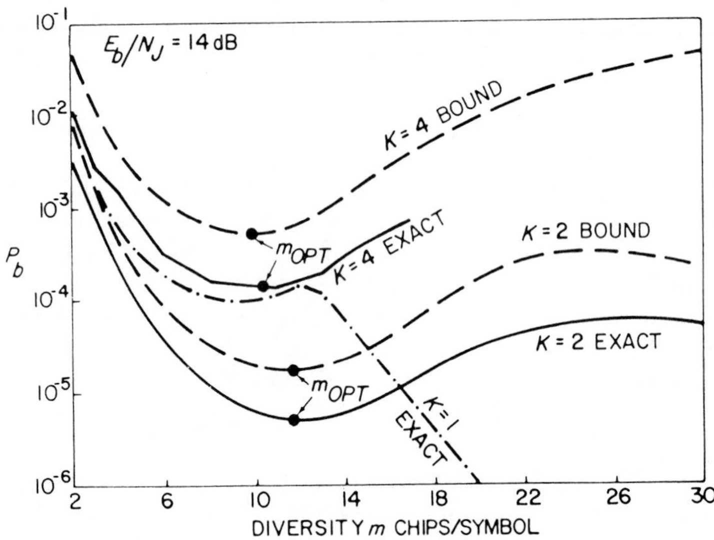

Figure 2.44. Accuracy of upperbound performance variation with diversity for FH/MFSK signals in worst case $n = 1$ band multitone jamming (refer to Figure 2.41). Performance for $K = 1$ is slightly better than $K = 4$ for small m, but improves drastically as 2^{-m} in the saturation region $m \geq E_b/2N_J$ where $\mu = 1$ (see (2.76)).

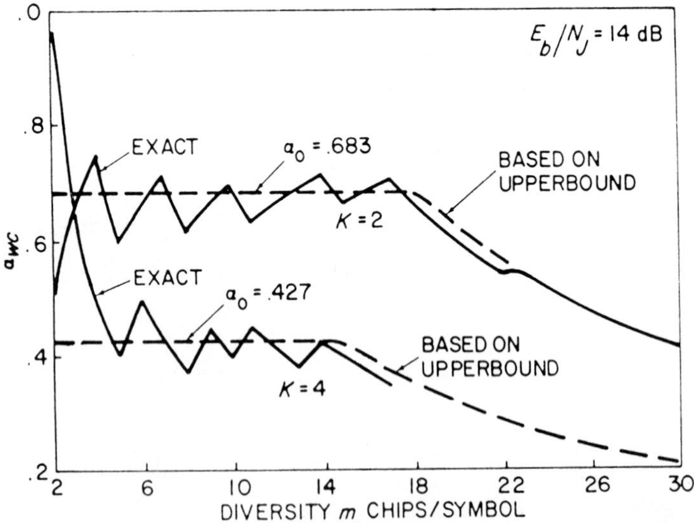

Figure 2.45. Comparison of "quasi-worst case" jamming parameter α_{wc} derived from P_b upperbound of (2.86) and (2.87) with actual worst case parameter based on (2.97)–(2.99) and (2.102) describing exact performance of FH/MFSK signals with diversity in $n = 1$ band multitone jamming.

performance improves so rapidly for $m \geq E_b/2N_J$ where $\mu = 1$ (refer to (2.76)), it is difficult to make a definite "optimum diversity" comparison with larger values of K. Figure 2.45 addresses the accuracy of the "quasi-worst case" jamming parameter α_{wc} derived from the P_b bound of (2.86) and (2.87). Prior to saturation, for smaller values of m, the exact α_{wc} fluctuates up and down due to the discrete nature of (2.102) (for each integer value of m, $\alpha_{wc} = k_{wc}/m$, where k_{wc} is the integer k that maximizes P_b in (2.97)–(2.99) subject to $\alpha m = k$), but the constant quasi-worst case $\alpha_{wc} = \alpha_0$ (see (2.90) and Table 2.7) is a good average fit to these fluctuations. In the saturation region, for sufficiently large m, both the quasi-worst case and exact parameters satisfy $\alpha_{wc} = KE_b/mMN_J$ (see (2.90) and (2.102)), so there is total agreement here.

We now consider the question of optimum diversity for $K \geq 2$. Recall that for $K = 1$, it was not clear whether to select the local minimum of the P_b versus m curves, or to use a moderately larger value of $m \geq m^*$ for which P_b became arbitrarily small (Figure 2.36 and (2.76) and (2.79)). Figure 2.44 shows that although P_b for $K \geq 2$ again decreases for sufficiently large m in the saturation region, the values of m for which this effect becomes significant are much larger than the initial local minima at m_{opt}, and are not of interest for realistic implementations. So we will look for the value of m that minimizes P_b for $\alpha = \alpha_{wc}$ in the region $\mu < 1$. For the bound of (2.90) (the relative simplicity of which we should all have a new appreciation for), this implies the restriction $E_b/N_J \geq \zeta m$; the minimum occurs at $\beta m/E_b/N_J = e^{-1}$, so that the performance with "quasi-optimum" diversity is defined by

$$P_b \leq \frac{M}{2} e^{-\delta E_b/N_J}; \quad \text{where } \delta \equiv \frac{1}{\beta e}$$

$$m_{\text{opt}} = \delta E_b/N_J$$

$$\alpha_{wc} = \alpha_0 \tag{2.104}$$

provided

$$\frac{E_b}{N_J} \geq \frac{1}{\delta} \equiv \gamma_0.$$

The constraint on E_b/N_J ensures that $m_{\text{opt}} \geq 1$. Of course, for the solution to be valid, we must verify that m_{opt} is in the pre-saturation region:

$$m_{\text{opt}} \leq \frac{E_b}{\zeta N_J}$$

$$\Downarrow$$

$$\zeta \leq \beta e. \tag{2.105}$$

Table 2.7 shows that this constraint is satisfied, and also lists the numerical values of δ and γ_0.

Table 2.7
Parameters associated with P_b upperbounds for FH/MFSK signals with diversity in worst case $n = 1$ band multitone jamming.

K	α_0	β	ζ	βe	δ	γ_0, dB
2	.683	.7945	1.366	2.160	.4631	3.34
3	.527	.8188	1.405	2.226	.4493	3.48
4	.427	.9583	1.708	2.605	.3839	4.16
5	.356	1.2204	2.278	3.317	.3014	5.21

For the exact P_b expressions of (2.97)–(2.99) and (2.102), there is no elegant way to compute the optimum diversity. The results involve several levels of computer number crunching. For each value of K and E_b/N_J, a value of m is selected within the range specified by (2.103). For this parameter set, the value of k that maximizes P_b is determined, corresponding to α_{wc}; the corresponding worst case P_b for that value of m is stored. The procedure is repeated for other values of m until the worst case P_b is minimized, defining m_{opt}. (This exercise shows the relative convenience of the performance bound.)

The resulting performance for optimum diversity and worst case $n = 1$ band multitone jamming is compared with the much simpler upperbound result in Figure 2.46. The bound is only pessimistic by 1/2 dB, which is a reasonable price to pay for its computational convenience. Interestingly, Figures 2.47 and 2.48 demonstrate that the quasi-optimum jamming parameters α and diversity m based on the upperbound agree quite well on the average with the exact parameters, whose variations are due to the discrete nature of the optimizations. So, for both the communicator and the jammer, the bound provides an accurate determination of the key system design parameter.

The effectiveness of optimum diversity against worst case $n = 1$ band multitone jamming is shown in Figures 2.49 and 2.50 for $K = 2$ and 4. The improvement in performance is substantial relative to the no diversity case: 36 dB at $K = 2$ and 38 dB at $K = 4$. (From the perspective of the E_b/N_J scale used in these graphs, the accuracy of the bounds seems to be quite adequate.) Recall that in the worst case partial-band noise case, optimum diversity provided performance less than 3 dB worse than in broadband noise for small P_b's. Worst case $n = 1$ band multitone jamming is more effective against FH/MFSK signals with optimum diversity for $K \geq 2$: the degradation relative to broadband noise is over 3 dB at $K = 2$, and almost 7 dB at $K = 4$.

The performance of FH/MFSK signals with optimum diversity in worst case $n = 1$ band multitone jamming is summarized in Figure 2.51 for $1 \leq K \leq 5$. As in the $m = 1$ case, P_b increases with K, except for the anomalous $K = 1$ case. For $K = 1$, the performance is plotted for the local extremum m_{opt}, but we can make P_b much smaller (easily below the $K = 2$ curve) for moderately larger amounts of diversity.

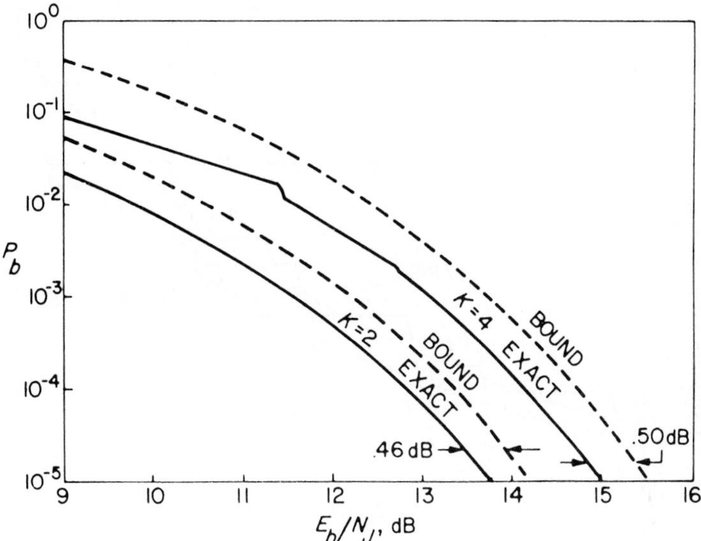

Figure 2.46. Performance of FH/MFSK signals with optimum diversity in worst case $n = 1$ band multitone jamming: comparison of upperbound with exact P_b.

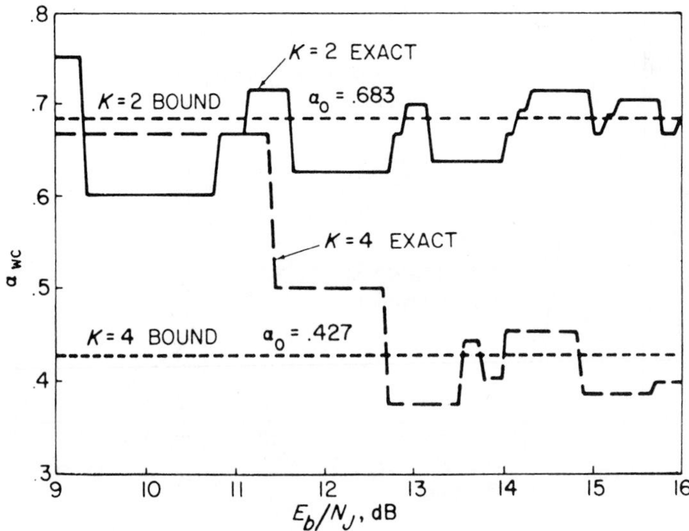

Figure 2.47. Comparison of worst case jamming power ratio α based on exact and upperbound performance of Figure 2.46. Agreement is good despite fluctuations in exact α_{wc} due to discrete nature of optimization, with exception of $K = 4$ for small E_b/N_J.

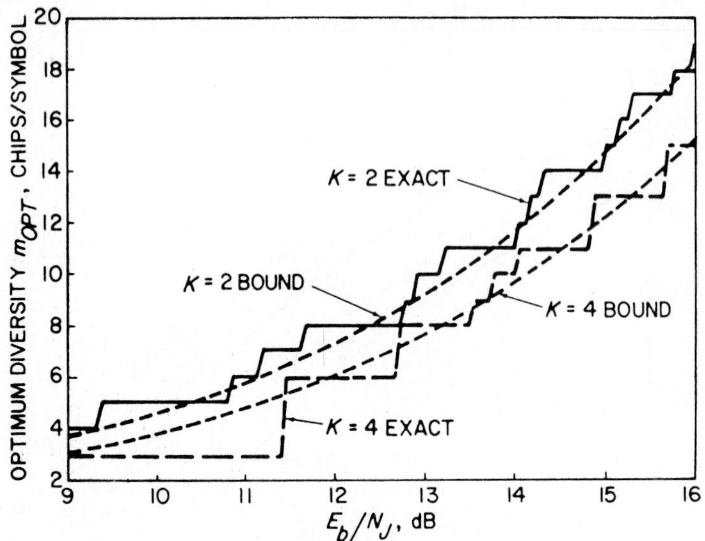

Figure 2.48. Comparison of optimum diversity for exact and upperbound performance of Figure 2.46.

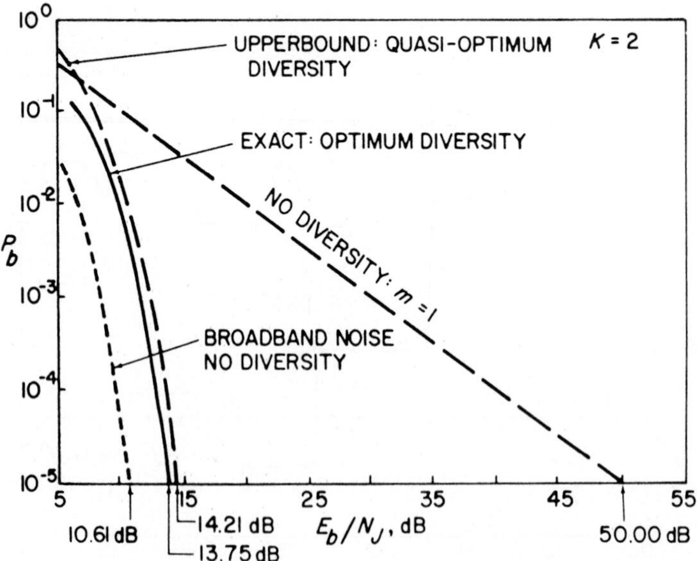

Figure 2.49. Effectiveness of diversity against worst case $n = 1$ band multitone jamming for FH/MFSK signals, with $K = 2$ above. Improvement relative to $m = 1$ case is over 36 dB, and performance is only 3.1 dB worse than in broadband noise, with $m = m_{\text{opt}}$ at $P_b = 10^{-5}$.

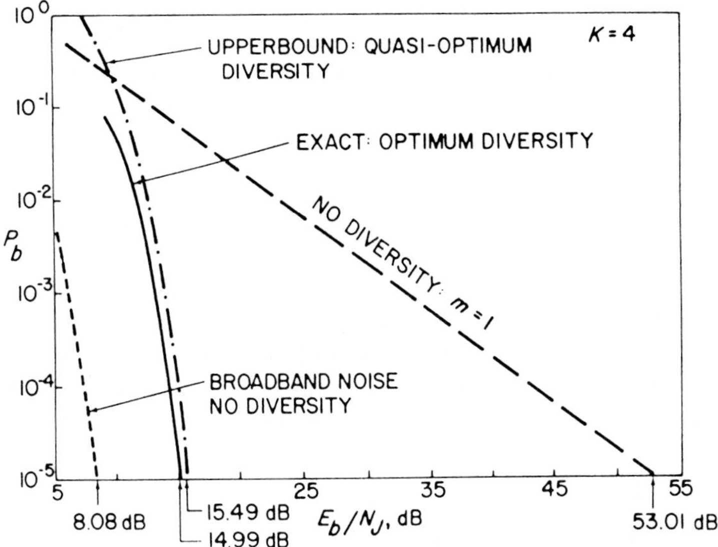

Figure 2.50. Same as Figure 2.49, except $K = 4$. Optimum diversity provides 38 dB improvement relative to $m = 1$ system, and is only 6.9 dB worse than in broadband noise at $P_b = 10^{-5}$.

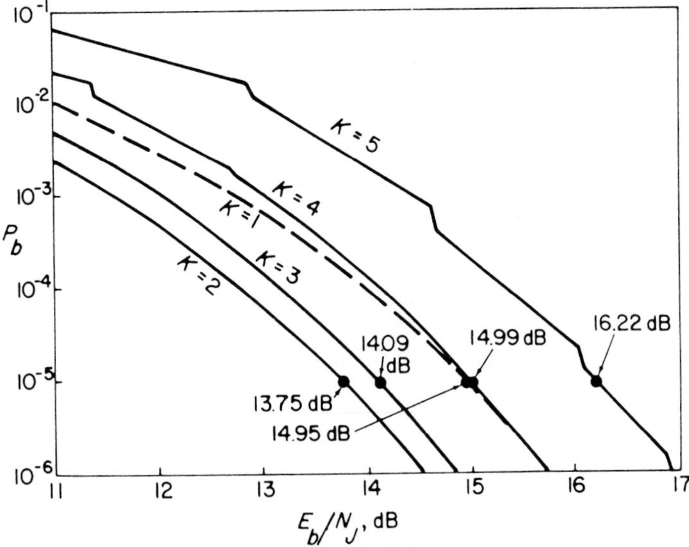

Figure 2.51. Overview of performance of FH/MFSK signals with optimum diversity in worst case $n = 1$ band multitone jamming. Note that the $K = 1$ curve is for the local minimum at m_{opt}, and arbitrarily better performance can be achieved for sufficiently large yet practically implementable values of m.

We now consider band multitone jamming for $n \in [2, M]$. To avoid the complexity of an exact performance analysis, we will again employ the union/Chernoff bound approach. Since $n \geq 2$, if an M-ary bound is jammed, we are guaranteed to have two or more high energy detector outputs. Therefore, from (2.74),

$$\Pr\{\boldsymbol{H}\} = \mu^m = \left[\frac{\alpha m M}{nKE_b/N_J}\right]^m. \tag{2.106}$$

Again assuming that symbol 1 is sent, we need the statistics of the differenced energy detector output $e_{2_j} - e_{1_j}$ conditioned on H_j. Referring to Table 2.2, which considers the relative phase ϕ of the received signal and jammer tones, and incorporating the joint likelihood that either or both symbols 1 and 2 are hit when the M-ary band is jammed, we can write

$$\Pr\{e_{2_j} - e_{1_j} = \beta | H_j, \phi\}$$

$$= \begin{cases} \dfrac{\binom{M-2}{n-2}}{\binom{M}{n}} = \dfrac{n(n-1)}{M(M-1)}; & \beta = -1 - \dfrac{2}{\sqrt{\alpha}}\cos\phi \\ \dfrac{\binom{M-2}{n-1}}{\binom{M}{n}} = \dfrac{n(M-n)}{M(M-1)}; & \beta = -1 - \dfrac{1}{\alpha} - \dfrac{2}{\sqrt{\alpha}}\cos\phi \\ \dfrac{n(M-n)}{M(M-1)}; & \beta = \dfrac{1}{\alpha} - 1 \\ \dfrac{\binom{M-2}{n}}{\binom{M}{n}} = \dfrac{(M-n)(M-n-1)}{M(M-1)}; & \beta = -1. \end{cases} \tag{2.107}$$

Since ϕ is assumed to be uniformly distributed over $[0, 2\pi)$,

$$\overline{e^{-(2\lambda/\sqrt{\alpha})\cos\phi}} = I_0\left(\frac{2\lambda}{\sqrt{\alpha}}\right) \tag{2.108}$$

where $I_0(\cdot)$ is the zeroeth-order modified Bessel function of the first kind. Then, as in (2.82), (2.83), and (2.86):

$$P_b \leq \frac{M}{2}F^m \tag{2.109}$$

where

$$F \equiv \min_{\lambda \geq 0} \left[\mu \overline{e^{\lambda(e_{2j} - e_{1j})}} |H_j \right]$$

$$= \min_{\lambda \geq 0} \left\{ \frac{\alpha m e^{-\lambda}}{nK(M-1)E_b/N_J} \left[n(n-1) I_0\left(\frac{2\lambda}{\sqrt{\alpha}}\right) \right. \right.$$

$$+ n(M-n)e^{-\lambda/\alpha} I_0\left(\frac{2\lambda}{\sqrt{\alpha}}\right) + n(M-n)e^{\lambda/\alpha}$$

$$\left. \left. + (M-n)(M-n-1) \right] \right\}. \qquad (2.110)$$

Because of the Bessel function, we cannot express the minimization over λ in closed form. Likewise, we must resort to numerical techniques to determine the worst case jamming performance, for which F must be maximized over $\alpha \in (0, 4)$. However, it can be demonstrated that this joint extremum is unique, and occurs at $\alpha = \alpha_0$, tabulated below for selected combinations of K and n. Defining the parameter β as in (2.90), for the region $\mu \geq 1$, we have

$$P_b \leq \frac{M}{2} \left(\frac{\beta m}{E_b/N_J} \right)^m \quad \text{and} \quad \alpha_{\text{wc}} = \alpha_0; \; \frac{E_b}{N_J} \geq \zeta m \qquad (2.111)$$

where β and $\zeta \equiv \alpha_0 M/nK$ are also given in Table 2.8 for various values of K and n. Unfortunately, in the saturation region $E_b/N_J \leq \zeta m$ (or $\mu = 1$), $\alpha_{\text{wc}} = (nK/mM)E_b/N_J$ and F must be minimized numerically over $\lambda \geq 0$ for each value of E_b/N_J (this is not typically a region of practical interest unless there is some additional channel coding since the M-ary error rate is relatively high).

As usual, the easiest way to observe the variation in performance with the parameters implicit in (2.111) is to examine different graphical representations. However, since a given two-dimensional parametric plot can only illustrate the relationship between three of the independent variables P_b, E_b/N_J, K, m, and n, there are many graphs to choose from; the few selected below provide some valuable insights. Figure 2.52 is representative of the behavior of P_b as a function of m and n for fixed K and E_b/N_J. We see that there is an optimum diversity m_{opt} which increases with n. And the performance appears to improve with n for a given m, which Table 2.8 indicates is due to the fact that β decreases with n for fixed K. This suggests that it is to the jammer's advantage to keep n small so as to place a jammer tone in as many M-ary bands as possible: this is a direct consequence of the assumption that the receiver has perfect jamming state side

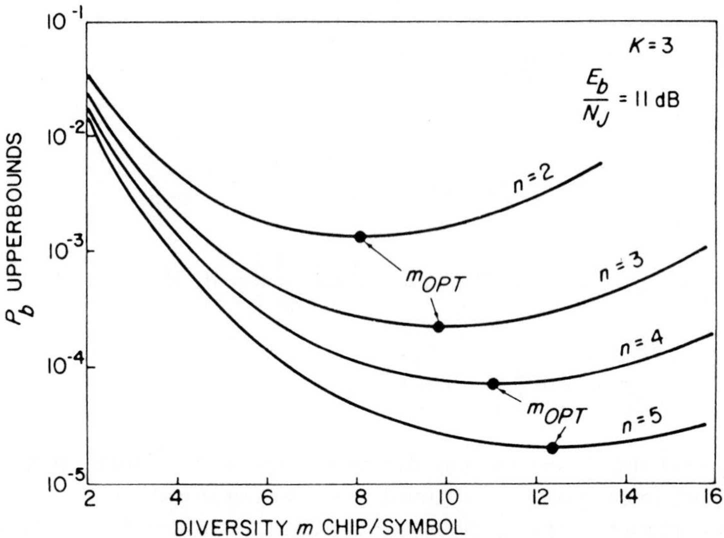

Figure 2.52. Performance of FH/8-ary FSK signals with m diversity chips/symbol in worst case band multitone jamming with n jamming tones per 8-ary band. These curves demonstrate the existence of an optimum diversity m_{opt}, and the decreased jamming effectiveness for larger n.

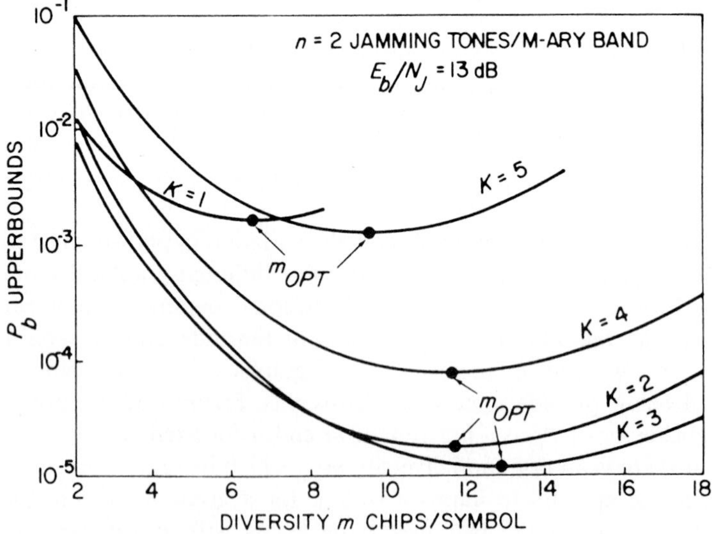

Figure 2.53. Variation in performance of FH/MFSK signals in worst case $n = 2$ band multitone jamming with alphabet size $M = 2^K$ and diversity m. Note the supremacy of the $K = 3$ case.

Table 2.8
Parameters associated with performance of FH/MFSK signals with diversity in worst case band multitone jamming.

K	n	α_0	β	ζ	δ	γ_0, dB	$\delta\zeta$
1	2	2.395	1.1381	2.395	.3232	4.91	.774
2	2	1.072	.6305	1.072	.5835	2.34	.626
	3	1.745	.5784	1.163	.6361	1.96	.740
	4	2.395	.5691	1.197	.6465	1.89	.774
3	2	.701	.5767	.935	.6379	1.95	.596
	3	.898	.4723	.798	.7790	1.08	.622
	4	1.169	.4237	.779	.8682	.61	.676
	5	1.488	.4009	.794	.9177	.37	.729
	6	1.804	.3894	.802	.9446	.25	.758
	7	2.106	.3832	.802	.9601	.18	.770
	8	2.394	.3794	.798	.9697	.13	.774
4	2	.535	.6354	1.070	.5790	2.37	.620
	3	.625	.5023	.833	.7324	1.35	.610
	4	.716	.4297	.716	.8560	.68	.613
	5	.816	.3844	.653	.9571	.19	.625
	6	.931	.3541	.621	1.0388	− .17	.645
	7	1.064	.3335	.608	1.1031	− .43	.671
	8	1.213	.3193	.607	1.1523	− .62	.699
	12	1.827	.2933	.609	1.2545	− .98	.764
	16	2.394	.2845	.598	1.2929	− 1.12	.774
5	2	.430	.7771	1.376	.4734	3.25	.651
	32	2.395	.2276	.479	1.6162	−2.08	.774

information. Figure 2.53 fixes n and E_b/N_J and illustrates the variation in P_b with m and K. Here we discover that m_{opt} does not vary monotonically with K. Also, the best performance with optimum diversity is realized when $K = 3$, for the selected case $n = 2$ and $E_b/N_J = 13$ dB; in fact, it will be shown below that this observation is true whenever E_b/N_J is large enough, and it extends to the $n = 3$ and 4 cases as well.

For the special case $n = M$, (2.110) reduces to

$$F = \min_{\lambda \geq 0} \left[\frac{m\alpha e^{-\lambda} I_0\left(\dfrac{2\lambda}{\sqrt{\alpha}}\right)}{KE_b/N_J} \right] \tag{2.112}$$

which implies that for $n = M$, β is inversely proportional to K in (2.111); consequently, the performance improves with K for $n = M$ as shown in Figure 2.54. Also, (2.112) reveals that the worst case jamming parameter α_0 is independent of K under this condition, an observation that is reinforced in Table 2.8.

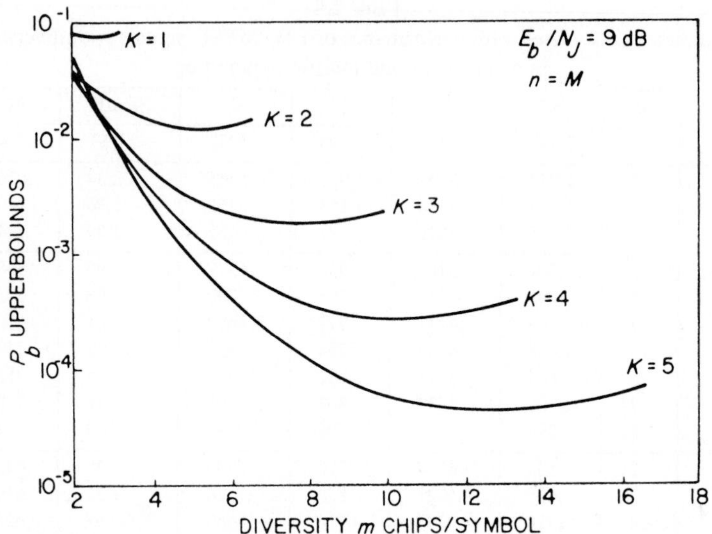

Figure 2.54. Special case of band multitone jamming where $n = M$, i.e., every symbol of a jammed M-ary band contains a jamming tone. For the record, the performance improves with K; however, this is a relatively ineffective jamming strategy which would probably not be used in practice.

Based on (2.111), we can define the optimum diversity condition:

$$P_b \le \frac{M}{2} e^{-\delta E_b/N_J} \quad \text{where } \delta \equiv \frac{1}{\beta e}$$

$$m_{\text{opt}} = \delta E_b/N_J \tag{2.113}$$

$$\alpha_{\text{wc}} = \alpha_0$$

provided

$$E_b/N_J \ge 1/\delta \equiv \gamma_0$$

so that $m_{\text{opt}} \ge 1$. We must also verify that we are not in the saturation region: that is,

$$m_{\text{opt}} \le \frac{1}{\zeta}(E_b/N_J)$$

$$\Downarrow \tag{2.114}$$

$$\delta\zeta \le 1.$$

The validity of this condition is demonstrated in Table 2.8, which also lists values of δ and γ_0.

We observed in connection with Figure 2.52 that the performance for arbitrary m and fixed K improves with n, since Table 2.8 shows that β decreases with n. Because δ is inversely proportional to β, the performance

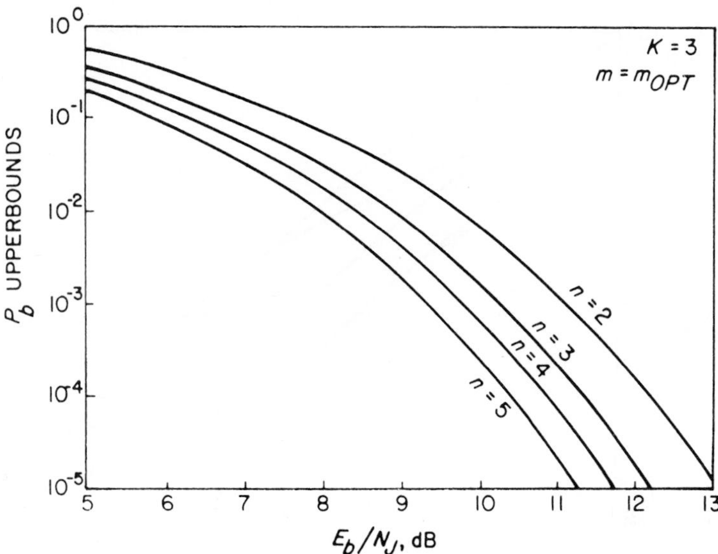

Figure 2.55. Variation in performance of FH/8-ary FSK signals with optimum diversity m_{opt} in worst case band multitone jamming as a function of the number n of jamming tones per jammed band. Jamming effectiveness deteriorates monotonically with n.

with optimum diversity also improves with n for a given K, as shown in Figure 2.55. Recall also that Figure 2.53 suggested that with optimum diversity and worst case band multitone jamming, the best performance for $n = 2$ is achieved when $K = 3$ over some range of E_b/N_J; Figure 2.56 supports this observation and shows that it is valid for $E_b/N_J \gtrsim 11$ dB. (2.113) says that the exponential component in the P_b bound, which determines the asymptotic performance for large E_b/N_J, decreases with δ for a given SNR. Table 2.8 shows that δ is in fact maximized at $K = 3$ when $n = 2$, as well as when $n = 3$ or 4 (but not for $n = 5$). So 8-ary FSK does have an advantage against the more effective band multitone jammers (except for the $n = 1$ case where 4-ary FSK is better) for low bit error rates (i.e., large E_b/N_J). Finally, for the special case $n = M$, Table 2.8 shows that δ increases with K so that the performance improves with K as illustrated in Figure 2.57.

2.3.1.3 Independent Multitone Jamming

As effective as band multitone jamming is against FH/MFSK signals, especially the $n = 1$ case, this strategy loses most of its potency if the M-ary band structure is removed. For example, a sophisticated anti-jam system might elect to use M frequency synthesizers to independently hop each transmitted symbol as a way of defeating band multitone or repeat-back

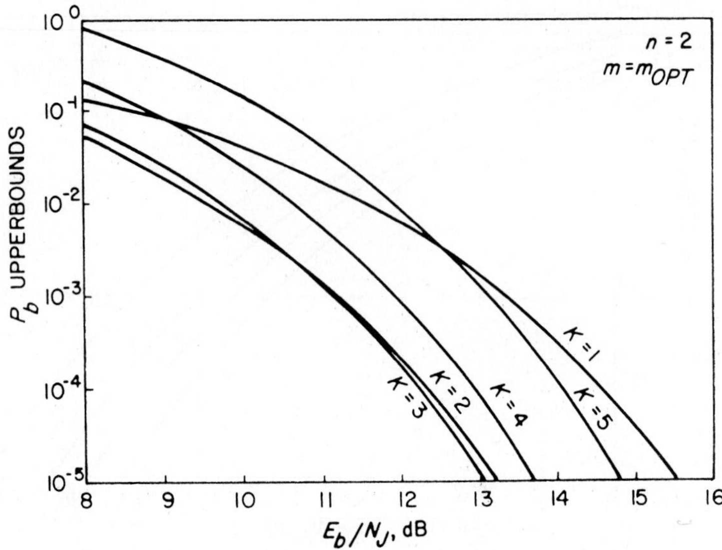

Figure 2.56. Superiority of FH/8-ary FSK signals with optimum diversity in worst case $n = 2$ band multitone jamming, for $E_b/N_J \lesssim 11$ dB.

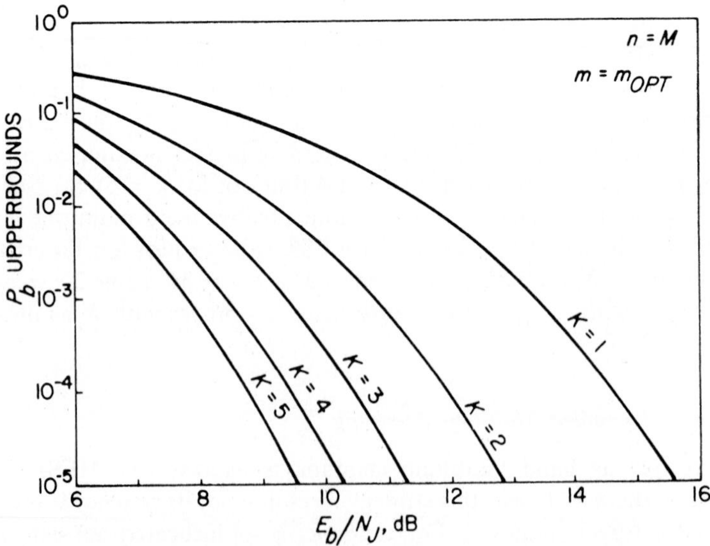

Figure 2.57. Performance of FH/MFSK signals with optimum diversity in worst case $n = M$ band multitone jamming improves with $K = \log_2 M$.

jamming [12]. Recognizing this possibility, a jammer may turn to the independent multitone jamming format as the best remaining ECM option.

Recall from Section 2.2.2.3 that the assumption implicit in the independent multitone strategy is that each FH tone frequency is independently jammed with a CW signal of power S/α with probability ρ; with m-diversity, the expression of (2.51) is modified to

$$\rho = \frac{\alpha m}{KE_b/N_J} \equiv \zeta\alpha. \tag{2.115}$$

With perfect side information, an error can only occur if at least one of the $M - 1$ untransmitted symbols is hit by a jamming tone on each diversity hop. The likelihood of this occurring on the j-th hop is

$$\Pr\{H_j\} = 1 - (1-\rho)^{M-1} \equiv \varepsilon. \tag{2.116}$$

Independent of H_j, the transmitted symbol on the j-th hop is hit with probability ρ; however, conditioned on H_j, a particular untransmitted symbol on that hop is jammed with probability ρ/ε. Again referring to Table 2.2 and assuming that symbol 1 is sent on the j-th hop, we can write

$$\Pr\left\{e_{2_j} - e_{1_j} = \beta | H_j, \phi\right\}$$

$$= \begin{cases} \dfrac{\rho^2}{\varepsilon}; & \beta = -1 - \dfrac{2}{\sqrt{\alpha}}\cos\phi \\ \rho\left(1 - \dfrac{\rho}{\varepsilon}\right); & \beta = -1 - \dfrac{1}{\alpha} - \dfrac{2}{\sqrt{\alpha}}\cos\phi \\ \dfrac{\rho}{\varepsilon}(1-\rho); & \beta = \dfrac{1}{\alpha} - 1 \\ (1-\rho)\left(1 - \dfrac{\rho}{\varepsilon}\right); & \beta = -1. \end{cases} \tag{2.117}$$

As in the band multitone jamming case of (2.107), an error can only occur if $\beta > 0$ with a non-zero probability, so α is restricted to the range $(0, 4]$. Note that from (2.116),

$$\varepsilon - \rho = (1-\rho)\left[1 - (1-\rho)^{M-2}\right]. \tag{2.118}$$

Applying the identity of (2.108), and expressing ρ as a function of α defined in terms of the parameter ζ in (2.115), the union/Chernoff bound on P_b is given by (2.109) with

$$F \equiv \min_{\lambda \geq 0}\left[\varepsilon \overline{e^{\lambda(e_{2_j} - e_{1_j})}|H_j}\right]$$

$$= \min_{\lambda \geq 0}\left(e^{-\lambda}\left[\zeta\alpha I_0\left(\frac{2\lambda}{\sqrt{\alpha}}\right) + (1-\zeta\alpha)e^{\lambda/\alpha}\right]\right.$$

$$\left.\times\left\{\zeta\alpha + (1-\zeta\alpha)\left[1 - (1-\zeta\alpha)^{M-2}\right]e^{-\lambda/\alpha}\right\}\right). \tag{2.119}$$

As in previous jammer cases analyzed in this section on diversity, we want to determine optimum values of α and m for arbitrary but fixed values of K and E_b/N_J. From (2.115), we can replace m by the normalized diversity parameter ζ:

$$m = \zeta K E_b/N_J \tag{2.120}$$

so that (2.109) becomes

$$P_b \leq \frac{M}{2} e^{-\zeta K \ln(1/F) E_b/N_J}. \tag{2.121}$$

Now we want to *minimize* the (positive) exponential coefficient $\zeta K \ln(1/F)$ over $\alpha \in (0, 4)$ for given values of K, E_b/N_J, and ζ; then we want to *maximize* the result over ζ.

As always, we must verify that all of the required extrema are unique. From the form of (2.119), it can be easily argued that the minimization over λ is always unique. However, it can be shown numerically that *the subsequent optimization over α and ζ is only unique for $K \geq 2$*. In the $K = 3$ case, for example, Figure 2.58 shows that the P_b bound has a well defined *saddlepoint* at the approximate values $\zeta = .28$ and $\alpha = .537$. The existence of a saddlepoint implies that it does not matter whether the optimization is performed first over α or ζ. Recall that this was not the case for partial-band noise [11], although it is in fact true for band multitone jamming. When

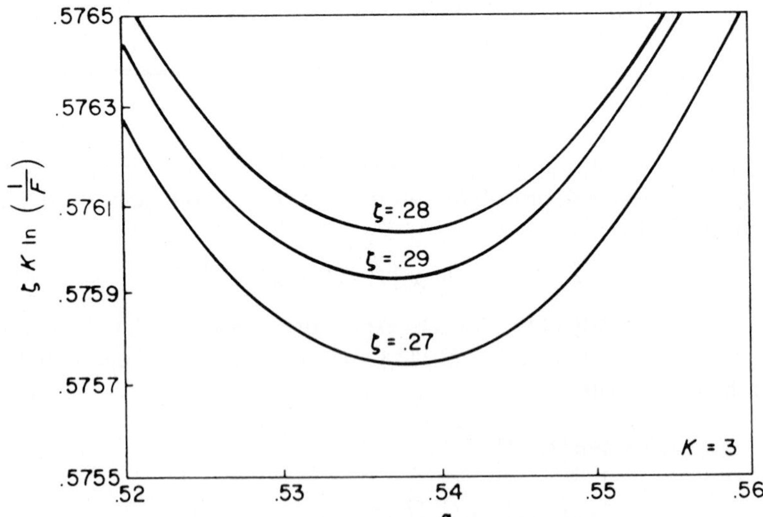

Figure 2.58. Demonstration that the P_b bound for FH/8-ary FSK signals with diversity in independent multitone jamming has a saddlepoint with respect to the normalized diversity ζ and the jammer power coefficient α. Similar results are obtained whenever $K \geq 2$.

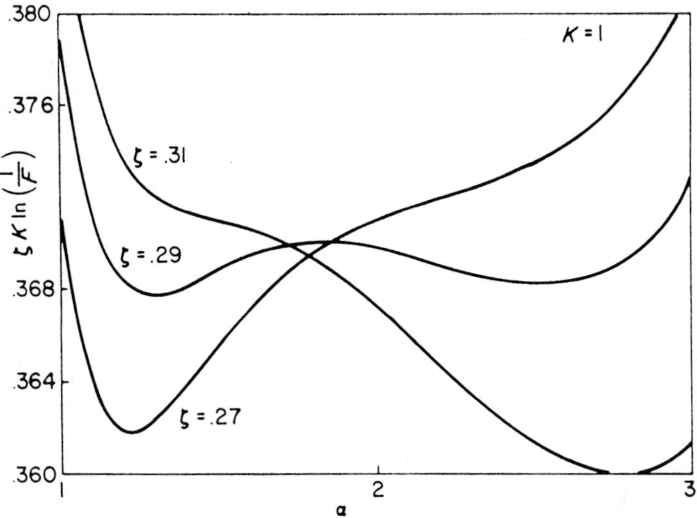

Figure 2.59. Unlike Figure 2.58, there is no saddlepoint when $K = 1$. Instead, the worst case α that minimizes the coefficient $\zeta K \ln(1/F)$ in the P_b bound of (2.121) has an abrupt discontinuity near $\zeta = .29$. In this case, the order in which the P_b bound is optimized over α and ζ affects the performance, although not as drastically as in the partial-band noise scenario.

$K = 1$, Figure 2.59 demonstrates that the optimum α has an abrupt discontinuity at $\zeta \cong .29$: to be more precise,

$$\alpha_{wc} = \begin{cases} 1.283; & \zeta = .2911_- \\ 2.552; & \zeta = .2911_+. \end{cases} \tag{2.122}$$

That is, the P_b bound coefficient $\zeta K \ln(1/F)$ has two *equal-valued* local minima at the disjoint values of α given in (2.122) when $\zeta = .2911$. And it is this value of ζ, denoted by ζ_{opt}, that subsequently determines the optimum diversity condition by maximizing $\zeta K \ln(1/F)$ for any α_{wc} when $K = 1$:

$$\begin{aligned} \delta &\equiv \max_{\zeta \geq (KE_b/N_J)^{-1}} \; \min_{0 < \alpha \leq \min(4, 1/\zeta)} \left[\zeta K \ln(1/F)\right] \\ &= .3679; \qquad K = 1 \end{aligned} \tag{2.123}$$

provided

$$E_b/N_J \geq \left(K\zeta_{opt}\right)^{-1} \equiv \gamma_0 = 5.36 \text{ dB}; \qquad K = 1.$$

Then the P_b bound of (2.121), jointly optimized over α and ζ, has the compact form

$$P_b \leq \frac{M}{2} e^{-\delta E_b/N_J}; \qquad E_b/N_J \geq \gamma_0 \tag{2.124}$$

Table 2.9
Parameters associated with performance of FH/MFSK signals with optimum diversity in worst case independent multitone jamming, as defined in (2.124).

K	α_{wc}	ρ_{opt}	δ	γ_0, dB
1	1.283 or 2.552	.291	.3679	5.36
2	.793	.354	.5495	1.50
3	.537	.282	.5760	0.73
4	.395	.213	.5243	0.70
5	.298	.158	.4379	1.02

where

$$m_{\text{opt}} = \zeta_{\text{opt}} K E_b/N_J = \frac{E_b/N_J}{\gamma_0}$$

from (2.120). In (2.123), the constraint on α ensures that $\rho \leq 1$ in (2.115), while the limit on ζ (which translates into the restriction that $E_b/N_J \geq \gamma_0$) guarantees that $m_{\text{opt}} \geq 1$. Interestingly, $e^{-1} = .3679$, but we have not been able to prove explicitly that $\delta = e^{-1}$ for $K = 1$. Since we do not have a saddlepoint for $K = 1$, it is illuminating to reverse the order of optimization in (2.123): we find that $\zeta_{\text{opt}} = .2911$ again, but

$$\delta' \equiv \min_{0<\alpha\leq 4} \max_{\alpha \leq 1/\zeta \leq KE_b/N_J} [\zeta K \ln(1/F)]$$
$$\cong .370 \quad \text{and} \quad \alpha_{wc} \cong 1.8; \qquad K = 1. \tag{2.125}$$

The performance improvement is only $\delta'/\delta = .025$ dB for $K = 1$, which is insignificant so that the absence of a saddlepoint here is only of academic interest, unlike the partial-band noise case.

(2.123) and (2.124) are valid for any K. The computed values of α_{wc}, ζ_{opt}, δ, and γ_0 are shown in Table 2.9 for various K. The effectiveness of diversity in combatting independent multitone jamming is illustrated in Figure 2.60 for 8-ary FSK. As a benchmark, at $P_b = 10^{-5}$, the improvement with optimum diversity relative to no diversity is at least 37.8 dB, and is closer than 4.4 dB to the broadband noise performance, since the m_{opt} curve is an upperbound. The best asymptotic performance for small P_b with optimum diversity is achieved at $K = 3$, which has the largest exponential coefficient δ; this is underscored graphically in Figure 2.61. (Recall that $K = 3$ was also asymptotically optimum for $n = 2$, 3, and 4 band multitone jamming.)

2.3.1.4 Time Diversity Overview

At this stage, we are in a position to assess the relative effectiveness of the different kinds of jammers we have analyzed against FH/MFSK systems with simple repetition coding. For sufficiently large E_b/N_J (how large

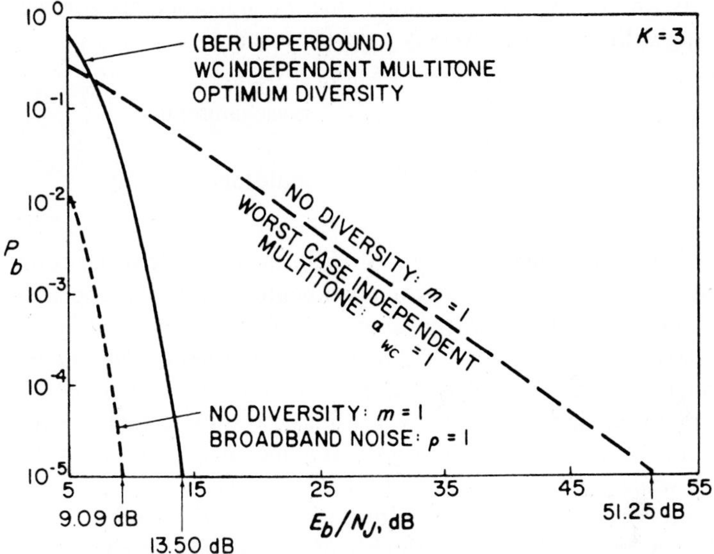

Figure 2.60. Effectiveness of diversity against worst case independent multitone jamming for FH/8-ary FSK signals. Improvement with optimum diversity relative to no diversity exceeds 37.8 dB, and performance is degraded less than 4.4 dB relative to broadband noise, at $P_b = 10^{-5}$.

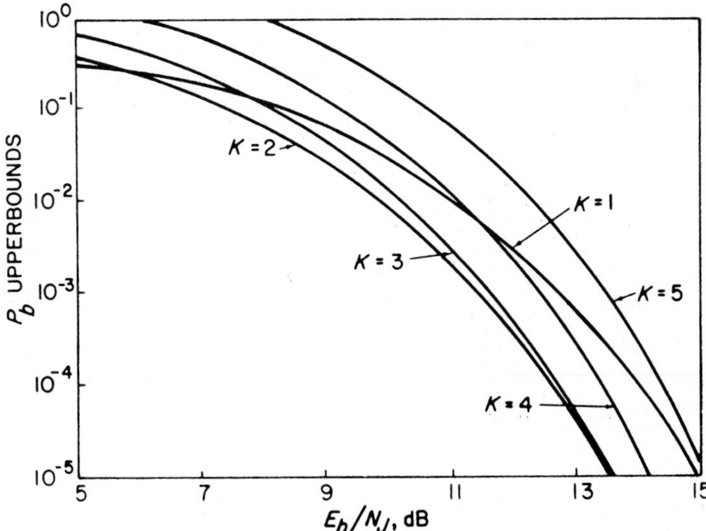

Figure 2.61. Comparison of performance of FH/MFSK systems with optimum diversity in worst case independent multitone jamming as a function of $K = \log_2 M$. Best performance for small P_b (large E_b/N_J) is achieved for 8-ary signalling.

depends on the type of jamming), the P_b upperbounds for worst case jamming with optimum diversity have the form

$$P_b \leq \begin{cases} \dfrac{M}{4} e^{-\delta E_b/N_J}; & \text{noise jamming} \\ \dfrac{M}{2} e^{-\delta E_b/N_J}; & \text{multitone jamming} \end{cases} \tag{2.126}$$

where δ is enumerated in Table 2.10. With the caveat that our comparisons are based on exponentially tight upperbounds, it would appear that *the worst case $n = 1$ band multitone jammer is the most asymptotically effective of those considered against FH/MFSK signals with optimum diversity for $K \geq 2$.* Although Table 2.10 suggests that partial-band noise is more effective than band multitone jamming for $K = 1$, it must be stressed that δ is pessimistically low for the partial-band noise case since it is based on a P_b upperbound, while the $n = 1$ band multitone δ is exact; so, it is conceivable that even in this case $n = 1$ band multitone jamming is the winner.

When we analyzed the performance of FH/MFSK signals without diversity in worst case jamming, we saw that for small enough P_b's, the $n = 1$ band and independent multitone jammers were equally effective (see Figure 2.21). We argued that the reason for this equivalence is that the worst case independent multitone jammer sets the probability ρ that a given FH slot is jammed so small that a jammed M-ary band is likely to contain a single jamming tone, just as in the $n = 1$ band multitone structure. Table 2.10 shows that with optimum diversity, $n = 1$ band multitone jamming is more

Table 2.10

P_b upperbound exponential coefficients (see (2.126)) for FH/MFSK signalling with optimum diversity in worst case jamming of various classes. The smaller δ is, the more effective the jammer is for a given E_b/N_J at low P_b. The upper bound for $n = 1$ band multitone jamming and $K = 1$ is identical with the exact performance.

	P_b Bound Exponential Coefficient δ				
Type of Jammer	$K = 1$	$K = 2$	$K = 3$	$K = 4$	$K = 5$
Broadband Noise	.5000	1.0000	1.5000	2.0000	2.5000
Partial-Band Noise	.2500	.5000	.7500	1.0000	1.2500
Independent Multitone	.3679	.5495	.5760	.5242	.4379
$n = 1$ Band Multitone	.3679 (Exact)	.4631	.4493	.3839	.3014
$n = 2$ Band Multitone	.3232	.5835	.6379	.5790	.4734
$n = M$ Band Multitone	.3232	.6465	.9697	1.2929	1.6162

effective than independent multitone jamming. The difference now is that the use of a detection metric that can make an error only if all m diversity transmissions are jammed (perfect side information assumption) forces the jammer to use a much larger value of ρ; these values, shown in Table 2.11, are based on the optimum values of α and ζ shown in Table 2.9 and (2.115). Note that the probability that k slots in an M-ary band are jammed is simply $\binom{M}{k}\rho^k(1-\rho)^{M-k}$. A relevant parameter is the likelihood that one slot in an M-ary band is jammed relative to the probability that two or more slots are jammed:

$$P_1 \equiv \frac{\Pr\{k=1\}}{\Pr\{2 \le k \le M\}} = \frac{M\rho(1-\rho)^{M-1}}{1-(1-\rho)^M - M\rho(1-\rho)^{M-1}}. \tag{2.127}$$

In the absence of diversity, $P_1 \gg 1$; with optimum diversity, Table 2.11 shows that $P_1 \sim 1$. This means that a jammed band will often contain two or more jamming tones, which is different from, and apparently a less efficient use of available jamming power than the $n = 1$ band multitone structure, for which P_1 is by definition infinite.

Table 2.10 also reiterates the relative impotence of $n = M$ band multitone jamming.

All of these observations are illustrated graphically in Figures 2.62–2.64. Note that as indicated in Figure 2.64, the optimum diversity m_{opt} varies with the type of jamming for a given K and E_b/N_J. Which raises an interesting point: with the exception of independent multitone jamming (refer to (2.124)), all of the remaining jammers have

$$m_{\text{opt}} = \delta E_b/N_J. \tag{2.128}$$

Now we know from (2.126) that a larger δ ensures better performance for a given E_b/N_J. But (2.128) reminds us that this benefit is balanced by increased system complexity due to the need for more diversity.

In designing an FH/MFSK system with diversity, it is prudent to select parameters that will allow it to achieve the desired performance under the

Table 2.11

Parameters associated with performance of FH/MFSK signals with optimum diversity in worst case independent multitone jamming, as defined in (2.115) and (2.127).

K	ρ_{wc}	P_1
1	.37 or .74	3.4 or .69
2	.28	1.3
3	.15	1.1
4	.084	.91
5	.047	.75

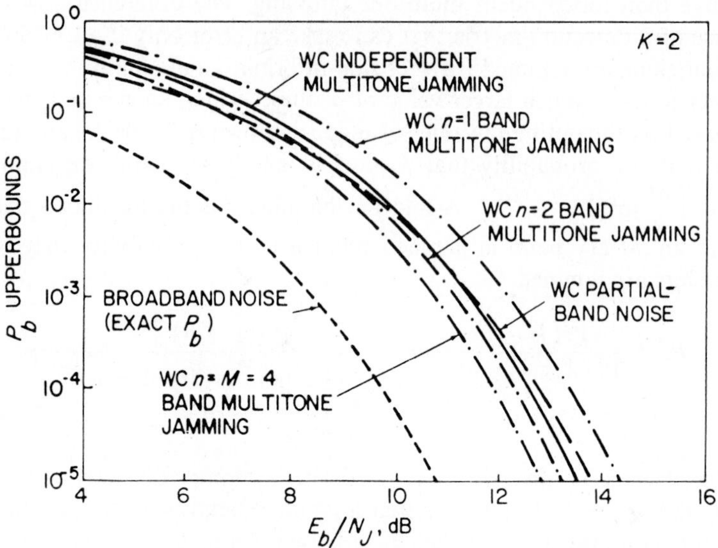

Figure 2.62. Relative performance of FH/4-ary FSK signalling with optimum diversity in different worst case jamming environments. Note that the optimum diversity varies with the type of jammer for a given E_b/N_J.

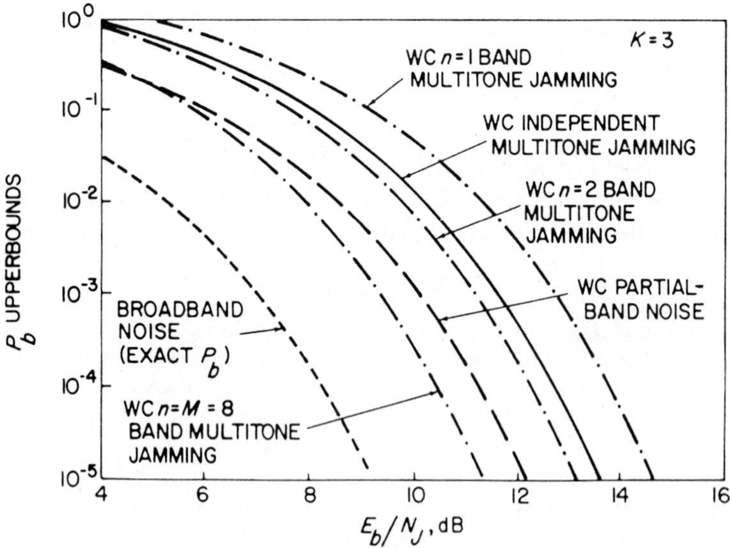

Figure 2.63. Same as Figure 2.62, but for 8-ary FSK.

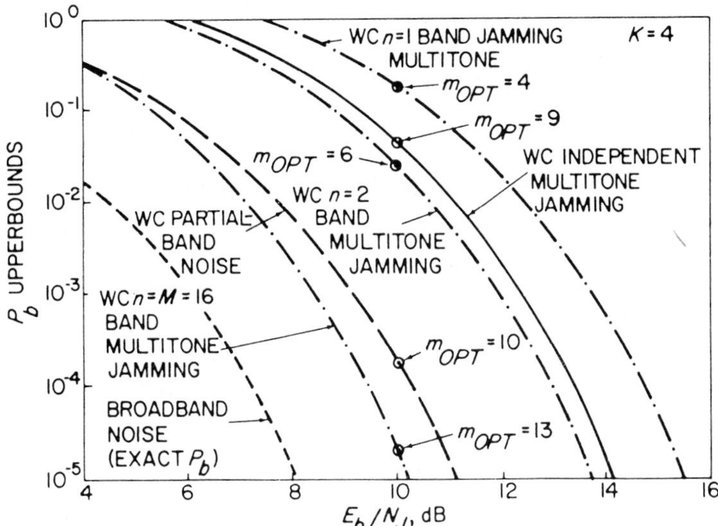

Figure 2.64. Same as Figures 2.62 and 2.63, but for 16-ary FSK. To emphasize the variation in optimum diversity m_{opt} with jammer type, values of m_{opt} are indicated for $E_b/N_J = 10$ dB.

worst conceivable jamming conditions. With the possible exception of $K = 1$ as discussed above, this implies the assumption of $n = 1$ band multitone jamming. However, since this class of jammer has the lowest δ for a given K, it calls for less diversity than is optimum for the other kinds of jamming. So we must verify that the suboptimum, degraded performance for these other jammers does not exceed the optimized P_b for $n = 1$ band multitone jamming. This kind of information is not available from curves of the form of Figures 2.62–2.64. As an example, using Table 2.10, we see that

$$\min_{K} \max_{\text{type of jammer}} \delta = .4493; \qquad n = 1 \text{ band multitone jamming}, \quad K = 3. \tag{2.129}$$

On this basis, it is reasonable to use $K = 3$, and if we assume a desired P_b of 10^{-5}, (2.126) and (2.128) suggest that we use $E_b/N_J = 14.58$ dB and $m = m_{\text{opt}} = 13$. Using previously derived bounds on P_b for worst case jamming with arbitrary diversity, curves of performance versus diversity are drawn in Figures 2.65 for $n = 1$ band multitone, independent multitone, and partial-band noise jamming with the selected K and E_b/N_J. Although $m_{\text{opt}} = 24$ and 22 respectively for the last two jammers, we see that the bound on P_b for these jammers at $m = 13$ does not exceed the desired bit error rate, so we do indeed have a viable system design.

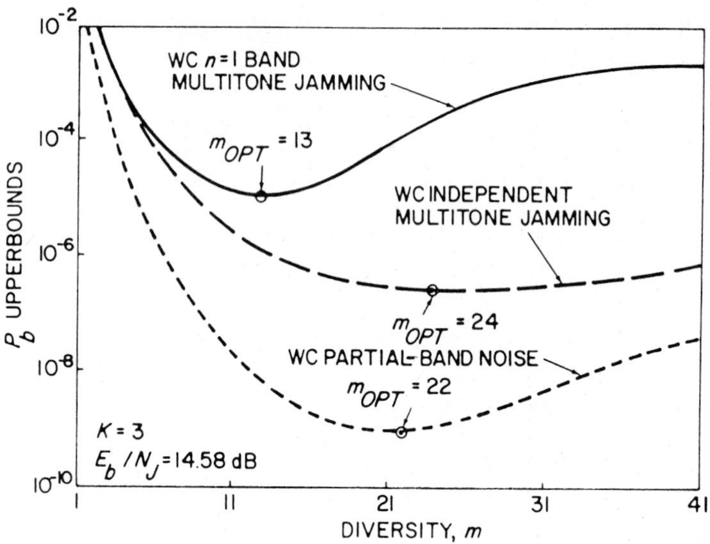

Figure 2.65. Variation in performance of FH/8-ary FSK systems with diversity for several kinds of worst case jamming when $E_b/N_J = 14.58$ dB, which was selected to achieve a P_b of 10^{-5} or better under any jamming conditions with $m = 13$.

2.3.2 Coding without Diversity

We have seen in the previous sections that time diversity techniques can significantly reduce the effectiveness of worst case noise and multitone jammers against FH/MFSK signals. In particular, optimum diversity restores the exponential relationship between P_b and E_b/N_J from the inverse linear dependence characterizing worst case jamming without any coding redundancy.

Yet, diversity transmission corresponds to a simple repetition code. And there are many block and convolutional codes that are much more powerful than repetition codes, based on experience with classical additive Gaussian noise channels. It remains to be seen how effective these codes are in a non-stationary, non-Gaussian jamming environment. In fact, it would probably be valuable to derive codes and detection metrics specifically matched to the more insidious pulsed, partial-band, or tone jamming channels characteristic of the electronic warfare era.

Several papers in the open literature have investigated the effectiveness of various block, convolutional, and concatenated codes for FH/MFSK systems in partial-band noise [2], [14]–[16]. Of these, the paper by Ma and Poole [16] is perhaps the most comprehensive. In this section, we will consider multitone as well as partial-band noise jamming. This is important since we have previously seen that $n = 1$ band multitone jamming is the most effective type of interference against uncoded FH/MFSK signals, with or without diversity, for $K \geq 2$. It will also provide some insights into the effect of the jamming channel characteristics on the performance of some of the more popular codes in use today.

Our intention is not to exhaustively analyze the performance of every known code in all types of jamming. The emphasis will be on providing the analytical tools for evaluating the effectiveness of coding against worst case FH/MFSK jammers. Specifically, we will consider several binary and M-ary convolutional codes, Reed-Solomon codes (because their burst error correction capabilities make them attractive for non-stationary interference), and concatenated schemes employing Reed-Solomon outer codes and convolutional inner codes. With regard to jamming categories, we will restrict our analysis to partial-band noise and $n = 1$ band multitone jamming. The detection metric remains the unweighted linear combination of received chip energies, with perfect jamming state side information. We will be concerned with the relative performance of these codes in worst case jamming, and how they compare with the unsophisticated repetition codes with optimum diversity previously analyzed.

2.3.2.1 Convolutional Codes

Our analytical approach mirrors that of Chapter 4, Part 1, and [8]. Simulation techniques aside, most coding performance analyses are based on bounds of the form (see (4.24), Volume I)

$$P_b \leq G(D) \tag{2.130}$$

where the structure of $G(D)$ depends only on the coder and decoder characteristics, while the parameter D is *separably* dependent only on the type of jamming and the detection metric.

In particular, for the special case of partial-band noise with spectral fill factor ρ, (2.130) is modified by the addition of the familiar factor of 1/2 (refer to [10] and Appendix 2A):

$$P_b \leq \tfrac{1}{2} G(D); \text{ noise jamming} \tag{2.131}$$

and, for the soft decision linear combining metric with perfect side information (see (4.92), Volume I),

$$D = \left(\frac{\rho}{1-\lambda^2}\right) e^{-(\lambda/1+\lambda)(\rho E_c/N_J)} \tag{2.132}$$

where

$$\lambda = \tfrac{1}{2}\left[\sqrt{1 + 6\beta + \beta^2} - \beta - 1\right]$$

$$\beta \equiv \frac{\rho E_c}{2N_J}.$$

The parameter E_c/N_J is the MFSK chip energy-to-jamming noise spectral power ratio (see (4.2), Volume I):

$$\frac{E_c}{N_J} = R\left(\frac{E_b}{N_J}\right) \tag{2.133}$$

where R is the code rate expressed in information bits/chip. Recall that the transmission of a chip represents a single use of the M-ary channel; a chip is an M-ary symbol from the innermost code. For example, in an uncoded system with diversity m (we could also regard this as a simple repetition code as discussed previously), each diversity transmission is a single M-ary chip and $R = K/m$.

For worst case partial-band noise [5], we want to maximize D over $\rho \in (0, 1]$:

$$D = \frac{4e^{-1}}{E_c/N_J} \quad \text{and} \quad \rho_{\text{wc}} = \frac{3}{E_c/N_J}; \qquad \frac{E_c}{N_J} \geq 3 \tag{2.134}$$

while for $E_c/N_J \leq 3$, D is given by (2.132) with $\rho = \rho_{\text{wc}} = 1$.

For multitone jamming, the P_b bound of (2.130) must be used. For $n = 1$ band multitone jamming, the performance bounds have the form (refer to (2.75), (2.86), and (2.87))

$$P_b \leq \frac{M}{2} F^m. \tag{2.135}$$

Referring to the definition of D in (4.20) in Volume I, we see that D is simply equal to F, with KE_b/mN_J replaced by E_c/N_J. In terms of the jammer power parameter α, which is restricted to the range (see (2.89))

$$0 < \alpha < \min\left(1, \frac{E_c}{MN_J}\right) \tag{2.136}$$

we have

$$D = \begin{cases} \dfrac{\alpha}{E_c/N_J}; & K = 1 \\[2ex] \dfrac{1}{E_c/N_J}\left[\dfrac{\alpha(M-2)}{1-\alpha}\right]^{1-\alpha}; & K \geq 2. \end{cases} \tag{2.137}$$

Maximizing D over α for worst case $n = 1$ band multitone jamming, for the special case $K = 1$,

$$D = \begin{cases} \dfrac{1}{E_c/N_J} \text{ and } \alpha_{\text{wc}} = 1_-; & \dfrac{E_c}{N_J} \geq 2 \\[2ex] \dfrac{1}{2} \text{ and } \alpha_{\text{wc}} = \dfrac{E_c}{2N_J}; & \dfrac{E_c}{N_J} < 2. \end{cases} \tag{2.138}$$

Similarly, for $K \geq 2$,

$$D = \begin{cases} \dfrac{\beta K}{E_c/N_J} \text{ and } \alpha_{\text{wc}} = \alpha_0; & \dfrac{E_c}{N_J} \geq \alpha_0 M \\ \dfrac{1}{E_c/N_J}\left[\dfrac{\alpha_{\text{wc}}(M-2)}{1-\alpha_{\text{wc}}}\right]^{1-\alpha_{\text{wc}}} & \\ \quad \text{and } \alpha_{\text{wc}} = \dfrac{E_c}{MN_J}; & \dfrac{E_c}{N_J} \leq \alpha_0 M \end{cases} \tag{2.139}$$

where β and α_0 are given in Table 2.7 for $2 \leq K \leq 5$.

We now want to specify $G(D)$ for the codes of interest in this section. As a reference point, for the m-diversity repetition code (see (2.62)),

$$G(D) = \frac{M}{2}D^m \quad \text{and} \quad R \doteq \frac{K}{m}. \tag{2.140}$$

In worst case partial-band noise, the diversity that minimizes D^m (the so-called quasi-optimum diversity that minimizes the bound on P_b in [2]) is given by (see (2.70))

$$m_{\text{opt}} = \frac{KE_b}{4N_J}; \qquad \frac{E_b}{N_J} \geq \frac{4}{K}. \tag{2.141}$$

Combining (2.131), (2.133), (2.134), (2.140), and (2.141), we have

$$P_b \leq \frac{M}{4}e^{-KE_b/4N_J}; \qquad \frac{E_b}{N_J} \geq \frac{4}{K}. \tag{2.142}$$

For the special case of $n = 1$ band multitone jamming with $K = 1$, we could use (see (2.77))

$$m_{\text{opt}} = e^{-1}\left(\frac{E_b}{N_J}\right); \qquad \frac{E_b}{N_J} \geq e \tag{2.143}$$

although we saw in Figure 2.36 that we could achieve arbitrarily small error rates by using large enough values of m. Here, we combine (2.130), (2.133), (2.138), (2.140), and (2.143) to yield the performance bound

$$P_b \leq e^{-e^{-1}(E_b/N_J)}; \qquad \frac{E_b}{N_J} \geq e. \tag{2.144}$$

For $n = 1$ band multitone jamming with $K \geq 2$, we want to use (see (2.104))

$$\left.\begin{aligned} m_{\text{opt}} &= \delta\left(\frac{E_b}{N_J}\right) \\ &\Downarrow \\ P_b &\leq \frac{M}{2}e^{-\delta(E_b/N_J)} \end{aligned}\right\} \frac{E_b}{N_J} \geq \frac{1}{\delta} \tag{2.145}$$

where δ is specified in Table 2.7 for $2 \leq K \leq 5$.

Perhaps the most commonly used convolutional codes for *binary* ($K = 1$) channels are the constraint length 7, rate 1/2 and 1/3 structures determined by Odenwalder [17]; assuming soft decision Viterbi decoding, the performance is given by

$$\begin{aligned} G(D) = {} & 36D^{10} + 211D^{12} + 1404D^{14} + 11{,}633D^{16} \\ & + 77{,}433D^{18} + 502{,}690D^{20} + 3{,}322{,}763D^{22} \\ & + 21{,}292{,}910D^{24} + 134{,}365{,}911D^{26} + \cdots \\ & \text{and } R = \tfrac{1}{2};\ (7, \tfrac{1}{2}) \text{ code} \end{aligned} \tag{2.146}$$

$$\begin{aligned} G(D) = {} & D^{14} + 20D^{16} + 53D^{18} + 184D^{20} + \cdots \\ & \text{and } R = \tfrac{1}{3};\ (7, \tfrac{1}{3}) \text{ code.} \end{aligned} \tag{2.147}$$

((2.147) is not accurate for $D \gtrsim 10^{-1}$.)

For larger channel alphabets, Trumpis found the optimum constraint length 7, rate 1/2 and 1/3 (over these larger alphabets) convolutional codes for 4-ary and 8-ary orthogonal signal sets, respectively [18]:

$$\begin{aligned} G(D) = {} & 7D^{7} + 39D^{8} + 104D^{9} \\ & + 352D^{10} + 1187D^{11} + \cdots;\ (7, \tfrac{1}{2}) \text{ code} \end{aligned} \tag{2.148}$$

$$\begin{aligned} G(D) = {} & D^{7} + 4D^{8} + 8D^{9} + 49D^{10} \\ & + 92D^{11} + \cdots;\ (7, \tfrac{1}{3}) \text{ code.} \end{aligned} \tag{2.149}$$

Since each information bit produces an M-ary code symbol above, $R = 1$ for both cases.

For $K \geq 2$, the M-ary orthogonal convolutional codes [19] have

$$G(D) = \frac{D^{K}(1 - D)^{2}}{(1 - 2D - D^{K})^{2}} \quad \text{and} \quad R = 1\,. \tag{2.150}$$

Finally, for all values of K, we have the powerful class of dual-K convolutional codes with code rate $1/\nu$ over GF(2^K) [2], [20]. That is, for every M-ary (K-bit) input word, ν M-ary code symbols are generated, corresponding to $R = K/\nu$ bits/chip. The performance is defined by

$$G(D) = \frac{MD^{2\nu}}{2\left[1 - \nu D^{\nu-1} - (M - \nu - 1)D^{\nu}\right]^{2}}\,. \tag{2.151}$$

We now want to investigate how effective these convolutional codes are at combatting worst case partial-band noise and $n = 1$ band multitone jamming. The performance of these codes with FH/MFSK signals is illustrated in Figures 2.66–2.75 for $1 \leq K \leq 5$ and both kinds of jamming. As a benchmark, each graph plots the upperbound on P_b for "uncoded" signalling with optimum diversity. In one sense, this comparison is unfavorable to the convolutional codes. The optimum diversity structure corresponds to the block repetition code with the code rate K/m that provides the best

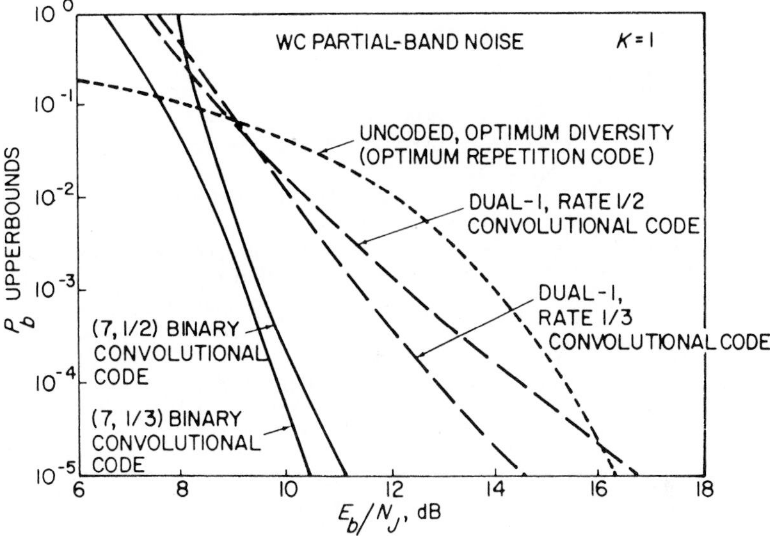

Figure 2.66. Performance of several convolutional codes and optimum repetition code with FH binary FSK signals in worst case partial-band noise. Odenwalder's binary convolutional codes are particularly effective (e.g., about 5–6 dB better than uncoded signalling with optimum diversity at $P_b = 10^{-5}$). Assumes soft decision energy detection, linear combining, and perfect side information.

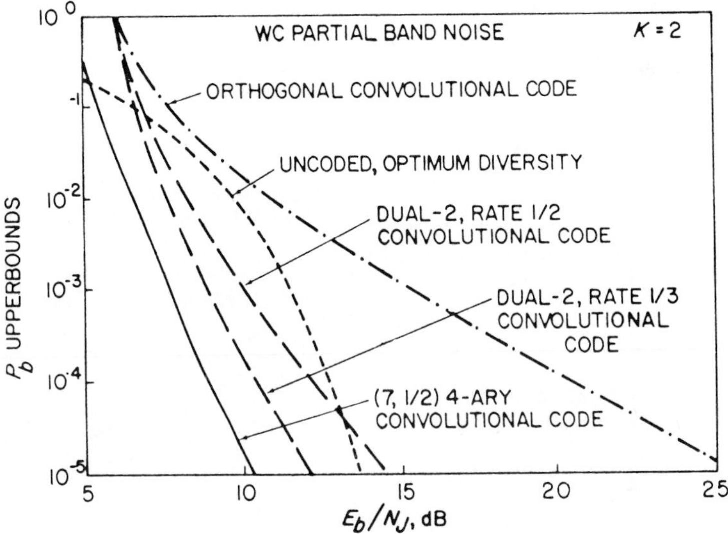

Figure 2.67. Same as Figure 2.66, except $K = 2$. The 4-ary orthogonal convolutional code performs poorly, with an inverse linear characteristic for small P_b's. Trumpis' optimum constraint length 7 convolutional code for 4-ary orthogonal signalling is about 3.5 dB better than optimum diversity at $P_b = 10^{-5}$.

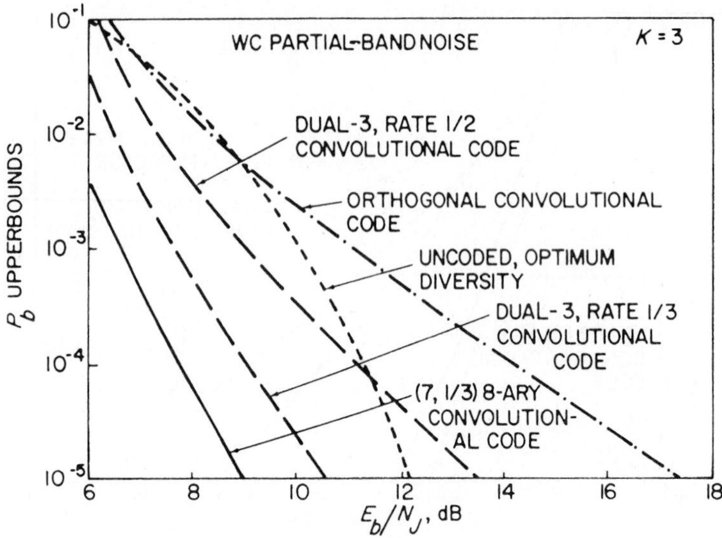

Figure 2.68. Same as Figures 2.66 and 2.67, except $K = 3$. The orthogonal convolutional code continues to be ineffective, while the dual-3, rate $1/3$ code outperforms the optimum diversity system over P_b's of interest. The best performance is again provided by Trumpis' optimum $(7, \frac{1}{3})$ code for 8-ary orthogonal channels.

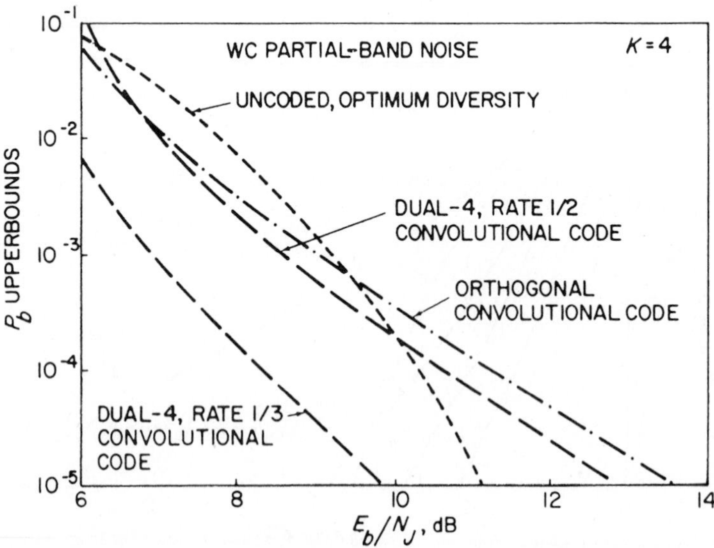

Figure 2.69. Same as previous figures with $K = 4$. The dual-4, rate $1/2$ convolutional code performance is almost as poor as orthogonal convolutional coding. The dual-4, rate $1/3$ performance is marginally better than optimum diversity (e.g., about 1 dB better at $P_b = 10^{-5}$).

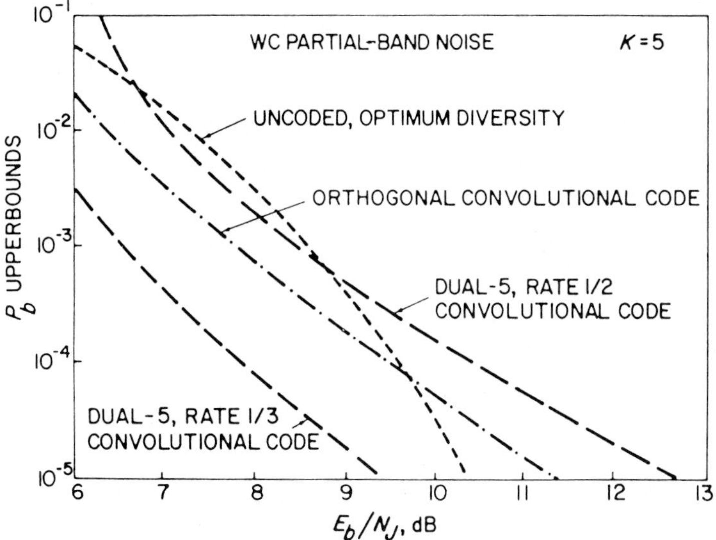

Figure 2.70. Same as previous figures, except $K = 5$. The 32-ary orthogonal convolutional code is now better than the dual-5, rate 1/2 code, although both codes perform poorly at low P_b's. The dual-5, rate 1/3 code is again about 1 dB better than optimum diversity at $P_b = 10^{-5}$.

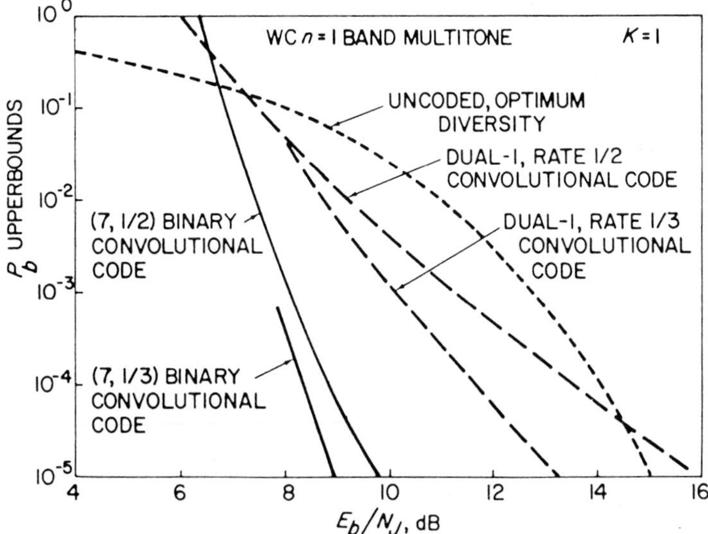

Figure 2.71. Same as Figure 2.66, but for worst case $n = 1$ band multitone jamming. Remember that this entire series of graphs is for the soft decision energy detection metric with linear combining and perfect side information. Odenwalder's codes again provide the best performance, with a 1.5 dB improvement over the noise jamming case at $P_b = 10^{-5}$. Some of the curves are truncated because $G(D)$ is invalid for small E_b/N_J.

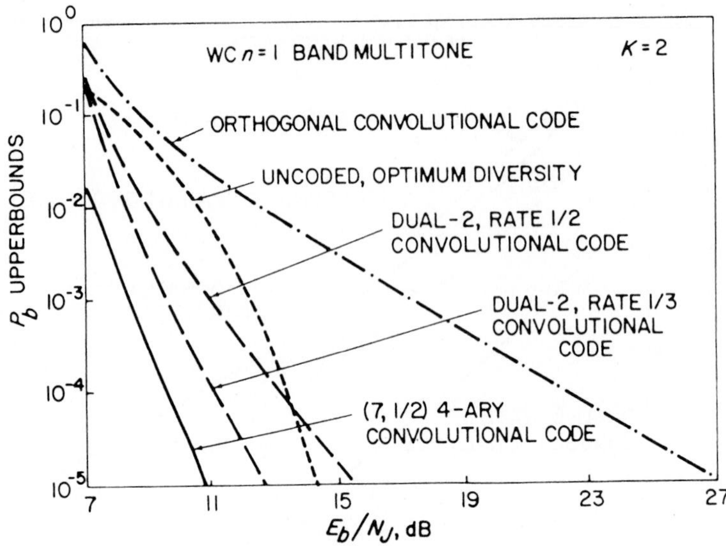

Figure 2.72. Same as Figure 2.67 for multitone jamming. The orthogonal convolution codes continue to be vulnerable to worst case jamming. Trumpis' $(7, \frac{1}{2})$ code is about 3.5 dB better than optimum diversity as in the noise jamming case, but the multitone jammer degrades its performance about .75 dB relative to the noise jammer.

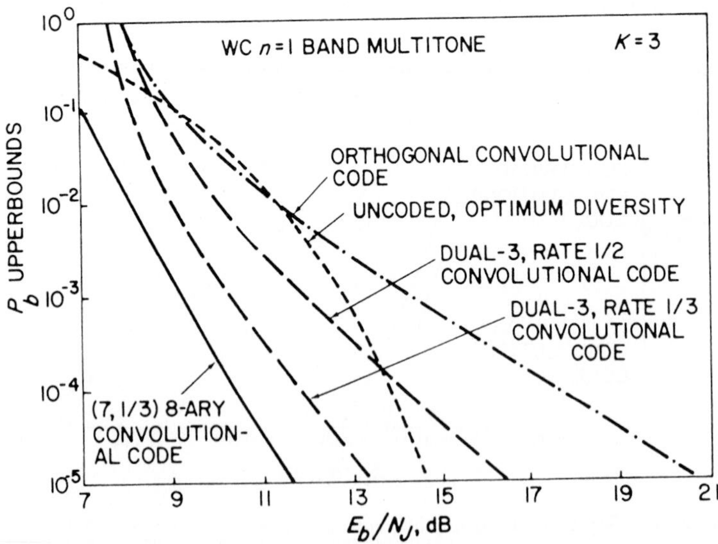

Figure 2.73. Same as Figure 2.68 for multitone jamming, which is more effective than partial-band noise. However, relative performance of codes is essentially unchanged, with Trumpis' $(7, \frac{1}{3})$ code on top.

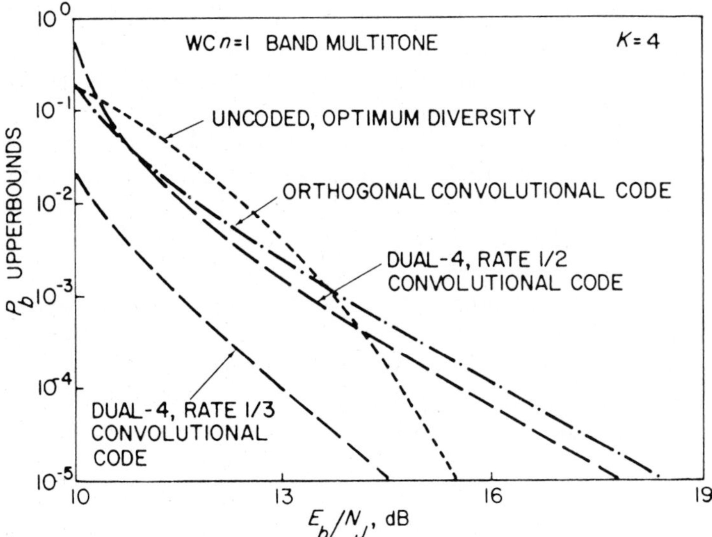

Figure 2.74. Same as Figure 2.69, with worst case multitone jamming proving more effective than partial-band noise again (this is generally true for smaller P_b's and $K \geq 2$).

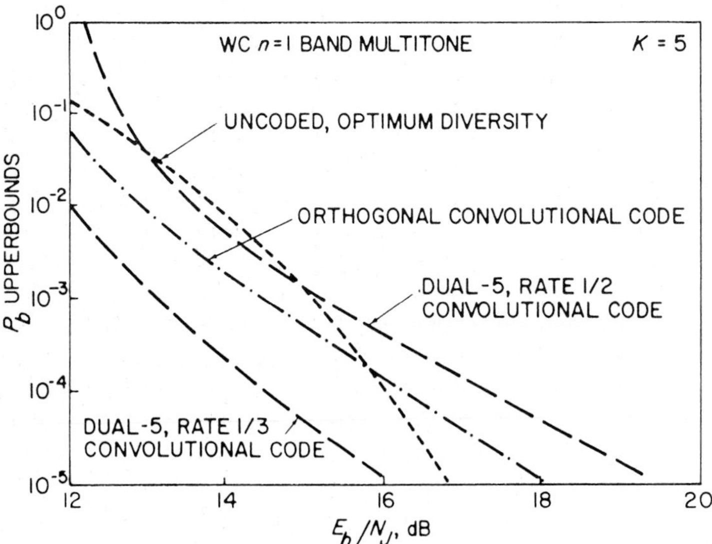

Figure 2.75. Same as Figure 2.70, except jamming is worst case $n = 1$ band multitone. Performance of dual-5, rate 1/3 code is about 6.5 dB worse than in partial-band noise, and 1.5 dB worse than for $K = 4$ in multitone jamming at $P_b = 10^{-5}$.

performance for a given combination of FH/MFSK signals and jamming. No attempt has been made to similarly optimize the convolutional code rates. We will examine this issue later in connection with block codes, particularly Reed-Solomon codes.

Some specific observations about the relative effectiveness of the various convolutional codes in worst case jamming are included in the commentaries with Figures 2.66–2.75. Overall, the Odenwalder optimum binary convolutional codes and the Trumpis optimum 4-ary and 8-ary convolutional codes are a significant improvement over uncoded FH/MFSK with optimum diversity. At the other extreme, orthogonal convolutional coding is quite vulnerable to worst case jamming, especially for smaller values of K; in fact, for lower P_b's the performance curves exhibit the inverse linear dependence characteristic of uncoded signalling. In between are the dual-K convolutional codes, which can be fairly effective against worst case jamming, with improved performance for lower code rates $1/\nu$.

For a given class of codes, there are observations to be made with regard to the impact of the channel dimensionality K and the type of jamming on system performance. The variation in performance with K is illustrated in Figures 2.76–2.81. Recall that for uncoded FH/MFSK signalling with optimum diversity, the performance in worst case partial-band noise improved monotonically with K for moderate and lower P_b's (Figure 2.31); this behavior is adhered to by the orthogonal and dual-K convolutional codes. On the other hand, for worst case $n = 1$ band multitone jamming, Figure 2.51 showed that the best performance for uncoded signalling with optimum diversity is achieved for $K = 2$, with increasingly degraded performance for larger values of K. (This should be qualified by the reminder that the $K = 1$ performance could be made arbitrarily good for large enough amounts of diversity.) The dual-K performance in worst case multitone jamming conforms to this behavior (without the $K = 1$ qualifier above), while the orthogonal convolutional codes in Figure 2.77 do not.

Focussing on the dual-K convolutional code behavior, since performance improves with K for worst case partial-band noise, and degrades with $K \geq 2$ for worst case $n = 1$ band multitone jamming, the impact of the type of jamming becomes more significant for larger values of K. This effect is illustrated in Figure 2.82 for the rate 1/3 codes. In particular, at $P_b = 10^{-5}$, noise jamming is about 1 dB more effective than multitone jamming for $K = 1$; the jamming effectiveness is reversed for $K \geq 2$, with multitone jamming exhibiting a 3 dB advantage at $K = 3$, and a 7 dB advantage at $K = 5$ for this P_b.

The relative performance of all of these codes in noise and multitone jamming is summarized in Table 2.12 at the benchmark $P_b = 10^{-5}$. From a min/max perspective, if we wanted to choose the coded system that required the smallest SNR to provide a guaranteed P_b of 10^{-5} *in any kind of non-adaptive jamming*, we would use the Odenwalder $(7, \frac{1}{3})$ binary convolutional code: this requires $E_b/N_J = 10.38$ dB for worst case partial-band noise, with better performance for any other jammer. By comparison, if we

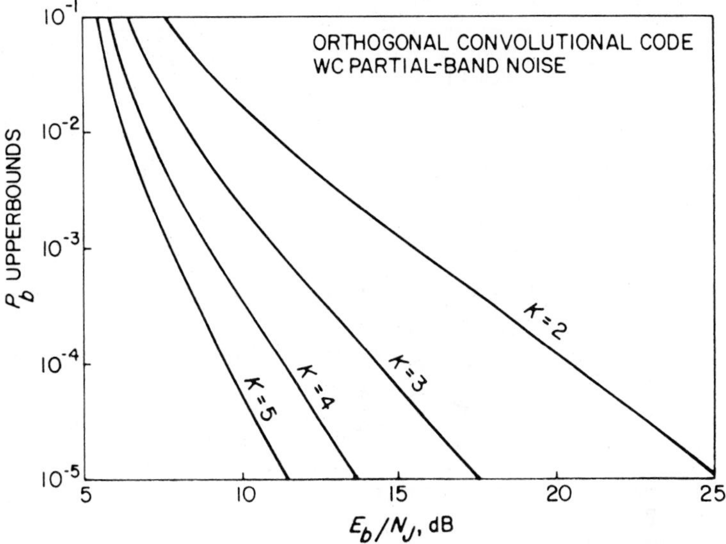

Figure 2.76. Variation with K in performance of orthogonal convolutional codes with FH/MFSK signals in worst case partial-band noise, assuming soft decision energy detection with linear combining metric and perfect jamming state side information. Performance is generally poor, but improves with K.

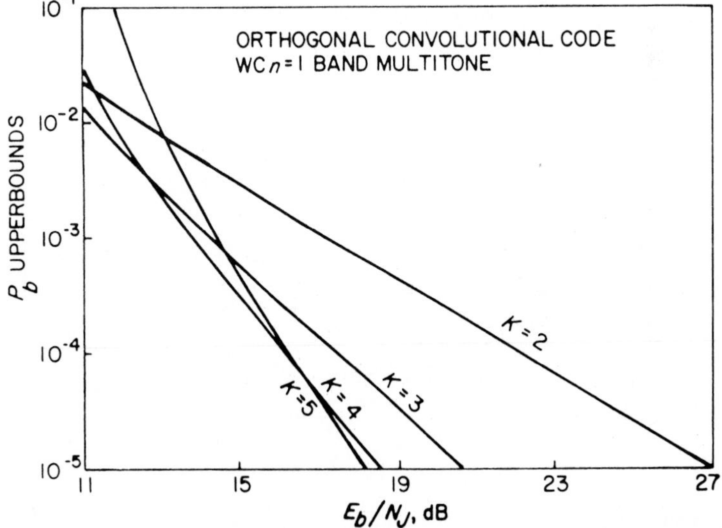

Figure 2.77. Same as Figure 2.76, but for worst case $n = 1$ band multitone jamming. For sufficiently small P_b's, performance improves with K.

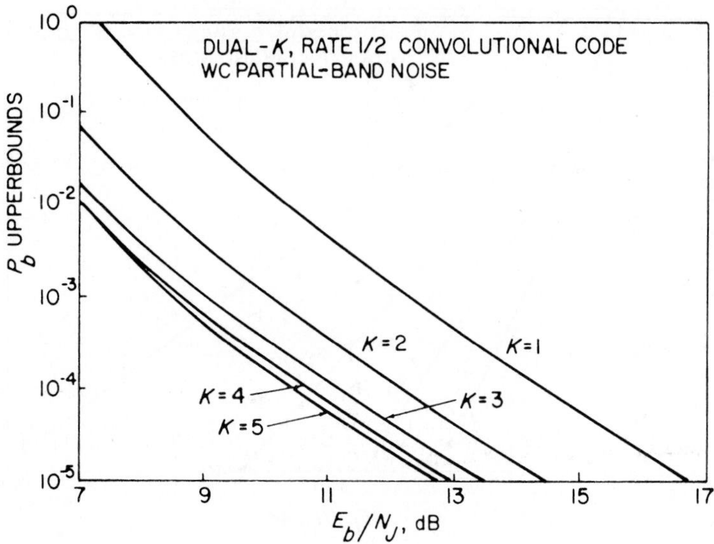

Figure 2.78. Same as Figure 2.76, but for dual-K, rate 1/2 convolutional coding. Performance improves with K for moderate to small P_b's, but improvement is minor for $K \gtrsim 4$.

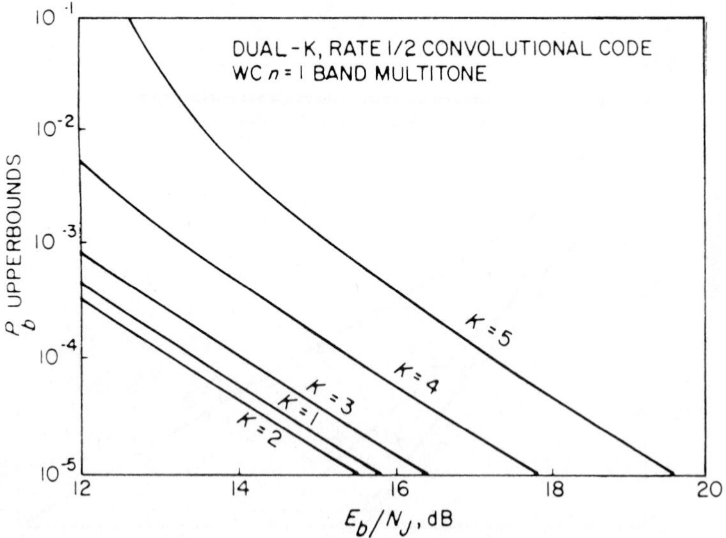

Figure 2.79. Same as Figure 2.78, but for multitone jamming. Performance is optimized over range of interest of P_b at $K = 2$. For $K \geq 2$, performance degrades with K (similar effect was observed for uncoded FH/MFSK signals with optimum diversity in Figure 1.51).

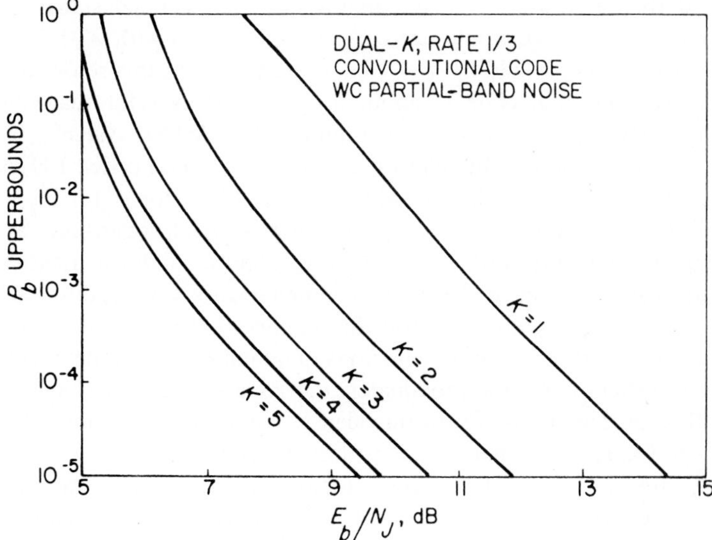

Figure 2.80. Same as Figure 2.78, but for rate 1/3, dual-K convolutional coding. Performance improves with K.

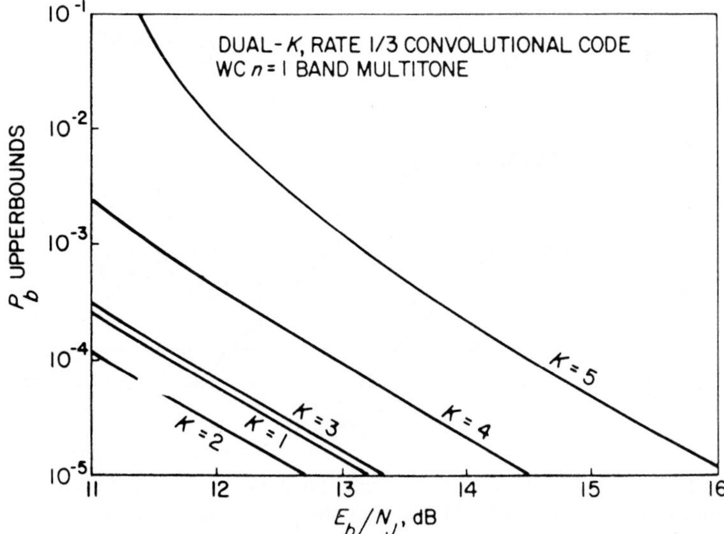

Figure 2.81. Same as Figure 2.79, but for rate 1/3, dual-K convolutional coding. Variation with K is qualitatively identical to rate 1/2 code in Figure 2.79.

adopted the same system design philosophy for uncoded signalling with optimum diversity, we would need $E_b/N_J = 14.21$ dB with $K = 2$, and the worst case jammer would be $n = 1$ band multitone. In this sense, the $(7, \frac{1}{3})$ binary convolutional code is about 4 dB more powerful than the best repetition code against worst case jamming of FH/MFSK systems.

Figure 2.83 examines the relative sensitivity of several coded FH/MFSK systems to variations in the partial-band noise fill factor ρ, for the specific case of $K = 4$ and $E_b/N_J = 10$ dB. The ρ-axis uses a logarithmic scale so that equal length intervals anywhere correspond to identical relative (e.g., percent) variations in ρ. From the communicator's viewpoint, a highly peaked curve is desirable because this implies that small deviations in ρ away from ρ_{wc} produce large reductions in jamming effectiveness. However, all three systems exhibit approximately the same sensitivity to changes in ρ. Note though that $\rho_{wc} = .75$ for uncoded signalling with optimum diversity, $\rho_{wc} = .30$ for 16-ary orthogonal convolutional coding, and $\rho_{wc} = .15$ for the dual-4, rate 1/2 convolutional code; furthermore, all three systems achieve comparable performance. This observation suggests a more sophisticated hybrid coding scheme for defeating partial-band noise jamming. Consider a two-way FH/16-FSK system which can select any of the coding schemes of Figure 2.83. The receivers in this link must be able to monitor the jamming parameter ρ (e.g., by performing a fast Fourier transform over the entire

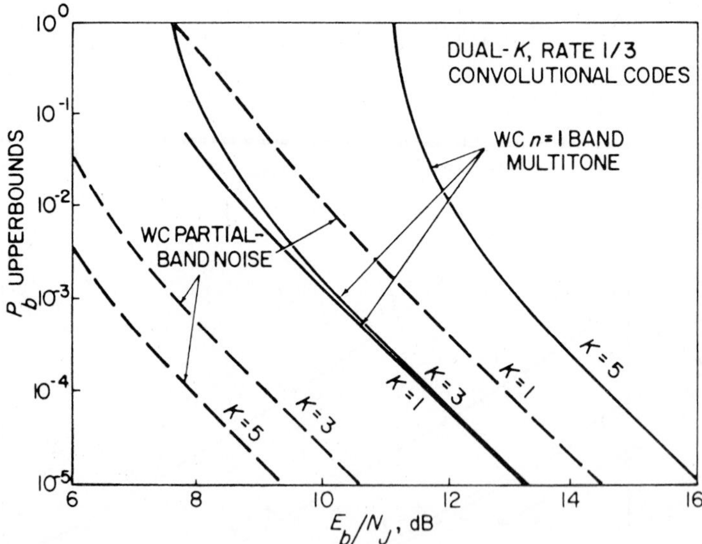

Figure 2.82. Impact of type of jamming on performance of dual-K, rate 1/3 convolutional codes with FH/MFSK signalling as a function of K. Assumes soft decision energy detection, linear combining metric, and perfect jamming state side information.

Table 2.12

Required E_b/N_J in dB to achieve $P_b = 10^{-5}$ for coded FH/MFSK ($M = 2^K$) system in worst case partial-band noise (upper number) and $n = 1$ band multitone jamming (lower number), assuming soft decision energy detection with perfect jamming state side information.

Type of Code	K				
	1	2	3	4	5
Optimum Diversity	16.36	13.62	12.12	11.11	10.36
(Repetition)	14.95	14.21	14.58	15.49	16.76
Optimum Binary	11.11	n/a	n/a	n/a	n/a
$(7, \frac{1}{2})$ Convolutional	9.71	n/a	n/a	n/a	n/a
Optimum Binary	10.38	n/a	n/a	n/a	n/a
$(7, \frac{1}{3})$ Convolutional	8.89	n/a	n/a	n/a	n/a
Optimum 4-ary	n/a	10.12	n/a	n/a	n/a
$(7, \frac{1}{2})$ Convolutional	n/a	10.84	n/a	n/a	n/a
Optimum 8-ary	n/a	n/a	8.95	n/a	n/a
$(7, \frac{1}{3})$ Convolutional	n/a	n/a	11.55	n/a	n/a
Orthogonal	n/a	25.19	17.42	13.58	11.30
Convolutional	n/a	27.03	20.63	18.46	18.05
Dual-K, Rate $\frac{1}{2}$	16.72	14.43	13.40	12.89	12.62
Convolutional	15.75	15.47	16.34	17.76	19.56
Dual-K, Rate $\frac{1}{3}$	14.38	11.86	10.60	9.85	9.39
Convolutional	13.19	12.68	13.31	14.49	16.04

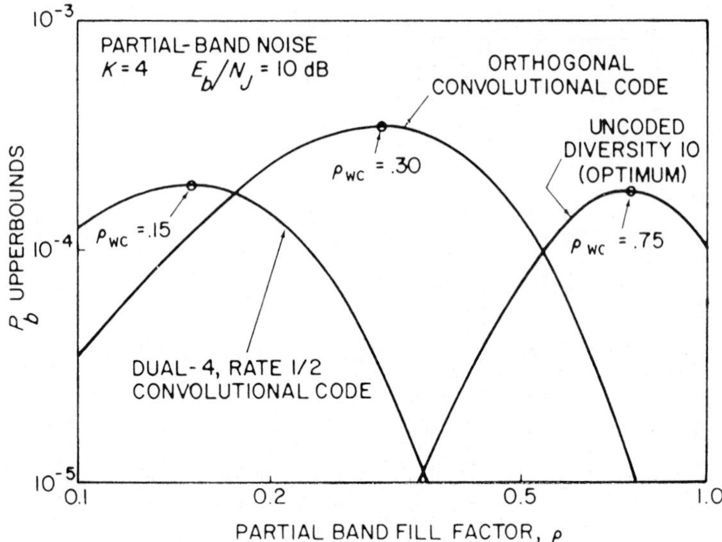

Figure 2.83. Sensitivity of three coded FH/MFSK systems to variations in partial-band noise fill factor ρ, for $K = 4$ and $E_b/N_J = 10$ dB. Although all three cases exhibit comparable sensitivity to ρ, differences in ρ_{wc} suggest a hybrid coding scheme for defeating partial-band noise jamming (see text for details).

spread-spectrum bandwidth). As an example, if one of the receivers determines that it is being jammed with partial-band noise for which $\rho = .75$, it could request that the transmitter at the other end of the link switch to the dual-4, rate 1/2 convolutional code. If the jammer can somehow detect this change and reduce ρ to .15, or if it simply varies ρ pseudorandomly, the FH system can react accordingly. If the link can monitor ρ and adjust its code quickly enough, it can maintain a mismatch between ρ and ρ_{wc} most of the time. The net effect of this mismatch is that the effectiveness of the partial-band noise jammer will be significantly reduced, to the extent that the jammer may in fact be better off emitting broadband noise.

2.3.2.2 Reed-Solomon Codes

We now consider Reed-Solomon (RS) codes (refer to Section 4.10.3, Part 1) in place of convolutional codes, with FH/MFSK signals in worst case partial-band noise and multitone jamming. These are block codes, with input and output characters (symbols) over GF(2^Q). The output block length of a conventional RS code is $2^Q - 1$ Q-bit characters, although extended RS codes can have block lengths of 2^Q or $2^Q + 1$.

As an example, the popular (255, 191) RS code uses $Q = 8$ bit characters. The 64-character redundancy of this code allows it to correct up to 32 character errors (or, equivalently, 256 bit errors) within each received block of length 255. The code rate over GF(2^8) is 191/255. If an FH/256-ary FSK channel is available, each RS character can be ideally transmitted as a single tone. Other less desirable implementations are the transmission of each RS character as two consecutive tones over a 16-ary channel, or four tones over a 4-ary channel, or even eight binary tones. In general, a Q-bit RS character can be sent as L tones over an $M = 2^K$-ary channel, where

$$M^L = 2^{KL} = 2^Q \Rightarrow L = \frac{Q}{K}. \tag{2.152}$$

Because of complexity considerations, RS decoders in use today typically make hard decisions on each received code symbol, and use this reduced observable space to recreate the transmitted data. Berlekamp has generated a table of 2^Q-ary RS character error rates P_Q required for a hard-decision decoder to achieve some selected P_b's for codes with power of 2 redundancies up to 64 [21]. If L uses of an M-ary channel are needed to send each RS character, and the channel K-bit symbol error rate is P_K, then

$$P_Q = 1 - (1 - P_K)^L. \tag{2.153}$$

With no diversity, the bit error rate for FH/MFSK signals in worst case partial-band noise and $n = 1$ band multitone jamming is specified by (2.25) and (2.41), respectively, except that E_b/N_J *must be reduced by the RS code rate*. The bit error rate over the M-ary channel then determines the symbol error rate P_K according to the familiar relation

$$P_b = \frac{M}{2(M-1)} P_K. \tag{2.154}$$

Using this procedure, we were able to measure the relative performance of various RS codes, without additional levels of coding or diversity, over an FH/MFSK channel in worst case jamming. The results are presented in Table 2.13 in the form of the E_b/N_J required to achieve $P_b = 10^{-5}$ out of the RS decoder. These are *exact* SNR's based on the tabulated P_Q's in [21]. For the sake of comparison, the convolutional code performance in Table 2.12 is generally much better, particularly in the multitone case, even though the tabulated values of E_b/N_J are upperbounds. As a single benchmark, the minimum E_b/N_J required to ensure $P_b = 10^{-5}$ for any non-adaptive jammer in Table 2.12 is less than 10.38 dB; for Table 2.13, the corresponding requirement is 19.70 dB (for $K = 2$, the (63, 31) RS code, with worst case $n = 1$ band multitone jamming). The performance might be improved for some of the higher order RS codes if redundancies greater than 64 were used; however, Berlekamp's tabulated values of P_Q do not extend to this region, and the complexity of high-speed RS coder/decoder implementations increases with redundancy [21, p. 571]. There are some expanded tables of P_Q covering a larger range of redundancies, and we will use these later to explore the issue of optimum RS code rates in the context of combined coding and diversity.

Table 2.13

Required E_b/N_J to achieve $P_b = 10^{-5}$ for Reed-Solomon coding with FH/MFSK signals in worst case partial-band noise and $n = 1$ band multitone jamming, assuming hard decisions on received code symbols. Terminology: Reed-Solomon codes over $GF(2^Q)$; $L = Q/K$ = number of $M = 2^K$-ary channel uses/code symbol; P_Q and P_K are code and channel symbol error rates, respectively.

K	RS Code	L	P_Q	P_K	E_b/N_J, dB for $P_b = 10^{-5}$	
					Noise	Multitone
1	(31, 15)	5	5.88×10^{-2}	1.20×10^{-2}	18.02	22.36
	(63, 31)	6	9.50×10^{-2}	1.65×10^{-2}	16.56	20.91
	(127, 63)	7	1.30×10^{-1}	1.97×10^{-2}	15.76	20.10
	(255, 191)	8	6.51×10^{-2}	8.38×10^{-3}	17.68	22.02
2	(15, 7)	2	2.81×10^{-2}	1.42×10^{-2}	17.22	23.55
	(63, 31)	3	9.50×10^{-2}	3.27×10^{-2}	13.37	19.70
	(255, 191)	4	6.51×10^{-2}	1.67×10^{-2}	14.46	20.79
	(1023, 959)	5	1.72×10^{-2}	3.46×10^{-3}	20.32	26.65
3	(7, 3)	1	9.51×10^{-3}	9.51×10^{-3}	19.24	27.58
	(63, 31)	2	9.50×10^{-2}	4.87×10^{-2}	11.54	19.88
	(511, 447)	3	3.33×10^{-2}	1.12×10^{-2}	15.43	23.77
4	(15, 7)	1	2.81×10^{-2}	2.81×10^{-2}	14.11	24.56
	(255, 191)	2	6.51×10^{-2}	3.31×10^{-2}	11.35	21.80
5	(31, 15)	1	5.88×10^{-2}	5.88×10^{-2}	10.78	23.38
	(1023, 959)	2	1.72×10^{-2}	8.64×10^{-3}	16.27	28.86

2.3.2.3 Concatenated Codes

Since we have determined that Reed-Solomon (RS) codes alone do not provide sufficient redundancy to produce acceptable FH/MFSK performance in worst case jamming, the next recourse is to concatenate an RS outer code with a suitable inner code (usually a convolutional code) as illustrated in Figure 4.21, Part 1.

In particular, the RS outer code generates Q-bit code symbols (or characters). These are decomposed into L smaller K-bit subsymbols, which are then scrambled by an interleaver. Suppose these subsymbols are then fed to an inner dual-K, rate $1/v$ convolutional encoder, producing K-bit chips that are transmitted over an FH/MFSK channel. In the receiver, the dual-K Viterbi decoder makes *hard* K-bit *subsymbol* decisions based on the *soft* decision *chip* energy, linear combining metric with perfect jammer state side information. These subsymbols are then deinterleaved to break up any burst error patterns, and reconstituted into Q-bit RS characters which are input to the outer RS decoder.

Suppose we want to achieve a particular P_b out of the RS decoder: this maps into a character error rate P_Q [22], which determines the subsymbol error rate P_K using (2.153). Even though the inner decoder makes hard subsymbol rather than bit decisions, its performance is characterized by the P_b of (2.154). Depending on whether we have worst case partial-band noise or multitone jamming, (2.130) or (2.131) is combined with (2.151) to compute the required D. If we have an (n, k) RS outer code (i.e., each block of k Q-bit data symbols produces $n > k$ code symbols), the concatenated code rate is

$$R = \left(\frac{k}{n}\right)\left(\frac{K}{v}\right) \text{ bits/chip} \tag{2.155}$$

which relates E_c/N_J and E_b/N_J via (2.133). Now the required E_b/N_J can be determined from D using (2.132) and (2.134), or (2.138) and (2.139), depending on the type of jamming.

As shown in Table 2.14 for selected combinations of (n, k) and K, the concatenated scheme above appears to be quite promising, with significant performance advantages over the dual-K or RS codes alone (Tables 2.12 and 2.13). Not too surprisingly, the concatenated systems with the rate 1/3 inner code outperform those with the rate 1/2 code by anywhere from about .5 to 2 dB. At $P_b = 10^{-5}$, the best system in Table 2.14 is the (1023, 959) RS outer code concatenated with the dual-2, rate 1/3 convolutional inner code: this system requires an E_b/N_J less than 9.38 dB (upperbound) for any non-adaptive jammer, versus 10.38 dB for the best convolutional code alone in Table 2.12.

In the terminology of Section 4.10, Part 1, or Figure 4.21, Part 1, the inner encoder and decoder, interleaver and deinterleaver, and FH/MFSK channel can be regarded as a super channel. When the inner

Table 2.14

Relative performance of Reed-Solomon (n, k) outer codes concatenated with dual-K, rate $1/\nu$ convolutional inner codes for FH/MFSK signals in worst case non-adaptive jamming. P_K denotes inner code symbol error rate.

			Inner Code	E_b/N_J, dB for $P_b = 10^{-5}$			
				Noise		Multitone	
K	(n, k)	P_K	P_b	$\nu = 2$	$\nu = 3$	$\nu = 2$	$\nu = 3$
1	(255, 191)	8.38×10^{-3}	Same	11.72	11.39	10.61	10.09
	(511, 447)	3.76×10^{-3}	as	11.70	9.95	10.61	9.88
	(1023, 959)	1.73×10^{-3}	P_K	12.06	10.03	11.00	10.05
2	(15, 7)	1.42×10^{-2}	9.47×10^{-3}	11.52	10.95	12.37	11.63
	(63, 31)	3.27×10^{-2}	2.18×10^{-2}	10.74	10.34	11.53	10.09
	(255, 191)	1.67×10^{-2}	1.11×10^{-2}	9.36	8.82	10.19	9.49
	(1023, 959)	3.46×10^{-3}	2.31×10^{-3}	9.57	8.65	10.49	9.38
3	(7, 3)	9.51×10^{-3}	5.43×10^{-3}	11.39	10.41	14.12	12.98
	(63, 31)	4.87×10^{-2}	2.78×10^{-2}	9.81	9.15	12.42	11.63
	(511, 447)	1.12×10^{-2}	6.40×10^{-3}	8.18	7.24	10.90	9.79
4	(15, 7)	2.81×10^{-2}	1.50×10^{-2}	10.11	9.02	14.64	13.43
	(255, 191)	3.31×10^{-2}	1.77×10^{-2}	7.98	6.91	12.49	11.31
5	(31, 15)	5.88×10^{-2}	3.03×10^{-2}	9.77	8.43	16.21	14.78
	(1023, 959)	8.64×10^{-3}	4.46×10^{-3}	7.76	6.14	14.36	12.61

code is a dual-K convolutional code, the input and output symbols for this super channel lie in GF(2^K). Suppose now that we use an Odenwalder or Trumpis convolutional inner code: although the FH/MFSK channel proper operates over GF(2^ν) for the rate $1/\nu$ Trumpis codes, the super channel digests and regurgitates *binary* data. Consequently, the interleaver between the outer and inner encoders has to scramble data at the binary level. In our earlier notation, each RS code symbol is transmitted over the super channel as Q binary subsymbols. Now the RS character error rate P_Q needed to produce a given overall (outer code) P_b is achieved by establishing a super channel (inner code) $P_b = P_K$ in (2.153) with $K = 1$ and $L = Q$:

$$\text{inner code } P_b = 1 - \left(1 - P_Q\right)^{1/Q}. \tag{2.156}$$

We will consider three particular inner codes: the Odenwalder $(7, \frac{1}{2})$ code for $K = 1$ (we would use the rate 1/3 code except that the $G(D)$ expression of (2.147) does not contain enough terms to be accurate at the higher P_b's defined by (2.156)), and the Trumpis $(7, \frac{1}{2})$ and $(7, \frac{1}{3})$ codes for $K = 2$ and 3, respectively (this K refers to the MFSK data modulation rather than the parameter in (2.152) and (2.153); with the dual-K inner code, the two parameters were synonymous). Analogous to (2.155), the overall code rate to be used in (2.133) is

$$R = \frac{k}{n} \times \text{inner code rate.} \tag{2.157}$$

We should note that the inner Viterbi decoder makes hard binary subsymbol decisions based on the soft decision/side information metric applied to the K-bit chips out of the FH/MFSK channel, so D is still given by (2.132), (2.134), (2.138), or (2.139).

The SNR's needed to achieve a system P_b of 10^{-5} with selected RS outer codes for worst case partial-band noise and multitone jamming are shown in Table 2.15. The concatenated systems employing the Trumpis inner codes are particularly attractive: in fact, the (511, 447) RS outer code combined with the Trumpis $(7, \frac{1}{2})$ convolutional inner code over the 4-ary channel achieves $P_b = 10^{-5}$ in any non-adaptive jamming with $E_b/N_J = 8.31$ dB, representing a 1 dB improvement over the best RS/Dual-K system in Table 2.14. Table 2.15 also adheres to the previously observed behavior that the worst case jammer is partial-band noise for $K = 1$ and multitone for $K \geq 2$. Also, whereas the performance improves with K in partial-band noise, it peaks at $K = 2$ in multitone jamming for small P_b's.

2.3.3 Coding with Diversity

We demonstrated in the previous section that convolutional codes and concatenated Reed-Solomon/convolutional codes can provide improved performance for FH/MFSK signals in worst case jamming over simple diversity. The next question to be answered is whether these codes are powerful enough for this type of non-stationary, non-Gaussian channel.

Table 2.15

Comparison of several Reed-Solomon outer codes concatenated with binary convolutional inner codes and FH/MFSK signalling in worst case partial-band noise and multitone jamming. Inner codes consist of $(7, \frac{1}{2})$ Odenwalder code for $K = \log_2 M = 1$, and $(7, \frac{1}{2})$ and $(7, \frac{1}{3})$ Trumpis codes for $K = 2$ and $K = 3$, respectively.

RS Code n, k	RS Code P_Q	Inner Code P_b	E_b/N_J, dB for $P_b = 10^{-5}$					
			Noise			Multitone		
			$K = 1$	$K = 2$	$K = 3$	$K = 1$	$K = 2$	$K = 3$
127, 63	1.30×10^{-1}	1.970×10^{-2}	11.74	9.32	8.27	10.23	9.98	10.81
255, 191	6.51×10^{-2}	8.379×10^{-3}	10.16	7.93	6.87	8.66	8.60	9.42
511, 447	3.33×10^{-2}	3.756×10^{-3}	9.69	7.64	6.57	8.20	8.31	9.12
1023, 959	1.72×10^{-2}	1.733×10^{-3}	9.60	7.72	6.63	8.13	8.39	9.19

Suppose we add diversity to the codes analyzed above; we will employ the usual scheme of transmitting each M-ary symbol as m chips on separate hops. Effectively, we will have a concatenated coding system with an m-fold repetition code as the innermost code. We will then determine the optimum diversity m_{opt} for a given coded FH/MFSK structure in worst case partial-band noise or multitone jamming. If the outer code has sufficient redundancy and is well matched to the jamming environment, we should find that $m_{\text{opt}} = 1$. If instead we discover that m_{opt} is significantly larger, the implication is that diversity is required to boost the capabilities of the given code.

As in Table 4.3, Volume I, an m-fold repetition code has

$$G(D) = \frac{M}{2} D^m \tag{2.158}$$

for an M-ary orthogonal channel. As a result, *all of the performance expressions in the previous section remain valid, except that D is replaced by* D^m *for m-diversity*. That is, (2.130) and (2.131) become

$$P_b \le \begin{cases} \frac{1}{2} G(D^m); & \text{noise jamming} \\ G(D^m); & \text{multitone jamming.} \end{cases} \tag{2.159}$$

Aside from this change of arguments, the functional form of $G(\cdot)$ for the various codes in (2.146)–(2.151) remains the same. Depending on the type of jamming, D is computed from (2.132), (2.134), (2.138), or (2.139), with E_c/N_J related to E_b/N_J by the overall code rate R. Since the diversity innermost code rate is $1/m$, it is convenient to use

$$\frac{E_c}{N_J} = \frac{R'}{m}\left(\frac{E_b}{N_J}\right) \tag{2.160}$$

in the expressions for D, where R' is the outer code rate in bits per M-ary symbol. This explicit dependence on m will be useful in determining the optimum diversity later.

As a check on (2.158)–(2.160), consider an uncoded FH/MFSK system with diversity m in worst case partial-band noise. Using (2.134) and (2.160), with $R' = K$ for uncoded M-ary signalling, we compute

$$D^m = \left(\frac{4mN_J}{eKE_b}\right)^m; \qquad \frac{E_b}{N_J} \ge \frac{3m}{K}. \tag{2.161}$$

This combines with (2.158) and (2.159) to produce the same P_b expression derived earlier for this system (i.e., (2.64)).

These m-diversity formulas can now be used to determine the variation in performance with m of any uncoded or coded FH/MFSK system in worst case jamming. As an example, consider the uncoded 4-ary system with diversity: Table 2.12 says that we require $E_b/N_J = 14.2$ dB to guarantee $P_b \le 10^{-5}$ in any non-adaptive jamming environment if we use the opti-

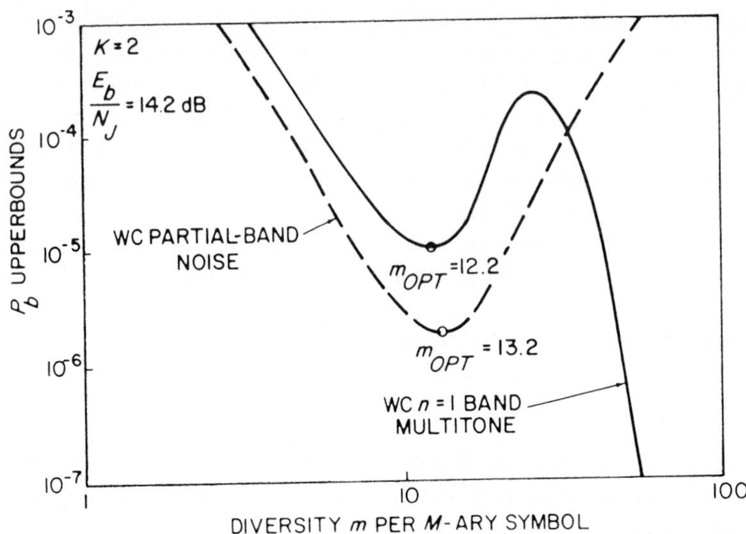

Figure 2.84. Variation in performance with diversity of uncoded FH/4-ary FSK signals in worst case jamming, for $E_b/N_J = 14.2$ dB; this SNR was selected to guarantee that $P_b \leq 10^{-5}$ at $m = m_{\text{opt}} = 12.2$ for any non-adaptive jamming.

mum amount of diversity. For this value of E_b/N_J, Figure 2.84 illustrates the dependence of the system performance on diversity for worst case partial-band noise and $n = 1$ band multitone jamming. (We have seen similar curves in Figures 2.30 and 2.41.) The multitone jamming curve reminds us that although there is a local minimum at $m = 12.2$, we can force P_b to be arbitrarily small for large enough m. However, as we previously argued in Section 2.3.1.2, for practical implementation considerations, we want to keep m small; consequently, we will continue to refer to the diversity at the local minimum P_b for worst case $n = 1$ band multitone jamming as m_{opt}, defined in (2.79) and (2.104).

The variation in performance of several coded systems in worst case noise and multitone jamming as a function of diversity is shown in Figures 2.85 and 2.86. Each curve is characterized by a different value of E_b/N_J, selected to achieve a P_b upperbound of 10^{-5} at the corresponding m_{opt}. In each graph, the curves are approximately lateral translations of each other, implying that all four systems are essentially equally sensitive to *proportional* deviations from m_{opt} (since the m axis is logarithmic). However, on an *absolute* basis, the curves with smaller values of m_{opt} are less robust with respect to m: for example, the performance of the $(7, \frac{1}{2})$ convolutionally coded system in Figure 2.85 is significantly degraded at $m = m_{\text{opt}} \pm 1$. (Recall that although it is analytically convenient to treat m as if it were continuously valued, only integer values are physically meaningful.) In the

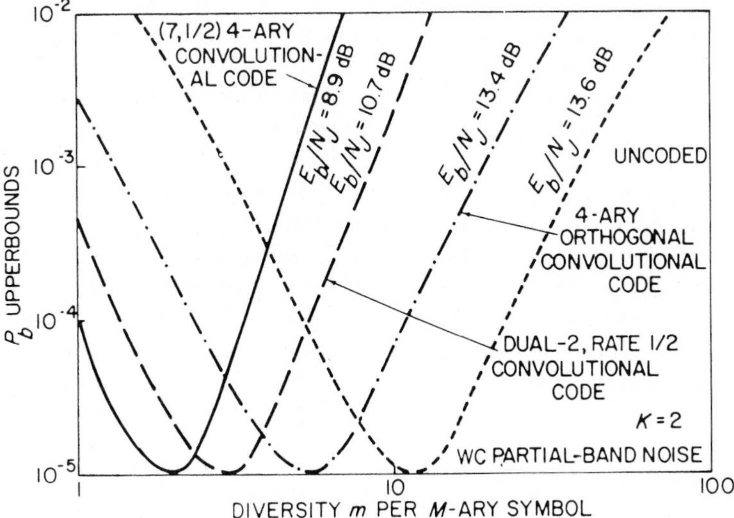

Figure 2.85. Comparison of sensitivities of various FH/MFSK systems to variations in diversity for $K = 2$ and worst case partial-band noise. More powerful codes (requiring smaller E_b/N_J to achieve $P_b = 10^{-5}$ at $m = m_{\text{opt}}$) need less diversity to combat jamming.

absence of diversity, we saw in Figures 2.67 and 2.72 and Table 2.12 that for FH/4-ary FSK signalling in worst case jamming, the most powerful of the convolutional codes considered was the $(7, \frac{1}{2})$ Trumpis code, followed by the dual-2 and 4-ary orthogonal codes. When these codes are combined with optimum diversity, this anti-jam effectiveness hierarchy is preserved as indicated by the required values of E_b/N_J in Figures 2.85 and 2.86. Furthermore, the more powerful codes need less additional diversity redundancy to cope with worst case jamming, although they all need some improvement since $m_{\text{opt}} > 1$ in all cases. The orthogonal convolutional code is particularly weak, providing a meager 0.2 dB advantage over uncoded signalling, both with optimum diversity. In the multitone jamming case of Figure 2.86, each curve has a local minimum, which we still use to define the "optimum" diversity m_{opt}, as well as a monotonically decreasing P_b for sufficiently large values of m. In the uncoded case, we argued that the values of m needed to provide better performance than at m_{opt} were too large for practical implementations; for example, in Figure 2.86, $E_b/N_J = 14.2$ dB will provide the uncoded system with $P_b = 10^{-5}$ at $m = m_{\text{opt}} \cong 12$, whereas lower bit error rates require diversities in excess of 40. However, the $(7, \frac{1}{2})$ Trumpis convolutional code has $m_{\text{opt}} = 2$ with extremely low P_b's for diversities of the order of 10. We will continue to use our previous definitions of m_{opt} (refer to (2.79) and (2.104)); however, we should remember that some of the more capable codes can achieve arbitrarily good performance in worst case $n = 1$ band multitone jamming for moderate amounts of diversity.

We will now mathematically define the performance of coded FH/MFSK systems concatenated with optimum diversity. For arbitrary diversity m, P_b for the concatenated system is proportional to $G(D^m)$, where D itself depends on m through (2.160). Since $G(\cdot)$ is monotonic for small P_b's, the optimum diversity is the value of m that minimizes D^m. Recall from (2.158) that the performance of uncoded FH/MFSK signals with diversity is proportional to D^m, and we computed m_{opt} for such systems in Section 2.3.1. The only difference here is that R' is arbitrary, whereas $R' = K$ in the previous analysis. Generalizing the earlier results for arbitrary outer code rates, we conclude that for values of E_b/N_J large enough to yield $m_{\text{opt}} > 1$,

$$D^m = e^{-m_{\text{opt}}} \tag{2.162}$$

as in (2.70), (2.77), and (2.104), where, for worst case noise or tone jamming, the optimum diversity has the form

$$m_{\text{opt}} = \frac{R'}{\gamma}\left(\frac{E_b}{N_J}\right) \tag{2.163}$$

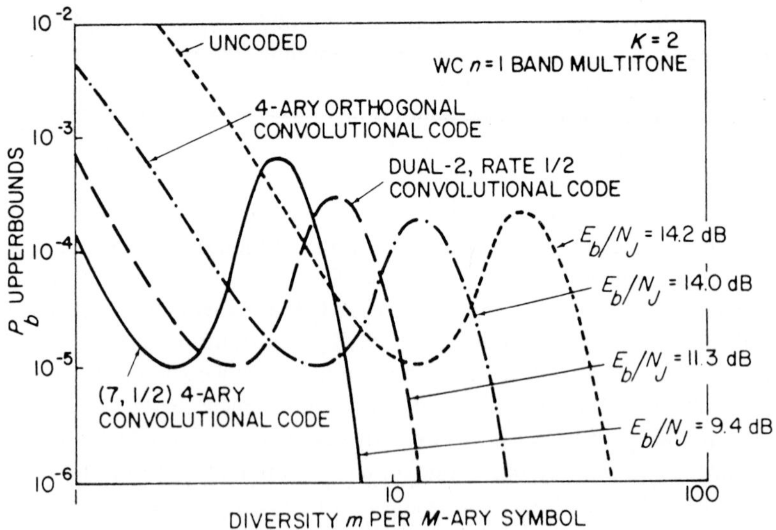

Figure 2.86. Same as Figure 2.85, but for worst case $n = 1$ band multitone jamming. Note that although we consider the local minimum to be m_{opt} in each curve, arbitrarily low P_b's can be achieved for sufficiently large values of m; *for the more powerful codes, these larger amounts of diversity are small enough to be of practical interest.*

and the factor γ varies with the type of jamming according to

$$\gamma = \begin{cases} 4; & WC \text{ partial-band noise} \\ \beta K e; & WC\ n = 1 \text{ band multitone} \end{cases} \tag{2.164}$$

with the definition of β in Table 2.7 extended to include $\beta = 1$ for $K = 1$. Of course, for smaller values of E_b/N_J, $m_{\text{opt}} = 1$ and the performance is based on formulas in Section 2.3.2.

In Figures 2.66–2.75, we compared the performance of convolutionally coded FH/MFSK systems in worst case noise and tone jamming for $1 \leq K \leq 5$. We are now in a position to extend the scope of that comparison to include optimum diversity inner codes; the results are illustrated in Figures 2.87–2.96. These graphs contain no major surprises: the more powerful codes without diversity still provide better performance with optimum diversity. Orthogonal convolutional codes continue to be relatively inadequate, although they manage to slightly outperform uncoded systems with optimum diversity. In all of the graphs, the performance of the rate 1/2 and 1/3 dual-K convolutional codes with optimum diversity converges for low P_b's. Furthermore, these systems are consistently 3 dB better than uncoded MFSK signals with optimum diversity for small enough P_b's. These observations are explained analytically later in this section.

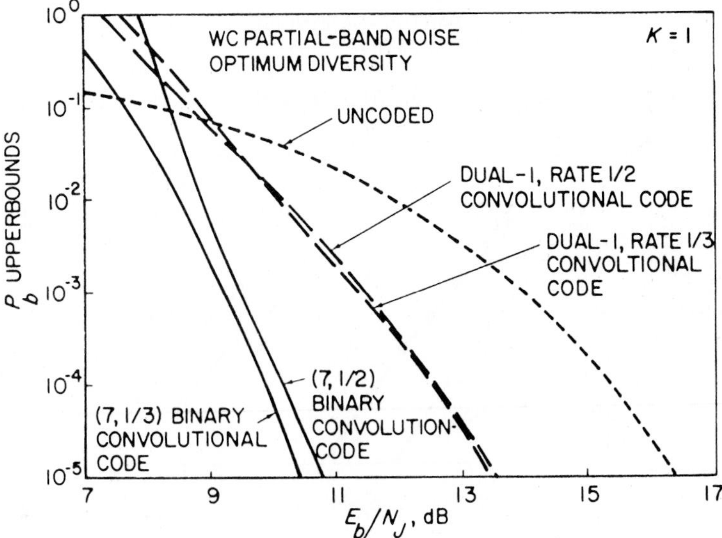

Figure 2.87. Comparison of performance of uncoded and several convolutionally coded FH/binary FSK systems with optimum diversity in worst case partial-band noise. With the addition of optimum diversity, the dual-1 system performance is almost identical for both code rates considered.

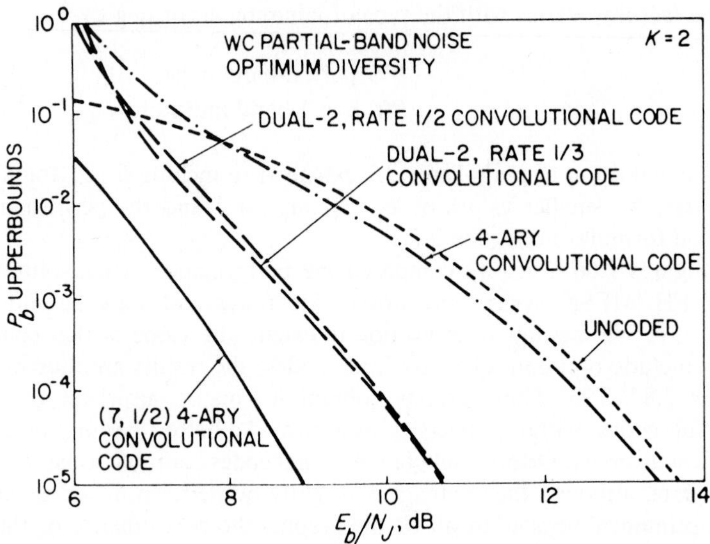

Figure 2.88. Same as Figure 2.87, but for $K = 2$. Again, with optimum diversity, we see that the dual-K system performance is negligibly affected by the code rate; in fact, we show in the text that this statement is asymptotically true for small P_b's for any K and all code rates $1/\nu$.

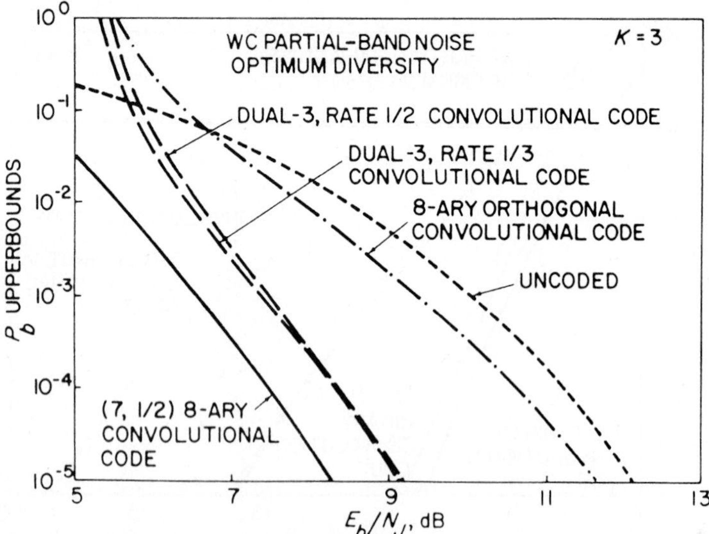

Figure 2.89. Same as Figure 2.87, but for $K = 3$. With the addition of optimum diversity, the M-ary orthogonal code performs moderately better than uncoded signalling, but it is clearly not a very strong code for worst case partial-band noise. The $(7, \frac{1}{3})$ Trumpis code with diversity is clearly superior (about 4 dB better than the uncoded case at $P_b = 10^{-5}$).

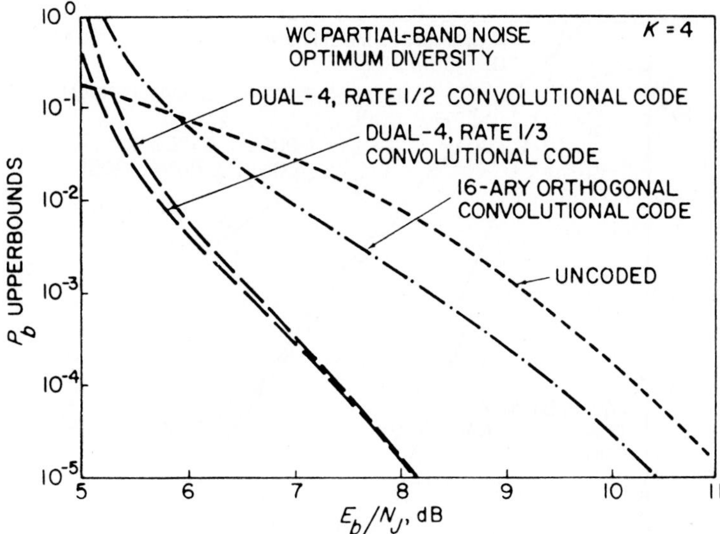

Figure 2.90. Same as Figure 2.87, but for $K = 4$. The dual-4 convolutional codes (both rates) perform about 3 dB better than uncoded signalling with optimum diversity at $P_b = 10^{-5}$.

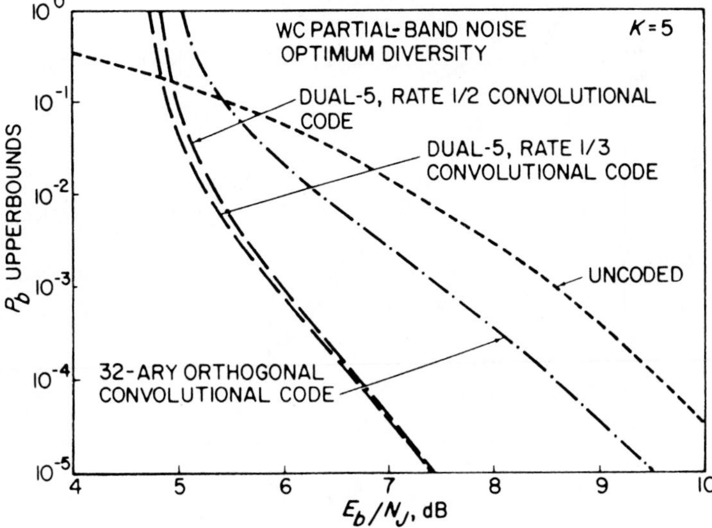

Figure 2.91. Same as Figure 2.87, but for $K = 5$. With optimum diversity, the orthogonal convolutional code is about 1 dB better than uncoded signalling at $P_b = 10^{-5}$, while the dual-K codes provide another 2 dB improvement.

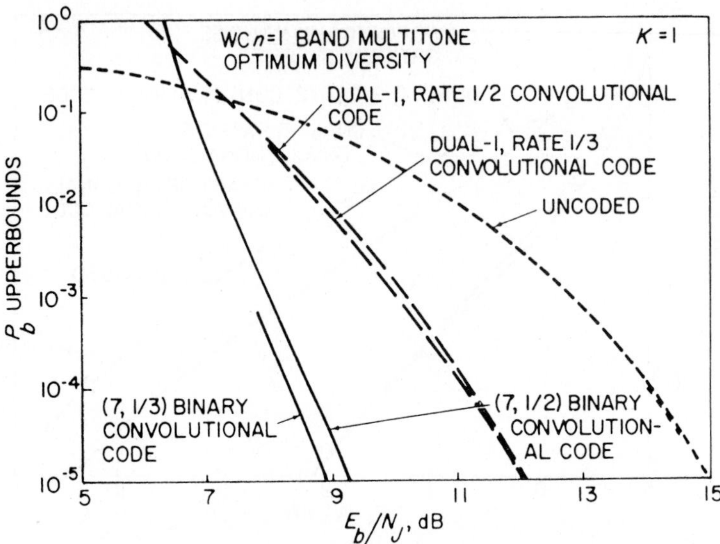

Figure 2.92. Performance of several uncoded and convolutionally coded FH/binary FSK systems with optimum diversity in worst case $n = 1$ band multitone jamming. At $P_b = 10^{-5}$, the dual-1 codes are about 3 dB better than uncoded signalling, and about 3 dB worse than the Odenwalder convolutional codes.

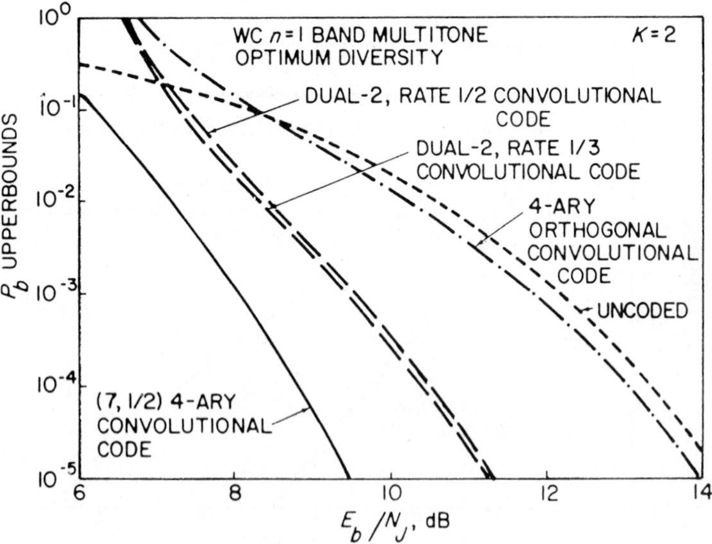

Figure 2.93. Same as Figure 2.92, but for $K = 2$. With diversity, we see that the uncoded and orthogonally coded systems have comparable performance, the dual-2 codes are about 3 dB better at $P_b = 10^{-5}$, and the Trumpis $(7, \frac{1}{2})$ code provides another 2 dB improvement.

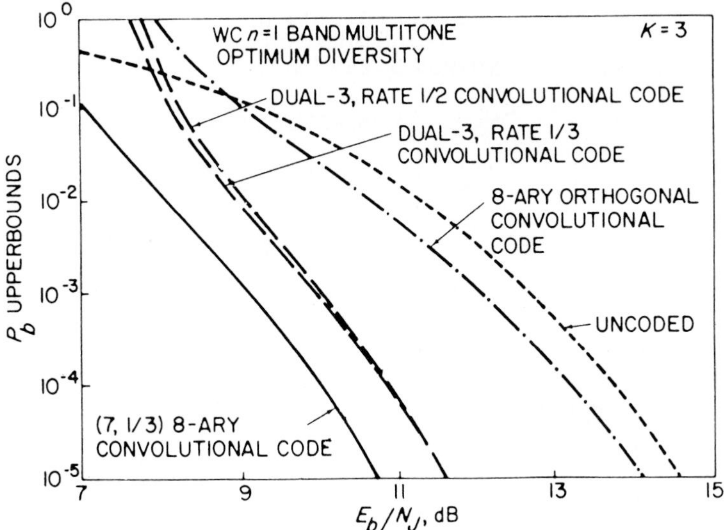

Figure 2.94. Same as Figure 2.92, but for $K = 3$. As in other cases considered, the dual-K convolutional codes provide a significant improvement over uncoded signalling with optimum diversity, while the Trumpis code is better still.

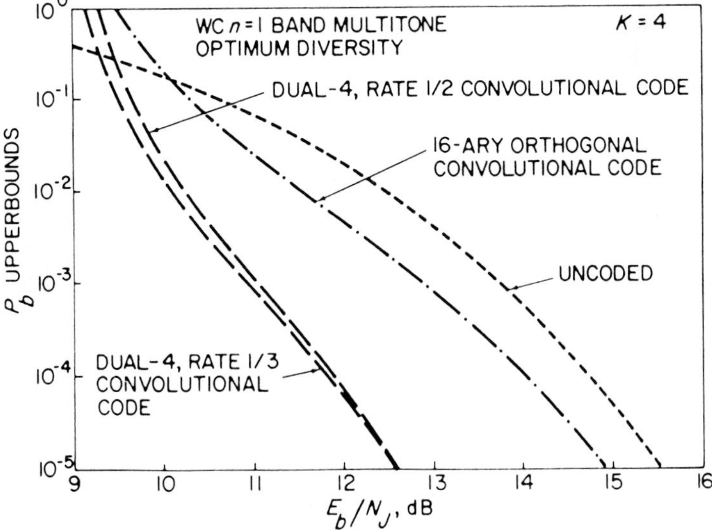

Figure 2.95. Same as Figure 2.92, but for $K = 4$. The dual-K code with optimum diversity is about 3 dB better than the uncoded system for small P_b's.

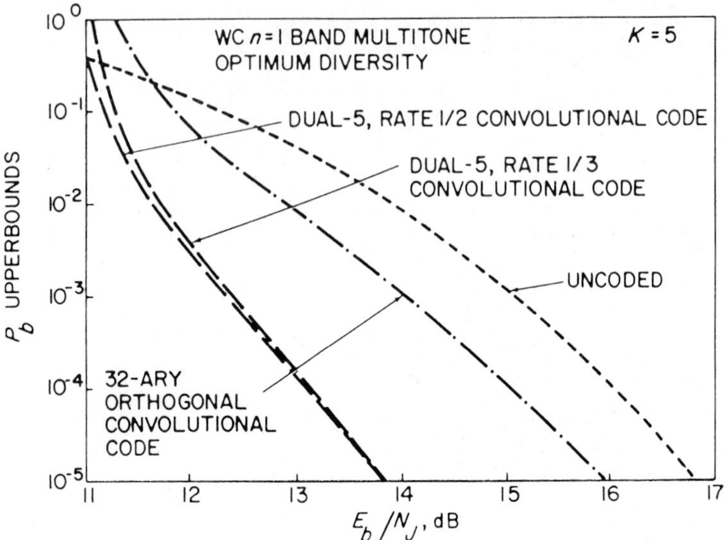

Figure 2.96. Same as Figure 2.92, but for $K = 5$. The 3 dB performance advantage of the dual-K code over the uncoded system with optimum diversity continues for small P_b's at $K = 5$.

The variation in performance of a given coded system concatenated with optimum diversity as a function of the channel dimensionality K and the type of jamming is exemplified by Figures 2.97 and 2.98. For both the M-ary orthogonal and dual-K convolutional codes in worst case partial-band noise, the performance improves with K, just as it did in Figures 2.76, 2.78, and 2.80 in the absence of diversity. However, unlike Figure 2.77 for orthogonal convolutionally coded systems in worst case $n = 1$ band multitone jamming, the addition of optimum diversity causes the performance in Figure 2.97 to degrade with increasing K. By comparison, for the dual-K convolutional codes in worst case $n = 1$ band multitone jamming, with or without diversity, Figures 2.79, 2.81, and 2.98 show that the best performance is obtained when $K = 2$ for low P_b's. In general, because the performance of coded FH/MFSK systems with optimum diversity tends to improve with K in worst case partial-band noise, and degrade with $K \geq 2$ for low bit error rates in worst case tone jamming, the impact of the type of jamming on the AJ capability becomes more significant for larger K. For example, at $P_b = 10^{-5}$, Figure 2.98 shows that worst case tone jamming is about .6 dB more effective against dual-K, rate 1/2 convolutional codes with optimum diversity than worst case noise jamming at $K = 2$; this difference rises to 6.4 dB at $K = 5$.

The performance improvements in various coded FH/MFSK systems provided by the addition of optimum diversity is illustrated in Figures

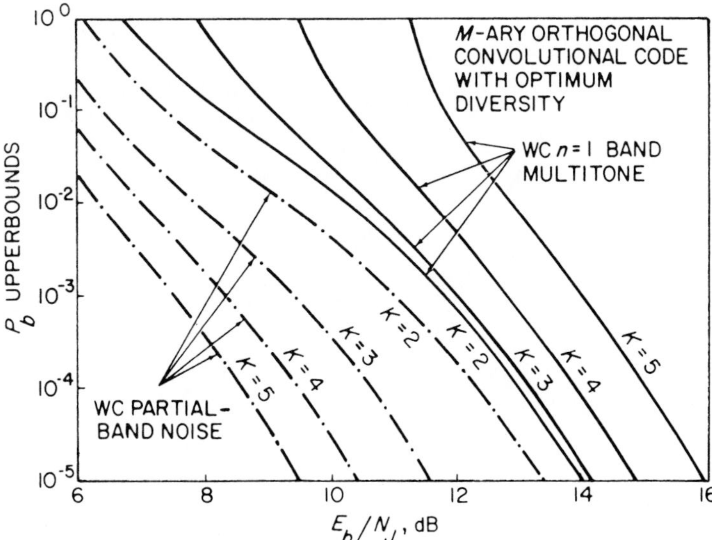

Figure 2.97. Variation in performance of FH/MFSK systems with orthogonal convolutional coding and optimum diversity versus $K = \log_2 M$ and type of jammer. By comparison with no diversity in multitone jamming (Figure 2.77), performance degrades with increasing K.

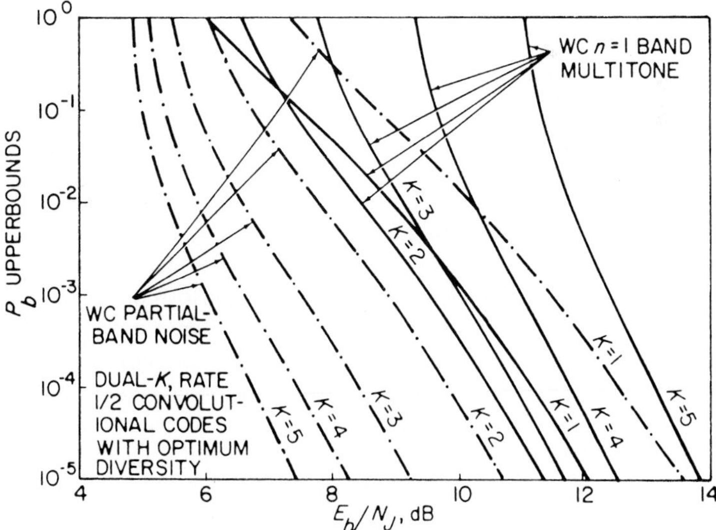

Figure 2.98. Same as Figure 2.97, but for dual-K, rate 1/2 coding. As in no diversity case with multitone jamming (Figure 2.79), best performance at low P_b's occurs when $K = 2$. Recall that all of these results are for soft decision energy detection, linear combining, and perfect side information.

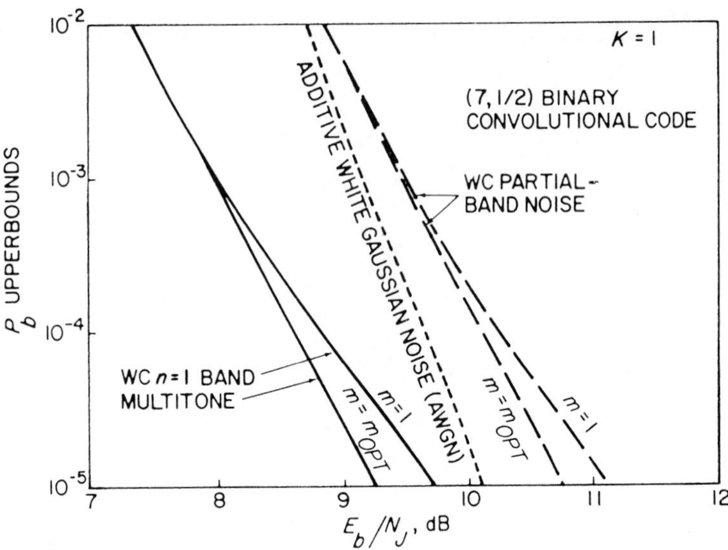

Figure 2.99. Performance improvement available from diversity inner code for FH/BFSK system employing Odenwalder $(7, \frac{1}{2})$ binary convolutional code in worst case noise and multitone jamming. In this case, diversity provides only a small performance gain. Note that broadband noise jamming (AWGN) is more effective than multitone jamming here.

2.99–2.102. Some codes are powerful enough over jamming channels that diversity does not produce significant performance gains: the Odenwalder binary convolutional codes fall into this category, and, in particular, the $(7, \frac{1}{3})$ code has $m_{\text{opt}} = 1$ for both noise and tone jamming implying no benefits from diversity. At the other extreme, the dual-K (Figure 2.102) and M-ary orthogonal (not illustrated) convolutional codes show major improvements with the addition of optimum diversity, indicating that these codes by themselves are not well-matched to the jamming channel and require additional redundancy to provide acceptable AJ performance. We also see in Figures 2.99 and 2.100 that *for the binary convolutional codes with FH/BFSK modulation, broadband noise jamming is more effective than worst case tone jamming*. This is not a general result for other $K = 1$ systems: for example, (2.20b) tells us that an uncoded FH/BFSK system in broadband noise requires $E_b/N_J = 13.35$ dB to produce $P_b = 10^{-5}$, whereas Table 2.12 shows that the same system with optimum diversity in worst case tone jamming needs $E_b/N_J = 14.95$ dB to achieve this performance.

As in previous sections, it is useful to compare the performance of all of these systems in worst case noise and tone jamming by tabulating the required E_b/N_J to achieve $P_b = 10^{-5}$: Table 2.16 does this for all of the FH/MFSK systems considered with convolutional outer codes and opti-

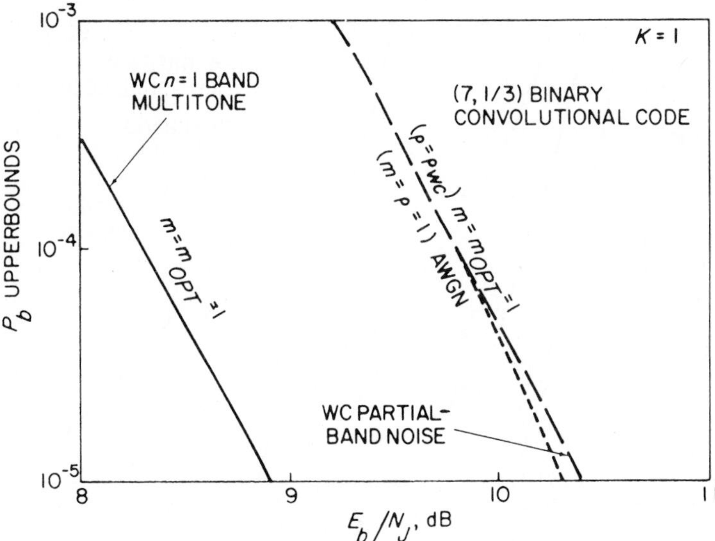

Figure 2.100. Same as Figure 2.99, except for $(7, \frac{1}{3})$ Odenwalder code; this is the only code of those considered in this section which is powerful enough by itself ($m_{\text{opt}} = 1$) to combat worst case non-adaptive jamming. In the noise case, the code is insensitive to ρ (ρ_{wc} is not much worse than $\rho = 1$), but performance is about 1.5 dB better in multitone jamming.

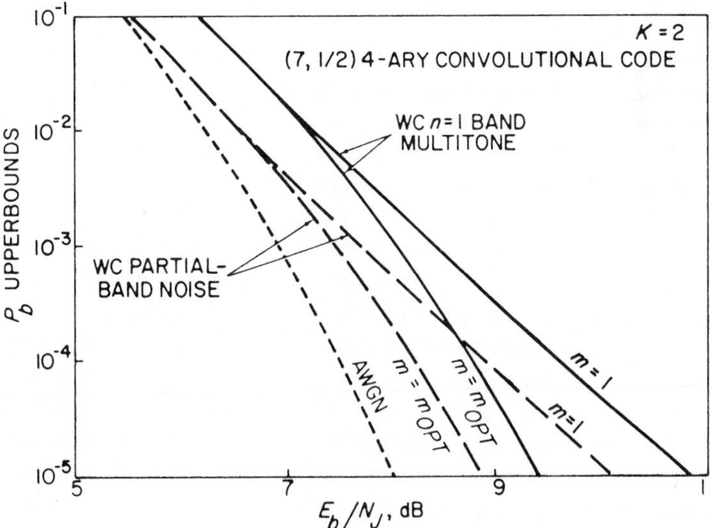

Figure 2.101. Effect of optimum diversity on FH/4-ary FSK system with Trumpis $(7, \frac{1}{2})$ code in worst case noise and multitone jamming. Optimum diversity provides a moderate improvement: e.g., it cuts the degradation due to worst case partial-band noise approximately in half.

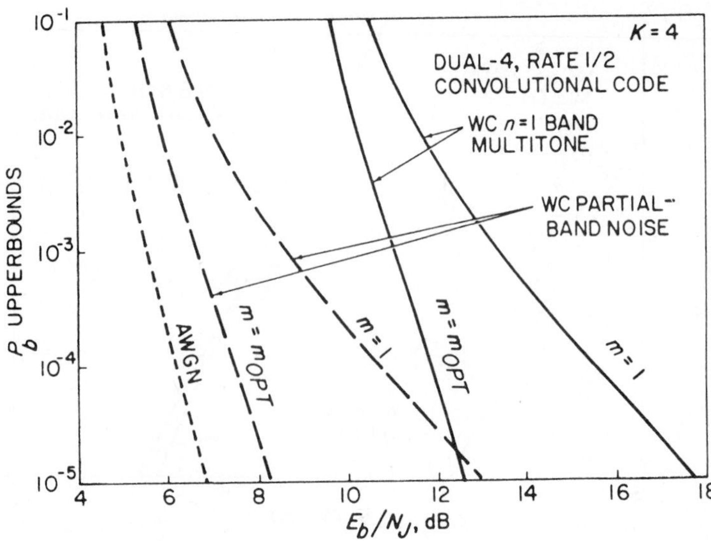

Figure 2.102. For FH/16-ary FSK system with dual-4, rate 1/2 convolutional code, diversity provides a major performance improvement; for example, optimum diversity recovers most of the degradation inflicted by worst case partial-band noise.

mum diversity inner codes. An overall benchmark is the system that requires the minimum E_b/N_J to achieve this P_b in any kind of non-adaptive jamming. Recall from Table 2.12 that without diversity, the Odenwalder $(7, \frac{1}{3})$ binary convolutional code gained this distinction with $E_b/N_J = 10.38$ dB; with the addition of optimum diversity, the Trumpis $(7, \frac{1}{2})$ 4-ary convolutional code is the overall winner with $E_b/N_J = 9.43$ dB, an improvement of almost 1 dB over the best convolutional code alone and nearly 5 dB better than optimum diversity alone ($E_b/N_J = 14.21$ dB at $K = 2$). Not surprisingly, m_{opt} is much smaller for the concatenated convolutionally coded systems (we already noted that the $(7, \frac{1}{3})$ binary convolutional code has $m_{\text{opt}} = 1$). In fact, m_{opt} is small enough that the overall code rate $R = R'/m_{\text{opt}}$ for the concatenated systems with the exception of the M-ary orthogonal codes is approximately double that of the uncoded systems with optimum diversity for a given K. Table 2.16 reiterates the close performance of the rate 1/2 and 1/3 dual-K convolutional codes with optimum diversity for low bit error rates; and, although m_{opt} is smaller for the lower rate (R') code, the overall code rate R is essentially independent of R' for any K.

We can illuminate this observation and provide further analytical insights by deriving asymptotic expressions for the performance of these concatenated systems in the region of large E_b/N_J. From (2.159), (2.162), and (2.163), we know that the performance of coded FH/MFSK systems with optimum diversity is given by

$$P_b \leq \eta G\left[e^{-R'/\gamma(E_b/N_J)}\right] \tag{2.165}$$

Table 2.16

Required E_b/N_J in dB (left columns) to achieve $P_b = 10^{-5}$ for coded FH/MFSK systems with optimum diversity m_{opt} (right columns) in worst case partial-band noise (upper rows) and $n = 1$ band multitone jamming (lower rows).

Type of Outer Code	$K = \log_2 M$									
	1		2		3		4		5	
Uncoded	16.36	10.8	13.62	11.5	12.12	12.2	11.11	12.9	10.36	13.6
	14.95	11.5	14.21	12.2	14.58	12.9	15.49	13.6	16.76	14.3
$(7, \frac{1}{2})$ Binary	10.73	1.5	n/a	n/a	n/a	n/a	n/a	n/a	n/a	n/a
Convolutional	9.24	1.5	n/a	n/a	n/a	n/a	n/a	n/a	n/a	n/a
$(7, \frac{1}{3})$ Binary	10.38	1.0	n/a	n/a	n/a	n/a	n/a	n/a	n/a	n/a
Convolutional	8.89	1.0	n/a	n/a	n/a	n/a	n/a	n/a	n/a	n/a
$(7, \frac{1}{2})$ 4-ary	n/a	n/a	8.91	1.9	n/a	n/a	n/a	n/a	n/a	n/a
Convolutional	n/a	n/a	9.43	2.0	n/a	n/a	n/a	n/a	n/a	n/a
$(7, \frac{1}{3})$ 8-ary	n/a	n/a	n/a	n/a	8.26	1.7	n/a	n/a	n/a	n/a
Convolutional	n/a	n/a	n/a	n/a	10.70	1.8	n/a	n/a	n/a	n/a
M-ary Orthogonal	n/a	n/a	13.36	5.4	11.61	3.6	10.40	2.7	9.48	2.2
Convolutional	n/a	n/a	13.96	5.8	14.10	3.8	14.81	2.9	15.90	2.3
Dual-K, Rate $\frac{1}{2}$	13.46	2.8	10.70	2.9	9.18	3.1	8.16	3.3	7.42	3.5
Convolutional	12.03	2.9	11.27	3.1	11.63	3.3	12.53	3.4	13.79	3.6
Dual-K, Rate $\frac{1}{3}$	13.41	1.8	10.66	1.9	9.15	2.1	8.13	2.2	7.39	2.3
Convolutional	11.99	1.9	11.24	2.1	11.60	2.2	12.51	2.3	13.78	2.4

where $\eta = \frac{1}{2}$ in worst case partial-band noise, $\eta = 1$ in worst case $n = 1$ band multitone jamming, and γ varies with the type of jamming according to (2.164). If E_b/N_J is large enough, the argument of $G(\cdot)$ in (2.165) is sufficiently small to approximate the expressions of (2.146)–(2.151) by their dominant terms, which all have the form

$$G(D) \cong CD^k; \qquad D \ll 1 \tag{2.166}$$

where C and k are listed in Table 2.17 for the systems under consideration. Therefore, the anti-jam performance of these systems for sufficiently large E_b/N_J is of the order of

$$P_b \lesssim \eta C e^{-(kR'/\gamma)(E_b/N_J)}. \tag{2.167}$$

This is a very succinct and useful gauge of the relative performance of all of these systems in worst case jamming for small bit error rates. Since the exponential term dominates the behavior of (2.167) in this region, a larger coefficient kR'/γ usually indicates a more capable anti-jam system; however, if two systems have comparable values of kR'/γ, the one with the smaller coefficient ηC will provide better performance. If we compare systems restricted to worst case partial-band noise ($\gamma = 4$), or worst case tone jamming with a fixed K, γ is fixed and the exponential coefficient kR' (see Table 2.17) is often a sufficient performance indicator, with a minor impact from C (η is fixed for a given jammer).

Table 2.17 shows us why the performance of the dual-K systems are asymptotically independent of the code rate $1/v$ for small P_b's: *C and kR' are not functions of v*. And since $kR' = K$ for both the uncoded and M-ary orthogonal convolutionally coded systems, their performance is asymptotically similar, with the orthogonal convolutional code achieving a slight advantage because its factor C is smaller for $K \geq 2$. Another observation made earlier based on Figures 2.87–2.96 and Table 2.16 is that the dual-K systems provide 3 dB better AJ performance than uncoded systems with optimum diversity at low error rates; Table 2.17 shows that this behavior occurs because both systems have the same factor C, while *the dual-K scheme's exponential coefficient kR' is double that of the uncoded implementation.*

Table 2.17 also reveals some other heretofore unnoted asymptotic performance comparisons. In particular, the $(7, \frac{1}{3})$ Odenwalder (binary) and Trumpis (M-ary) convolutional codes are modestly superior to their $(7, \frac{1}{2})$ counterparts primarily because of their smaller values of C rather than due to any exponential advantage: this is underscored by the fact that kR' is actually *smaller* for the rate $1/3$ binary convolutional code.

If we temporarily restrict our attention to the noise jamming case where $\gamma = 4$ independent of K, we can use Table 2.17 to make some interesting comparisons of systems with different channel alphabets. For example, based on the exponential coefficient kR', we see that the uncoded system with optimum diversity begins to exceed the asymptotic performance of the

Table 2.17

For given outer code with rate R', and optimum diversity, performance of FH/MFSK system is approximated by $P_b \lesssim \eta C e^{-(kR'/\gamma)(E_b/N_J)}$ (see (2.167)), where η and γ vary with the type of jamming.

Type of Outer Code	R'	C	k	kR'	Range of $K = \log_2 M$
Uncoded	K	$\frac{M}{2}$	1	K	≥ 1
$(7, \frac{1}{2})$ Binary Convolutional	$\frac{1}{2}$	36	10	5	1
$(7, \frac{1}{3})$ Binary Convolutional	$\frac{1}{3}$	1	14	$\frac{14}{3} = 4.7$	1
$(7, \frac{1}{2})$ 4-ary Convolutional	1	7	7	7	2
$(7, \frac{1}{3})$ 8-ary Convolutional	1	1	7	7	3
M-ary Orthogonal Convolutional	1	1	K	K	≥ 2
Dual-K, Rate $\frac{1}{\nu}$ Convolutional	$\frac{K}{\nu}$	$\frac{M}{2}$	2ν	$2K$	≥ 1

binary convolutional codes when the former operates with $K \geq 5$: this is supported by the results in Table 2.16. Similarly, we conclude that the dual-K systems with $K \geq 4$ asymptotically outperform the Trumpis codes in worst case partial-band noise, an observation that is again corroborated by Table 2.16.

Recall that at the beginning of this chapter we considered an unsophisticated AJ communication system using uncoded FH/MFSK signals confronted by equally simplistic broadband noise (i.e., additive white Gaussian noise or AWGN) jamming. The asymptotic performance of this system is approximated by the upperbound of (2.20c), repeated here for convenience:

$$P_b \leq \frac{M}{4} e^{-KE_b/2N_J}.$$

Interestingly, this is *identical* to the asymptotic upperbound of (2.167) for the dual-K system with optimum diversity operating in worst case partial-band noise. Imagine then an electronic warfare (EW) scenario in which both adversaries begin with innocuous equipment and then feel compelled to alternately escalate the EW ante. Initially, there is an uncoded FH/MFSK system opposed by a broadband noise jammer. Then the ECM opponent introduces a worst case partial-band noise jammer, with the dramatic result that the communication link performance degrades severely to the inverse linear relationship of (2.21). To combat this increased threat, the communication system counters with a series of increasingly more sophisticated coding techniques, beginning with simple diversity. Each improved coding scheme brings the AJ performance closer to the initial AWGN situation, and with the concatenated dual-K/optimum diversity system, a balance is achieved between the ECM and ECCM upgrade effectiveness. Of course, the jammer can still resort to the increased capability of worst case multitone jamming if $K \geq 2$, but the communicator has an arsenal of even more powerful codes (such as the RS/convolutional code/optimum diversity scheme analyzed below) to neutralize this ploy.

We can also use the asymptotic results to explain some of the multitone jamming behavior that we have previously observed graphically and in Table 2.16. From (2.164) and Table 2.17, we see that the exponential performance coefficient kR'/γ in (2.167) is proportional to $(\beta e)^{-1}$ for uncoded, M-ary orthogonal, and dual-K convolutionally coded signals with optimum diversity in worst case multitone jamming; the same coefficient is proportional to $K/4$ in worst case partial-band noise. These quantities are shown in Table 2.18. Since a larger coefficient kR'/γ contributes to a smaller P_b, we can understand why the noise jamming performance of these systems improves monotonically with K, while the tone jamming performance is best at $K = 2$, as seen earlier in Figures 2.97 and 2.98 and Table 2.16. In the uncoded and dual-K cases, we also see why worst case noise jamming is more effective than worst case tone jamming for $K = 1$, whereas the reverse is true for $K \geq 2$.

Table 2.18
Relative performance of coded FH/MFSK signals with optimum diversity in worst case multitone and partial-band noise jamming based on exponential coefficient kR'/γ in (2.167).

K	$(\beta e)^{-1}$	$K/4$
1	.368	.250
2	.463	.500
3	.449	.750
4	.384	1.000
5	.301	1.250

Now let us briefly consider the performance of FH/MFSK systems employing RS outer codes concatenated with optimum diversity. Using the notation introduced in Section 2.3.2.2, each RS code symbol over GF(2^Q) is sent by using the M-ary channel L times. Although the soft decision/side information metric is used with linear combining of the m diversity chip energies, hard decisions are made on each M-ary symbol, and these are combined in groups of L to recreate the received RS characters. Using Berlekamp's table of RS symbol error rates P_Q required to achieve a given P_b for a particular (n, k) RS code [21], (2.153) converts it to an M-ary channel symbol error rate P_K, which implies an effective *channel* P_b defined by (2.154). For worst case noise and tone jamming, the channel P_b is related to E_b/N_J by (2.159) and (2.162)–(2.164), where

$$G(D) = \frac{M}{2} D \tag{2.168}$$

for uncoded M-ary signalling, and

$$R' = \frac{k}{n} K \tag{2.169}$$

is the overall code rate exclusive of diversity. These equations reduce to

$$\frac{E_b}{N_J} = \left(\frac{\gamma n}{Kk}\right) m_{\text{opt}}$$

$$m_{\text{opt}} \leq \begin{cases} \ln\left(\dfrac{M-1}{2P_K}\right); & WC \text{ noise} \\ \ln\left(\dfrac{M-1}{P_K}\right); & WC \text{ multitone.} \end{cases} \tag{2.170}$$

Table 2.19 compares the performance of various combinations of RS codes, M-ary channels, and worst case jamming for the system P_b of 10^{-5}. The results are not as good as those in Table 2.16 for convolutional outer codes: for example, the best system in Table 2.16 required $E_b/N_J = 9.43$ dB for any kind of non-adaptive jamming, whereas we need $E_b/N_J = 11.75$ dB

Table 2.19

Required SNR to achieve $P_b = 10^{-5}$ for FH/MFSK systems with (n, k) Reed-Solomon outer codes and optimum diversity m_{opt}, in worst case partial-band noise and $n = 1$ band multitone jamming; P_K is M-ary ($M = 2^K$) channel symbol error rate.

K	n, k	P_K	Noise		Multitone	
			E_b/N_J, dB	m_{opt}	E_b/N_J, dB	m_{opt}
1	31, 15	1.20×10^{-2}	14.89	3.7	13.95	4.4
	63, 31	1.65×10^{-2}	14.43	3.4	13.56	4.1
	127, 63	1.97×10^{-2}	14.16	3.2	13.33	3.9
	255, 191	8.38×10^{-3}	13.39	4.1	12.39	4.8
	511, 447	3.76×10^{-3}	13.49	4.9	12.39	5.6
	1023, 959	1.73×10^{-3}	13.83	5.7	12.66	6.4
2	15, 7	1.42×10^{-2}	13.00	4.7	13.94	5.4
	63, 31	3.27×10^{-2}	11.92	3.8	12.97	4.5
	255, 191	1.67×10^{-2}	10.80	4.5	11.75	5.2
	1023, 959	3.46×10^{-3}	11.12	6.1	11.93	6.8
3	7, 3	9.51×10^{-3}	12.64	5.9	15.35	6.6
	63, 31	4.87×10^{-2}	10.64	4.3	13.52	5.0
	511, 447	1.12×10^{-2}	9.42	5.7	12.14	6.4
4	15, 7	2.81×10^{-2}	10.78	5.6	15.45	6.3
	255, 191	3.31×10^{-2}	8.60	5.4	13.28	6.1
5	31, 15	5.88×10^{-2}	9.65	5.6	16.33	6.3
	1023, 959	8.64×10^{-3}	8.06	7.5	14.62	8.2

in Table 2.19, and the diversity required for the RS systems is also larger by more than a factor of 2.

As in the section on coding without diversity, we again conclude that RS codes need to be concatenated with other good codes to achieve satisfactory performance. In particular, we want to look at systems that combine RS outer codes with convolutional inner codes over FH/MFSK channels with optimum diversity.

First assume that the inner code is a dual-K, rate 1/2 convolutional code. Each RS code symbol over GF(2^Q) is composed of L inner code symbols over GF(2^K). The M-ary channel symbols are transmitted as m_{opt} diversity chips which are energy detected in the receiver. These chip energies are linearly combined using the soft decision metric with perfect side information. The convolutional decoder uses these observables to make hard M-ary decisions. These M-ary symbols are unscrambled (assuming interleaving between the inner and outer codes) and reformatted into Q-bit RS characters, which are then fed to the RS decoder.

As before, a given outer code P_b maps into an RS symbol error rate P_Q [21], which translates into an M-ary symbol error rate P_K, corresponding to an inner code P_b: combining (2.153) and (2.154), we have

$$\text{inner code } P_b = \frac{M}{2(M-1)}\left[1-(1-P_Q)^{1/L}\right]. \tag{2.171}$$

Finally, this inner code P_b is converted into a required SNR for a dual-K, rate 1/2 convolutional code with optimum diversity using (2.151), (2.159), and (2.162)–(2.164), with overall code rate

$$R' = \frac{k}{n}\left(\frac{K}{2}\right) \tag{2.172}$$

exclusive of diversity. That is,

$$\text{inner code } P_b \le \begin{cases} \frac{1}{2}G(e^{-m_{\text{opt}}}); & \text{noise} \\ G(e^{-m_{\text{opt}}}); & \text{multitone} \end{cases} \tag{2.173}$$

and

$$m_{\text{opt}} = \frac{kK}{2n\gamma}\left(\frac{E_b}{N_J}\right) \tag{2.174}$$

where $G(\cdot)$ and γ are defined in (2.151) and (2.164), respectively.

The performance of these systems is illustrated in Table 2.20 for an overall bit error rate of 10^{-5} and worst case noise and tone jamming. The best of these systems requires $E_b/N_J = 9.39$ dB to achieve the desired P_b in any non-adaptive jamming environment. Recall that the best concatenated FH/MFSK system with an RS outer code, a dual-K inner code, and *no diversity* required $E_b/N_J = 9.38$ dB under the same design constraints (Table 2.14); however, this was with a rate 1/3 inner code, whereas Table 2.20 is restricted to rate 1/2 inner codes. (If we extended Table 2.20 to

Table 2.20

Required SNR and optimum diversity m_{opt} to achieve $P_b = 10^{-5}$ for FH/MFSK systems with RS outer codes, dual-K, rate 1/2 inner codes, and optimum diversity for worst case partial-band noise and $n = 1$ band multitone jamming. Note that $m_{opt} \sim 2$ in almost all cases, implying concatenated RS/dual-K coding is quite powerful even without diversity.

K	RS Code n, k	Inner Code P_b	Noise		Multitone	
			$\frac{E_b}{N_J}$, dB	m_{opt}	$\frac{E_b}{N_J}$, dB	m_{opt}
1	255, 191	8.38×10^{-3}	11.52	1.3	10.25	1.5
	511, 447	3.76×10^{-3}	11.32	1.5	10.02	1.6
	1023, 959	1.73×10^{-3}	11.44	1.6	10.13	1.8
2	15, 7	9.47×10^{-3}	11.11	1.5	11.77	1.6
	63, 31	2.18×10^{-2}	10.49	1.4	11.14	1.5
	255, 191	1.11×10^{-2}	8.98	1.5	9.64	1.6
	1023, 959	2.31×10^{-3}	8.74	1.8	9.39	1.9
3	7, 3	5.43×10^{-3}	10.48	1.8	12.98	1.9
	63, 31	2.78×10^{-2}	9.29	1.6	11.76	1.7
	511, 447	6.40×10^{-3}	7.32	1.8	9.81	1.9
4	15, 7	1.50×10^{-2}	9.05	1.9	13.40	2.0
	255, 191	1.77×10^{-2}	6.95	1.9	11.29	1.9
5	31, 15	3.03×10^{-2}	8.32	2.1	14.62	2.1
	1023, 959	4.46×10^{-3}	5.85	2.3	12.21	2.4

include rate 1/3 inner codes, the performance with optimum diversity would not improve much as argued earlier.) The 9.39 dB SNR benchmark in Table 2.20 should more fairly be compared with the best rate 1/2 inner code in Table 2.14, which requires $E_b/N_J = 10.19$ dB, to measure the improvement due to diversity. And the amount of diversity in Table 2.20 is small (of the order of 2). Still, to place this result in perspective, the best RS/dual-K/optimum diversity system is only slightly improved over the $E_b/N_J = 9.43$ dB requirement of Table 2.16 for the best binary convolutional code with optimum diversity.

So, as a final exercise, we will now determine how much additional improvement is afforded by combining an RS outer code, a binary convolutional inner code, and optimum diversity. As in Section 2.3.2.3 when we considered the same systems without diversity, because the inner code operates on binary data, the RS outer code sees a binary rather than an M-ary super channel. Analytically, this requires that we use (2.171) with $M = 2$ and $L = Q$, which reduces it to (2.156). As before, we will use the Odenwalder $(7, \frac{1}{2})$ convolutional inner code for the $K = 1$ FH/MFSK system, and the Trumpis $(7, \frac{1}{2})$ and $(7, \frac{1}{3})$ codes for $K = 2$ and $K = 3$, respectively. The inner code P_b translates into a required E_b/N_J and m_{opt} through (2.163–2.164) and (2.173), with $G(\cdot)$ specified by (2.146), (2.148), or (2.149) depending on the particular inner code, and

$$R' = \frac{k}{n} \times \text{inner code rate}\,. \tag{2.175}$$

These systems are compared in Table 2.21 for an overall $P_b = 10^{-5}$ in worst case noise and tone jamming. In all cases, $m_{\text{opt}} \sim 1$ so that the concatenated RS/binary convolutional coding structure is capable of coping with the jamming without the need for additional coding redundancy through diversity; this is underscored by the similarity between the results in Tables 2.15 and 2.21. In fact, the addition of optimum diversity only provides an improvement of .2 dB in the sense that the best system in Table 2.21 (the (1023, 959) RS outer code with the $(7, \frac{1}{2})$ Trumpis convolutional inner code over a 4-ary channel) requires $E_b/N_J = 8.11$ dB to achieve the benchmark bit error rate of 10^{-5} in worst case non-adaptive jamming, whereas $E_b/N_J = 8.31$ dB for the best system in Table 2.15. Still, this particular coding scheme provides the best performance of all implementations considered so far.

Lest these results be taken out of context without regard for the associated design constraints, we should note that there are realistic scenarios which reduce the E_b/N_J requirement for a given P_b. For example, band multitone jamming is only possible if the M-ary bands are distinct; that is, the MFSK tones on a given hop occupy M adjacent FH slots as shown in Figure 2.3(a) or (b). If this band structure is destroyed, for example, by hopping each MFSK tone independently as suggested in [22] (a relatively expensive implementation requiring not one but M separate frequency

Table 2.21

Performance of several concatenated FH/MFSK systems employing RS outer codes, binary convolutional inner codes, and optimum diversity on the M-ary symbols. The inner codes are the $(7, \frac{1}{2})$ Odenwalder code for $K = \log_2 M = 1$, and the $(7, \frac{1}{2})$ and $(7, \frac{1}{3})$ Trumpis codes for $K = 2$ and $K = 3$, respectively. Hard decisions are made on inner code M-ary symbols based on soft decision diversity chip metric with perfect jamming state side information and linear chip energy combining.

RS Code n, k	Convolutional Code P_b	E_b/N_J, dB and m_{opt} (lower parameter) for $P_b = 10^{-5}$					
		Noise			Multitone		
		$K = 1$	$K = 2$	$K = 3$	$K = 1$	$K = 2$	$K = 3$
255, 191	8.379×10^{-3}	10.16	7.89	6.87	8.66	8.50	9.42
		1.0	1.2	1.0	1.0	1.2	1.0
511, 447	3.756×10^{-3}	9.69	7.53	6.57	8.19	8.13	9.11
		1.0	1.2	1.0	1.1	1.3	1.1
1023, 959	1.733×10^{-3}	9.59	7.53	6.62	8.10	8.11	9.14
		1.1	1.3	1.1	1.1	1.4	1.2

synthesizers), the worst case multitone jammer must use the independent tone placement strategy. And we have already seen that independent multitone jamming is less effective than $n = 1$ band multitone jamming. If we assume only worst case partial-band noise jamming, the best system considered is the (1023, 959) RS outer code with the dual-5, rate 1/2 convolutional inner code and optimum diversity (~ 2), which achieves $P_b = 10^{-5}$ with $E_b/N_J = 5.85$ dB; furthermore, the performance improves as K and the RS block length increase.

2.3.3.1 Optimum Code Rates

Many different combinations of coding and optimum diversity have been considered in this section. Using a system $P_b = 10^{-5}$ as a benchmark, in most cases with worst case noise or tone jamming, the optimum diversity was greater than unity, implying that the coding without diversity did not provide enough (or the appropriate kind of) redundancy to effectively counter the assumed threat. Some notable exceptions where diversity was not needed (i.e., $m_{\text{opt}} = 1$) were the $(7, \frac{1}{3})$ Odenwalder convolutional code (see Table 2.16), and several of the concatenated Reed-Solomon/binary convolutional codes (Table 2.21).

The RS codes by themselves were particularly ineffective, as evidenced by Table 2.19. This poor performance could in part be attributed to the use of a hard decision decoder. However, it has been shown that for a given signalling scheme and jamming environment, there is a unique code rate which optimizes the system performance [23]. So far, we have only considered a single (n, k) RS code (rate k/n) over GF(2^Q) for each block length $n = 2^Q - 1$.

To investigate the significance of optimizing the RS code rate for FH/MFSK systems in worst case jamming, we will examine the values of m_{opt} and E_b/N_J required to achieve $P_b = 10^{-5}$ for the class of $(255, k)$ RS codes with optimum diversity used over a 16-ary channel. Recall from Table 2.19 that the (255, 191) code over this channel required $m_{\text{opt}} \sim 5$ or 6 depending on whether the jamming was noise or multitone. It is certainly plausible that a lower rate $n = 255$ RS code might have sufficient redundancy to provide better system performance with less or no diversity.

In general, the performance is specified by (2.153) and (2.170): for the case of interest (i.e., $M = 16$, $K = 4$, $Q = 8$, $L = \frac{1}{2}$, $n = 255$), with γ defined by (2.164) and Table 2.7, these equations reduce to

$$m_{\text{opt}} \le \begin{cases} \ln\left[\dfrac{7.5}{1 - \sqrt{1 - P_Q}}\right]; & \text{noise} \\[2ex] \ln\left[\dfrac{15}{1 - \sqrt{1 - P_Q}}\right]; & \text{multitone} \end{cases}$$

where

$$\frac{E_b}{N_J} = \begin{cases} \left(\frac{255}{k}\right) m_{\text{opt}}; & \text{noise} \\ \left(\frac{255 \times .9583 \times e}{k}\right) m_{\text{opt}}; & \text{multitone} \end{cases} \quad (2.176)$$

The RS code rate is k/n over GF(2^Q); however, the entire FH/MFSK system including the RS outer code and the optimum diversity has an overall code rate

$$r = \frac{R}{K} = \frac{k}{nm_{\text{opt}}} \quad (2.177)$$

over GF(2^K). Recall that R was defined in Section 2.3.2 (e.g., see (2.133)) as the system code rate in information *bits* per M-ary channel use: r is the same parameter expressed in *M-ary* information *symbols* per channel use, so that $r \leq 1$. Therefore, $E_b/N_J \propto r^{-1}$ for both kinds of jamming, and *the optimum RS code rate that minimizes the required E_b/N_J is the one that maximizes the overall system code rate.*

Berlekamp's table of RS character error rates P_Q for a given block length n and P_b with hard decision decoding was limited to redundancies $n - k$ that were powers of 2 up to a maximum of 64 [21]. In an unpublished report, L. Deutsch and R. Miller of the Jet Propulsion Laboratory in Pasadena, California, extended Berlekamp's table to include *all* odd values of k; these results were used in conjunction with (2.176) to derive the performance curves of Figure 2.103. We found that for the system under consideration, with worst case partial-band noise jamming, the optimum RS code rate $k/n = .81$, for which $E_b/N_J \leq 8.55$ dB, $m_{\text{opt}} \leq 5.8$, and $r \geq .14$; for worst case $n = 1$ band multitone jamming, the optimum $k/n = .83$, with $E_b/N_J \leq 13.19$ dB, $m_{\text{opt}} \leq 6.6$, and $r \geq .12$. These results are only marginally better than the (255, 191) RS code in Table 2.19. But, what is really surprising is that the system performance is optimized by a weak, high rate RS outer code concatenated with a simple repetition code, rather than a more powerful low rate RS code alone. Thus, although the overall system code rate r is quite low, indicating that a significant amount of redundancy is needed to counter the postulated threats, *the RS code by itself with hard decision decoding is apparently poorly matched to the worst case FH/MFSK jamming channel.*

In general, the traditional codes in use today were designed to provide good performance in stationary, additive Gaussian noise. *The worst case jamming environment is often neither stationary nor Gaussian*, so we should not be terribly surprised if these codes are vulnerable to this kind of pathological interference. What is really needed is the development of new codes specifically matched to the various anticipated jamming threats.

Do such codes exist? To provide some insight into this issue, let us apply random coding arguments to the FH/MFSK channel with worst case noise

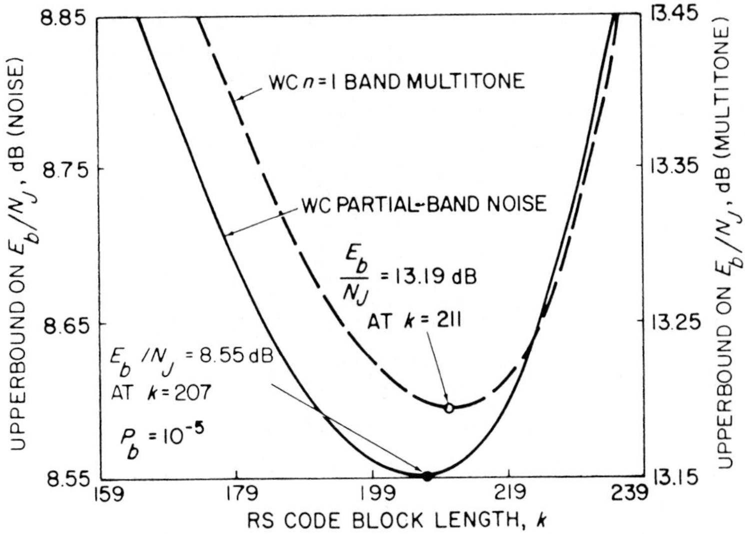

Figure 2.103. Required E_b/N_J to achieve $P_b = 10^{-5}$ for FH/16-ary FSK system with $(255, k)$ Reed-Solomon code and optimum diversity in worst case noise and tone jamming. Minima occur at RS code rates $k/n > .8$, with $m_{\text{opt}} > 6$.

and tone jamming. And since the convolutional codes performed generally better than the one class of block codes considered (i.e., the Reed-Solomon codes), we will restrict this exercise to random (n, k) block codes with characters over $GF(2^K)$. So, for each block of k K-bit information symbols, the encoder generates a block of n K-bit code symbols, according to a randomly generated mapping as in [9, pp. 309–320]; this corresponds to a code rate

$$R' = \frac{kK}{n} \frac{\text{information bits}}{M\text{-ary channel use}} \tag{2.178}$$

in the notation of Section 2.3.3. The random coding scheme selects a set of $M^k = 2^{Kk} = 2^{nR'}$ codewords $\{\boldsymbol{s}_i\} \in \text{GF}(2^K)$, with a mapping of the j-th message, m_j, into codeword $\boldsymbol{s}_j$. If all sets of codewords and messages are equally probable, the union bound on the word error rate is [9, (5.47)]

$$\begin{aligned} P_{\text{w}} &= \Pr\{\text{word error}|m_j\} \\ &\le \sum_{\substack{l=1 \\ (l \ne j)}}^{2^{nR'}} \overline{P_2(\boldsymbol{s}_l, \boldsymbol{s}_j)}^{\{\boldsymbol{s}_i\}} \\ &\le (2^{nR'} - 1)\, 2^{-nR_0} \end{aligned} \tag{2.179}$$

where $P_2(\boldsymbol{s}_l, \boldsymbol{s}_j)$ is the probability that codeword $\boldsymbol{s}_j$ is sent and the decoder decides message m_l was intended, the expectation is over the codeword set $\{s_i\}$, and R_0 is the M-ary channel cutoff rate in bits/channel use (see Chapter 4, Part 1). We can convert R_0 to the parameter D used in this chapter according to (see (4.27), Part 1)

$$R_0 = \log_2\left[\frac{M}{1+(M-1)D}\right] \tag{2.180}$$

which implies that

$$2^{-nR_0} = \left[\frac{1+(M-1)D}{M}\right]^n. \tag{2.181}$$

By analogy with (2.20a), with $M^k = 2^{nR'}$ replacing M,

$$\begin{aligned} P_b &= \frac{2^{nR'-1}}{2^{nR'}-1}P_w \\ &\le 2^{nR'-1}\left[\frac{1+(M-1)D}{M}\right]^n. \end{aligned} \tag{2.182}$$

Suppose we concatenate the (n, k) random block code with an m-diversity inner code. That is, the block code operates over an M-ary channel with D replaced by D^m as in Section 2.3.3. When this diversity is optimized, (2.162)–(2.164) apply for worst case noise and tone jamming: substituting these expressions into (2.182), we find that

$$\begin{aligned} m_{\text{opt}} &\le \ln\left[\frac{M-1}{M2^{-R'}(2P_b)^{1/n}-1}\right] \\ \frac{E_b}{N_J} &= \left(\frac{\gamma}{R'}\right)m_{\text{opt}}. \end{aligned} \tag{2.183}$$

As an example, (2.183) was used to plot an upperbound on E_b/N_J required to achieve $P_b = 10^{-5}$ as a function of R' with parameter n, for $K = \log_2 M = 2$ and worst case partial-band noise jamming. Figure 2.104 shows that for each n, the required E_b/N_J upperbound is minimized at an interior code rate $R' = R_{\text{opt}}$. If we compute m_{opt} at this optimum code rate as a function of n, Figure 2.105 shows that m_{opt} decreases monotonically with n, finally reaching unity at $n = n^* \cong 92$, for which $R_{\text{opt}} = .76$. Remember that (2.183) represents the *average* performance over all possible code sets $\{s_i\}$, with the obvious implication that some *particular* codes must perform even better. Generalizing these results for arbitrary system parameters, we know that *for sufficiently large block lengths and optimized code rates, codes exist that are powerful enough to defeat any kind of non-adaptive jamming without the need for additional diversity redundancy.* It remains for information theorists to determine how to generate these codes.

We can derive closed form solutions for n^* and the corresponding R_{opt}. Independent of the kind of jamming, (2.183) tells us that E_b/N_J is bounded

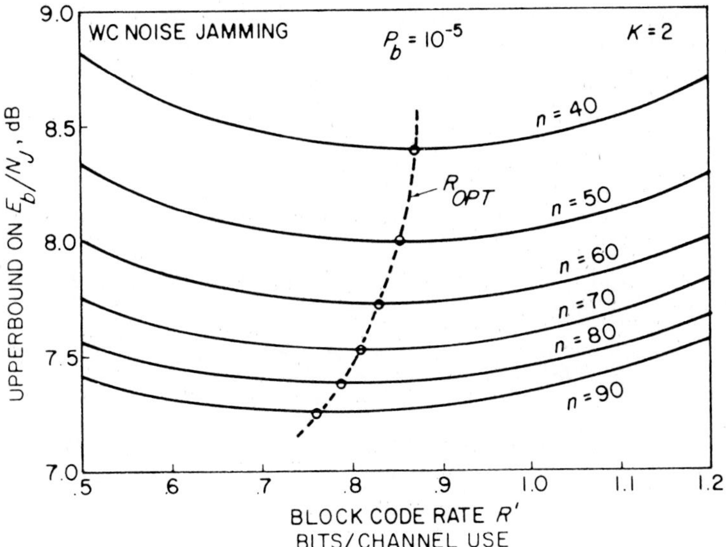

Figure 2.104. Performance of FH/4-ary FSK system employing $(n, nR'/2)$ random block code with optimum diversity in worst case partial-band noise. For a given block length n over the 4-ary field, the required E_b/N_J to achieve $P_b = 10^{-5}$ is minimized at $R' = R_{\text{opt}}$.

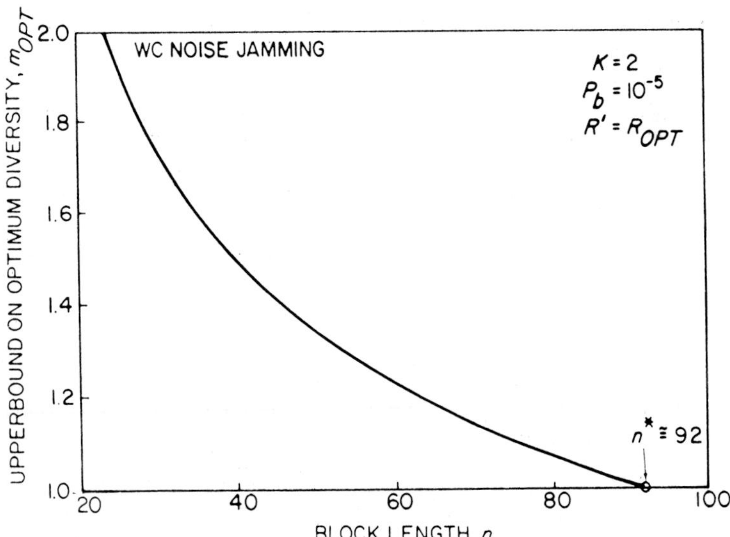

Figure 2.105. Variation in optimum diversity with block length n for FH/4-ary FSK system with (n, k) random block code and optimized code rate, when $P_b = 10^{-5}$ and signals are received in worst case partial-band noise. For $n > n^* \cong 92$, $m_{\text{opt}} = 1$, implying that diversity is not required.

by an expression that is proportional to

$$f(R') \equiv \frac{1}{R'} \ln\left(\frac{A}{B2^{-R'} - 1}\right)$$

where, for convenience,

$$A \equiv M - 1$$
$$B \equiv M(2P_b)^{1/n}. \tag{2.184}$$

Differentiating $f(R')$ with respect to R' and setting this result equal to zero shows that R_{opt} must satisfy the transcendental constraint

$$\ln\left(\frac{A}{B2^{-R_{\text{opt}}} - 1}\right) = \frac{R_{\text{opt}} B2^{-R_{\text{opt}}} \ln 2}{B2^{-R_{\text{opt}}} - 1} \tag{2.185}$$

for a given n (remember that B depends on n). If we further require that the bound on m_{opt} in (2.183) be unity at $n = n^*$, we have the additional constraint

$$B2^{-R_{\text{opt}}} = Ae^{-1} + 1. \tag{2.186}$$

For this particular value of n, (2.185) simplifies to

$$R_{\text{opt}} = \frac{Ae^{-1}}{(Ae^{-1} + 1)\ln 2} \tag{2.187}$$

in bits/channel use. Since $m_{\text{opt}} = 1$ at $n = n^*$, R_{opt} in (2.187) is the *overall* system code rate. If we prefer to express this parameter in M-ary information symbols/channel use, as in (2.177), we have

$$r_{\text{opt}} \equiv \frac{R_{\text{opt}}}{K} = \frac{(M-1)e^{-1}}{K \ln 2\left[(M-1)e^{-1} + 1\right]}. \tag{2.188}$$

Finally, from (2.184) and (2.186) and (2.187), we find that

$$n^* = \frac{\ln(2P_b)}{\ln\left[\dfrac{(M-1)e^{-1} + 1}{M}\right] - \left[\dfrac{(M-1)e^{-1}}{(M-1)e^{-1} + 1}\right]}. \tag{2.189}$$

Note that r_{opt} depends only on K, n^* depends only on K and P_b, and neither parameter depends on the type of jamming. From (2.183), the corresponding SNR is

$$\frac{E_b}{N_J} = \frac{\gamma \ln 2\left[(M-1)e^{-1} + 1\right]}{(M-1)e^{-1}} \tag{2.190}$$

which does depend on the jamming environment through (2.164), as well as K, *but not explicitly on* P_b. These parameters are shown in Table 2.22 as a function of K for worst case noise and tone jamming when $P_b = 10^{-5}$. The random block coding results perpetuate a pattern that we observed for

Table 2.22
Random (n, k) block coding with FH/MFSK signals in worst case jamming. If $n \geq n^*$, the performance cannot be improved by adding diversity; at n^*, $r_{\text{opt}} = k/n^*$ minimizes the required E_b/N_J.

K	n^*	r_{opt}	E_b/N_J, dB for $P_b = 10^{-5}$	
			Noise	Tone
1	97.5	.39	10.13	8.45
2	91.7	.38	7.23	7.56
3	127.1	.35	5.85	8.08
4	210.5	.31	5.15	9.31
5	382.1	.27	4.79	10.97

almost all of the specific codes considered in this chapter. *The performance improves monotonically with K in worst case partial-band noise, but it peaks at* $K = 2$ *for worst case multitone jamming. If we must be capable of dealing with either threat, the best performance for a coded FH/MFSK system is usually achieved at* $K = 2$. Recall that of all of the coded FH/MFSK systems considered, the smallest E_b/N_J that could guarantee $P_b \leq 10^{-5}$ in any non-adaptive jamming environment was 8.11 dB, realized for the (1023, 959) RS outer code combined with the $(7, \frac{1}{2})$ Trumpis 4-ary convolutional inner code and optimum diversity. Table 2.22 says that block codes exist that can perform at least .5 dB better than that system, presumably because they are better matched to the jamming channel; the incentive to find these codes is evident.

2.4 SLOW FADING UNIFORM CHANNELS

We assume a slow fading channel where each hopped FH/MFSK signal experiences an independent fade with the same statistics. In particular, assume that during each hop the signal amplitude A at the receiver is a Rayleigh random variable with probability density function

$$p_A(a) = \frac{a}{\sigma^2} e^{-a^2/2\sigma^2}, \qquad a \geq 0 \tag{2.191}$$

where this fade is independent from hop to hop. Amplitude A is constant during each hop interval. This is called a uniform channel since the probability density function (2.191) does not depend on which part of the spread spectrum frequency band the signal hops to at any time.

Consider a CW signal of T seconds duration at frequency ω_0 with amplitude A and phase ϕ together with white Gaussian noise $n(t)$ of double-sided power spectral density $N_0/2$, which is given by

$$y(t) = A \sin(\omega_0 t + \phi) + n(t)$$
$$0 \leq t \leq T. \tag{2.192}$$

Using the sine expansion

$$y(t) = A \sin\phi \cos\omega_0 t + A \cos\phi \sin\omega_0 t + n(t)$$
$$0 \leq t \leq T. \tag{2.193}$$

In detecting such a signal, there is no loss of generality[3] in basing decisions on the normalized cosine and sine components of $y(t)$ given by

$$y_c = \int_0^T y(t)\sqrt{\frac{2}{T}} \cos\omega_0 t \, dt = \sqrt{\frac{T}{2}} A \sin\phi + n_c$$
$$y_s = \int_0^T y(t)\sqrt{\frac{2}{T}} \sin\omega_0 t \, dt = \sqrt{\frac{T}{2}} A \cos\phi + n_s \tag{2.194}$$

[3] This is because the signal has only cosine and sine components.

where n_c and n_s are independent zero mean Gaussian random variables with variance $N_0/2$.

Note that if A is a Rayleigh random variable with probability density given by (2.191) and ϕ is independent of A and uniformly distributed over $[0, 2\pi]$, then

$$z_s = A \sin \phi$$

and

$$z_c = A \cos \phi \tag{2.195}$$

are independent zero mean Gaussian random variables with variance σ^2. Thus, y_c and y_s are independent zero mean Gaussian random variables with variance $\sigma^2 T/2 + N_0/2$. Denoting

$$\overline{E} = \sigma^2 T \tag{2.196}$$

as the average signal energy, the joint density for y_c and y_s is given by

$$p_1(y_c, y_s) = \frac{1}{\pi(\overline{E} + N_0)} e^{-(y_c^2 + y_s^2)/(\overline{E} + N_0)}. \tag{2.197}$$

If the received signal was noise alone then

$$y(t) = n(t) \tag{2.198}$$

and the joint probability density of y_c and y_s is

$$p_0(y_c, y_s) = \frac{1}{\pi N_0} e^{-(y_c^2 + y_s^2)/N_0}. \tag{2.199}$$

Thus in a Rayleigh fading channel, at the receiver each FH/MFSK signal is a narrowband Gaussian random process with the resulting sine and cosine components being zero mean independent Gaussian random variables with variance $(\overline{E} + N_0)/2$. At a frequency[4] where there is no FH/MFSK signal, the corresponding cosine and sine components would be zero mean Gaussian random variables with variance $N_0/2$.

Note that when the CW signal is present and A and ϕ are known, then y_c and y_s are nonzero mean Gaussian random variables with variance $N_0/2$. The conditional probability density function is

$$p_1(y_c, y_s | A, \phi) = \frac{1}{\pi N_0} \cdot \exp\left\{ - \frac{\left(y_c - \sqrt{\frac{T}{2}} A \sin \phi \right)^2 + \left(y_s - \sqrt{\frac{T}{2}} A \cos \phi \right)^2}{N_0} \right\}. \tag{2.200}$$

[4] We assume all possible carrier frequencies are spaced so as to result in orthogonal signals.

Averaging this probability density over ϕ, which is uniformly distributed over $[0, 2\pi]$ and independent of A, gives [9]

$$p_1(y_c, y_s|A) = \frac{1}{\pi N_0} e^{-(y_c^2+y_s^2)/N_0} e^{-A^2T/2N_0} I_0\left(\sqrt{2(y_c^2 + y_s^2)A^2T/N_0^2}\right). \tag{2.201}$$

Averaging this result over the Rayleigh random variable A returns us to the unconditioned probability density function given by (2.197).

2.4.1 Broadband Jamming—No Diversity

The performance of the FH/MFSK system against broadband noise jamming is the same as that of conventional non-coherent MFSK systems in white Gaussian noise with single-sided spectral density $N_J = J/W_{ss}$. Denote

$$\mathbf{y}_m = (y_{mc}, y_{ms})$$
$$m = 1, 2, \ldots, M \tag{2.202}$$

as the cosine and sine components of the received signal at the M possible tones representing an M-ary symbol. For the Rayleigh fading channel described above, the maximum-likelihood (ML) decision rule is based on probability density functions

$$p(\mathbf{y}_1, \mathbf{y}_2, \ldots, \mathbf{y}_M | m \text{ is sent}) = F(\mathbf{y}_1, \mathbf{y}_2, \ldots, \mathbf{y}_M) \frac{p_1(\mathbf{y}_m)}{p_0(\mathbf{y}_m)} \tag{2.203}$$

where

$$F(\mathbf{y}_1, \mathbf{y}_2, \ldots, \mathbf{y}_M) = \prod_{l=1}^{M} p_0(\mathbf{y}_l) \tag{2.204}$$

and $p_1(\mathbf{y})$ and $p_0(\mathbf{y})$ are given by (2.197) and (2.199), respectively. Without any coding or diversity, the ML decision rule is to choose that symbol m that yields the maximum value of

$$\frac{p_1(\mathbf{y}_m)}{p_0(\mathbf{y}_m)} = \frac{N_J}{\overline{E} + N_J} \exp\left\{ \frac{\overline{E}/N_J}{\overline{E} + N_J} (y_{mc}^2 + y_{ms}^2) \right\} \tag{2.205}$$

or equivalently the maximum value of

$$e_m = y_{mc}^2 + y_{ms}^2, \tag{2.206}$$

the energy of the m-th frequency component of the received signal. Thus, the optimum decision rule is the same as that for the non-fading channel when there is no coding or diversity.

Since the decision rule is the same whether or not the fading amplitude A is given, consider the conditional bit error probability given A (see Section 2.1)

$$P_b(A) = \frac{\frac{1}{2}M}{M-1} \sum_{l=1}^{M-1} \binom{M-1}{l} \frac{(-1)^{l+1}}{l+1} e^{-(l/l+1)(A^2T/2N_J)}. \tag{2.207}$$

Averaging this over the Rayleigh random variable with probability density function (2.191) results in the bit error probability expression

$$P_b = \frac{\frac{1}{2}M}{M-1} \sum_{l=1}^{M-1} \binom{M-1}{l} \frac{(-1)^{l+1}}{1 + l[1 + (\bar{E}/N_J)]} \qquad (2.208)$$

where $\bar{E}$ is given by (2.196). In Chapter 4, Section 4.7.1, Part 1, a simple union bound for (2.207) was given by

$$P_b(A) \leq \tfrac{1}{4} M e^{-A^2 T/4N_J} \qquad (2.209)$$

which, when averaged over the Rayleigh fading random variable, becomes

$$P_b \leq \frac{M}{4 + 2(\bar{E}/N_J)}. \qquad (2.210)$$

In Figure 2.106 we plot P_b and its bound versus $\bar{E}_b/N_J$ where $\bar{E}_b = \bar{E}/K$ is the average bit energy and $M = 2^K$ with $K = 1, 2, 3, 4$, and 5. Note that

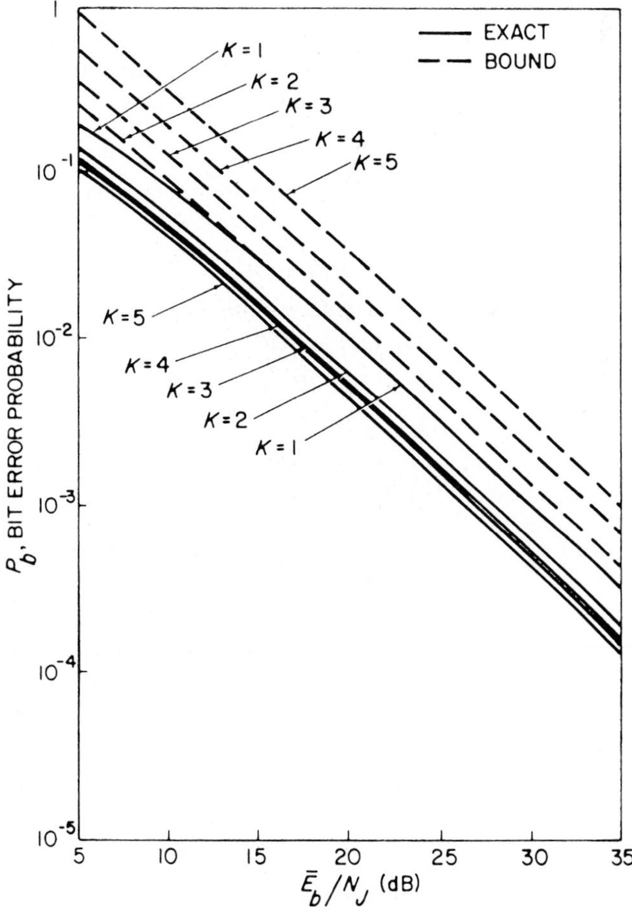

Figure 2.106. Rayleigh fading–uncoded.

the impact of fading is similar to the worst case partial-band and multitone jammer. Also notice that although the union bound is very tight for the non-fading case (see Figure 4.11 in Chapter 4, Part 1), this bound is quite weak in this uncoded Rayleigh fading case. Furthermore, the bound increases as K increases, whereas the true bit error probability decreases with increasing K. With no fading the union bound results in a sum of terms that decrease exponentially with E_b/N_J, whereas in the Rayleigh case these terms decrease at a much slower rate, namely inversely with $\bar{E}_b/N_J$.

We saw earlier that coding and/or diversity can improve the performance of worst case partial-band jamming. These techniques similarly improve the performance in Rayleigh fading channels.

2.4.2 Broadband Jamming—Diversity and Coding

Consider diversity of order m where each MFSK signal of duration T seconds is transmitted as m MFSK chip tones each of duration $T_c = T/m$ seconds. Each chip is independently hopped over the spread-spectrum frequency band. Also assume that each chip tone has independent Rayleigh fading of the same statistics. This is a reasonable assumption for FH/MFSK signals that hop over a wide frequency band W_{ss} where

$$W_{ss} \gg \Delta f_c \tag{2.211}$$

where Δf_c is the "coherence bandwidth" of the fading channel [24].

If we denote

$$y_{lk} = (y_{lkc}, y_{lks}) \tag{2.212}$$

as the cosine and sine components of the received signal at the l-th frequency during the k-th chip interval and

$$\boldsymbol{Y}_l = (y_{l1}, y_{l2}, \ldots, y_{lm}) \tag{2.213}$$

as the sequence of such components for the l-th tone, then the conditional probability of the entire set of mM chip cosine and sine components given the l-th tone was transmitted is

$$p(\boldsymbol{Y}_1, \boldsymbol{Y}_2, \ldots, \boldsymbol{Y}_M | l \text{ is sent}) = F(\boldsymbol{Y}_1, \boldsymbol{Y}_2, \ldots, \boldsymbol{Y}_M) \frac{p_{1m}(\boldsymbol{Y}_l)}{p_{0m}(\boldsymbol{Y}_l)} \tag{2.214}$$

where

$$F(\boldsymbol{Y}_1, \boldsymbol{Y}_2, \ldots, \boldsymbol{Y}_M) = \prod_{j=1}^{M} p_{0m}(\boldsymbol{Y}_j), \tag{2.215}$$

$$p_{0m}(\boldsymbol{Y}_j) = \prod_{k=1}^{m} p_0(y_{jk}) \tag{2.216}$$

and

$$p_{1m}(\boldsymbol{Y}_j) = \prod_{k=1}^{m} p_1(y_{jk}). \tag{2.217}$$

The ML decision rule chooses l that maximizes

$$\frac{p_{1m}(\mathbf{Y}_l)}{p_{0m}(\mathbf{Y}_l)} = \left(\frac{N_J}{\bar{E}+N_J}\right)^m \exp\left\{\frac{\bar{E}/N_J}{\bar{E}+N_J}\sum_{k=1}^{m}\left(y_{lkc}^2 + y_{lks}^2\right)\right\} \tag{2.218}$$

or equivalently maximizes

$$e_l = \sum_{k=1}^{m} e_{lk} \tag{2.219}$$

where

$$e_{lk} = y_{lkc}^2 + y_{lks}^2 \tag{2.220}$$

is the energy of the l-th tone in the k-th chip interval. $\bar{E}$ is the average energy per MFSK chip.

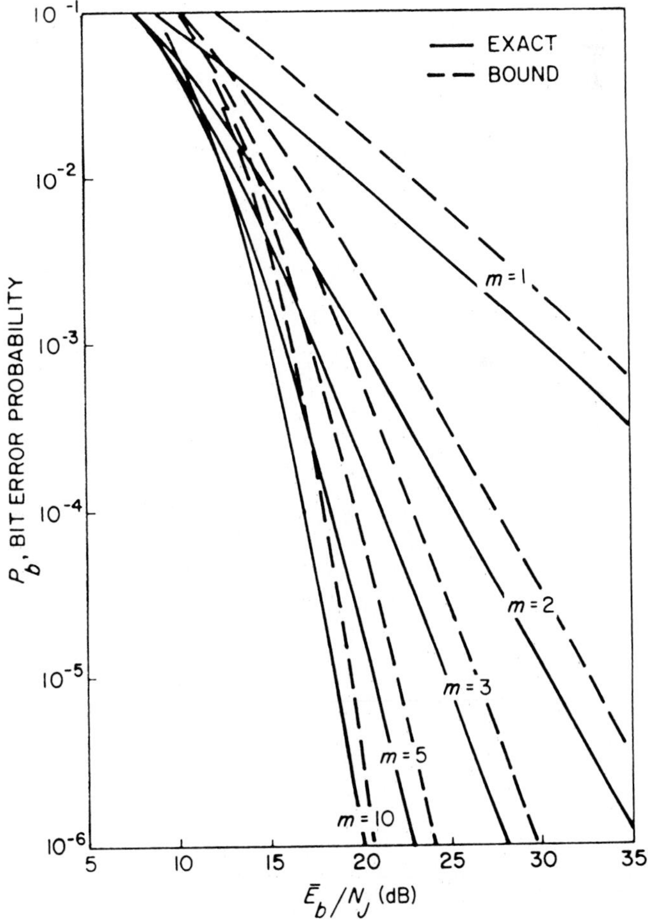

Figure 2.107. Rayleigh fading BFSK—diversity.

Note that here the ML decision rule is based on the sum of the m chip energies for each of the M tones. The energy metric is thus optimum for the Rayleigh fading channel with equivalent white Gaussian noise or broadband noise jamming. This was not the case with coding over a non-fading white Gaussian noise channel. There, however, the energy metric was used since it is convenient.

For m diversity, the bit error probability is given by [24],

$$P_b = \frac{\frac{1}{2}M}{M-1} \sum_{l=1}^{M-1} \frac{\binom{M-1}{l}(-1)^{l+1}}{\{1 + l[1 + (\bar{E}/N_J)]\}^m} \cdot \sum_{k=0}^{l(m-1)} \beta_{kl} \frac{(m-1+k)!}{(m-1)!} \left(\frac{1 + (\bar{E}/N_J)}{1 + l[1 + (\bar{E}/N_J)]} \right)^k \tag{2.221}$$

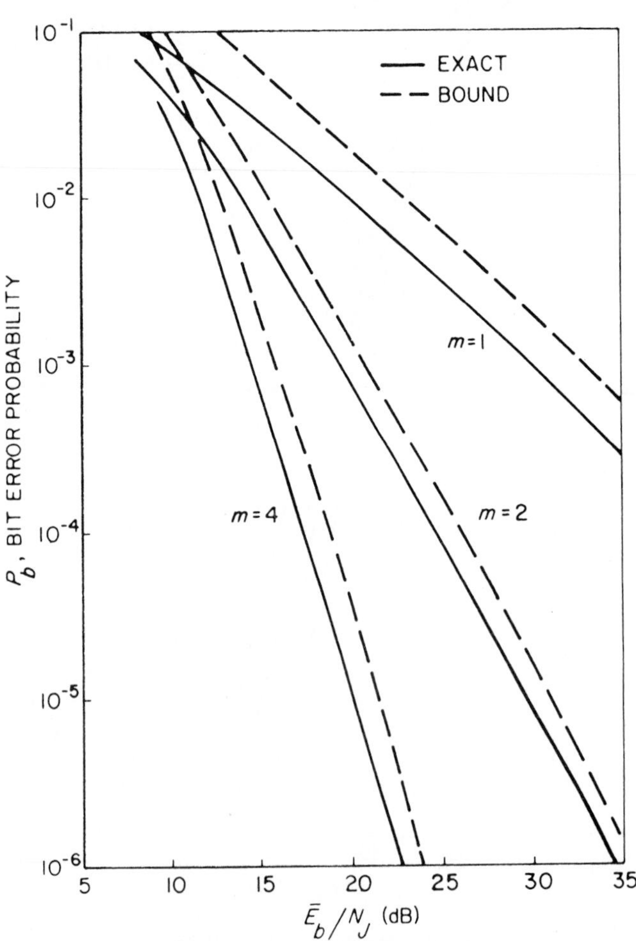

Figure 2.108. Rayleigh fading 4FSK—diversity.

where $\bar{E} = (K/m)\bar{E}_b$, $M = 2^K$, and β_{kl} satisfies

$$\left(\sum_{k=0}^{m-1} \frac{x^k}{k!}\right)^l = \sum_{k=0}^{l(m-1)} \beta_{kl} x^k. \tag{2.222}$$

For the binary case where $M = 2$, the bit error probability is simply

$$P_b = \delta^m \sum_{k=0}^{m-1} \binom{m-1+k}{k} (1-\delta)^k \tag{2.223}$$

where

$$\delta = \frac{m}{2m + (\bar{E}_b/N_J)}. \tag{2.224}$$

Figure 2.107 shows this bit error probability versus $\bar{E}_b/N_J$ for various values of diversity. Note that, for each value of $\bar{E}_b/N_J$, there is an optimum

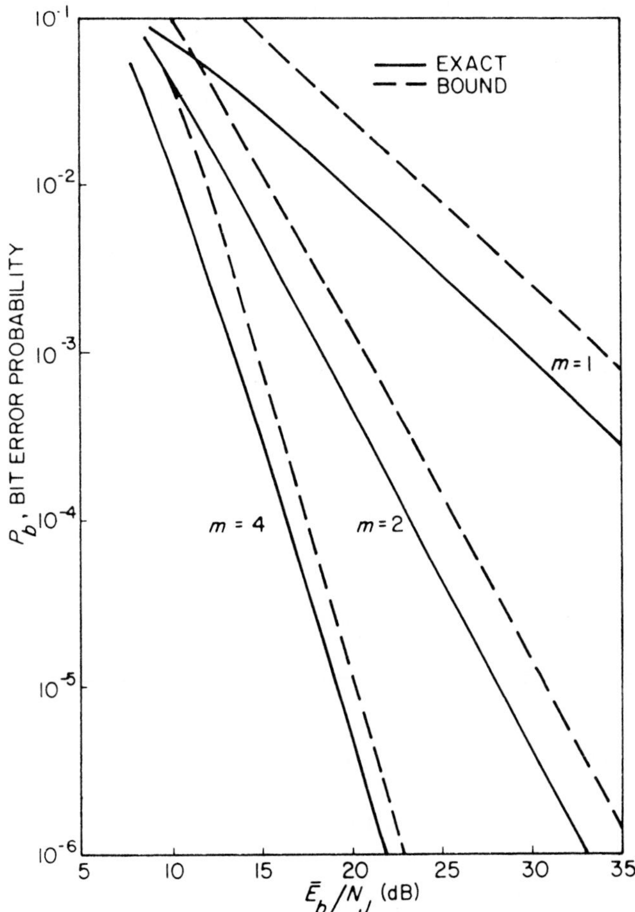

Figure 2.109. Rayleigh fading 8FSK—diversity.

diversity. Excessive diversity results in non-coherent combining losses that begin to cancel the beneficial effects of having independent observations.

Next, a Chernoff bound will be derived for the bit error probability when $M = 2$. Assuming the ML metric, the optimized Chernoff bound is the Bhattacharyya bound given by

$$P_b \le \frac{1}{2}\int \sqrt{p(\mathbf{Y}_1, \mathbf{Y}_2 | l = 1)\, p(\mathbf{Y}_1, \mathbf{Y}_2 | l = 2)}\, d\mathbf{Y}_1\, d\mathbf{Y}_2$$

$$= \frac{1}{2}\int F(\mathbf{Y}_1, \mathbf{Y}_2)\sqrt{\frac{p_{1m}(\mathbf{Y}_1)\, p_{1m}(\mathbf{Y}_2)}{p_{0m}(\mathbf{Y}_1)\, p_{0m}(\mathbf{Y}_2)}}\, d\mathbf{Y}_1\, d\mathbf{Y}_2$$

$$= \frac{1}{2}\int F(\mathbf{Y}_1, \mathbf{Y}_2)\prod_{k=1}^{m}\left(\frac{N_J}{\bar{E} + N_J}\right)\cdot \tag{2.225}$$

$$\exp\left\{\frac{\bar{E}/N_J}{\bar{E} + N_J}\left(\frac{y_{1kc}^2 + y_{1ks}^2 + y_{2kc}^2 + y_{2ks}^2}{2}\right)\right\} d\mathbf{Y}_1\, d\mathbf{Y}_2.$$

But $F(\mathbf{Y}_1, \mathbf{Y}_2)$ is the joint Gaussian density function where all random variables are i.i.d. with zero mean and variance $N_J/2$. Thus

$$P_b \le \frac{1}{2}\left[\frac{4m(m + (\bar{E}_b/N_J))}{(2m + (\bar{E}_b/N_J))^2}\right]^m \tag{2.226}$$

Figure 2.107 shows this bound (dotted lines) together with the exact bit error probability.

For $M > 2$ the union bound can be combined with the above Chernoff bound. The symbol error probability is union bounded by

$$\begin{aligned}
P_s &= Pr\{\hat{l} \ne 1 | l = 1\} \\
&\le \sum_{k=2}^{M} Pr\{\hat{l} = k | l = 1\} \\
&= \sum_{k=2}^{M} Pr\{1 \to k\} \\
&= (M - 1) Pr\{1 \to 2\}
\end{aligned} \tag{2.227}$$

where $l = 1$ was assumed to be the transmitted symbol and $Pr\{1 \to \hat{l}\}$ is the pairwise error bound, which is the same as the $M = 2$ bit error probability. Thus, using the Chernoff bound

$$Pr\{1 \to 2\} \le \frac{1}{2}\left[\frac{4m(m + (\bar{E}/N_J))}{(2m + (\bar{E}/N_J))^2}\right]^m \tag{2.228}$$

and noting that here $\bar{E} = K\bar{E}_b$, we obtain the bit error bound

$$P_b = \frac{\frac{1}{2}M}{M-1} P_s$$
$$\leq 2^{K-2}\left[\frac{4m(m + K(\bar{E}_b/N_J))}{(2m + K(\bar{E}_b/N_J))^2}\right]^m. \tag{2.229}$$

Figures 2.108 to 2.111 show these bounds for various values of K and diversity m together with the corresponding exact bit error probabilities given by (2.221) and (2.222).

Next choose the value of diversity m that minimizes the bound in (2.228). This is shown in Figure 2.12. Figure 2.113 shows the same bound with

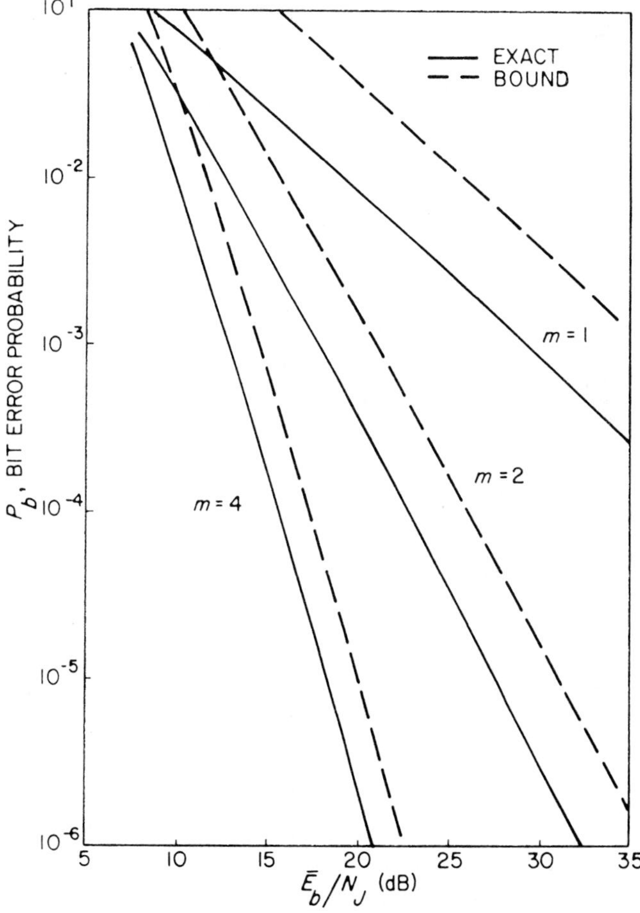

Figure 2.110. Rayleigh fading 16FSK—diversity.

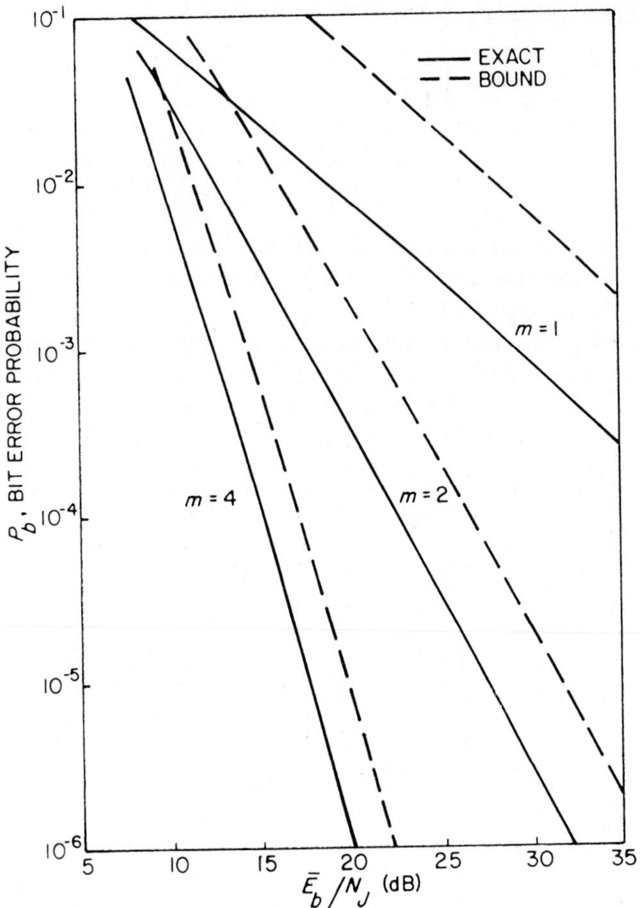

Figure 2.111. Rayleigh fading 32FSK—diversity.

$m = K$ where $M = 2^K$. For fixed data rate, this case results in the bandwidth of each FH/MFSK chip signal being the same for $M = 2, 4, 8, 16$, and 32.

Regarding each FH/MFSK chip as a coded M-ary symbol, a coding channel (see Figure 4.1 in Chapter 4, Part 1) with output

$$y = (y_1, y_2, \ldots, y_M) \tag{2.230}$$

where y_l is the cosine and sine components of the channel output signal at the l-th chip tone is obtained. In a coded system, a sequence of coded chips is transmitted and the channel outputs are the corresponding vectors of these cosine and sine components. Any coding system uses a metric $m(y, l)$ which assigns a value to each channel output corresponding to each possible

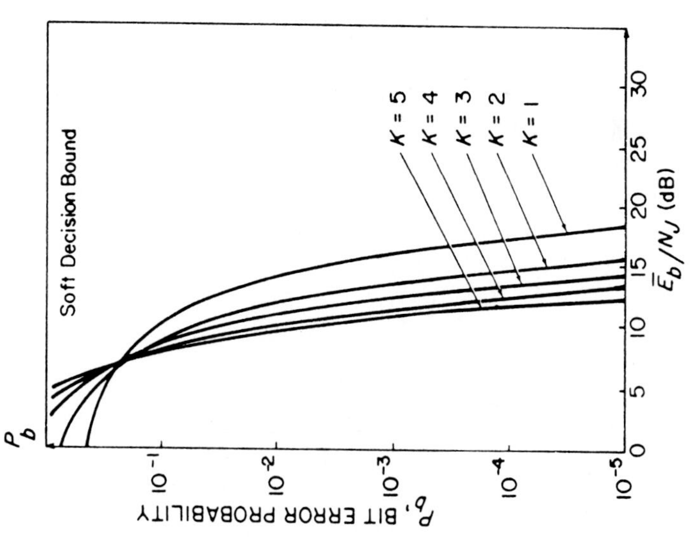

Figure 2.112. P_b-FH/MFSK optimal diversity.

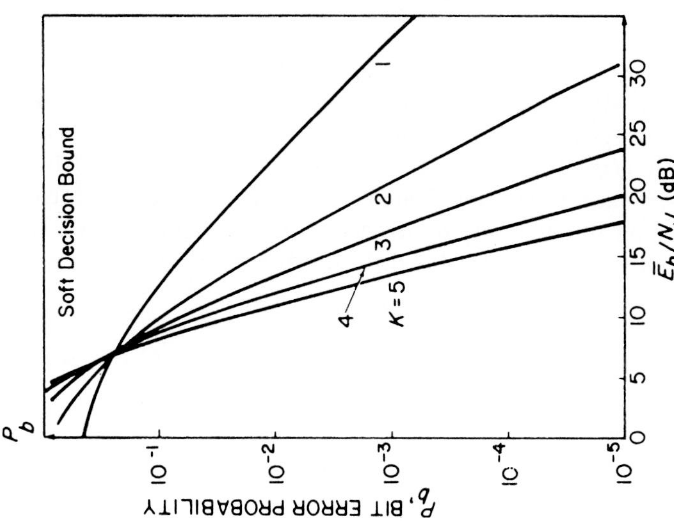

Figure 2.113. P_b-FH/MFSK, $m = K$ diversity.

input. The ML energy metric we have considered previously is

$$\begin{aligned} m(y,l) &= e_l \\ &= y_{lc}^2 + y_{ls}^2 \\ l &= 1,2,\ldots,M. \end{aligned} \tag{2.231}$$

For the ML metric and simple diversity, the expression for the bit error probability given by (2.221) and (2.222) is quite complex. Obtaining an exact bit error probability expression is much more difficult with other metrics. Hence we examine bounds on the coded bit error probabilities.

Based on the general approach of Chapter 4, Part 1, for an arbitrary metric $m(y, l)$, the general coded bit error bound is given by

$$P_b \le G(D) = B(R_0) \tag{2.232}$$

where for FH/MFSK the cutoff rate R_0 is given by (2.180) where

$$D = \min_{\lambda \ge 0} E\left\{ \exp\lambda\left[m(y,l') - m(y,l)\right] \mid l\right\} \tag{2.233}$$

with $l' \neq l$. For the energy metric (2.231), D is given by

$$D = \frac{4(1+(\bar{E}/N_J))}{(2+(\bar{E}/N_J))^2}. \tag{2.234}$$

Also, for the special case of an m diversity code, the function $G(\cdot)$ is

$$G(D) = 2^{K-2}D^m \tag{2.235}$$

with code rate $R = K/m$ bits per chip and $\bar{E} = R\bar{E}_b = (K/m)\bar{E}_b$. This is the result given by (2.229).

Rather than the energy metric, if a hard decision is made for each MFSK chip then

$$D = 2\sqrt{\frac{(1-\varepsilon)\varepsilon}{M-1}} + \left(\frac{M-2}{M-1}\right)\varepsilon \tag{2.236}$$

where

$$\varepsilon = \sum_{l=1}^{M-1} \binom{M-1}{l} \frac{(-1)^{l+1}}{1 + l[1+(\bar{E}/N_J)]} \tag{2.237}$$

which is the chip error probability given by (2.208). Figures 2.114 and 2.115 show the performance for optimum diversity and diversity $m = K$ where $M = 2^K$ for the hard decision metric.

2.4.3 Partial-Band Jamming

Next consider the case of a Rayleigh fading channel together with a partial-band noise jammer with average power J that jams a fraction ρ of the total spread-spectrum band. Assume that when an FH/MFSK signal

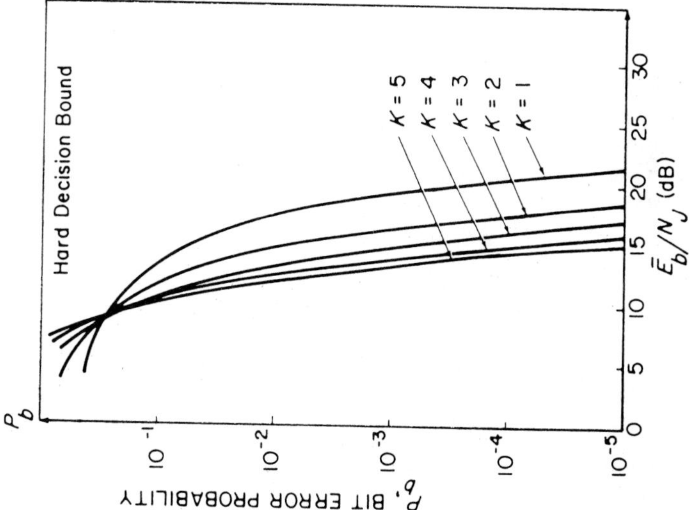

Figure 2.114. P_b-FH/MFSK optimal diversity.

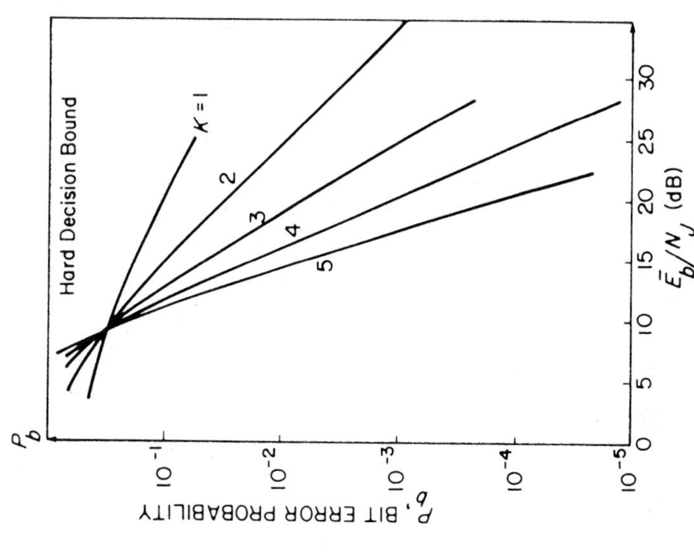

Figure 2.115. P_b-FH/MFSK, $m = K$ diversity.

hops into the part of the band where there is no noise jamming, the bit error probability is negligibly small since the signal-energy-to-background noise is large.[5] When a noise jamming signal is present in the transmitted signal band, the symbol-energy-to-noise ratio is $\rho E/N_J$. Thus, with no coding or diversity, the bit error probability is given by

$$\begin{aligned} P_b &= \rho P_b(\rho \bar{E}/N_J) + (1-\rho) P_b(\infty) \\ &= \rho P_b(\rho \bar{E}/N_J) \end{aligned} \tag{2.238}$$

where $P_b(x)$ is the uncoded bit error probability when the symbol-energy-to-noise ratio is x. For the binary case, $M = 2$,

$$P_b = \frac{\rho}{2 + \rho(\bar{E}_b/N_J)}. \tag{2.239}$$

The choice of the worst partial-band parameter ρ that maximizes this bit error probability is $\rho = 1$. *Thus, the broadband jammer is the worst noise jammer in a Rayleigh fading channel.* This is primarily due to the fact that Rayleigh fading has already created the same impact as the worst case partial-band jammer with a resulting uncoded bit error probability that changes slowly with increasing values of $\bar{E}_b/N_J$. Changes in the signal-to-noise ratio caused by the signal hopping to a jammed part of the frequency band no longer results in large changes in the uncoded bit error probability and the broadband jammer turns out to be the worst case. Coding in the form of diversity still shows dramatic improvements, but this time to overcome the effects of Rayleigh fading.

In general, for arbitrary fade statistics, if the derivative with respect to ρ of the bit error probability given in (2.238) is positive for a given symbol-energy-to-noise ratio and all $\rho \varepsilon [0,1]$, then $\rho = 1$ maximizes the bit error probability. Taking the derivative of (2.238) with respect to ρ gives

$$P_b'(\rho \bar{E}/N_J) > -\frac{P_b(\rho \bar{E}/N_J)}{\rho(\bar{E}/N_J)} \tag{2.240}$$

which must be satisfied for all $\rho \varepsilon [0,1]$ where $P_b'(x)$ is the derivative of $P_b(x)$. This condition defines how slowly the bit error probability must decrease with $\bar{E}/N_J$ in order to have broadband noise jamming as the worst case. It is satisfied by all uncoded FH/MFSK signals in a Rayleigh fading channel. For small values of $\bar{E}/N_J$, condition (2.240) is usually satisfied for non-fading channels as well.

With the use of coding, the worst fraction ρ of the partial-band noise jammer depends on the coding metric used. With Rayleigh fading, and the ML metric, which assumes jammer state information, the broadband jammer ($\rho = 1$) is again the worst case. This is not true, however, for the energy metric with no jammer state information. We show this next with a more general noise jammer power distribution.

[5] We assume it is infinite.

2.5 WORST NOISE JAMMER DISTRIBUTION—SLOW FADING UNIFORM CHANNEL

Most of this chapter assumed the worst case noise jammer was a partial band jammer that jammed some fraction, ρ, of the spread-spectrum frequency band with constant noise power spectral density. In this section consider the Rayleigh fading channel with arbitrary power spectral density for the noise jammer and then find the worst noise power spectral density. This presentation sets the stage for our discussion of slowly fading non-uniform channels in Section 2.6, which is based on the work of Avidor [25], [26].

Assume that whenever a hopped MFSK signal is transmitted the average signal energy at the receiver is $\bar{E}$ independent of the part of the spread-spectrum frequency band that the signal hopped into during its transmission. This is what we refer to as the uniform channel and is the channel assumed in Section 2.4.

Divide the spread-spectrum frequency band into Q equal size sub-bands where in each sub-band the jammer places noise with constant spectral density across the sub-band. Let J_q be the jammer noise power in the q-th sub-band of bandwidth $W_q = W_{ss}/Q$. Thus, the q-th sub-band has white Gaussian noise of single-sided spectral density

$$\begin{aligned} N_q &= J_q/W_q \\ &= QJ_q/W_{ss} \\ q &= 1, 2, \ldots, Q. \end{aligned} \tag{2.241}$$

This is illustrated in Figure 2.116. Note that for large values of Q this can accurately approximate all noise jammer power spectral densities of interest. With total jammer power J, the total power constraint is

$$J = \sum_{q=1}^{Q} J_q. \tag{2.242}$$

2.5.1 Uncoded

The uncoded (no diversity) FH/MFSK signal that hops with uniform probability across the total spread-spectrum frequency band has a bit error probability given by[6]

$$\begin{aligned} P_b &= \sum_{q=1}^{Q} \frac{1}{Q} P_b\left(\frac{\bar{E}}{N_q}\right) \\ &= \sum_{q=1}^{Q} \frac{1}{Q} P_b\left(\frac{\bar{E}W_{ss}}{QJ_q}\right) \end{aligned} \tag{2.243}$$

[6]We assume the FH/MFSK signal will hop into each sub-band with equal probability $1/Q$.

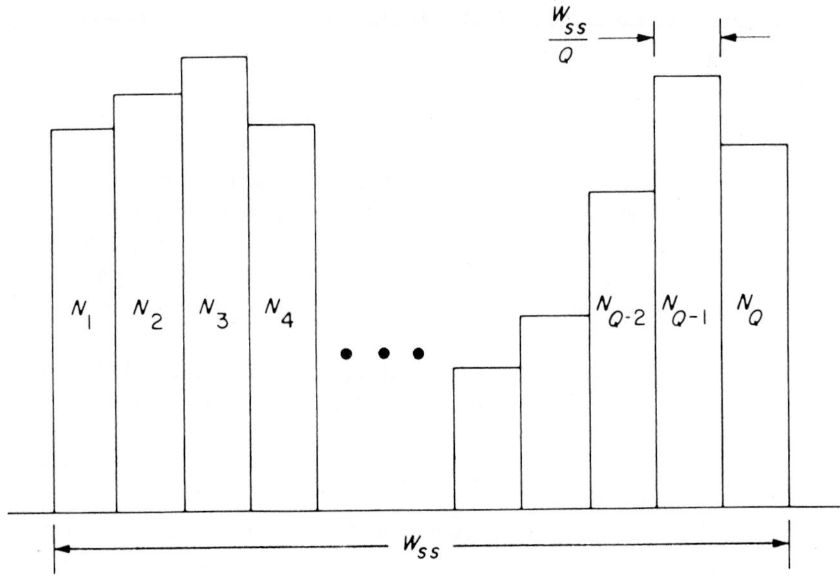

Figure 2.116. Jammer noise power distribution.

where $P_b(x)$ is the Rayleigh fading uncoded non-coherent MFSK bit error probability in white Gaussian noise with average symbol-energy-to-noise ratio x. This is given by (2.208).

As was done in Section 2.5, consider uncoded FH/BFSK in a Rayleigh fading uniform channel where the Rayleigh fading statistics are the same in each sub-band. In this case from (2.208)

$$P_b(x) = \frac{1}{2 + x} \tag{2.244}$$

and the average bit error probability is

$$P_b = \sum_{q=1}^{Q} \frac{1}{Q}\left(\frac{J_q Q}{2J_q Q + \bar{E}_b W_{ss}}\right). \tag{2.245}$$

Now consider the worst distribution of jammer power $\boldsymbol{J} = (J_1, J_2, \ldots, J_Q)$ which satisfies constraint (2.242). This equality constraint can be incorporated into the maximization of P_b given by (2.243) by using a Lagrange multiplier $\lambda \geq 0$ and considering the maximization of

$$C(\boldsymbol{J}) = \sum_{q=1}^{Q} \frac{1}{Q} P_b\left(\frac{\bar{E}_b W_{ss}}{Q J_q}\right) - \lambda \sum_{q=1}^{Q} J_q \tag{2.246}$$

with respect to $J_1, J_2, \ldots, J_Q$ where

$$J_q \geq 0 \text{ for all } q. \tag{2.247}$$

Suppose $\boldsymbol{J}^* = (J_1^*, J_2^*, \ldots, J_Q^*)$ maximizes $C(\boldsymbol{J})$. Then for values of l where

$$J_l^* > 0 \tag{2.248}$$

we have the necessary condition

$$\left.\frac{\partial C(\boldsymbol{J})}{\partial J_l}\right|_{J_l = J_l^*} = 0 \tag{2.249}$$

or

$$\left.\frac{d}{dJ_l} P_b\left(\frac{\bar{E}_b W_{ss}}{J_l Q}\right)\right|_{J_l = J_l^*} = \lambda Q. \tag{2.250}$$

For those values of l where

$$J_l^* = 0 \tag{2.251}$$

we have the necessary condition

$$\left.\frac{\partial C(\boldsymbol{J})}{\partial J_l}\right|_{J_l = J_l^*} \leq 0 \tag{2.252}$$

or

$$\left.\frac{d}{dJ_l} P_b\left(\frac{\bar{E}_b W_{ss}}{J_l Q}\right)\right|_{J_l = J_l^*} \leq \lambda Q. \tag{2.253}$$

These necessary conditions become both necessary and sufficient if $P_b(1/z)$ is a concave function of z. (See the Kuhn-Tucker Theorem [19]). In this case, the minimizing jammer noise power distribution is unique.

For the Rayleigh fading FH/BFSK case, $P_b(1/z)$ is concave in z so the necessary and sufficient conditions become

$$\frac{\bar{E}_b W_{ss}}{\left(2J_l^* Q + \bar{E}_b W_{ss}\right)^2} \leq \lambda \tag{2.254}$$

with equality when $J_l^* > 0$. The unique worst jammer noise power distribution is

$$J_l^* = \frac{J}{Q} \tag{2.255}$$

$$l = 1, 2, \ldots, Q$$

which is the broadband jammer with uniform power distribution. This generalizes to arbitrary uncoded FH/MFSK signals including background white Gaussian noise together with the noise jammer.

With no fading, the worst distribution for uncoded FH/MFSK is the usual two-level partial-band noise jammer considered previously in this chapter. To show this for the binary case, suppose that the distinct values of

J_q, $q = 1, 2, \ldots, Q$ are given by $\Delta_1, \Delta_2, \ldots, \Delta L$ where L is the number of these values of the jammer power levels in the sub-bands. Let F_l be the number of sub-bands that have jammer power Δ_l. Then

$$\rho_l = \frac{F_l}{Q} \tag{2.256}$$

is the fraction of sub-bands with jammer power Δ_l for $l = 1, 2, \ldots, L$. The bit error probability thus has the form

$$\begin{aligned} P_b &= \sum_{q=1}^{Q} \frac{1}{Q} e^{-E_b W_{ss}/2J_q Q} \\ &= \sum_{l=1}^{L} \frac{F_l}{Q} e^{-E_b W_{ss}/2\Delta_l Q} \\ &= \sum_{l=1}^{L} \rho_l e^{-\rho_l E_b W_{ss}/2F_l \Delta_l}. \end{aligned} \tag{2.257}$$

Using the bound

$$\begin{aligned} \rho e^{-\rho\alpha} &\leq \max_{\rho'} \rho' e^{-\rho'\alpha} \\ &= \frac{e^{-1}}{\alpha} \end{aligned} \tag{2.258}$$

which is easily obtained by direct differentiation,

$$\begin{aligned} P_b &\leq \sum_{l=1}^{L} F_l \Delta_l \frac{2e^{-1}}{E_b W_{ss}} \\ &= \frac{2Je^{-1}}{E_b W_{ss}} \\ &= \frac{2e^{-1}}{E_b/N_J} \end{aligned} \tag{2.259}$$

using the relationship

$$\begin{aligned} J &= \sum_{q=1}^{Q} J_q \\ &= \sum_{l=1}^{L} F_l \Delta_l. \end{aligned} \tag{2.260}$$

The bound in (2.259) can be achieved with two levels ($L = 2$) where

$$\begin{aligned} \Delta_1 &= 0 \\ \Delta_2 &= J/\rho \end{aligned} \tag{2.261}$$

with

$$\rho_1 = 1 - \rho$$
$$\rho_2 = \rho = \frac{2}{E_b/N_J} \tag{2.262}$$

provided that

$$E_b/N_J \geq 2. \tag{2.263}$$

If this condition is not satisfied, then the broadband jammer is the worst noise jammer.

2.5.2 Diversity and Coding

Next assume that a coded sequence of FH/MSFK chips is transmitted over the slowly varying Rayleigh fading uniform channel where the noise jammer power is distributed according to $\boldsymbol{J}$. Each chip is hopped with uniform probability across the spread-spectrum frequency band and assume all chip signals have independent Rayleigh fade envelopes with the same statistics.

If y_c and y_s are the cosine and sine components of the received signal at a carrier frequency in the q-th sub-band, then y_c and y_s are independent Gaussian random variables with joint probability density function

$$p_1(y_c, y_s) = \frac{1}{\pi(\bar{E} + N_q)} e^{-(y_c^2 + y_s^2)/(\bar{E} + N_q)} \tag{2.264}$$

if a chip signal is present at this carrier frequency and

$$p_0(y_c, y_s) = \frac{1}{\pi N_q} e^{-(y_c^2 + y_s^2)/N_q} \tag{2.265}$$

when only jammer noise is present. Here N_q is given by (2.241). The ratio of these probabilities is

$$\frac{p_1(y_c, y_s)}{p_0(y_c, y_s)} = \frac{N_q}{\bar{E} + N_q} \exp\left\{ \frac{\bar{E}/N_q}{\bar{E} + N_q} \left(y_c^2 + y_s^2 \right) \right\}. \tag{2.266}$$

With diversity of order m where the m chips fall into frequency sub-bands indexed by

$$\boldsymbol{q} = (q_1, q_2, \ldots, q_m), \tag{2.267}$$

and following the same discussion as in Section 2.4.2, the ML decision rule is to choose symbol l that maximizes

$$e_l = \sum_{k=1}^{m} \frac{\bar{E}}{N_{q_k}(\bar{E} + N_{q_k})} e_{lk} \tag{2.268}$$

where e_{lk} is the energy corresponding to the k-th chip of the l-th symbol. Defining the k-th channel output as the vector of M chip energy detector outputs

$$\boldsymbol{e}_k = (e_{1k}, e_{2k}, \ldots, e_{Mk}) \tag{2.269}$$

then the ML metric is

$$m(\boldsymbol{e}_k, l | J_{q_k}) = \frac{\bar{E}}{N_{q_k}(\bar{E} + N_{q_k})} e_{lk}. \tag{2.270}$$

This is the ideal receiver that assumes knowledge of $\boldsymbol{J}$ and corresponds to the case of known jammer state information.

For binary communication ($M = 2$), follow the same discussion leading to (2.226) except now assume the sequence of sub-bands $\boldsymbol{q}$ is given. Thus the Chernoff bit error bound using the ML metric (2.270) is the Bhattacharyya bound given by

$$P_b(\boldsymbol{q}) \leq \frac{1}{2} \prod_{k=1}^{m} \left[\frac{4m(m + (\bar{E}_b/N_{q_k}))}{(2m + (\bar{E}_b/N_{q_k}))^2} \right]. \tag{2.271}$$

Assuming each hop is independent of other hops, then averaging (2.271) over the hop sequence gives the m diversity bit error bound

$$P_b \leq \frac{1}{2} \left\{ \sum_{q=1}^{Q} \frac{1}{Q} \left[\frac{4m(m + (\bar{E}_b/N_q))}{(2m + (\bar{E}_b/N_q))^2} \right] \right\}^m. \tag{2.272}$$

For arbitrary $M = 2^K$ the corresponding bit error bound is

$$P_b \leq 2^{K-2} \left\{ \sum_{q=1}^{Q} \frac{1}{Q} \left[\frac{4m(m + K(\bar{E}_b/N_q))}{(2m + K(\bar{E}_b/N_q))^2} \right] \right\}^m \tag{2.273}$$

For arbitrary coded FH/MFSK signals,

$$P_b \leq G(D(\boldsymbol{J})) \tag{2.274}$$

where

$$\begin{aligned} D(\boldsymbol{J}) &= \sum_{q=1}^{Q} \frac{1}{Q} \left[\frac{4(1 + (\bar{E}/N_q))}{(2 + (\bar{E}/N_q))^2} \right] \\ &= \sum_{q=1}^{Q} \frac{1}{Q} \left[\frac{4J_q Q(J_q Q + \bar{E} W_{ss})}{(2J_q Q + \bar{E} W_{ss})^2} \right] \end{aligned} \tag{2.275}$$

and $\bar{E}$ is the average chip energy. For a code rate of R bits per chip, $\bar{E} = RE_b$. With diversity m and $M = 2^K$ this is the special case of $R = K/m$ and $G(D) = 2^{K-2}D^m$ given in (2.274). The union Chernoff bound given by (2.274) and (2.275) applies for the ML metric that assume jammer state information $\boldsymbol{J}$, namely, the jammer noise power distribution.

The jammer noise power distribution that maximizes the coded bit error bound (2.274) is the one that maximizes $D(\boldsymbol{J})$ given in (2.275). Applying the Kuhn-Tucker Theorem to maximizing $D(\boldsymbol{J})$ under equality constraint (2.242) results in the necessary and sufficient conditions

$$\frac{4\bar{E}^2 W_{ss}^2}{\left(2J_q^*Q + \bar{E}W_{ss}\right)^3} \le \lambda \quad \text{for all } q \tag{2.276}$$

with equality for values of q where $J_q^* > 0$. Here the function $D(\boldsymbol{J})$ is concave in $\boldsymbol{J}$ so the maximizing $\boldsymbol{J} = \boldsymbol{J}^*$ is unique. Again we see that the worst jammer noise distribution is the broadband noise jammer with

$$J_q^* = \frac{J}{Q} \quad \text{for all } q. \tag{2.277}$$

For this worst distribution

$$D(\boldsymbol{J}^*) = \frac{4(1 + (\bar{E}/N_J))}{(2 + (\bar{E}/N_J))^2} \tag{2.278}$$

which is the result shown earlier in (2.234).

Again for a slowly varying Rayleigh fading uniform channel, the worst jammer noise power distribution is uniform across the band which is the broadband jammer. This is exactly true for uncoded FH/MFSK signals and was shown here for the union Chernoff bound for coded FH/MFSK signals with ideal ML decoders having jammer state information. For coded systems using other metrics, similar union Chernoff bounds can be obtained in which the broadband jammer is not necessarily the worst noise jammer.

Consider the coded FH/MFSK signal using the energy metric

$$m(\boldsymbol{e}, x) = e_x \tag{2.279}$$

which assumes no knowledge of $\boldsymbol{J}$, the jammer state. This is known to be the optimum metric when there is broadband noise. Since the broadband noise jammer was the worst case in the uncoded case, we might expect good performance with this metric. The coding parameter obtained using the Chernoff bound has the form

$$\begin{aligned} D(\boldsymbol{J}) &= \min_{\lambda \ge 0} \sum_{q=1}^{Q} \frac{1}{Q} E\left\{ e^{\lambda[e_l' - e_l]} | l, q \right\} \\ &= \min_{\lambda \ge 0} \sum_{q=1}^{Q} \frac{1}{Q} E\{ e^{\lambda e_l'} | l, q \} E\{ e^{-\lambda e_l} | l, q \} \end{aligned} \tag{2.280}$$

for $l' \neq l$. Here

$$\begin{aligned} E\left\{ e^{\lambda e_l'} | l, q \right\} &= \left[\int_{-\infty}^{\infty} e^{\lambda x^2} \frac{1}{\sqrt{\pi N_q}} e^{-x^2/N_q} \, dx \right]^2 \\ &= \frac{1}{1 - \lambda N_q}; \quad 0 \le \lambda \le \frac{1}{N_q} \end{aligned} \tag{2.281}$$

and

$$E\{e^{-\lambda e_l}|l,q\} = \left[\int_{-\infty}^{\infty} e^{-\lambda x^2} \frac{1}{\sqrt{\pi(\bar{E}+N_q)}} e^{-x^2/(\bar{E}+N_q)}\,dx\right]^2$$
$$= \frac{1}{1+\lambda(\bar{E}+N_q)}. \tag{2.282}$$

Thus,

$$D(J) = \min_{0\le\lambda\le\lambda^*} \sum_{q=1}^{Q} \frac{1}{Q}\left[\frac{1}{(1-\lambda N_q)(1+\lambda\bar{E}+\lambda N_q)}\right] \tag{2.283}$$

where

$$\lambda^* = \min_q \frac{1}{N_q}. \tag{2.284}$$

Consider the two-level partial-band jammer where

$$N_1 = QJ/W_{ss}$$
$$= QN_J \tag{2.285}$$

and

$$N_q = 0 \qquad q = 2, 3, \ldots, Q.$$

Then

$$D(J) = \min_{0\le\lambda\le\frac{1}{QN_J}} \left\{\frac{1}{Q(1-\lambda QN_J)(1+\lambda\bar{E}+\lambda QN_J)} + \frac{Q-1}{Q(1+\lambda\bar{E})}\right\}. \tag{2.286}$$

Note that as $Q \to \infty$, we have $\lambda \to 0$ and thus

$$D(J) \underset{Q\to\infty}{\to} 1. \tag{2.287}$$

Since in general $D(J) \le 1$, this shows that the asymptotically worst noise jammer power distribution is the two-level partial-band jammer where the fraction of the sub-band that is jammed approaches zero.

The above example points out the important fact that in coded systems the choice of metric is crucial even in Rayleigh fading channels where the broadband jammer is worst in the uncoded case. Here, without jammer state information, the usual energy metric which is optimum for a broadband noise jammer case gives very poor performance for the worst jammer noise power distribution.

2.6 WORST NOISE JAMMER DISTRIBUTION—SLOW FADING NON-UNIFORM CHANNEL

Based on the work of Avidor [25] a consideration now follows of the non-uniform fading channel where there is Rayleigh fading that can be different for each of the Q sub-bands. In particular, let the average energy of an FH/MFSK symbol transmitted in the q-th sub-band have average energy

$$\bar{E}_q = \alpha_q \bar{E} \tag{2.288}$$
$$q = 1, 2, \ldots, Q.$$

Also assume that the noise jammer's power is non-uniformly attenuated across the band. For the q-th sub-band the jammer's single-sided noise power spectral density is constant at

$$N_q = \beta_q J_q \tag{2.289}$$

where as before the jammer power distribution $\boldsymbol{J} = (J_1, J_2, \ldots, J_Q)$ satisfies the constraint given by (2.242). The channel parameters $\alpha_1, \alpha_2, \ldots, \alpha_Q$ and $\beta_1, \beta_2, \ldots, \beta_Q$ are fixed throughout this section.

Since the channel is no longer uniform, assume the frequency hopping is also non-uniform across the total spread-spectrum frequency band. Certainly if $\bar{E}_q = 0$, it does not make sense to hop into the q-th sub-band. Thus we let p_q be the probability that the FH/MFSK signal hops into the q-th sub-band and define the hopping probability vector

$$\boldsymbol{p} = (p_1, p_2, \ldots, p_Q). \tag{2.290}$$

The non-uniform fading channel described here might model the HF channel where $\alpha_1, \alpha_2, \ldots, \alpha_Q$ describe the propagation conditions across the HF band (3MHz to 30 MHz). These may be known to the transmitter and receiver by using channel sounder signals that periodically measure the channel. The jammer may also be transmitting the jammer signal over the non-uniform channel, thus resulting in propagation parameters $\beta_1, \beta_2, \ldots, \beta_Q$. The jammer has control over the noise power distribution $\boldsymbol{J} = (J_1, J_2, \ldots, J_Q)$ under constraint (2.242) while the FH/MFSK anti-jam system controls the frequency hopping pattern defined by the probability vector $\boldsymbol{p} = (p_1, p_2, \ldots, p_Q)$.

In addition to the generalizations described above, assume there is receiver white Gaussian noise with single-sided spectral density N_0 across the total spread-spectrum band.

2.6.1 Uncoded

The uncoded (no diversity) FH/MFSK signal has conditional symbol error probability

$$P_q(J_q) = \sum_{k=1}^{M-1} \binom{M-1}{k} \frac{(-1)^{k+1}}{1 + k\left(1 + \dfrac{\alpha_q \bar{E}}{N_0 + \beta_q J_q}\right)} \tag{2.291}$$

when the FH/MFSK signal hops into the q-th sub-band. This is the usual symbol error probability for non-coherent Rayleigh fading channels of average signal energy $\alpha_q \bar{E}$ in additive white Gaussian noise of single-sided spectral density $N_0 + \beta_q J_q$. The symbol error probability averaged over the random hopping depends on the jammer noise power distribution $\boldsymbol{J}$ and the hopping probability vector $\boldsymbol{p}$ as follows:

$$P_s(\boldsymbol{p}, \boldsymbol{J}) = \sum_{q=1}^{Q} p_q P_q(J_q)$$

$$= \sum_{q=1}^{Q} p_q \sum_{k=1}^{M-1} \binom{M-1}{k} \frac{(-1)^{k+1}}{1 + k\left(1 + \dfrac{\alpha_q \overline{E}}{N_0 + \beta_q J_q}\right)} \tag{2.292}$$

which is a concave function of $\boldsymbol{J}$.

Without loss of generality let

$$\alpha_1 \geq \alpha_2 \geq \cdots \geq \alpha_Q. \tag{2.293}$$

Thus with no jammer the sub-band symbol error probabilities satisfy

$$P_1(0) \leq P_2(0) \leq \cdots \leq P_Q(0). \tag{2.294}$$

Suppose the jammer is very weak so that even if the jammer used all its power to jam the 1st sub-band, it would still have lower symbol error probability than the other sub-bands. That is, with $J_1 = J$ and $J_q = 0$, $q = 2, 3, \ldots, Q$

$$P_1(J) \leq P_2(0) \leq \cdots \leq P_Q(0). \tag{2.295}$$

Clearly in this case the optimum choice for the hopping probability vector is $p_1 = 1$ and $p_q = 0$, $q = 2, 3, \ldots, Q$. Using only the 1st sub-band would maximize the bit error probability.

Now define threshold τ_1 that satisfies

$$\frac{\alpha_1 \overline{E}}{N_0 + \beta_1 \tau_1} = \frac{\alpha_2 \overline{E}}{N_0} \tag{2.296}$$

or

$$\tau_1 = \frac{N_0}{\beta_1}\left[\frac{\alpha_1}{\alpha_2} - 1\right]. \tag{2.297}$$

Then τ_1 is the jammer power in sub-band 1 that makes it exactly as bad as sub-band 2 without jamming. It is clear that if $J > \tau_1$, then the optimum hopping probability would not have $p_1 = 1$. Now consider the general choice for $\boldsymbol{p}$ under a minimax criterion.

We assume the transmitter has no prior knowledge of the jammer noise power distribution $\boldsymbol{J}$ and so the probability vector $\boldsymbol{p}$ does not depend on $\boldsymbol{J}$. Consider here the choice of $\boldsymbol{p}$ that minimizes the maximum error probability. Specifically we choose $\boldsymbol{p} = \boldsymbol{p}^*$ to minimize

$$\max_{\boldsymbol{J}} P_s(\boldsymbol{p}, \boldsymbol{J}) \tag{2.298}$$

under the constraint that $\boldsymbol{p}$ is a probability vector. The maximization of $P_s(\boldsymbol{p}, \boldsymbol{J})$ with respect to $\boldsymbol{J}$ is under the constraints of (2.242) and $\boldsymbol{J}$ have non-negative components. Here the minimax error probability is given by

$$\begin{aligned} P_s^* &= P_s(\mathbf{p}^*, \boldsymbol{J}^*) \\ &= \min_{\mathbf{p}} \max_{\boldsymbol{J}} P_s(\mathbf{p}, \boldsymbol{J}). \end{aligned} \tag{2.299}$$

Necessary and sufficient conditions for $(\boldsymbol{p}, \boldsymbol{J})$ to be the minimax point $(\boldsymbol{p}^*, \boldsymbol{J}^*)$ have been found and analyzed by Avidor [25]. The minimax solution corresponds to the jammer noise power distribution resulting in the sub-band symbol error probabilities

$$P_1(J_1^*) = P_2(J_2^*) = \cdots = P_L(J_L^*) < P_{L+1}(0) \le \cdots \le P_Q(0) \tag{2.300}$$

for some L where

$$J = \sum_{l=1}^{L} J_l^*. \tag{2.301}$$

For the minimax solution the jammer distributes its power so that the strongest sub-bands without jammer noise receive the most jammer power, thus reducing all the better sub-bands to the same level of performance. Here the effective signal-to-noise ratios for the L sub-bands are

$$\delta = \frac{\alpha_q \bar{E}}{N_0 + \beta_q J_q^*} \qquad q = 1, 2, \ldots, L \tag{2.302}$$

and for the remaining sub-bands

$$\delta > \frac{\alpha_q \bar{E}}{N_0} \qquad q = L+1, L+2, \ldots, Q. \tag{2.303}$$

Note that the minimax jammer noise power distribution is

$$J_q^* = \begin{cases} \dfrac{\alpha_q \bar{E} - \delta N_0}{\beta_q \delta}, & q = 1, 2, \ldots, L \\ 0, & q = L+1, L+2, \ldots, Q \end{cases} \tag{2.304}$$

and from the constraint (2.242)

$$\begin{aligned} J &= \sum_{q=1}^{L} \left(\frac{\alpha_q \bar{E} - \delta N_0}{\beta_q \delta} \right) \\ &= \frac{1}{\delta} \sum_{q=1}^{L} \left(\frac{\alpha_q}{\beta_q} \right) \bar{E} - \sum_{q=1}^{L} \left(\frac{N_0}{\beta_q} \right) \end{aligned} \tag{2.305}$$

or

$$\delta = \frac{\sum_{q=1}^{L} \left(\frac{\alpha_q}{\beta_q}\right) \bar{E}}{J + \sum_{q=1}^{L} \left(\frac{N_0}{\beta_q}\right)}. \tag{2.306}$$

Thus, in terms of the total power J the smallest L is found to satisfy (2.304) and (2.306). Only these L sub-bands are jammed by the noise jammer.

The minimax choice of $\boldsymbol{p}^*$ has the form

$$p_q^* = \begin{cases} \dfrac{\alpha_q/\beta_q}{\sum_{i=1}^{L} (\alpha_i/\beta_i)}, & q = 1, 2, \ldots, L \\ 0, & q = L+1, \ldots, Q. \end{cases} \tag{2.307}$$

with resulting minimax bit error probability

$$\begin{aligned} P_b^* &= \frac{\frac{1}{2}M}{M-1} P_s(\boldsymbol{p}^*, \boldsymbol{J}^*) \\ &= \frac{\frac{1}{2}M}{M-1} \sum_{k=1}^{M-1} \binom{M-1}{k} \frac{(-1)^{k+1}}{1 + k(1+\delta)} \end{aligned} \tag{2.308}$$

where δ and $\boldsymbol{J}^*$ satisfies (2.302) and (2.304) and L is the smallest integer satisfying (2.306).

2.6.2 Diversity and Coding

Following the discussion leading to (2.270), with coding and diversity the soft decision ML metric is

$$m(\boldsymbol{e}, x | J_q) = \frac{\alpha_q \bar{E} e_x}{(N_0 + \beta_q J_q)(\alpha_q \bar{E} + N_0 + \beta_q J_q)} \tag{2.309}$$

when the chip hops into the q-th sub-band. This ideal receiver assumes knowledge of $\alpha_1, \alpha_2, \ldots, \alpha_Q$; $\beta_1, \beta_2, \ldots, \beta_Q$; and $\boldsymbol{J}$, the jammer noise power distribution. Here $\alpha_q \bar{E}$ is the average chip energy at the receiver when the signal hops into the q-th sub-band. In this case the coding parameter is

$$D(\boldsymbol{p}, \boldsymbol{J}) = \sum_{q=1}^{Q} p_q \left[\frac{4\left(1 + \dfrac{\alpha_q \bar{E}}{N_0 + \beta_q J_q}\right)}{\left(2 + \dfrac{\alpha_q \bar{E}}{N_0 + \beta_q J_q}\right)^2} \right] \tag{2.310}$$

where any coded bit error bound has the form

$$P_b \leq G(D(\boldsymbol{p}, \boldsymbol{J})) \tag{2.311}$$

and $G(\cdot)$ is determined by the code used. This follows from generalizing the discussion leading to (2.275).

For the coded FH/MFSK system with the ML metric, the minimax point $(\boldsymbol{p}^*, \boldsymbol{J}^*)$ satisfies

$$\begin{aligned} D^* &= D(\boldsymbol{p}^*, \boldsymbol{J}^*) \\ &= \min_{\boldsymbol{p}} \max_{\boldsymbol{J}} D(\boldsymbol{p}, \boldsymbol{J}). \end{aligned} \tag{2.312}$$

This is similar to the uncoded case and in fact, the minimax point $(\boldsymbol{p}^*, \boldsymbol{J}^*)$ is exactly the same. This is because $D(\boldsymbol{p}, \boldsymbol{J})$ is a concave function of $\boldsymbol{J}$ and the unique minimax point gives the condition

$$D^* = \frac{4\left(1 + \dfrac{\alpha_q \bar{E}}{N_0 + \beta_q J_q^*}\right)}{\left(2 + \dfrac{\alpha_q \bar{E}}{N_0 + \beta_q J_q^*}\right)^2} \tag{2.313}$$

$$q = 1, 2, \ldots, L$$

and

$$D^* < \frac{4\left(1 + \dfrac{\alpha_q \bar{E}}{N_0}\right)}{\left(2 + \dfrac{\alpha_q \bar{E}}{N_0}\right)^2} \tag{2.314}$$

$$q = L+1, L+2, \ldots, Q.$$

This implies $\boldsymbol{J}^*$ satisfies (2.304) where δ is given by (2.302) and L is the smallest integer where (2.306) is true.

For the hard decision case assume a hard M-ary decision is made for each FH/MFSK chip. If the FH/MFSK signal is hopped into the q-th sub-band, then the coding channel has M inputs and M outputs with conditional channel probabilities

$$p(y|x, q) = \begin{cases} 1 - P_q(J_q), & y = x \\ P_q(J_q)/(M-1), & y \neq x \end{cases} \tag{2.315}$$

where $P_q(J_q)$ is given by (2.291) and $x, y \in \{1, 2, \ldots, M\}$. For a sequence of symbols $\boldsymbol{x}$ and $\boldsymbol{y}$ and hop sequence $\boldsymbol{q}$ we have the conditional probability

$$\begin{aligned} p(\boldsymbol{y}|\boldsymbol{x}, \boldsymbol{q}) &= \prod_k p(y_k|x_k, q_k) \\ &= \prod_k \left[1 - P_{q_k}(J_{q_k})\right]^{1 - w(y_k, x_k)} \left[P_{q_k}(J_{q_k})/(M-1)\right]^{w(y_k, x_k)} \\ &= \prod_k \left[\frac{P_{q_k}(J_{q_k})}{(M-1)\left(1 - P_{q_k}(J_{q_k})\right)}\right]^{w(y_k, x_k)} \left(1 - P_{q_k}(J_{q_k})\right). \end{aligned} \tag{2.316}$$

Here the ML hard decision metric is

$$m(y, x|J_q) = w(y, x)\log\left[\frac{P_q(J_q)}{(M-1)(1-P_q(J_q))}\right]. \tag{2.317}$$

With this metric the coding parameter is

$$D(\boldsymbol{p}, \boldsymbol{J}) = \sum_{q=1}^{Q} p_q\left[2\sqrt{\frac{(1-P_q(J_q))P_q(J_q)}{M-1}} + \frac{M-2}{M-1}P_q(J_q)\right]. \tag{2.318}$$

Again $D(\boldsymbol{p}, \boldsymbol{J})$ is a concave function of $\boldsymbol{J}$ and thus there is a unique minimax solution where the minimax point $(\boldsymbol{p}^*, \boldsymbol{J}^*)$ satisfies (2.302), (2.303), and (2.304) where L is the minimum integer where (2.306) is satisfied.

For the special case of the uniform channel where

$$\alpha_q = 1 \tag{2.319}$$

and

$$\beta_q = 1$$
$$q = 1, 2, \ldots, Q$$

for the soft decision ML metric, broadband jamming is the worst case when jammer state information, $\boldsymbol{J}$, is assumed. This was shown in Section 2.5.2 and also follows directly from the general results here. Also for the hard decision ML metric, the broadband jammer is the worst case noise jammer. In Section 2.5.2 we had shown that for the energy metric without jammer state information, the broadband jammer was not the worst case for the uniform channel. We shall examine the hard decision channel with no jammer state information after deriving the general coding parameter expression for arbitrary metrics.

For more general metrics the general Chernoff bound can be used to compute the coding parameter D. To examine metrics that assume no knowledge of $\boldsymbol{J}$, consider the jammer state information or metrics with various quantizations on the chip energy out of each detector. Here assuming the most general metric form, $m(y, x|J_q)$, the usual pairwise error Chernoff bound is

$$\begin{aligned} P(\boldsymbol{x} \to \hat{\boldsymbol{x}}|\boldsymbol{q}) &= \Pr\left\{ \sum_k m(y_k, \hat{x}_k|J_{q_k}) \geq \sum_k m(y_k, x_k|J_{q_k}) \middle| \boldsymbol{x}, \boldsymbol{q}\right\} \\ &\leq E\left\{\exp\lambda\left(\sum_k\left[m(y_k, \hat{x}_k|J_{q_k}) - m(y_k, x_k|J_{q_k})\right]\right)\middle|\boldsymbol{x}, \boldsymbol{q}\right\} \\ &= \prod_k E\left\{\exp\lambda\left[m(y_k, \hat{x}_k|J_{q_k}) - m(y_k, x_k|J_{q_k})\right] \middle| x_k, q_k\right\} \end{aligned} \tag{2.320}$$

where $E\{\cdot\}$ is the expectation over all channel statistics including jammer noise when $\boldsymbol{x}$ is sent and $\boldsymbol{q}$ is the hopping sequence. Averaging this over the hopping sequence according to probability $\boldsymbol{p}$ and minimizing over the Chernoff bound parameter, λ, gives the final pairwise error bound

$$P(\boldsymbol{x} \to \hat{\boldsymbol{x}}) \le [D(\boldsymbol{p}, \boldsymbol{J})]^{w(\boldsymbol{x}, \hat{\boldsymbol{x}})} \tag{2.321}$$

where

$$D(\boldsymbol{p}, \boldsymbol{J}) = \min_{\lambda \ge 0} \sum_{q=1}^{Q} p_q E\left\{\exp \lambda \left[m(y, \hat{x}|J_q) - m(y, x|J_q)\right] \middle| x, q\right\} \tag{2.322}$$

when $\hat{x} \ne x$. The minimax bound is

$$P(\boldsymbol{x} \to \hat{\boldsymbol{x}}) \le [D^*]^{w(\boldsymbol{x}, \hat{\boldsymbol{x}})} \tag{2.323}$$

where

$$D^* = \min_{\boldsymbol{p}} \max_{\boldsymbol{J}} D(\boldsymbol{p}, \boldsymbol{J}). \tag{2.324}$$

The parameter D^* can be computed for non-fading channels as well as fading channels with any fading statistics. These can all be included in the general analysis discussed in Chapter 4, Part 1.

As an example consider the hard decision metric

$$m(y, x) = -w(y, x) \tag{2.325}$$

which assumes no knowledge of the jammer state $\boldsymbol{J}$. Here when $\hat{x} \ne x$

$$\begin{aligned} &E\{\exp \lambda\, [m(y, \hat{x}) - m(y, x)] | x, q\} \\ &\quad = E\{\exp \lambda\, [w(y, x) - w(y, \hat{x})] | x, q\} \\ &\quad = \left(1 - P_q(J_q)\right)e^{-\lambda} + \frac{P_q(J_q)}{M-1}e^{\lambda} + \left(\frac{M-2}{M-1}\right)P_q(J_q) \end{aligned} \tag{2.326}$$

and

$$\begin{aligned} D(\boldsymbol{p}, \boldsymbol{J}) &= \min_{\lambda \ge 0} \sum_{q=1}^{Q} p_q \left[\left(1 - P_q(J_q)\right)e^{-\lambda} + \frac{P_q(J_q)}{M-1}e^{\lambda} + \left(\frac{M-2}{M-1}\right)P_q(J_q)\right] \\ &= \min_{\lambda \ge 0} \left[(1 - \bar{\varepsilon})e^{-\lambda} + \frac{\bar{\varepsilon}}{M-1}e^{\lambda} + \left(\frac{M-2}{M-1}\right)\bar{\varepsilon}\right] \\ &= 2\sqrt{\frac{(1-\bar{\varepsilon})\bar{\varepsilon}}{M-1}} + \left(\frac{M-2}{M-1}\right)\bar{\varepsilon} \end{aligned} \tag{2.327}$$

where

$$\bar{\varepsilon} = \sum_{q=1}^{Q} p_q P_q(J_q). \tag{2.328}$$

Note that for the hard decision metric (2.325) where no jammer state information is used, the minimax point $(\boldsymbol{p}^*, \boldsymbol{J}^*)$ for $D(\boldsymbol{p}, \boldsymbol{J})$ is also the minimax point for $\bar{\varepsilon}$ given by (2.328). But $\bar{\varepsilon}$ is exactly the uncoded symbol error probability with the same minimax point as specified by (2.302), (2.304), and (2.306). For the uniform channel specified by (2.319) the worst noise jammer is again the broadband jammer. Thus with the hard decision uniform channel with no jammer state information the worst noise jammer is again the broadband jammer.

2.7 OTHER CODING METRICS

In this section we continue with the general slow fading non-uniform channel where there are Q sub-bands, jammer noise power distribution given by $\boldsymbol{J}$, and hopping probability vector $\boldsymbol{p}$ where the channel parameters are $\boldsymbol{\alpha} = (\alpha_1, \alpha_2, \ldots, \alpha_Q)$ and $\boldsymbol{\beta} = (\beta_1, \beta_2, \ldots, \beta_Q)$. Each coded FH/MFSK chip signal has a Rayleigh fading envelope which is independent from hop to hop and there is white Gaussian receiver noise with parameter N_0. Up to this point the two extreme types of coding metrics, soft decision and hard decision, were examined. In this section other coding metrics are now considered. The basic approach illustrated here and the various metrics considered can be applied to other types of channels and jammers such as non-fading channels with multitone jamming.

Recall that each time an M-ary coded symbol $x \in \{1, 2, \ldots, M\}$ is modulated as an FH/MFSK chip signal the receiver dehops the received signal and samples the outputs of M energy detectors. Denote the M-sampled energy detector outputs as $\boldsymbol{e} = (e_1, e_2, \ldots, e_M)$. If the signal hopped into the q-th sub-band, then $\boldsymbol{\varepsilon}$ has conditional probability density,

$$p(\boldsymbol{e}|x, q) = \prod_{m=1}^{M} p(e_m|x, q) \tag{2.329}$$

where

$$p(e_m|x, q) = \begin{cases} \dfrac{1}{\alpha_q \bar{E} + N_0 + \beta_q J_q} e^{-e_m/(\alpha_q \bar{E} + N_0 + \beta_q J_q)}, & m = x \\[2ex] \dfrac{1}{N_0 + \beta_q J_q} e^{-e_m/(N_0 + \beta_q J_q)}, & m \neq x \end{cases} \tag{2.330}$$

Thus the energy detector outputs are independent central chi-square random variables of order 2 and their square root values are Rayleigh random variables.

When the M energy detector outputs are taken as the channel output, then the maximum-likelihood metric is given as $m(\boldsymbol{e}, x|J_q)$ defined by

(2.309). This is the soft decision ML metric which assumes knowledge of jammer state information represented by $\boldsymbol{J}$, the jammer noise power distribution. The suboptimum soft decision energy metric without jammer state information is denoted $m(\boldsymbol{e}, x)$ and is given by (2.279).

In practical applications coded systems require a receiver that uses the coding metric in a digital processing algorithm or decoding process. This means the coding metric must be some quantized function of the M-sampled energy detector outputs. Generally, smaller number of bits used to represent metric values means faster decoding speeds with less memory requirements.[7] Consider the channel output in the form

$$y = f(\boldsymbol{e}) \tag{2.331}$$

where $f(\cdot)$ is some function of the sampled M energy detector outputs. The simplest form of this function is the hard decision output defined by

$$y = m \tag{2.332}$$

if

$$e_m \geq e_k \quad \text{all } k \neq m.$$

For this case the channel conditional probability $p(y|x, q)$ is given by (2.315) where $P_q(J_q)$ is the symbol error probability given by (2.291).

For the hard decision channel the ML metric $m(y, x|J_q)$ is given by (2.317). This assumes jammer state information $\boldsymbol{J}$ is known. The suboptimum hard decision metric without jammer station information is given by (2.325), which can be represented by a single binary digit.

The above soft decision and hard decision channels are special cases of the demodulator-to-decoder interface function $f(\cdot)$. This is illustrated in Figure 2.117, where the dotted line shows the equivalent coding channel with input x, output y, and conditional probability $p(y|x, q)$. For a given interface function $y = f(\boldsymbol{e})$, the conditional probabilities can be computed.

Once a coding channel is defined by the input symbols, output symbols, and conditional probabilities, a coding metric $m(y, x|J_q)$ is chosen. For the given channel and chosen coding metric, the coding parameter is

$$D(\boldsymbol{p}, \boldsymbol{J}) = \min_{\lambda \geq 0} \sum_{q=1}^{Q} p_q E\{ e^{\lambda[m(y, \hat{x}|J_q) - m(y, x|J_q)]} | x, q\} \tag{2.333}$$

for $\hat{x} \neq x$. Here the expectation $E\{\cdot\}$ is over the random variable y given x, $\hat{x}$, and q. In terms of a given $\boldsymbol{J}$ and $\boldsymbol{p}$ the cutoff rate is then

$$R_0(\boldsymbol{p}, \boldsymbol{J}) = \log_2 M - \log_2[1 + (M-1)D(\boldsymbol{p}, \boldsymbol{J})] \tag{2.334}$$

in bits per FH/MFSK chip. When an ML metric of the form[8]

$$m(y, x|J_q) = a \log p(y|x, q) + b \tag{2.335}$$

---

[7] Memory requirements in both the decoder and the deinterleaver.

[8] This is a maximum likelihood metric for the given function $y = f(\boldsymbol{e})$.

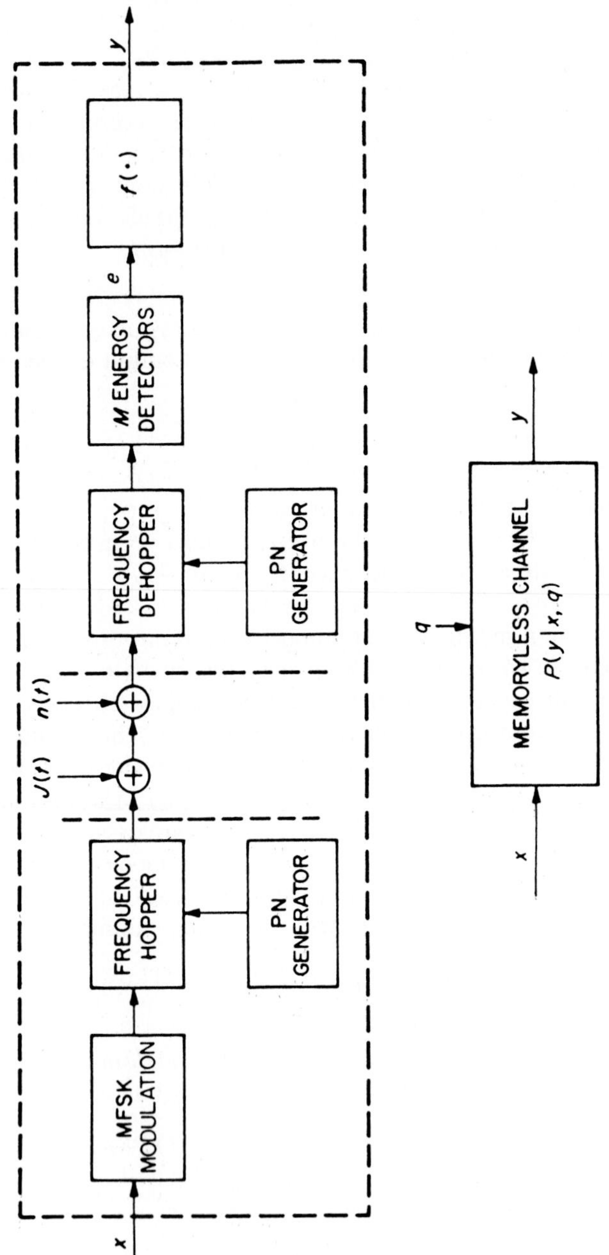

Figure 2.117. Equivalent coding channel.

for any $a > 0$ and b is used, the expression for $D(\boldsymbol{p}, \boldsymbol{J})$ becomes

$$D(\boldsymbol{p}, \boldsymbol{J}) = \sum_{q=1}^{Q} p_q \int \sqrt{p(y|\hat{x}, q)p(y|x, q)}\, dy \tag{2.336}$$

for $\hat{x} \neq x$ and where the integral may be a summation when y is a discrete random variable.

We now investigate various quantized channels defined by (2.331) and consider examples of coding metrics associated with these equivalent coding channels.

2.7.1 Energy Quantizer

Consider the function

$$\begin{aligned} y &= f(\boldsymbol{e}) \\ &= (y_1, y_2, \ldots, y_M) \end{aligned} \tag{2.337}$$

where

$$y_m = \begin{cases} 0, & 0 \le \sqrt{e_m} < v \\ 1, & v \le \sqrt{e_m} < 2v \\ 2, & 2v \le \sqrt{e_m} < 3v \\ 3, & 3v \le \sqrt{e_m} \end{cases} \tag{2.338}$$

$$m = 1, 2, \ldots, M.$$

This function just quantizes each sampled energy detector output into one of four levels (two-bit quantizer) where the quantization interval is of length v.

Suppose x is the transmitted symbol. Then define probabilities

$$\begin{aligned} p_0(k|v, q) &= \Pr\left\{ kv \le \sqrt{e_m} < (k+1)v \middle| m \neq x, q \right\} \\ p_1(k|v, q) &= \Pr\left\{ kv \le \sqrt{e_m} < (k+1)v \middle| m = x, q \right\} \\ k &= 0, 1, 2 \end{aligned} \tag{2.339}$$

and

$$\begin{aligned} p_0(3|v, q) &= \Pr\left\{ 3v \le \sqrt{e_m} \middle| m \neq x, q \right\} \\ p_1(3|v, q) &= \Pr\left\{ 3v \le \sqrt{e_m} \middle| m = x, q \right\}. \end{aligned} \tag{2.340}$$

Using the probability density for e_m given by (2.330)

$$\begin{aligned} p_i(k|v, q) &= e^{-k^2v^2/2\sigma_i^2} - e^{-(k+1)^2v^2/2\sigma_i^2} \\ p_i(3|v, q) &= e^{-9v^2/2\sigma_i^2} \\ i &= 0, 1;\ k = 0, 1, 2 \end{aligned} \tag{2.341}$$

where

$$2\sigma_i^2 = \begin{cases} N_0 + \beta_q J_q, & i = 0 \\ \alpha_q \bar{E} + N_0 + \beta_q J_q, & i = 1. \end{cases} \tag{2.342}$$

The coding channel conditional probability density is then

$$\begin{aligned} p(y|v, q) &= \prod_{m=1}^{M} p(y_m|v, q) \\ &= \prod_{m=1}^{M} p_0(y_m|v, q) \cdot \frac{p_1(y_x|v, q)}{p_0(y_x|v, q)} \\ &= F(y|v, q) \frac{p_1(y_x|v, q)}{p_0(y_x|v, q)} \end{aligned} \tag{2.343}$$

where

$$F(y|v, q) = \prod_{m=1}^{M} p_0(y_m|v, q) \tag{2.344}$$

is independent of the channel input symbol x.

For this channel the maximum-likelihood metric is

$$m(y, x|J_q) = \log p_1(y_x|v, q) - \log p_0(y_x|v, q) \tag{2.345}$$

which will give a coding parameter

$$D(\boldsymbol{p}, \boldsymbol{J}) = \sum_{q=1}^{Q} p_q \sum_{k=0}^{3} \sum_{j=0}^{3} \sqrt{p_0(k|v, q) p_0(j|v, q) p_1(k|v, q) p_1(j|v, q)}\,. \tag{2.346}$$

For the uniform channel with no receiver noise where parameters $\boldsymbol{\alpha}$ and $\boldsymbol{\beta}$ are given by (2.319),

$$J_q = \frac{J}{Q}$$

and

$$p_q = \frac{1}{Q}$$

$$q = 1, 2, \ldots, Q \tag{2.347}$$

the choice of v that minimizes this coding parameter can be found numerically. Figure 2.118 shows the minimizing value of $\bar{v} = v/N_J$ versus $\bar{E}/N_J$ along with corresponding values of the cutoff rate R_0 for $M = 2$ defined by (2.334).

Instead of the ML metric (2.335) for this coding channel, a simpler metric is to approximate the soft decision energy metric with no jammer state information by choosing metric

$$m(y, x) = y_x. \tag{2.348}$$

This uses no jammer state information and has coding parameter given by (2.333), which becomes

$$D(\mathbf{p}, \mathbf{J}) = \min_{\lambda \geq 0} \sum_{q=1}^{Q} p_q E\{ e^{\lambda[y_{\hat{x}} - y_x]} | x, q \}$$

$$= \min_{\lambda \geq 0} \sum_{q=1}^{Q} p_q \sum_{k=0}^{3} \sum_{j=0}^{3} e^{k\lambda} e^{-j\lambda} p_0(k|v, q) p_1(j|v, q)$$

$$= \min_{\lambda \geq 0} \sum_{q=1}^{Q} p_q \left(\sum_{k=0}^{3} e^{k\lambda} p_0(k|v, q) \right) \left(\sum_{j=0}^{3} e^{-j\lambda} p_1(j|v, q) \right). \tag{2.349}$$

This, too, can be minimized over $v \geq 0$ and examined for special cases such as the uniform channel. For the uniform channel with large values of $\overline{E}/N_J$ we expect similar results to the ML metric since the two metrics are approximately equal. This follows from the approximation

$$p_i(k|v, q) \cong e^{-k^2 v^2 / 2\sigma_i^2} \tag{2.350}$$

for large values of signal-to-noise ratios and the optimized choice of $\bar{v} = v/N_J$.

The difficulty with the energy quantization presented here is that a good choice of $\bar{v}$ depends on channel measurements which may be difficult to accurately obtain in jamming and fading channels.

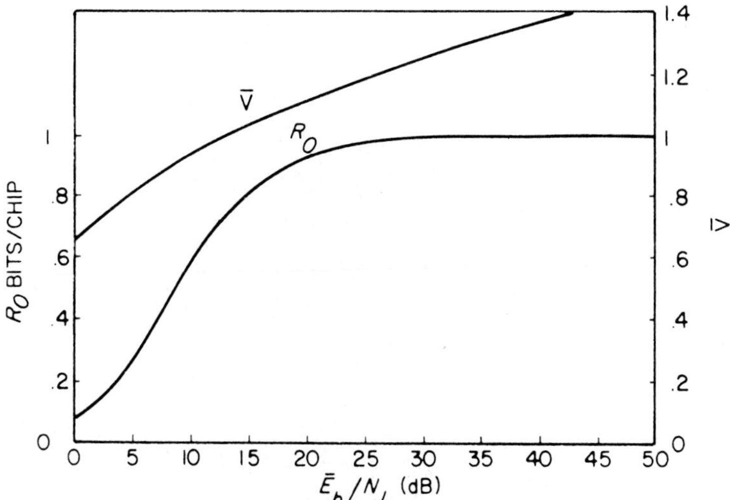

Figure 2.118. Energy quantizer parameters.

2.7.2 Hard Decision with One Bit Quality Measure

The demodulator-to-decoder interface is used to reduce the number of bits representing each channel output. The fewest bits correspond to the hard decision interface function (2.332). A practical compromise is to pass over this interface, a binary vector of low dimension. Viterbi [27] noted that the first (most significant) bits of this vector will correspond to the demodulator's hard decision while subsequent bits provide information on the quality of the channel which require some modification in the conventional demodulator design. He concentrated on adding one quality bit to the modulator's hard decision. This metric is presented here.

Define a modified hard decision demodulator-to-decoder interface function as follows:

$$y = \begin{cases} (m,1) & \text{if } e_m \geq \gamma \max\limits_{k \neq m} e_k \\ (m,0), & \text{if } \gamma \max\limits_{k \neq m} e_k > e_m \geq \max\limits_{k \neq m} e_k \end{cases} \tag{2.351}$$

for some parameter $\gamma \geq 1$. This is the hard decision function with a quality bit where "1" indicates a "good" channel while a "0" indicates a "poor" channel. For FH/MFSK this results in a coding channel with M inputs and $2M$ outputs. Figure 2.119 illustrates this for $M = 4$. Now what remains is to determine the coding channel conditional probabilities.

Note that output $y = (1,1)$ is a correct decision if $x = 1$. This occurs when

$$e_1 \geq \gamma e_m \qquad m = 2, 3, \ldots, M. \tag{2.352}$$

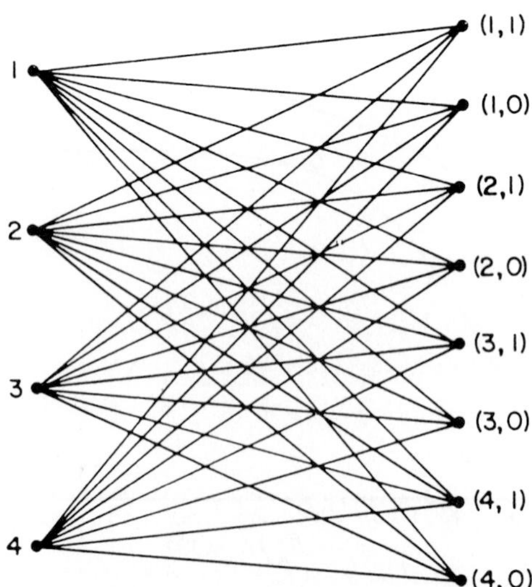

Figure 2.119. FH/4FSK coding channel.

The channel conditional probability is

$$p((1,1)|1) = \Pr\left\{ e_1 \geq \gamma \max_{m \neq 1} e_m \middle| x = 1 \right\}$$

$$= \int_0^\infty \Pr\left\{ \max_{m \neq 1} e_m \leq \frac{z}{\gamma} \middle| x = 1 \right\} p_1(z|q)\, dz \qquad (2.353)$$

where

$$p_i(z|q) = \frac{1}{2\sigma_i^2} e^{-z/2\sigma_i^2}, \qquad z \geq 0$$

$$i = 0, 1 \qquad (2.354)$$

and

$$2\sigma_i^2 = \begin{cases} \alpha_q \bar{E} + N_0 + \beta_q J_q, & i = 1 \\ N_0 + \beta_q J_q, & i = 0. \end{cases} \qquad (2.355)$$

Since

$$\Pr\left\{ \max_{m \neq 1} e_m \leq \frac{z}{\gamma} \middle| x = 1 \right\}$$

$$= \prod_{m=2}^{M} Pr\left\{ e_m \leq \frac{z}{\gamma} \middle| x = 1 \right\}$$

$$= \prod_{m=2}^{M} \int_0^{z/\gamma} p_0(w|q)\, dw$$

$$= \left[1 - e^{-z/2\gamma\sigma_0^2}\right]^{M-1}$$

$$= \sum_{k=0}^{M-1} \binom{M-1}{k} (-1)^k e^{-kz/2\gamma\sigma_0^2}, \qquad (2.356)$$

the conditional probability is

$$p((1,1)|1) = \sum_{k=0}^{M-1} \binom{M-1}{k} (-1)^k \int_0^\infty e^{-kz/2\gamma\sigma_0^2} \frac{1}{2\sigma_1^2} e^{-z/2\sigma_1^2}\, dz$$

$$= \sum_{k=0}^{M-1} \binom{M-1}{k} \frac{(-1)^k}{1 + k\dfrac{\sigma_1^2}{\gamma\sigma_0^2}}. \qquad (2.357)$$

Defining the parameterized probabilities

$$P(a, S, M) = \begin{cases} \displaystyle\sum_{k=1}^{M-1} \binom{M-1}{k} \frac{(-1)^{k+1}}{a + kS}, & M \geq 2 \\ 0, & \text{otherwise} \end{cases} \qquad (2.358)$$

where, recall from (2.291) the hard decision symbol error probability is

$$\varepsilon = P\left(1, \frac{\sigma_1^2}{\sigma_0^2}, M\right), \qquad (2.359)$$

we have

$$p((1,1)|1) = 1 - P\left(1, \frac{\sigma_1^2}{\gamma\sigma_0^2}, M\right). \tag{2.360}$$

Next note that

$$\begin{aligned} p((1,0)|1) &= \Pr\left\{ \max_{m\neq 1} e_m \leq e_1 \leq \gamma \max_{m\neq 1} e_m \middle| x = 1\right\} \\ &= \Pr\left\{ e_1 \geq \max_{m\neq 1} e_m \middle| x = 1\right\} - \Pr\left\{ e_1 \geq \gamma \max_{m\neq 1} e_m \middle| x = 1\right\} \\ &= P\left(1, \frac{\sigma_1^2}{\gamma\sigma_0^2}, M\right) - P\left(1, \frac{\sigma_1^2}{\sigma_0^2}, M\right). \end{aligned} \tag{2.361}$$

Similarly when errors occur

$$\begin{aligned} p((2,1)|1) &= \Pr\left\{ e_2 \geq \gamma \max_{m\neq 2} e_m \middle| x = 1\right\} \\ &= \int_0^\infty \Pr\left\{ \max_{m\neq 2} e_m \leq \frac{z}{\gamma} \middle| x = 1\right\} p_0(z|q)\, dz \end{aligned} \tag{2.362}$$

where now

$$\begin{aligned} &\Pr\left\{ \max_{m\neq 2} e_m \leq \frac{z}{\gamma} \middle| x = 1\right\} \\ &\quad = \Pr\left\{ e_1 \leq \frac{z}{\gamma} \middle| x = 1\right\} \prod_{m=3}^{M} \Pr\left\{ e_m \leq \frac{z}{\gamma} \middle| x = 1\right\} \\ &\quad = \left(1 - e^{-z/2\gamma\sigma_1^2}\right)\left[1 - e^{-z/2\gamma\sigma_0^2}\right]^{M-2} \\ &\quad = \left(1 - e^{-z/2\gamma\sigma_1^2}\right) \sum_{k=0}^{M-2} \binom{M-2}{k} (-1)^k e^{-kz/2\gamma\sigma_0^2} \end{aligned} \tag{2.363}$$

and thus

$$\begin{aligned} p((2,1)|1) &= \sum_{k=0}^{M-2} \binom{M-2}{k} \frac{(-1)^k}{1+\dfrac{k}{\gamma}} - \sum_{k=0}^{M-2} \binom{M-2}{k} \frac{(-1)^k}{1+\dfrac{\sigma_0^2}{\gamma\sigma_1^2}+\dfrac{k}{\gamma}} \\ &= P\left(1+\frac{\sigma_0^2}{\gamma\sigma_1^2}, \frac{1}{\gamma}, M-1\right) - P\left(1, \frac{1}{\gamma}, M-1\right) \\ &= \begin{cases} \dfrac{1}{1+\gamma\dfrac{\sigma_1^2}{\sigma_0^2}}, & M = 2 \\[2ex] \dfrac{1}{1+\gamma\dfrac{\sigma_1^2}{\sigma_0^2}} + P\left(1+\dfrac{\sigma_0^2}{\gamma\sigma_1^2}, \dfrac{1}{\gamma}, M-1\right) - P\left(1, \dfrac{1}{\gamma}, M-1\right), & M > 2. \end{cases} \end{aligned} \tag{2.364}$$

By similar steps we have

$$p((2,0)|1) = \Pr\left\{ \max_{m\neq 2} e_m \leq e_2 \leq \gamma \max_{m\neq 2} e_m \middle| x = 1\right\}$$

$$= \Pr\left\{ e_2 \geq \max_{m\neq 2} e_m \middle| x = 1\right\} - \Pr\left\{ e_2 \geq \gamma \max_{m\neq 2} e_m \middle| x = 1\right\}$$

$$= \begin{cases} \dfrac{\sigma_0^2/\sigma_1^2}{1+\sigma_0^2/\sigma_1^2} - \dfrac{\sigma_0^2/\sigma_1^2}{\gamma+\sigma_0^2/\sigma_1^2}, & M = 2 \\ \dfrac{\sigma_0^2/\sigma_1^2}{1+\sigma_0^2/\sigma_1^2} - \dfrac{\sigma_0^2/\sigma_1^2}{\gamma+\sigma_0^2/\sigma_1^2} & \\ +P\left(1+\dfrac{\sigma_0^2}{\sigma_1^2}, 1, M-1\right) - P(1,1,M-1) & \\ +P\left(1, \dfrac{1}{\gamma}, M-1\right) - P\left(1+\dfrac{\sigma_0^2}{\gamma\sigma_1^2}, \dfrac{1}{\gamma}, M-1\right), & M \geq 2 \end{cases} \tag{2.365}$$

and by symmetry for $y = (m,b)$

$$p((m,b)|x) = \begin{cases} p((1,b)|1), & m = x \\ p((2,b)|1), & m \neq x \end{cases} \tag{2.366}$$
$$b = 0, 1.$$

Assuming an ML metric where $m(y, x|\boldsymbol{J}) = ln\, p(y|x)$, then the coding parameter is

$$D(\boldsymbol{p}, \boldsymbol{J}) = \sum_{q=1}^{Q} p_q D_q(\boldsymbol{J}) \tag{2.367}$$

where

$$D_q(\boldsymbol{J}) = \sum_y \sqrt{p(y|x)p(y|\hat{x})}$$
$$= 2\sqrt{p((1,1)|1)p((2,1)|1)} + 2\sqrt{p((1,0)|1)p((2,0)|1)}$$
$$+(M-2)p((2,1)|1) + (M-2)p((2,0)|1). \tag{2.368}$$

For a suboptimum metric of the general form

$$m(y,x) = \begin{cases} m_{c,1}, & y = (x,1) \\ m_{c,0}, & y = (x,0) \\ m_{e,1}, & y = (\hat{x},1), & \hat{x} \neq x \\ m_{e,0}, & y = (\hat{x},0), & \hat{x} \neq x \end{cases} \tag{2.369}$$

the coding parameter is given by (2.367) with

$$
\begin{aligned}
D_q(J) &= \min_{\lambda \geq 0} E\{ {}^{\lambda[m(y,\hat{x})-m(y,x)]}|x\} \\
&= \min_{\lambda \geq 0} \{ p((1,1)|1)e^{\lambda[m_{e,1}-m_{c,1}]} \\
&\quad + p((1,0)|1)e^{\lambda[m_{e,0}-m_{c,0}]} + p((2,1)|1)e^{\lambda[m_{c,1}-m_{e,1}]} \\
&\quad + p((2,0)|1)e^{\lambda[m_{c,0}-m_{e,0}]} \\
&\quad + (M-2)p((2,1)|1) + (M-2)p((2,0)|1)\}. \qquad (2.370)
\end{aligned}
$$

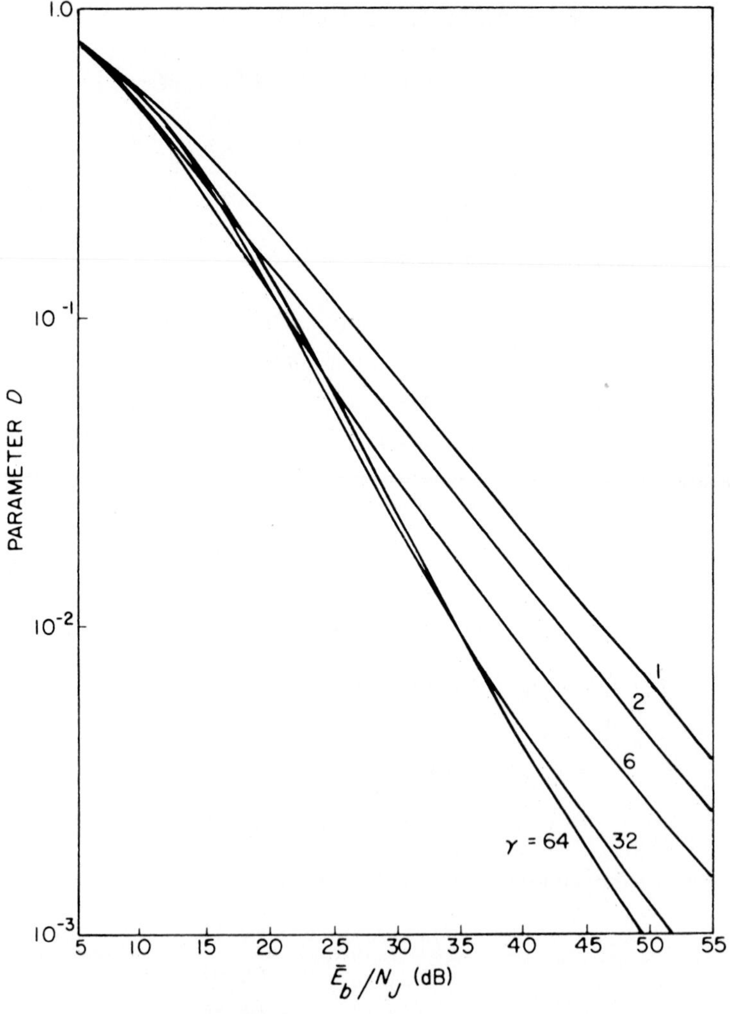

Figure 2.120. D for $M = 2$.

For the special case of the uniform channel with broadband noise jamming, the coding parameter D with various values of the parameter γ is shown in Figures 2.120 to 2.123. Shown in Figure 2.124 are the corresponding cutoff rates for $M = 2$. These figures also show the hard decision examples ($\gamma = 1$) so that the advantage of one additional quality bit can be seen.

2.7.3 List Metric

Another useful metric is based on a channel output that provides an ordered list of the M energy detector output samples. For the M energy detector

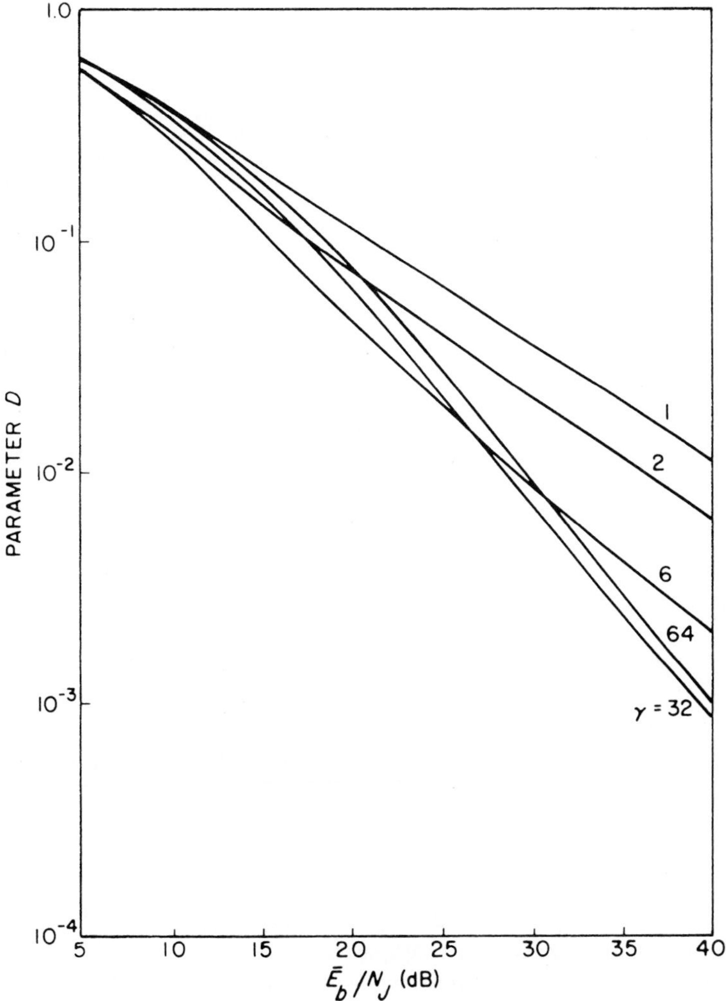

Figure 2.121. D for $M = 4$.

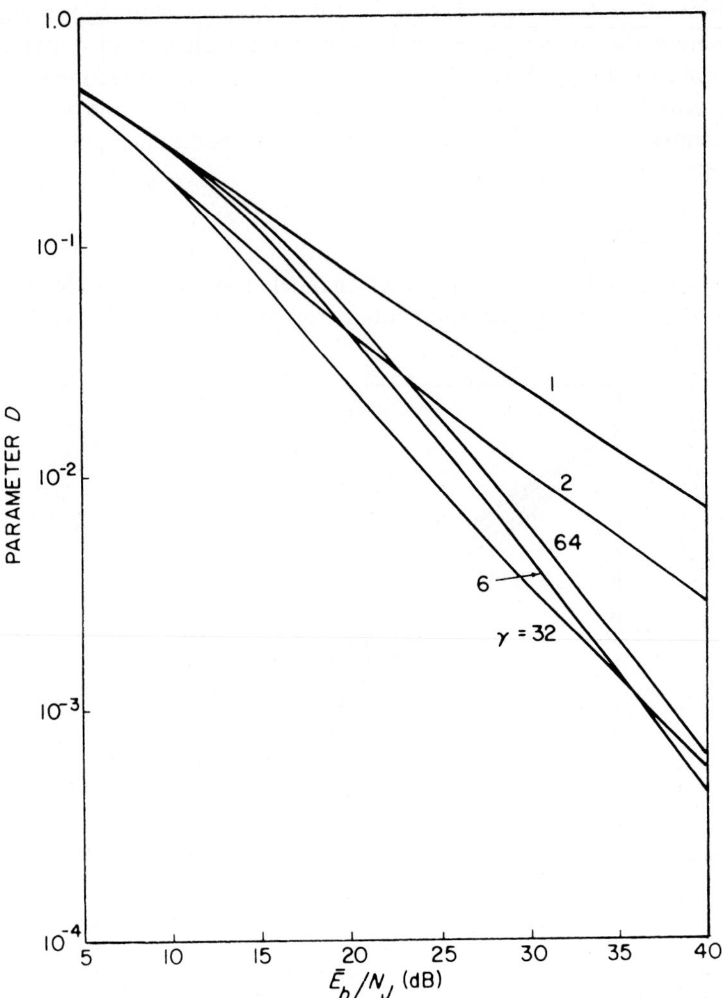

Figure 2.122. D for $M = 8$.

output samples $\boldsymbol{e} = (e_1, e_2, \ldots, e_M)$, the demodulator-to-decoder interface function is the list

$$y = f(\boldsymbol{e}) = (y_1, y_2, \ldots, y_M) \tag{2.371}$$

where $y_l = k$ if e_l is the k-th largest energy term among the M energy detector output samples. For example, for $M = 4$ if $e_3 > e_2 > e_1 > e_4$ then $y = (3, 2, 1, 4)$. Here $y_1 = 3$ indicates e_1 was the third largest energy sample, $y_2 = 2$ indicates e_2 was the second largest, etc.

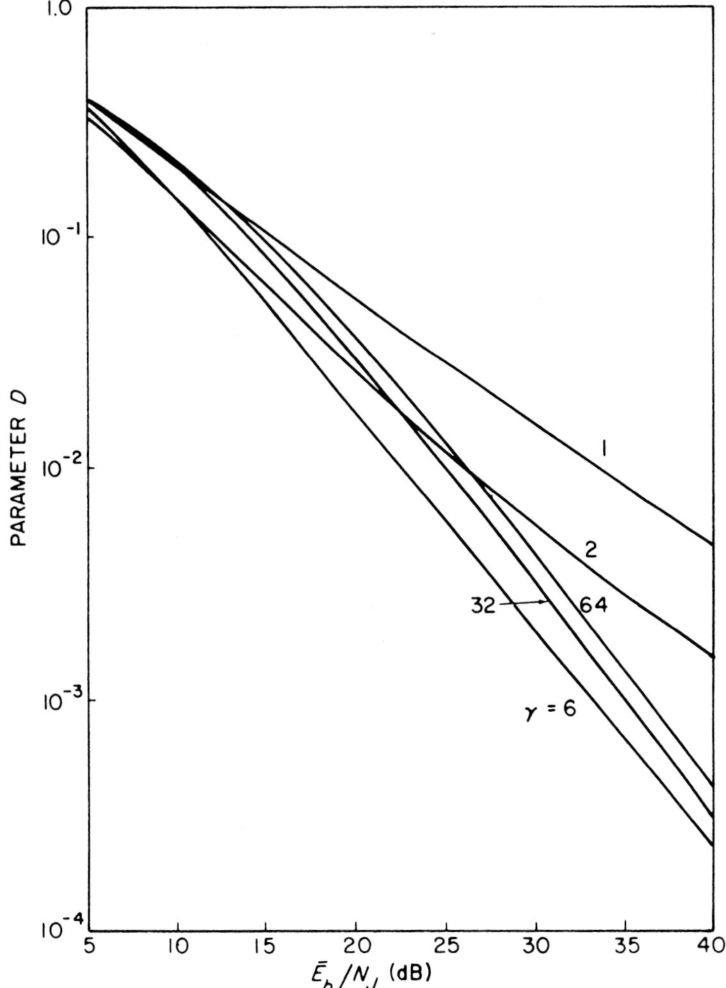

Figure 2.123. D for $M = 16$.

Note that list output can be obtained without using any AGC to maintain optimum thresholds such as in the energy quantizer. Previous work [28], [29] that considered list-of-L detection with optimum metrics has shown that this is inferior to energy quantization for AWGN channels. This, however, is not necessarily true in jamming and multiple access channels.

For the channel that outputs the ordered list of the M energy detector output samples, there are $M!$ distinct possible outputs or ordered lists. For this M input, $M!$ output coding channel we now derive expressions for the channel conditional probabilities $\{p(y|x)\}$.

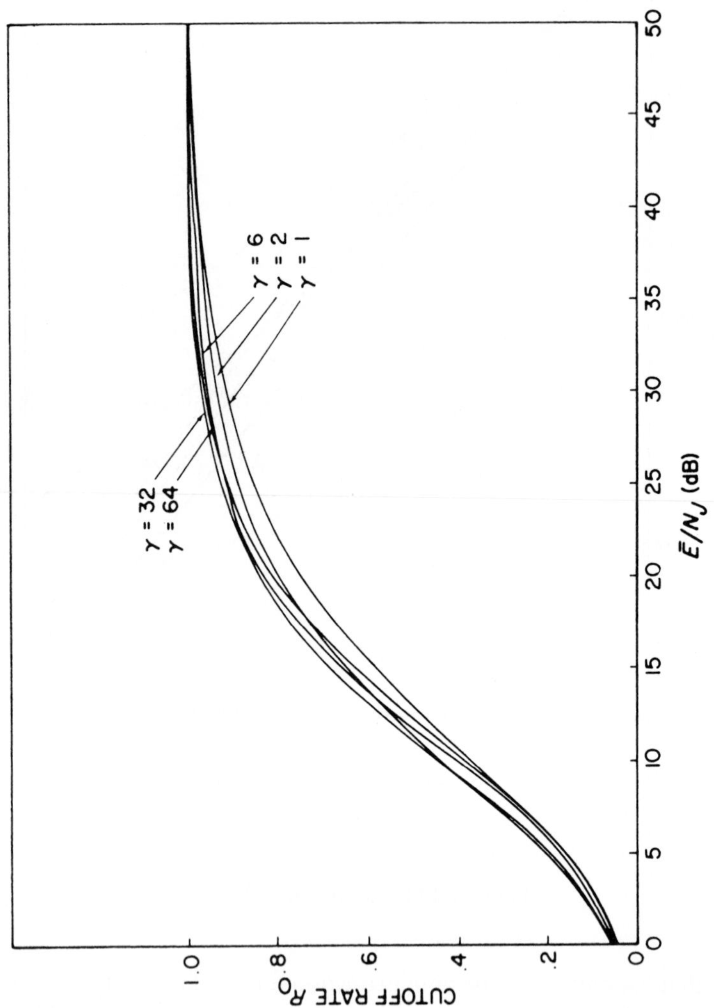

Figure 2.124. Cutoff rate for $M = 2$.

Suppose $x = 1$ and e_1 is the l-th largest energy detector output sample so that $y_1 = l$. Assume further the M energy detector output samples satisfy

$$e_2 > e_3 > ,\dots, > e_l > e_1 > e_{l+1} > ,\dots, > e_M \tag{2.372}$$

so that the channel output becomes

$$y = (l, 1, 2, \dots, l-1, l+1, \dots, M). \tag{2.373}$$

It is difficult to find an expression for $p(y|x)$ directly. By symmetry, since $\{e_m : m \neq 1\}$ are i.i.d. random variables and there are $(l-1)!$ ways to order $e_2, e_3, \dots, e_l$ and $(M-l)!$ ways to order $e_{l+1}, \dots, e_M$, we have the relationship

$$p(y|1) = \frac{1}{(M-l)!(l-1)!}\Pr\left\{ \min_{2 \le k \le l} e_k \ge e_1 \ge \max_{l \le k \le M} e_k \middle| x = 1 \right\} \tag{2.374}$$

where y is given by (2.373). This merely states that different ordering of the largest $l-1$ energy samples and the smallest $M-l$ energy samples all have the same conditional probability when ε_1 is the l-th largest and $x = 1$.

Next consider the probability

$$\Pr\left\{ \min_{2 \le k \le l} e_k \ge e_1 \ge \min_{l \le k \le M} e_k \middle| x = 1 \right\}$$

$$= \int_0^\infty \Pr\{e_2 \ge z, \dots, e_l \ge z, e_{l+1} \le z, \dots, e_M \le z | x = 1\} p_1(z|q)\, dz$$

$$= \int_0^\infty \left(e^{-z/2\sigma_0^2}\right)^{l-1} \left(1 - e^{-z/2\sigma_0^2}\right)^{M-l} p_1(z|q)\, dz$$

$$= \sum_{k=0}^{M-l} \binom{M-l}{k} (-1)^k \int_0^\infty e^{-(k+l-1)z/2\sigma_0^2} p_1(z|q)\, dz$$

$$= \sum_{k=0}^{M-l} \binom{M-l}{k} \frac{(-1)^k}{1 + (k+l-1)\dfrac{\sigma_1^2}{\sigma_0^2}}$$

$$= \frac{1}{1 + (l-1)\dfrac{\sigma_1^2}{\sigma_0^2}} - P\left(1 + (l-1)\frac{\sigma_1^2}{\sigma_0^2}, \frac{\sigma_1^2}{\sigma_0^2}, M - l + 1\right)[1 - \delta_{lM}]. \tag{2.375}$$

Thus the conditional probability of the input x with output y where $y_x = l$

is given by

$$p(y|x) = \frac{1}{(M-l)!(l-1)!}\left\{\frac{1}{1+(l-1)\frac{\sigma_1^2}{\sigma_0^2}} - P\left(1+(l-1)\frac{\sigma_1^2}{\sigma_0^2}, \frac{\sigma_1^2}{\sigma_0^2}, M-l+1\right)[1-\delta_{lM}]\right\}. \tag{2.376}$$

Since there are $(M-1)!$ outputs y with $y_x = l$,

$$\begin{aligned} P_l &= Pr\{y_x = l|x\} \\ &= \binom{M-1}{l-1}\left\{\frac{1}{1+(l-1)\frac{\sigma_1^2}{\sigma_0^2}} - P\left(1+(l-1)\frac{\sigma_1^2}{\sigma_0^2}, \frac{\sigma_1^2}{\sigma_0^2}, M-l+1\right)[1-\delta_{lM}]\right\}. \end{aligned} \tag{2.377}$$

This is the probability that the transmitted symbol has a corresponding energy detector output that is the l-th largest among the M energy detector outputs. Comparing (2.376) and (2.377)

$$p(y|x) = \frac{1}{(M-1)!}p_{y_x} \tag{2.378}$$

when y is any output with component y_x which is the place on the list that resulted for the energy detector output corresponding to input x.

We now have an expression for the conditional probabilities of the coding channel created by the demodulator-to-decoder interface function that provides an ordered list of the M energy detector output samples. Here the ML metric is clearly

$$m(y, x|J) = \log p_{y_x}. \tag{2.379}$$

This ML decision rule results in the coding parameter

$$D(p, J) = \sum_{q=1}^{Q} p_q D_q(J) \tag{2.380}$$

where

$$
\begin{aligned}
D_q(\boldsymbol{J}) &= \sum_y \sqrt{p(y|x)p(y|\hat{x})} \\
&= \sum \frac{1}{(M-1)!} \sqrt{P_l P_{\hat{l}}} \\
&= \sum_{k=1}^{M} \sum_{j \neq k} \frac{(M-2)!}{(M-1)!} \sqrt{P_k P_j} \\
&= \sum_{k=1}^{M} \sum_{j=1}^{M} \frac{1}{M-1} \sqrt{P_k P_j} - \sum_{k=1}^{M} \frac{1}{M-1} P_k \\
&= \frac{1}{M-1} \left[\sum_{k=1}^{M} \sum_{j=1}^{M} \sqrt{P_k P_j} - 1 \right]
\end{aligned} \tag{2.381}
$$

with $\{P_k\}$ given by (2.377).

Next consider a suboptimum metric that assigns a value or number to each place on the list in the output. In particular let the metric be given by

$$m(y, x) = N_{y_x}. \tag{2.382}$$

This assignment is defined by the vector

$$\boldsymbol{N} = (N_1, N_2, \ldots, N_M) \tag{2.383}$$

where N_l is the assigned number placed on the energy detector output with the l-th largest value.

For the general metric defined by (2.382) the coding parameter is given by

$$
\begin{aligned}
D_q(\boldsymbol{J}) &= \min_{\lambda \geq 0} E\{ e^{\lambda[m(y,\hat{x}) - m(y,x)]} | x \} \\
&= \min_{\lambda \geq 0} E\{ e^{\lambda[N_{y_{\hat{x}}} - N_{y_x}]} | x \} \\
&= \min_{\lambda \geq 0} \sum_{k=1}^{M} \sum_{j \neq k} e^{\lambda[N_j - N_k]} Pr\{ y_x = k, y_{\hat{x}} = j | x \}
\end{aligned} \tag{2.384}
$$

where

$$
\begin{aligned}
\Pr\{ y_x = k, y_{\hat{x}} = j | x \} &= \Pr\{ y_{\hat{x}} = j | y_k = k, x \} \Pr\{ y_k = k | x \} \\
&= \frac{1}{M-1} P_k.
\end{aligned} \tag{2.385}
$$

Thus

$$D_q(\boldsymbol{J}) = \min_{\lambda \geq 0} \frac{1}{M-1} \sum_{k=1}^{M} P_k \left[\sum_{j=1}^{M} e^{\lambda[N_j - N_k]} - 1 \right]. \tag{2.386}$$

Creighton [30] considered this list metric for the uniform channel with no background noise where there is Rayleigh fading and partial-band noise jamming. For the partial-band noise jammer that jams ρ fraction of the band, define the binary random variable Z where $Pr(Z=1) = \rho$ and $Pr(Z=0) = 1-\rho$. Since the probabilities $\{P_k\}$ depend on the jammer noise level, we emphasize this by writing $P_k = P_k(Z)$ showing this dependence. Recall that each probability depended on the hopped sub-band that had a jammer noise level characterized by $\beta_q J_q$. Here there are only two levels of noise jamming characterized by the random variable Z. The general metric now has the form

$$m(y, x|Z) = N_{y_x}(Z) \tag{2.387}$$

where for the ML metric with jammer state information (JSI) where Z is known at the receiver

$$N_{y_x}(Z) = \log P_{y_x}(Z). \tag{2.388}$$

When the receiver does not have JSI, then we have average probability

$$\overline{P}_k = \rho P_k(1) + (1-\rho) P_k(0) \tag{2.389}$$

$$k = 1, 2, \ldots, M$$

and the ML metric without JSI given by

$$N_{y_x}(Z) = \log \overline{P}_{y_x}. \tag{2.390}$$

In general an arbitrary assignment of numbers to the list values in y is possible. Here too we can consider the case with JSI where Z is known and different assignments are used for $Z=1$ and $Z=0$. In general, the ML metric requires knowledge of $P_k(Z)$ or $\overline{P}_k$ while having JSI requires knowledge of the random variable Z in the partial-band case and $\boldsymbol{J}$ for a more general noise power distribution.

For the ML metric with or without JSI the worst case partial-band noise jammer is again found to be the broadband noise jammer ($\rho = 1$). Figure 2.125 shows the cutoff rates for ML metrics (2.388) and (2.390) with worst case partial-band noise jamming and compares the results with no Rayleigh fading. Figures 2.126 to 2.130 compare cutoff rates for $M = 2$, 4, 8, 16, and 32 where the curves are labelled as follows:

1. Soft decision energy metric with JSI
2. Soft decision energy metric without JSI
3. ML list metric with JSI
4. ML list metric without JSI.

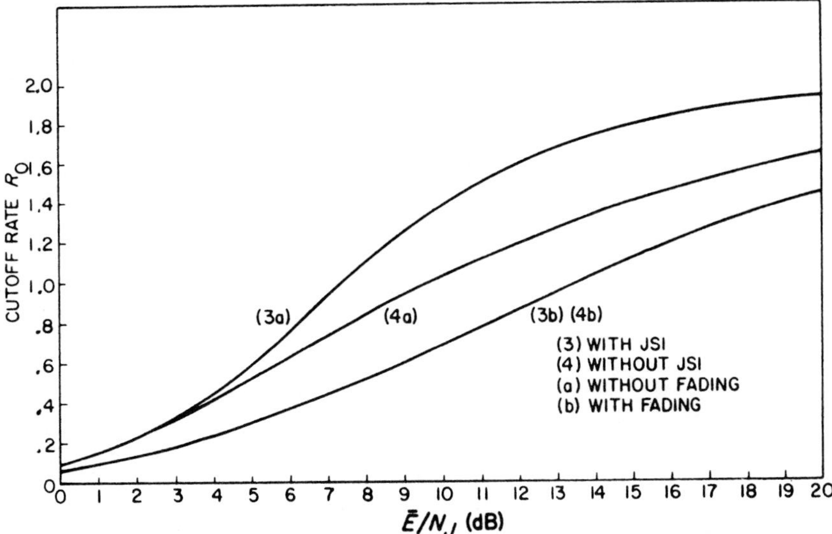

Figure 2.125. List metric R_0 for FH/4FSK against worst case noise jammer.

Although the unquantized soft decision energy metric with JSI gives better performance, its advantage over the list metrics decreases as the alphabet size increase. Furthermore, with other types of jamming or interference in the channel the list metric can outperform the soft decision energy metric. Multitone jamming and multiple access interference cases are where the list

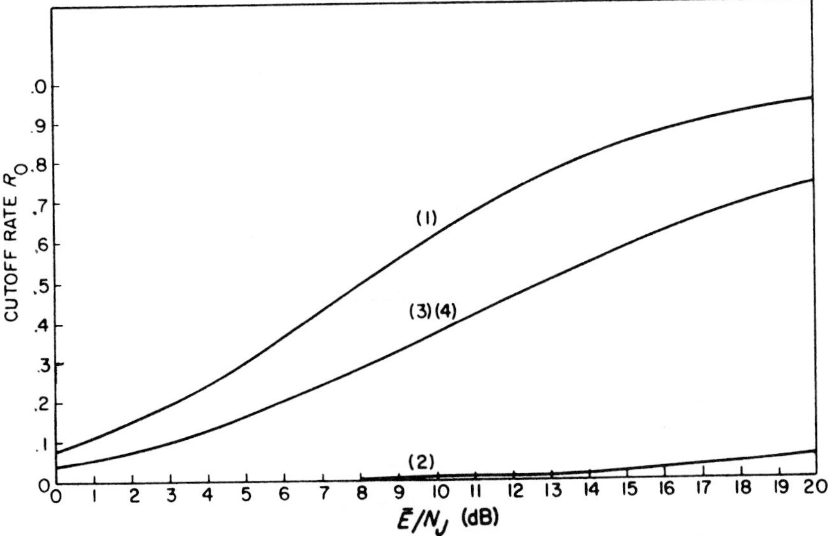

Figure 2.126. List and energy metrics R_0 for FH/8FSK against worst case noise jammer.

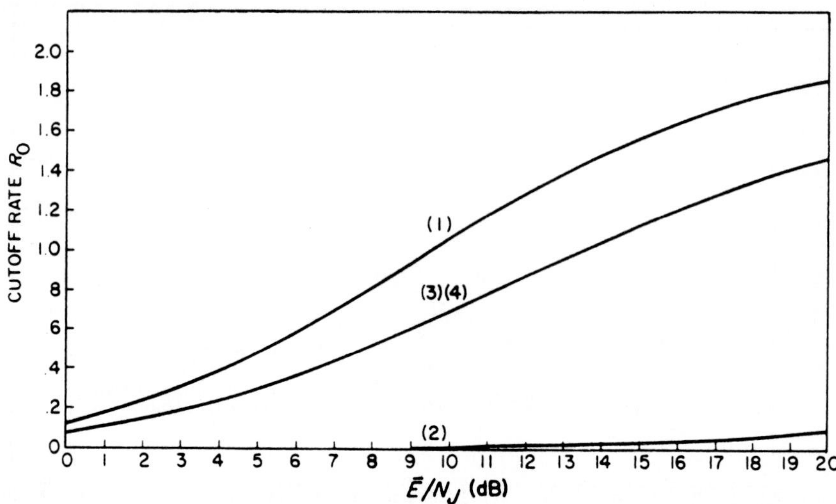

Figure 2.127. List and energy metrics R_0 for FH/4FSK against worst case noise jammer.

metric can do better than the energy metric [30], [31] (see Chapter 5, Part 5).

The results presented here generalize to arbitrary memoryless channels with FH/MFSK signals with list output as long as P_l is the probability that the transmitted symbol has a corresponding energy detector output sample

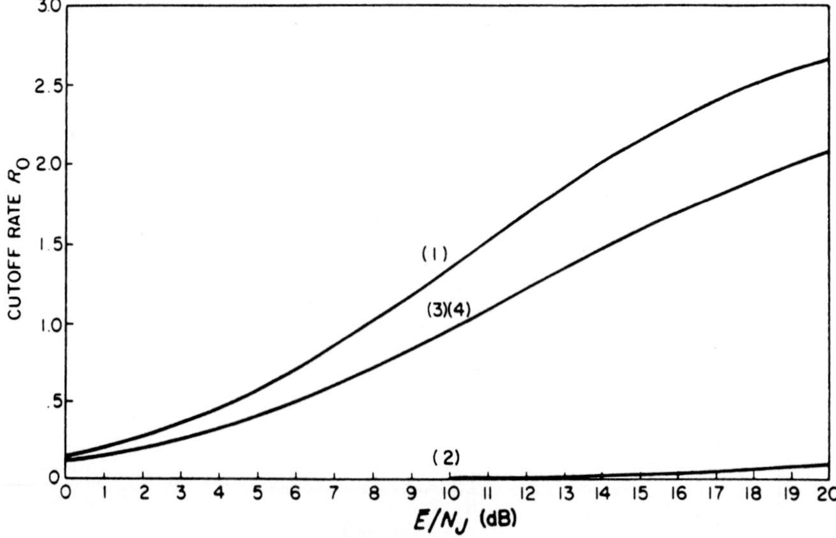

Figure 2.128. List and energy metrics R_0 for FH/8FSK against worst case noise jammer.

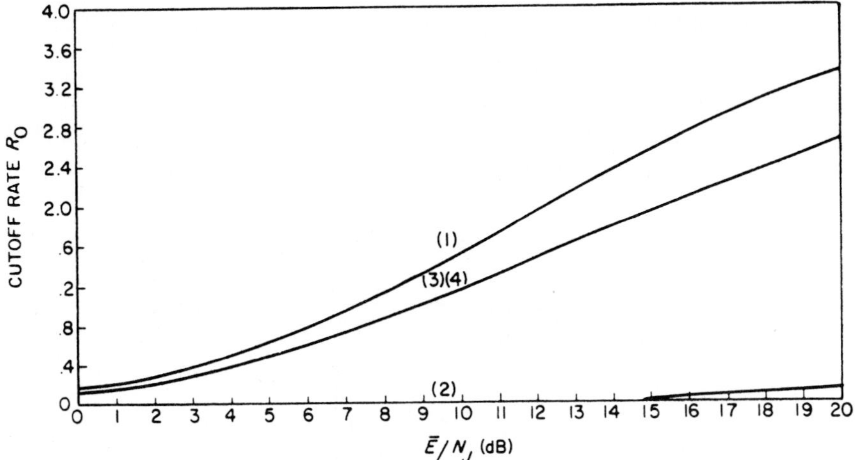

Figure 2.129. List and energy metrics R_0 for FH/16FSK against worst case noise jammer.

that is the l-th largest among all M energy detector samples. Indeed, with the usual symmetry assumptions, the same expressions apply for the coding parameter D.

In some circumstances it may be desirable to shorten the list to the L largest energy detector outputs where $L < M$. In this case the lowest $M - L$ energy detector outputs are treated indistinguishably as a single off-list group. Here the probability of the correct symbol energy detector sample

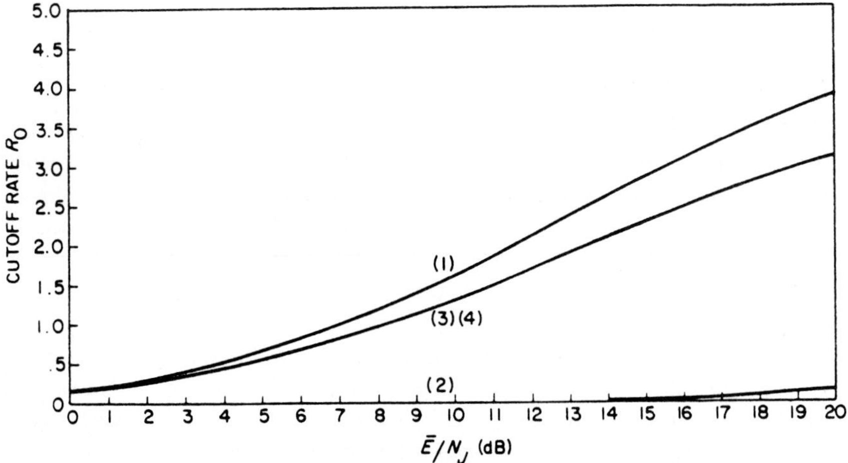

Figure 2.130. List and energy metrics R_0 for FH/32FSK against worst case noise jammer.

being l-th on the list is

$$P_l(L) = \begin{cases} P_l; & l = 1, 2, \ldots, L \\ \dfrac{\sum\limits_{j=L+1}^{M} P_j}{M - L}; & l = L+1, \ldots, M. \end{cases} \tag{2.391}$$

With the ML metric the coding parameter is then

$$\begin{aligned} D_q(\boldsymbol{J}) &= \frac{1}{M-1}\left[\sum_{k=1}^{M}\sum_{j=1}^{M}\sqrt{P_k(L)P_j(L)} - 1\right] \\ &= \frac{1}{M-1}\left[\left(\sum_{k=1}^{M}\sqrt{P_k(L)}\right)^2 - 1\right] \\ &= \frac{1}{M-1}\left[\left(\sum_{k=1}^{L}\sqrt{P_k} + \sqrt{(M-L)\sum_{j=L+1}^{M} P_j}\right)^2 - 1\right]. \end{aligned} \tag{2.392}$$

This is the list-of-L detection scheme presented in [28], [29], and [32].

For the uniform channel with no receiver noise, Crepeau [32] has evaluated the performance of the ML metric with a list-of-L where there is worst case multitone jamming and broadband noise jamming with slowly varying Rayleigh fading. Figure 2.131 shows the $M = 16$ case with Rayleigh fading for R_0 in bits per symbol. There is little difference in the performance due to increasing the list size. For worst case multitone jamming, Figures 2.132 to 2.135 show a more dramatic difference in just going from $L = 1$ to $L = 2$. In general, the list metric is a useful metric when there are multiple tones in the channel due to a jammer and/or other users.

2.7.4 Metrics for Binary Codes

For FH/MFSK signals there are three well-known types of codes one can use that have M-ary code symbols. Reed-Solomon codes [21] are natural block codes to use where the decoders generally require a hard decision M-ary channel. M-ary alphabet convolutional codes include those found by Trumpis [18] and dual-K codes[9] [20] where $M = 2^K$. These codes can be decoded using the Viterbi algorithm with all metrics discussed in this chapter.

Today, however, most codes used in practice are binary codes, especially binary convolutional codes. These have been used primarily with coherent BPSK and QPSK modulations with one-bit (hard decision), two-bit, and three-bit quantized channel outputs. For binary convolutional codes LSI Viterbi decoders chips and sequential decoder chips have been developed. It

[9] These are convolutional codes using the Galois Field GF(2^K).

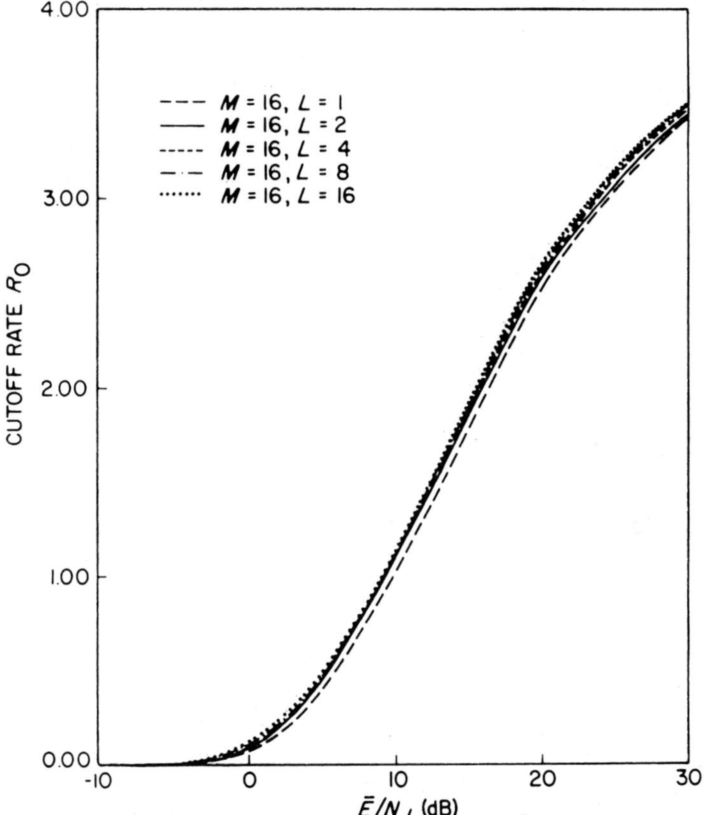

Figure 2.131. List metric cutoff rates for broadband noise jammer.

seems reasonable to exploit these developments and use binary convolutional codes with the FH/MFSK signals. Here we examine how the M-ary input channel with outputs of M energy detector samples can be converted into a binary input channel with one-bit, two-bit, and three-bit outputs that will be suitable for binary codes with corresponding decoders.

For $M = 2^K$ there are K bits associated with each M-ary channel input symbol. For example, with $K = 3$ ($M = 8$), we have a channel with eight input symbols and the output samples as seen in Table 2.23.

Between the M-ary input and the M energy detector outputs there exists MFSK modulation, frequency hopping, the real channel, dehopping and M energy detectors. To create a binary input channel with one-bit output, we merely make a hard decision as to which M-ary symbol was sent. For example, for $M = 8$ above if e_4 is the largest energy detector output then the channel output hard decision bits would be 011. Here the probability of a bit error is denoted δ_q if the signal hopped into the q-th sub-band. If the bits are interleaved before converting them into M-ary symbols and then deinterleaved, the hard decision bits obtained are the outputs of the usual

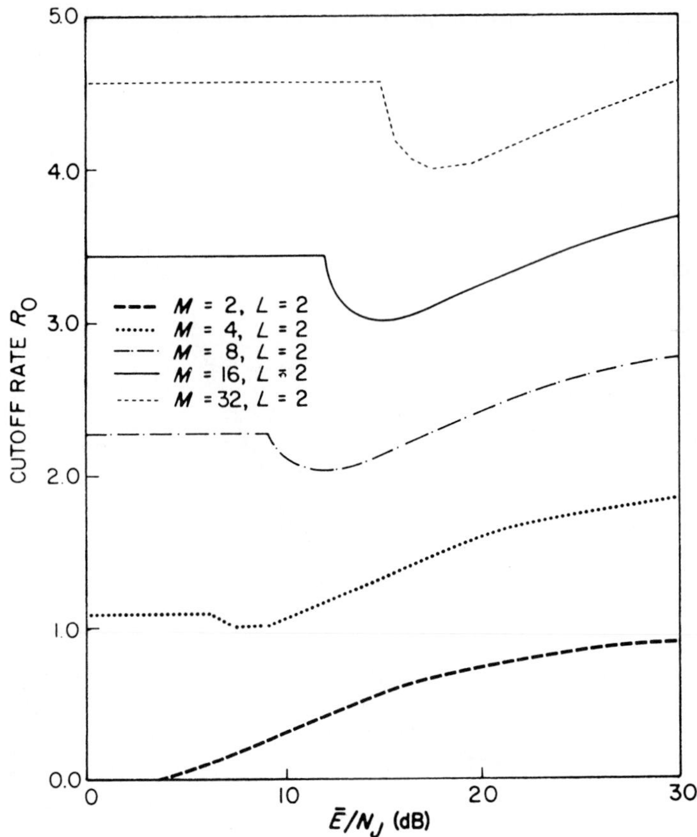

Figure 2.132. List metric cutoff rates for worst case tone jammer.

binary symmetric channel (BSC) with crossover probability δ_q, which is the uncoded bit error probability for the FH/MFSK system.

For the above BSC a binary code can be used with a decoder that uses jammer state information (JSI) with metric given by (2.317) and the resulting coding parameter given by (2.318). Without JSI the decoder metric becomes (2.325) with the resulting coding parameter given by (2.327) and (2.328).

Suppose next we want a binary input channel with two-bit outputs. Here the hard decision with 1-bit quality measure suggested by Viterbi [27] and discussed in Section 2.7.2 can be used. For $M = 8$ there are 16 outputs here of the form $(m, 1)$ and $(m, 0)$ for $M = 1, 2, \ldots, 8$. We can now convert these into two-bit binary channel outputs by taking, for example, the output $(4, 1)$ and converting it into three two-bit binary outputs of the form

$$(4,1) \rightarrow (0,1)\ (1,1), (1,1) \tag{2.393}$$

where recall $m = 4$ corresponds to the 011 bits. Similarly, if $(4,0)$ is the

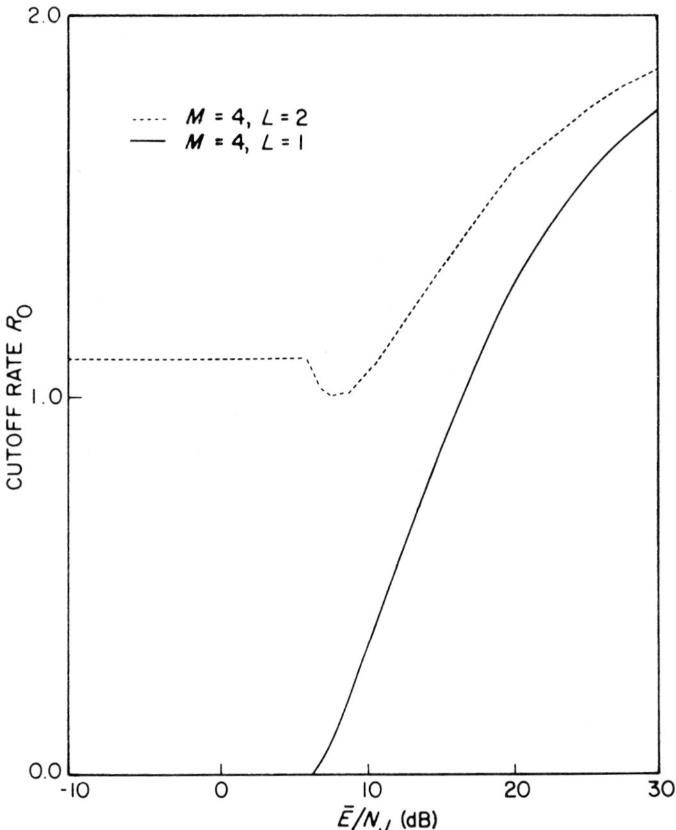

Figure 2.133. List metric cutoff rates for worst case tone jammer.

output of the channel in Section 2.7.2, then we have the conversion

$$(4,0) \to (0,0),\,(1,0),\,(1,0). \tag{2.394}$$

With interleaving and deinterleaving the result is a binary input channel with two-bit outputs as shown in Figure 2.136 where the transition probabilities can be obtained using the type of analysis given in Section 2.7.2 (see Viterbi [27]).

This approach can be extended to three-bit outputs for each input bit by using three threshold levels $\gamma_1 > \gamma_2 > \gamma_3 \geq 1$ where (2.351) is generalized as

$$y = \begin{cases} (m,11), & e_m \geq \gamma_1 \max\limits_{k \neq m} e_k \\ (m,10), & \gamma_1 \max\limits_{k\neq m} e_k > e_m \geq \gamma_2 \max\limits_{k \neq m} e_k \\ (m,01), & \gamma_2 \max\limits_{k\neq m} e_k > e_m \geq \gamma_3 \max\limits_{k \neq m} e_k \\ (m,00), & \gamma_3 \max\limits_{k\neq m} e_k > e_m \geq \max\limits_{k \neq m} e_k. \end{cases} \tag{2.395}$$

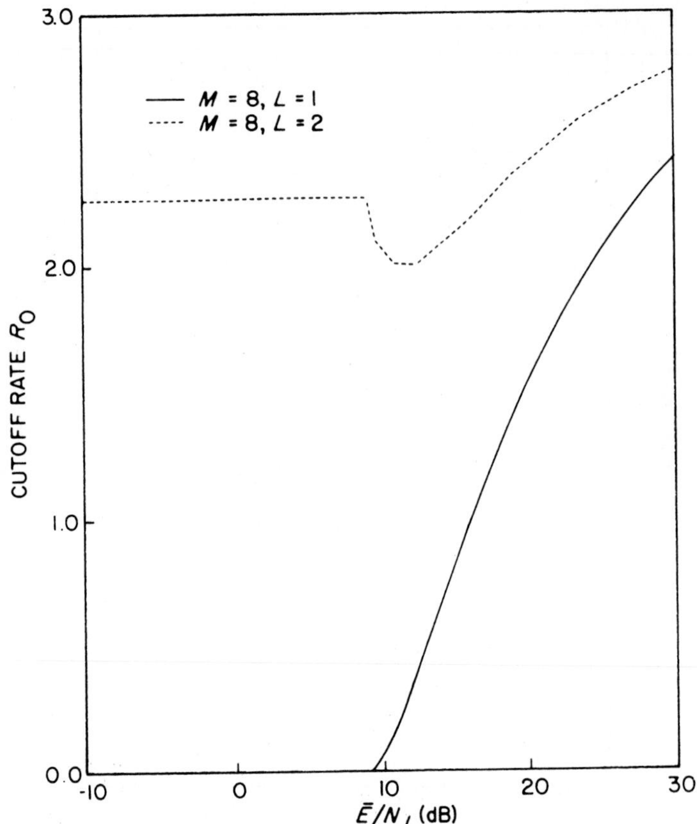

Figure 2.134. List metric cutoff rates for worst case tone jammer.

Again for the $M = 8$ example we have the conversion

$$(4,01) \rightarrow (001), (101), (101) \tag{2.396}$$

where the hard decision bits are followed by two "quality" bits. With interleaving and deinterleaving there are three-bit outputs for each binary input into the channel which can be used in the usual three-bit soft decision decoder for binary codes.

Another approach to obtaining a binary input channel with a quantized output is to consider the conditional probability of each transmitted bit given the M energy detector outputs. In general let $b_1, b_2, \ldots, b_K$ be the K coded bits that result in an M-ary symbol m with corresponding energy detector output e_m. Using Bayes rule (see Lee [33])

$$\Pr\{b_l|e\} = \frac{\Pr\{e|b_l\}\Pr\{b_l\}}{\Pr\{e\}}. \tag{2.397}$$

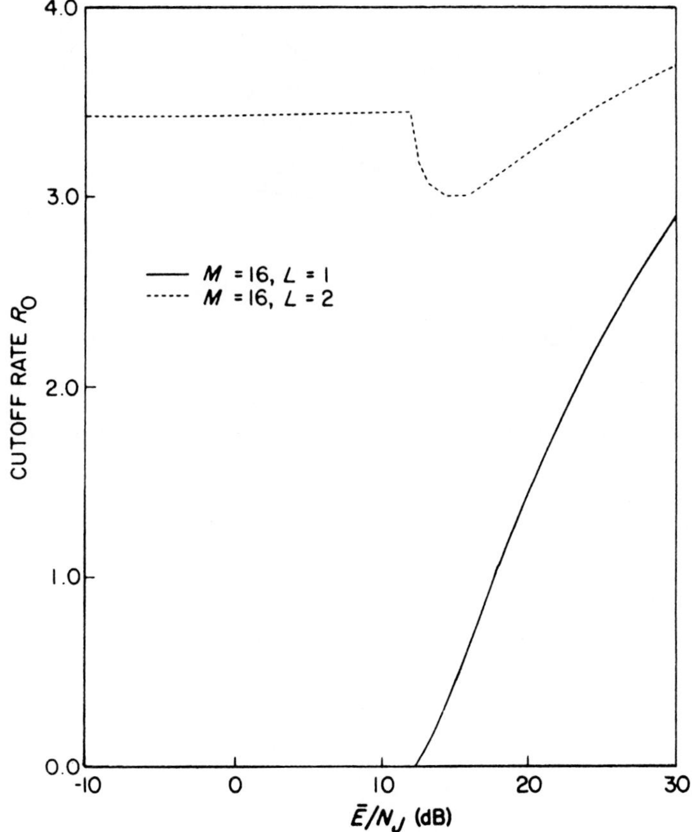

Figure 2.135. List metric cutoff rates for worst case tone jammer.

Table 2.23
Bits to symbol conversion, $K = 3$, $M = 8$.

Bits $b_1 b_2 b_3$	8-ary Input m	Energy Detector Output e
0 0 0	→ 1	e_1
0 0 1	→ 2	e_2
0 1 0	→ 3	e_3
0 1 1	→ 4	e_4
1 0 0	→ 5	e_5
1 0 1	→ 6	e_6
1 1 0	→ 7	e_7
1 1 1	→ 8	e_8

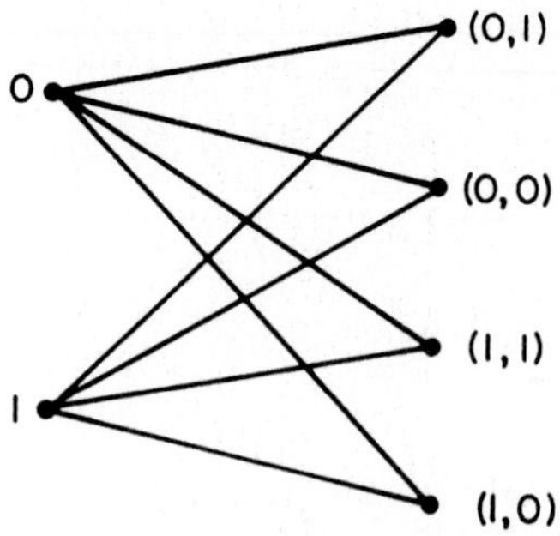

Figure 2.136. Binary input 2-bit output channel.

Next observing that there are several possible M-ary symbols having the l-th bit, b_l,

$$\Pr\{e|b_l\} = \sum_{m=1}^{M} \Pr\{e|m, b_l\}\Pr\{m|b_l\}. \tag{2.398}$$

Defining

$$\mathcal{M}(b_l) = \{m: l\text{-th bit is } b_l\}, \tag{2.399}$$

by symmetry

$$\Pr\{m|b_l\} = \begin{cases} \dfrac{2}{M}, & m \in \mathcal{M}(b_l) \\ 0, & m \notin \mathcal{M}(b_l). \end{cases} \tag{2.400}$$

Recall

$$\begin{aligned} \Pr\{e|m, b_l\} &= \Pr\{e|m\} \\ &= \prod_{k=1}^{M} p(e_k|m, q) \end{aligned} \tag{2.401}$$

where $p(e_k|m, q)$ is given by (2.330) for the general slowly fading non-uniform channel with jammer power distribution $\boldsymbol{J}$. Defining

$$r(e_k) = \frac{N_0 + \beta_q J_q}{\alpha_q \overline{E} + N_0 + \beta_q J_q} \exp\left\{ \frac{\alpha_q \overline{E} e_k}{(N_0 + \beta_q J_q)(\alpha_q \overline{E} + N_0 + \beta_q J_q)} \right\} \tag{2.402}$$

the final form is

$$Pr\{b_l|e\} = G(e) \sum_{m \in \mathcal{M}(b_l)} r(e_m) \tag{2.403}$$

where

$$G(\boldsymbol{e}) = \frac{\dfrac{1}{M}\displaystyle\prod_{k=1}^{M}\left(\frac{1}{N_0 + \beta_q J_q} e^{-1/(N_0 + \beta_q J_q)}\right)}{\Pr\{\boldsymbol{e}\}}. \tag{2.404}$$

But $\Pr\{\mathrm{b}_l|\boldsymbol{e}\}$ is a sum of exponential functions of e_m, $m \in \mathcal{M}(b_l)$ and for signal-to-noise ratios of interest such a sum is dominated by the largest term. Thus, using the approximation

$$\Pr\{b_l|\boldsymbol{e}\} \cong G(\boldsymbol{e}) \max_{m \in \mathcal{M}(b_l)} r(e_m) \tag{2.405}$$

gives an approximate ML metric (taking logarithm) given by

$$m(\boldsymbol{e}, b_l) = \max_{m \in \mathcal{M}(b_l)} e_m. \tag{2.406}$$

For the $K = 3$ ($M = 8$) example of Table 2.23

$$\begin{aligned}
\mathcal{M}(b_1 = 0) &= \{1,2,3,4\}\\
\mathcal{M}(b_1 = 1) &= \{5,6,7,8\}\\
\mathcal{M}(b_2 = 0) &= \{1,2,5,6\}\\
\mathcal{M}(b_2 = 1) &= \{3,4,7,8\}\\
\mathcal{M}(b_3 = 0) &= \{1,3,5,7\}\\
\mathcal{M}(b_3 = 1) &= \{2,4,6,8\}
\end{aligned} \tag{2.407}$$

and the metrics for each of the three coded binary inputs,

$$\begin{aligned}
m(\boldsymbol{e}, b_1 = 0) &= \max\{e_1, e_2, e_3, e_4\}\\
m(\boldsymbol{e}, b_1 = 1) &= \max\{e_5, e_6, e_7, e_8\}\\
m(\boldsymbol{e}, b_2 = 0) &= \max\{e_1, e_2, e_5, e_6\}\\
m(\boldsymbol{e}, b_2 = 1) &= \max\{e_3, e_4, e_7, e_8\}\\
m(\boldsymbol{e}, b_3 = 0) &= \max\{e_1, e_3, e_5, e_7\}\\
m(\boldsymbol{e}, b_3 = 1) &= \max\{e_2, e_4, e_6, e_8\}.
\end{aligned} \tag{2.408}$$

The above metrics are approximate ML metrics with no quantizations. They result in a binary input channel with real valued outputs. Various quantized outputs can be obtained for each coded input bit in the form

$$\begin{aligned}
y_l &= f(m(\boldsymbol{e}, b_l = 0) - m(\boldsymbol{e}, b_l = 1))\\
&= f\left(\max_{m \in \mathcal{M}(b_l = 0)} e_m - \max_{m \in \mathcal{M}(b_l = 1)} e_m\right)
\end{aligned} \tag{2.409}$$

where $f(\cdot)$ is typically a uniform quantizer function. Here the difference

$$\max_{m \in \mathcal{M}(b_l = 0)} e_m - \max_{m \in \mathcal{M}(b_l = 1)} e_m \tag{2.410}$$

is treated like the correlator output of the coherent BPSK demodulator. With interleaving and deinterleaving we have a discrete memoryless binary input quantized output coding channel suitable for the usual binary codes with corresponding decoders.

Although the above conversion of an FH/MFSK channel into a discrete memoryless binary input channel was based on a Rayleigh fading channel with receiver and jammer Gaussian noise statistics, it can certainly be used in other cases as well. It is a straightforward conversion and should be robust in the sense of being good for all cases of interest. Generally, for Gaussian noise and optical signals with M-ary pulse position modulation good binary convolutional codes with these converted binary input channels perform as well or better than M-ary input channels for roughly the same complexity (see Lee [33]). For very high speeds and large M, Reed-Solomon codes look attractive for the hard decision M-ary channels. Reed-Solomon codes at data rates over 100 Mbps exist for $M = 2^8 = 256$ [21].

2.8 REFERENCES

[1] R. C. Dixon, *Spread Spectrum Systems*, New York: John Wiley, 1976.

[2] A. J. Viterbi and I. M. Jacobs, "Advances in Coding and Modulation for Noncoherent Channels Affected by Fading, Partial Band, and Multiple Access Interference," in *Advances in Communication Systems*, Vol. 4. New York: Academic Press, 1975, pp. 279–308.

[3] A. J. Viterbi, *Principles of Coherent Communication*, New York: McGraw-Hill, 1966.

[4] J. I. Marcum, "Table of Q-Functions," Rand Corporation Report RM-339, Jan. 1, 1950.

[5] S. W. Houston, "Modulation Techniques for Communication, Part I: Tone and Noise Jamming Performance of Spread Spectrum M-ary FSK and 2, 4-ary DPSK Waveforms," *Proceedings of the IEEE National Aerospace and Electronics Conference (NAECON '75)*, Dayton, Ohio, June 10–12, 1975, pp. 51–58.

[6] A. J. Viterbi, "Spread spectrum communications—Myths and realities," *IEEE Commun. Mag.*, vol. 17, pp. 11–18, May 1979.

[7] B. D. Trumpis, "On the optimum detection of fast frequency hopped MFSK signals in worst case jamming," TRW internal memorandum, June 1981.

[8] J. K. Omura and B. K. Levitt, "Coded error probability evaluation for antijam communication systems," *IEEE Trans. Commun.*, COM-30, pp. 896–903, May 1982.

[9] J. M. Wozencraft and I. M. Jacobs, *Principles of Communication Engineering*, New York: John Wiley, 1976.

[10] I. M. Jacobs, "Probability of error bounds for binary transmission on the slowly fading Rician channel," *IEEE Trans. Inform. Theory*, IT-12, pp. 431–441, October 1966.

[11] B. K. Levitt, "Strategies for FH/MFSK signaling with diversity in worst case partial band noise," in *Record of Joint USC/ARO Workshop on "Research Trends in Military Communications*," Wickenburg, AZ, May 1–4, 1983.

[12] D. J. Torrieri, *Principles of Military Communication Systems*, Dedham, MA: Artech House, 1981.

[13] J. K. Omura and T. Kailath, "Some useful probability distributions," Technical Report No. 7050-6, Stanford Electronics Laboratories, Stanford University, p. 83, September 1965.

[14] B. K. Levitt and J. K. Omura, "Coding tradeoffs for improved performance of FH/MFSK systems in partial band noise," *Record of the National Telecommunications Conference (NTC '81)*, pp. D 9.1.1–D 9.1.5, November 1981.

[15] W. E. Stark, "Coding for Frequency-Hopped Spread Spectrum Channels with Partial-Band Interference," Ph.D. Dissertation, University of Illinois, 1982.

[16] H. H. Ma and M. A. Poole, "Error-correcting codes against the worst-case partial-band jammer," *IEEE Trans. Commun.*, COM-32, pp. 124–133, February 1984.

[17] J. P. Odenwalder, "Optimal Decoding of Convolutional Codes," Ph.D. Dissertation, University of California, Los Angeles, 1970, pp. 62–68.

[18] B. D. Trumpis, "Convolutional Coding for *M*-ary Channels," Ph.D. Dissertation, University of California, Los Angeles, 1975.

[19] A. J. Viterbi and J. K. Omura, *Principles of Digital Communication and Coding*, New York: McGraw-Hill, 1979, p. 253.

[20] J. P. Odenwalder, "Dual-*K* convolutional codes for noncoherently demodulated channels," in *Proceedings of the IEEE International Telecommunications Conference (ITC '76)*, pp. 165–174, October 1976.

[21] E. R. Berlekamp, "The technology of error-correcting codes," *Proceedings of the IEEE*, vol. 68, pp. 570–572, May 1980.

[22] R. S. Orr, "Quasi-independent frequency hopping—A new spread spectrum multiple access technique," *Record of the IEEE International Conference on Communications (ICC '81)*, pp. 76.2.1–76.2.6, June 1981.

[23] R. J. McEliece and W. E. Stark, "The optimal code rate vs. a partial band noise jammer," *Record of the IEEE Military Communications Conference (MILCOM '82)*, pp. 8.5-1 to 8.5-4, October 1982.

[24] J. G. Proakis, *Digital Communications*, McGraw-Hill, New York: 1983.

[25] D. Avidor, "Anti-Jam Analysis of FH/MFSK Communication Systems in HF Rayleigh Fading Channels," Ph.D. Dissertation, University of California at Los Angeles, 1981.

[26] D. Avidor and J. K. Omura, "Analysis of FH/MFSK systems in nonuniform Rayleigh fading channels," *MILCOM '82*, October 17–20, 1982.

[27] A. J. Viterbi, "A robust ratio-threshold technique to mitigate tone and partial-band jamming in coded MFSK systems," *MILCOM '82*, October 18–20, 1982.

[28] K. L. Jordan, Jr., "The performance of sequential decoding in conjunction with efficient modulation," *IEEE Trans. Commun. Tech.*, COM-14 (3), pp. 283–297, June 1966.

[29] J. M. Wozencraft and R. S. Kennedy, "Modulation and demodulation for probabilistic decoding," *IEEE Trans. Inform. Theory*, IT-12, pp. 291–297, July 1966.

[30] M. A. Creighton, "Analysis of List Decoding Metrics for Jamming and Multiple Access Channels," Ph.D. Dissertation, University of California, Los Angeles, 1985.

[31] P. J. Crepeau, M. A. Creighton, and J. K. Omura, "Performance of FH/MFSK with list metric detection against partial band noise and random tone jamming," *MILCOM '83*, October 31–November 2, 1983.

[32] P. J. Crepeau, "Generalized list detection for coded MFSK/FH signaling on fading and jamming channels," NRL Report 8708, Naval Research Laboratory, Washington, DC, June 1983.

[33] P. J. Lee, "Decomposition of 2^L ~ ary Input Channel into L Parallel Binary Input Component Channels and Independent Binary Coding," Ph.D. Dissertation, University of California, Los Angeles, 1985.

APPENDIX 2A: JUSTIFICATION OF FACTOR OF ONE-HALF FOR FH / MFSK SIGNALS WITH DIVERSITY IN PARTIAL-BAND NOISE

Chapter 2 employed a factor of 1/2 in the Chernoff performance bounds for FH/MFSK signals with diversity in partial-band noise. This factor was originally introduced by Viterbi and Jacobs [2] based on an earlier existence proof by Jacobs [10]. However, some analysts were left with the erroneous belief that the result was valid only for maximum-likelihood metrics, which would disqualify the suboptimum linear combination metric of (2.57). Furthermore, Jacobs did not stress that his result does not usually apply to discrete-valued metrics such as those we encountered in the multitone jamming scenarios neglecting thermal noise.

Appendix 4B in Part 1 derived many general conditions under which the factor of 1/2 is valid. In particular, using (4B.31), (4B.38), (4B.39b), and (4B.43), we conclude that

$$\Pr\{x \geq 0\} \leq \min_{\lambda}\left(\tfrac{1}{2}\overline{e^{\lambda x}}\right) \tag{2A.1}$$

provided that

$$p(x) \leq p(-x); \qquad \forall\, x \geq 0 \tag{2A.2}$$

where $p(x)$ is the probability density function of the random variable x. (2A.1) is distinguished from the conventional Chernoff bound by the factor of 1/2 and the absence of the restriction that the Chernoff parameter λ be non-negative. (In fact, the condition of (2A.2) guarantees that the minimizing $\lambda \geq 0$.) Since (2A.2) must be satisfied for every non-negative x, it cannot apply to discrete-valued random variables which are asymmetric about $x = 0$. We will now prove that (2A.2) is valid for the particular cases of interest.

Consider the reception of FH/MFSK signals with m diversity chips per M-ary symbol over the partial-band noise channel. Assume non-coherent energy detection of the diversity chips, linear summation of the detected chip energies for each symbol, and perfect jamming state side information. Let the random variable x above represent the detection metric: (2.61) shows that x is the difference of a non-central and a central chi-square random variable, each with $2m$ degrees of freedom. In particular, since the received signal energy over all m chips is KE_b, where $M = 2^K$, and the side information assumption requires that all m chips be jammed with noise of power spectral density N_J/ρ for an error to occur (designated by the event $\boldsymbol{H}$ in (2.61)),

$$x = \sum_{i=1}^{2m} \left(y_i^2 - z_i^2 \right) \tag{2A.3}$$

where the y_i's and z_i's are independent Gaussian random variables, statistically defined by

$$\begin{aligned} y_i &= N\left(0, \frac{N_J}{2\rho}\right) \\ z_i &= N\left(a_i, \frac{N_J}{2\rho}\right) \\ \sum_{i=1}^{2m} a_i^2 &= KE_b. \end{aligned} \tag{2A.4}$$

From [13], we can express the probability density function of x as

$$p(x) = b^m e^{-c} |x|^{m-1} \sum_{k=0}^{\infty} \frac{\left(bc^2|x|\right)^{k/2}}{k!} \times \begin{cases} \dfrac{W_{-k/2,\, m+(k-1)/2}(4bx)}{m!}; & x \geq 0 \\[2ex] \dfrac{W_{k/2,\, m+(k-1)/2}(-4bx)}{(k+m-1)!}; & x < 0 \end{cases} \tag{2A.5}$$

where

$$b \equiv \frac{\rho}{2N_J}, \qquad c \equiv \frac{\rho K E_b}{N_J}$$

and $W(\cdot)$ is the Whittaker function defined by

$$W_{\alpha,\beta}(x) \equiv \frac{x^{\beta+1/2} e^{-x/2}}{\left(\beta - \alpha - \frac{1}{2}\right)!} \int_0^{\infty} dy\, e^{-xy} y^{\beta-\alpha-1/2} (1+y)^{\beta+\alpha-1/2};$$

$$\beta - \alpha + \tfrac{1}{2} > 0. \tag{2A.6}$$

Since $m \geq 1$ and $k \geq 0$ in (2A.5), the constraint on the indices of the Whittaker function in (2A.6) is satisfied.

Now we need to demonstrate that (2A.5) is compatible with (2A.2); that is, we must prove that

$$\sum_{k=0}^{\infty} \frac{\left(bc^2 x\right)^{k/2}}{k!(k+m-1)!} W_{k/2,\, m+(k-1)/2}(4bx) \geq \sum_{k=0}^{\infty} \frac{\left(bc^2 x\right)^{k/2}}{k!m!} W_{-k/2,\, m+(k-1)/2}(4bx); \qquad \forall\, x \geq 0. \tag{2A.7}$$

A sufficient condition is simply

$$m!\ W_{k/2,\,m+(k-1)/2}(4bx) \geq (k+m-1)!\ W_{-k/2,\,m+(k-1)/2}(4bx); \qquad \forall\, k, x \geq 0. \tag{2A.8}$$

Substituting (2A.6) into (2A.8), we need to show that

$$\int_0^\infty dy\, e^{-xy}[y(1+y)]^{m-1}\left[m(1+y)^k - y^k\right] \geq 0; \qquad \forall\, k, x \geq 0. \tag{2A.9}$$

However, since $m \geq 1$, the integrand is non-negative whenever $y \geq 0$. Consequently, (2A.9) is valid, completing the desired proof.

APPENDIX 2B: COMBINATORIAL COMPUTATION FOR $n = 1$ BAND MULTITONE JAMMING

This is a combinatorial problem required to compute the exact performance for FH/MFSK signals with diversity in $n = 1$ band multitone jamming, assuming non-coherent linear combining and perfect side information. The problem is deceptively simple to state, and difficult to resolve under certain conditions.

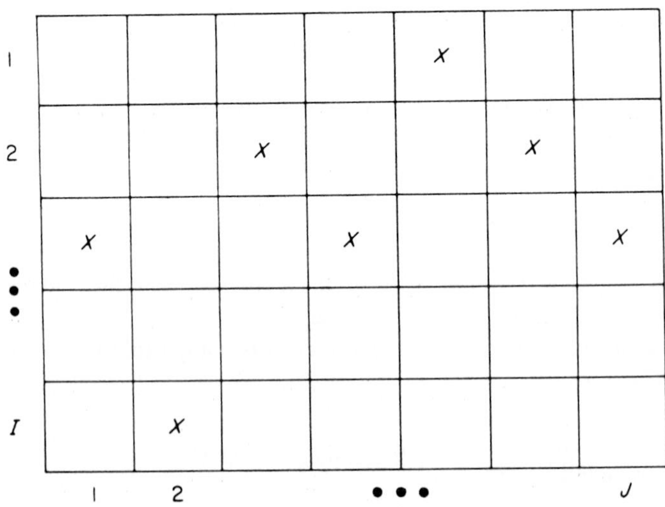

Figure 2B.1. Frequency (row)-time (column) grid for computing probabilities associated with $n = 1$ band multitone jamming.

Consider a grid containing I rows and J columns, as shown in Figure 2B.1. One X is placed in each column: the row location is random, equally likely, and independent from column to column. The number of X's in the i-th row is denoted by $l_i \in [0, J]$, and $l_{\max} \equiv \max_{1 \le i \le I}(l_i)$. There are I^J distinct patterns of X's that can arise; we want to compute subsets of these defined by

$$N_L \equiv \text{number of patterns} \ni l_{\max} = L. \tag{2B.1}$$

The difficulty here is that while the columns are statistically independent, the rows (specifically, the l_i's) are not.

Clearly, $1 \le l_{\max} \le J$, so that $N_L = 0$ for $L \notin [1, J]$. For $L = 1$, each X must lie in a different row, which can only occur if $I \ge J$:

$$N_1 = \begin{cases} \dfrac{I!}{(I-J)!}; & I \ge J \\ 0; & I < J \end{cases}. \tag{2B.2}$$

For $J/2 < L \le J$, only *one* row can have L X's: there are I ways to choose that row, $\binom{J}{L}$ ways to choose the columns that contain the X's in that row, and $(I-1)^{J-L}$ ways to place the remaining X's (all of these $I - 1$ other l_i's will be less than L since $J - L < J/2$), so that

$$N_L = \binom{J}{L} I (I-1)^{J-L}; \qquad J/2 < L \le J. \tag{2B.3}$$

For smaller values of L, it is more difficult to derive a general, explicit expression for N_L, but not impossible. For example, consider the next level of complexity, $J/3 < L \le J/2$. There are now $\binom{I}{2}\binom{J}{L}\binom{J-L}{L}(I-2)^{J-2L}$ patterns with two rows of L X's and $I - 2$ other rows with less than L X's; these patterns are counted twice in (2B.3). Furthermore, if $2L + 1 \le J$ (which always occurs in the region $J/3 < L \le J/2$ except when J is even and $L = J/2$ exactly), we must eliminate those patterns which contain L X's in one row and $L + 1$ or more X's in another row. The resulting modification to (2B.3) is[1]

$$\begin{aligned} N_L = \binom{J}{L} I (I-1)^{J-L} - \binom{I}{2}\binom{J}{L}\binom{J-L}{L}(I-2)^{J-2L} \\ - I(I-1)\binom{J}{L} \sum_{j=L+1}^{J-L} \binom{J-L}{j} (I-2)^{J-L-j}; \end{aligned}$$

$$\frac{J}{3} < L \le \frac{J}{2} \tag{2B.4}$$

where the summation is understood to be zero for the singular case $L > (J-1)/2$ discussed above.

[1] Derived by Dr. Laif Swanson of the Jet Propulsion Laboratory, Pasadena, California.

For the band multitone jamming application, we do not actually need the individual N_L's. A sufficient parameter is

$$\begin{aligned} S_{I,J}(L) &\equiv \text{number of patterns} \ni \bigcup_{i=1}^{I} (l_i \geq L) \\ &= \text{number of patterns} \ni l_{\max} \geq L \\ &= \sum_{i=L}^{J} N_i \end{aligned} \tag{2B.5}$$

where we have made use of the disjointness of the N_L's (i.e., none of the patterns in N_i coincide with any pattern in N_j for $i \neq j$). As noted earlier, before $S_{I,J}(L)$ was defined,

$$S_{I,J}(1) = I^J. \tag{2B.6}$$

Also,

$$\begin{aligned} S_{I,J}(2) &= S_{I,J}(1) - N_1 \\ &= \begin{cases} I^J - \dfrac{I!}{(I-J)!}; & I \geq J \\ I^J; & I < J. \end{cases} \end{aligned} \tag{2B.7}$$

Finally, adopting the conventions that $\lfloor x$ denotes the integer portion of x and $\Sigma_{i=a}^{b} c_i = 0$ if $a > b$, we can write

$$\begin{aligned} S_{I,J}(L) = {} & I \sum_{i=L}^{J} \binom{J}{i} (I-1)^{J-i} \\ & - \binom{I}{2} \sum_{i=L}^{\lfloor J/2} \binom{J}{i} \binom{J-i}{i} (I-2)^{J-2i} \\ & - I(I-1) \sum_{i=L}^{\lfloor J/2} \binom{J}{i} \sum_{j=i+1}^{J-i} \binom{J-i}{j} (I-2)^{J-i-j}; \\ & \qquad \frac{J}{3} < L \leq J. \end{aligned} \tag{2B.8}$$

So for $J \leq 8$, we can compute $S_{I,J}(L)$ for the entire range of $L \in [1, J]$; for $J > 8$, we are missing the region $3 \leq L \leq \lfloor J/3$. In principle, we could extend (2B.4) to the next region, $J/4 < L \leq J/3$, and so on, but this is increasingly more complex and not really a worthwhile exercise.

Part 3

OTHER FREQUENCY-HOPPED SYSTEMS

Chapter 3

COHERENT MODULATION TECHNIQUES

Thus far in our discussions, we have considered only those frequency-hopped (FH) systems in which the carrier phases of the individual transmitted hop frequency pulses bear no relation to one another. Such a spread-spectrum (SS) technique was referred to as *non-coherent FH* and the method for recovering the data modulation appropriately employed some form of energy detection. Clearly, another possibility exists for implementing the FH modulator, wherein phase continuity is maintained from one hop pulse to another thereby resulting in so-called *coherent FH*. Assuming that the coherent frequency synthesizer in the receiver is capable of estimating and correcting for the phase errors associated with the electrical path length over the transmission channel and the Doppler shift, then following the dehopping operation one could employ coherent detection techniques for recovery of the data modulation.

Of all the modulation techniques which lend themselves to coherent detection, those that are most commonly found in present-day applications are the so-called quadrature modulations which include quadriphase-shift-keying (QPSK), quadrature amplitude-shift-keying (QASK), and quadrature partial response (QPR).[1] We shall consider binary phase-shift-keying (BPSK) as a degenerate case of QPSK. The performance of these modulation techniques over the additive white Gaussian noise (AWGN) channel is well documented in the literature [1], [2], [3]. This chapter presents the comparable results when an FH/SS modulation is superimposed on these conventional techniques in order to combat the intentional interference introduced by a jammer [4], [5]. The receiver structures that will be analyzed will be those normally employed for coherent detection of these modulations in an AWGN background. As such, our intent here is not to consider optimum

[1] The QPR Class I modulation, which is the only case we shall consider, is also referred to in the literature as duobinary-encoded QPSK [1].

receiver structures based upon jamming state information, but rather to demonstrate the effect of the despread jammer on the conventional structures.

The scenario under which the jammer is assumed to operate here is the same as that proposed in the previous chapters for the design of non-coherent FH/SS systems. In particular, we assume an intelligent jammer that has knowledge of the form of data and SS modulations, including such items as data rate, spreading bandwidth and hop rate, but no knowledge of the code selected for determining the spectrum-spreading hop frequencies. Once again, the strategy employed is to design for the worst case jammer in the sense that, given the modulation form of the communicator, the jammer is assumed to employ the type of jamming which is most deleterious to the communication receiver. The two most common jammer types are still the partial-band noise and partial-band multitone jammers. Hence, for each form of coherent data modulation considered, we shall direct all of our attention to these two jammer types, developing in each case the performance corresponding to the worst case jamming strategy.

Although the primary emphasis of this chapter is on pure FH quadrature modulation systems, later on we shall consider the additional improvement in jam resistance offered by superimposing a balanced pseudonoise (PN) modulation on the individual hop frequencies. This hybrid SS technique is referred to as FH/PN modulation and is normally employed in situations where the system requires anti-jam protection beyond that which FH or PN modulation is capable of producing on its own.

3.1 PERFORMANCE OF FH/QPSK IN THE PRESENCE OF PARTIAL-BAND MULTITONE JAMMING

An FH/QPSK signal is characterized by transmitting (Figure 3.1)

$$s^{(i)}(t) = \sqrt{2S}\,\sin\left(\omega_h^{(i)}t + \theta^{(i)}\right) \tag{3.1}$$

in the i-th signalling interval $(i-1)T_s \le t \le iT_s$, where $\omega_h^{(i)}$ is the particular carrier radian frequency selected by the frequency hopper for this interval.[2] According to the designated SS code, $\theta^{(i)}$ is the information symbol which ranges over the set of possible values

$$\theta_m = \frac{m\pi}{4}; \qquad m = 1, 3, 5, 7 \tag{3.2}$$

and S is the transmitted average power.

[2] We assume here the case of slow frequency hopping (SFH), i.e., the hop rate is equal to or a submultiple of the information symbol rate and that the frequency hopper and symbol clock are synchronous. Thus, in a given symbol interval, the signal frequency is constant and the jammer, if transmitting a tone at that frequency, affects the entire symbol interval.

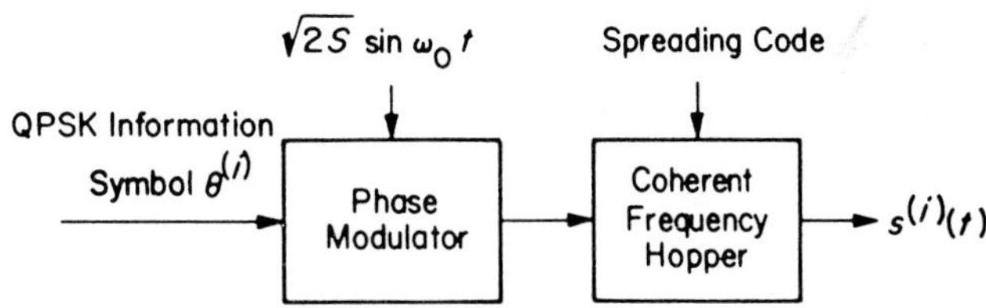

Figure 3.1. Block diagram of a coherent FH/QPSK modulator.

At the receiver (Figure 3.2), the sum of additive white Gaussian noise $n(t)$, the jammer $J(t)$, and a random phase-shifted version of the transmitted signal $s^{(i)}(t;\theta)$ are first frequency dehopped, then coherently demodulated by a conventional QPSK demodulator.

The band-pass noise $n(t)$ has the usual narrowband representation

$$n(t) = \sqrt{2}\left[N_c(t)\cos\left(\omega_h^{(i)}t + \theta\right) - N_s(t)\sin\left(\omega_h^{(i)}t + \theta\right)\right] \qquad (3.3)$$

where $N_c(t)$ and $N_s(t)$ are statistically independent low-pass white Gaussian noise processes with single-sided noise spectral density N_0 w/Hz. The partial-band multitone jammer $J(t)$ is assumed to have a total power J which is evenly divided among Q jammer tones. Thus, each tone has power

$$J_0 = \frac{J}{Q}. \qquad (3.4)$$

Furthermore, since the jammer is assumed to have knowledge of the exact location of the spreading bandwidth W_{ss} and the number N of hops in this bandwidth, then, as was done in our previous discussions, we shall assume that he will randomly locate each of his Q tones coincident with Q of the N hop frequencies. Thus,

$$\rho \triangleq \frac{Q}{N} \qquad (3.5)$$

represents the fraction of the total band which is continuously jammed with tones, each having power J_0. Once again, the jammer's strategy is to distribute his total power J (i.e., choose ρ and J_0) in such a way as to cause the communicator to have maximum probability of error.

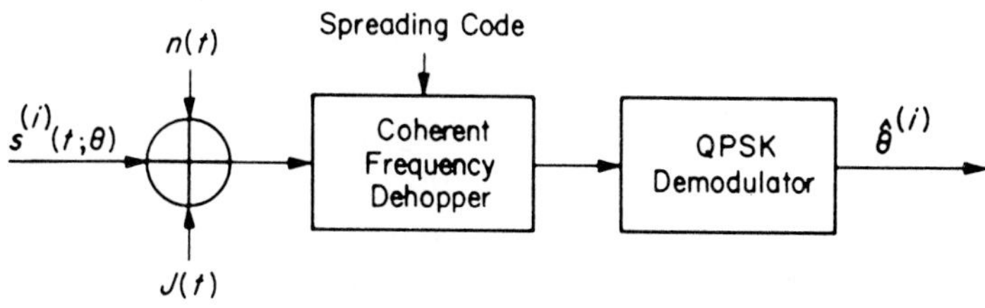

Figure 3.2. Block diagram of a coherent FH/QPSK demodulator.

In view of the foregoing, the total received signal in a signalling interval which contains a jamming tone at the hop frequency is given by

$$y^{(i)}(t) = s^{(i)}(t;\theta) + n(t) + J(t) \tag{3.6}$$

where

$$s^{(i)}(t;\theta) = \sqrt{2S}\,\sin\left(\omega_h^{(i)}t + \theta^{(i)} + \theta\right), \tag{3.7}$$

$n(t)$ is given by (3.3) and

$$J(t) = \sqrt{2J_0}\,\cos\left(\omega_h^{(i)}t + \theta_J + \theta\right) \tag{3.8}$$

with θ_J uniformly distributed on $(0, 2\pi)$ and independent of the information symbol phase $\theta^{(i)}$. Over an integral number of hop bands, the fraction ρ of the total number of signalling intervals will have a received signal characterized by (3.6). In the remaining fraction $(1-\rho)$ of the signalling intervals, the received signal is simply characterized by

$$y^{(i)}(t) = s^{(i)}(t;\theta) + n(t). \tag{3.9}$$

After ideal coherent demodulation by the frequency hopper, the in-phase and quadrature components of the received signal become[3]

$$\begin{aligned}\varepsilon_I(t) &\triangleq y^{(i)}(t)\left[\sqrt{2}\,\sin\left(\omega_h^{(i)}t + \theta\right)\right] = \sqrt{S}\,\cos\theta^{(i)} - \sqrt{J_0}\,\sin\theta_J - N_s(t)\\ \varepsilon_Q(t) &\triangleq y^{(i)}(t)\left[\sqrt{2}\,\cos\left(\omega_h^{(i)}t + \theta\right)\right] = \sqrt{S}\,\sin\theta^{(i)} + \sqrt{J_0}\,\cos\theta_J + N_c(t).\end{aligned} \tag{3.10}$$

These signals are then passed through integrate-and-dump filters of duration equal to the information symbol interval T_s to produce the in-phase and quadrature decision variables

$$\begin{aligned}z_I &\triangleq \int_{(i-1)T_s}^{iT_s} \varepsilon_I(t)\,dt = \sqrt{S}\,T_s\cos\theta^{(i)} - \sqrt{J_0}\,T_s\sin\theta_J + N_I\\ &= a_i\sqrt{\frac{S}{2}}\,T_s - \sqrt{J_0}\,T_s\sin\theta_J + N_I\\ z_Q &\triangleq \int_{(i-1)T_s}^{iT_s} \varepsilon_Q(t)\,dt = \sqrt{S}\,T_s\sin\theta^{(i)} + \sqrt{J_0}\,T_s\cos\theta_J + N_Q\\ &= b_i\sqrt{\frac{S}{2}}\,T_s + \sqrt{J_0}\,T_s\cos\theta_J + N_Q\end{aligned} \tag{3.11}$$

where

$$\begin{aligned}N_I &\triangleq -\int_{(i-1)T_s}^{iT_s} N_s(t)\,dt\\ N_Q &\triangleq \int_{(i-1)T_s}^{iT_s} N_c(t)\,dt\end{aligned} \tag{3.12}$$

[3] We ignore double-harmonic terms.

are zero mean Gaussian random variables with variance $N_0T_s/2$ and, in view of the possible values for $\theta^{(i)}$ given in (3.2), $\{a_i\}$ and $\{b_i\}$ are the equivalent independent in-phase and quadrature binary information sequences which take on values ± 1.

The receiver estimates of a_i and b_i are obtained by passing z_I and z_Q through hard limiters, giving

$$\hat{a}_i = \operatorname{sgn} z_I; \qquad \hat{b}_i = \operatorname{sgn} z_Q. \tag{3.13}$$

Hence, given a_i, b_i and θ_J, the probability that the i-th symbol is in error is the probability that either $\hat{a}_i$ or $\hat{b}_i$ is in error, i.e.,

$$\begin{aligned} P_{s_i}(\theta_J) &= \Pr\{\hat{a}_i \neq a_i \text{ or } \hat{b}_i \neq b_i\} \\ &= \Pr\{\hat{a}_i \neq a_i\} + \Pr\{\hat{b}_i \neq b_i\} \\ &\quad - \Pr\{\hat{a}_i \neq a_i\}\Pr\{\hat{b}_i \neq b_i\}. \end{aligned} \tag{3.14}$$

Since the signal set is symmetric, we can compute (3.14) for any of the four possible signal points and obtain the average probability of symbol error conditioned on the jammer phase $P_s(\theta_J)$. Thus, assuming for simplicity that $a_i = 1$, $b_i = 1$, we compute $P_s(\theta_J)$ from (3.14), combined with (3.11) and (3.13), as

$$\begin{aligned} P_s(\theta_J) &= \Pr\{z_I < 0 | a_i = 1\} + \Pr\{z_Q < 0 | b_i = 1\} \\ &\quad - \Pr\{z_I < 0 | a_i = 1\}\Pr\{z_Q < 0 | b_i = 1\} \\ &= P_I(\theta_J) + P_Q(\theta_J) - P_I(\theta_J)P_Q(\theta_J) \end{aligned} \tag{3.15}$$

where

$$\begin{aligned} P_I(\theta_J) &= \Pr\left\{N_I < -\sqrt{\frac{S}{2}}\,T_s + \sqrt{J_0}\,T_s \sin\theta_J\right\} \\ &= Q\left[\sqrt{\frac{ST_s}{N_0}}\left(1 - \sqrt{\frac{2J_0}{S}}\,\sin\theta_J\right)\right] \\ P_Q(\theta_J) &= \Pr\left\{N_Q < -\sqrt{\frac{S}{2}}\,T_s - \sqrt{J_0}\,T_s \cos\theta_J\right\} \\ &= Q\left[\sqrt{\frac{ST_s}{N_0}}\left(1 + \sqrt{\frac{2J_0}{S}}\,\cos\theta_J\right)\right] \end{aligned} \tag{3.16}$$

with $Q(x)$ the Gaussian probability integral as used in previous chapters.

Finally, the unconditional average probability of symbol error P_{s_J} for symbol intervals which are jammed is obtained by averaging $P_s(\theta_J)$ of (3.15) over the uniform distribution of θ_J. Thus,

$$P_{s_J} = \frac{1}{2\pi}\int_0^{2\pi}\left[P_I(\theta_J) + P_Q(\theta_J) - P_I(\theta_J)P_Q(\theta_J)\right] d\theta_J. \tag{3.17}$$

Recognizing that, for a QPSK signal, the symbol time T_s is twice the bit time T_b, letting $E_b = ST_b$ denote the bit energy, we then have

$$\frac{ST_s}{N_0} = \frac{2ST_b}{N_0} = \frac{2E_b}{N_0}. \tag{3.18}$$

Furthermore, from (3.4) and (3.5),

$$\frac{2J_0}{S} = \frac{2J}{\rho NS}. \tag{3.19}$$

Now, if the hop frequency slots are $1/T_s$ wide, in terms of the total hop frequency band W_{ss} and the number of hop slots N in that band, we then have

$$N = \frac{W_{ss}}{1/T_s} = W_{ss}T_s = 2W_{ss}T_b. \tag{3.20}$$

Substituting (3.20) into (3.19) gives

$$\frac{2J_0}{S} = \frac{J/W_{ss}}{\rho ST_b} = \frac{J/W_{ss}}{\rho E_b} \triangleq \frac{N_J}{\rho E_b}. \tag{3.21}$$

As in previous chapters, the quantity J/W_{ss} represents the *effective jammer power spectral density* in the hop band; thus, we have again introduced the notation N_J to represent this quantity.

Finally, rewriting (3.16) using (3.18) and (3.21) gives

$$P_I(\theta_J) = Q\left[\sqrt{\frac{2E_b}{N_0}}\left(1 - \sqrt{\frac{N_J}{\rho E_b}}\sin\theta_J\right)\right]$$

$$P_Q(\theta_J) = Q\left[\sqrt{\frac{2E_b}{N_0}}\left(1 + \sqrt{\frac{N_J}{\rho E_b}}\cos\theta_J\right)\right]. \tag{3.22}$$

For the fraction $(1-\rho)$ of symbol (hop) intervals where the jammer is absent, the average symbol error probability is given by the well-known result [1]

$$P_{s_0} = 2Q\left(\sqrt{\frac{2E_b}{N_0}}\right) - Q^2\left(\sqrt{\frac{2E_b}{N_0}}\right). \tag{3.23}$$

Thus, the average error probability over all symbols (jammed and unjammed) is simply

$$P_s = \rho P_{s_J} + (1-\rho)P_{s_0}, \tag{3.24}$$

where P_{s_J} is given by (3.17), together with (3.22), and P_{s_0} is given in (3.23).

Before presenting numerical results illustrating the evaluation of (3.24), it is of interest to examine its limiting behavior as $N_0 \to 0$. Clearly, from (3.23) we have

$$\lim_{E_b/N_0 \to \infty} P_{s_0} = 0 \tag{3.25}$$

Also,

$$\lim_{E_b/N_0 \to \infty} P_{s_J} = \begin{cases} 0; & \dfrac{\rho E_b}{N_J} > 1 \\ \dfrac{2}{\pi}\cos^{-1}\sqrt{\dfrac{\rho E_b}{N_J}}; & \dfrac{1}{2} < \dfrac{\rho E_b}{N_j} \le 1 \\ \dfrac{1}{\pi}\cos^{-1}\sqrt{\dfrac{\rho E_b}{N_J}} + \dfrac{1}{4}; & 0 < \dfrac{\rho E_b}{N_J} \le \dfrac{1}{2}. \end{cases} \quad (3.26)$$

This result can be obtained directly from the graphical interpretation given in Figure 3.3. Finally, substituting (3.25) and (3.26) in (3.24) gives the

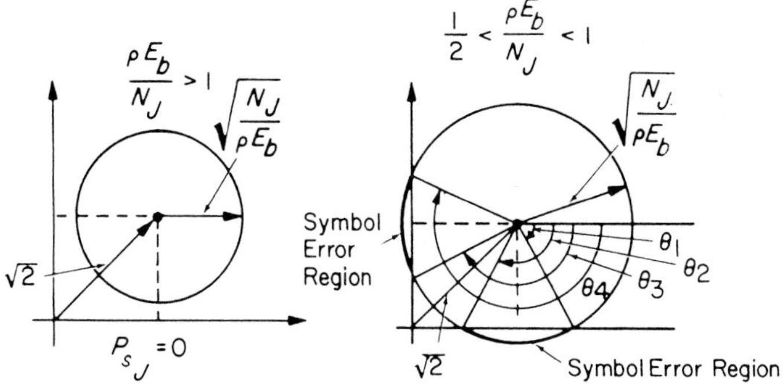

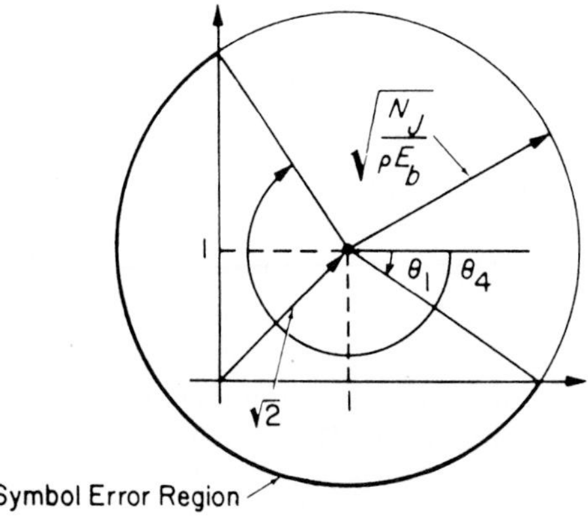

Figure 3.3. Graphical interpretation of (3.26).

desired limiting behavior for the average symbol error probability, namely,

$$\lim_{E_b/N_0 \to \infty} P_s = \begin{cases} 0; & \dfrac{\rho E_b}{N_J} > 1 \\ \dfrac{2\rho}{\pi} \cos^{-1}\sqrt{\dfrac{\rho E_b}{N_J}}; & \dfrac{1}{2} < \dfrac{\rho E_b}{N_J} \le 1 \\ \dfrac{\rho}{\pi} \cos^{-1}\sqrt{\dfrac{\rho E_b}{N_J}} + \dfrac{\rho}{4}; & 0 < \dfrac{\rho E_b}{N_J} \le \dfrac{1}{2}. \end{cases} \tag{3.27}$$

The partial-band fraction ρ corresponding to the worst case jammer (maximum P_s) can be obtained by differentiating (3.27) with respect to ρ and equating to zero. Assuming that, for a fixed E_b/N_J, this worst case ρ occurs when $1/2 < \rho E_b/N_J \le 1$, then

$$\frac{d}{d\rho}\left[\frac{2\rho}{\pi} \cos^{-1}\sqrt{\frac{\rho E_b}{N_J}}\right] = 0 \tag{3.28}$$

implies

$$\tan^{-1} Z = \frac{1}{2Z} \tag{3.29}$$

where

$$Z \triangleq \sqrt{\frac{1 - \rho E_b/N_J}{\rho E_b/N_J}}. \tag{3.30}$$

The solution to (3.29) may be numerically found to be

$$Z = 0.7654 \tag{3.31}$$

or

$$\rho_{\text{wc}} = \begin{cases} \dfrac{0.6306}{E_b/N_J}; & E_b/N_J > 0.6306 \\ 1; & E_b/N_J \le 0.6306. \end{cases} \tag{3.32}$$

Note that, since Q and N are integers, then ρ as defined in (3.5) is not a continuous variable. Thus, for a given N, the true worst case ρ would be the rational number nearest to (3.32) which yields an integer value of Q. Also, the second part of (3.32) comes about from the fact that Q is constrained to be less than or equal to N. Thus, when E_b/N_J is such that the solution of (3.30) and (3.31) gives a value of $\rho > 1$, we take $\rho = 1$ (full-band jamming) as the worst case jammer. Substituting (3.32) into (3.27) gives the limiting average symbol error probability performance corresponding to the worst case jammer, namely,

$$\lim_{E_b/N_0 \to \infty} P_{s_{\max}} = \begin{cases} \dfrac{0.2623}{E_b/N_J}; & E_b/N_J > 0.6306 \\ \dfrac{2}{\pi} \cos^{-1}\sqrt{\dfrac{E_b}{N_J}}; & 0.5 < E_b/N_J \le 0.6306 \\ \dfrac{1}{\pi} \cos^{-1}\sqrt{\dfrac{E_b}{N_J}} + \dfrac{1}{4}; & 0 < E_b/N_J \le 0.5. \end{cases} \tag{3.33}$$

The final step in the characterization of the performance of FH/QPSK in the presence of multitone jamming is the conversion of average symbol error probability to average bit error probability. If one encodes the information symbols using a Gray code, the average bit error probability, P_b, for a multiple phase-shift-keyed (MPSK) signal is then approximated for large

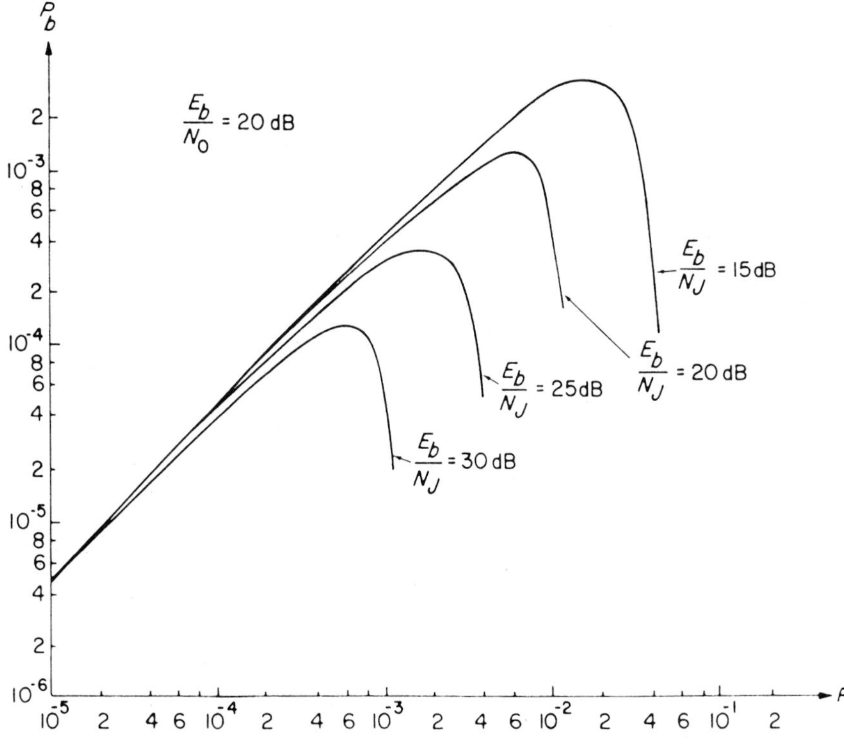

Figure 3.4. P_b versus ρ—FH/QPSK (tone jamming).

E_b/N_0 by

$$P_b \cong \frac{P_s}{\log_2 M} \tag{3.34}$$

where $\log_2 M$ is the number of bits/symbol. The approximation in (3.34) refers to the fact that only errors in symbols whose corresponding signal phases are adjacent to that of the transmitted signal are accounted for. Since a Gray code has the property that adjacent symbols differ in only a single bit, then an error in an adjacent symbol is accompanied by one, and only one, bit error.

Since QPSK is the particular case of MPSK corresponding to $M = 4$, then from (3.34),

$$P_b \cong \tfrac{1}{2} P_s \tag{3.35}$$

where P_s is given by (3.24) or its limiting form in (3.27).

Fortunately, for the case of QPSK, it is straightforward to account for the diagonal symbol errors which result in two bit errors and, thus, arrive at an *exact* expression for P_b. In fact, P_b for QPSK is identical to P_b for binary PSK (BPSK) and is given by

$$\begin{aligned} P_b &= \rho\left[\frac{1}{2\pi}\int_0^{2\pi} P_I(\theta_J)\,d\theta_J\right] + (1-\rho)Q\left(\sqrt{\frac{2E_b}{N_0}}\right) \\ &= \rho\left[\frac{1}{2\pi}\int_0^{2\pi} P_Q(\theta_J)\,d\theta_J\right] + (1-\rho)Q\left(\sqrt{\frac{2E_b}{N_0}}\right) \end{aligned} \tag{3.36}$$

where $P_I(\theta_J)$ and $P_Q(\theta_J)$ are given in (3.22). Thus, comparing the approximate result of (3.35) (using (3.17), (3.22), and (3.24)) with the exact result of (3.36), we observe that the difference between the two resides in the terms resulting from the *product* of error probabilities, namely,

$$\frac{1}{2\pi}\int_0^{2\pi} P_I(\theta_J)P_Q(\theta_J)\,d\theta_J$$

and $Q^2(\sqrt{2E_b/N_0})$. Also, by analogy with (3.27), the exact limiting form of P_b becomes

$$\lim_{E_b/N_0\to\infty} P_b = \begin{cases} 0; & \dfrac{\rho E_b}{N_J} > 1 \\ \dfrac{\rho}{\pi}\cos^{-1}\sqrt{\dfrac{\rho E_b}{N_J}}; & 0 < \dfrac{\rho E_b}{N_J} \le 1 \end{cases} \tag{3.37}$$

with a worst case ρ as in (3.32) and corresponding maximum error probability

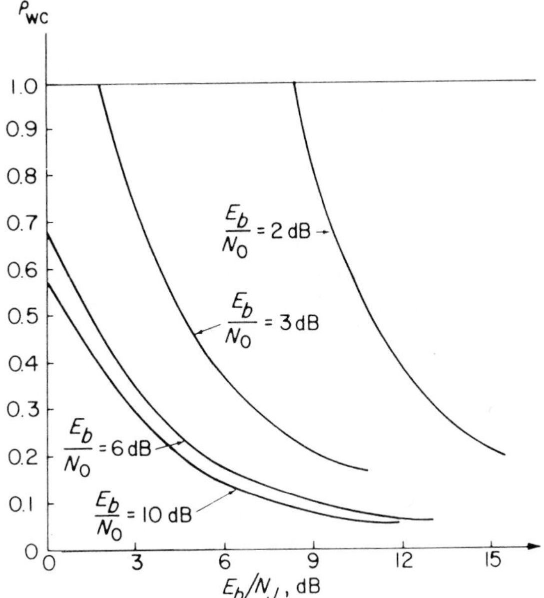

Figure 3.5. Worst case ρ versus E_b/N_J—FH/QPSK (tone jamming).

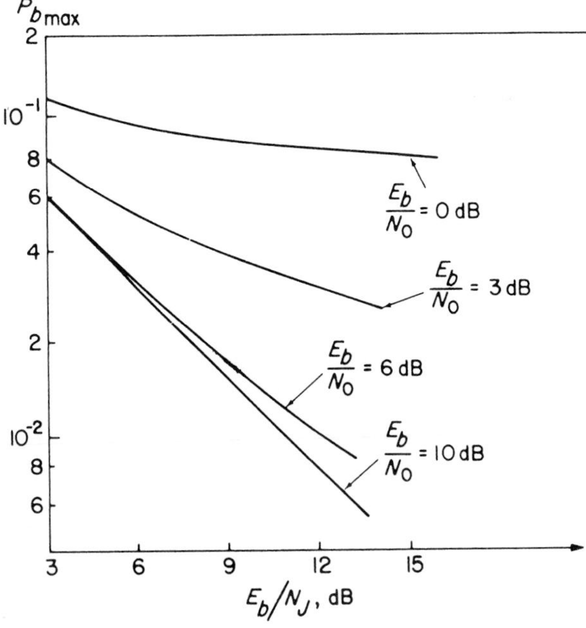

Figure 3.6. Worst case P_b versus E_b/N_J—FH/QPSK (tone jamming).

$$\lim_{E_b/N_0 \to \infty} P_{b_{\max}} = \begin{cases} \dfrac{0.1311}{E_b/N_J}; & E_b/N_J > 0.6306 \\ \dfrac{1}{\pi}\cos^{-1}\sqrt{\dfrac{E_b}{N_J}}; & E_b/N_J \le 0.6306. \end{cases} \tag{3.38}$$

Figure 3.4 is a typical plot of P_b versus ρ, with E_b/N_J as a parameter for the case $E_b/N_0 = 20$ dB. It is seen that, for fixed E_b/N_0 and E_b/N_J, there exists a value of ρ which maximizes P_b and, thus, represents the worst case multitone jammer situation. In the limit, as E_b/N_0 approaches infinity, this value of ρ becomes equal to that given by (3.32). Figure 3.5 is a plot of worst case ρ versus E_b/N_J, with E_b/N_0 as a parameter. Figure 3.6 illustrates the corresponding plot of $P_{b_{\max}}$ versus E_b/N_J, with E_b/N_0 fixed.

3.2 PERFORMANCE OF FH/QASK IN THE PRESENCE OF PARTIAL-BAND MULTITONE JAMMING

An FH/QASK-M signal is characterized by transmitting

$$s^{(i)}(t) = \sqrt{2}\,\delta\left[b_n \cos\omega_h^{(i)}t + a_m \sin\omega_h^{(i)}t\right] \tag{3.39}$$

in the i-th signalling interval. The total number of signals possible M is typically the square of an even number K, and the quadrature amplitudes a_m and b_n take on equally likely values m and n, respectively, with $m, n = \pm 1, \pm 3, \ldots \pm(K-1)$. Also, δ is a parameter which is related to the average power S of the signal set by

$$S = \tfrac{2}{3}(K^2 - 1)\delta^2. \tag{3.40}$$

Analogous to the step leading to (3.11), we can arrive at expressions for the in-phase and quadrature decision variables, namely,

$$\begin{aligned} z_I &= a_i \delta T_s - \sqrt{J_0}\,T_s \sin\theta_J + N_I \\ z_Q &= b_i \delta T_s + \sqrt{J_0}\,T_s \cos\theta_J + N_Q. \end{aligned} \tag{3.41}$$

The QASK receiver estimates of a_i and b_i are obtained by passing z_I and z_Q through K-level quantizers

$$\hat{a}_i = Q_K(z_I); \qquad \hat{b}_i = Q_K(z_Q) \tag{3.42}$$

where

$$Q_K(x) = \begin{cases} 1; & 0 \le x \le 2\delta T_s \\ 3; & 2\delta T_s \le x \le 4\delta T_s \\ \vdots & \\ (K-3); & (K-4)\delta T_s \le x \le (K-2)\delta T_s \\ (K-1); & (K-2)\delta T_s \le x \le \infty \end{cases} \tag{3.43}$$

and $Q_K(x) = -Q_K(-x)$. Hence, given a_i, b_i, and θ_J, the probability that the i-th symbol is in error is the probability that $\hat{a}_i$ or $\hat{b}_i$ is in error. Thus, once again, (3.14) is valid. Here, however, we must compute (3.14) for the $K^2/4$ points in any quadrant in order to obtain the average probability of symbol error conditioned on the jammer phase. Thus, using QASK-16 ($K = 4$) as an example, we have

$$\begin{aligned}\Pr\{\hat{a}_i \neq a_i\} &\triangleq P_I(\theta_J)\\ &= \tfrac{1}{2}\Pr\{0 > z_I > 2\delta T_s | a_i = 1\} + \tfrac{1}{2}\Pr\{z_I < 2\delta T_s | a_i = 3\}\\ \Pr\{\hat{b}_i \neq b_i\} &\triangleq P_Q(\theta_J)\\ &= \tfrac{1}{2}\Pr\{0 > z_Q > 2\delta T_s | b_i = 1\} + \tfrac{1}{2}\Pr\{z_Q < 2\delta T_s | b_i = 3\}\end{aligned} \tag{3.44}$$

or

$$\begin{aligned}P_I(\theta_J) &= \tfrac{1}{2}\Pr\left\{\delta T_s + \sqrt{J_0}\,T_s\sin\theta_J < N_I < -\delta T_s + \sqrt{J_0}\,T_s\sin\theta_J\right\}\\ &+ \tfrac{1}{2}\Pr\left\{N_I < -\delta T_s + \sqrt{J_0}\,T_s\sin\theta_J\right\}\\ &= Q\left[\sqrt{\frac{2\delta^2 T_s}{N_0}}\left(1 - \sqrt{\frac{J_0}{\delta^2}}\sin\theta_J\right)\right] + \frac{1}{2}Q\left[\sqrt{\frac{2\delta^2 T_s}{N_0}}\left(1 + \sqrt{\frac{J_0}{\delta^2}}\sin\theta_J\right)\right]\end{aligned} \tag{3.45}$$

and

$$\begin{aligned}P_Q(\theta_J) &= \tfrac{1}{2}\Pr\left\{\delta T_s - \sqrt{J_0}\,T_s\cos\theta_J < N_Q < -\delta T_s - \sqrt{J_0}\,T_s\cos\theta_J\right\}\\ &+ \tfrac{1}{2}\Pr\left\{N_Q < -\delta T_s - \sqrt{J_0}\,T_s\cos\theta_J\right\}\\ &= Q\left[\sqrt{\frac{2\delta^2 T_s}{N_0}}\left(1 + \sqrt{\frac{J_0}{\delta^2}}\cos\theta_J\right)\right] + \frac{1}{2}Q\left[\sqrt{\frac{2\delta^2 T_s}{N_0}}\left(1 - \sqrt{\frac{J_0}{\delta^2}}\cos\theta_J\right)\right].\end{aligned} \tag{3.46}$$

Letting $K = 4$ in (3.40) and recognizing that $T_s = 4T_b$, we now have

$$\frac{2\delta^2 T_s}{N_0} = \frac{ST_s}{5N_0} = 2\left(\frac{2}{5}\frac{ST_b}{N_0}\right) \triangleq \frac{2E_b'}{N_0} \tag{3.47}$$

where

$$E_b' \triangleq \tfrac{2}{5}E_b. \tag{3.48}$$

Also,

$$\frac{J_0}{\delta^2} = \frac{10J}{\rho NS} = \frac{10J}{\rho(4W_{ss}T_b)S} = \frac{J/W_{ss}}{\rho E_b'} = \frac{N_J}{\rho E_b'}. \tag{3.49}$$

Finally, then, the unconditional average probability of symbol error P_{s_J} for symbol intervals which are jammed is given by (3.17) with (for QASK-16)

$$P_I(\theta_J) = Q\left[\sqrt{\frac{2E_b'}{N_0}}\left(1 - \sqrt{\frac{N_J}{\rho E_b'}}\sin\theta_J\right)\right] + \frac{1}{2}Q\left[\sqrt{\frac{2E_b'}{N_0}}\left(1 + \sqrt{\frac{N_J}{\rho E_b'}}\sin\theta_J\right)\right]$$

$$P_Q(\theta_J) = Q\left[\sqrt{\frac{2E_b'}{N_0}}\left(1 + \sqrt{\frac{N_J}{\rho E_b'}}\cos\theta_J\right)\right] + \frac{1}{2}Q\left[\sqrt{\frac{2E_b'}{N_0}}\left(1 - \sqrt{\frac{N_J}{\rho E_b'}}\cos\theta_J\right)\right]. \tag{3.50}$$

For symbol intervals which are not jammed, the average symbol error probability is given by the well-known result [2]

$$P_{s_0} = 3Q\left(\sqrt{\frac{2E_b'}{N_0}}\right) - \frac{9}{4}Q^2\left(\sqrt{\frac{2E_b'}{N_0}}\right). \tag{3.51}$$

Thus, the average error probability over all symbols is once again given by (3.24) with, however, P_{s_J} of (3.17) together with (3.50) and P_{s_0} of (3.51).

As was done for FH/QPSK, one can compute the limiting performance of FH/QASK as E_b/N_0 approaches infinity. In particular, using a graphical interpretation analogous to Figure 3.3, we obtain the following result:

$$\lim_{E_b/N_0 \to \infty} P_{s_J} = \begin{cases} 0; & \dfrac{\rho E_b'}{N_J} > 1 \\ \dfrac{3}{\pi}\cos^{-1}\sqrt{\dfrac{\rho E_b'}{N_J}}; & \dfrac{1}{2} < \dfrac{\rho E_b'}{N_J} \leq 1 \\ \dfrac{3}{4\pi}\cos^{-1}\sqrt{\dfrac{\rho E_b'}{N_J}} + \dfrac{9}{16}; & 0 < \dfrac{\rho E_b'}{N_J} \leq \dfrac{1}{2}. \end{cases} \tag{3.52}$$

Finally, realizing that (3.25) also applies to P_{s_0} of (3.51), substituting (3.25) and (3.52) into (3.24) then gives the desired limiting behavior of the average symbol error probability of QASK-16, namely,

$$\lim_{E_b/N_0 \to \infty} P_s = \begin{cases} 0; & \dfrac{\rho E_b'}{N_J} > 1 \\ \dfrac{3\rho}{\pi}\cos^{-1}\sqrt{\dfrac{\rho E_b'}{N_J}}; & \dfrac{1}{2} < \dfrac{\rho E_b'}{N_J} \leq 1 \\ \dfrac{3\rho}{4\pi}\cos^{-1}\sqrt{\dfrac{\rho E_b'}{N_J}} + \dfrac{9\rho}{16}; & 0 < \dfrac{\rho E_b'}{N_J} \leq \dfrac{1}{2}. \end{cases} \tag{3.53}$$

To determine the worst case jamming situation, we again differentiate P_s, now given by (3.53), with respect to ρ and equate to zero. Recognizing that the expression for P_s of QASK-16 in the interval $1/2 < \rho E_b'/N_J \le 1$ is $3/2$ times that for P_s of QPSK in the interval $1/2 < \rho E_b/N_J \le 1$, we can immediately observe that the worst case ρ is now

$$\rho_{\text{wc}} = \begin{cases} \dfrac{0.6306}{E_b'/N_J} = \dfrac{1.5765}{E_b/N_J}; & E_b'/N_J > 0.6306 \\ 1; & E_b'/N_J \le 0.6306 \end{cases} \tag{3.54}$$

and the corresponding worst case average symbol error probability performance is

$$\lim_{E_b/N_0 \to \infty} P_{s_{\max}} = \begin{cases} \dfrac{3}{2}\left(\dfrac{0.2623}{E_b'/N_J}\right) = \dfrac{0.9835}{E_b/N_J}; & E_b'/N_J > 0.6306 \\ \dfrac{3}{\pi}\cos^{-1}\sqrt{\dfrac{E_b'}{N_J}} & 0.5 < E_b'/N_J \le 0.6306 \\ \dfrac{3}{4\pi}\cos^{-1}\sqrt{\dfrac{E_b'}{N_J}} + \dfrac{9}{16}; & 0 < E_b'/N_J \le 0.5 \end{cases} \tag{3.55}$$

where we have also made use of (3.48).

If one encodes the QASK symbols with a perfect Gray code, then accounting only for adjacent symbol errors (which is equivalent to one bit error per symbol error), the average bit error probability for large E_b/N_0 and $\rho E_b/N_J$ is related to the average symbol error probability by (3.34), where now $M = K^2$ is the total number of symbols or $\log_2 M = \log_2 K^2$ is the number of bits/symbol. Clearly, for QASK-16,

$$P_b \cong \tfrac{1}{4} P_s \qquad (\text{for } E_b/N_0 \gg 1, \rho E_b/N_J \gg 1). \tag{3.56}$$

(3.56) provides an optimistic estimate of P_b. The exact expression can be calculated via the fact that QASK-16 is obtained from independent amplitude-shift-keying on two quadrature components of a carrier. Assuming a perfectly coherent receiver, no interchannel effects exist in the demodulation process. Hence, the bit error probability P_b for QASK-16 is identical to P_b for each individual channel and is given by

$$P_b = \rho P_{b_J} + (1-\rho) P_{b_0} \tag{3.57}$$

where

$$P_{b_J} = \frac{1}{4\pi}\int_0^{2\pi}\left[P_Q(\theta_J) + P_Q^*(\theta_J)\right] d\theta_J \tag{3.58}$$

with $P_Q(\theta_J)$ as in (3.50) and $P_Q^*(\theta_J)$ equal to

$$P_Q^*(\theta_J) = Q\left[\sqrt{\frac{2E_b'}{N_0}}\left(3 + \sqrt{\frac{N_J}{\rho E_b'}}\cos\theta_J\right)\right] - \frac{1}{2}Q\left[\sqrt{\frac{2E_b'}{N_0}}\left(5 + \sqrt{\frac{N_J}{\rho E_b'}}\cos\theta_J\right)\right]. \tag{3.59}$$

Furthermore, P_{b_0} of (3.57) represents the average bit error probability in the presence of noise only and is given by

$$P_{b_0} = \frac{3}{4}Q\left[\sqrt{\frac{2E_b'}{N_0}}\right] + \frac{1}{2}Q\left[3\sqrt{\frac{E_b'}{N_0}}\right] - \frac{1}{4}Q\left[5\sqrt{\frac{2E_b'}{N_0}}\right]. \tag{3.60}$$

Once again before presenting numerical results illustrating the evaluation of (3.57), it is of interest to examine its limiting behavior as $N_0 \to 0$. Following the approach taken for FH/QPSK, we can arrive at the following result:

$$\lim_{E_b/N_0\to\infty} P_b = \begin{cases} 0; & \dfrac{\rho E_b'}{N_J} > 1 \\[2ex] \dfrac{3\rho}{4\pi}\cos^{-1}\sqrt{\dfrac{\rho E_b'}{N_J}}; & \dfrac{1}{9} < \dfrac{\rho E_b'}{N_J} \le 1 \\[2ex] \dfrac{3\rho}{4\pi}\cos^{-1}\sqrt{\dfrac{\rho E_b'}{N_J}} + \dfrac{2\rho}{4\pi}\cos^{-1}\sqrt{\dfrac{9\rho E_b'}{N_J}}; & \dfrac{1}{25} < \dfrac{\rho E_b'}{N_J} \le \dfrac{1}{9} \\[2ex] \dfrac{3\rho}{4\pi}\cos^{-1}\sqrt{\dfrac{\rho E_b'}{N_J}} + \dfrac{2\rho}{4\pi}\cos^{-1}\sqrt{\dfrac{9\rho E_b'}{N_J}} - \dfrac{\rho}{\pi}\cos^{-1}\sqrt{\dfrac{25\rho E_b'}{N_J}}; & 0 < \dfrac{\rho E_b'}{N_J} \le \dfrac{1}{25}. \end{cases} \tag{3.61}$$

The partial-band fraction ρ corresponding to the worst case jammer (maximum P_b) is obtained by differentiating (3.61) with respect to ρ and equating to zero. Assuming that, for a fixed E_b'/N_J this worst case ρ occurs when $1/9 < \rho E_b'/N_J < 1$, then the solution to the transcendental equation which results from the differentiation is identical to (3.54). Substituting (3.54) into (3.61) gives the limiting average bit error probability performance corre-

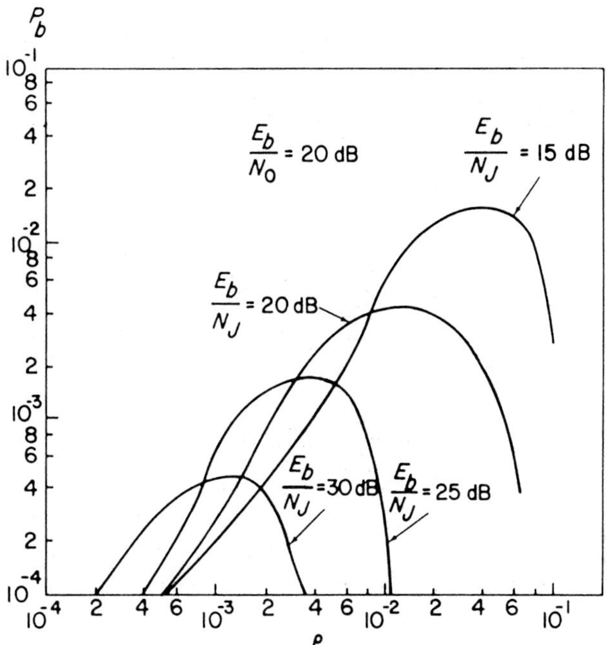

Figure 3.7. P_b versus ρ for FH/QASK-16 in tone jamming with $E_b/N_0 = 20$ dB.

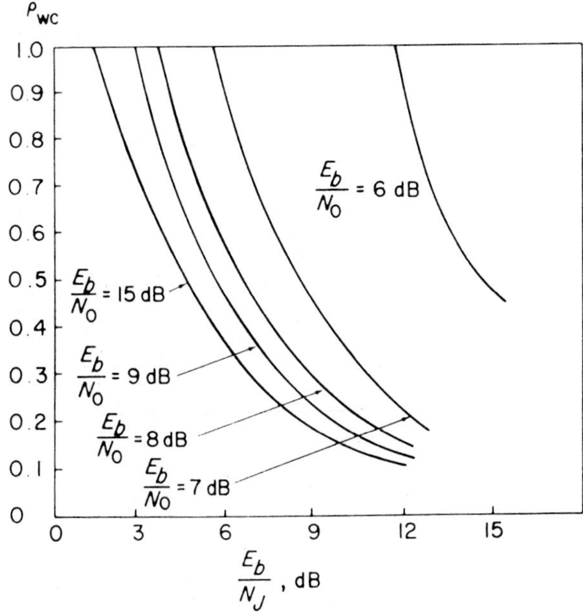

Figure 3.8. Worst case ρ versus E_b/N_J—FH/QASK-16 (tone jamming).

sponding to the worst case jammer, namely,

$$\lim_{E_b/N_0\to\infty} P_{b_{\max}} = \begin{cases} \dfrac{0.0984}{E_b'/N_J} = \dfrac{0.2459}{E_b/N_J}; & E_b'/N_J > 0.6306 \\ \dfrac{3}{4\pi}\cos^{-1}\sqrt{\dfrac{E_b'}{N_J}}; & 1/9 < E_b'/N_J \le 0.6306 \\ \dfrac{3}{4\pi}\cos^{-1}\sqrt{\dfrac{E_b'}{N_J}} + \dfrac{2}{4\pi}\cos^{-1}\sqrt{\dfrac{9E_b'}{N_J}}; & 1/25 < E_b'/N_J \le 1/9 \\ \dfrac{3}{4\pi}\cos^{-1}\sqrt{\dfrac{E_b'}{N_J}} + \dfrac{2}{4\pi}\cos^{-1}\sqrt{\dfrac{9E_b'}{N_J}} - \dfrac{1}{\pi}\cos^{-1}\sqrt{\dfrac{25E_b'}{N_J}}; & 0 < E_b'/N_J \le 1/25. \end{cases} \tag{3.62}$$

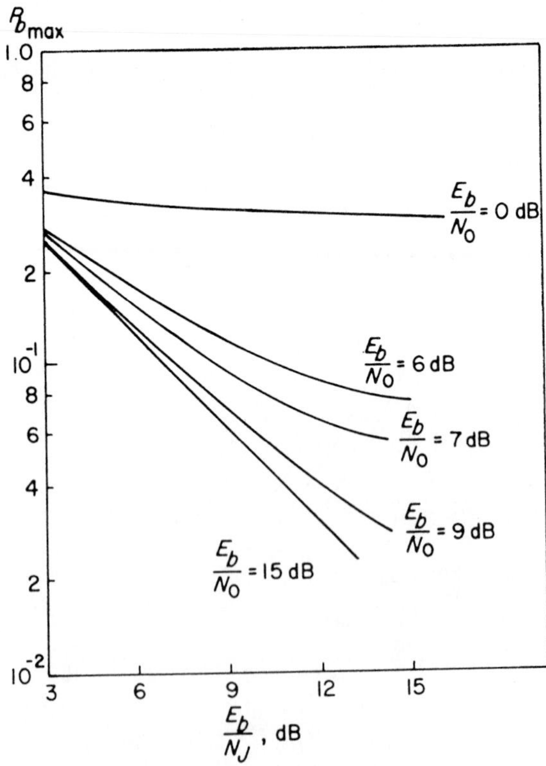

Figure 3.9. Worst case P_b versus E_b/N_J—FH/QASK-16 (tone jamming).

Figures 3.7–3.9 are the numerical evaluations of FH/QASK-16 performance which are analogous to those in Figures 3.4–3.6 characterizing FH/QPSK.

3.3 PERFORMANCE OF FH/QPSK IN THE PRESENCE OF PARTIAL-BAND NOISE JAMMING

Now assume that the jammer $J(t)$ spreads his total power J uniformly across a fraction ρ of the total hop frequency band W_{ss}. Then, insofar as the data demodulation process is concerned, the jammer appears as an additional additive noise source of power spectral density

$$N_J' = \frac{J}{\rho W_{ss}} = \frac{N_J}{\rho}. \tag{3.63}$$

Note that the power spectral density of the noise jammer defined in (3.63) is identical to the effective power spectral density defined for the multitone jammer in (3.21).

Since the jammer noise can be assumed to be independent of the background AWGN, one can add their power spectral densities and use this sum to represent the total noise perturbing the receiver. Thus, the error probability performance of FH/QPSK in the presence of partial-band noise jamming is characterized by taking the well-known results for just an AWGN background and replacing N_0 by $N_0 + N_J'$.

Without going into great detail, we then see that the average symbol error probability is once again given by (3.24), with P_{s_0} as in (3.23); however,

$$P_{s_J} = 2Q\left(\sqrt{\frac{2E_b}{N_0 + N_J'}}\right) - Q^2\left(\sqrt{\frac{2E_b}{N_0 + N_J'}}\right). \tag{3.64}$$

Substituting (3.63) into (3.64), we can rewrite P_{s_J} in the alternate form:

$$P_{s_J} = 2Q\left(\left[\left(\frac{2E_b}{N_0}\right)^{-1} + \left(\frac{2\rho E_b}{N_J}\right)^{-1}\right]^{-1/2}\right)$$
$$-Q^2\left(\left[\left(\frac{2E_b}{N_0}\right)^{-1} + \left(\frac{2\rho E_b}{N_J}\right)^{-1}\right]^{-1/2}\right). \tag{3.65}$$

Also, the average bit error probability is now

$$P_b = \rho Q\left(\left[\left(\frac{2E_b}{N_0}\right)^{-1} + \left(\frac{2\rho E_b}{N_J}\right)^{-1}\right]^{-1/2}\right) + (1-\rho)Q\left(\sqrt{\frac{2E_b}{N_0}}\right) \tag{3.66}$$

which is identical to the result for noise jamming of FH/BPSK.

The limiting behavior of (3.66) as E_b/N_0 approaches infinity is easily seen to be

$$\lim_{E_b/N_0 \to \infty} P_b = \rho Q\left(\sqrt{\frac{2\rho E_b}{N_J}}\right). \tag{3.67}$$

Differentiating (3.67) with respect to ρ and equating the result to zero gives the transcendental equation

$$Q\left(\sqrt{\frac{2\rho E_b}{N_J}}\right) = \sqrt{\frac{\rho E_b}{N_J}}\left(\frac{e^{-\rho E_b/N_J}}{2\sqrt{\pi}}\right), \tag{3.68}$$

whose solution for ρ corresponds to the worst case jammer situation. In particular, letting

$$x = \sqrt{\frac{\rho E_b}{N_J}}, \tag{3.69}$$

(3.68) then becomes

$$Q(\sqrt{2}\,x) = \frac{xe^{-x^2}}{2\sqrt{\pi}} \tag{3.70}$$

which, when solved numerically, yields

$$x = 0.842. \tag{3.71}$$

Equating (3.69) and (3.71) gives the partial-band fraction for the worst case

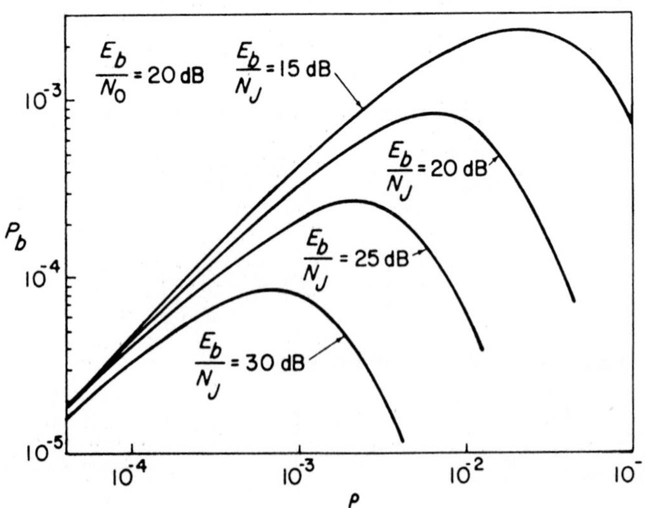

Figure 3.10. P_b versus ρ for FH/QPSK in noise jamming with $E_b/N_0 = 20$ dB.

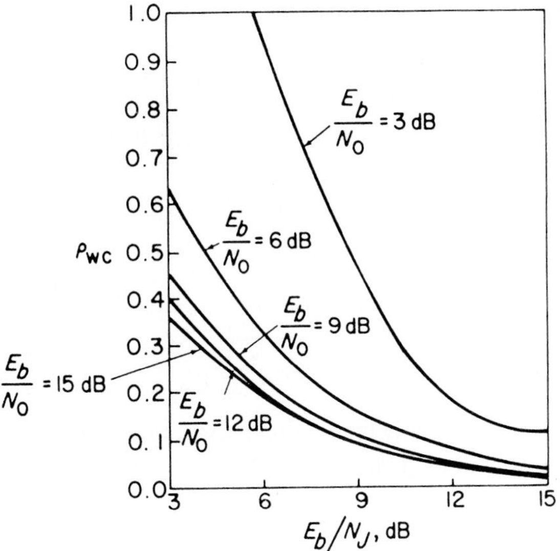

Figure 3.11. Worst case ρ versus E_b/N_J—FH/QPSK (noise jamming).

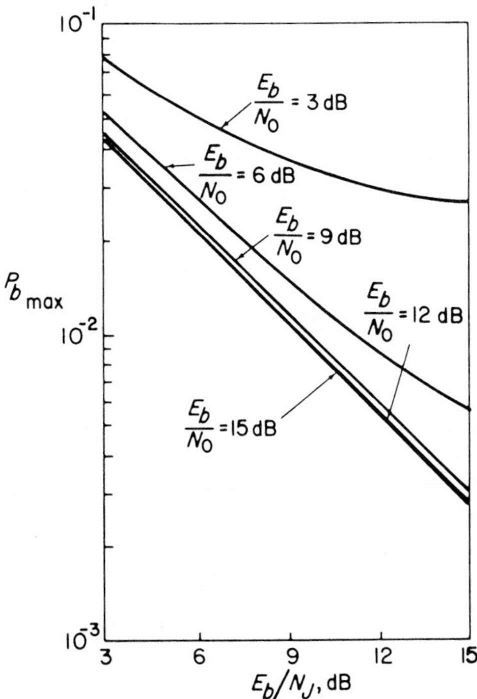

Figure 3.12. Worst case P_b versus E_b/N_J—FH/QPSK (noise jamming).

jammer, namely,

$$\rho_{wc} = \begin{cases} \dfrac{0.7090}{E_b/N_J}; & E_b/N_J > 0.7090 \\ 1; & E_b/N_J \le 0.7090 \end{cases} \tag{3.72}$$

and a corresponding maximum average bit error probability

$$\lim_{E_b/N_0 \to \infty} P_{b_{\max}} = \begin{cases} \dfrac{0.0829}{E_b/N_J}; & E_b/N_J > 0.7090 \\ Q\left(\sqrt{2E_b/N_J}\right); & E_b/N_J \le 0.7090. \end{cases} \tag{3.73}$$

Figures 3.10–3.12 characterize the performance of FH/QPSK in the presence of noise jamming, as computed from (3.66).

3.4 PERFORMANCE OF FH/QASK IN THE PRESENCE OF PARTIAL-BAND NOISE JAMMING

Assuming the same noise jammer model as that discussed in the previous section for FH/QPSK, the average symbol error probability of FH/QASK-16 is then given by (3.24), with P_{s_0} as in (3.51), but now

$$P_{s_J} = 3Q\left(\left[\left(\frac{2E_b'}{N_0}\right)^{-1} + \left(\frac{2\rho E_b'}{N_J}\right)^{-1}\right]^{-1/2}\right) - \frac{9}{4}Q^2\left(\left[\left(\frac{2E_b'}{N_0}\right)^{-1} + \left(\frac{2\rho E_b'}{N_J}\right)^{-1}\right]^{-1/2}\right). \tag{3.74}$$

The limiting behavior of (3.24), together with (3.51) and (3.74) as E_b/N_0 approaches infinity is simply

$$\lim_{E_b/N_0 \to \infty} P_s = 3\rho Q\left(\sqrt{\frac{2\rho E_b'}{N_J}}\right) - \frac{9\rho}{4}Q^2\left(\sqrt{\frac{2\rho E_b'}{N_J}}\right) \tag{3.75}$$

which yields a partial-band fraction for the worst case jammer given by the solution to

$$3Q(\sqrt{2}\,x) - 3x\frac{e^{-x^2}}{\sqrt{\pi}} - \frac{9}{4}Q^2(\sqrt{2}\,x) + \frac{9}{2}Q(\sqrt{2}\,x)\left[\frac{xe^{-x^2}}{2\sqrt{\pi}}\right] = 0, \tag{3.76}$$

with

$$x = \sqrt{\frac{\rho E_b'}{N_J}}. \tag{3.77}$$

Numerical solution of (3.76) yields

$$\rho_{\text{wc}} = \begin{cases} \dfrac{0.7921}{(2/5)E_b/N_J} = \dfrac{1.9802}{E_b/N_J}; & E_b/N_J > 1.9802 \\ 1; & E_b/N_J \le 1.9802 \end{cases} \tag{3.78}$$

and a corresponding worst case average symbol error probability

$$\lim_{E_b/N_0 \to \infty} P_{s_{\max}} = \begin{cases} \dfrac{0.5700}{E_b/N_J}; & E_b/N_J > 1.9802 \\ 3Q\left(\sqrt{\dfrac{2E_b'}{N_J}}\right) - \dfrac{9}{4}Q^2\left(\sqrt{\dfrac{2E_b'}{N_J}}\right); & E_b/N_J \le 1.9802. \end{cases} \tag{3.79}$$

The average bit error probability P_b is obtained from (3.57), where P_{b_0} is given by (3.60) and P_{b_J} is given by

$$P_{b_J} = \tfrac{3}{4}Q(x) + \tfrac{1}{2}Q(3x) - \tfrac{1}{4}Q(5x) \tag{3.80}$$

with

$$x = \left[\left(\frac{2E_b'}{N_0}\right)^{-1} + \left(\frac{2\rho E_b'}{N_J}\right)^{-1}\right]^{-1/2}. \tag{3.81}$$

The limiting behavior of P_b as E_b/N_0 approaches infinity is then

$$\lim_{E_b/N_0 \to \infty} P_b = \rho\left[\tfrac{3}{4}Q(x_\infty) + \tfrac{1}{2}Q(3x_\infty) - \tfrac{1}{4}Q(5x_\infty)\right] \tag{3.82}$$

where x_∞ is the corresponding limit of x in (3.81), namely,

$$x_\infty = \sqrt{\frac{2\rho E_b'}{N_J}}. \tag{3.83}$$

The worst case jammer is found through a procedure analogous to the one in Section 3.3:

$$\rho_{\text{wc}} = \begin{cases} \dfrac{1.758}{E_b/N_J}; & E_b/N_J > 1.758 \\ 1; & E_b/N_J \le 1.758 \end{cases} \tag{3.84}$$

and a corresponding maximum average bit error probability of

$$\lim_{E_b/N_0\to\infty} P_{b_{\max}} = \begin{cases} \dfrac{0.1555}{E_b/N_J}; & E_b/N_J > 1.758 \\ \dfrac{3}{4}Q\left[\sqrt{\dfrac{2E_b'}{N_J}}\right] + \dfrac{1}{2}Q\left[3\sqrt{\dfrac{2E_b'}{N_J}}\right] - \dfrac{1}{4}Q\left[5\sqrt{\dfrac{2E_b'}{N_J}}\right]; & \\ & E_b/N_J \le 1.758. \end{cases} \tag{3.85}$$

It is interesting to note that the ratio ($\lim P_{b_{\max}}/\lim P_{s_{\max}}$), as computed from (3.79) and (3.85) is 0.2728, which is slightly higher than the approximate value of 1/4 as in (3.56). Furthermore, those limits are achieved for values of ρ (see (3.78) and (3.84)) which are different but relatively close.

Figures 3.13–3.15 characterize the performance of FH/QASK-16 in the presence of noise jamming, as computed from the results given in this section. In Figure 3.13 the dashed line represents the locus of the maxima of P_b versus ρ, with E_b/N_J as a parameter. It can be seen that the value of 20 dB for E_b/N_0 is sufficiently high to warrant an almost linear relationship between $P_{b_{\max}}$ and ρ, which closely conforms with the theoretically predicted line (see (3.84) and (3.85))

$$\lim_{E_b/N_0\to\infty} P_{b_{\max}} = 0.0878\rho. \tag{3.86}$$

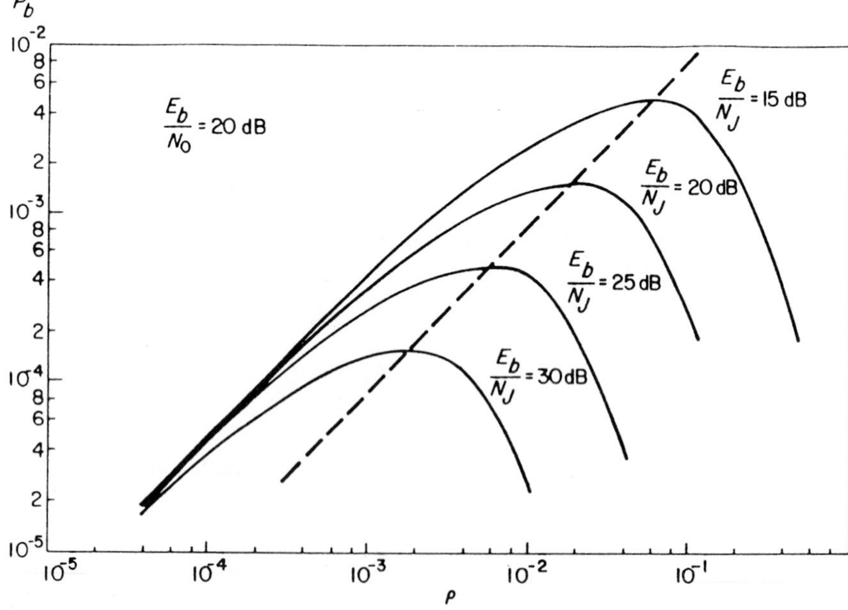

Figure 3.13. P_b versus ρ for FH/QASK-16 in noise jamming with $E_b/N_0 = 20$ dB.

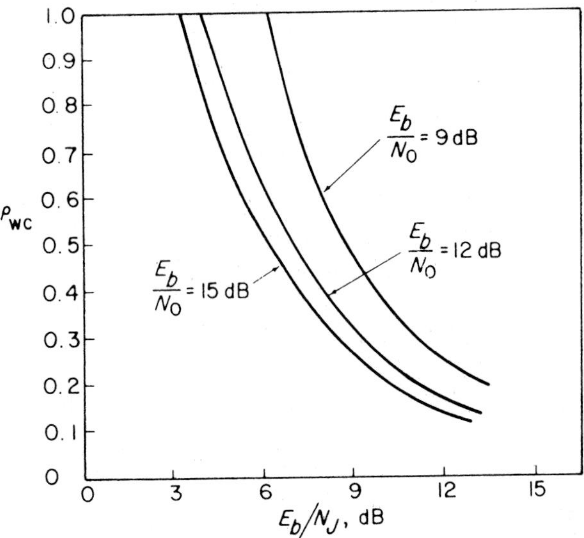

Figure 3.14. Worst case ρ versus E_b/N_J—FH/QASK-16 (noise jamming).

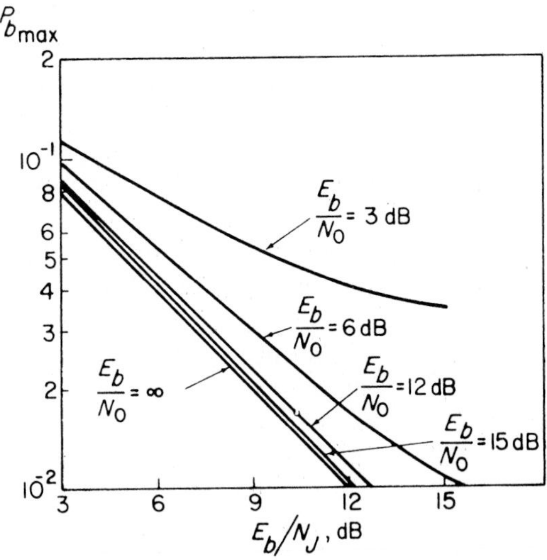

Figure 3.15. Worst case P_b versus E_b/N_J—FH/QASK-16 (noise jamming).

3.5 PERFORMANCE OF FH / PN / QPSK IN THE PRESENCE OF PARTIAL-BAND MULTITONE JAMMING

When a pseudonoise (PN) balanced modulation is superimposed on an FH/QPSK signal, each jammer tone of power J_0 is then spread over a bandwidth equal to the PN chip rate R_c. Let $R_s = 1/T_s$ be the information symbol rate and R_c/R_s represent the *processing gain associated with the PN spreading*, herein taken to be a larger integer I. It follows from the assumption of a large processing gain that the spread tone jammer possesses a fairly flat power spectral density within the data modulation bandwidth and is now caused to behave like a white noise jammer of spectral density

$$N_J' = J_0/R_c = J_0 T_c. \tag{3.87}$$

Using (3.4) and (3.5), we can rewrite (3.87) as

$$N_J' = J/\rho N R_c. \tag{3.88}$$

Since the hop frequency slots (assumed to be *contiguous*) must now be R_c wide to accommodate the PN modulation, in terms of the total hop frequency band W_{ss} and the number of hop slots N in that band, we then have

$$N = W_{ss}/R_c. \tag{3.89}$$

Combining (3.88) and (3.89) gives

$$N_J' = \frac{J/W_{ss}}{\rho} = \frac{N_J}{\rho}, \tag{3.90}$$

which is identical to (3.63) (the case of FH/QPSK in the presence of partial-band noise jamming) *independent of the chip rate* R_c.

The above discussion concerns the spectral characteristics of the spread tone jammer which, as concluded, resembles a white noise jammer with identical spectral density. We shall now discuss the assumptions and theoretical adjustments under which the spread tone jammer can also be treated as a *Gaussian* noise interference.

Consider an FH/PN/QPSK demodulator, similar to the one in Figure 3.2, where the despreading process now also includes a PN code correlator following the frequency dehopper. Let p represent the PN code length (in number of chips). Accounting for the effects of the spread jammer only (i.e., neglecting thermal noise), it follows that the decision variable z_I for the in-phase channel (see (3.11)) becomes

$$z_I = a_i\sqrt{\frac{S}{2}}\,T_s - \sqrt{J_0}\,\sin\theta_J C_{\mathrm{PN}} \tag{3.91}$$

where

$$C_{\mathrm{PN}} = \int_{(i-1)T_s}^{iT_s} c(t)\,dt \tag{3.92}$$

and $c(t)$ is the ± 1-valued PN waveform. In deriving (3.91), ideal PN code synchronization at the receiver has been assumed. Recalling that the processing gain is the ratio of the PN chip rate to the data symbol rate, or equivalently $T_s/T_c = I$, then it follows that the integral in (3.92) amounts to a partial correlation of the PN code, starting from some random phase, provided that the number I of integrated chips does not equal the code length p. Phrased differently, the conclusions to follow hold when $1 \ll I \ll p$ (or in a weaker sense when $1 \ll I$ modulo $p \ll p$). This is because, as is well known, the full-period integration of a PN code equals the constant $1/p$, in which case, no randomness about C_{PN} exists. On the other hand, when p is very large, successive code chips can be considered almost independent, identically distributed ± 1-valued random variables, in which case the condition $I \ll p$ would provide an approximate binomial distribution for the random variable C_{PN}. The additional constraint $I \gg 1$ then causes this binomial distribution to behave like a Gaussian distribution.

Arguments similar to the above were made in Chapter 1 in connection with the evaluation of the performance of pulse-jammed direct-sequence spread-spectrum systems. A more rigorous treatment of the validity of the Gaussian assumption for C_{PN} has been examined in [6] for a variety of PN and Gold codes, with sufficient evidence that it holds, at least approximately, for a wide class of such codes.

Let us now return to (3.91). Conditioned on the $(0, 2\pi)$-uniformly distributed phase θ_J, z_I is, according to the above, a Gaussian random variable whose conditional variance is

$$\operatorname{var}\{z_I|\theta_J\} = T_s T_c J_0 \sin^2\theta_J. \tag{3.93}$$

Hence, when the jammer is present, the average bit error probability for the I channel (identically for the Q channel) is given by

$$P_{b_J}^t = \frac{1}{2\pi}\int_0^{2\pi} Q\left(\sqrt{\frac{ST_s}{2T_c J_0}}\,\frac{1}{|\sin\theta_J|}\right)d\theta_J = \frac{2}{\pi}\int_0^{\pi/2} Q\left(\sqrt{\frac{\rho E_b}{N_J}}\,\frac{1}{\sin\theta_J}\right)d\theta_J \tag{3.94}$$

where (3.18), (3.87), (3.90), and (3.93) have been used in arriving at this result. Finally, multiplying (3.94) by ρ gives the average bit error probability of FH/PN/QPSK in the presence of partial-band multitone jamming, namely,

$$P_b^t = \frac{2\rho}{\pi}\int_0^{\pi/2} Q\left(\sqrt{\frac{\rho E_b}{N_J}}\,\frac{1}{\sin\theta_J}\right)d\theta_J. \tag{3.95}$$

Although (3.95) can be used in assessing the effect of a spread tone jammer on system performance, we shall now indicate an even simpler way of evaluating the tone interference effect by means of converting the spread tone jammer to an *equivalent* AWGN interference, where the equivalence is understood *in terms of its effect on bit error probability*. Let N_{0_J} represent the one-sided power spectral density of AWGN interference whose statistical characteristics remain the same after the PN despreader. Clearly, the bit error probability in this case is given by

$$P_{b_J}^n = Q\left(\sqrt{\frac{2E_b}{N_{0_J}}}\right). \tag{3.96}$$

Equations (3.94) and (3.96) have been plotted in Figure 3.16. The abscissa is the signal-to-jammer power ratio SJR in decibels where, for the spread tone case $(\text{SJR})^t = E_b/N_J$ while, for the noise case, $(\text{SJR})^n = E_b/N_{0_J}$. A careful examination of Figure 3.16 reveals that, for values of $(\text{SJR})^t$ up to approximately 12 dB, the difference $(\text{SJR})^t_{(\text{dB})} - (\text{SJR})^n_{(\text{dB})}$ between the signal-to-jammer ratios which achieve the same performance is, to a high degree of accuracy, linearly increasing with $(\text{SJR})^t_{(\text{dB})}$, the slope of the line being 0.2. It is therefore concluded that, given a spread tone jammer of $(\text{SJR})^t_{(\text{dB})}$, an

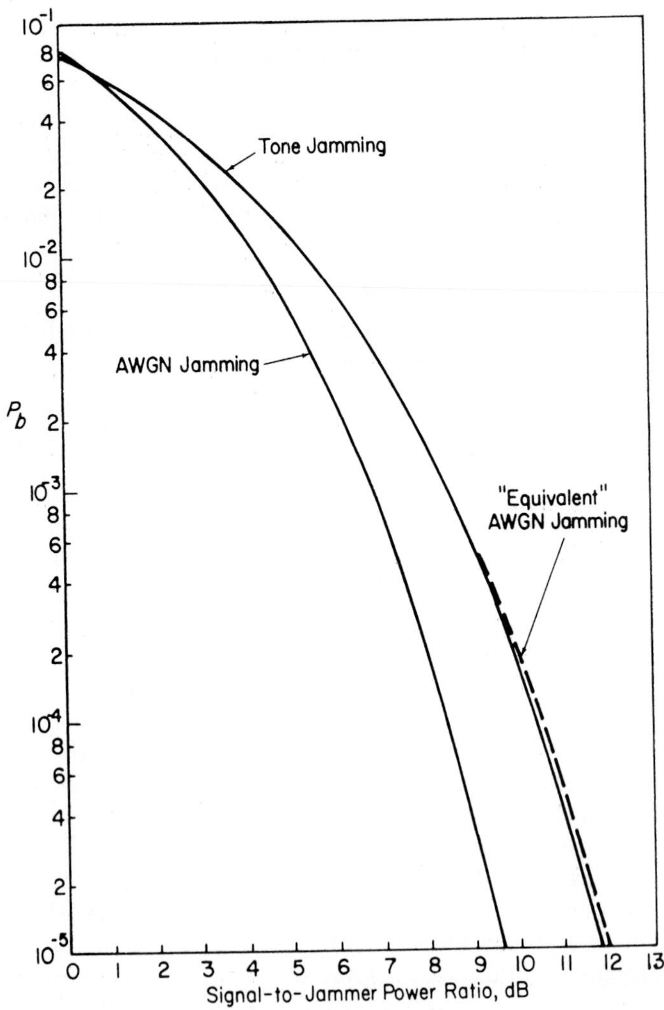

Figure 3.16. QPSK bit error probability versus $\text{SJR}_{(\text{dB})}$ for AWGN and tone jamming and spread tone "equivalent" AWGN jamming.

"*equivalent*" AWGN jammer can be devised for which

$$(\mathrm{SJR})^{n}_{\mathrm{equiv(dB)}} = (0.8) \times (\mathrm{SJR})^{t}_{(\mathrm{dB})}. \tag{3.97}$$

If the SJR's are measured in ordinary numbers rather than decibels, then (3.97) implies that

$$(\mathrm{SJR})^{n}_{\mathrm{equiv}} = \left((\mathrm{SJR})^{t}\right)^{0.8}. \tag{3.98}$$

From (3.96) and (3.98), it then follows that the spread tone jammer can be conveniently thought of as an "*equivalent*" AWGN jammer with corresponding bit error probability

$$P^{t}_{b_J} = Q\left(\sqrt{2\left(\frac{\rho E_b}{N_J}\right)^{0.8}}\right). \tag{3.99}$$

Equation (3.99) has been plotted in Figure 3.16 (dashed lines), from which the high degree of agreement with the exact expression for $P^{t}_{b_J}$ can be witnessed. The range of applicability of (3.99) is, for the current purposes, more than adequate since, in the frequency bands where the jammer is present, the system is forced to operate at high bit error probabilities (this is especially true when the jammer strategy, i.e., choice of ρ, has been optimized). From (3.99), it follows that the overall average bit error probability (accounting for partial-band jamming) is given by

$$P^{t}_{b} = \rho Q\left(\sqrt{2\left(\frac{\rho E_b}{N_J}\right)^{0.8}}\right). \tag{3.100}$$

The worst case jammer can be found from (3.100), with the result

$$\rho_{\mathrm{wc}} = \begin{cases} \dfrac{0.9220}{E_b/N_J}; & E_b/N_J \geq 0.9220 \\ 1; & E_b/N_J < 0.9220 \end{cases} \tag{3.101}$$

with corresponding

$$P^{t}_{b_{\max}} = \begin{cases} \dfrac{0.0789}{E_b/N_J}; & E_b/N_J \geq 0.9220 \\ Q\left(\sqrt{2\left(\dfrac{E_b}{N_J}\right)^{0.8}}\right); & E_b/N_J < 0.9220. \end{cases} \tag{3.102}$$

A comparison of (3.102) with (3.73) indicates that the worst tone jammer for FH/PN/QPSK is slightly less effective than the worst noise jammer for FH/QPSK.

3.6 PERFORMANCE OF FH / PN / QASK IN THE PRESENCE OF PARTIAL-BAND MULTITONE JAMMING

A line of thought similar to that of Section 3.6 also applies here. The tone/noise jamming equivalence discussed in Section 3.6 is also applicable because the first Q function in (3.82) dominates over the other terms in the range of interest. Without belaboring the point, we summarize here the pertinent results (also in the absence of thermal noise)

$$P_b^t = \rho P_{b_J} \tag{3.103}$$

where P_{b_J} is given by (3.80) with

$$x = \sqrt{2\left(\frac{2\rho E_b}{5N_J}\right)^{0.8}}. \tag{3.104}$$

The corresponding worst case results are

$$\rho_{\text{wc}} = \begin{cases} \dfrac{2.3050}{E_b/N_J}; & E_b/N_J \geq 2.3050 \\ 1; & E_b/N_J < 2.3050 \end{cases} \tag{3.105}$$

and

$$P_{b_{\max}}^t = \begin{cases} \dfrac{0.1483}{E_b/N_J}; & E_b/N_J \geq 2.3050 \\ \frac{3}{4}Q(x_1) + \frac{1}{2}Q(3x_1) - \frac{1}{4}Q(5x_1); & E_b/N_J < 2.3050 \end{cases} \tag{3.106}$$

where

$$x_1 = \sqrt{2\left(\frac{2E_b}{5N_J}\right)^{0.8}}. \tag{3.107}$$

Thus far in this chapter, we have focussed our entire attention on how augmenting "ideal" QPSK and QASK with a FH/SS technique allows them to combat a partial-band multitone or noise jammer. The word "ideal" is used here to indicate that although the underlying modulations are so-called "bandwidth efficient" because of the structure of their signal constellations, we have not considered any additional bandwidth conservation produced by transmitter and receiver filtering. Stated another way, we have assumed throughout that the basic transmission pulse is rectangular in shape. In the remainder of this chapter, we examine the detection efficiency of quadrature partial response Class I signals in the presence of the identical jamming scenario postulated thus far. Consideration of this form of modulation represents a departure from the basic assumption mentioned above as discussed in the next section.

3.7 PERFORMANCE OF FH / QPR IN THE PRESENCE OF PARTIAL-BAND MULTITONE JAMMING

In the design of most digital data transmission systems, the occurrence of intersymbol interference is ordinarily treated as an undesirable phenomenon. Certain signalling systems, however, utilize a controlled amount of intersymbol interference to achieve certain beneficial effects. These systems have been called, variously, *duobinary*, *polybinary*, and *partial response* [7]–[10]. When such a modulation type is transmitted on quadrature carriers over a common channel, the acronym *quadrature partial response* (QPR) has been applied. A typical modulator, which generates an FH three-level QPR signal,[4] is illustrated in Figure 3.17. The transmitted signal in the i-th hop interval is

$$s^{(i)}(t) = \sqrt{2}A\left[\sum_{n=-\infty}^{\infty} c_n h_T(t - 2nT_b)\right]\cos\omega_h^{(i)}t$$
$$+\sqrt{2}A\left[\sum_{n=-\infty}^{\infty} d_n h_T(t - (2n+1)T_b)\right]\sin\omega_h^{(i)}t, \quad (3.108)$$

where again $\omega_h^{(i)}$ is the particular carrier frequency selected by the frequency hopper for this interval according to the designated SS code, $h_T(t)$ is the impulse response of the transmit filter $H_T(\omega)$, and T_b is the bit time interval. The amplitude A will soon be related to the average transmitted power S.

The conventional demodulator for an FH three-level QPR signal corrupted by additive Gaussian noise $n(t)$ is illustrated in Figure 3.18. From a noise power standpoint, it is advantageous to split the overall partial response (duobinary) signal shaping equally between the transmit and receive filters. Since, for a three-level signal, the overall shaping characteristic is given by

$$H(\omega) = \begin{cases} 4T_b\cos\omega T_b; & |\omega| < \dfrac{\pi}{2T_b} \\ 0; & \text{otherwise,} \end{cases} \quad (3.109)$$

then, based on the above statement, we have

$$H_T(\omega) = H_R(\omega) = \left(H(\omega)\right)^{1/2} = \begin{cases} (4T_b\cos\omega T_b)^{1/2}; & |\omega| < \dfrac{\pi}{2T_b} \\ 0; & \text{otherwise.} \end{cases} \quad (3.110)$$

[4] We shall concentrate our efforts on only FH three-level QPR. Extension to the case of FH $(2L-1)$-level QPR is straightforward.

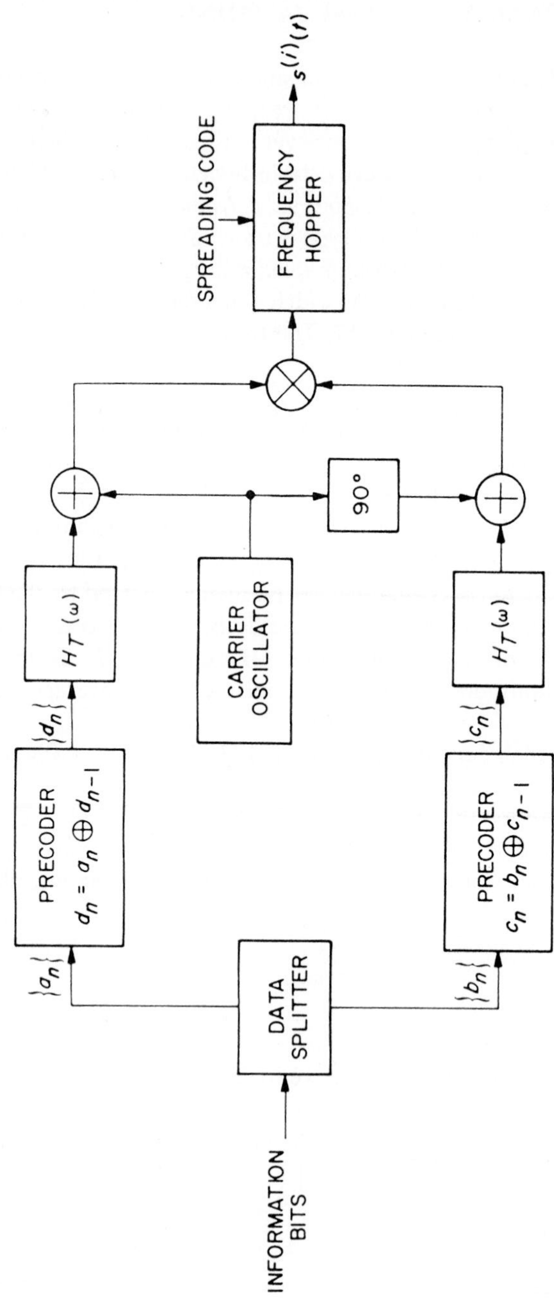

Figure 3.17. An FH three-level QPR modulator.

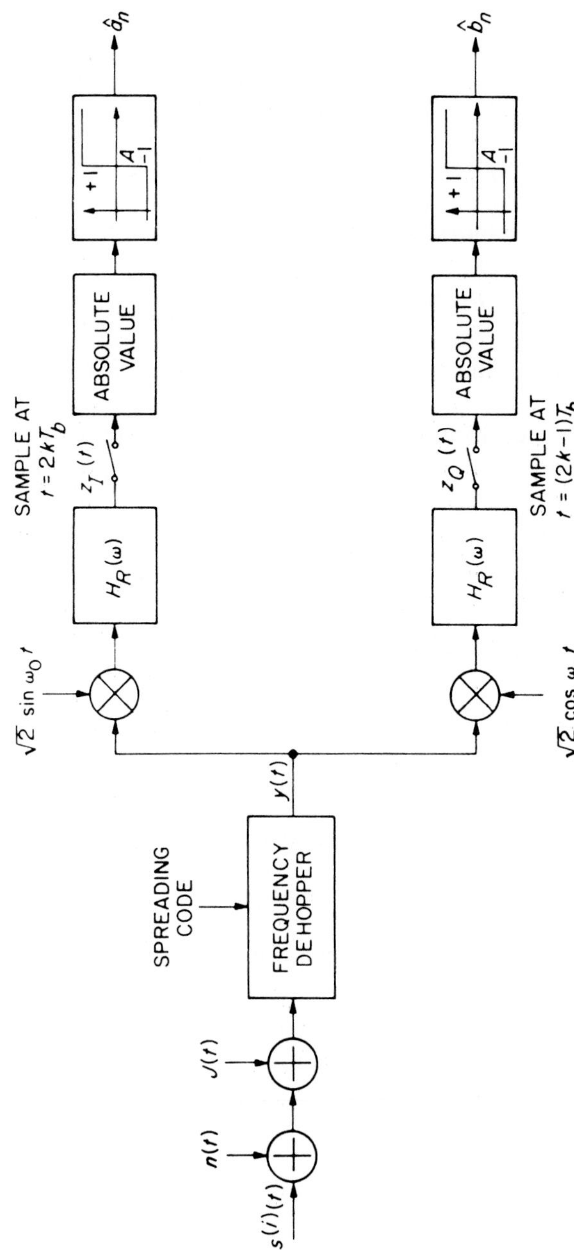

Figure 3.18. An FH three-level QPR demodulator.

Also, the impulse response $h(t)$ corresponding to $H(\omega)$ of (3.109) is given by

$$h(t) = \frac{4}{\pi}\left[\frac{\cos\dfrac{\pi t}{2T_b}}{1 - \dfrac{t^2}{T_b^2}}\right]. \tag{3.111}$$

Notice that, if the response sampling time t_0 is chosen to be $-T_b$, then

$$h_n \triangleq h(t)|_{t=2nT_b+t_0} = \begin{cases} 1; & n = 0,1 \\ 0; & \text{otherwise,} \end{cases} \tag{3.112}$$

and the controlled intersymbol interference comes from the preceding symbol only.

In a hop interval which contains the partial-band multitone jammer $J(t)$, the total received signal $y(t)$ after dehopping can be expressed in the form

$$\begin{aligned} y(t) &= \sqrt{2}\left[A \sum_{n=-\infty}^{\infty} c_n h_T(t - 2nT_b) + N_c(t)\right]\cos\omega_0 t \\ &+ \sqrt{2}\left[A \sum_{n=-\infty}^{\infty} d_n h_T(t - (2n+1)T_b) - N_s(t)\right]\sin\omega_0 t \\ &+ \sqrt{2J_0}\cos(\omega_0 t + \theta_J). \end{aligned} \tag{3.113}$$

After demodulation by the in-phase and quadrature reference signals,

$$\begin{aligned} r_I(t) &= \sqrt{2}\sin\omega_0 t \\ r_Q(t) &= \sqrt{2}\cos\omega_0 t, \end{aligned} \tag{3.114}$$

and receive filtering by $H_R(\omega)$, the following signals result:

$$\begin{aligned} z_Q(t) &\triangleq \left[y(t)(\sqrt{2}\cos\omega_0 t)\right] \circledast h_R(t) \\ &= A \sum_{n=-\infty}^{\infty} c_n h(t - 2nT_b) + \sqrt{J_0}\, H_R(0)\cos\theta_J + \hat{N}_c(t) \\ z_I(t) &\triangleq \left[y(t)(\sqrt{2}\sin\omega_0 t)\right] \circledast h_R(t) \\ &= A \sum_{n=-\infty}^{\infty} d_n h(t - (2n+1)T_b) - \sqrt{J_0}\, H_R(0)\sin\theta_J - \hat{N}_s(t), \end{aligned} \tag{3.115}$$

where

$$\hat{N}_c(t) \triangleq H_R(p) N_c(t)$$
$$\hat{N}_s(t) \triangleq H_R(p) N_s(t) \tag{3.116}$$

with p the Heaviside operator and

$$\hat{\sigma}^2 \triangleq E\{\hat{N}_c^2(t)\} = E\{\hat{N}_s^2(t)\}$$
$$= \frac{N_0}{2}\left[\frac{1}{2\pi}\int_{-\infty}^{\infty} |H_R(\omega)|^2 \, d\omega\right] = \frac{2N_0}{\pi}. \tag{3.117}$$

The sampled values of $z_c(t)$ and $z_s(t)$ are given by

$$z_{Qk} \triangleq z_Q[(2k-1)T_b] = A(c_k + c_{k-1}) + \sqrt{4J_0T_b}\cos\theta_J + \hat{N}_{ck}$$
$$z_{Ik} \triangleq z_I(2kT_b) = A(d_k + d_{k-1}) - \sqrt{4J_0T_b}\sin\theta_J - \hat{N}_{sk} \tag{3.118}$$

where

$$\hat{N}_{ck} \triangleq \hat{N}_c[(2k-1)T_b]$$
$$\hat{N}_{sk} \triangleq \hat{N}_s(2kT_b) \tag{3.119}$$

and we have made use of the fact (see (3.110)) that $H_R(0) = \sqrt{4T_b}$.

Table 3.1 lists the four possible combinations of precoded symbols c_k and c_{k-1} (or d_k and d_{k-1}) and the corresponding duobinary values $c_k + c_{k-1}$ (or $d_k + d_{k-1}$). Here we use $+1$ and -1 symbols rather than zeros and ones; hence, the modulo-2 operation in the precoder is replaced by arithmetic multiplication.

From Table 3.1, it is clear that the detection criteria should be

$$\hat{b}_k = \begin{cases} 1 & \text{if } |z_{ck}| > A \\ -1 & \text{if } |z_{ck}| < A \end{cases}; \qquad \hat{a}_k = \begin{cases} 1 & \text{if } |z_{sk}| > A \\ -1 & \text{if } |z_{sk}| < A \end{cases}. \tag{3.120}$$

Thus, since the a_k's and b_k's are equally likely, the in-phase and quadrature

Table 3.1
Transformation of the input symbols into their duobinary equivalents.

Transmitted Symbol b_k	Received Symbols c_k	c_{k-1}	Duobinary Value $c_k + c_{k-1}$
-1	$+1$	-1	0
-1	-1	$+1$	0
$+1$	$+1$	$+1$	$+2$
$+1$	-1	-1	-2

bit error probabilities are given by

$$\begin{aligned}P_Q(\theta_J) \triangleq \Pr\{\hat{b}_k \neq b_k\} &= \tfrac{1}{2}\Pr\{|z_{Qk}| > A|\, c_k + c_{k-1} = 0\}\\ &+ \tfrac{1}{4}\Pr\{|z_{Qk}| < A|\, c_k + c_{k-1} = 2\}\\ &+ \tfrac{1}{4}\Pr\{|z_{Qk}| < A|\, c_k + c_{k-1} = -2\}\\ P_I(\theta_J) \triangleq \Pr\{\hat{a}_k \neq a_k\} &= \tfrac{1}{2}\Pr\{|z_{Ik}| > A|\, d_k + d_{k-1} = 0\}\\ &+ \tfrac{1}{4}\Pr\{|z_{Ik}| < A|\, d_k + d_{k-1} = 2\}\\ &+ \tfrac{1}{4}\Pr\{|z_{Ik}| < A|\, d_k + d_{k-1} = -2\}\end{aligned} \tag{3.121}$$

or, using (3.118),

$$\begin{aligned}P_Q(\theta_J) &= \frac{3}{4}Q\left(\frac{A + \sqrt{4J_0T_b}\cos\theta_J}{\hat{\sigma}}\right) - \frac{1}{4}Q\left(\frac{3A + \sqrt{4J_0T_b}\cos\theta_J}{\hat{\sigma}}\right)\\ &+ \frac{3}{4}Q\left(\frac{A - \sqrt{4J_0T_b}\cos\theta_J}{\hat{\sigma}}\right) - \frac{1}{4}Q\left(\frac{3A - \sqrt{4J_0T_b}\cos\theta_J}{\hat{\sigma}}\right)\\ P_I(\theta_J) &= \frac{3}{4}Q\left(\frac{A - \sqrt{4J_0T_b}\sin\theta_J}{\hat{\sigma}}\right) - \frac{1}{4}Q\left(\frac{3A - \sqrt{4J_0T_b}\sin\theta_J}{\hat{\sigma}}\right)\\ &+ \frac{3}{4}Q\left(\frac{A + \sqrt{4J_0T_b}\sin\theta_J}{\hat{\sigma}}\right) - \frac{1}{4}Q\left(\frac{3A + \sqrt{4J_0T_b}\sin\theta_J}{\hat{\sigma}}\right)\end{aligned} \tag{3.122}$$

To express (3.122) in terms of more meaningful parameters such as signal-to-Gaussian noise ratio and signal-to-jamming noise ratio, we must relate the signal amplitude A to the average transmitted power S. Since,

$$\overline{c_n c_m} = \overline{d_n d_m} = \begin{cases}1; & n = m\\ 0; & n \neq m\end{cases} \tag{3.123}$$

then from (3.108), we have that

$$\begin{aligned}S &= (\sqrt{2}\,A)^2\left[\frac{1}{2T_b}\int_0^{2T_b}\sum_{n=-\infty}^{\infty} h_T^2(t - 2nT_b)\,dt\right]\\ &= 2A^2\left[\frac{1}{2T_b}\int_{-\infty}^{\infty} h_T^2(t)\,dt\right] = 2A^2\left[\frac{1}{2T_b}\left(\frac{1}{2\pi}\int_{-\infty}^{\infty}|H_T(\omega)|^2\,d\omega\right)\right].\end{aligned} \tag{3.124}$$

Substituting (3.110) into (3.124) and evaluating the integral gives

$$S = \frac{4A^2}{\pi T_b}. \tag{3.125}$$

Combining (3.117) and (3.125) gives an effective rms signal-to-Gaussian noise ratio of

$$\frac{A}{\hat{\sigma}} = \sqrt{\frac{\pi^2}{16}\left(\frac{2E_b}{N_0}\right)}. \tag{3.126}$$

Also, from (3.21) and (3.125), we have

$$\frac{\sqrt{4J_0T_b}}{A} = \sqrt{\frac{8N_J}{\rho\pi E_b}} = \sqrt{\frac{\pi}{2}\left(\frac{16}{\pi^2}\right)\left(\frac{N_J}{\rho E_b}\right)}. \tag{3.127}$$

Finally, substituting (3.126) and (3.127) into (3.122) results in

$$\begin{aligned}
P_Q(\theta_J) = \frac{3}{4}\Bigg\{ & Q\left[\sqrt{\frac{2E_b'}{N_0}}\left(1 + \sqrt{\frac{\pi}{2}\left(\frac{N_J}{\rho E_b'}\right)}\cos\theta_J\right)\right] \\
& + Q\left[\sqrt{\frac{2E_b'}{N_0}}\left(1 - \sqrt{\frac{\pi}{2}\left(\frac{N_J}{\rho E_b'}\right)}\cos\theta_J\right)\right]\Bigg\} \\
& - \frac{1}{4}\Bigg\{Q\left[\sqrt{\frac{2E_b'}{N_0}}\left(3 - \sqrt{\frac{\pi}{2}\left(\frac{N_J}{\rho E_b'}\right)}\cos\theta_J\right)\right] \\
& + Q\left[\sqrt{\frac{2E_b'}{N_0}}\left(3 + \sqrt{\frac{\pi}{2}\left(\frac{N_J}{\rho E_b'}\right)}\cos\theta_J\right)\right]\Bigg\} \\
P_I(\theta_J) = \frac{3}{4}\Bigg\{ & Q\left[\sqrt{\frac{2E_b'}{N_0}}\left(1 - \sqrt{\frac{\pi}{2}\left(\frac{N_J}{\rho E_b'}\right)}\sin\theta_J\right)\right] \\
& + Q\left[\sqrt{\frac{2E_b'}{N_0}}\left(1 + \sqrt{\frac{\pi}{2}\left(\frac{N_J}{\rho E_b'}\right)}\sin\theta_J\right)\right]\Bigg\} \\
& - \frac{1}{4}\Bigg\{Q\left[\sqrt{\frac{2E_b'}{N_0}}\left(3 + \sqrt{\frac{\pi}{2}\left(\frac{N_J}{\rho E_b'}\right)}\sin\theta_J\right)\right] \\
& + Q\left[\sqrt{\frac{2E_b'}{N_0}}\left(3 - \sqrt{\frac{\pi}{2}\left(\frac{N_J}{\rho E_b'}\right)}\sin\theta_J\right)\right]\Bigg\}
\end{aligned} \tag{3.128}$$

where we have further introduced the notation

$$E_b' = \frac{\pi^2}{16}E_b. \tag{3.129}$$

The average probability of bit error P_{b_J} in a detection interval which is jammed is obtained by averaging $P_Q(\theta_J)$ or $P_I(\theta_J)$ of (3.128) over the uniform distribution of θ_J; namely,

$$P_{b_J} = \frac{1}{2\pi}\int_0^{2\pi} P_Q(\theta_J)\, d\theta_J = \frac{1}{2\pi}\int_0^{2\pi} P_I(\theta_J)\, d\theta_J. \tag{3.130}$$

Since, on the average, the fraction ρ of the total number of detection intervals is jammed, the average bit error probability over all detection intervals (jammed and unjammed) is given by (3.57) where

$$P_{b_0} = \frac{3}{2}Q\left(\sqrt{\frac{2E_b'}{N_0}}\right) - \frac{1}{2}Q\left(3\sqrt{\frac{2E_b'}{N_0}}\right) \tag{3.131}$$

represents the average bit error probability of duobinary QPSK in the absence of jamming. Note that the average bit error probability performance of duobinary, as given by [7, Eq. (4.114)], agrees only with the leading term of (3.131) and is thus only asymptotically correct as E_b/N_0 approaches infinity.

The symbol error probability of duobinary QPSK is, as for any QPSK system, the probability that either the in-phase or the quadrature bit is in error. Thus,

$$\begin{aligned} P_s &= \Pr\{\hat{a}_i \neq a_i \text{ or } \hat{b}_i \neq b_i\} = \Pr\{\hat{a}_i \neq a_i\} + \Pr\{\hat{b}_i \neq b_i\} \\ &\quad - \Pr\{\hat{a}_i \neq a_i\}\Pr\{\hat{b}_i \neq b_i\}, \end{aligned} \tag{3.132}$$

which when averaged over all symbols (jammed and unjammed) gives the result in (3.24) where P_{s_J} is given by (3.17) together with now (3.122) and

$$\begin{aligned} P_{s_0} &= 3Q\left(\sqrt{\frac{2E_b'}{N_0}}\right) - \frac{9}{4}Q^2\left(\sqrt{\frac{2E_b'}{N_0}}\right) - Q\left(3\sqrt{\frac{2E_b'}{N_0}}\right) \\ &\quad + \frac{3}{2}Q\left(\sqrt{\frac{2E_b'}{N_0}}\right)Q\left(3\sqrt{\frac{2E_b'}{N_0}}\right) - \frac{1}{4}Q^2\left(3\sqrt{\frac{2E_b'}{N_0}}\right). \end{aligned} \tag{3.133}$$

Note that the first two terms of (3.133) resemble the functional form of the average symbol error probability expression for QASK-16 as in (3.51). There, however, E_b' is related to the true bit energy E_b by $E_b' = (2/5)E_b$.

Figure 3.19 is a typical plot of P_b (as evaluated from (3.57) versus ρ, with E_b/N_J as a parameter and $E_b/N_0 = 20$ dB. One again observes that, by fixing E_b/N_0 and E_b/N_J, there exists a value of ρ which maximizes P_b and thus represents the worst case multitone jammer situation. Figure 3.20 is a

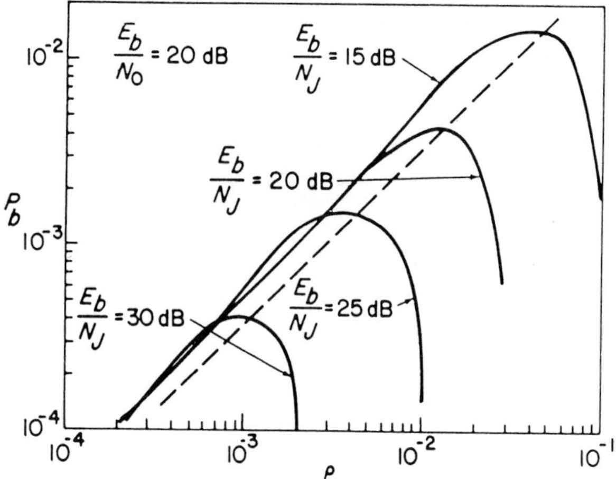

Figure 3.19. P_b versus ρ for FH/QPR in tone jamming with $E_b/N_0 = 20$ dB.

plot of worst case ρ versus E_b/N_J, with E_b/N_0 as a parameter. Figure 3.21 illustrates the corresponding plot of $P_{b_{\max}}$ versus E_b/N_J, with E_b/N_0 fixed.

As was true for the FH/QPSK and FH/QASK modulations considered previously, it is of interest to study the limiting behavior of FH/QPR in the presence of multitone jamming as the Gaussian noise (e.g., N_0) goes to zero. Let

$$N_J' \triangleq \frac{\pi}{2} N_J. \tag{3.134}$$

Then, for FH/QPR, we obtain the following results:

$$\lim_{E_b/N_0 \to \infty} P_{b_J}$$

$$= \begin{cases} 0; & \dfrac{\rho E_b'}{N_J'} > 1 \\[2ex] \dfrac{3}{2\pi} \cos^{-1} \sqrt{\dfrac{\rho E_b'}{N_J'}}; & \dfrac{1}{9} < \dfrac{\rho E_b'}{N_J'} < 1 \\[2ex] \dfrac{1}{2\pi} \left[3 \cos^{-1} \sqrt{\dfrac{\rho E_b'}{N_J'}} - \cos^{-1}\left(3 \sqrt{\dfrac{\rho E_b'}{N_J'}} \right) \right]; & 0 < \dfrac{\rho E_b'}{N_J'} < \dfrac{1}{9}. \end{cases} \tag{3.135}$$

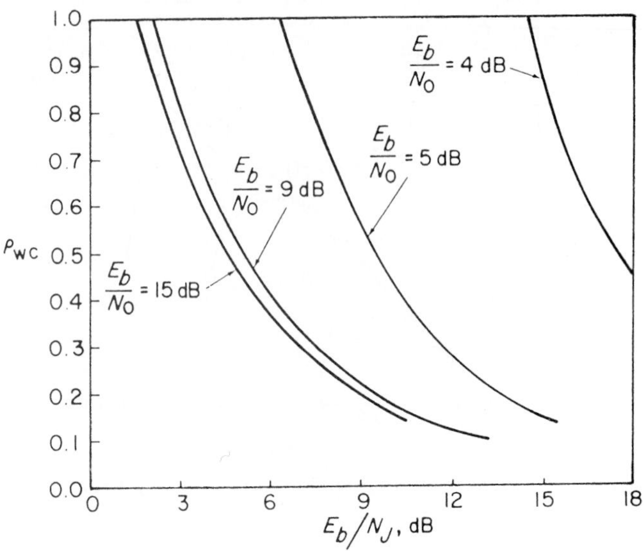

Figure 3.20. Worst case ρ versus E_b/N_J—FH/QPR (tone jamming).

Also, recognizing that $P_{b_0} \to 0$ in the limit as $E_b/N_0 \to \infty$, we obtain from (3.135) and (3.57) the desired limiting behavior to the average bit error probability, namely,

$$\lim_{E_b/N_0 \to \infty} P_b$$

$$= \begin{cases} 0; & \dfrac{\rho E_b'}{N_J'} > 1 \\ \dfrac{3\rho}{2\pi} \cos^{-1} \sqrt{\dfrac{\rho E_b'}{N_J'}}; & \dfrac{1}{9} < \dfrac{\rho E_b'}{N_J'} < 1 \\ \dfrac{\rho}{2\pi} \left[3 \cos^{-1} \sqrt{\dfrac{\rho E_b'}{N_J'}} - \cos^{-1} \left(3 \sqrt{\dfrac{\rho E_b'}{N_J'}} \right) \right]; & 0 < \dfrac{\rho E_b'}{N_J'} < \dfrac{1}{9}. \end{cases}$$

(3.136)

The partial-band fraction ρ corresponding to the worst case jammer (maximum P_b) can be obtained by differentiating (3.136) with respect to ρ and equating to zero. Assuming that, for a fixed E_b'/N_J', this worst case ρ occurs when $1/9 < \rho E_b'/N_J' < 1$, then analogous to (3.32), we immediately

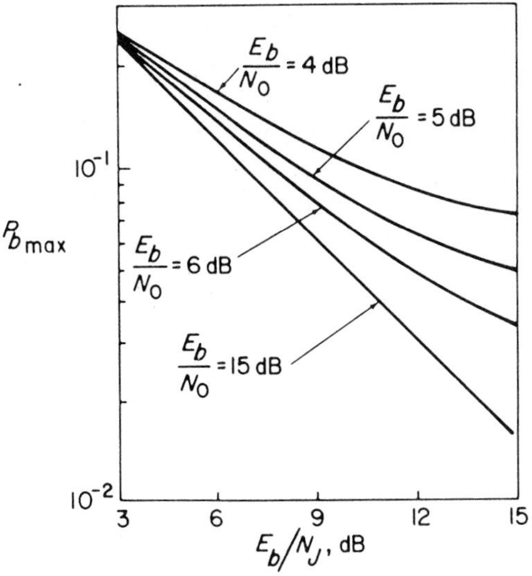

Figure 3.21. Worst case P_b versus E_b/N_J—FH/QPR (tone jamming).

obtain

$$\rho_{wc} = \begin{cases} \dfrac{0.6306}{E_b'/N_J'} = \dfrac{1.6058}{E_b/N_J}; & E_b/N_J \geq 1.6058 \\ 1; & E_b/N_J < 1.6058. \end{cases} \tag{3.137}$$

Substituting (3.137) into (3.136) gives the limiting average bit error probability performance corresponding to the worst case jammer, namely,

$$\lim_{E_b/N_0 \to \infty} P_{b_{\max}} = \begin{cases} \dfrac{3}{4}\left(\dfrac{0.2623}{E_b'/N_J'}\right) = \dfrac{0.5009}{E_b/N_J}; & E_b/N_J \geq 1.6058 \\ \dfrac{3}{2\pi}\cos^{-1}\sqrt{\dfrac{\pi E_b}{8N_J}}; & 8/9\pi \leq E_b/N_J < 1.6058 \\ \dfrac{1}{2\pi}\left[3\cos^{-1}\sqrt{\dfrac{\pi E_b}{8N_J}} - \cos^{-1}\left(3\sqrt{\dfrac{\pi E_b}{8N_J}}\right)\right]; & \\ & 0 \leq E_b/N_J < 8/9\pi. \end{cases} \tag{3.138}$$

3.8 PERFORMANCE OF FH/QPR IN THE PRESENCE OF PARTIAL-BAND NOISE JAMMING

Once again, modeling the partial-band noise jammer as an additional additive noise source with power spectral density given by (3.63), the average bit error probability performance in the presence of partial-band noise jamming is obtained from (3.131) by replacing N_0 by $N_0 + N_J/\rho$, namely,

$$P_{b_J} = \frac{3}{2}Q\left(\left[\left(\frac{2E_b'}{N_0}\right)^{-1} + \left(\frac{2\rho E_b'}{N_J}\right)^{-1}\right]^{-1/2}\right) - \frac{1}{2}Q\left(3\left[\left(\frac{2E_b'}{N_0}\right)^{-1} + \left(\frac{2\rho E_b'}{N_J}\right)^{-1}\right]^{-1/2}\right). \tag{3.139}$$

A similar result can be obtained from (3.133) for average symbol error probability in the presence of partial-band noise jamming. Finally, substituting (3.139) and (3.131) in (3.57) then gives the average bit error probability over all detection intervals, namely,

$$\begin{aligned} P_b = {} & \frac{3\rho}{2}Q\left(\left[\left(\frac{2E_b'}{N_0}\right)^{-1} + \left(\frac{2\rho E_b'}{N_J}\right)^{-1}\right]^{-1/2}\right) \\ & - \frac{\rho}{2}Q\left(3\left[\left(\frac{2E_b'}{N_0}\right)^{-1} + \left(\frac{2\rho E_b'}{N_J}\right)^{-1}\right]^{-1/2}\right) \\ & + \frac{3(1-\rho)}{2}Q\left(\sqrt{\frac{2E_b'}{N_0}}\right) - \frac{(1-\rho)}{2}Q\left(3\sqrt{\frac{2E_b'}{N_0}}\right). \end{aligned} \tag{3.140}$$

The limiting behavior of (3.140) as E_b/N_0 approaches infinity is easily seen to be

$$\lim_{E_b/N_0 \to \infty} P_b = \frac{3\rho}{2}Q\left(\sqrt{\frac{2\rho E_b'}{N_J}}\right) - \frac{\rho}{2}Q\left(3\sqrt{\frac{2\rho E_b'}{N_J}}\right) \tag{3.141}$$

which yields a partial-band fraction for the worst case jammer given by

$$\rho_{wc} = \begin{cases} \dfrac{0.7114}{E_b'/N_J} = \dfrac{1.1532}{E_b/N_J}; & E_b/N_J \geq 1.1532 \\ 1; & E_b/N_J < 1.1532 \end{cases} \tag{3.142}$$

and a corresponding worst case average bit error probability

$$\lim_{E_b/N_0 \to \infty} P_{b_{max}} = \begin{cases} \dfrac{0.2014}{E_b/N_J}; & E_b/N_J \geq 1.1532 \\ \dfrac{3}{2}Q\left(\sqrt{\dfrac{\pi^2 E_b}{8N_J}}\right) - \dfrac{1}{2}Q\left(3\sqrt{\dfrac{\pi^2 E_b}{8N_J}}\right); & E_b/N_J < 1.1532. \end{cases} \tag{3.143}$$

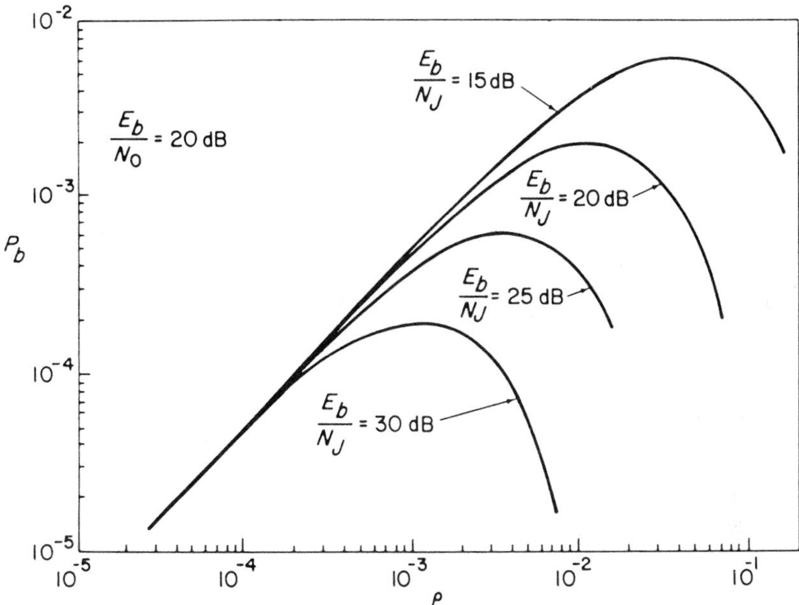

Figure 3.22. P_b versus ρ for FH/QPR in noise jamming with $E_b/N_0 = 20$ dB.

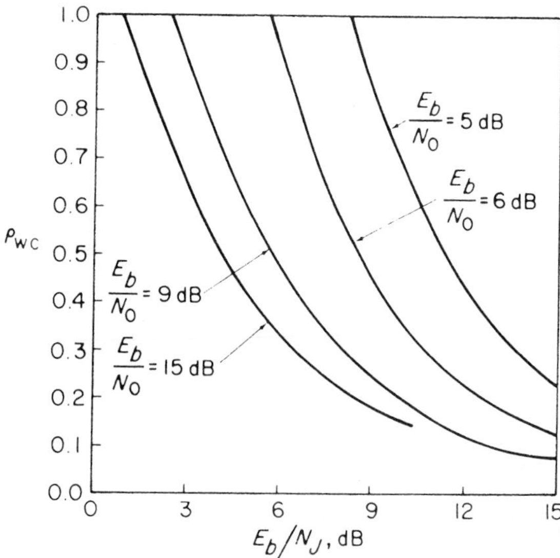

Figure 3.23. Worst case ρ versus E_b/N_J—FH/QPR (noise jamming).

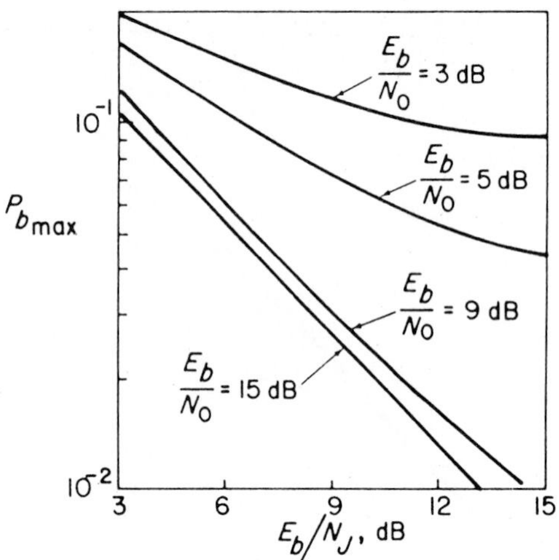

Figure 3.24. Worst case P_b versus E_b/N_J—FH/QPR (noise jamming).

Table 3.2
Worst case jammer performance for various modulations and jammer types.

$$\text{Worst case partial-band fraction } \rho_{\text{wc}} = \frac{K_\rho}{E_b/N_J}$$

$$\text{Maximum average bit error probability } P_{b_{\max}} = \frac{K_P}{E_b/N_J}$$

Spread-Spectrum Modulation	Jammer Type	K_ρ	K_P
FH/QPSK	Multitone Noise	0.6306 0.7090	0.1311 0.0829
FH/QASK-16	Multitone Noise	1.5765 1.758	0.2459 0.1555
FH/PN/QPSK	Multitone Noise	0.9220 0.7090	0.0789 0.0829
FH/PN/QASK-16	Multitone Noise	2.3050 1.758	0.1483 0.1555
FH/QPR-3	Multitone Noise	1.6058 1.1532	0.5009 0.2014

Figures 3.22–3.24 characterize the performance of FH/QPR in the presence of partial-band noise jamming as computed from the results given in this section.

3.9 SUMMARY AND CONCLUSIONS

We conclude this chapter by summarizing the asymptotic worst case jammer performance results for the various modulations and jammer types in the form of Table 3.2. In all cases, we consider the limiting behavior as E_b/N_0 approaches infinity so that both the worst case partial-band fraction and corresponding maximum average bit error probability are inversely related to E_b/N_J.

Based on the table entries, the following conclusions can be reached:

- FH/QASK-16 is more susceptible to jamming (noise or multitone) than FH/QPSK by about 2.73 dB.
- Both FH/QPSK and FH/QASK are more susceptible to multitone jamming by about 2 dB.
- FH three-level QPR is more susceptible to multitone jamming than noise jamming by about 4 dB.
- FH three-level QPR is more susceptible to tone and noise jammers than FH/QASK-16 by 3.09 dB and 1.12 dB, respectively.

3.10 REFERENCES

[1] D. P. Taylor and D. Cheung, "The effect of carrier phase error on the performance of a duobinary shaped QPSK signal," *IEEE Trans. Commun.*, COM-25, no. 7, pp. 738–744, July 1977.

[2] W. C. Lindsey and M. K. Simon, *Telecommunication Systems Engineering*, Englewood Cliffs, NJ: Prentice-Hall, 1973, chapter 5.

[3] M. K. Simon and J. G. Smith, "Carrier synchronization and detection of QASK signal sets," *IEEE Trans. Commun.*, COM-22, no. 2, February 1974.

[4] M. K. Simon and A. Polydoros, "Coherent detection of frequency-hopped quadrature modulations in the presence of jamming; Part I: QPSK and QASK modulations," *IEEE Trans. Commun.*, COM-29, no. 11, pp. 1644–1660, November 1981.

[5] M. K. Simon, "Coherent detection of frequency-hopped quadrature modulations in the presence of jamming; Part II: QPR Class I modulation," *IEEE Trans. Commun.*, COM-29, no. 11, pp. 1660–1668, November 1981.

[6] N. E. Bekir, "Bounds on the Distribution of Partial Correlation for PN and Gold Sequences," Ph.D. Dissertation, Electrical Engineering Department, University of Southern California, January 1978.

[7] R. W. Lucky, J. Salz and E. J. Weldon, Jr., *Principles of Data Communications*, New York: McGraw-Hill, pp. 85–86, 1968.

[8] A. Lender, "The duobinary technique for high-speed data transmission," *AIEE Trans. Commun. Electr.*, vol. 82, pp. 214–218, May 1963.

[9] E. R. Kretzmer, "Generalization of a technique for binary data communication," *IEEE Trans. Commun. Syst.*, COM-14, pp. 67–68, February 1966.

[10] P. Kabal and S. Pasupathy, "Partial Response Signaling," *IEEE Trans. Commun.*, COM-23, pp. 921–935, September 1975.

Chapter 4

DIFFERENTIALLY COHERENT MODULATION TECHNIQUES

Traditionally coherent modulations such as multiple phase-shift-keying (MPSK) and quadrature amplitude-shift-keying (QASK) can also be detected using differentially coherent techniques. These techniques are useful in applications where the receiver is unable to provide an exact carrier reference phase for demodulating each data symbol but is capable of establishing a phase reference to within an arbitrary number of radians, say ϕ_a, of the exact phase. By differentially encoding the transmitted phase information and using a form of phase difference detection, the ϕ_a phase ambiguity can be resolved and the system is then capable of credible data detection. Obviously, because of the lack of perfect phase information per symbol, some degradation in system performance over coherent detection of the same modulation will exist.

In the spread-spectrum (SS) application, the need for differentially coherent detection comes about as follows [1]–[4]. Conventional frequency hopping (FH) as used to protect communication systems from radio frequency interference (RFI) or jamming has non-continuous carrier phase from hop to hop. For the fast hop rates needed in most RFI and jamming environments, the receiver dehopper does not have a chance to acquire the phase of each new carrier in the hop sequence. Differentially coherent detection provides a possible solution to the effect of phase discontinuities introduced by frequency hopping since the *absolute* phase of each carrier in the hop sequence is irrelevant insofar as the data detection process is concerned. More explicitly, the case of interest in FH differentially coherent modulation systems is where there are many (at least two) data symbols per hop, i.e., the so-called slow frequency hopping (SFH) case. Thus, for all the data symbols on a given hop, the carrier phase is constant and, regardless of its value, the combination of differential phase encoding and phase difference detection is sufficient to produce reliable communication. Of course, as in any differentially coherent system, the first data symbol in the sequence (here the first data symbol in each hop) is lost since a phase reference has not yet been established for its detection. This again emphasizes the necessity of having many symbols per hop so as to reduce this effective loss in information rate to a minimum.

As in the previous chapter, we shall again examine the performance of the various modulations considered in the presence of partial-band noise and partial-band multitone jamming. In each case, the worst case jamming strategy will be determined, which, as before, consists of specifying the worst case partial-band fraction and the corresponding maximum average error probability. To simplify the ensuing analysis, we shall ignore the presence of the additive white Gaussian noise (AWGN) background in favor of the degradation produced by the jamming interference. Modification of the results to include the quiescent noise contribution would follow along the same lines as the approach taken in the previous chapter for coherent detection of these same modulations.

4.1 PERFORMANCE OF FH / MDPSK IN THE PRESENCE OF PARTIAL-BAND MULTITONE JAMMING

In a differentially encoded frequency-hopped M-ary differential phase-shift-keyed (FH/MDPSK) system, the information to be transmitted in the i-th signalling interval $(i-1)T_s \le t \le iT_s$ is conveyed by appropriately selecting one of M phases

$$\theta_m = \frac{(2m-1)\pi}{M}; \qquad m = 1, 2, \ldots, M \tag{4.1}$$

and adding it to the total accumulated phase in the $(i-1)$-st signalling interval of a constant amplitude (A), fixed frequency (assumed known at the receiver) sinusoid. Typically $M = 2^K$ with K integer, and these are the only cases we shall consider in detail. Furthermore, since the derivation of the performance of FH/MDPSK in the presence of a partial-band multitone jammer will rely largely on certain geometric relations, it is expedient to deal with both the signal and the jammer as phasors. Thus, the transmitted signal $s^{(i)}(t)$ in the i-th signalling interval is conveniently represented in complex form by

$$\boldsymbol{S}^{(i)} = Ae^{j(\theta^{(i)} + \theta_T^{(i-1)})} \tag{4.2}$$

where $\theta_T^{(i-1)}$ is the total accumulated phase in the $(i-1)$-st signalling interval and $\theta^{(i)}$ ranges over the set $\{\theta_m\}$ of (4.1).

In the presence of multitone jamming interference as characterized in the previous chapter, a jamming tone $J(t)$, constant in both phase and magnitude (amplitude), is added to the transmitted signal. Since, when the jammer "hits," he is assumed[1] to be of the same frequency as the signal, then we may also represent the jammer in complex form, namely,

$$J = Ie^{j\theta_J} \tag{4.3}$$

where θ_J is a random phase uniformly distributed in the interval $(0, 2\pi)$. Thus, in any hop interval which is hit by the jammer (the probability of this occurring is the partial-band fraction ρ), the signals on which a decision for the i-th signalling interval is to be based are given (in complex form) by

$$Y^{(i-1)} = Ae^{j\theta_T^{(i-1)}} + Ie^{j\theta_J}$$

$$Y^{(i)} = Ae^{j(\theta^{(i)} + \theta_T^{(i-1)})} + Ie^{j\theta_J}. \tag{4.4}$$

Assuming a receiver structure that is optimum in the absence of the jammer, i.e., it employs the optimum decision rule for MDPSK against wideband noise, then in the presence of the on-tune jammer this rule would result in the estimate

$$\hat{\theta}^{(i)} = \theta_k \tag{4.5}$$

where k is such that

$$|\arg(Y^{(i)} - Y^{(i-1)}) - \theta_k| \le \frac{\pi}{M}. \tag{4.6}$$

Then if θ_n is indeed the true value of $\theta^{(i)}$, a symbol (phase) error is made, i.e., $\hat{\theta}^{(i)} \ne \theta^{(i)}$ whenever

$$|\arg(Y^{(i)} - Y^{(i-1)}) - \theta_n| > \frac{\pi}{M}. \tag{4.7}$$

Without loss in generality, we shall, for convenience, rotate the actual transmitted signal vectors by π/M radians so that the possible transmitted signal phases of (4.1) become

$$\theta_m = \frac{2\pi m}{M}; \quad m = 0, \pm 1, \pm 2, \ldots, \pm\left(\frac{M-2}{2}\right), \frac{M}{2}. \tag{4.8}$$

Finally, letting $Q_{2\pi n/M}$; $n = 0, \pm 1, \pm 2, \ldots \pm(M-2)/2, M/2$ denote the probability of the error event in (4.7), namely,

$$Q_{2\pi n/M} = \Pr\left\{|\arg(Y^{(i)} - Y^{(i-1)}) - \theta_n| > \frac{\pi}{M}\right\} \tag{4.9}$$

and noting that since we have assumed the absence of an AWGN background, the probability of error in hop intervals which are not hit by the jammer is zero, then the average symbol error probability for MDPSK in

[1] The assumption of on-tune jamming is made solely to simplify the analysis, as has been done in previous chapters. Both the analytical technique and the sensitivity of the results that follow from its application depend heavily on this assumption. Some evidence of this statement will be discussed at the end of this section.

the presence of multitone jamming is given by

$$P_s(M) = \frac{\rho}{M} \sum_n Q_{2\pi n/M} \tag{4.10}$$

where the summation on n ranges over the set $n = 0, \pm 1, \pm 2, \ldots, \pm (M-2)/2, M/2$. Since θ_J is uniformly distributed, we can recognize the symmetry

$$Q_{2\pi n/M} = Q_{-2\pi n/M}; \quad n = 1, 2, \ldots, \frac{M-2}{2}. \tag{4.11}$$

Also if $\theta_n = 0$ is transmitted, then, from (4.4), $\boldsymbol{Y}^{(i-1)}$ and $\boldsymbol{Y}^{(i)}$ are identical vectors. Equivalently,

$$|\arg(\boldsymbol{Y}^{(i)} - \boldsymbol{Y}^{(i-1)}) - \theta_0| = 0 \tag{4.12}$$

and, from (4.9),

$$Q_0 = 0. \tag{4.13}$$

Thus, using (4.11) and (4.13), $P_s(M)$ of (4.10) simplifies to

$$P_s(M) = \frac{\rho}{M}\left[Q_\pi + 2\sum_{n=1}^{\frac{M-2}{2}} Q_{2\pi n/M}\right]. \tag{4.14}$$

Finally, using the relation between average symbol and bit error probabilities, namely,

$$P_b(M) = \left[\frac{M}{2(M-1)}\right] P_s(M), \tag{4.15}$$

the average bit error probability for MDPSK in the presence of multitone jamming is given by

$$P_b(M) = \frac{\rho}{2(M-1)}\left[Q_\pi + 2\sum_{n=1}^{\frac{M-2}{2}} Q_{2\pi n/M}\right]. \tag{4.16}$$

Actually, the relation in (4.15) holds as an equality only for orthogonal signal sets [5]. However, for low signal-to-jammer noise ratios, the right-hand side of (4.15) becomes a tight upper bound for the average bit error probability performance of FH/MDPSK. For binary DPSK ($M = 2$), the equality in (4.15) is exact.

We shall see shortly that, for the evaluation of $Q_{2\pi n/M}$, it is convenient to renormalize the problem in terms of the ratio of jamming power per tone $J_0 = J/Q$ to signal power S. Let β^2 denote this ratio, i.e.,

$$\beta^2 = \frac{J/Q}{S}. \tag{4.17}$$

Then, recalling from the previous chapter that the number of hop slots N in the total hop frequency band W_{ss} is

$$N = \frac{W_{ss}}{1/T_s} = W_{ss}T_b\log_2 M \tag{4.18}$$

then, the partial-band fraction ρ can be expressed in terms of β^2 and the bit energy-to-jammer noise spectral density ratio E_b/N_J by

$$\rho \triangleq \frac{Q}{N} = \frac{J}{\beta^2 S W_{ss} T_b \log_2 M} = \frac{1}{(\log_2 M)\beta^2 E_b/N_J}. \tag{4.19}$$

Using (4.19), we can rewrite (4.16) in the form

$$P_b(M) = \frac{1}{2(M-1)(\log_2 M)\beta^2 E_b/N_J}\left[Q_\pi + 2\sum_{n=1}^{\frac{M-2}{2}} Q_{2\pi n/M}\right]. \tag{4.20}$$

Before proceeding to the evaluation of $Q_{2\pi n/M}$; $n = 1, 2, \ldots, M/2$ we make the final observation that the per tone jamming-to-signal power ratio β^2 can also be expressed in terms of the vector definitions of the signal and tone jamming interference. Since from (4.2) and (4.3) the signal power and jammer power per tone are given by

$$S = \frac{A^2}{2}; \qquad \frac{J}{Q} = \frac{I^2}{2}, \tag{4.21}$$

then equivalently from (4.17) we have that

$$\beta^2 = \frac{I^2}{A^2}. \tag{4.22}$$

4.1.1 Evaluation of $Q_{2\pi n/m}$

In view of (4.22), $Q_{2\pi n/M}$ of (4.9) may be restated in the normalized form

$$Q_{2\pi n/M} = \Pr\{|\arg(\mathbf{Z}^{(i)} - \mathbf{Z}^{(i-1)}) - 2n\theta| > \theta\} \tag{4.23}$$

where

$$\theta \triangleq \frac{\pi}{M} \tag{4.24}$$

and

$$\begin{aligned} \mathbf{Z}^{(i-1)} &= e^{-jn\theta} + \beta e^{j\theta_J} \triangleq R_1 e^{j(-n\theta+\psi_1)} \\ \mathbf{Z}^{(i)} &= e^{jn\theta} + \beta e^{j\theta_J} \triangleq R_2 e^{j(n\theta+\psi_2)}. \end{aligned} \tag{4.25}$$

Note that, in obtaining (4.25) from (4.4), we have substituted for $\theta^{(i)}$ its assumed true value, namely, $\theta_n = 2\pi n/M - 2n\theta$, and, since θ_J is uniformly distributed, we have arbitrarily established the symmetry $\theta_T^{(i-1)} = -\pi n/M = -n\theta$. Figure 4.1 is a graphical representation of (4.25) where we have further introduced the notation

$$\psi \triangleq \arg(\boldsymbol{Z}^{(i)} - \boldsymbol{Z}^{(i-1)}). \tag{4.26}$$

Thus, using (4.25) and (4.26),

$$\begin{aligned}\arg(\boldsymbol{Z}^{(i)} - \boldsymbol{Z}^{(i-1)}) - 2n\theta &= \psi - 2n\theta \\ &= n\theta + \psi_2 - (-n\theta + \psi_1) - 2n\theta \\ &= \psi_2 - \psi_1\end{aligned} \tag{4.27}$$

and, hence,

$$Q_{2\pi n/M} = \Pr\{|\psi_2 - \psi_1| > \theta\} = 1 - \Pr\{|\psi_2 - \psi_1| \le \theta\}. \tag{4.28}$$

Consider the product (asterisk denotes complex conjugate)

$$\begin{aligned}(\boldsymbol{Z}^{(i-1)})^* \boldsymbol{Z}^{(i)} e^{-j2n\theta} &= R_1 R_2 e^{j(n\theta - \psi_1)} e^{j(n\theta + \psi_2)} e^{-j2n\theta} \\ &= R_1 R_2 e^{j(\psi_2 - \psi_1)}.\end{aligned} \tag{4.29}$$

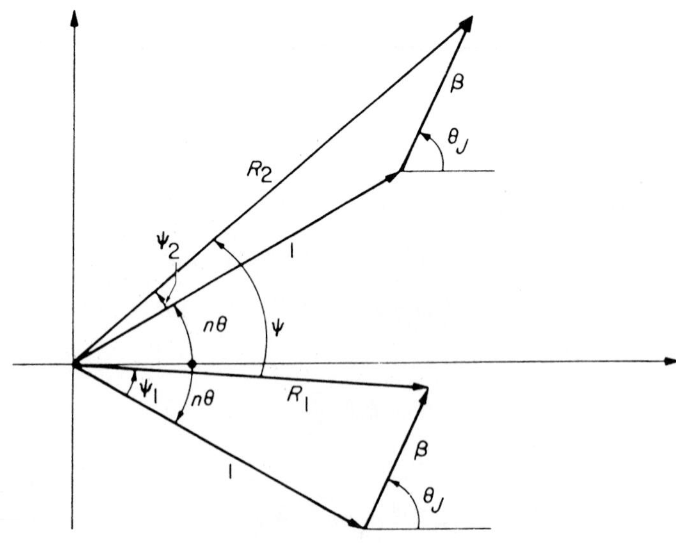

Figure 4.1. A graphical representation of (4.25).

The above product can also be written in the form

$$\begin{aligned}(\boldsymbol{Z}^{(i-1)})^*\boldsymbol{Z}^{(i)}e^{-j2n\theta} &= (e^{jn\theta} + \beta e^{-j\theta_J})(e^{jn\theta} + \beta e^{j\theta_J})e^{-j2n\theta} \\ &= \left[e^{j2n\theta} + \beta^2 + \beta e^{jn\theta}(e^{j\theta_J} + e^{-j\theta_J})\right]e^{-j2n\theta} \\ &= 1 + \beta^2 e^{-j2n\theta} + 2\beta\cos\theta_J e^{-jn\theta}. \end{aligned} \tag{4.30}$$

Thus, using (4.29) and (4.30) in (4.28) results in the equivalent relation

$$\begin{aligned} Q_{2\pi n/M} &= 1 - \Pr\left\{-\theta \le \arg\left[(\boldsymbol{Z}^{(i-1)})^*\boldsymbol{Z}^{(i)}e^{-j2n\theta}\right] \le \theta\right\} \\ &= 1 - \Pr\left\{-\theta \le \arg\left[1 + \beta^2 e^{-j2n\theta} + 2\beta\cos\theta_J e^{-jn\theta}\right] \le \theta\right\}. \end{aligned} \tag{4.31}$$

Equation (4.31) can be given a geometric interpretation as in Figure 4.2. Here the vector $\boldsymbol{OQ}$ (a line drawn from point O to either point Q)

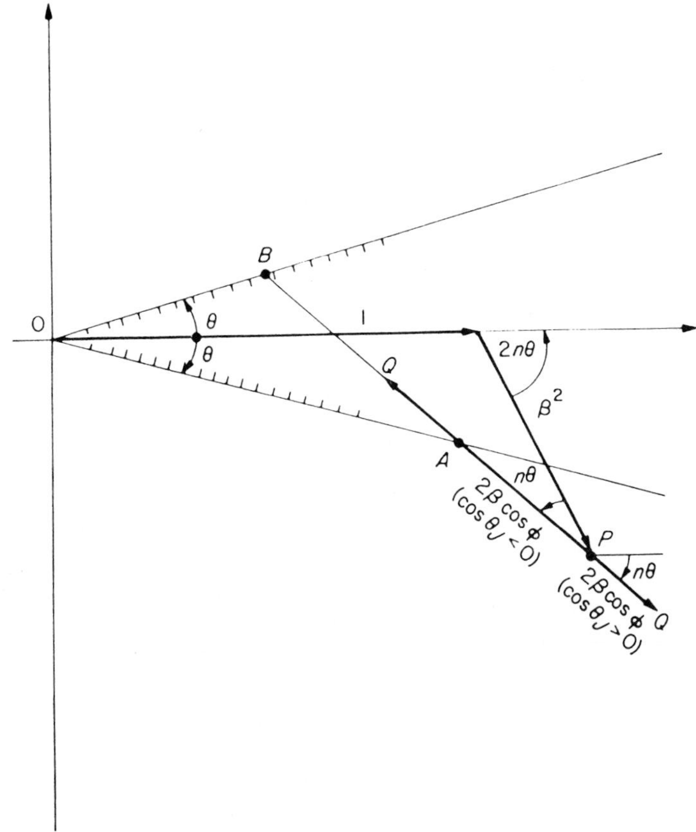

Figure 4.2. A geometric interpretation of (4.31).

represents the complex number whose argument is required in (4.31), i.e.,

$$\boldsymbol{OQ} = 1 + \beta^2 e^{-j2n\theta} + 2\beta\cos\theta_J e^{jn\theta}. \tag{4.32}$$

Thus, in terms of the geometry in Figure 4.2, (4.31) may be written in the alternate form

$$\begin{aligned} Q_{2\pi n/M} &= 1 - \Pr\{\text{point } Q \text{ is within the } 2\theta \text{ wedge}\} \\ &= 1 - \Pr\{\text{point } Q \text{ lies along the line } AB\}. \end{aligned} \tag{4.33}$$

Considering separately the cases where point P falls outside and inside the 2θ wedge, which expressed mathematically corresponds to the inequalities (see Figure 4.3)

$$\beta^2 \gtrless \frac{\sin\theta}{\sin[(2n-1)\theta]}; \tag{4.34}$$

then after much routine trigonometry, it can be shown that

$$Q_{2\pi n/M} = Q_{2n\theta}$$

$$= \begin{cases} \dfrac{1}{\pi}\cos^{-1}\left[\dfrac{\beta^2\sin[(2n+1)\theta] + \sin\theta}{2\beta\sin[(n+1)\theta]}\right] u(\beta - \beta_n) \\ \quad + \dfrac{1}{\pi}\cos^{-1}\left[\dfrac{\sin\theta - \beta^2\sin[(2n-1)\theta]}{2\beta\sin[(n-1)\theta]}\right] u(\beta - \beta_{n-1}); \quad 0 < \beta < 1 \\ 1; \quad \beta \geq 1 \quad n = 2, 3, \ldots, \dfrac{M}{2} - 1, \end{cases} \tag{4.35}$$

where $u(\beta)$ is the unit step function and

$$\beta_{n-1} \triangleq \frac{-\sin[(n-1)\theta] + \sin n\theta}{\sin[(2n-1)\theta]}. \tag{4.36}$$

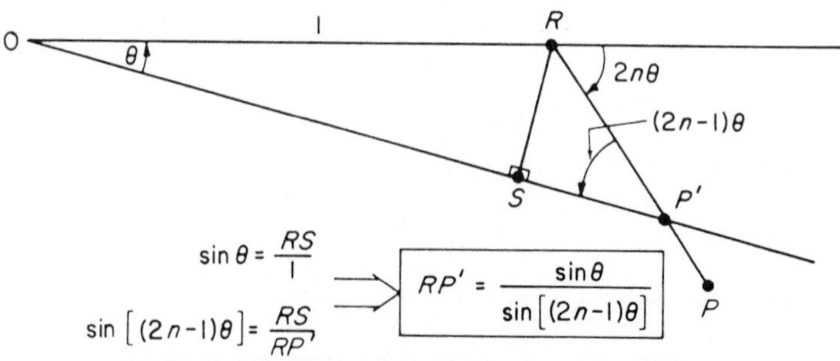

Figure 4.3. The geometry needed to establish (4.34).

Note that

$$\lim_{\beta\to 1} Q_{2n\theta} = \frac{1}{\pi}\left\{\cos^{-1}\left[\frac{\sin[(2n+1)\theta] + \sin\theta}{2\sin[(n+1)\theta]}\right] + \cos^{-1}\left[\frac{\sin\theta - \sin[(2n-1)\theta]}{2\sin[(n-1)\theta]}\right]\right\} = 1 \tag{4.37}$$

For $n = 1$, the appropriate result analogous to (4.35) is

$$Q_{2\theta} = \begin{cases} 0; & 0 < \beta < \beta_1 \\ \dfrac{1}{\pi}\cos^{-1}\left[\dfrac{\beta^2 \sin 3\theta + \sin\theta}{2\beta\sin 2\theta}\right]; & \beta_1 \le \beta < 1 \\ 1; & \beta \ge 1 \end{cases}$$

$$\beta_1 = \frac{\sin 2\theta - \sin\theta}{\sin 3\theta} = \frac{\sin\dfrac{2\pi}{M} - \sin\dfrac{\pi}{M}}{\sin\dfrac{3\pi}{M}}. \tag{4.38}$$

Here

$$\lim_{\beta\to 1} Q_{2\theta} = \frac{1}{\pi}\cos^{-1}\left[\frac{\sin 3\theta + \sin\theta}{2\sin 2\theta}\right] < 1. \tag{4.39}$$

Finally, for $n = M/2$, we have the result

$$Q_{M\theta} = Q_{\pi} = \begin{cases} 0; & 0 < \beta < \beta_{M/2-1} \\ \dfrac{2}{\pi}\cos^{-1}\left[\dfrac{\left(\sin\dfrac{\pi}{M}\right)(1-\beta^2)}{2\beta\cos\dfrac{\pi}{M}}\right]; & \beta_{M/2-1} \le \beta < 1 \\ 1; & \beta \ge 1 \end{cases}$$

$$\beta_{M/2-1} = \frac{1 - \cos\dfrac{\pi}{M}}{\sin\dfrac{\pi}{M}} \tag{4.40}$$

Also,

$$\lim_{\beta\to 1} Q_{\pi} = 1. \tag{4.41}$$

As an example, Figure 4.4 is a plot of $Q_{2n\theta}$; $n = 1, 2, 3, 4, 8$ versus β for $M = 16$. These probabilities are computed from (4.35), (4.38), and (4.40). Using these results in (4.20), Figure 4.5 illustrates the product $(E_b/N_J) \times P_b$ (16) versus β. This curve has a maximum value of 1.457 at $\beta = 0.1614$, which, from (4.19), corresponds to the optimal (worst case) jamming strategy.

$$\rho_{wc} = \begin{cases} \dfrac{9.597}{E_b/N_J}; & E_b/N_J \geq 9.597 \\ 1; & E_b/N_J < 9.597 \end{cases} \tag{4.42}$$

Thus, the average bit error probability performance of FH/MDPSK ($M = 16$) in the presence of the worst case tone jammer is given by

$$P_{b_{\max}} = \begin{cases} \dfrac{1}{30}\left[Q_\pi + 2\displaystyle\sum_{n=1}^{7} Q_{n\pi/8}\right]\Bigg|_{\beta=1/(2\sqrt{E_b/N_J})}; & 0.25 < E_b/N_J < 9.597 \\ \dfrac{1.457}{E_b/N_J}; & E_b/N_J \geq 9.597 \\ 0.5; & E_b/N_J < 0.25. \end{cases} \tag{4.43}$$

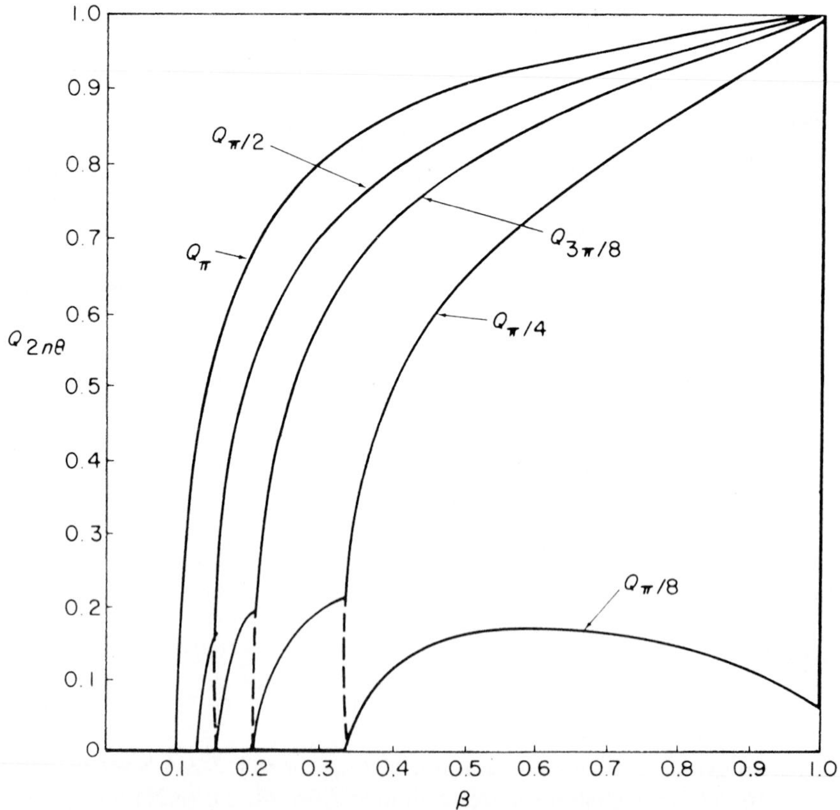

Figure 4.4. Individual signal point error probability components as a function of square root of jamming (per tone)-to-signal power ratio.

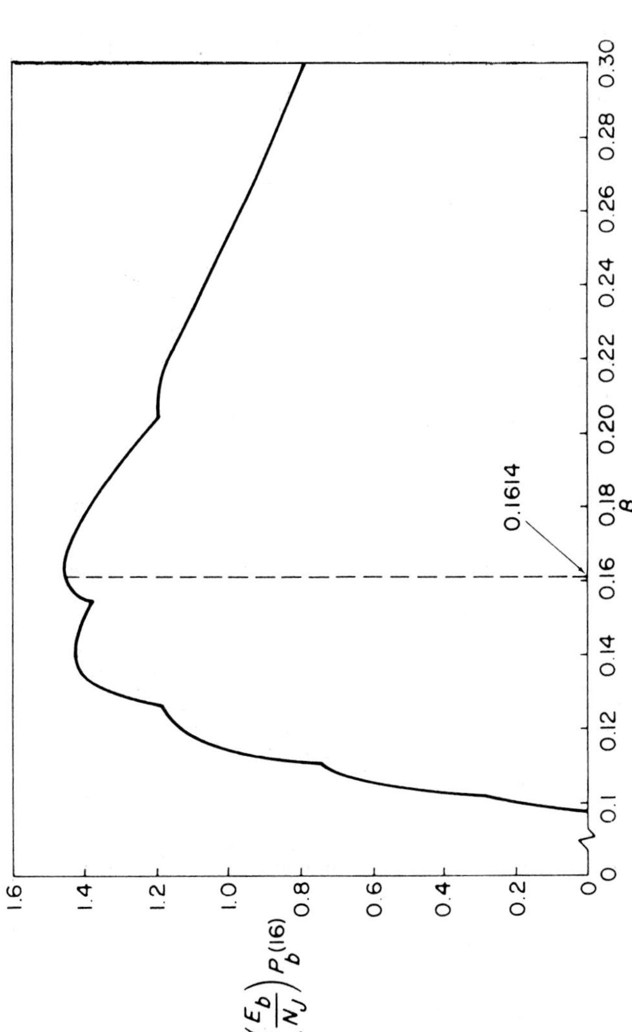

Figure 4.5. Bit error probability performance of FH/MDPSK ($M = 16$) as a function of square root of jamming (per tone)-to-signal power ratio.

Table 4.1
Asymptotic performance of FH/MDPSK for worst case partial-band multitone jamming.

Worst case partial-band fraction $\rho_{wc} = \dfrac{K_\rho}{E_b/N_J}$

Maximum average bit error probability $P_{b_{\max}} = \dfrac{K_P}{E_b/N_J}$

M	β	K_ρ	K_P
2	1	1	0.50
4	0.5220	1.835	0.2593
8	0.2760	4.376	0.5280
16	0.1614	9.597	1.457

Similar results can be obtained[2] for FH/MDPSK with $M = 2$, 4, and 8. The asymptotic behavior of these results (i.e., ρ and P_b inversely related to E_b/N_J) is given in Table 4.1. Using the results in Table 4.1 and the fact that, for any M,

$$P_{b_{\max}} = P_b(M)\big|_{\beta=1/\sqrt{(\log_2 M)E_b/N_J}}; \quad E_b/N_J \le K_\rho \tag{4.44}$$

with $P_b(M)$ given by (4.20), Figure 4.6 is an illustration of the average bit error probability performance of FH/MDPSK for worst case partial-band multitone jamming.

Before concluding this section, we wish to alert the reader to a point of pathological behavior that is directly attributable to the assumption of an on-tune tone jammer and is perhaps not obvious from the analytical or graphical results given. In particular, we observe from Figure 4.4 that $Q_{\pi/8}$ has a jump discontinuity at $\beta = 1$ and thus $P_{b_{\max}}$ of (4.43) will have a similar jump discontinuity at $E_b/N_J = 0.25$ (-6 dB). In fact, since from (4.39), $Q_{\pi/8} = .0625$ as β approaches one from below, then at $E_b/N_J = -6$ dB, $P_{b_{\max}}$ jumps from .4375 to .5. For other values of $M \ge 4$, a similar jump

[2] It should be noted here that the results in [1] for the performance of FH/MDPSK ($M = 4$) in the presence of the worst case tone jammer are partially incorrect. In particular, Houston finds $\beta = 0.52$ as the maximizing value. However, since the fraction of the band jammed, which is given by $\rho = 1/(2\beta^2 E_b/N_J)$, cannot exceed one, the value $\beta = 0.52$ can only be achieved if $E_b/N_J > 1.85$. For smaller values of E_b/N_J, the relation $\beta = 1/\sqrt{2E_b/N_J}$ must be used. Thus, we arrive at the following corrected results for $M = 4$:

$$P_{b_{\max}} = \begin{cases} \dfrac{0.2592}{E_b/N_J}; & E_b/N_J > 1.85 \\ \dfrac{1}{3\pi}\left[\cos^{-1}\left(\dfrac{2E_b/N_J - 1}{2\sqrt{2E_b/N_J}}\right) + \cos^{-1}\left(\dfrac{2E_b/N_J + 1}{4\sqrt{E_b/N_J}}\right)\right]; & 0.5 < E_b/N_J < 1.85 \\ 0.5; & E_b/N_J < 0.5 \end{cases}$$

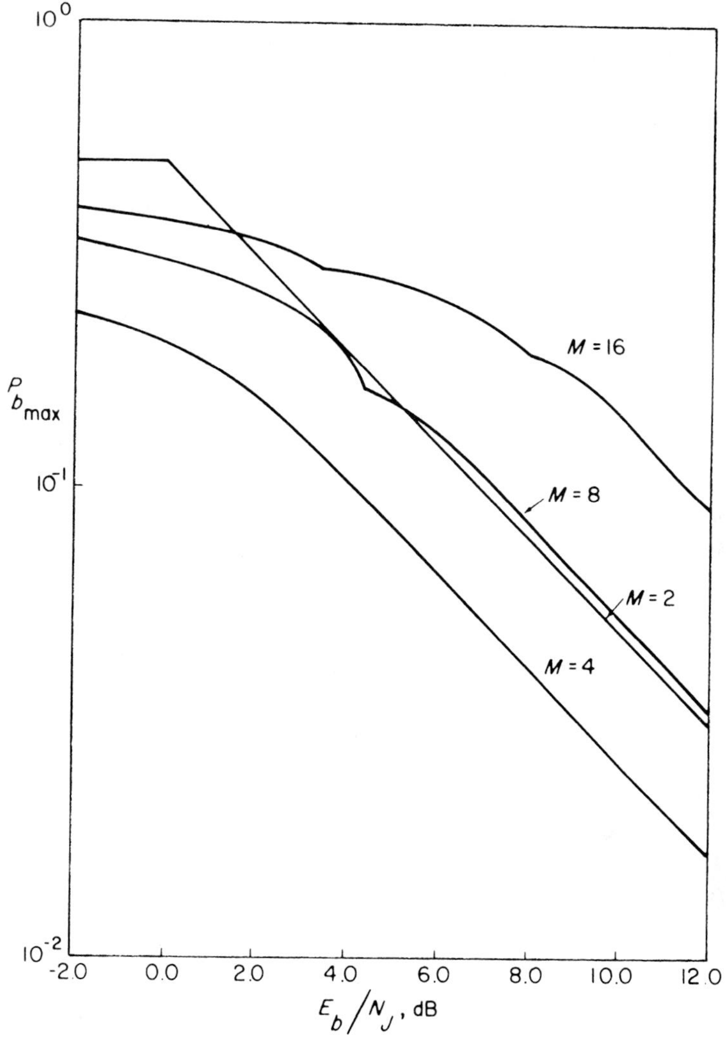

Figure 4.6. Worst case bit error probability performance of FH/MDPSK for partial-band multitone jamming.

discontinuity in the worst case tone jammer bit error probability will occur at $\beta = 1$ and $\rho = 1$, or equivalently, from (4.19), $E_b/N_J = 1/\log_2 M$. Since the range of E_b/N_J in Figure 4.6 extends only down to -2 dB, these jump discontinuities are not visible on this plot, i.e., the largest value of E_b/N_J at which a discontinuity occurs would correspond to $M = 4$ ($E_b/N_J = 1/2 = -3$ dB).

4.2 PERFORMANCE OF FH/MDPSK IN THE PRESENCE OF PARTIAL-BAND NOISE JAMMING

The average symbol error probability performance of MDPSK on an AWGN channel is given by [5], [6]

$$P_s(M) = \int_{\pi/M}^{\pi} \int_0^{\pi/2} \frac{\sin\alpha}{\pi} \left[1 + (\log_2 M)\frac{E_b}{N_0}(1 + \cos\psi \sin\alpha)\right] \times \exp\left[-(\log_2 M)\frac{E_b}{N_0}(1 - \cos\psi\sin\alpha)\right] d\alpha\, d\psi \qquad (4.45)$$

where E_b/N_0 is the bit energy-to-noise ratio. More recently, the double integral in (4.45) has been shown [7] to be expressible as a single integral, namely,

$$P_s(M) = \left(\frac{\sin\frac{\pi}{M}}{\pi}\right) \int_0^{\pi/2} \frac{\exp\left[-(\log_2 M)\frac{E_b}{N_0}\left(1 - \cos\frac{\pi}{M}\cos\alpha\right)\right]}{1 - \cos\frac{\pi}{M}\cos\alpha} d\alpha \qquad (4.46)$$

which lends itself to more convenient numerical evaluation.

To obtain the performance of FH/MDPSK in partial-band noise jamming, one has merely to replace E_b/N_0 by $\rho E_b/N_J$ in (4.46) and multiply the result by ρ where again ρ is the partial-band fraction. Thus, also using (4.15), the average bit error probability performance of FH/MDPSK in partial-band noise jamming is given by

$$\begin{aligned} P_b(M) &= \frac{\rho M}{2(M-1)}\left(\frac{\sin\frac{\pi}{M}}{\pi}\right) \times \int_0^{\pi/2} \frac{\exp\left[-(\log_2 M)\frac{\rho E_b}{N_J}\left(1 - \cos\frac{\pi}{M}\cos\alpha\right)\right]}{1 - \cos\frac{\pi}{M}\cos\alpha} d\alpha \\ &= \left(\frac{E_b}{N_J}\right)^{-1}\left(\frac{M}{2(M-1)}\right) \times \left[Z\left(\frac{\sin\frac{\pi}{M}}{\pi}\right)\int_0^{\pi/2} \frac{\exp\left[-(\log_2 M)Z\left(1 - \cos\frac{\pi}{M}\cos\alpha\right)\right]}{1 - \cos\frac{\pi}{M}\cos\alpha} d\alpha\right] \end{aligned} \qquad (4.47)$$

where

$$Z \triangleq \frac{\rho E_b}{N_J}. \qquad (4.48)$$

Comparing (4.47) with (4.46), we observe that to determine the worst case partial-band noise jammer, one merely uses a tabulation of $P_s(M)$ versus E_b/N_0 (or Z), such as that found in Table 5-5 of [5], multiplies these error probabilities by Z, and locates the value of Z, say $Z_{\max}$ which yields the maximum, say $P_{\max}$, of this product. Then, from (4.47) and (4.48), the worst case jammer strategy corresponds to a partial-band fraction

$$\rho_{wc} = \left(\frac{E_b}{N_J}\right)^{-1} Z_{\max} \tag{4.49}$$

and maximum bit error probability

$$P_{b_{\max}} = \begin{cases} \left(\dfrac{E_b}{N_J}\right)^{-1}\left[\dfrac{MP_{\max}}{2(M-1)}\right]; & \dfrac{E_b}{N_J} \geq Z_{\max} \\[2ex] \dfrac{M}{2(M-1)}\left(\dfrac{\sin\dfrac{\pi}{M}}{\pi}\right)\displaystyle\int_0^{\pi/2} \dfrac{\exp\left[-(\log_2 M)\dfrac{E_b}{N_J}\left(1-\cos\dfrac{\pi}{M}\cos\alpha\right)\right]}{1-\cos\dfrac{\pi}{M}\cos\alpha}\,d\alpha; & \\ & \dfrac{E_b}{N_J} < Z_{\max}. \end{cases} \tag{4.50}$$

Although, for arbitrary M, the single integral of (4.46) cannot be evaluated in closed form, the special case of 2-ary MDPSK (often just abbreviated as DPSK) allows one to obtain the simple result

$$P_s(2) = P_b(2) = \frac{1}{2}\exp\left(-\frac{E_b}{N_0}\right) \tag{4.51}$$

or for FH/DPSK in partial-band noise jamming

$$P_b(2) = \frac{\rho}{2}\exp\left(-\frac{\rho E_b}{N_J}\right). \tag{4.52}$$

Directly differentiating (4.52) with respect to ρ and equating the result to zero yields the worst case performance

$$\rho_{wc} = \left(\frac{E_b}{N_J}\right)^{-1} \tag{4.53}$$

and

$$P_{b_{\max}} = \begin{cases} \dfrac{1}{2e\left(\dfrac{E_b}{N_J}\right)}; & \dfrac{E_b}{N_J} \geq 1 \\[2ex] \dfrac{1}{2}\exp\left(-\dfrac{E_b}{N_J}\right); & \dfrac{E_b}{N_J} < 1 \end{cases} \tag{4.54}$$

Figure 4.7 illustrates $ZP_s(M)$ versus Z in dB for $M = 2$, 4, 8, and 16. Table 4.2 provides the corresponding values of Z_{max} and P_{max} from which the asymptotic performance of FH/MDPSK for worst case partial-band noise jamming is computed using (4.49) and (4.50). Comparing Tables 4.1 and 4.2, we observe that for all values of M, FH/MDPSK is more sensitive to worst case partial-band multitone jamming than it is to worst case partial-band noise jamming.

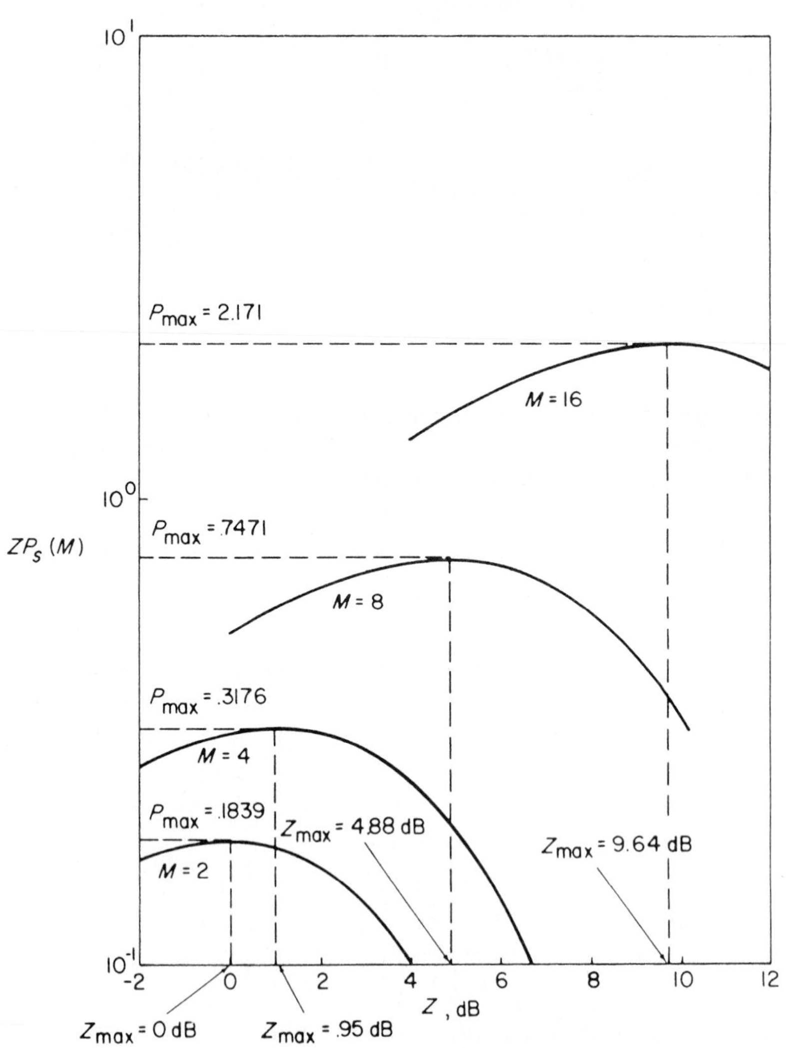

Figure 4.7. A plot of $ZP_s(M)$ versus Z in dB.

Table 4.2
Asymptotic performance of FH/MDPSK
for worst case partial-band noise jamming.

$$\text{Worst case partial-band fraction } \rho_{wc} = \frac{K_\rho}{E_b/N_J}$$

$$\text{Maximum average bit error probability } P_{b_{max}} = \frac{K_P}{E_b/N_J}$$

M	P_{max}	$K_\rho(Z_{max})$	K_P
2	.1839	1.000	.1839
4	.3176	1.245	.2118
8	.7471	3.076	.4269
16	2.171	9.204	1.1579

4.3 PERFORMANCE OF DQASK IN THE PRESENCE OF ADDITIVE WHITE GAUSSIAN NOISE

Having now discussed the jamming performance of the most classical differentially coherent modulation technique, namely FH/MDPSK, we turn our attention to the SS application of differentially coherent detection to multiple-amplitude-and phase-shift-keying (MAPSK). In particular, we introduce the concept of differentially coherent detection of differentially phase-encoded quadrature amplitude-shift-keyed signals (DQASK) [2] which when augmented with an FH modulation can be used to protect the system from RFI or the intentional jammer [3]. Since we have already seen many times before that the performance of an FH modulation technique in the presence of a partial-band noise jammer is directly obtained from the corresponding performance of the unspread modulation over the AWGN channel, we begin our discussion by first considering the symbol error probability performance of DQASK in such a Gaussian noise environment.

4.3.1 Characterization of the Transmitted Signal

As a brief review of our presentation in the previous chapter, an M-ary (QASK-M) is characterized by transmitting in each symbol interval one of M possible signals of the form

$$s(t) = \sqrt{2}\,\delta[b_n \cos\omega_0 t + a_m \sin\omega_0 t] = \sqrt{2}\,\mathrm{Re}\{s\,e^{j\omega_0 t}\} \qquad (4.55)$$

where ω_0 is the carrier radian frequency. The total number of signals M is typically the square of an even number K, and the quadrature amplitudes a_m and b_n take on equally likely values m and n with $m, n = \pm 1, \pm 3, \ldots \pm(K-1)$. Here, δ is a parameter which is related to the average power S of the signal set by

$$S = \tfrac{2}{3}(K^2 - 1)\delta^2. \qquad (4.56)$$

In order to describe the manner in which a QASK signal may be differentially phase encoded so that differentially coherent phase detection may be performed at the receiver, a polar coordinate representation of the signal set is preferable to the rectangular coordinate representation in (4.55).[3] In particular, if. in the i-th signalling interval $(i-1)T_s \le t \le iT_s$, it is desired to transmit a signal corresponding to the signal point vector

$$\mathbf{s}^{(i)} = \delta\left[b_n^{(i)} - ja_m^{(i)}\right] = A^{(i)}e^{-j\phi^{(i)}}, \tag{4.57}$$

the differentially phase-encoded QASK signal in this interval would then appear as

$$s^{(i)}(t) = \sqrt{2}\,A^{(i)}\cos\left(\omega_0 t + \theta^{(i)}\right), \tag{4.58}$$

where

$$\theta^{(i)} = \theta^{(i-1)} - \phi^{(i)}. \tag{4.59}$$

Note that, while $\phi^{(i)}$ is restricted to take on values

$$\phi = \tan^{-1}\left(\frac{m}{n}\right); \qquad m, n = \pm 1, \pm 3, \ldots \pm(K-1), \tag{4.60}$$

the actual transmitted phase, $\theta^{(i)}$ in the i-th interval has no such restriction. Consequently, an estimate of $\theta^{(i)}$ alone conveys no information regarding the phase, $\phi^{(i)}$ of the transmitted information symbol. This is a consequence of the differential phase-encoding operation described by (4.59).

Immediately, then, one observes that, in order to estimate $\phi^{(i)}$ in the absence of absolute phase information, what is needed is a receiver which forms estimates of $\theta^{(i)}$ and $\theta^{(i-1)}$ and computes their difference. Furthermore, since the QASK signal set is obviously not constant envelope, the amplitude, $A^{(i)}$, must also be estimated by the receiver in order to complete the decision on $\mathbf{s}^{(i)}$. Again, since absolute phase information is assumed to be unavailable at the receiver, the estimate of $A^{(i)}$ is obtained from a non-coherent envelope detector.

In the next section, we describe and derive the performance of a receiver which performs the above two functions, namely, differentially coherent detection of phase and non-coherent detection of envelope (amplitude).

4.3.2 Receiver Characterization and Performance

Figure 4.8 depicts a receiver used to perform differentially coherent detection of differentially phase-encoded QASK. The structure combines the elements of a differentially coherent receiver for a constant envelope modulation such as MPSK with a non-coherent envelope detector. The output from these two receiver components, namely, detected envelope and dif-

[3] When we discuss the differentially coherent detection process in the next section, we shall switch back to the rectangular representation to accommodate the rectangular-shaped decision regions.

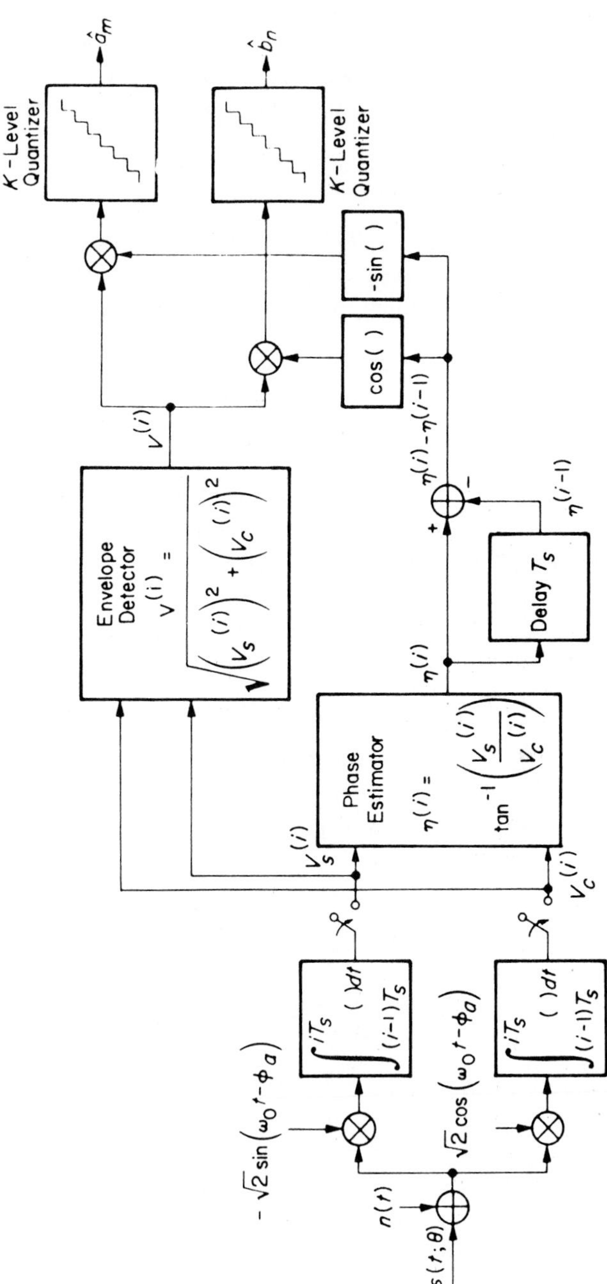

Figure 4.8. A receiver for differentially coherent detection of differentially phase-encoded QASK.

ferential phase are then converted to equivalent in-phase and quadrature signals upon which multilevel decisions are made, as is done in the more conventional coherent QASK receiver.

Appearing at the receiver input in the i-th signalling interval is the transmitted signal of (4.58) to which the channel has added a random phase shift θ and an AWGN which has the usual narrowband representation (repeated here for convenience)

$$n(t) = \sqrt{2}\left[N_c(t)\cos(\omega_0 t + \theta) - N_s(t)\sin(\omega_0 t + \theta)\right], \tag{4.61}$$

where $N_c(t)$ and $N_s(t)$ are statistically independent low-pass Gaussian noise processes with single-sided power spectral density N_0 w/Hz. Thus, the received signal in the i-th signalling interval is of the form

$$y^{(i)}(t) = s[t,\theta] + n(t) = \sqrt{2}\,A^{(i)}\cos\left(\omega_0 t + \theta^{(i)} + \theta\right) + n(t). \tag{4.62}$$

The receiver first performs in-phase and quadrature carrier demodulation with a pair of quadrature reference signals of known frequency ω_0 but unknown phase ϕ_a. The results of these demodulations are then passed through integrate-and-dump (I & D) filters whose outputs are given by[4]

$$\begin{aligned} V_s^{(i)} &= \int_{(i-1)T_s}^{iT_s} y^{(i)}(t)\left[-\sqrt{2}\,\sin(\omega_0 t - \phi_a)\right] dt \\ &= A^{(i)}T_s\sin\left(\theta^{(i)} + \phi_a\right) + n_c\sin\phi_a + n_s\cos\phi_a \\ V_c^{(i)} &= \int_{(i-1)T_s}^{iT_s} y^{(i)}(t)\left[\sqrt{2}\,\cos(\omega_0 t - \phi_a)\right] dt \\ &= A^{(i)}T_s\cos\left(\theta^{(i)} + \phi_a\right) + n_c\cos\phi_a - n_s\sin\phi_a, \end{aligned} \tag{4.63}$$

where

$$\begin{aligned} n_c &\triangleq \int_{(i-1)T_s}^{iT_s} \cdot N_c(t)\,dt \\ n_s &\triangleq \int_{(i-1)T_s}^{T_s} N_s(t)\,dt. \end{aligned} \tag{4.64}$$

The receiver next generates the equivalent envelope and phase of the I & D outputs, namely,

$$\begin{aligned} V^{(i)} &= \sqrt{\left(V_s^{(i)}\right)^2 + \left(V_c^{(i)}\right)^2} \\ \eta^{(i)} &= \tan^{-1}\left(\frac{V_s^{(i)}}{V_c^{(i)}}\right). \end{aligned} \tag{4.65}$$

[4]Without any loss in generality, we shall set $\theta = 0$ for simplicity of notation.

Finally, the differential phase $\eta^{(i)} - \eta^{(i-1)}$ is formed and used to produce the in-phase and quadrature decision variables $V^{(i)}\cos(\eta^{(i)} - \eta^{(i-1)})$ and $-V^{(i)}\sin(\eta^{(i)} - \eta^{(i-1)})$ upon which K-level decisions ($\hat{a}_m$ and $\hat{b}_n$) are made.

At this point, it is convenient to redraw Figure 4.8 in its equivalent form illustrated in Figure 4.9 by recognizing that

$$\begin{aligned} V^{(i)}\cos\left(\eta^{(i)} - \eta^{(i-1)}\right) &= \underbrace{V^{(i)}\cos\eta^{(i)}}_{V_c(i)}\cos\eta^{(i-1)} + \underbrace{V^{(i)}\sin\eta^{(i)}}_{V_s(i)}\sin\eta^{(i-1)} \\ -V^{(i)}\sin\left(\eta^{(i)} - \eta^{(i-1)}\right) &= \underbrace{-V^{(i)}\sin\eta^{(i)}}_{V_s(i)}\cos\eta^{(i-1)} + \underbrace{V^{(i)}\cos\eta^{(i)}}_{V_c(i)}\sin\eta^{(i-1)}. \end{aligned} \tag{4.66}$$

Figure 4.9 has the advantage of resembling a conventional *coherent* QASK receiver [8] with a noisy carrier demodulation reference and thus its error probability performance can be obtained almost by inspection. In particular, from (4.63) and (4.66), we obtain the decision variables

$$\begin{aligned} U_s^{(i)} &= -A^{(i)}T_s\sin\left(\theta^{(i)} + \phi_a - \eta^{(i-1)}\right) - n_c\sin\left(\phi_a - \eta^{(i-1)}\right) \\ &\quad - n_s\cos\left(\phi_a - \eta^{(i-1)}\right) \\ U_c^{(i)} &= A^{(i)}T_s\cos\left(\theta^{(i)} + \phi_a - \eta^{(i-1)}\right) + n_c\cos\left(\phi_a - \eta^{(i-1)}\right) \\ &\quad - n_s\sin\left(\phi_a - \eta^{(i-1)}\right). \end{aligned} \tag{4.67}$$

Letting

$$\eta_a^{(i-1)} = \eta^{(i-1)} - \theta^{(i-1)} - \phi_a \tag{4.68}$$

and using (4.59), we can rewrite (4.67) as

$$\begin{aligned} U_s^{(i)} &= A^{(i)}T_s\sin\left(\phi^{(i)} + \eta_a^{(i-1)}\right) + n_c\sin\left(\theta^{(i-1)} + \eta_a^{(i-1)}\right) \\ &\quad - n_s\cos\left(\theta^{(i-1)} + \eta_a^{(i-1)}\right) \\ &= A^{(i)}T_s\sin\left(\phi^{(i)} + \eta_a^{(i-1)}\right) - N_1\cos\eta_a^{(i-1)} + N_2\sin\eta_a^{(i-1)} \\ U_c^{(i)} &= A^{(i)}T_s\cos\left(\phi^{(i)} + \eta_a^{(i-1)}\right) + n_c\cos\left(\theta^{(i-1)} + \eta_a^{(i-1)}\right) \\ &\quad + n_s\sin\left(\theta^{(i-1)} + \eta_a^{(i-1)}\right) \\ &= A^{(i)}T_s\cos\left(\phi^{(i)} + \eta_a^{(i-1)}\right) + N_1\sin\eta_a^{(i-1)} + N_2\cos\eta_a^{(i-1)} \end{aligned} \tag{4.69}$$

where

$$\begin{aligned} N_1 &= n_s\cos\theta^{(i-1)} - n_c\sin\theta^{(i-1)} \\ N_2 &= n_s\sin\theta^{(i-1)} + n_c\cos\theta^{(i-1)}. \end{aligned} \tag{4.70}$$

Finally, recognizing that (4.69) resembles the decision variables for a coherent QASK receiver whose carrier demodulation reference signals are in error by $\eta_a^{(i-1)}$ radians, we can immediately write down an expression for

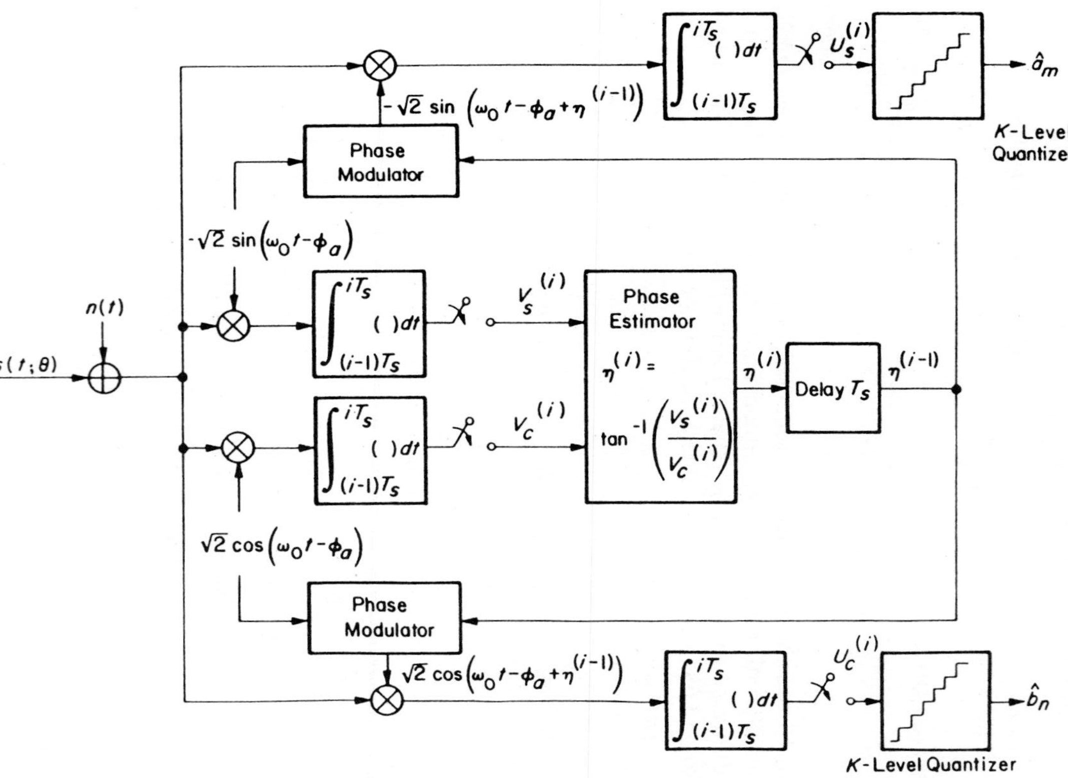

Figure 4.9. An alternate and equivalent implementation of the receiver shown in Figure 4.8.

the symbol error probability of differentially coherent detected QASK (conditioned on the $(i-1)$-st symbol SNR), namely,

$$P_s\left(\gamma_s^{(i-1)}\right) = \int_{-\pi}^{\pi} P_s\left(\eta_a^{(i-1)}\right) p_1\left(\eta_a^{(i-1)}; \gamma_s^{(i-1)}\right) d\eta_a^{(i-1)} \tag{4.71}$$

where $p_1(\eta_a^{(i-1)}; \gamma_s^{(i-1)})$, the probability density function (pdf) of the normalized phase $\eta_a^{(i-1)}$ in the $(i-1)$-st signalling interval, is given by [2]

$$p_1\left(\eta_a^{(i-1)}; \gamma_s^{(i-1)}\right) = \begin{cases} \dfrac{1}{2\pi}\exp\left(-\gamma_s^{(i-1)}\right)\Big\{1 + 2\sqrt{\pi\gamma_s^{(i-1)}}\cos\eta_a^{(i-1)}\exp\left(\gamma_s^{(i-1)}\cos^2\eta_a^{(i-1)}\right) \\ \qquad \times Q\left[-\sqrt{2\gamma_s^{(i-1)}}\cos\eta_a^{(i-1)}\right]\Big\}; \quad \left|\eta_a^{(i-1)}\right| \le \pi \\ 0; \quad \text{elsewhere} \end{cases} \tag{4.72}$$

with the $(i-1)$-st *transmission interval symbol SNR* $\gamma_s^{(i-1)}$ defined by

$$\gamma_s^{(i-1)} = \frac{\left(A^{(i-1)}\right)^2 T}{N_0}, \tag{4.73}$$

and $Q(x)$ denoting, as in previous chapters, the Gaussian probability integral. Also from (51) of [8], with ϕ replaced by $\eta_a^{(i-1)}$,

$$\begin{aligned} P_s\left(\eta_a^{(i-1)}\right) = {} & \frac{4}{K^2}\sum_{j,l} Q\left\{\Delta\left[l + (1-l)\cos\eta_a^{(i-1)} - j\sin\eta_a^{(i-1)}\right]\right\} \\ & - \frac{4}{K^2}\sum_{k,l} Q\left\{\Delta\left[k + (1-k)\cos\eta_a^{(i-1)} + (l-1)\sin\eta_a^{(i-1)}\right]\right\} \\ & \times Q\left\{\Delta\left[l + (1-l)\cos\eta_a^{(i-1)} - (k-1)\sin\eta_a^{(i-1)}\right]\right\}. \end{aligned} \tag{4.74}$$

In (4.74), the sum over j is for values $\pm 1, \pm 3, \ldots \pm (K-1)$ while the sums over k and l are for values $0, \pm 2, \pm 4, \ldots, \pm (K-2)$. Also,

$$\Delta \triangleq \sqrt{\frac{3\gamma_s}{K^2 - 1}} \tag{4.75}$$

where

$$\gamma_s \triangleq \frac{ST_s}{N_0} \tag{4.76}$$

is the average symbol SNR of the QASK-K^2 signal set with average power S defined in (4.56).

Finally, the average symbol error probability, P_s, is obtained by averaging (4.71) over the pdf of $\gamma_s^{(i-1)}$. To obtain this pdf, we note that, for a given K, the $(i-1)$-st symbol signal power $(A^{(i-1)})^2$ ranges over $K(K+2)/8$ different values. $K/2$ of these values correspond to signal points on the diagonal of any quadrant and occur with probability $4/K^2$. The remaining $K(K-2)/8$ values correspond to off-diagonal signal points *either* above or below the diagonal of any quadrant and occur with probability $8/K^2$. Thus, $\gamma_s^{(i-1)}$ takes on the discrete set, $\mathscr{R}$, of values $\Delta^2(m^2+n^2)/2$; $m, n = 1, 3 \ldots, (K-1)$; $m \le n$ and the corresponding pdf is then

$$p\left(\gamma_s^{(i-1)}\right) = \begin{cases} \dfrac{4}{K^2}; & \gamma_s^{(i-1)} = m^2\Delta^2; \qquad m = 1, 3, \ldots, (K-1) \\ \dfrac{8}{K^2}; & \gamma_s^{(i-1)} = \left(\dfrac{m^2+n^2}{2}\right)\Delta^2; \\ & m, n = 1, 3, \ldots (K-1); \qquad m < n \end{cases} \tag{4.77}$$

where Δ is defined in (4.75). Averaging (4.71) over the pdf of (4.77) gives the desired result

$$\begin{aligned} P_s &= \sum_{\mathscr{R}} P_s\left(\gamma_s^{(i-1)}\right) p\left(\gamma_s^{(i-1)}\right) \\ &= \int_{-\pi}^{\pi} P_s\left(\eta_a^{(i-1)}\right)\left[\sum_{\mathscr{R}} p_1\left(\eta_a^{(i-1)}; \gamma_s^{(i-1)}\right) p\left(\gamma_s^{(i-1)}\right)\right] d\eta_a^{(i-1)} \end{aligned} \tag{4.78}$$

Equivalently, letting

$$\begin{aligned} p\left(\eta_a^{(i-1)}\right) &= \sum_{\mathscr{R}} p_1\left(\eta_a^{(i-1)}; \gamma_s^{(i-1)}\right) p\left(\gamma_s^{(i-1)}\right) \\ &= \frac{4}{K^2} \sum_{m=1,3,\ldots}^{K-1} p_1\left(\eta_a^{(i-1)}; m^2\Delta^2\right) \\ &\quad + \frac{8}{K^2} \sum_{\substack{m,n=1,3\ldots \\ m<n}}^{K-1} p_1\left(\eta_a^{(i-1)}; \left(\frac{m^2+n^2}{2}\right)\Delta^2\right) \end{aligned} \tag{4.79}$$

represent the "effective" pdf of the $(i-1)$-st symbol phase, then (4.78) becomes the simple result

$$P_s = \int_{-\pi}^{\pi} P_s\left(\eta_a^{(i-1)}\right) p\left(\eta_a^{(i-1)}\right) d\eta_a^{(i-1)}. \tag{4.80}$$

Figure 4.10 is a plot of P_s versus γ_s in decibels as evaluated from (4.80) for $K = 4$ (DQASK-16). Also shown is the corresponding result for coherent detection of QASK which, for $K = 4$, is given by [8]:

$$P_s = 3Q(\Delta)\left[1 - \tfrac{3}{4}Q(\Delta)\right]. \tag{4.81}$$

For comparison, the performance of coherent and differentially coherent detection of MPSK with $M = 16$ (i.e., PSK-16 and DPSK-16) is presented in Figure 4.10 [5]. For small γ_s, the coherent PSK-16 and the DQASK-16 perform almost identically but, for large γ_s, the DQASK-16 approaches the performance of DPSK-16. Also, for large γ_s, coherent QASK-16 is about 4 dB better than coherent PSK-16 showing the more favorable exchange of average power for bandwidth with the QASK-16 than with the PSK-16. While it is true that DQASK-16 suffers a significant performance degrada-

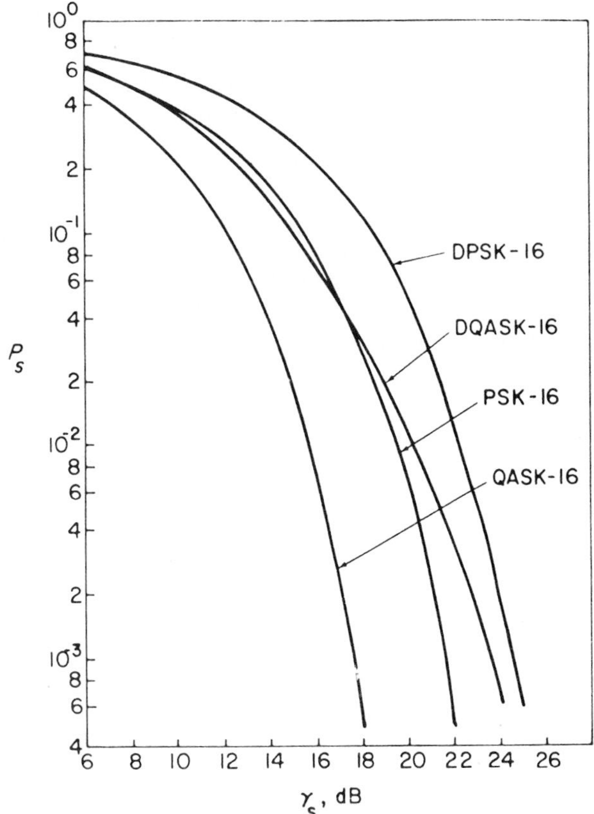

Figure 4.10. Symbol probability of error versus symbol SNR for coherent and differentially coherent detection of QASK-16 and PSK-16.

tion with respect to coherent QASK-16 at large γ_s, we must recall our initial motivation, namely to use DQASK-16 along with frequency hopping (i.e., FH/DQASK) to protect a conventional QASK communication system against jamming. In the next two sections, we present the FH/DQASK performance in the presence of partial-band multitone and noise jamming.

4.4 PERFORMANCE OF FH/DQASK IN THE PRESENCE OF PARTIAL-BAND MULTITONE JAMMING

A frequency-hopped, differentially coherent M-ary QASK modulation (FH/DQASK-M) is characterized by transmitting in the i-th symbol interval $[(i-1)T_s \le t \le iT_s]$ one of M possible signals of the form

$$s^{(i)}(t) = \sqrt{2}\,\delta\left[b_n^{(i)}\cos\left(\omega_h^{(i)}t + \theta^{(i-1)}\right) + a_m^{(i)}\sin\left(\omega_h^{(i)}t + \theta^{(i-1)}\right)\right], \tag{4.82}$$

where $\omega_h^{(i)}$ is the particular carrier frequency selected by the hopper for this interval, and $\theta^{(i-1)}$ is again the transmitted phase in the $(i-1)$-st interval. In analyzing the performance of FH/DQASK in the presence of the tone jammer (assuming the i-th transmission interval is jammed)

$$J(t) = \sqrt{2J_0}\cos\left(\omega_h^{(i)}t + \theta_J\right), \tag{4.83}$$

it is convenient to adopt a vector diagram approach analogous to that taken for MDPSK. As such, the transmitted signal will be represented by a normalized vector with x and y components respectively given by $n = b_n^{(i)}/\delta$ and $m = a_m^{(i)}/\delta$. The jammer is then represented by a normalized vector with phase θ_J and amplitude[5]

$$\beta \triangleq \frac{\sqrt{J_0}}{\delta} = \frac{\sqrt{\dfrac{J}{Q}}}{\delta}. \tag{4.84}$$

Recalling that $M = K^2$, then combining (4.18), (4.19), (4.56), and (4.84),

$$\beta = \sqrt{\frac{K^2-1}{3\rho\log_2 K}\left(\frac{N_J}{E_b}\right)}. \tag{4.85}$$

For example, for FH/DQASK-16 ($K = 4$), (4.85) becomes

$$\beta = \sqrt{\frac{5}{2}\left(\frac{N_J}{\rho E_b}\right)}. \tag{4.86}$$

In the remainder of this chapter, we shall deal specifically with FH/DQASK-16 as a matter of convenience. However, whenever results are obtained in their final form, they shall be given in the generalized form suitable to FH/DQASK-K^2, with arbitrary K.

Figure 4.11 is the normalized signal point constellation corresponding to QASK-16. The dashed lines indicate the decision region boundaries appropriate for coherent or differentially coherent detection of the various signal points. Now suppose that we wish to transmit signal point ① with differentially encoded phase in the i-th interval. The signal transmitted in the $(i-1)$-st interval could have been any of the 16 signal points. Thus, the vector representation of Figure 4.12 is adequate for characterizing the signal and jammer in these two intervals. For convenience, we shall always draw the vector representing the signal transmitted in the $(i-1)$-st interval along the positive x-axis. The amplitude A_1 corresponds to the normalized envelope of the signal point transmitted in the $(i-1)$-st interval and, from

[5] Note that the normalized vector amplitude β as defined here is not the same as a similar quantity denoted by β in Section 4.1 and defined in (4.17).

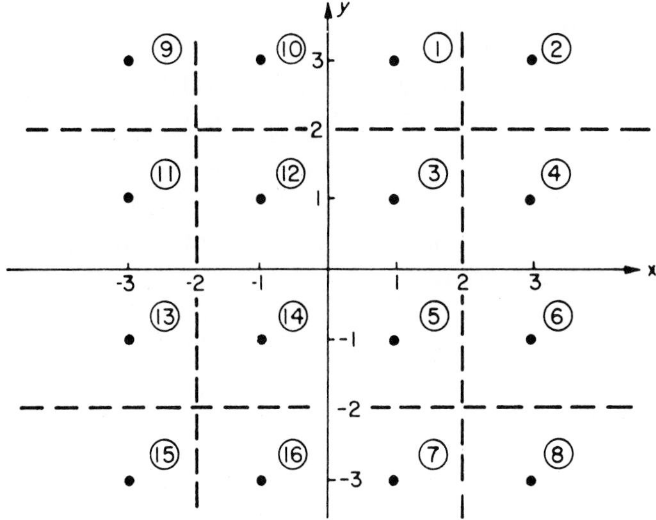

Figure 4.11. Normalized signal point constellation for QASK-16.

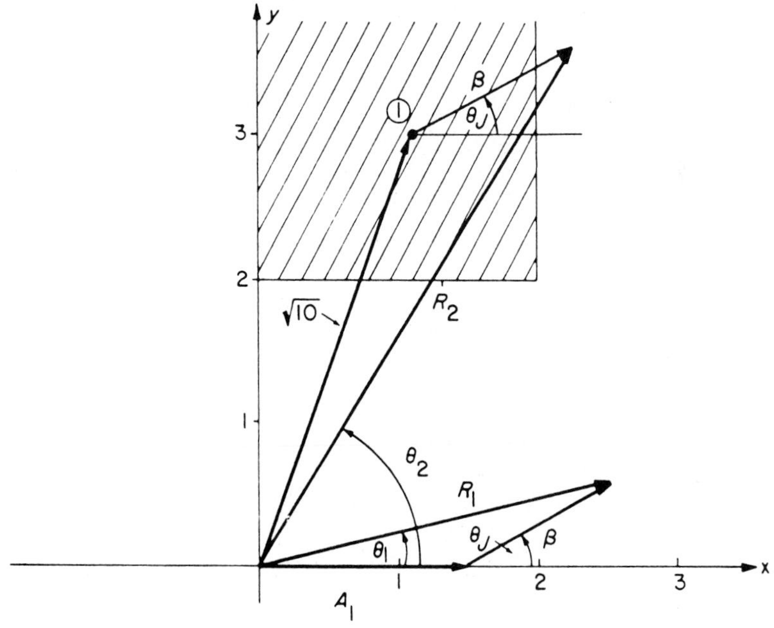

Figure 4.12. A vector diagram representation of the signal and jammer in the i-th and $(i-1)$-st transmission intervals (signal point in first quadrant).

Figure 4.11, takes on values

$$A_1 = \begin{cases} \sqrt{2} & \text{with Prob. } 1/4 \\ \sqrt{10} & \text{with Prob. } 1/2 \\ \sqrt{18} & \text{with Prob. } 1/4. \end{cases} \tag{4.87}$$

From the results of the previous section, we observe that signal point ① will be correctly detected if

$$\begin{aligned} 0 &< R_2 \cos(\theta_2 - \theta_1) < 2 \\ 2 &< R_2 \sin(\theta_2 - \theta_1) < \infty. \end{aligned} \tag{4.88}$$

The boundaries on the inequalities in (4.88) correspond to the x and y coordinates of the decision region indicated by the shaded area in Figure 4.12.

Expanding the sine and cosine of the difference angle $\theta_2 - \theta_1$ and noting, from Figure 4.12, that

$$\begin{aligned} R_2 \cos\theta_2 &= 1 + \beta\cos\theta_J \\ R_2 \sin\theta_2 &= 3 + \beta\sin\theta_J \end{aligned}$$

$$\begin{aligned} \cos\theta_1 &= \frac{A_1 + \beta\cos\theta_J}{\sqrt{(A_1 + \beta\cos\theta_J)^2 + (\beta\sin\theta_J)^2}} = \frac{A_1 + \beta\cos\theta_J}{\sqrt{A_1^2 + 2\beta A_1 \cos\theta_J + \beta^2}} \\ \sin\theta_1 &= \frac{\beta\sin\theta_J}{\sqrt{(A_1 + \beta\cos\theta_J)^2 + (\beta\sin\theta_J)^2}} = \frac{\beta\sin\theta_J}{\sqrt{A_1^2 + 2\beta A_1 \cos\theta_J + \beta^2}}, \end{aligned} \tag{4.89}$$

the inequalities of (4.88) can be rewritten as

$$\begin{aligned} 0 &< \frac{(1 + \beta\cos\theta_J)(A_1 + \beta\cos\theta_J) + (3 + \beta\sin\theta_J)(\beta\sin\theta_J)}{\sqrt{A_1^2 + 2\beta A_1 \cos\theta_J + \beta^2}} < 2 \\ 2 &< \frac{(3 + \beta\sin\theta_J)(A_1 + \beta\cos\theta_J) - (1 + \beta\cos\theta_J)(\beta\sin\theta_J)}{\sqrt{A_1^2 + 2\beta A_1 \cos\theta_J + \beta^2}} < \infty. \end{aligned} \tag{4.90}$$

Dividing the numerator and denominator of each inequality in (4.90) by A_1

and simplifying results in

$$0 < \frac{1 + \beta\cos\theta_J + \dfrac{\beta}{A_1}(\beta + \cos\theta_J + 3\sin\theta_J)}{\sqrt{1 + 2\left(\dfrac{\beta}{A_1}\right)\cos\theta_J + \left(\dfrac{\beta}{A_1}\right)^2}} < 2$$

$$2 < \frac{3 + \beta\sin\theta_J + \dfrac{\beta}{A_1}(3\cos\theta_J - \sin\theta_J)}{\sqrt{1 + 2\left(\dfrac{\beta}{A_1}\right)\cos\theta_J + \left(\dfrac{\beta}{A_1}\right)^2}} < \infty. \quad (4.91)$$

Let $P_{c①}(\theta_J; \beta, A_1)$ denote the conditional probability of correctly detecting signal point ① for given θ_J, β, and A_1. Then, from (4.91),

$$P_{c①}(\theta_J; \beta, A_1) = \begin{cases} 1; & \text{for values of } \theta_J \text{ such that} \\ & 0 < X_{1,3}(\theta_J; \beta, A_1) < 2 \text{ and} \\ & 2 < Y_{1,3}(\theta_J; \beta, A_1) < \infty \\ 0; & \text{all other values of } \theta_J \text{ in } (0, 2\pi), \end{cases} \quad (4.92)$$

where we have defined the generalized functions

$$X_{i,j}(\theta_J; \beta, A_1) = \frac{i + \beta\cos\theta_J + \dfrac{\beta}{A_1}(\beta + i\cos\theta_J + j\sin\theta_J)}{\sqrt{1 + 2\left(\dfrac{\beta}{A_1}\right)\cos\theta_J + \left(\dfrac{\beta}{A_1}\right)^2}}$$

$$Y_{i,j}(\theta_J; \beta, A_1) = \frac{j + \beta\sin\theta_J + \dfrac{\beta}{A_1}(j\cos\theta_J - i\sin\theta_J)}{\sqrt{1 + 2\left(\dfrac{\beta}{A_1}\right)\cos\theta_J + \left(\dfrac{\beta}{A_1}\right)^2}};$$

$$i, j = \pm 1, \pm 3. \quad (4.93)$$

Further defining

$$G(X) \triangleq \frac{1 - \operatorname{sgn} X}{2} = \begin{cases} 1; & X < 0 \\ 0; & X > 0, \end{cases} \quad (4.94)$$

then, for $a > 0$,

$$1 - G(X - a) = \begin{cases} 0; & -\infty < X < a \\ 1; & a < X < \infty \end{cases}$$

$$G(X - a) - G(X) = \begin{cases} 1; & 0 < X < a \\ 0; & \text{otherwise.} \end{cases} \quad (4.95)$$

In view of (4.95), we may rewrite (4.92) as

$$P_{c①}(\theta_J;\beta,A_1) = \left[G\left(X_{1,3}(\theta_J;\beta,A_1)-2\right) - G\left(X_{1,3}(\theta_J;\beta,A_1)\right)\right] \times\left[1 - G\left(Y_{1,3}(\theta_J;\beta,A_1)-2\right)\right]. \tag{4.96}$$

As our next example, consider the problem of correctly detecting signal point ⑩ of Figure 4.13. The vector diagram describing this situation is given in Figure 4.13. Noting again that the shaded area corresponds to the correct decision region, analogous to (4.88), we then have

$$\begin{gathered} -2 < R_2\cos(\theta_2-\theta_1) < 0 \\ 2 < R_2\sin(\theta_2-\theta_1) < \infty. \end{gathered} \tag{4.97}$$

Once again expanding the sine and cosine of the difference angle $\theta_2 - \theta_1$ and making use of relations similar to (4.89), we obtain the equivalent inequalities

$$\begin{gathered} -2 < X_{-1,3}(\theta_J;\beta,A_1) < 0 \\ 2 < Y_{-1,3}(\theta_J;\beta,A_1) < \infty, \end{gathered} \tag{4.98}$$

where $X_{i,j}(\theta_J,\beta,A_1)$ and $Y_{i,j}(\theta_J;\beta,A_1)$ are given by (4.93). Noting from (4.94) that, for $a > 0$,

$$G(X) - G(X+a) = \begin{cases} 1; & -a < X < 0 \\ 0; & \text{otherwise} \end{cases} \tag{4.99}$$

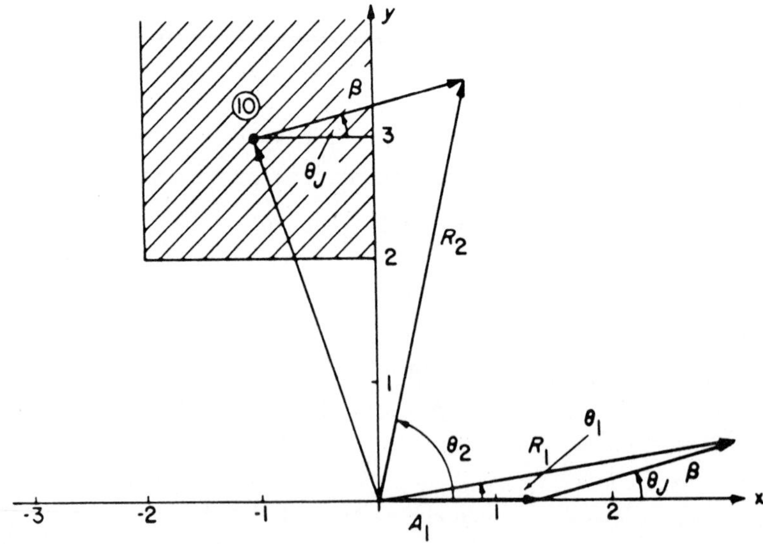

Figure 4.13. A vector diagram of the signal and jammer in the i-th and $(i-1)$-st transmission intervals (signal point in second quadrant).

then letting $P_{c⑩}(\theta_J; \beta, A_1)$ denote the conditional probability of correctly detecting signal point ⑩, we have, from (4.98) together with (4.95) and (4.99), that

$$P_{c⑩}(\theta_J; \beta, A_1) = [G(X_{-1,3}(\theta_J; \beta, A_1)) - G(X_{-1,3}(\theta_J; \beta, A_1) + 2)] \times [1 - G(Y_{-1,3}(\theta_J; \beta, A_1) - 2)]. \quad (4.100)$$

At this point, one can write down the remainder of the conditional probabilities of correct decision by inspection. Without going into great detail, the results are given as follows:[6]

$$\begin{aligned}
P_{c②}(\theta_J; \beta, A_1) &= [1 - G(X_{3,3} - 2)][1 - G(Y_{3,3} - 2)] \\
P_{c③}(\theta_J; \beta, A_1) &= [G(X_{1,1} - 2) - G(X_{1,1})][G(Y_{1,1} - 2) - G(Y_{1,1})] \\
P_{c④}(\theta_J; \beta, A_1) &= [1 - G(X_{3,1} - 2)][G(Y_{3,1} - 2) - G(Y_{3,1})] \\
P_{c⑤}(\theta_J; \beta, A_1) &= [G(X_{1,-1} - 2) - G(X_{1,-1})] \\
&\quad \times [G(Y_{1,-1}) - G(Y_{1,-1} + 2)] \\
P_{c⑥}(\theta_J; \beta, A_1) &= [1 - G(X_{3,-1} - 2)][G(Y_{3,-1}) - G(Y_{3,-1} + 2)] \\
P_{c⑦}(\theta_J; \beta, A_1) &= [G(X_{1,-3} - 2) - G(X_{1,-3})]G(X_{1,-3} + 2) \\
P_{c⑧}(\theta_J; \beta, A_1) &= [1 - G(X_{3,-3} - 2)]G(Y_{3,-3} + 2) \\
P_{c⑨}(\theta_J; \beta, A_1) &= G(X_{-3,3} + 2)[1 - G(Y_{-3,3} - 2)] \\
P_{c⑪}(\theta_J; \beta, A_1) &= G(X_{-3,1} + 2)[G(Y_{-3,1} - 2) - G(Y_{-3,1})] \\
P_{c⑫}(\theta_J; \beta, A_1) &= [G(X_{-1,1}) - G(X_{-1,1} + 2)] \\
&\quad \times [G(Y_{-1,1} - 2) - G(Y_{-1,1})] \\
P_{c⑬}(\theta_J; \beta, A_1) &= G(X_{-3,-1} + 2)[G(Y_{-3,-1}) - G(Y_{-3,-1} + 2)] \\
P_{c⑭}(\theta_J; \beta, A_1) &= [G(X_{-1,-1}) - G(X_{-1,-1} + 2)] \\
&\quad \times [G(Y_{-1,-1}) - G(Y_{-1,-1} + 2)] \\
P_{c⑮}(\theta_J; \beta, A_1) &= G(X_{-3,-3} + 2)G(Y_{-3,-3} + 2) \\
P_{c⑯}(\theta_J; \beta, A_1) &= [G(X_{-1,-3}) - G(X_{-1,-3} + 2)]G(Y_{-1,-3} + 2).
\end{aligned} \quad (4.101)$$

Since, as previously mentioned, the jammer phase θ_J is uniformly distributed in the interval $(0, 2\pi)$, the average symbol error probability (condi-

[6] For simplicity of notation, we delete the dependence of $X_{i,j}$ and $Y_{i,j}$ on θ_J, β, and A_1.

tioned on A_1) is then given by

$$P_s(\beta, A_1) = 1 - \frac{1}{2\pi}\int_0^{2\pi}\left[1 - \frac{1}{16}\sum_{k=1}^{16} P_{c\textcircled{k}}(\theta_J; \beta, A_1)\right] d\theta_J. \quad (4.102)$$

Finally, making use of (4.86) and (4.87) and the fact that only the fraction ρ of the total number of hop intervals are jammed, then the average unconditional symbol error probability is given by

$$P_s = \rho\left\{\frac{1}{4}P_s\left(\sqrt{\frac{5}{2}\left(\frac{N_J}{\rho E_b}\right)}, \sqrt{2}\right) + \frac{1}{2}P_s\left(\sqrt{\frac{5}{2}\left(\frac{N_J}{\rho E_b}\right)}, \sqrt{10}\right) + \frac{1}{4}P_s\left(\sqrt{\frac{5}{2}\left(\frac{N_J}{\rho E_b}\right)}, \sqrt{18}\right)\right\}. \quad (4.103)$$

Before leaving this subject, we note that the result of substituting (4.96), (4.100), and (4.101) in (4.102) can be put into a compact form. In particular, by replacing each $G(X)$ term in (4.96), (4.100), and (4.101) with its equivalent form $1 - G(-X)$ and summing all terms, we obtain the following result:

$$P_s(\beta, A_1) = \frac{1}{2\pi}\int_0^{2\pi} P_s(\theta_J; \beta, A_1)\, d\theta_J, \quad (4.104)$$

where

$$\begin{aligned} &P_s(\theta_J; \beta, A_1) \\ &\triangleq 1 - \frac{1}{16}\sum_{k=1}^{16} P_{c\textcircled{k}}(\theta_J; \beta, A_1) \\ &= \frac{1}{16}\sum_{m=\pm 1}\sum_{j=\pm 1, \pm 3}\sum_{l=0, \pm 2}\left[G(mX_{m(1-l), j} + l) + G(mY_{j, m(1-l)} + l)\right] \\ &\quad - \frac{1}{16}\sum_{m=\pm 1}\sum_{n=\pm 1}\sum_{l=0, \pm 2}\sum_{k=0, \pm 2} G(mX_{m(1-l), n(1-k)} + l) \\ &\quad \times G(nY_{m(1-l), n(1-k)} + k). \end{aligned} \quad (4.105)$$

For the more general case of FH/DQASK-K^2 with arbitrary K, the summation on j is for values $j = \pm 1, \pm 3, \ldots, \pm(K-1)$, while the summations on l and k are for values $l, k = 0, \pm 2, \pm 4, \ldots, \pm(K-2)$.

It is of interest to evaluate the limit of P_s of (4.103) as E_b/N_J approaches zero ($\beta \to \infty$). From (4.93), we first note that

$$\lim_{\beta\to\infty} X_{i,j}(\theta_J; \beta, A_1) = \infty$$

$$\lim_{\beta\to\infty} Y_{i,j}(\theta_J; \beta, A_1) = A_1 \sin\theta_J + j\cos\theta_J - i\sin\theta_J. \quad (4.106)$$

Then, substituting (4.106) into (4.105) and simplifying gives

$$\lim_{\beta\to\infty} P_s(\theta_J; \beta, A_1)$$
$$= \frac{1}{16}\left\{12 + \sum_{m=\pm 1}\ \sum_{l=0,\pm 2} G\left(m\left[A_1 \sin\theta_J + m(1-l)\cos\theta_J - 3\sin\theta_J\right] + l\right)\right\}, \tag{4.107}$$

which when averaged over θ_J results in

$$\lim_{\beta\to\infty} P_s(\beta, A_1) = \frac{1}{2\pi}\int_0^{2\pi} \lim_{\beta\to\infty} P_s(\theta_J; \beta, A_1)\, d\theta_J$$
$$= \frac{15}{16} \text{ independent of } A_1. \tag{4.108}$$

Thus, applying (4.108) to (4.103) gives the final desired result, namely,

$$\lim_{\beta\to\infty} P_s = \lim_{E_b/N_J\to 0} P_s = \rho\left(\frac{15}{16}\right). \tag{4.109}$$

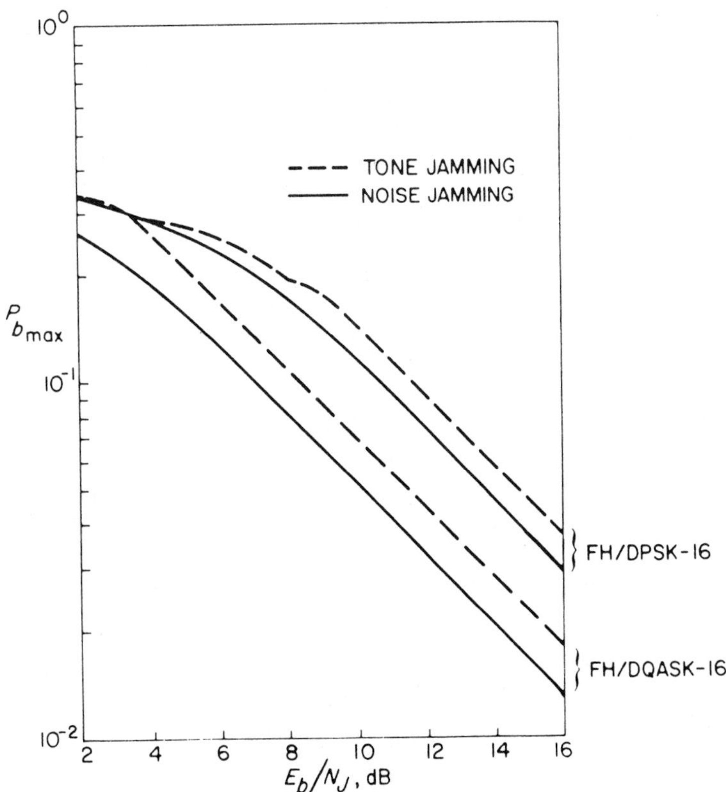

Figure 4.14. Worst case P_b versus E_b/N_J for FH/DQASK-16 and FH/DPSK-16.

Finally, using the same relation between average symbol and bit error probabilities as for FH/MDPSK, namely (4.15), then the worst case jamming strategy for FH/DQASK-16 can be determined to be

$$\rho_{\text{wc}} = \begin{cases} \dfrac{2.4}{E_b/N_J}; & E_b/N_J \geq 2.4 \\ 1; & E_b/N_J < 2.4 \end{cases} \tag{4.110}$$

and

$$P_{b_{\max}} = \begin{cases} \dfrac{0.67}{E_b/N_J}; & E_b/N_J \geq 2.4 \\ \dfrac{8}{15} P_s\Big|_{\rho=1}; & E_b/N_J < 2.4 \end{cases} \tag{4.111}$$

where $P_s|_{\rho=1}$ is given by (4.103) with $\rho = 1$. Figure 4.14 illustrates this worst case jammer bit error probability performance.

4.5 PERFORMANCE OF FH/DQASK IN THE PRESENCE OF PARTIAL-BAND NOISE JAMMING

Since we are ignoring the background AWGN, the results for the performance in the presence of a partial-band noise jammer are then directly obtained from the Gaussian results in Section 4.3 by replacing N_0 with N_J/ρ. In particular, the average symbol error probability performance is given by (4.80), multiplied by ρ, namely

$$P_s = \rho \int_{-\pi}^{\pi} P_s\left(\eta_a^{(i-1)}\right) p\left(\eta_a^{(i-1)}\right) d\eta_a^{(i-1)}, \tag{4.112}$$

where the dependence of the integrand on ρ is entirely contained within the parameter Δ of (4.75) which now becomes

$$\Delta = \sqrt{\frac{6\rho \log_2 K}{K^2 - 1}\left(\frac{E_b}{N_J}\right)} \tag{4.113}$$

Once again using (4.15) to obtain P_b from P_s, we obtain the worst case jammer performance given by

$$\rho_{\text{wc}} = \begin{cases} \dfrac{5.0}{E_b/N_J}; & E_b/N_J \geq 5.0 \\ 1; & E_b/N_J < 5.0 \end{cases} \tag{4.114}$$

and

$$P_{b_{\max}} = \begin{cases} \dfrac{0.51}{E_b/N_J}; & E_b/N_J \geq 5.0 \\ \dfrac{8}{15} P_s\Big|_{\rho=1}; & E_b/N_J < 5.0 \end{cases} \tag{4.115}$$

where now $P_s|_{\rho=1}$ corresponds to (4.112) with $\rho = 1$. The behavior of $P_{b_{\max}}$ of (4.115) as a function of E_b/N_J in dB is also illustrated in Figure 4.14.

Finally, for the purpose of comparison, the results of (4.43) and (4.50), corresponding to the worst case tone and noise jammer performances of FH/DPSK-16, have been superimposed on Figure 4.14. We note that, asymptotically, FH/DQASK-16 outperforms FH/DPSK-16 by 3.283 dB for worst case tone jamming and 3.55 dB for worst case noise jamming.

4.6 REFERENCES

[1] S. W. Houston, "Modulation techniques for communication, Part I: Tone and noise jamming performance of spread spectrum M-ary FSK and 2, 4-ary DPSK waveforms," *NAECON'75 Record*, pp. 51–58.

[2] M. K. Simon, G. K. Huth, and A. Polydoros, "Differentially coherent detection of QASK for frequency-hopping systems; Part I: Performance in the presence of a Gaussian noise background," *IEEE Trans. Commun.*, COM-30, no. 1, pp. 158–164, January 1982.

[3] M. K. Simon, "Differentially coherent detection of QASK for frequency-hopping systems; Part II: Performance in the presence of jamming," *IEEE Trans. Commun.*, COM-30, no. 1, pp. 164–172, January 1982.

[4] M. K. Simon, "The Performance of M-ary DPSK/FH in the Presence of Partial-Band Multitone Jamming," *IEEE Trans. Commun.*, Special Issue on Spread Spectrum Communications, COM-30, no. 5, pp. 953–958, May 1982.

[5] W. C. Lindsey and M. K. Simon, *Telecommunication Systems Engineering*, Englewood Cliffs, NJ: Prentice-Hall, 1973, Chapter 5.

[6] J. T. Fleck and E. A. Trabka, "Error Probabilities of Multiple-State Differentially Coherent Phase Shift Keyed Systems in the Presence of White, Gaussian Noise," Detect Memo No. 2A in Investigation of Digital Data Communication Systems, Report No. UA-1420-S-1, J. G. Lawton, ed., Cornell Aeronautical Laboratory, Inc., Buffalo, NY, January 1961. Available as ASTIA Document No. AD 256 584.

[7] J. H. Roberts, S. O. Rice, and R. F. Pawula, "Distribution of the phase angle between two vectors perturbed by Gaussian noise," *IEEE Trans. Commun.*, COM-30, no. 8, pp. 1828–1841, August 1982.

[8] M. K. Simon and J. G. Smith, "Carrier synchronization and detection of QASK signal sets," *IEEE Trans. Commun.*, COM-22, no. 2, pp. 98–106, February 1974.

Part 4

SYNCHRONIZATION OF SPREAD-SPECTRUM SYSTEMS

Chapter 1

PSEUDONOISE CODE ACQUISITION IN DIRECT-SEQUENCE RECEIVERS

One of the primary functions of a direct-sequence (DS) spread-spectrum (SS) receiver is to despread the received pseudonoise (PN) code. This is accomplished by generating a local replica of the PN code in the receiver and then synchronizing this local PN signal to the one which is superimposed on the incoming (received) waveform. Multiplication or remodulation of the incoming signal by the synchronized local PN code replica then produces the desired despreading process.

The process of synchronizing the local and received PN signals is ordinarily accomplished in two stages. Initially, a coarse alignment of the two PN signals is produced to within a small (typically less than a fraction of a chip) residual relative timing offset. The process of bringing the two codes into coarse alignment is referred to as *PN acquisition*. Once the incoming PN code has been acquired, a fine synchronization system takes over and continuously maintains the best possible waveform alignment by means of a closed loop operation. The process of maintaining the two codes in fine synchronism is referred to as *PN tracking*. In this chapter, we focus our attention on techniques and their performance for accomplishing PN acquisition. Chapter 2 deals with the companion problem of PN tracking.

1.1 HISTORICAL SURVEY

If one searches through the literature which discusses PN acquisition techniques, the common denominator among almost all the methods is that the received and local PN signals are first multiplied[1] to produce a measure of correlation between the two. This correlation measure is then processed by a suitable detector/decision rule and search strategy to decide whether the two codes are in synchronism and what to do if they're not. The

[1] The word "multiplied" is used here in the broadest sense allowing for the possibilities of active or passive, analog or digital, time continuous or time discrete correlation operations. The specific differences among these various forms of multiplication will be partly responsible for the classification of PN acquisition systems to be discussed shortly.

differences between the various schemes depend on (1) the type of detector (and decision strategy) used, which, in turn, is dependent on the form of the received signal and the particular application at hand, and (2) the nature of the search algorithm which acts on the detector outputs to reach the final verdict.[2]

All known detectors for PN acquisition systems, in one form or another, fall into two basic categories, namely, *coherent* or *non-coherent*. By far the most common found in acquisition systems for DS/SS receivers is the non-coherent detector which, for example, might be comprised of a band-pass filter centered at the frequency of the received carrier upon which the PN signal is direct modulated, followed by a square-law envelope detector,[3] an integrate-and-dump circuit which operates over a finite time interval, and a simple threshold device [1]. The reason why the non-coherent detector is most commonly found is that the despreading operation typically takes place ahead of the carrier synchronization function; thus, at the point in time at which PN acquisition is to be accomplished, the carrier phase must be assumed to be unknown.

Consideration has also been given in the literature to PN acquisition systems which operate under the assumption that the receiver is capable of determining good estimates of the carrier phase and frequency shifts brought about by the propagation delay and Doppler produced by the transmission channel, in which case, the carrier can be "demodulated" prior to PN despreading. In these instances, the PN acquisition system can employ a coherent detector which typically might consist of a low-pass filter (possibly implemented as an integrate-and-dump circuit) followed by an optimum Bayes detector [2], [3] or instead just a simple threshold device [4], [5].

It is convenient insofar as our discussion is concerned to perform a further classification of detectors for PN acquisition schemes depending upon whether they are of the *fixed* or *variable* integration time type. Within the category of *fixed* integration time detectors, one can further subdivide them into single dwell [1], [6] and multiple dwell types [7], [8] depending, respectively, upon whether the detector's decision is made on the basis of a single (suitably processed) fixed time observation of received signal plus noise or many such observations (not necessarily independent of one another). Depending upon the duration of the observation, or equivalently, the time allotted to make a decision, relative to the PN code period, single dwell time detectors can be further differentiated according to whether they utilize partial or full period code correlation. The multiple dwell detectors differ from one another in the way in which the additional observations are

[2] Much of the ensuing discussion on classification, as well as the unified approach presented in Sections 1.4 through 1.6, is based on the theory as formulated by Polydoros [38], Polydoros and Weber [14], and Polydoros and Simon [39].

[3] An envelope detector followed by a square-law device.

used to *verify* the temporary decision made based on the first observation alone.

More specifically, since all of the detector structures of interest make decisions based on a threshold comparison test of one form or another, following a threshold exceedance of the first dwell (integration) output, the additional dwells in combination with threshold testing are used in accordance with a specified *verification algorithm* to produce a final decision on whether the code phase position under test corresponds to true synchronization. This verification mode of operation of the detector structure typically falls into one of two categories. In the type of multiple dwell acquisition system discussed by DiCarlo [7], [8], a code phase position is immediately rejected or dismissed as corresponding to an incorrect synchronization condition as soon as *any* dwell output fails to satisfy its threshold exceedance test. All other types of verification modes of operation, often referred to as *search/lock* strategies [9], employ algorithms which require repeated threshold testing of a given dwell output or use a majority logic type of decision on the total set of multiple dwell threshold tests (coincidence detectors).

Finally, the category of variable integration time detectors is reserved for those cases where the dwell time, here being the time for a continuously integrated stochastic process to exceed a threshold, is a random variable. As such, the various PN acquisition systems that contain a variable integration time detector typically employ the classical method of *sequential detection* [10] which finds its roots in the detection of radar signals [11].

The next classification of detector structures is in accordance with the rate at which decisions are made on each code phase position under test. High decision rate detectors, such as those used in *matched filter* (passive correlation) PN acquisition systems [12], [13], refer to those structures that make their decisions on the out-of-sync code phase offsets between incoming and local codes at the PN code chip rate or an integer multiple of it. Low decision rate detectors, which employ active correlation, make these same decisions at a rate significantly slower than the code chip rate. As such, many of these structures employ little or no verification.

To complete our classification of detector types, we further categorize them according to the criterion used for deciding between in-sync and out-of-sync hypotheses, e.g., Bayes (minimum average risk), Neyman-Pearson (minimum probability of an error of the second kind—missed detection—for a given probability of an error of the first kind—false alarm), etc.

A summary of the above classification of the structure of detectors used for PN acquisition purposes is illustrated in Figure 1.1, which was originally suggested in [14]. A more detailed discussion of the various forms of the structures themselves and how they fit into the overall acquisition scheme will follow shortly.

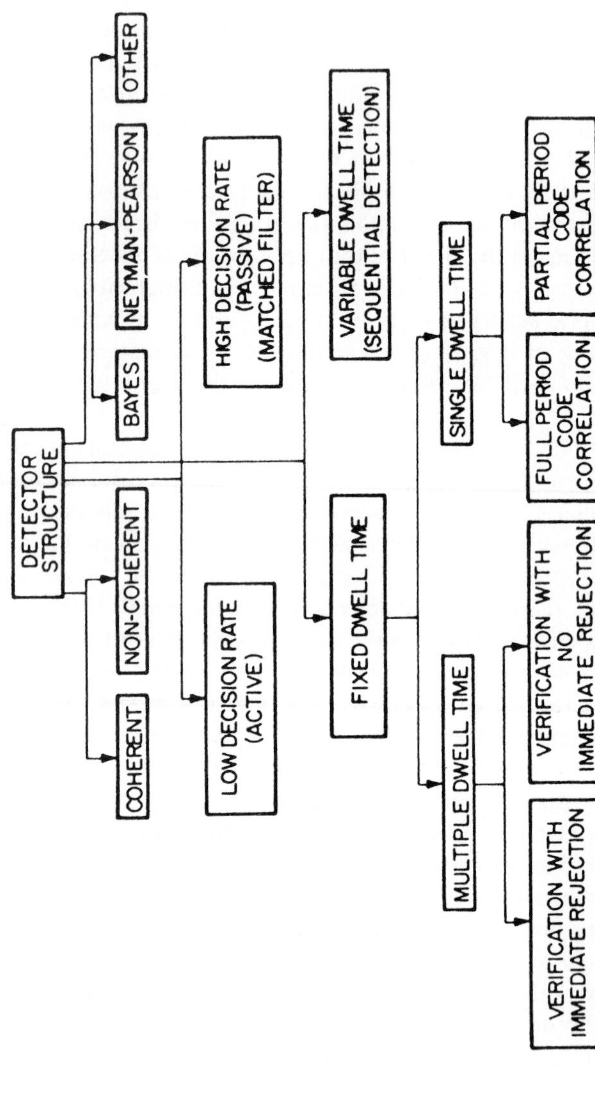

Figure 1.1. Structure of detectors for acquisition purposes (reprinted from [38]).

Not unlike the classification of detector types, the classification of acquisition schemes according to search strategy follows a tree structure [14] (see Figure 1.2) where many of the categories produce the next level of the tree by a simple dichotomy. Perhaps the simplest, at least conceptually, of the search techniques on the first level of the hierarchy is the *maximum-likelihood* algorithm. In its strictest form, the algorithm requires that the input PN signal be correlated with all possible code positions (or perhaps fractional code positions) of the local PN code replica. The correlations are assumed to be performed in parallel and as such the corresponding detector outputs all pertain to the identical observation of received signal plus noise. The correct PN alignment is chosen as that local code phase position which produced the maximum detector output. In a less strict version, the maximum-likelihood algorithm[4] can be implemented in a serial fashion (see Figure 1.3). Here the input PN signal is serially correlated with all possible code positions (or perhaps again fractional code positions) of the local PN code replica and the corresponding detector outputs stored. At the end of the test, the correct PN alignment is again chosen as that local code phase position which produced the maximum detector output. Such a brute force acquisition procedure, whether implemented in parallel or serial form, clearly has the advantage that a definite decision will be made after only a single examination of all code phase positions, or a single search through the entire code period. Thus, multiple examination of each code phase position or multiple searches through the code are avoided by this procedure. However, this rudimentary advantage is overwhelmed by the obvious disadvantage that a decision cannot be reached unless every code phase position has been examined or until the entire code period has been searched. For long codes, as are required in spread-spectrum systems with large processing gain, complexity of the parallel implementation or the time to search the entire code and thus reach a synchronization decision in the serial version is often prohibitive.

Another scheme, which dates back more than two and a half decades, was first introduced by Ward [4] and is based on a sequential estimation[5] of the shift register states of the PN generator. In particular, the RASE (Rapid Acquisition by Sequential Estimation) system of Figure 1.4 makes its best estimate of the first n received PN code chips (n is the number of stages in the code generator) and loads the receiver sequence generator with that estimate, thus defining a particular initial condition (starting state) from which the generator begins its operation. Since a PN sequence has the

[4] Note that the serial implementation of the maximum-likelihood algorithm is not true maximum-likelihood since the various hypotheses (code phase positions) are tested using different observations of the received signal.

[5] This should not be confused with the method of sequential detection [10] associated with variable integration time acquisition systems.

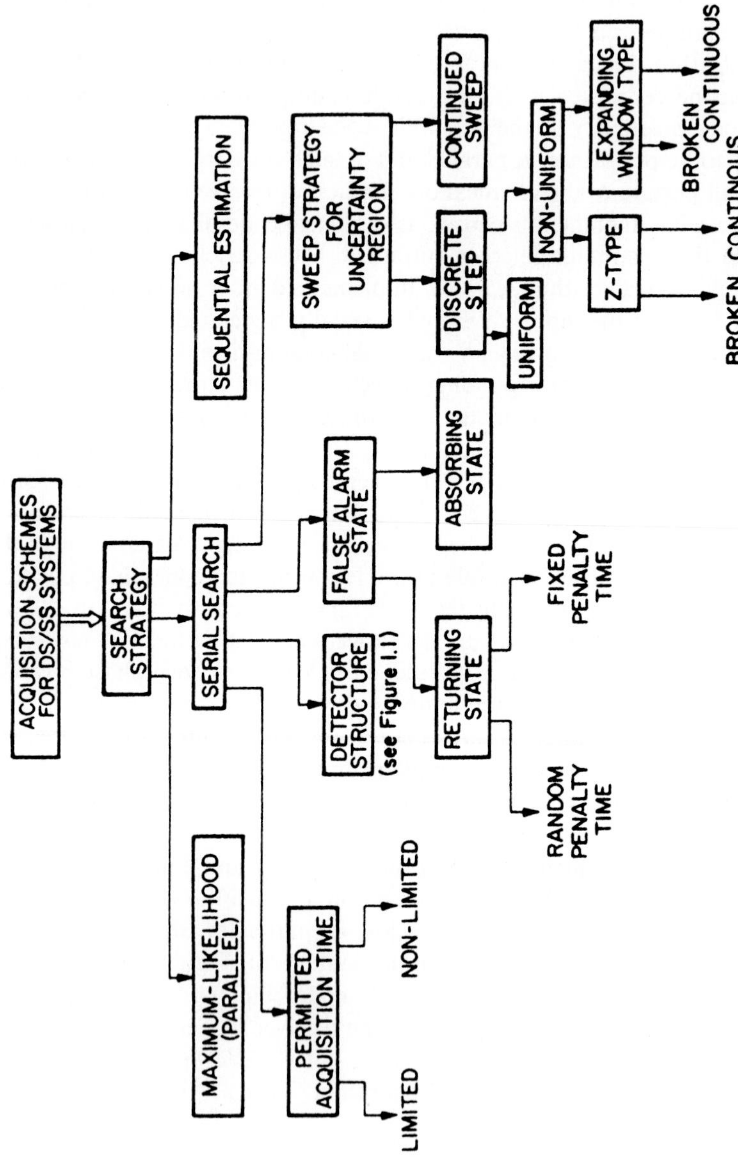

Figure 1.2. Classification of acquisition schemes (reprinted from [38]).

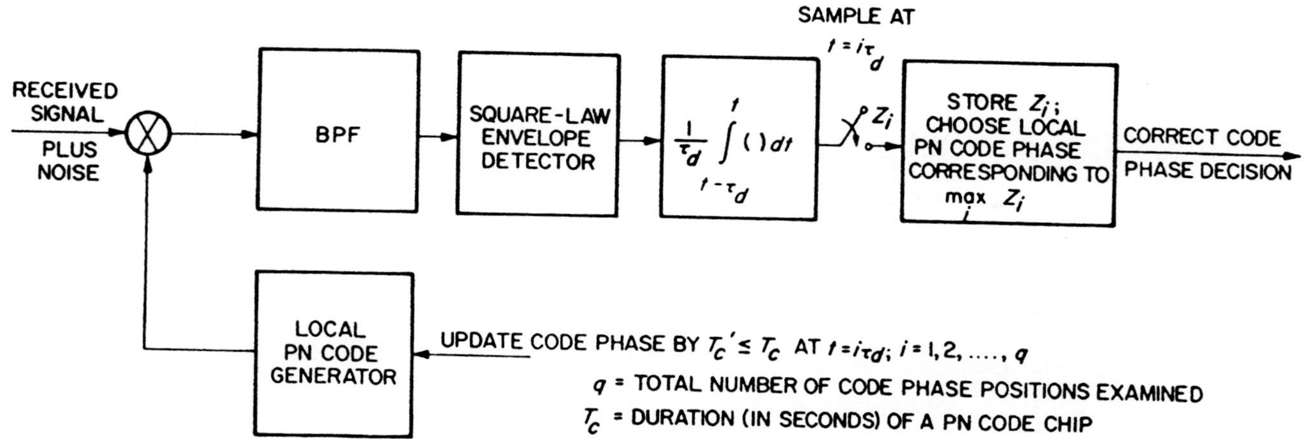

Figure 1.3. A serial realization of the maximum-likelihood search technique.

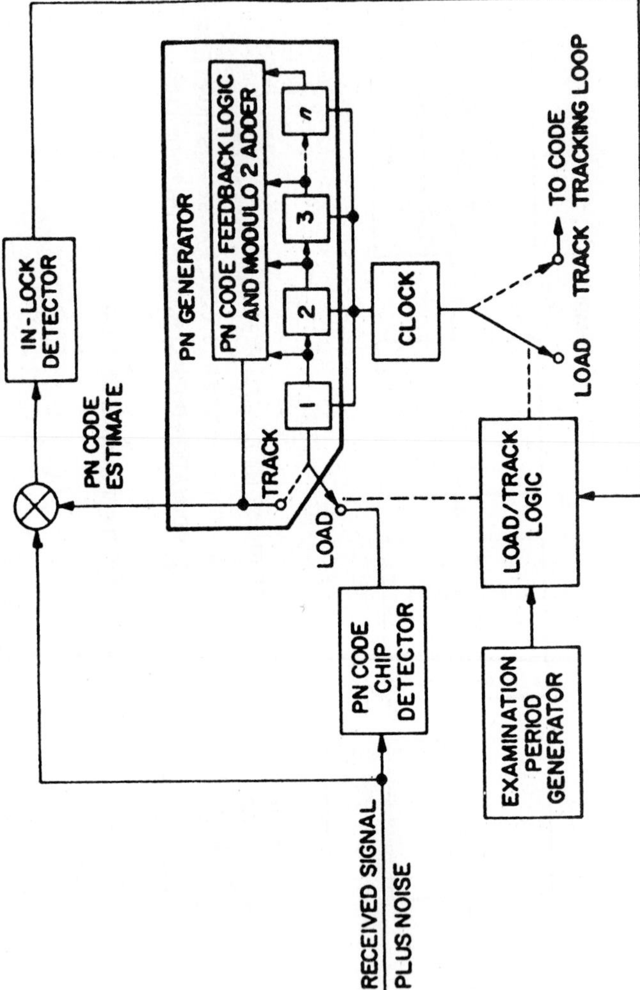

Figure 1.4. A rapid acquisition by sequential estimation (RASE) technique.

property that the next combination of register states depends only on the present combination of states, if indeed this present combination is correct (i.e., all n input chips are correctly estimated), all the following states can be predicted based on the knowledge of only this initial condition. Such is the manner in which the RASE maintains synchronization once it has been determined that the n detected chips provide the correct starting position, i.e., from that point on it no longer needs estimates of the input code chips. Until such time, however, the local PN shift registers must be periodically, at a rate determined by an examination period generator, loaded with new estimates where the decision when to stop the reload procedure is based upon a threshold crossing of an in-lock detector. The test statistic upon which this in-lock detector makes its decision is the cross-correlation of the input code with that produced by the local PN generator whose shift register contents correspond to the present estimate of the input state. Once it is determined that a correct estimate was made, the lock detector threshold crossing inhibits further reloading of the local shift register. This register is then closed within the PN tracking loop which is responsible for maintaining code phase from that time on.

At this point, several features of the RASE system are worthy of note. Clearly, since the success of this acquisition scheme depends on the ability to make credible estimates of the received PN code chips in the presence of noise, for a PN modulated carrier as an input signal, the estimation process would consist of a simple demodulation and hard-limiting detection of this signal in the same way that one would demodulate and detect any PSK data stream.[6] As such this scheme falls into the class requiring *coherent* detection and is thus of limited use in most spread-spectrum applications. Nevertheless, it warrants discussion since it does have the advantage of being a rapid acquisition technique for *moderate* input signal-to-noise ratios, and in fact, when compared with the simplest serial search (stepping correlator) system to be discussed next, it offers significant improvement in acquisition time even for signal-to-noise ratios down to -15 dB [4]. Despite its rapid acquisition capability, the RASE technique has the drawback of being highly vulnerable to noise and interference signals. The reason for this vulnerability stems from the fact that the estimation process is performed on a chip-by-chip basis and as such makes no use of the interference rejection capabilities of PN signals.

A modification of the RASE system, which was given the acronym RARASE (Recursion-Aided Rapid Acquisition Sequential Estimation), was reported more than a decade later by Ward and Yiu [5]. Here additional estimated code chips are summed to form a sync-worthiness indicator (SWI)

[6]In the original version of the RASE as suggested by Ward, the incoming signal was an unmodulated PN waveform and the code chip estimator consisted of a low-pass filter followed by a limiter.

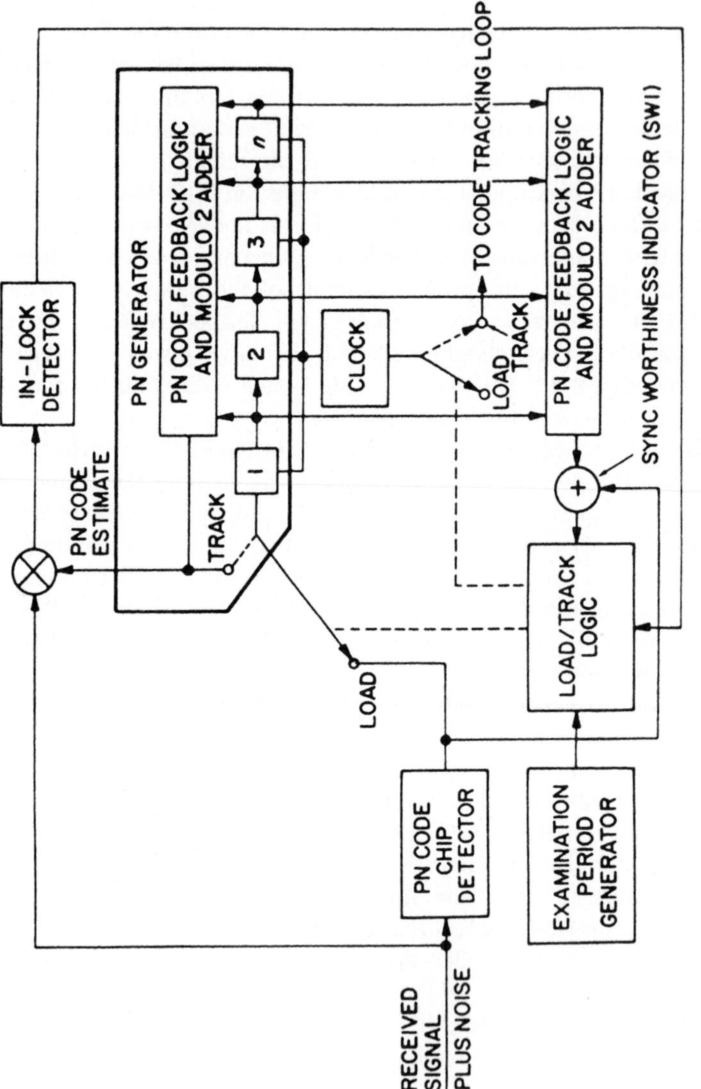

Figure 1.5. A recursion-aided rapid acquisition by sequential estimation (RARASE) technique.

which is used along with the in-lock indicator to determine when the n-stage shift register should switch from a reload to a tracking condition (see Figure 1.5). When compared with the basic RASE system which uses only a simple in-lock detector, the RARASE system was shown [5] to achieve an acquisition time reduction by a factor of 7.5 for a PN code of length $2^{15} - 1$ (15 stage shift register). Other modifications of Ward's initial RASE system have also been investigated [15], [16] which use the recursion relation of the PN code to improve the initial n-chip estimates. For example, Kilgus [15] suggests obtaining a number (η) of independent estimates of each of the n chips and making a majority logic vote among all η estimates to determine the initial n-chip load of the local shift register. Alternately, Pearce and Ristenblatt [16] suggest a threshold decoding type of estimator similar to that used for block codes. Finally, Alem and Weber [2] suggest replacing the simple threshold decision contained within the in-lock detector of the RASE system with an optimum Bayes detector based on the first two statistical moments of the decision random variable, which is assumed to be Gaussian distributed.

Historically, the serial synchronization of pseudonoise signals as introduced by Sage [17] was reported one year earlier than the RASE system. In this original version, a serial search was performed by *linearly* varying the time difference between the PN modulation on the incoming carrier and the PN waveform generated at the receiver with a *continuous* decision process determining when synchronization was achieved. Such a system is also referred to in the literature as a *sliding correlator* PN acquisition circuit [12], [18], [19]. Since the test for synchronization was based on the crossing of a threshold by the output of either a coherent or non-coherent detector, when compared with the serial realization of the maximum-likelihood technique discussed earlier, this scheme trades off shorter acquisition time (i.e., the search can terminate anywhere within the uncertainty region rather than having to wait till the end of the code period) against reduced accuracy in detection of synchronization.

When compared with Ward's sequential estimation technique, the serial search technique, as mentioned, will yield shorter acquisition time for input signal-to-noise ratios less than approximately -15 dB. Although at first glance -15 dB input SNR might seem unusually low, PN spread-spectrum communication systems which operate at, or below, this value are becoming increasingly common. The primary reason for this is that with modern technology we can now produce devices capable of handling the rapid switching rates needed to generate the high chip rate codes required for large processing gain. The need for a high code chip rate carries with it the attendant requirement of a compatibly high detector input bandwidth, which in turn results in a low input SNR. Since in addition to the above considerations serial search techniques have the advantage of being easy to implement, their application, particularly in SS receivers, is becoming increasingly popular. Although Sage's original analysis applied to the case where the input signal was a carrier direct-modulated only by the PN code, the technique is easily extended to include the case of angle-modulated (such as that produced by data modulation) carriers in which the non-coherent detector would include a post-detection filter between the envelope detector and threshold comparison [19].

In more recent years, the trend has been to accomplish the variation of the time difference between the incoming and local PN waveforms by a discrete stepping process wherein the phase of the local PN code is, at uniform increments in time, advanced (or retarded) by a fixed amount (typically a fraction of a chip). This time-discrete sweep of the uncertainty region can be accomplished by a uniform (unidirectional) search from one end of the region to the other, as in the case of no *a priori* information about the received PN code phase, or by a non-uniform search typically starting in the region of highest code phase certainty and expanding as a function of time to regions of lesser certainty. Such *expanding window* serial search strategies [20]–[24], or the simpler *z*-type search strategies [24], are well suited to applications where the length of the code makes it not feasible to search the whole code and thus some *a priori* information about the code phase must be provided by other means.

Continuing our subclassification of search strategies, we can distinguish two different philosophies with regard to the time elapsed before reaching the final acquisition state. In one case, the search is allowed to proceed as long as is necessary to achieve acquisition with the given fidelity criterion, although it is clearly desirable to accomplish this state as fast as possible. Such serial search techniques are classified as having *non-limited* permitted acquisition time and are typically employed in applications where information modulation is always present in the received waveform. Serial search strategies with *limited* permitted acquisition time are characteristic of DS/SS systems where information modulation commences to be transmitted only after PN code acquisition has been ensured. In such applications, a fixed time is usually allotted to achieve code acquisition, and furthermore this achievement must be accomplished with high probability.

The final classification of serial search strategies is in accordance with the way in which the false alarm event (state) is handled. Analogous to radar terminology, a false alarm in serial search PN code acquisition occurs when the detector (including the verification mode if it exists) erroneously decides that an in-sync condition has occurred and proceeds to direct the appropriate logic circuitry to initiate PN code tracking. Under normal circumstances, an erroneous entry into the tracking mode of operation will be detected (by the code loop lock detector) and after a given amount of time (referred to as the *false alarm penalty time*), which, in reality, is a random variable but is often mathematically modelled as being fixed, the system will return to the acquisition mode and continue searching where it last left off. Such a recoverable false alarm state is referred to as a *returning* state. Occasionally, entry into the false alarm state is catastrophic in that the system cannot recover from this event. In this instance code acquisition is completely lost and thus this type of false alarm state is referred to as *absorbing*.

In the remainder of this chapter, we shall focus our attention on the serial search strategy subclass of DS/SS acquisition schemes since, as previously mentioned, these are most attractive in the low signal-to-noise ratio environments in which these systems normally operate. We begin with a detailed discussion of the simplest of the uniform stepping, serial search techniques, namely, the *single dwell* system where a single detector is used to examine each of the possible waveform alignments for a fixed period of time in a serial fashion until the correct one has been located [1]. A recent application of such a system was the code acquisition portion of the S-band despreader aboard the Space Shuttle Orbiter System [25]. In the succeeding sections we discuss the theoretical acquisition time and acquisition probability performance of such a system along with all of the practical considerations required to apply the results. Following this, we shall return to our introductory classification of PN acquisition systems to discuss and give the performance of the conventional *multiple dwell* serial search system with immediate rejection verification mode [7], [8]. Next, we will present a unified approach [14] to serial stepped search acquisition with fixed dwell times in which the previously discussed single dwell and multiple dwell schemes appear as special cases. Another special case of this general approach is the rapid acquisition matched filter system whose behavior and performance are the subject of the following section. The treatment of fixed dwell time systems is completed with a discussion of some optimum PN sync search procedures and sweep strategies for applications where the *a priori* probability density function of the uncertainty region is not necessarily uniform [20]–[24], [26]. Here again the unified approach of [14] along with its equivalent circular state diagram are invaluable in assessing the acquisition performance of these non-uniform stepping strategies [24]. Next comes a combination of analytical and computer simulation results [27]–[30] pertaining to the performance of variable dwell time systems based on the classical method of sequential detection. Finally, as a bridge to the next chapter, we conclude with a discussion of the handover process between acquisition and tracking including some suggestions for search/lock strategies [9], and a brief consideration of parallel search.

1.2 THE SINGLE DWELL SERIAL PN ACQUISITION SYSTEM

Consider the simple model of a single dwell serial PN acquisition system illustrated in Figure 1.6. Since our interest is in the case where the PN code is acquired without knowledge of the carrier phase, the model employs a standard type, non-coherent (square-law) detector. Briefly, the received signal plus noise is actively correlated with a local replica of the PN code

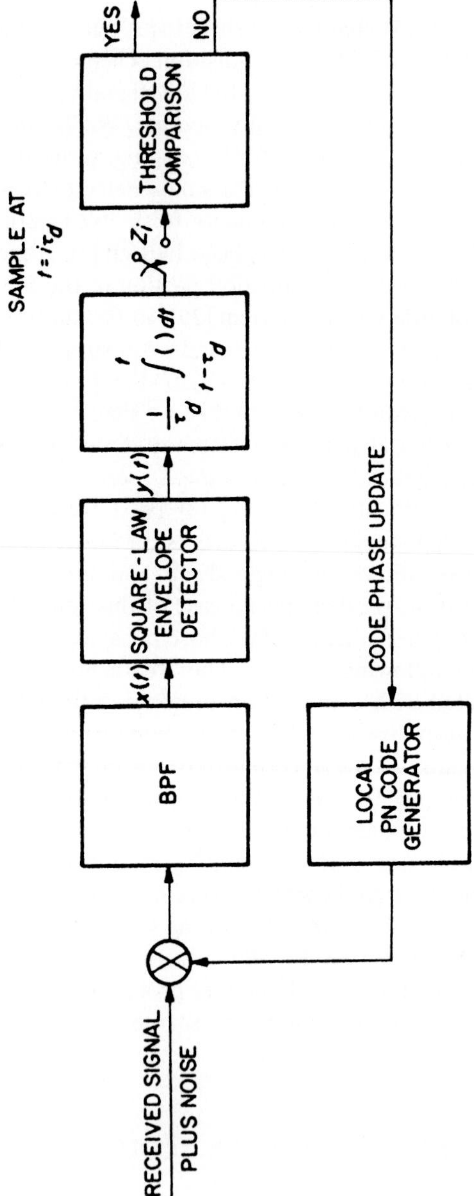

Figure 1.6. Block diagram of a single dwell time PN acquisition system with non-coherent detection.

and then passed through a band-pass (pre-detection) filter. The filter output is then square-law envelope detected with the detector output being integrated for a fixed time duration, τ_d (the "dwell time"), in an integrate-and-dump (I & D) circuit (post-detection integration) and then compared to a preset threshold.

An equivalent low-pass version of the single dwell acquisition system is illustrated in Figure 1.7. Here the received signal plus noise is first demodulated by inphase and quadrature carrier reference signals $I(t)$ and $Q(t)$ whose frequency is equal to that of the receiver carrier on which the PN waveform is direct modulated but whose phase is arbitrary. The demodulated and despread signals are now passed through identical low-pass filters which are the low-pass equivalents of the band-pass filter in Figure 1.6. Square-law detecting the filter outputs and summing produces the signal required for post-detection integration and threshold comparison. Although our analysis of the performance of the single dwell system will directly relate to the band-pass representation of Figure 1.6, our primary reason for introducing Figure 1.7 at this point is to allow for comparison later on in the chapter with an analogous configuration of a matched filter type of acquisition system. Also, in a later chapter on synchronization of frequency-hopped signals, we shall again draw a parallel with the low-pass version of the acquisition scheme as illustrated in Figure 1.7.

1.2.1 Markov Chain Acquisition Model

The Markov chain nature of the acquisition model stems from the way in which the integrate-and-dump (I & D) output is processed. In particular, if the I & D output is above the preset threshold, then a "hit" is declared. If this hit represents a true hit (i.e., the correct code phase has been determined), then the system has officially acquired and the search comes to an end. If the hit is a false alarm, then verification cannot be consummated and the search must continue. In either case, we shall assume that the verification is characterized by an extended dwell time (e.g., $K\tau_d$ sec; $K \gg 1$) assumed to be fixed and an entering into the code tracking loop mode. Understanding that a true hit corresponds to a single code phase position and that this can occur only once per search through the code, we can regard the time interval $K\tau_d$ sec as the "penalty" of obtaining a false alarm, since a false alarm can occur on any code phase position. If the I & D output falls below the preset threshold, then the local PN code generator steps to its next position and the search proceeds. Thus, at each test position (aside from the single true code phase position), one of the two events can take place, each characterized by a probability of occurrence; namely, a false alarm can happen i.e., an indication that acquisition has occurred when the PN codes are actually misaligned, with probability P_{FA}, causing a penalty of $K\tau_d$ sec, or no false alarm occurs with probability $(1 - P_{FA})$, resulting in only a single dwell time of τ_d sec—hence, the Markov chain model. Furthermore, at the

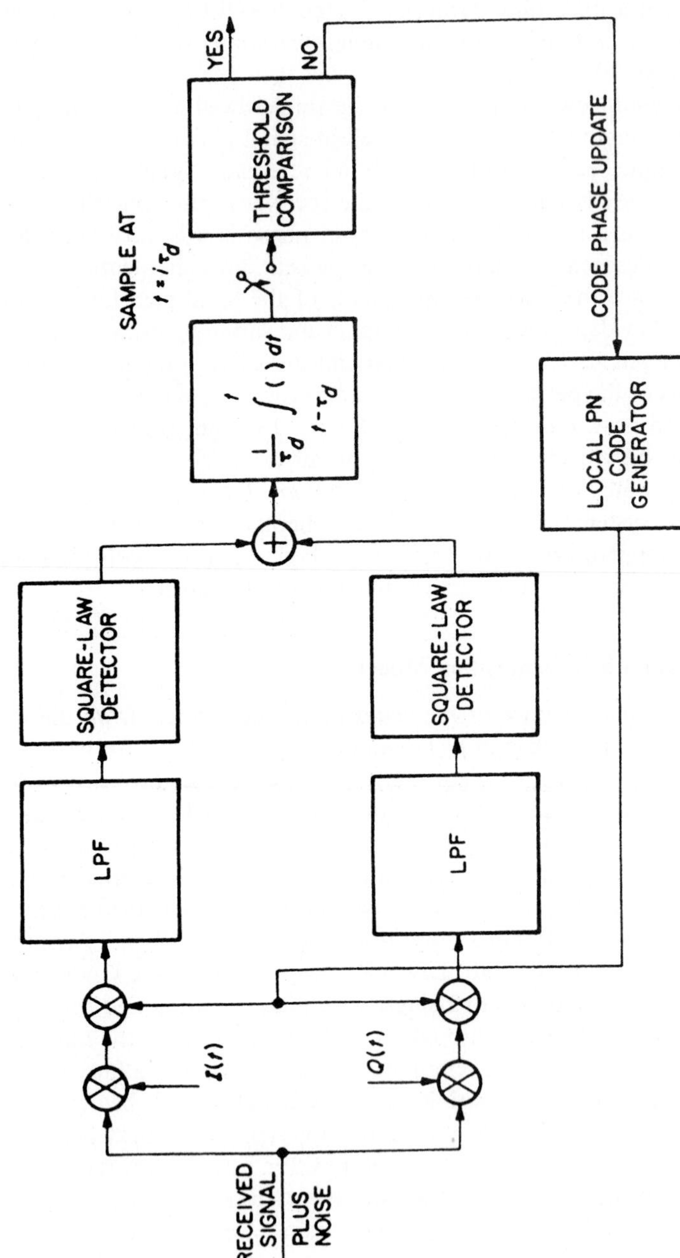

Figure 1.7. An equivalent low-pass representation of the single dwell time PN acquisition system.

true code phase position, either a correct detection can happen, i.e., an indication that acquisition has occurred when the PN codes are indeed aligned, with probability P_D, or no detection occurs, with probability $(1 - P_D)$.

In the absence of any *a priori* information regarding the true code phase position, the uncertainty in misalignment between the received PN code and the local replica of it could be as much as a full code period. Thus for long PN codes, the corresponding time uncertainty to be resolved could typically be quite large. In order to represent a reasonable compromise between the time required to search through this code phase uncertainty region and the accuracy within which the final alignment position is determined, the amount by which the local PN code generator is stepped in position as the search proceeds must be judiciously chosen. It is typical in practice to require that the received and local PN code signals be aligned to within one-half a code chip period ($T_c/2$) before relinquishing control to the fine synchronization (tracking) system. In accordance with this requirement, the time delay of the local PN code signal would be retarded (or advanced) in discrete steps of one-half a chip period and a check for acquisition made after each step. Thus, if $T_u = N_u T_c$ is the time uncertainty[7] to be resolved, then $q = 2N_u$ would be the number of possible code alignments (in serial search parlance, these are referred to as *cells*) to be examined during each search through the uncertainty region. In the more general case where the local code update size is arbitrary, we shall still use q to denote the number of cells to be searched.

The *time to acquire*, T_{ACQ}, i.e., the time to declare a true hit, is a random variable and, in general, depends on the initial (at the beginning of the search) code phase position of the local PN generator relative to that of the received code. The most complete statistical description of this random variable would be given by its probability density function, whose determination would ultimately allow computation of the probability of successful synchronization for the single dwell serial synchronization system. Although the probability of successful synchronization provides the most complete statistical description of system performance, one is often content with measuring performance in terms of the first two moments of the probability density function of T_{ACQ}, namely, *the mean acquisition time*, $\bar{T}_{ACQ}$, and the *acquisition time variance*, σ^2_{ACQ}, both of which come at a considerable savings in computation. Since, historically, the evaluation of $\bar{T}_{ACQ}$ and σ^2_{ACQ} for the single dwell system preceded the evaluation of the probability of successful acquisition for this system, we shall follow the same pattern in our discussions. In this way, the reader is first afforded the insight into the nature of the acquisition process itself which is allowed by

[7]It is convenient to assume that T_u is (or is bounded by) an integer multiple of the code time period pT_c.

computation of the simpler performance parameters $\overline{T}_{ACQ}$ and σ_{ACQ}^2, before being thrust into the complex mathematical developments needed to compute acquisition probability.

Furthermore, to make matters even simpler at first, we shall assume that *no* code Doppler is present in the received PN signal and that the detection probability P_D is constant (time invariant), the latter being equivalent to assuming that only one cell corresponds to a "correct" code alignment. Since the PN code correlation function is triangular over an interval of plus and minus one chip $(-T_c, T_c)$, for a search in increments of $T_c/2$, as is typical, there are, in reality, four[8] cells which correspond to non-zero code correlation. Clearly, the cell corresponding to the largest of these code correlations (nearest to the peak of the triangular correlation curve) would be the one yielding the "correct" code alignment. However, because of the constant P_D assumption, we must appropriately modify the results to be presented based on this assumption so as to apply to the true situation as described above. A discussion of how this is done, based upon a worst case correlation error assumption, will be given in Section 1.2.5. Later on in the chapter, we present a more exact accounting of the effects of having multiple cells with non-zero code correlation.

1.2.2 Single Dwell Acquisition Time Performance in the Absence of Code Doppler

In the absence of *a priori* knowledge concerning the relative code phase positions of the received and locally generated codes, the local PN generator is assumed to start the search at any code phase position with equal probability. Stated in mathematical terms, the probability P_1 of having the signal present (true hit) in the first cell searched is $1/q$, and the probability of it not being present there is $1 - 1/q$. For example, if the number of code chips to be searched is denoted by N_u and the search proceeds in half-chip increments, then $q = 2N_u$ and $P_1 = 1/2N_u$. More generally, if it has been determined that the signal is not present in the first $k - 1$ cells, then the *a priori* probability P_k of finding it present in the k-th cell is $1/(q + 1 - k)$, where $q + 1 - k$ is obviously the number of *remaining* cells to be searched, each possessing an equal probability of having the signal present.

A generating function flow graph for the q-state Markov chain which characterizes the acquisition process of the single dwell system is illustrated in Figure 1.8. As is customary in such flow graphs, each branch is labelled with the product of the transition probability associated with going from the node at the originated end of the branch to the node at its terminating end, and an integer (including zero) power of a parameter denoted here by z. The parameter z is used to mark time as one proceeds through the graph and its power represents the number of time units (dwell times) spent in traversing

[8] If one of the cells corresponds to perfect sync., i.e., the peak of the triangular correlation curve, then there are only three cells which correspond to non-zero code correlation.

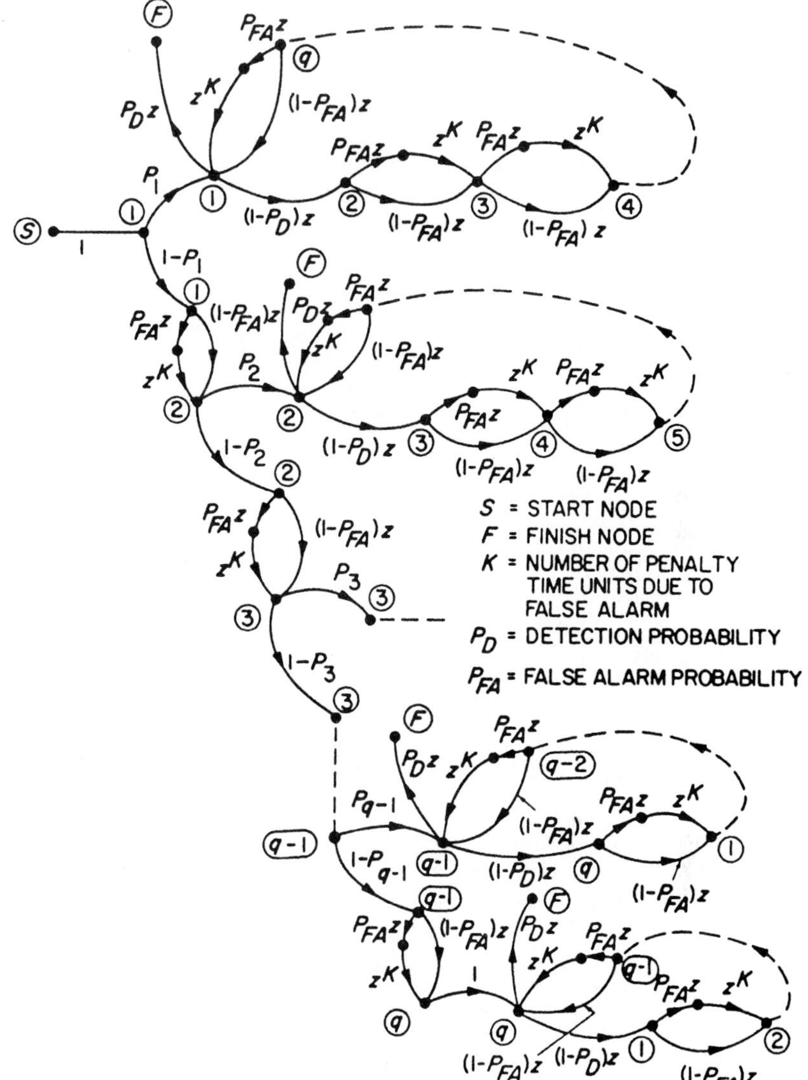

Figure 1.8. Generating function flow graph for acquisition time.

that branch. Furthermore, note that the sum of the branch probabilities (letting $z = 1$) emanating from each node equals unity.

Using standard signal flow graph reduction techniques [31]–[33], one can show that the *generating function* for the flow graph in Figure 1.8 is given by [1]

$$U(z) = \frac{(1-\beta)z}{1-\beta z H^{q-1}(z)} \left[\frac{1}{q} \sum_{l=0}^{q-1} H^{l}(z) \right] \tag{1.1}$$

where

$$\beta = 1 - P_D$$
$$H(z) = P_{FA} z^{K+1} + (1 - P_{FA}) z. \tag{1.2}$$

The mean acquisition time $\overline{T}_{ACQ}$ is obtained by differentiating $U(z^{\tau_d})$[9] with respect to z and evaluating the result at $z = 1$. After some routine algebra, one arrives at the desired result, namely,

$$\begin{aligned}\overline{T}_{ACQ} &= \left.\frac{d \ln U(z^{\tau_d})}{dz}\right|_{z=1} \\ &= \frac{2 + (2 - P_D)(q-1)(1 + KP_{FA})}{2P_D}\tau_d \end{aligned} \tag{1.3}$$

which for $q \gg 1$ (the case of practical interest) simplifies to

$$\overline{T}_{ACQ} = \frac{(2 - P_D)(1 + KP_{FA})}{2P_D}(q\tau_d). \tag{1.4}$$

The variance of the acquisition time is determined from the first two derivatives of $U(z)$ by

$$\sigma_{ACQ}^2 = \left.\left[\frac{d^2U(z^{\tau_d})}{dz^2} + \frac{dU(z^{\tau_d})}{dz} - \left(\frac{dU(z^{\tau_d})}{dz}\right)^2\right]\right|_{z=1} \tag{1.5}$$

or, since $U(1) = 1$, by the equivalent relation

$$\sigma_{ACQ}^2 = \left.\left[\frac{d^2 \ln U(z^{\tau_d})}{dz^2} + \frac{d \ln U(z^{\tau_d})}{dz}\right]\right|_{z=1} \tag{1.6}$$

Taking the natural logarithm of (1.1) together with its first two derivatives, substituting them into (1.6), and simplifying the resulting algebraic expressions, one obtains (for $q \gg 1$ and $K \ll q$) the desired result, namely,

$$\sigma_{ACQ}^2 = \tau_d^2 (1 + KP_{FA})^2 q^2 \left(\frac{1}{12} + \frac{1}{P_D^2} - \frac{1}{P_D}\right). \tag{1.7}$$

We hasten to point out that although Figure 1.6 was drawn for a single dwell system with a non-coherent band-pass detector, the above results apply equally to a single dwell system with a coherent detector, the only difference between the two cases being the interrelation of the parameters τ_d, P_{FA}, and P_D for the detector. This interrelationship, which is essential for computing acquisition time performance, will be discussed later on for the non-coherent band-pass detector.

The above analytical results for the mean and variance of the acquisition time can also be obtained by a simple heuristic approach [34] which, although lacking the mathematical elegance of the Markov chain signal flow graph technique, provides additional insight into the acquisition process in

[9] Note that since the generating function has the property that $U(1) = 1$, we can, if convenient, equivalently differentiate the natural logarithm of $U(z^{\tau_d})$ and evaluate it at $z = 1$.

terms of the underlying tradeoff between false alarm and detection probabilities. As before, we start out with the same basic assumptions, namely, that no *a priori* knowledge of the correct cell's location within the total uncertainty region is available and the cell-by-cell search of the entire uncertainty region is repeated until the correct cell is detected. Although not explicitly stated previously, each cell is assumed to be tested only once during each search of the uncertainty region and the order of the cells in the search is inconsequential.

To make matters simple, we assume at first that during each examination of a cell, the detector is characterized by a constant (time-invariant) detection probability P_D as before, but now, however, a zero false alarm probability. Then, if k (integer) denotes the particular search of the uncertainty region during which the correct cell is *first* detected, then k has the geometric probability density function (pdf)

$$p(k) = P_D(1 - P_D)^{k-1}; \qquad k = 1, 2, 3, \ldots. \tag{1.8}$$

Note that since, by assumption, $P_{FA} = 0$, then the detection probability for each complete search of the entire uncertainty region is equal to the detection probability for the correct cell, namely, P_D. Furthermore, $k - 1$ represents the number of unsuccessful searches of the uncertainty region, each having passed through q cells. Thus,

$$N_u' \triangleq q(k - 1) \tag{1.9}$$

is an integer random variable which represents *the number of cells searched without success of detection prior to the k-th search during which the correct cell will be detected*. Since each of these N_u' cell examinations occupied a single dwell time τ_d,

$$T_u' \triangleq N_u'\tau_d = q\tau_d(k - 1) \tag{1.10}$$

represents the time expired in passing through this unsuccessful series of searches.

The mean and variance of T_u' are readily computed as follows:

$$\begin{aligned} E\{T_u'\} \triangleq \overline{T}_u' &= \sum_{k=1}^{\infty} T_u' p(k) \\ &= q\tau_d \sum_{k=1}^{\infty} (k - 1) P_D (1 - P_D)^{k-1}. \end{aligned} \tag{1.11}$$

Since, by definition, $p(k)$ is a probability density function,

$$\sum_{k=1}^{\infty} P_D(1 - P_D)^{k-1} = 1. \tag{1.12}$$

Furthermore, differentiating both sides of (1.12) with respect to P_D and simplifying gives

$$\sum_{k=1}^{\infty} k P_D (1 - P_D)^{k-1} = \frac{1}{P_D}. \tag{1.13}$$

Thus, combining (1.12) and (1.13) gives the desired result, namely,

$$\overline{T}_u' = q\tau_d\left(\frac{1}{P_D} - 1\right). \tag{1.14}$$

Similarly,

$$\begin{aligned} E\left\{\left(T_u' - \overline{T}_u'\right)^2\right\} \triangleq \sigma_u^2 &= E\left\{T_u'^2\right\} - \overline{T}_u'^2 \\ &= q^2\tau_d^2 \sum_{k=1}^{\infty} (k-1)^2 P_D(1-P_D)^{k-1} \\ &\quad - q^2\tau_d^2\left(\frac{1}{P_D} - 1\right)^2. \end{aligned} \tag{1.15}$$

Differentiating (1.13) with respect to P_D and simplifying by using (1.13) prior to differentiation gives

$$\sum_{k=1}^{\infty} k^2 P_D(1-P_D)^{k-1} = \frac{2}{P_D^2} - \frac{1}{P_D}. \tag{1.16}$$

Finally, expanding the square in (1.15) and substituting (1.12), (1.13), and (1.16) gives the desired result, namely,

$$\sigma_u^2 = q^2\tau_d^2\left(\frac{1}{P_D^2} - \frac{1}{P_D}\right). \tag{1.17}$$

Having now characterized the period of unsuccessful search, we turn our attention to the k-th search interval during which the acquisition process will terminate at the location of the correct cell. Letting m denote this correct cell location, the time required to successfully reach this point from the time the k-th search is initiated is clearly

$$T_s = m\tau_d. \tag{1.18}$$

Since, for lack of any *a priori* information regarding correct cell location within the uncertainty region, m will be uniformly distributed in this region, i.e.,

$$p(m) = \frac{1}{q};\; m = 1,2,3,\ldots,q \tag{1.19}$$

with mean

$$\overline{m} = \sum_{m=1}^{q} mp(m) = \frac{1}{q}\sum_{m=1}^{q} m = \frac{q+1}{2} \tag{1.20}$$

and variance

$$\begin{aligned} \sigma_m^2 &= \sum_{m=1}^{q} m^2 p(m) - \left(\frac{q+1}{2}\right)^2 \\ &= \frac{(q+1)(2q+1)}{6} - \left(\frac{q+1}{2}\right)^2 = \frac{q^2-1}{12} \end{aligned} \tag{1.21}$$

then the mean and variance of T_s are respectively given by

$$\bar{T}_s = \left(\frac{q+1}{2}\right)\tau_d$$

$$\sigma_s^2 = \left(\frac{q^2-1}{12}\right)\tau_d^2. \tag{1.22}$$

Finally, the total acquisition time T_{ACQ_0} [10] is the sum of T_u' and T_s with mean

$$\begin{aligned}\overline{T_{ACQ_0}} &= \bar{T}_u' + \bar{T}_s \\ &= \tau_d\left[q\left(\frac{1}{P_D}-1\right)+\left(\frac{q+1}{2}\right)\right] = \left[\frac{(2-P_D)q+P_D}{2P_D}\right]\tau_d \end{aligned}\tag{1.23}$$

and variance[11]

$$\begin{aligned}\sigma_{ACQ_0}^2 &= \sigma_u^2 + \sigma_s^2 \\ &= \tau_d^2\left[q^2\left(\frac{1}{P_D^2}-\frac{1}{P_D}\right)+\frac{q^2-1}{12}\right]\end{aligned}\tag{1.24}$$

which for $q \gg 1$ becomes

$$\sigma_{ACQ_0}^2 = q^2\tau_d^2\left(\frac{1}{12}+\frac{1}{P_D^2}-\frac{1}{P_D}\right). \tag{1.25}$$

All that remains is to include the effect of a non-zero false alarm probability on the results in (1.23) and (1.25). Since out of the total of $N_u' + m$ cells searched, k of them are actually correct (one per each of the k searches of the entire uncertainty region), then there is a possibility of a false alarm only on any of the

$$N_{FA} \triangleq N_u' + m - k = q(k-1) + m - k \tag{1.26}$$

remaining cells. Equivalently, N_{FA} is the *maximum* number of false alarms that can occur. If n denotes the actual number of false alarms that occur, each with probability P_{FA} of occurrence, then conditioned on N_{FA}, n has the binomial pdf

$$p(n|N_{FA}) = \binom{N_{FA}}{n}P_{FA}^n(1-P_{FA})^{N_{FA}-n};$$

$$n = 0,1,2,3,\ldots,N_{FA} \tag{1.27}$$

with conditional mean

$$E\{n|N_{FA}\} = N_{FA}P_{FA} \tag{1.28}$$

and conditional variance

$$\sigma_{n|N_{FA}}^2 = N_{FA}P_{FA}(1-P_{FA}). \tag{1.29}$$

---

[10] The zero subscript is used to denote the fact that we have assumed $P_{FA} = 0$.

[11] It is reasonable to assume that T_u and T_s are essentially independent.

Since for each of the n false alarms a penalty of $K\tau_d$ sec is assessed, then the penalty time due to false alarm is

$$T_p = nK\tau_d. \tag{1.30}$$

Finally, the total acquisition time T_{ACQ} is the sum of T_{ACQ_0} and T_p, i.e.,

$$T_{ACQ} = T_{ACQ_0} + T_p = \left[N_u' + m + nK\right]\tau_d. \tag{1.31}$$

The mean acquisition time is obtained by averaging T_{ACQ} of (1.31). Thus, making use of (1.23) and (1.28), we obtain

$$\overline{T}_{ACQ} = \left[\frac{(2-P_D)q + P_D}{2P_D} + \overline{N}_{FA}KP_{FA}\right]\tau_d. \tag{1.32}$$

Using (1.26), we have

$$\begin{aligned}\overline{N}_{FA} &= \overline{N_u' + m} - \overline{k} \\ &= \frac{(2-P_D)q + P_D}{2P_D} - \frac{1}{P_D} = \frac{(2-P_D)q + P_D - 2}{2P_D}.\end{aligned} \tag{1.33}$$

Thus, substituting (1.33) into (1.32) gives the desired result, namely,

$$\overline{T}_{ACQ} = \left[\frac{2 + (2-P_D)(q-1)(1+KP_{FA})}{2P_D}\right]\tau_d \tag{1.34}$$

which agrees identically with (1.3).

To obtain the variance of T_{ACQ}, we first rewrite (1.26) as

$$N_{FA} = (q-1)k - q + m \tag{1.35}$$

which for $q \gg 1$ becomes

$$N_{FA} = q(k-1) + m = N_u' + m. \tag{1.36}$$

Thus, for large q, we may evaluate the conditional second moment of T_{ACQ} as

$$\begin{aligned}E\left\{T_{ACQ}^2|N_{FA}\right\} &= E\left\{(N_{FA} + nK)^2|N_{FA}\right\}\tau_d^2 \\ &= E\left\{\left(N_{FA}^2 + 2KnN_{FA} + n^2K^2\right)|N_{FA}\right\}\tau_d^2.\end{aligned} \tag{1.37}$$

Since from (1.28) and (1.29)

$$E\left\{n^2|N_{FA}\right\} = N_{FA}P_{FA}(1-P_{FA}) + (N_{FA}P_{FA})^2 \tag{1.38}$$

and from (1.28)

$$E\left\{nN_{FA}|N_{FA}\right\} = N_{FA}^2P_{FA} \tag{1.39}$$

then

$$\begin{aligned}E\left\{T_{ACQ}^2|N_{FA}\right\} &= \left\{N_{FA}^2 + 2K\left(N_{FA}^2P_{FA}\right)\right. \\ &\quad \left.+K^2\left[N_{FA}P_{FA}(1-P_{FA}) + N_{FA}^2P_{FA}^2\right]\right\}\tau_d^2 \\ &= \left\{N_{FA}^2(1+KP_{FA})^2 + N_{FA}K^2P_{FA}(1-P_{FA})\right\}\tau_d^2.\end{aligned} \tag{1.40}$$

Similarly,

$$\begin{aligned} E\{T_{ACQ}|N_{FA}\} &= E\{(N_{FA} + nK)|N_{FA}\}\tau_d \\ &= (N_{FA} + KN_{FA}P_{FA})\tau_d \\ &= N_{FA}(1 + KP_{FA})\tau_d. \end{aligned} \tag{1.41}$$

Averaging (1.40) and (1.41) over the distribution of N_{FA} gives the unconditional second and first moments of T_{ACQ}, namely,

$$\begin{aligned} E\{T_{ACQ}^2\} &= \left\{\overline{N_{FA}^2}(1 + KP_{FA})^2 + \overline{N}_{FA}K^2P_{FA}(1 - P_{FA})\right\}\tau_d^2 \\ E\{T_{ACQ}\} &= \overline{N_{FA}}(1 + KP_{FA})\tau_d. \end{aligned} \tag{1.42}$$

Finally, the variance of the acquisition time is obtained as

$$\begin{aligned} \sigma_{ACQ}^2 &= \overline{T_{ACQ}^2} - (\overline{T}_{ACQ})^2 \\ &= \left[\sigma_{N_{FA}}^2(1 + KP_{FA})^2 + \overline{N}_{FA}K^2P_{FA}(1 - P_{FA})\right]\tau_d^2. \end{aligned} \tag{1.43}$$

In view of the approximation in (1.36)

$$\sigma_{ACQ_0}^2 = \sigma_{N_{FA}}^2\tau_d^2 \tag{1.44a}$$

and

$$\overline{T_{ACQ_0}} = \overline{N}_{FA}\tau_d. \tag{1.44b}$$

Thus, using (1.25) and (1.23) in (1.43) gives

$$\begin{aligned} \sigma_{ACQ}^2 &= \tau_d^2(1 + KP_{FA})^2 q^2\left(\frac{1}{12} + \frac{1}{P_D^2} - \frac{1}{P_D}\right) \\ &+ \tau_d^2\left[\frac{(2 - P_D)q + P_D}{2P_D}\right]K^2P_{FA}(1 - P_{FA}). \end{aligned} \tag{1.45}$$

Finally, if in addition $K \ll q$, then (1.45) simplifies to

$$\sigma_{ACQ}^2 = \tau_d^2(1 + KP_{FA})^2 q^2\left(\frac{1}{12} + \frac{1}{P_D^2} - \frac{1}{P_D}\right) \tag{1.46}$$

which is in exact agreement with (1.7).

Although somewhat lengthy, the heuristic derivation of (1.34) and (1.46) is important in that false alarms and missed detections are readily identified in terms of their individual contributions to the mean acquisition time and variance.

1.2.3 Single Dwell Acquisition Time Performance in the Presence of Code Doppler and Doppler Rate

When code Doppler is present, the acquisition time performance of the system of Figure 1.6 is affected in two ways. First, the code Doppler causes the relative code phase between received and locally generated PN codes to be time varying during the dwell time of the integrate-and-dump. This has the effect of increasing or decreasing the probability of detection P_D, depending on whether the code Doppler is causing the relative code phase to increase or decrease. The second and potentially more dominant effect is that code Doppler affects the average search rate. In fact, if the code phase shift caused by the Doppler over a single dwell time is equal to the step size (phase update) of the search, then the average search rate is reduced to zero.

To take both of these effects into account when computing mean acquisition time is indeed a difficult, if not impossible, analytical task. However, it is possible to account for just the effect of Doppler on average search rate in a way which represents an obvious extension of the previous results. Letting Δf_c denote the code Doppler in chips/sec, then the mean search (code phase) update μ in chips is given by [1]:

$$\mu = \frac{N_u}{q'} + \Delta f_c \tau_d + \Delta f_c K \tau_D P_{FA}, \tag{1.47}$$

where[12] N_u/q' represents the search update in the absence of Doppler or, equivalently, the step size of the search in fractions of a chip, $\Delta f_c \tau_d$ is the code phase shift due to Doppler during the dwell time, and $\Delta f_c K \tau_d$ is the code phase shift during verification caused by a false alarm. Thus, replacing q by N_u/μ in (1.4) and (1.7) gives expressions for the mean and variance of the acquisition time in the presence of code Doppler, namely [1],

$$\bar{T}_{ACQ} = \frac{(2 - P_D)(1 + KP_{FA})N_u\tau_d}{2P_D\left[\dfrac{N_u}{q'} + \Delta f_c\tau_d(1 + KP_{FA})\right]} = \frac{\bar{T}_{ACQ}\big|_{\text{no code Doppler}}}{1 + \dfrac{q'}{N_u}\Delta f_c\tau_d(1 + KP_{FA})} \tag{1.48a}$$

$$\sigma^2_{ACQ} = \frac{\tau_d^2(1 + KP_{FA})^2 N_u^2\left(\dfrac{1}{12} + \dfrac{1}{P_D^2} - \dfrac{1}{P_D}\right)}{\left[\dfrac{N_u}{q'} + \Delta f_c\tau_d(1 + KP_{FA})\right]^2} = \frac{\sigma^2_{ACQ}\big|_{\text{no code Doppler}}}{\left[1 + \dfrac{q'}{N_u}\Delta f_c\tau_d(1 + KP_{FA})\right]^2}. \tag{1.48b}$$

Since Δf_c can be either positive or negative, depending upon its sign, the code Doppler can either speed up or slow down the search. With regard to

[12] The prime on q is used here to denote the number of cells searched *in the absence of Doppler.*

the magnitude of the code Doppler, we shall assume that $|\Delta f_c|\tau_d(1 + KP_{FA}) \ll N_u/q'$, so that the denominator of (1.48a) and (1.48b) never approaches zero and the search always proceeds in the direction dictated by the code phase update provided by the local PN generator. Finally, note that, when $\Delta f_c = 0$, then $q' = q$ and (1.48a) and (1.48b) reduce to (1.4) and (1.7), respectively as they should.

The way in which code Doppler is accounted for in extending the results of (1.4) and (1.7) to those given in (1.48a) and (1.48b) can also be applied to further extend them to include the effect of code Doppler rate. In particular, one computes the mean search update analogous to (1.47) and again replaces q by N_u/μ in the expression for mean acquisition time and acquisition time variance.

When code Doppler alone was present, we observed that the mean (statistical) search update was time invariant, i.e., the expression in (1.47) characterizes every cell being searched. When, in addition, code Doppler rate is present, the mean search update is now time dependent in the sense that it is now a function of the cell being searched.

In general, the mean search update μ in any given search cell is equal to the nominal search update N_u/q' (typically, 1/2 for half-chip search increments) of the local PN code generator plus the *mean change in phase* of the received code over the search time of that cell.[13] Thus, letting μ_n denote the mean search update in the n-th cell being searched, and $\Delta\dot{f}_c$ the code Doppler rate in chips/sec^2, then from the Markov model previously established for the single dwell time system, we have that

$$\mu_{n+1} = \frac{N_u}{q'} + \Delta f_c\tau_d(1 + KP_{FA}) + \frac{1}{2}\Delta\dot{f}_c\tau_d^2\left[1 + P_{FA}(K^2 + 2K)\right]$$

$$+ n\Delta\dot{f}_c\left[\tau_d(1 + KP_{FA})\right]^2; \; n \geq 0. \tag{1.49}$$

Note from (1.49) that the mean search update is a linear function of the search cell. Because of this dependence on n, we cannot directly replace q by N_u/μ in (1.4) to arrive at a formula for mean acquisition in the presence of code Doppler and Doppler rate. Rather, we should first find the *average mean search update* μ obtained by averaging μ_{n+1} of (1.49) over all q search cells, i.e.,

$$\mu \triangleq \frac{1}{q}\sum_{n=0}^{q-1}\mu_{n+1} \tag{1.50}$$

and then make the above suggested replacement in (1.4). Thus, from (1.49)

[13] We continue to assume, as before, that the code phase derivatives are positive when they are in such a direction as to aid the search (reduce the acquisition time).

and (1.50), we have that

$$\mu = \frac{N_u}{q'} + \Delta f_c \tau_d (1 + KP_{FA}) + \frac{1}{2}\Delta \dot{f}_c \tau_d^2 \left\{ q(1 + KP_{FA})^2 + K^2 P_{FA}(1 - P_{FA}) \right\}. \tag{1.51}$$

Since the total mean search update must correspond to the total number of chips searched, we have that[14]

$$q\mu = \sum_{n=0}^{q-1} \mu_{n+1} = N_u. \tag{1.52}$$

Thus, substituting N_u/μ for q in (1.51) results in a quadratic equation in μ, namely,

$$\mu^2 - \mu\left[\frac{N_u}{q'} + \Delta f_c \tau_d (1 + KP_{FA}) + \frac{1}{2}\Delta \dot{f}_c \tau_d^2 K^2 P_{FA}(1 - P_{FA})\right] - \frac{1}{2}\Delta \dot{f}_c \tau_d^2 N (1 + KP_{FA})^2 = 0. \tag{1.53}$$

Letting

$$\begin{aligned} A &= 1 \\ B &= \frac{N_u}{q'} + \Delta f_c \tau_d (1 + KP_{FA}) + \frac{1}{2}\Delta \dot{f}_c \tau_d^2 K^2 P_{FA}(1 - P_{FA}) \\ C &= \tfrac{1}{2}\Delta \dot{f}_c \tau_d^2 N_u (1 + KP_{FA})^2, \end{aligned} \tag{1.54}$$

then

$$\mu = \frac{B}{2A}\left[1 + \sqrt{1 + \frac{4AC}{B^2}}\right]. \tag{1.55}$$

Finally, substituting N/μ for q in (1.4), with μ defined by (1.55), gives the resulting expression for mean acquisition time in the presence of code Doppler and code Doppler rate, namely,

$$\overline{T}_{ACQ} = \frac{(2 - P_D)(1 + KP_{FA}) N \tau_d}{2P_D \left[\dfrac{B\left(1 + \sqrt{1 + \dfrac{4AC}{B^2}}\right)}{2A}\right]}. \tag{1.56}$$

[14] Here we have made the assumption that $|\Delta f_c|$ and $|\Delta \dot{f}_c|$ are small enough such that $\mu_{n+1} > 0$ for all $n = 0, 1, \ldots, q - 1$ and thus the search proceeds only in one direction, namely, that dictated by the local PN generator code phase update.

Also, the acquisition time variance in the presence of code Doppler and code Doppler rate becomes

$$\sigma_{ACQ}^2 = \frac{\tau_d^2 (1 + KP_{FA})^2 N_u^2 \left(\frac{1}{12} + \frac{1}{P_D^2} - \frac{1}{P_D} \right)}{\left[\frac{B\left(1 + \sqrt{1 + \frac{4AC}{B^2}}\right)}{2A} \right]^2}. \tag{1.57}$$

Note again that, when $\Delta f_c = \Delta \dot{f}_c = 0$, we have that $B = N/q' = N/q$, $C = 0$, whereby (1.56) and (1.57) reduce to (1.4) and (1.7), respectively.

1.2.4 Evaluation of Detection Probability P_D and False Alarm Probability P_{FA} in Terms of PN Acquisition System Parameters

The formulas for mean acquisition time and acquisition time variance developed in the previous section are all functions of the detection probability P_D, false alarm probability P_{FA}, and dwell time τ_d. Thus, it would appear at first glance that, for specified values of detection probability and false alarm probability, one could arbitrarily select the dwell time to achieve any desired mean acquisition time. Upon closer examination, one realizes that indeed this is not possible with the fallacy lying in the fact that, for a given P_{FA} and pre-detection signal-to-noise ratio, P_D is implicitly a function of τ_d. To place this statement in evidence, we begin by evaluating P_D and P_{FA} in terms of the PN acquisition system parameters for the simple case of no code Doppler or Doppler derivatives.

When signal is present (i.e., the cell being searched corresponds to a sample value on the PN correlation curve), then the input to the square-law envelope detector can be expressed in the form[15]

$$\begin{aligned} x(t) = s(t) + n(t) &= \sqrt{2} A \cos(\omega_0 t + \psi) + \sqrt{2}\, n_c(t) \cos(\omega_0 t + \psi) \\ &\quad - \sqrt{2}\, n_s(t) \sin(\omega_0 t + \psi) \\ &= \sqrt{2}\, R(t) \cos(\omega_0 t + \psi + \theta(t)), \end{aligned} \tag{1.58}$$

where

$$R(t) = \sqrt{(A + n_c(t))^2 + n_s^2(t)}\,;\ \theta(t) = \tan^{-1} \frac{n_s(t)}{A + n_c(t)}. \tag{1.59}$$

[15] To keep the presentation simple, we shall, at this point, ignore partial correlation effects produced by the filtering of the product of incoming and local PN waveforms over less than a full code period. Later in the chapter, we shall present both exact and approximate approaches for accounting for these effects and their significance.

In (1.58), A is the rms signal amplitude,[16] ω_0 the radian carrier frequency, and $n_c(t), n_s(t)$ are band-limited, independent, low-pass, zero-mean Gaussian noise processes with variance $\sigma^2 = N_0 B/2$, where N_0 is the single-sided noise spectral density and B is the noise bandwidth of the pre-detection band-pass filter.

The output of the square-law envelope detector in Figure 1.6, in response to the input $x(t)$ of (1.58), is (ignoring second harmonics of the carrier):

$$y(t) \triangleq x^2(t) = R^2(t) = \left(A + n_c(t)\right)^2 + n_s^2(t) \tag{1.60}$$

and has a non-central chi-squared pdf which is given by

$$p(y) = \begin{cases} \dfrac{1}{2\sigma^2}\exp\left[-\left(\dfrac{y}{2\sigma^2} + \gamma\right)\right] I_0\left(2\sqrt{\dfrac{\gamma y}{2\sigma^2}}\right); & y \geq 0 \\ 0; & \text{otherwise} \end{cases} \tag{1.61}$$

where

$$\gamma \triangleq \frac{A^2}{N_0 B} = \frac{A^2}{2\sigma^2} \tag{1.62}$$

is the pre-detection signal-to-noise ratio. In the absence of signal, i.e., $A = 0$, (1.61) reduces to the central chi-squared pdf:

$$p(y) = \begin{cases} \dfrac{1}{2\sigma^2}\exp\left(-\dfrac{y}{2\sigma^2}\right); & y \geq 0, \\ 0; & \text{otherwise} \end{cases} \tag{1.63}$$

which characterizes the square-law output in all search cells that contain noise only.

If $y(t)$ is sampled at intervals $T = 1/B$, then these samples are approximately independent, and furthermore, the integrate-and-dump output can be approximated by a summation over these sampled values, namely,[17]

$$Z \triangleq \frac{1}{\tau_d}\int_0^{\tau_d} y(t)\,dt \cong \frac{1}{N_B}\sum_{k=0}^{N_B - 1} y(kT) \tag{1.64}$$

where

$$N_B \triangleq \frac{\tau_d}{T} = B\tau_d. \tag{1.65}$$

[16] For the moment, we shall not enter into a discussion concerning the various system losses and gains which enter into the calculation of the effective signal amplitude to be used in predicting true system signal-to-noise ratio behavior. Such a discussion will be given later on in the development.

[17] For simplicity of notation, we assume that $i = 0$ in Figure 1.6 and set $Z_0 = Z$. Furthermore, it is convenient to assume that N_B is integer, although the results which follow are, for large N_B, valid for N_B non-integer.

Using the approximation in (1.64) and the first order pdf's of (1.61) and (1.63), the pdf of Z, namely, $p(Z)$, for signal present is given by

$$p(Z) = \begin{cases} \dfrac{N_B}{2\sigma^2}\left(\dfrac{Z}{2\gamma\sigma^2}\right)^{(N_B-1)/2} \exp\left[-N_B\left(\dfrac{Z}{2\sigma^2}+\gamma\right)\right] & \\ \times I_{N_B-1}\left[2\sqrt{N_B^2\gamma\dfrac{Z}{2\sigma^2}}\right]; & Z \geq 0 \\ 0; & \text{otherwise} \end{cases} \tag{1.66}$$

and for signal absent is given by

$$p(Z) = \begin{cases} \left(\dfrac{N_B}{2\sigma^2}\right)\dfrac{\left(\dfrac{ZN_B}{2\sigma^2}\right)^{N_B-1}}{(N_B-1)!}\exp\left(-\dfrac{ZN_B}{2\sigma^2}\right); & Z \geq 0 \\ 0; & \text{otherwise.} \end{cases} \tag{1.67}$$

Normalizing Z by $2\sigma^2/N_B = N_0/\tau_d$ or, equivalently, letting $Z^* \triangleq ZN_B/2\sigma^2$, we can rewrite (1.66) and (1.67), respectively, in the simpler form,

$$p(Z^*) = \begin{cases} \left(\dfrac{Z^*}{N_B\gamma}\right)^{(N_B-1)/2} \exp(-Z^* - N_B\gamma) & \\ \times I_{N_B-1}\left[2\sqrt{N_B\gamma Z^*}\right]; & Z^* \geq 0 \\ 0; & \text{otherwise} \end{cases} \tag{1.68}$$

and

$$p(Z^*) = \begin{cases} \dfrac{(Z^*)^{(N_B-1)}}{(N_B-1)!}\exp(-Z^*); & Z^* \geq 0 \\ 0; & \text{otherwise.} \end{cases} \tag{1.69}$$

The probability of false alarm, P_{FA}, is the probability that Z exceeds the threshold η when signal is absent or, equivalently, in terms of the normalized random variable Z^* and the normalized threshold $\eta^* \triangleq \eta N_B/2\sigma^2$,

$$P_{FA} = \int_{\eta^*}^{\infty} p(Z^*)\,dZ^* = 1 - \int_0^{\eta^*}\frac{(Z^*)^{(N_B-1)}}{(N_B-1)!}\exp(-Z^*)\,dZ^*$$

$$= e^{-\eta^*}\sum_{k=0}^{N_B-1}\frac{(\eta^*)^k}{k!}. \tag{1.70}$$

The detection probability P_D is the probability that Z exceeds the threshold

η when signal is present. Thus, using (1.68) rather than (1.69), we get

$$P_D = 1 - \int_0^{\eta^*} \left(\frac{Z^*}{N_B \gamma} \right)^{(N_B - 1)/2} \exp(-Z^* - N_B \gamma) I_{N_B - 1}\left[2\sqrt{N_B \gamma Z^*}\right] dZ^* \tag{1.71}$$

which, if desired, can be expressed in terms of a generalized Marcum's Q-function.

For large N_B (the case of most practical interest), things become quite a bit simpler. Defining $y_k^* = y(kT)/2\sigma^2$, then from (1.61) and (1.63), the pdf's of y_k^* in the presence and absence of signal are, respectively,

$$p(y_k^*) = \begin{cases} e^{-(y_k^* + \gamma)} I_0\left(2\sqrt{\gamma y_k^*}\right); & y_k^* \geq 0 \\ 0; & \text{otherwise} \end{cases} \tag{1.72}$$

$$p(y_k^*) = \begin{cases} e^{-y_k^*}; & y_k^* \geq 0 \\ 0; & \text{otherwise.} \end{cases} \tag{1.73}$$

Also, from (1.64) and the definition of Z^* in terms of Z, we have

$$Z^* = \sum_{k=0}^{N_B - 1} y_k^*. \tag{1.74}$$

Since, by previous assumption, the y_k^*s are independent random variables, then for large N_B, Z^* is approximately Gaussian distributed with mean $\overline{Z^*} = N_B \overline{y^*}$ and variance $\sigma_{Z^*}^2 = N_B \sigma_{y^*}^2$. The means and variance of the pdf's in (1.72) and (1.73) are well known [35] to be

$$\overline{y^*} = 1 + \gamma;\ \sigma_{y^*}^2 = 1 + 2\gamma;\ \text{signal present} \tag{1.75}$$

$$\overline{y^*} = 1;\ \sigma_{y^*}^2 = 1;\ \text{signal absent.} \tag{1.76}$$

Thus,

$$\overline{Z^*} = N_B(1 + \gamma);\ \sigma_{Z^*}^2 = N_B(1 + 2\gamma);\ \text{signal present} \tag{1.77}$$

$$\overline{Z^*} = N_B;\ \sigma_{Z^*}^2 = N_B;\ \text{signal absent.} \tag{1.78}$$

Using the Gaussian assumption, the false alarm probability is

$$\begin{aligned} P_{FA} &= \int_{\eta^*}^{\infty} \frac{1}{\sqrt{2\pi N_B}} \exp\left[-\frac{(Z^* - N_B)^2}{2N_B} \right] dZ^* \\ &= Q\left(\frac{\eta^* - N_B}{\sqrt{N_B}} \right) \\ &\triangleq Q(\beta) \end{aligned} \tag{1.79}$$

where $Q(x)$ is the Gaussian probability integral. Thus, if P_{FA} is specified, β

can be determined. The corresponding detection probability under the same assumption is

$$P_D = \int_{\eta^*}^{\infty} \frac{1}{\sqrt{2\pi N_B(1+2\gamma)}} \exp\left[-\frac{\left(Z^* - N_B(1+\gamma)\right)^2}{2N_B(1+2\gamma)}\right] dZ^*$$

$$= Q\left(\frac{\beta - \sqrt{N_B}\gamma}{\sqrt{1+2\gamma}}\right). \tag{1.80}$$

Combining (1.79) and (1.80) and reidentifying N_B and γ in terms of the system parameters gives the final relation

$$P_D = Q\left(\frac{Q^{-1}(P_{FA}) - \sqrt{B\tau_d}\left(\frac{A^2}{N_0 B}\right)}{\sqrt{1 + 2\left(\frac{A^2}{N_0 B}\right)}}\right). \tag{1.81}$$

Thus, given P_D, P_{FA}, A^2/N_0 and B, the dwell time τ_d is determined.

Before we use (1.81) and the dwell time determined from it in the formulas derived in the previous section for mean acquisition time and acquisition time variance, several modifications based upon practical considerations must be made.

1.2.5 Effective Probability of Detection and Timing Misalignment

The calculation of detection probability as in (1.71) or (1.80) implicitly assumed that only one cell in the entire search satisfies the "signal present" hypothesis. In actuality, since the PN correlation curve exists over an interval of ± 1 chip around the peak, a system which updates the locally generated code phase, for example, in half-chip increments would yield several cells for which signal could be considered present.

Typically, the system is designed on the basis of the worst case correlation, which for the half-chip update case would correspond to the pair of correlation points one-quarter chip away from the correlation peak. Since the normalized correlation value at these points is 0.75 (relative to a peak of 1), then the *single* signal point calculation of detection probability as in (1.71) or (1.80) would be based on an effective reduction in the nominal signal-to-noise ratio A^2/N_0 of $10\log_{10}(.75)^2 = 2.5$ dB. Since, however, in reality there exist two worst case correlation positions, then the *effective probability of detection* P_D' for use in computing mean acquisition time is computed as

$$P_D' = P_D + (1 - P_D)P_D = 2P_D - P_D^2, \tag{1.82}$$

where the first term in (1.82) represents the probability of detecting signal present on the first correlation point and the second term is the joint probability of not detecting signal on the first correlation point and detecting signal present on the second correlation point. Clearly, for low signal-to-noise ratios (small P_D), the effective detection probability is approximately twice that computed on the basis of a single signal present cell [(1.71) or (1.80)]. In summary, then, the computation procedures would be as follows: For a given P_{FA}, determine β from (1.79). For a specified P_D', find P_D from (1.82), degrade the given nominal value of γ by 2.5 dB and solve for N_B in (1.80). Determine the dwell time from $\tau_d = N_B/B$, where B is the given band-pass filter bandwidth determined by considerations on allowable modulation distortion (to be discussed next). Using P_D', P_{FA}, and τ_d in (1.4) and (1.7), solve for $\overline{T}_{ACQ}$ and σ_{ACQ}^2.

1.2.6 Modulation Distortion Effects

Typically, the PN modulated carrier is also biphase modulated by data. Depending on the ratio of pre-detection filter bandwidth B to data rate R, this data modulation will suffer distortion and an equivalent power reduction as it passes through this filter. The equivalent power reduction factor M_2 is computed from[18]

$$M_2 = \int_{-\infty}^{\infty} S_m(f)|H(j2\pi f)|^2\, df, \tag{1.83}$$

where $S_m(f)$ is the power spectral density of the data modulation and $H(j2\pi f)$ is the equivalent low-pass transfer function of the pre-detection band-pass filter. Thus, the nominal signal power A^2 must be multiplied by M_2 to account for this effect when computing the effective signal-to-noise ratio to be used in the previous detection and false alarm probability computations.

1.2.7 Reduction in Noise Spectral Density Caused by PN Despreading

Multiplication of the equivalent noise process at the PN acquisition system input by the locally generated PN sequence spreads the spectrum of this noise process and simultaneously reduces its effective spectral height into the data filter. Letting N_0' denote this effective noise spectral density, then since the bandwidth of the data (pre-detection) filter is much narrower than that of the PN process, we have that

$$N_0' \cong N_0 \int_{-\infty}^{\infty} T_c \left(\frac{\sin \pi f T_c}{\pi f T_c} \right)^2 |H(j2\pi f)|^2\, df. \tag{1.84}$$

In (1.84), we have assumed for simplicity of the calculation that the PN line

[18] We shall again encounter this equivalent power reduction factor in our discussion of PN tracking loops in the next chapter.

spectrum is approximated by its envelope. Thus, again in computing the effective signal-to-noise ratio of the system, N_0 should be replaced by N_0'.

Finally, summing up the effects discussed in Sections 1.2.5–1.2.7, the effective signal-to-noise ratio γ' in the pre-detection filter bandwidth is given by

$$\gamma' = \frac{A^2 M_2 L}{N_0' B}, \tag{1.85}$$

where M_2 is defined in (1.83), N_0' in (1.84), and L, the loss due to a chip misalignment τ from the correlation curve peak, is given by

$$L = \left(1 - \frac{\tau}{T_c}\right)^2. \tag{1.86}$$

Again, for half-chip search updates, the worse case loss corresponds to $\tau/T_c = 1/4$.

1.2.8 Code Doppler and Its Derivative

When code Doppler and its derivative characterize the received signal dynamics, the timing error between received and local PN codes is not constant over the dwell time of the detection process. This "smearing" effect has a direct bearing on the calculation of the loss due to fractional chip timing misalignment and thus the expression for this loss given in (1.86) requires modification.

Considering the case where the received signal is characterized by code Doppler and Doppler rate, the normalized signal input to the acquisition dwell time integrator in Figure 1.6 is (under the signal present hypothesis):

$$\tilde{s}(t) = \left(1 - \frac{\tau}{T_c} - \Delta f_c t - \frac{1}{2}\Delta \dot{f}_c t^2\right)^2. \tag{1.87}$$

The corresponding normalized dwell time integrator output is

$$\begin{aligned} L &= \frac{1}{\tau_d}\int_0^{\tau_d} \tilde{s}(t)\, dt \\ &= \left(1 - \frac{\tau}{T_c}\right)^2 - \left[\Delta f_c \tau_d + \frac{1}{3}\Delta \dot{f}_c \tau_d^2\right]\left(1 - \frac{\tau}{T_c}\right) \\ &\quad + \frac{\Delta f_c^2 \tau_d^2}{3} + \frac{\Delta f_c \Delta \dot{f}_c \tau_d^3}{4} + \frac{\Delta \dot{f}_c^2 \tau_d^4}{20}. \end{aligned} \tag{1.88}$$

For small Δf_c and $\Delta \dot{f}_c$, the loss L of (1.88) is well approximated by

$$\tilde{L} = \left[\left(1 - \frac{\tau}{T_c}\right) - \frac{\Delta f_c \tau_d + \frac{1}{3}\Delta \dot{f}_c \tau_d^2}{2}\right]^2. \tag{1.89}$$

Using (1.88) or (1.89) in (1.85), one is able to compute, to a first-order approximation, the effective signal-to-noise ratio in the pre-detection filter bandwidth when the received signal dynamics are characterized by code Doppler and its derivative.

Because of the dependence of L on dwell time τ_d, the procedure for ultimately calculating mean acquisition time is more complex but may be summarized as follows:

1. For a given detection probability (P_D'), solve for P_D from (1.82).
2. For a specified bandwidth B and filter type, compute M_2 from (1.83) and N_0' from (1.84). (Actually, carrier and code Doppler affect these computations but we shall assume these are second-order effects.)
3. Using M_2 and N_0' computed in (2) and L from (1.88) or $\tilde{L}$ from (1.89), determine γ' from (1.85) (assume A^2/N_0 is given).
4. Letting $N_B = B\tau_d$, then for a given P_{FA}, solve for β from (1.79), which together with P_D determined from (1) and γ' from (3), allows us to solve (transcendentally) for τ_d from (1.80).
5. Using τ_d as determined in (4), and the given values of P_D' and P_{FA}, calculate $\bar{T}_{ACQ}$ from (4) and σ^2_{ACQ} from (1.7).

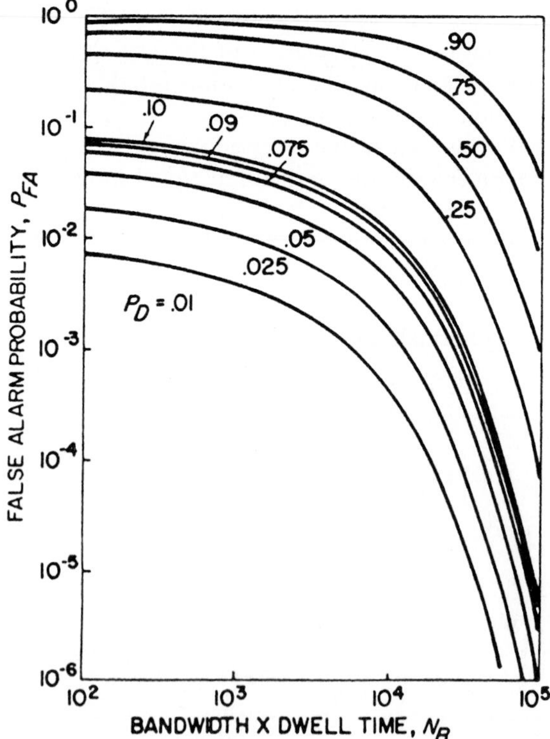

Figure 1.9. False alarm and detection probability performance of non-coherent (square-law) detector; $\gamma' = -20$ dB.

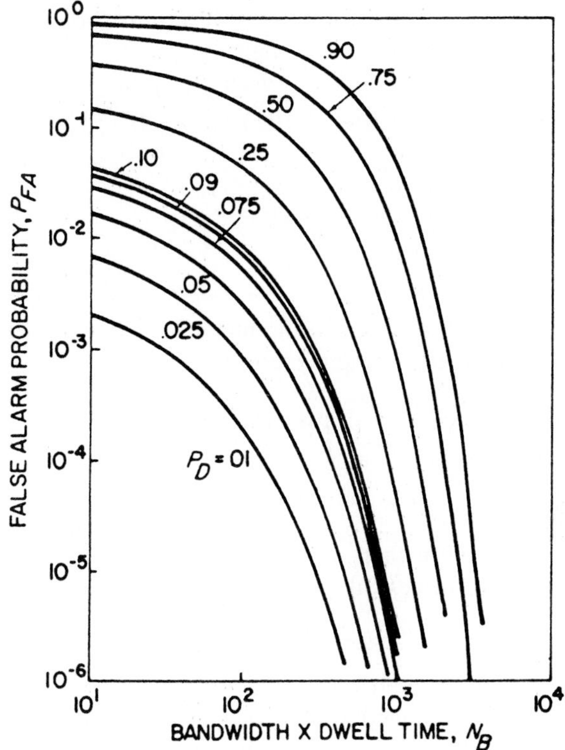

Figure 1.10. False alarm and detection probability performance of non-coherent (square-law) detector; $\gamma' = -10$ dB.

To aid in carrying out step (4), Figures 1.9 and 1.10 illustrate P_{FA} versus N_B with P_D as a parameter for $\gamma' = -20$ dB and -10 dB respectively. These curves are computed using (1.81). Clearly, for fixed P_D and γ', the square-law detector performance improves (P_{FA} decreases) as N_B increases. However, increasing N_B for fixed bandwidth B increases the dwell time τ_d, which acts to increase mean acquisition time.

1.2.9 Probability of Acquisition for the Single Dwell System

A more complete statistical characterization of the acquisition time performance of a single dwell PN acquisition system can be had by considering the *probability of acquisition in k or fewer dwells*. Computation of this cumulative probability requires first obtaining an expression for the probability density function of the number of dwells to obtain successful synchronization [6].

Once again in order to readily gain immediate and exact results, one resorts to the signal flow graph approach which provides the system generating function as in (1.1). Starting with this expression, we first rewrite it in the form of a power series in z, namely,

$$U(z) = (1-\beta)z\sum_{i=0}^{\infty}\left(H^{q-1}(z)\beta z\right)^{i}\left[\frac{1}{q}\sum_{l=0}^{q-1}H^{l}(z)\right]$$
$$= \frac{P_D z}{q}\sum_{i=0}^{\infty}\sum_{l=0}^{q-1}\left[P_{FA}z^{K}+(1-P_{FA})\right]^{i(q-1)+l}(1-P_D)^{i}z^{iq+l}. \tag{1.90}$$

Applying the binomial theorem to the factor involving P_{FA}, the generating function can be rewritten as the triple sum

$$U(z) = \frac{P_D z}{q}\sum_{i=0}^{\infty}\sum_{l=0}^{q-1}\sum_{h=0}^{i(q-1)+l}\binom{i(q-1)+l}{h}P_{FA}^{h}(1-P_{FA})^{i(q-1)+l-h}\cdot$$
$$\times(1-P_D)^{i}z^{iq+l+hK} \tag{1.91}$$

In order to proceed further, we must relate the generating function $U(z)$ to the probability of successful synchronization. Recalling (1.31), then

$$N_{ACQ} \triangleq N_u' + m + nK \tag{1.92}$$

is the integer valued random variable which represents the total number of cells that have been examined when successful synchronization (acquisition) occurs. Letting p_j denote the probability that the system acquires on the j-th cell tested, or, in terms of N_{ACQ},

$$p_j = Pr\{N_{ACQ} = j\}; \qquad j = 1,2,3\ldots \tag{1.93}$$

then z has the moment generating function

$$U(z) = \sum_{j=0}^{\infty} z^{j}p_j. \tag{1.94}$$

Thus, equating the coefficients of z^j; $j = 1,2,3,\ldots$ in (1.91) to p_j produces, at least in principle, the desired result.

Determination of these coefficients in (1.91) is possible [7] but quite tedious. To make matters more tractable, but still meaningful, we shall make the assumption that the system acquires within a single search of q cells, or equivalently we impose the restriction $N_{ACQ} < q$. Indeed, if this were not the case in practice, then the serial search synchronization system would give way to the maximum-likelihood system discussed earlier since if all the cells were to be examined there would be no need for a threshold test on each. Returning now to (1.91), we recognize that the restriction $N_{ACQ} < q$ is equivalent to considering only the $i = 0$ term in the summation on i, since the index i represents the number of times that the entire group of cells has been *previously* examined. Thus, $i = 0$ implies that the q cells are being examined for the first time. Making this simplification in (1.91) produces the result

$$U(z)|_{i=0} = \frac{P_D}{q}\sum_{l=0}^{q-1}\sum_{h=0}^{l}\binom{l}{h}P_{FA}^h(1-P_{FA})^{l-h}z^{l+hK+1}. \tag{1.95}$$

Now making the equivalence between the coefficients of z^j in (1.95) and (1.94) produces, after much simplification, the desired result, namely [6], [7]

$$p_j = \frac{P_D}{q}\sum_{h=0}^{\hat{h}+1}\binom{j-1-hK}{h}P_{FA}^h(1-P_{FA})^{j-1-h(K+1)};$$
$$\left\lfloor\frac{j}{K}\right\rfloor K+1 \le j \le \min\left\{\left(\left\lfloor\frac{j}{K}\right\rfloor+1\right)K, q\right\} \tag{1.96}$$

where

$$\hat{h} \triangleq \left\lfloor\frac{\left\lfloor\frac{j}{K}\right\rfloor K}{K+1}\right\rfloor \tag{1.97}$$

and the notation $\lfloor a \rfloor$ represents the largest integer less than or equal to a. Furthermore, the term corresponding to $h = \hat{h}+1$ clearly has meaning only if $j-1-(\hat{h}+1)K \ge 0$; otherwise its contribution is assumed equal to zero.

The cumulative distribution of N_{ACQ}, namely,

$$P_{ACQ}(j) \triangleq \Pr\{N_{ACQ} \le j\} = \sum_{i=0}^{j} p_i \tag{1.98}$$

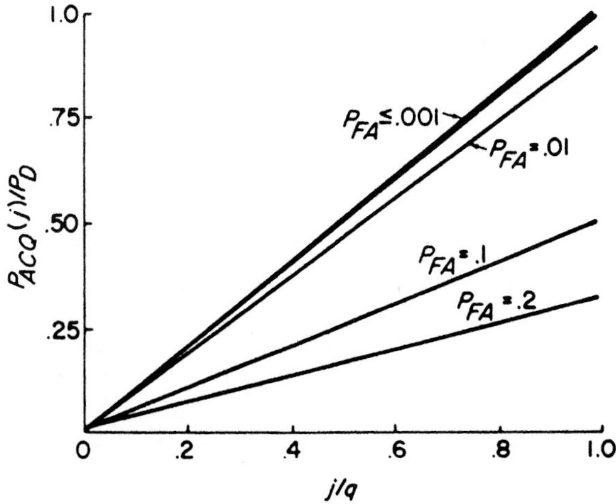

Figure 1.11. Normalized cumulative distribution function for $q = 10^2$, $K = 10$ and various values of P_{FA} (reprinted from [6]).

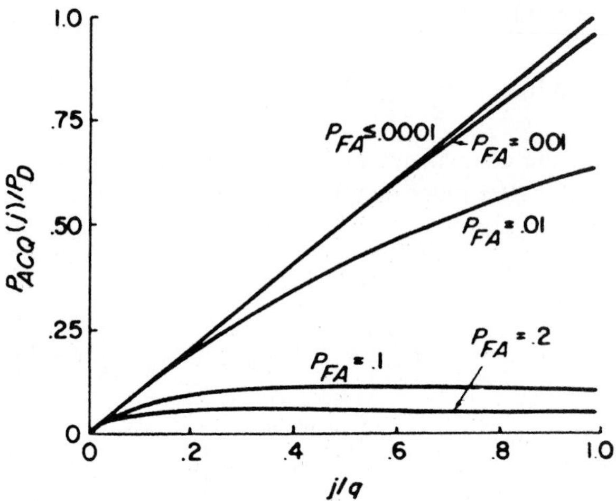

Figure 1.12. Normalized cumulative distribution for $q = 10^2$, $K = 10^2$ and various values of P_{FA} (reprinted from [6]).

represents the probability of acquisition in j or fewer dwells. Although a closed form expression for $P_{ACQ}(j)$ using p_j of (1.96) appears impossible, one can readily obtain numerical results for moderate values of q using digital computation. Figures 1.11–1.14 illustrate the normalized acquisition probability $P_{ACQ}(j)/P_D$ as a function of j/q for various values of q, K, and P_{FA}. In all cases, as P_{FA} goes to zero, we obtain the optimum

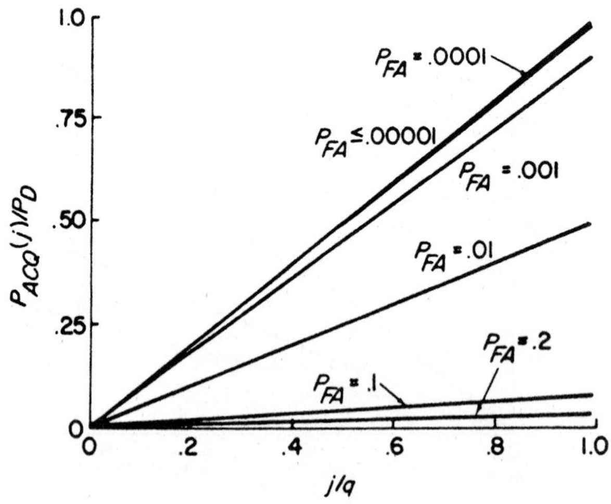

Figure 1.13. Normalized cumulative distribution function for $q = 5 \times 10^3$, $K = 10^2$ and various values of P_{FA} (reprinted from [6]).

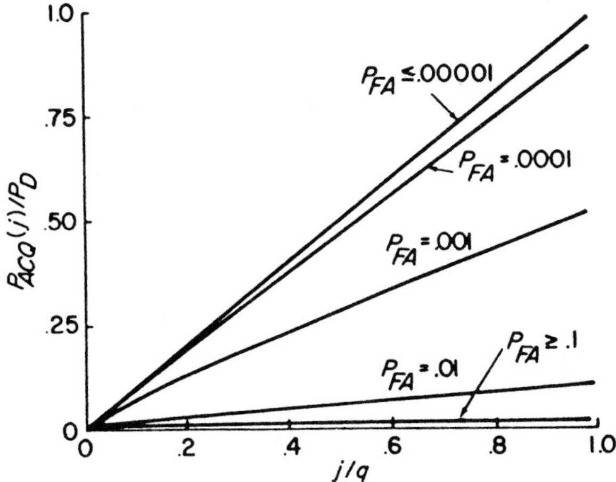

Figure 1.14. Normalized cumulative distribution function for $q = 5 \times 10^3$, $K = 10^3$ and various values of P_{FA} (reprinted from [6]).

performance corresponding to $P_{ACQ}(j)/P_D = j/q$. For a given q, increasing K (the number of dwell penalty time units) requires an attendant decrease in P_{FA} to achieve the same level of performance. In this regard, the value of K is critical in determining the value of P_{FA} which yields near optimum performance.

Before leaving this section we point out that the heuristic approach used to verify the mean time to acquisition and acquisition variance results derived from the flow graph diagram can also be applied here to obtain the acquisition probability behavior. The details are left as an exercise for the reader. As a head start, one can easily show that for $P_{FA} = 0$, convolution of (1.8) with (1.19) gives the probability density function for $N'_{ACQ} \triangleq q(k-1) + m$ as

$$p'_j \triangleq \Pr\{N'_{ACQ} = j\} = \frac{1}{q} P_D (1 - P_D)^j. \tag{1.99}$$

As a final note, we point out the relation of the single dwell system with stepped search discussed here to an equivalent acquisition system using a continuous sweep. In the latter case, the local PN code generator is clocked at a frequency $f_c + \delta f_c$ which differs from the clock frequency $f_c = 1/T_c$ of the incoming PN code by a small amount $\delta f_c \ll f_c$. As such, the epoch difference between the incoming and local PN codes vanishes at instants of time which are $p/\delta f_c$ apart where p is again the period of the PN code in chips. When the input and local codes are actively correlated, the result is a periodic train of "impulses" (triangular pulses of width $2/\delta f_c$) which occur at the instants of vanishing epoch difference. These impulses are detected by means of a non-coherent detection circuit consisting, as we have already seen, of a pre-detection band-pass filter, a quadratic detector, a post-detection low-pass filter, and a threshold device. The first detected "impulse" declares a "hit," sets the local clock frequency to f_c, and activates the tracking loop.

To extend the performance results obtained for the discrete stepping search to the continuous sweep procedure, one must merely equivalence $q\tau_d$ in the former with the time $p/\delta f_c$ to equivalently search one code period in the latter. Furthermore, since KP_{FA} can be written as $(K\tau_d)(P_{FA}/\tau_d)$, then for the continuous system $K\tau_d$ is equivalenced to the false alarm penalty time T_p and in view of the above, P_{FA}/τ_d is equivalenced with the false alarm *rate* $\eta_{FA} = P_{FA}(p\delta f_c/q)$.

1.3 THE MULTIPLE DWELL SERIAL PN ACQUISITION SYSTEM

A generalization of the single dwell serial PN acquisition system is a multiple dwell technique which, by virtue of its additional threshold testing, does not constrain the examination interval per cell to be a constant interval of time. Nevertheless, this scheme falls into the class of fixed dwell time PN acquisition systems as discussed earlier in the introduction in the sense that the variation in integration time is achieved here by allowing the examination interval to consist of a series of fixed short dwell periods (each longer than its predecessor) with a decision being made after each. Allowing the integration time in a given cell examination interval to increase toward its maximum value in *discrete steps*, as per the above, permits dismissal of an incorrect alignment earlier than would be possible in a single dwell system which is constrained to always integrate over the full examination interval. Since most of the cells searched indeed correspond to incorrect alignments, this ability to quickly eliminate them produces a considerable reduction in acquisition time, particularly for long codes.

Consider the N-dwell serial synchronization system illustrated in Figure 1.15. The received PN code signal plus noise multiplied by the local replica of the PN code and the output of the multiplier is applied to each of N non-coherent[19] detectors. The i-th detector, $i = 1, 2, \ldots, N$, is characterized by a detection probability P_{Di}, a false alarm probability P_{FAi}, and a dwell time τ_{di}. These three parameters are for a non-coherent detector, related to each other as per the discussion in Section 1.2.4, in particular, (1.81). On the assumption that the detector dwell times are ordered such that

$$\tau_{d1} \leq \tau_{d2} \leq \tau_{d3} \leq \cdots \leq \tau_{dN} \tag{1.100}$$

[19]Again, as in the single dwell case, the multiple dwell technique can also be used with coherent detectors. In fact, the results in this section are independent of the type of detector used. However, when it becomes necessary to relate the performance to the acquisition system parameters, we shall pursue only the non-coherent case.

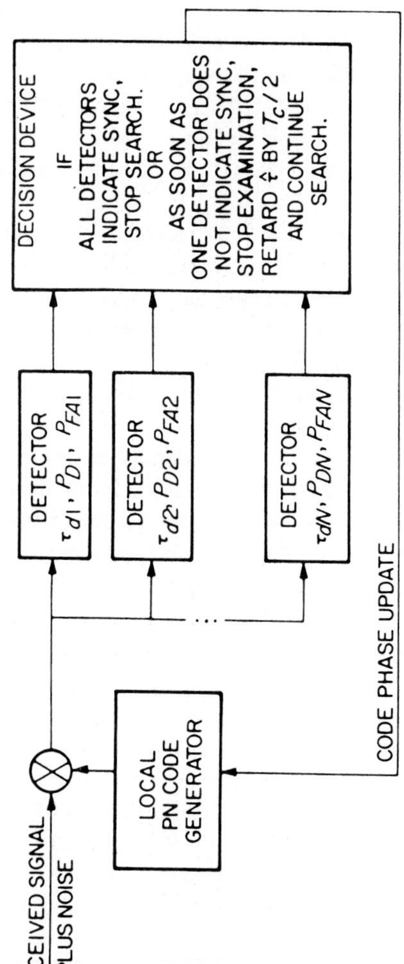

Figure 1.15. The N-dwell serial synchronization system with half chip search.

the decision to continue or stop the search at the present cell is made by sequentially examining the N detector outputs (starting with the first) and applying the following algorithm:

(1) If *all* of the N detectors (tested in succession) indicate that the present cell is correct, i.e., each produces a threshold crossing, then the decision is made to stop the search.

(2) If *any* one detector fails to indicate that the present cell is correct, i.e., it fails to produce a threshold crossing, then the decision is made to continue the search and the time delay $\hat{\tau}$ of the local PN generator is retarded by the chosen phase update increment, whereupon the next cell is examined. Thus, as soon as one detector indicates that the codes are misaligned, the search may move on without waiting for the decisions of the remaining detectors.

Note from the foregoing that the maximum time to search a given cell is τ_{dN}, whereas the minimum time is τ_{d1}. Herein lies the power of the N-dwell system, namely, that most of the cells can be dismissed after a dwell time τ_{dk}; $k \ll N$, whereas the single dwell system requires that each and every cell be examined for a time equivalent to τ_{dN}.

A block diagram of an N-dwell time PN acquisition system using non-coherent detection is illustrated in Figure 1.16. In the form in which the configuration is drawn, all of the N integrate-and-dump circuits initiate their integration at the same instant in time, each one dumping, however, at a later and later time instant in view of (1.100). Thus, because of this overlap in the integration times of the integrate-and-dump circuits, the outputs $Z_1, Z_2, \ldots, Z_N$ represent a set of fully dependent random variables.[20] As such, the probability that Z_i crosses its threshold depends on the probability that Z_k; $k = 1, 2, \ldots, i-1$ crossed their respective thresholds. This fact will be important in what follows later on. In accordance with the search update algorithm, the output of the i-th integrate-and-dump is sampled and compared to a threshold only if all of the previous $i-1$ integrate-and-dump outputs have previously exceeded their respective thresholds. Otherwise, the first integrate-and-dump output to fall below its threshold causes the local code to update its phase and search the next cell thereby resetting all of the integrate-and-dump circuits.

In reality, Figure 1.16 represents only a conceptual implementation of the N-dwell system. In practice, the N integrate-and-dumps would be realized by a *single continuous-time* integrator whose output is sequentially sampled (but not dumped) at time instants $t = \tau_{d1}, \tau_{d1} + \tau_{d2}, \ldots, \tau_{d1} + \tau_{d2} + \tau_{d3} + \cdots + \tau_{di}$ depending, as above, on the outcomes of the first $i-1$ threshold comparisons. This single integrator would again be reset only after a

[20] In [8], an N-dwell configuration is considered wherein the N integrate-and-dump outputs $Z_1, Z_2, \ldots, Z_N$ are independent by virtue of the fact that the i-th integrate-and-dump, $i = 2, 3, \ldots, N$, initiates its integration at the instant in time at which the $(i-1)$-st is dumped.

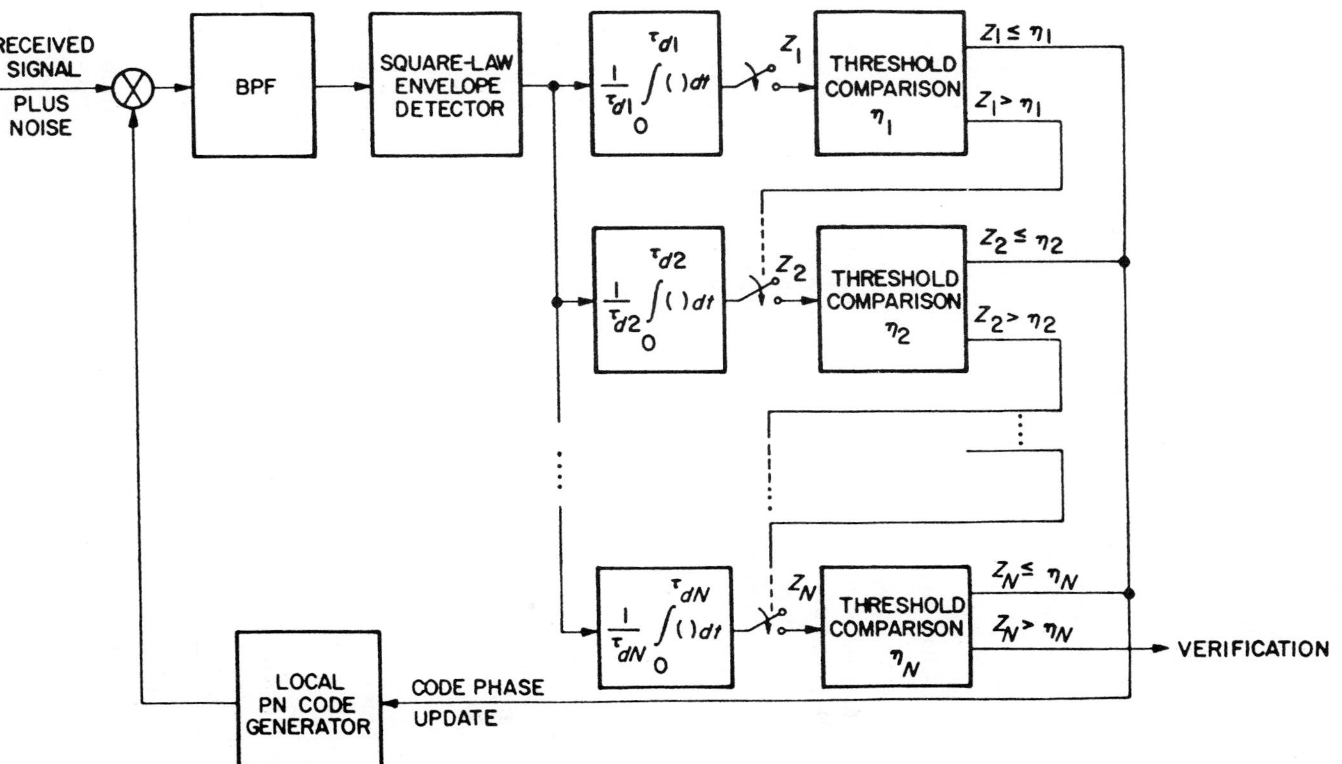

Figure 1.16. Block diagram of an N-dwell time PN acquisition system with non-coherent detection.

decision is made to search the next cell. From the standpoint of functional operation, these two systems are identical. Hence, in what follows we shall not draw any distinction between the two.

In addition to all of the foregoing, one must, as in the single dwell case, characterize the penalty time T_p for a false alarm. This occurs when all N detector outputs exceed their respective thresholds for a cell which does not correspond to the correct code alignment. Regardless of the means for identifying the false alarm (we shall discuss some of these toward the end of the chapter), it is convenient to model T_p as an integer multiple of the *additional* time required by the N-th dwell, i.e.,

$$T_p = K_N(\tau_{dN} - \tau_{d,N-1}). \tag{1.101}$$

1.3.1 Markov Chain Acquisition Model

The procedure for evaluating acquisition performance of the N-dwell system is to once again determine a suitable flow graph model for the process which when reduced results in the system generating function. Since the cell-to-cell or *inter*-cell behavior of the N-dwell system is identical to that of the single dwell system, one should expect that the generating function flow graphs for the two systems would have the same *macro*scopic (coarse) structure. This realization enables one to immediately use the structure of Figure 1.8 for the flow graph representation of the N-dwell system which is illustrated in Figure 1.17.

The *micro*scopic (fine) structure of each of the branches in Figure 1.17 which depicts the *intra*-cell behavior of the N-dwell process, is represented by the series of exploded flow graphs in Figure 1.18. Analogous to Figure 1.8 each branch is labelled with the product of the transition probability associated with going from the node at the originating end of the branch to the node at its terminating end, and an integer (including zero) power of a parameter z_i; $i = 1, 2, \ldots, N$. As before, the parameter z_i is used to indicate the unit time delay as flow propagates along that branch and its power represents the number of such time delay units.

Since Figures 1.17 and 1.18 are to be used to compute a generating function for acquisition time, the z_i's have the following associations: z_1 represents a time delay of τ_{d1}, z_2 a time delay of $\tau_{d2} - \tau_{d1}, \ldots,$ and z_N a time delay of $\tau_{dN} - \tau_{d,N-1}$. Thus z_i; $i = 1, 2, \ldots, N$ represents the additional dwell time one must wait before testing the i-th threshold after the $(i-1)$-st threshold has been tested.

The detection transition probability $P_{Di|i-1}$; $i = 1, 2, \ldots, N$ corresponds to the probability that, for the cell containing signal plus noise, the i-th dwell integrate-and-dump output Z_i exceeds its threshold *conditioned* on $Z_1, Z_2, \ldots, Z_{i-1}$ all having exceeded their respective thresholds. In mathematical terms, letting η_i; $i = 1, 2, \ldots, N$ denotes the i-th threshold; then

$$P_{Di|i-1} = \Pr\{Z_i > \eta_i | Z_1 > \eta_1, Z_2 > \eta_2, \ldots, Z_{i-1} > \eta_{i-1}\}. \tag{1.102}$$

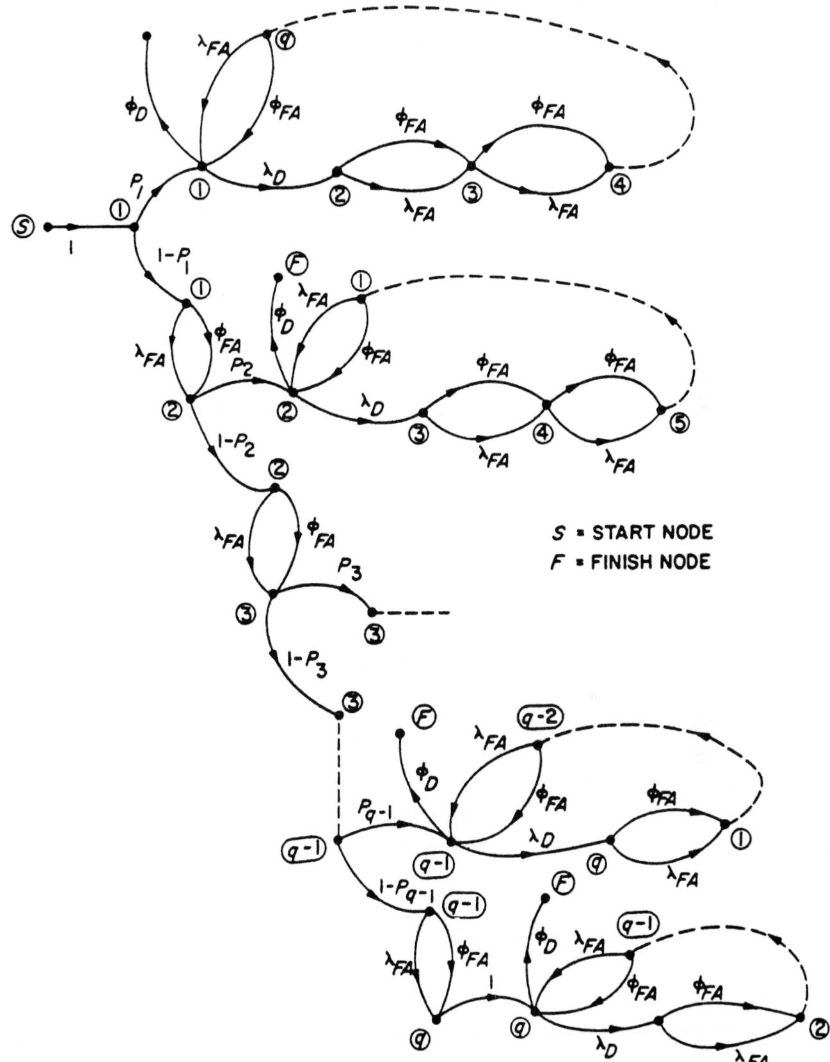

Figure 1.17. Generating function flow graph for acquisition time of the N-dwell process.

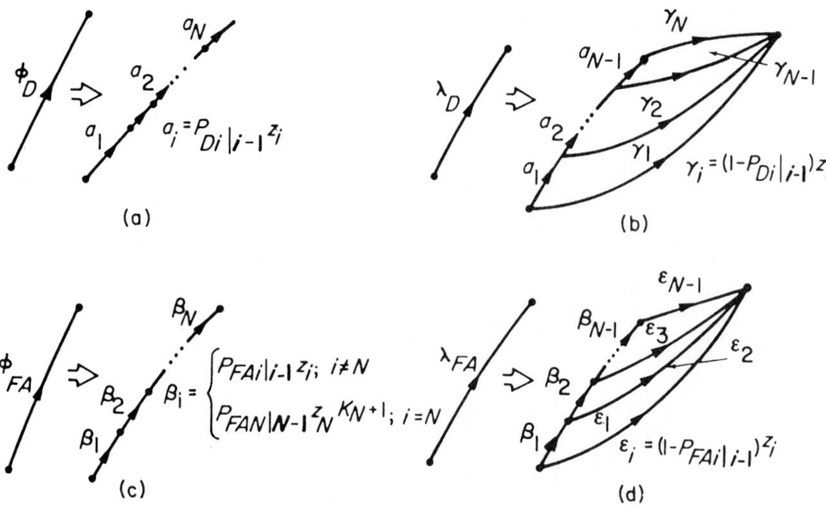

Figure 1.18. Flow graphs for *intra*-cell behavior of N-dwell process.

Similarly, for a cell containing noise only the false alarm transition probability $P_{FAi|i-1}$ is defined identically to (1.102).

With the meaning of the branch labels having been defined in Figure 1.18, the significance of each of the sub-flow graphs (actually a collection of branches corresponding to a single branch in Figure 1.17) is explained as follows. Figure 1.18(a) corresponds to reaching the event of a successful acquisition, i.e., reaching the finish node starting at a node corresponding to the *correct* cell. This event can occur only if *all* of the N integrate-and-dump outputs exceed their thresholds. Hence each node along ϕ_D represents one of the N dwells and the probability P_{ϕ_D} associated with the traversing this entire branch is the system detection probability[21]

$$P_D = \prod_{i=1}^{N} P_{Di|i-1}$$

$$= \Pr\{Z_1 > \eta_1, Z_2 > \eta_2, \ldots, Z_N > \eta_N\}. \quad (1.103)$$

Figure 1.18(b) corresponds to the event of causing a code phase update, i.e., advancing the search to the next cell starting at a node corresponding to the correct cell. This event will occur if *any* of the N integrate-and-dump outputs fails to exceed its threshold as one progresses through the N-dwell

[21] By definition, $P_{D1|0} = P_{D1} = \Pr\{Z_1 > \eta_1\}$.

system. Thus, the probability associated with λ_D is[22]

$$P_{\lambda_D} = \sum_{i=1}^{N} \left(\prod_{k=1}^{i-1} P_{Dk|k-1} \right) (1 - P_{Di|i-1})$$

$$= \Pr\{ Z_1 < \eta_1 \text{ or } Z_2 < \eta_2 \text{ or } \cdots \text{ or } Z_N < \eta_N \}. \qquad (1.104)$$

Figure 1.18(c) corresponds to a false alarm, i.e., all N integrate-and-dumps exceed their thresholds starting at a node corresponding to an *incorrect* cell. Note that the last sub-branch of ϕ_{FA} has associated with it $Z_N^{K_N+1}$ which represents the additional K_N penalty time units in accordance with (1.101). The probability $P_{\phi_{FA}}$ associated with this event is clearly the system false alarm probability

$$P_{FA} = \prod_{i=1}^{N} P_{FAi|i-1}$$

$$= \Pr\{ Z_1 > \eta_1, Z_2 > \eta_2, \ldots, Z_N > \eta_N \} \qquad (1.105)$$

where again $P_{FA1|0} \triangleq P_{FA1} = \Pr\{ Z_1 < \eta_1 \}$.

Finally, Figure 1.18(d) is analogous to Figure 1.18(b) and represents the event of updating the search starting from a node corresponding to an incorrect cell. Again a code search update will occur if any of the N integrate-and-dump outputs fails to exceed its threshold which occurs with probability

$$P_{\lambda_{FA}} = \sum_{i=1}^{N} \left(\prod_{k=1}^{i-1} P_{FAk|k-1} \right) (1 - P_{FAi|i-1})$$

$$= \Pr\{ Z_1 < \eta_1 \text{ or } Z_2 < \eta_2 \text{ or } \cdots \text{ or } Z_N < \eta_N \}. \qquad (1.106)$$

1.3.2 Multiple Dwell Acquisition Time Performance

With the same standard flow graph reduction techniques [31]–[33] as were used to obtain the generating function for the single dwell system, the flow graph of Figure 1.17 together with Figure 1.18 can be reduced to a single branch whose label is then the N-dimensional generating function for the N-dwell system, namely [7]

$$U(z) = C(z) \left[\frac{1}{q} \sum_{l=0}^{q-1} H^l(z) \right] \qquad (1.107)$$

---

[22] For the $i = 1$ term, we define $\prod_{k=1}^{0} P_{Dk|k-1} = 1$.

where now

$$H(z) = \lambda_{FA} + \phi_{FA} = \sum_{i=1}^{N}\left(\prod_{k=1}^{i-1} P_{FAk|k-1} z_k\right)(1 - P_{FAi|i-1}) z_i$$
$$+ P_{FA} z_N^{K_N} \prod_{i=1}^{N} z_i$$
$$C(z) = \frac{\phi_D}{1 - \lambda_D H^{q-1}(z)}$$
$$= \frac{P_D \prod_{i=1}^{N} z_i}{1 - \sum_{i=1}^{N}\left(\prod_{k=1}^{i-1} P_{Dk|k-1} z_k\right)(1 - P_{Di|i-1}) z_i H^{q-1}(z)}. \quad (1.108)$$

With i_n defined as the integer-valued random variable that represents the number of time delay units of duration $\tau_{dn} - \tau_{d,n-1}$ that have elapsed when the final node F is reached (acquisition occurs), the acquisition time T_{ACQ} is given by[23]

$$T_{ACQ} = \sum_{n=1}^{N} i_n(\tau_{dn} - \tau_{d,n-1}). \quad (1.109)$$

With $U(z)$ as the moment-generating function for the joint probability density function $p(i_1, i_2, \ldots, i_N)$, i.e.,

$$U(z) = \sum_{i_1=0}^{\infty} \sum_{i_2=0}^{\infty} \cdots \sum_{i_N=0}^{\infty} z_1^{i_1} z_2^{i_2} \cdots z_N^{i_N} p(i_1, i_2, \ldots, i_N) \quad (1.110)$$

then, analogous to (1.3), the mean acquisition time $\overline{T}_{ACQ}$ is obtained from[24]

$$\overline{T}_{ACQ} = \sum_{j=1}^{N} \left.\frac{\partial U(z^{\Delta\tau_d})}{\partial z_j}\right|_{z=1}. \quad (1.111)$$

Substituting (1.107) in (1.111) and carrying out the required differentiations of the N-dimensional polynomials $H(z)$ and $C(z)$ gives after much simplification [7]

$$\overline{T}_{ACQ} = \frac{1}{2P_D} \sum_{j=1}^{N} \Bigg[(2 - P_D)(q - 1)$$
$$\times \left\{\prod_{i=1}^{j-1} P_{FAi|i-1} + K_N P_{FA} \delta_{jN}\right\} + 2 \prod_{i=1}^{j-1} P_{Di|i-1}\Bigg]$$
$$\times (\tau_{dj} - \tau_{d,j-1}) \quad (1.112)$$

[23] For convenience we set $\tau_{d0} = 0$.

[24] The notation $z^{\Delta\tau_d}$ represents a vector whose j-th component, $j = 1, 2, \ldots, N$ is $z_j^{\tau_{d_j} - \tau_{d_{j-1}}}$.

which for $q \gg 1$ simplifies to

$$\overline{T}_{ACQ} = \frac{(2-P_D)q\sum_{j=1}^{N}\left[\left(\prod_{i=1}^{j-1}P_{FAi|i-1}\right)(\tau_{dj}-\tau_{d,j-1}) + K_N P_{FA}\delta_{jN}(\tau_{dN}-\tau_{d,N-1})\right]}{2P_D} \tag{1.113}$$

In (1.112) and (1.113), the Kronecker delta function has the usual definition

$$\delta_{ij} = \begin{cases} 1; & i=j \\ 0; & i \neq j \end{cases}. \tag{1.114}$$

Also, for $N = 1$ (a single dwell system) and $K_1 = K$, (1.113) reduces to (1.4), as it should.

Comparing the forms of (1.113) and (1.4), it is apparent that for the same false alarm penalty time, i.e., $K\tau_d = K_N(\tau_{dN} - \tau_{d,N-1})$, the N-dwell system can yield a smaller mean acquisition time than the single dwell system if

$$\sum_{j=1}^{N}\left(\prod_{i=1}^{j-1}P_{FAi|i-1}\right)(\tau_{dj}-\tau_{d,j-1}) < \tau_d. \tag{1.115}$$

The ability to design the N-dwell system to satisfy (1.115) depends upon the functional relationship between the conditional false alarm probabilities and the dwell times. More will be said about this relationship shortly.

The generating function of (1.107) can also be used to obtain an approximate expression for the acquisition time variance σ^2_{ACQ} of the N-dwell system. In particular,

$$\sigma^2_{ACQ} = \sum_{i=1}^{N}\sum_{l=1}^{N}\left.\frac{\partial^2 U(z^{\Delta\tau_d})}{\partial z_i\,\partial z_l}\right|_{z=1} + \overline{T}_{ACQ}(1-\overline{T}_{ACQ}). \tag{1.116}$$

Taking the required second partial derivatives using $U(z)$ defined in (1.107) and (1.108) and making the assumption of large q, then together with $\overline{T}_{ACQ}$ of (1.113) one obtains after much simplification the relation [7]

$$\sigma^2_{ACQ} = q^2\left\{\sum_{j=1}^{N}\left[\left(\prod_{i=1}^{j-1}P_{FAi|i-1}\right)(\tau_{dj}-\tau_{d,j-1}) + K_N P_{FA}\delta_{jN}(\tau_{dN}-\tau_{d,N-1})\right]\right\}^2 \times\left(\frac{1}{12}+\frac{1}{P_D^2}-\frac{1}{P_D}\right). \tag{1.117}$$

Again for the special case of $N = 1$ and $K_1 = K$, (1.117) reduces to (1.7).

Once again comparing (1.117) and (1.7) we observe that if (1.115) is satisfied, the N-dwell system yields a smaller acquisition time variance than the single dwell system. In fact, for large q, both $\overline{T}_{ACQ}$ and the standard deviation σ_{ACQ} are directly proportional to the same function $F(N)$ of false alarm probabilities and dwell times, namely,

$$F(N) = \sum_{j=1}^{N} \left[\left(\prod_{i=1}^{j-1} P_{FAi|i-1} \right) (\tau_{dj} - \tau_{d,j-1}) + K_N P_{FA} \delta_{jN} (\tau_{dN} - \tau_{d,N-1}) \right]. \tag{1.118}$$

To proceed further with the evaluation of the first two moments of acquisition time one must relate the *conditional* false alarm probabilities $\{P_{FAi|i-1}\}$ defined in (1.102) to the dwell times $\{\tau_{di}\}$ and the detection thresholds $\{\eta_i\}$. Since, as previously mentioned, the overlap in the integration times of the integrate-and-dump circuits causes the outputs $Z_1, Z_2, \ldots, Z_N$ to be a set of fully dependent random variables, computation of $P_{FAi|i-1}$ involves evaluation of an i-dimensional integral over the joint probability density function $p(Z_1, Z_2, \ldots, Z_i)$. Such evaluations are at best tedious if not altogether impossible.

To circumvent this computational bottleneck, we consider a procedure for obtaining an upper bound on the acquisition performance of the N-dwell system. This will allow direct comparison with the comparable performance of the single dwell system to assess how much improvement can be gained as function of the number of dwells N. To illustrate the procedure as clearly as possible, we shall first present its details for the simple case of a two-dwell system, i.e., $N = 2$.

Consider that we choose the decision thresholds η_1 and η_2 such that the *unconditional* detection probabilities P_{D1} and P_{D2} are equal, i.e.,

$$P_{D1} = P_{D2} \triangleq P. \tag{1.119}$$

This choice does not necessarily guarantee an optimum decision; however, it allows us to obtain a simple upper bound on performance that will be sufficient to indicate the benefit in going to an N-dwell system.

Next, we note from the law of total probability that

$$P_{D2} = P_{D2|1} P_{D1} + P_{D2|\bar{1}} P_{D\bar{1}} \tag{1.120}$$

where the overbar denotes the complement of the event. For example,

$$P_{D\bar{1}} = \Pr\{Z_1 < \eta_1\} \tag{1.121}$$

when signal is present. Since $P_{D2|\bar{1}} \le 1$ and $P_{D\bar{1}} = 1 - P_{D1}$, then from (1.120),

$$P_{D2} \le P_{D2|1} P_{D1} + 1 - P_{D1} \tag{1.122}$$

or, using (1.119),

$$P_{D2|1} P \ge 2P - 1. \tag{1.123}$$

Since, from (1.103), the left-hand side of (1.123) represents the system detection probability for the double dwell system, if P_D denotes the system detection probability of the single dwell system and we set

$$2P - 1 = P_D \tag{1.124}$$

then we are guaranteed that the two-dwell system will have an equal or higher detection probability. This in turn implies, from (1.113) and (1.117) an equal or smaller acquisition time mean and variance. Thus, in conclusion, evaluation of (1.113) and (1.117) using (1.124) for the choice of unconditional detection probabilities, i.e.,

$$P = \frac{1 + P_D}{2} \tag{1.125}$$

gives an upper bound on $\overline{T}_{ACQ}$ and σ_{ACQ}^2 for the double dwell system.

To proceed further, we note that, analogous to (1.120),

$$P_{FA2} = P_{FA2|1}P_{FA1} + P_{FA2|\bar{1}}P_{FA\bar{1}}. \tag{1.126}$$

Since $P_{FA2|\bar{1}} \geq 0$, then

$$P_{FA2} \geq P_{FA2|1}P_{FA1}. \tag{1.127}$$

The right-hand side of (1.127) represents [see (1.105)] the system false alarm probability for the two-dwell system. Thus, if P_{FA} denotes the system false alarm probability of the single dwell system and we set

$$P_{FA2} = P_{FA} \tag{1.128}$$

then we are guaranteed that the two-dwell system will have an equal or lower false alarm probability. Thus, including (1.128) as a condition on the design will once again produce upper bounds on $\overline{T}_{ACQ}$ and σ_{ACQ}^2 as evaluated from (1.113) and (1.117), respectively.

Since, as previously shown, both (1.113) and (1.117) depend on $F(N)$ of (1.118), we shall focus our attention on the evaluation of $F(2)$ using (1.125) and (1.128), or, for equal false alarm penalty times for the single and double dwell systems, the simpler function

$$G(N) = \sum_{j=1}^{N}\left(\prod_{i=1}^{j-1} P_{FAi|i-1}\right)(\tau_{dj} - \tau_{d,j-1}) \tag{1.129}$$

evaluated for $N = 2$. Letting $N = 2$ in (1.129) gives

$$G(2) = \tau_{d1} + P_{FA1}(\tau_{d2} - \tau_{d1}) \tag{1.130}$$

which, from (1.115), when less than τ_d of the single dwell system, will yield an improved acquisition performance.

From the general relationship among false alarm probability, detection probability, pre-detection signal-to-noise ratio, and IF bandwidth-dwell time product for a non-coherent detector (see (1.81)) we can write, for the single dwell system,

$$B\tau_d = f(P_D, P_{FA}; \gamma') \tag{1.131}$$

where A^2/N_0B is replaced by γ', the effective pre-detection signal-to-noise ratio, and $f(\cdot)$ represents the solution of (1.81) for $B\tau_d$. Similarly, for the double dwell system,

$$B\tau_{d1} = f\left(P_{D1}, P_{FA1}; \gamma'\right) = f\left(\frac{1 + P_D}{2}, P_{FA1}; \gamma'\right)$$

$$B\tau_{d2} = f\left(P_{D2}, P_{FA2}; \gamma'\right) = f\left(\frac{1 + P_D}{2}, P_{FA}; \gamma'\right) \geq B\tau_d. \quad (1.132)$$

Then, since by definition $\tau_{d1} \leq \tau_{d2}$, we conclude that $P_{FA1} \geq P_{FA2}$, or in view of (1.128),

$$P_{FA} = P_{FA2} \leq P_{FA1} \leq 1. \quad (1.133)$$

Now, if $P_{FA1} = P_{FA2}$, then $\tau_{d1} = \tau_{d2}$ and from (1.130)

$$G(2) = \tau_{d2} \geq \tau_d. \quad (1.134)$$

Alternately, if $P_{FA1} = 1$ and $P_{FA2} = P_{FA} < 1$, then, from (1.130)

$$G(2) = \tau_{d1} + \tau_{d2} - \tau_{d1} = \tau_{d2} \geq \tau_d, \quad (1.135)$$

which is the same result as (1.134). Clearly, then, for some $P_{FA} < P_{FA1} < 1$, say P_{FA1}^*, there exists a corresponding value of τ_{d1}, namely,

$$B\tau_{d1}^* = f\left(\frac{1 + P_D}{2}, P_{FA1}^*; \gamma'\right) \quad (1.136)$$

which minimizes $G(2)$. Letting $G^*(2)$ denote this minimum value, i.e.,

$$G^*(2) = \tau_{d1}^* + P_{FA1}^*\left(\tau_{d2} - \tau_{d1}^*\right) \quad (1.137)$$

then the ratio $\tau_d/G^*(2)$ is a measure of the minimum improvement in acquisition time and variance of the double dwell system over the single dwell system.

Figures 1.19 and 1.20 are plots of $\tau_d/G^*(2)$ versus P_{FA} with P_D as a parameter and $\gamma' = -20$ dB and -10 dB respectively. We note from these results that for fixed γ' and small P_{FA}, the minimum performance improvement offered by the two-dwell system over the single dwell system improves with increasing detection probability up to a certain point. Beyond that point, $\tau_d/G^*(2)$ decreases with increasing P_D. In fact, as P_D approaches unity, then from (1.125), P also approaches unity, and, from (1.131) and (1.132), τ_{d2} approaches τ_d. Also from (1.81), when P_D approaches unity then P_{FA} tends to unity for any γ' and all $N_B = B\tau_d$. Thus, from (1.133), P_{FA1} also approaches unity, and, from (1.132), τ_{d1} approaches τ_{d2}. Finally, using the above facts in (1.130), we see that $G(2) = G^*(2)$ approaches τ_d or $\tau_d/G^*(2)$ approaches unity.

To generalize the above procedure to arbitrary N, we begin by generalizing (1.119) to become

$$P_{Di} \triangleq P; \qquad i = 1, 2, \ldots, N, \quad (1.138)$$

i.e., all N unconditional detection probabilities are made equal by appropriate choice of the N detection thresholds. Next, following steps analogous to (1.120)–(1.122), it can be shown that the following recursion

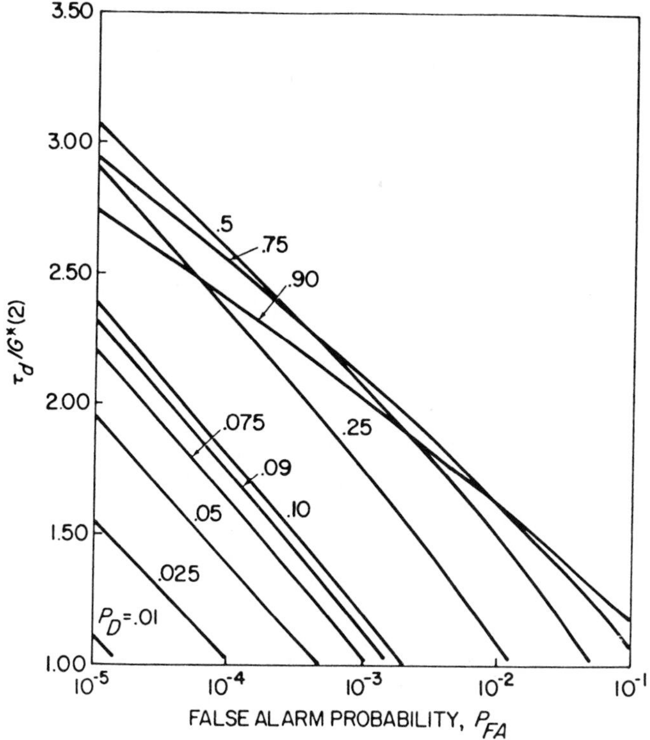

Figure 1.19. Acquisition performance improvement factor for two-dwell system over single dwell system versus false alarm probability with detection probability as a parameter; $\gamma' = -20$ dB.

relation holds:

$$\prod_{i=1}^{N} P_{Di|i-1} \geq P + \prod_{i=1}^{N-1} P_{Di|i-1} - 1 \tag{1.139}$$

Since the left-hand side of (1.139) again represents the system detection probability for the N-dwell system, and the product on the right-hand side represents the same probability for an $(N-1)$-dwell system, starting with (1.123), we may, by induction, arrive at the result

$$\prod_{i=1}^{N} P_{Di|i-1} \geq NP - (N-1). \tag{1.140}$$

Thus, we wish to set

$$P_D = NP - (N-1) \tag{1.141}$$

or

$$P = \frac{N - 1 + P_D}{N}. \tag{1.142}$$

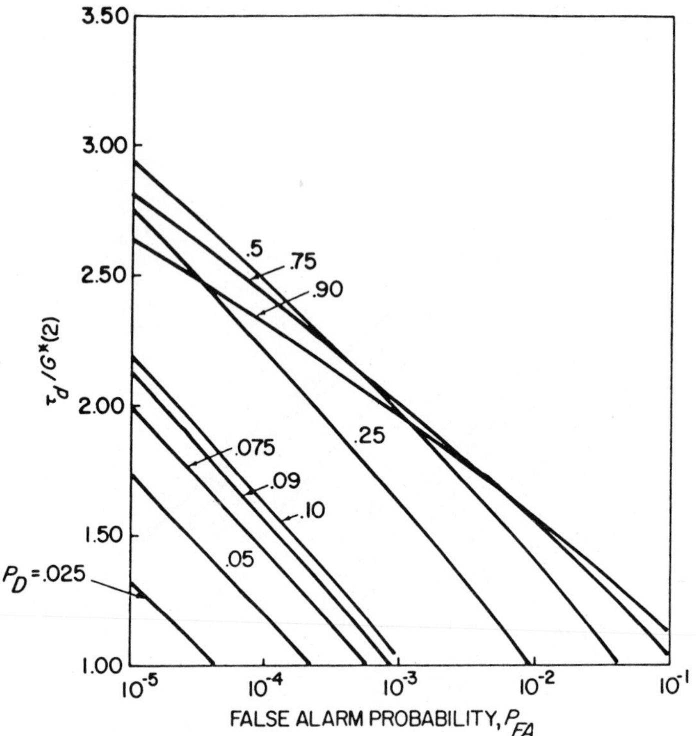

Figure 1.20. Acquisition performance improvement factor for two-dwell system over single dwell system versus false alarm probability with detection probability as a parameter; $\gamma' = -10$ dB.

Similarly, generalizing (1.126), it is simple to show that

$$P_{FAk} \geq \prod_{i=1}^{k} P_{FAi|i-1}; \qquad k = 1, 2, \ldots, N. \tag{1.143}$$

Since the right-hand side of (1.113) with $k = N$ is again the system false alarm probability of the N-dwell system, we wish to set

$$P_{FAN} = P_{FA}. \tag{1.144}$$

Finally, using (1.143) in (1.129), we have

$$\begin{aligned} G(N) &\leq \sum_{j=1}^{N} P_{FA, j-1}(\tau_{dj} - \tau_{d, j-1}) \\ &\triangleq G_u(N). \end{aligned} \tag{1.145}$$

For the non-coherent detector, the analogous relationships to (1.132) are

$$B\tau_{di} = f\left(\frac{N-1+P_D}{N}, P_{FAi}; \gamma'\right); \qquad i = 1, 2, \dots, N-1$$

$$B\tau_{dN} = f\left(\frac{N-1+P_D}{N}, P_{FA}; \gamma'\right) \geq B\tau_d. \tag{1.146}$$

Again since $\tau_{d1} \leq \tau_{d2} \leq \cdots \leq \tau_{dN}$, we have

$$P_{FA} = P_{FAN} \leq P_{FA,N-1} \leq \cdots \leq P_{FA1} \leq 1. \tag{1.147}$$

For $P_{FA1} = P_{FA2} = \cdots P_{FAN}$ or $P_{FA1} = P_{FA2} = \cdots P_{FA,N-1} = 1$ and $P_{FAN} = P_{FA} < 1$, (1.145) becomes

$$G_u(N) = \tau_{dN} \geq \tau_d. \tag{1.148}$$

Thus, for some set of false alarm probabilities

$$P_{FA} < P^*_{FA,N-1} < P^*_{FA,N-2} < \cdots < P^*_{FA2} < P^*_{FA1} < 1 \tag{1.149}$$

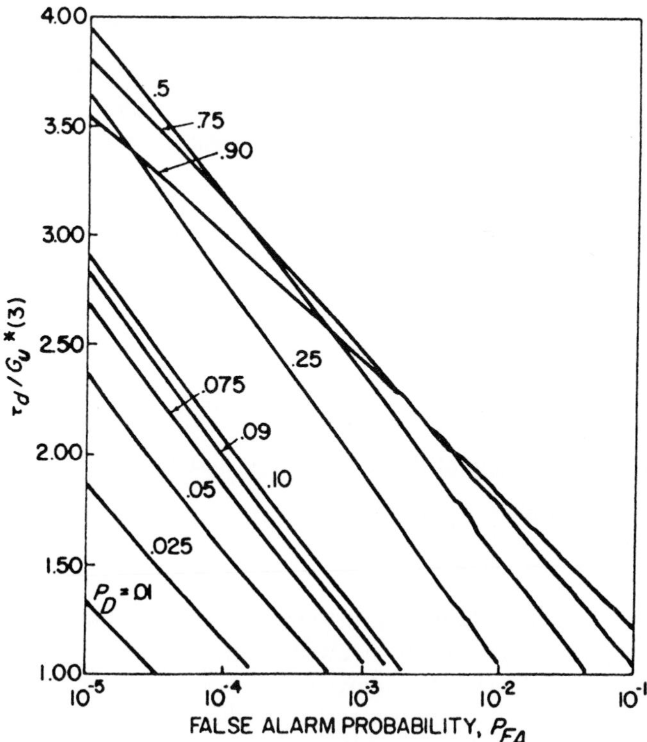

Figure 1.21. Acquisition performance improvement factor for three-dwell system over single dwell system versus false alarm probability with detection probability as a parameter; $\gamma' = -20$ dB.

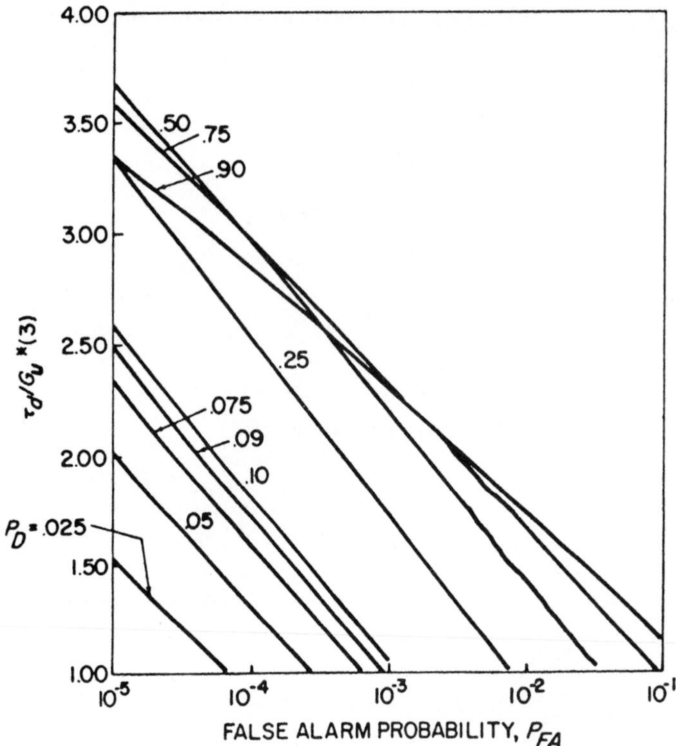

Figure 1.22. Acquisition performance improvement factor for three-dwell system over single dwell system versus false alarm probability with detection probability as a parameter; $\gamma' = -10$ dB.

and corresponding dwell times

$$\tau_{d1}^* < \tau_{d2}^* < \cdots < \tau_{d,N-1}^* \tag{1.150}$$

there exists a minimum of the function $G_u(N)$, namely,

$$G_u^*(N) = \tau_{d1}^* + P_{FA1}^*\left(\tau_{d2}^* - \tau_{d1}^*\right) + P_{FA2}^*\left(\tau_{d3}^* - \tau_{d2}^*\right) + \cdots + P_{FA,N-1}^*\left(\tau_{dN} - \tau_{d,N-1}^*\right). \tag{1.151}$$

The ratio $\tau_d/G_u^*(N)$ is then a measure of the minimum improvement in acquisition performance of the N-dwell system over the single dwell system. Note that obtaining (1.151) requires an $(N-1)$-dimensional minimization. Figures 1.21 and 1.22 illustrate the relative performance improvement results for a three-dwell system ($N = 3$) analogous to those given in Figures 1.19 and 1.20, respectively, for the two-dwell system. Once again as the detection probability P_D approaches unity, the performance improvement ratio $\tau_d/G_u^*(3)$ approaches unity.

1.4 A UNIFIED APPROACH TO SERIAL SEARCH ACQUISITION WITH FIXED DWELL TIMES

We now present a unified approach [14] to predicting the performance of serial search acquisition systems which employ fixed dwell time detector structures. Included as special cases in this generalized approach are the single dwell time system and the multiple dwell time system discussed in Sections 1.2 and 1.3, respectively, as well as a fast decision-rate matched filter acquisition system, which will be discussed in detail in Section 1.5. The restriction of the approach to systems with predetermined and fixed dwell times[25] is based upon the desire to utilize the discrete Markov nature of the imbedded process in such systems to allow application of the flow graph techniques previously demonstrated. We begin our discussion with a description and analysis of a generalized flow graph technique suitable for predicting the acquisition performance of serial search fixed dwell time systems.

1.4.1 The Flow Graph Technique

Consider a generalized serial search system of the type mentioned above where H_1 denotes the hypothesis that the received and local codes are misaligned by less than a code chip (previously designated as a "hit") and H_0 the alternate hypothesis, i.e., the relative alignment is greater than or equal to a chip. The discrete Markovian nature of the underlying process of such a system allows it to be represented by a $\nu + 2$-state flow graph, where $\nu - 1$ of the states belong to the cells corresponding to H_0, and one state (the ν-th) corresponds to H_1. Since, depending on the actual value of relative offset (misalignment) between the codes, up to either $2q/N_u$ or $(2q/N_u) - 1$ cells correspond to H_1 (recall that N_u/q corresponds to the fractional search update in chips), and the total number of cells for H_0 and H_1 combined is q, then ν is determined from either

$$\nu - 1 + \frac{2q}{N_u} = q \tag{1.152a}$$

or

$$\nu - 1 + \frac{2q}{N_u} - 1 = q. \tag{1.152b}$$

These ν states are indexed in a circular arrangement (see Figure 1.23) with the i-th state, $i = 1, 2, \ldots, q - 1$ corresponding to the i-th offset code phase position to the right of the "true" sync position (H_1). The remaining two states are the *false alarm* (*FA*) *state* and the *correct acquisition* (*ACQ*)

[25] This excludes schemes based on sequential detection methods, which will be discussed by themselves later on in the chapter.

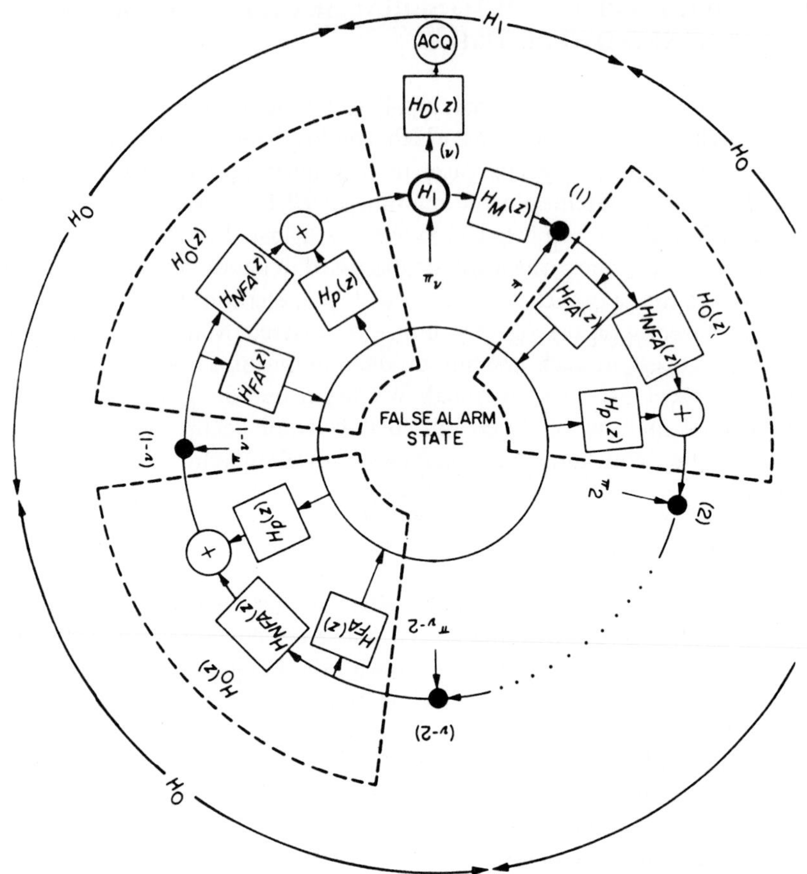

Figure 1.23. A flow graph representation of a generalized serial search acquisition system—the circular state diagram.

state. These are also indicated in Figure 1.23 where it is observed that the acquisition state can be directly reached only from the ν-th (H_1) state, whereas the false alarm state can be directly reached from any of the $\nu - 1$ states corresponding to the offset cells (H_0).

A flow graph model such as that illustrated in Figure 1.23 is an exact representation of the state transition diagram of serial search acquisition systems with no absolute limit on acquisition time. Although we are primarily interested in this class of systems (since their underlying process is indeed Markovian), we shall briefly mention at the conclusion of this section how the above model can be used in the presence of a finite limit on acquisition time.

The first way in which the flow graph model of Figure 1.23 is a generalization of those previously considered is that the *a priori* probability distribution $\{\pi_j;\ j = 1, 2, \ldots, \nu\}$ assigned to the ν states at which the search process can be entered is *arbitrary*. In the absence of any *a priori* information concerning the initial relative position of the codes, the system designer would assign a uniform distribution to the model, i.e., $\{\pi_j = 1/\nu;\ j = 1, 2, \ldots, \nu\}$. This is the case which we have discussed thus far. Another special case of the more general formulation might be a worst case distribution ($\pi_1 = 1,\ \pi_j = 0;\ j \neq 1$) corresponding to an initial relative code position furthest from the correct sync position.

The second way in which Figure 1.23 is a generalization of the previous notions is that each branch of the flow graph is assigned a generalized gain $H(z)$ which characterizes all possible ways by which the process can move along that branch. The significance of the subscripts on these branches is as follows:

$H_D(z)$ = gain for verification of detection
$H_M(z)$ = gain for missed verification of detection
$H_{FA}(z)$ = gain for false alarm occurrence
$H_{NFA}(z)$ = gain for no false alarm occurrence
$H_p(z)$ = gain for penalty after false alarm occurrence

Proper combination of these gains then allows computation of the gain associated with the "generalized" branch between any pair of nodes, e.g.,

$$H_0(z) = H_{NFA}(z) + H_{FA}(z)H_p(z) \tag{1.153}$$

represents the gain in going from node i to node $i+1$ for $i = 1, 2, \ldots, \nu - 1$.

As before, the flow graph representation of the system is used to compute the moment generating function $U(z)$ of the underlying acquisition process. Using standard flow graph reduction techniques, it can be shown [14] that

$$U(z) = \frac{H_D(z)}{1 - H_M(z)H_0^{\nu-1}(z)} \sum_{i=1}^{\nu} \pi_i H_0^{\nu-i}(z). \tag{1.154}$$

For the two special cases of uniform and worst case *a priori* state probability distributions, (1.154) reduces to

$$U(z) = \frac{1}{\nu}\frac{H_D(z)(1 - H_0^{\nu}(z))}{(1 - H_M(z)H_0^{\nu-1}(z))(1 - H_0(z))}, \text{ (uniform)} \tag{1.155a}$$

and

$$U(z) = \frac{H_D(z)H_0^{\nu-1}(z)}{1 - H_M(z)H_0^{\nu-1}(z)}, \text{ (worst case)}. \tag{1.155b}$$

The complete statistical description of the acquisition process is obtained by substituting for the various $H(z)$'s in (1.154) the expressions appropriate to the particular configuration at hand and then, as before, expanding the result in a power series in z (see (1.94)). In general, obtaining the complete set of coefficients of this series is a difficult task and approximations must be made in the manner discussed in [7]. Alternately, if one is pleased with the first few moments of the acquisition time, then the relations of (1.3) and (1.6) as applied to $U(z)$ of (1.154) or its special cases in (1.155) are appropriate. In particular, for the mean acquisition time $\overline{T}_{ACQ}$, we obtain from (1.3) and (1.155) the results

$$\underset{(\text{uniform})}{\overline{T}_{ACQ}} = \tau_d \times \begin{cases} P_{ACQ}\left\{\dfrac{H_D'(1)}{H_D(1)} + \dfrac{H_0'(1)}{1-H_0(1)} - \dfrac{\nu H_0'(1)H_0^{\nu-1}(1)}{1-H_0^{\nu}(1)} \right. \\ \quad \left. + \dfrac{(\nu-1)H_M(1)H_0^{\nu-2}(1)H_0'(1) + H_M'(1)H_0^{\nu-1}(1)}{1-H_M(1)H_0^{\nu-1}(1)}\right\} \\ \quad \ldots \text{if } H_0(1) < 1 \\ \dfrac{1}{H_D(1)}\left[H_D'(1) + H_M'(1) + (\nu-1)H_0'(1)\left(1 - \dfrac{H_D(1)}{2}\right)\right] \\ \quad \ldots \text{if } H_0(1) = 1 \end{cases} \tag{1.156a}$$

and

$$\underset{(\text{worst case})}{\overline{T}_{ACQ}} = \tau_d \times \begin{cases} \dfrac{P_{ACQ}}{H_D(1)}\left\{H_D'(1) + H_M'(1)P_{ACQ} + (\nu-1)\dfrac{H_0'(1)}{H_0(1)} \right. \\ \quad \left. \times \left(H_D(1) + H_M(1)P_{ACQ}\right)\right\} \ldots \text{if } H_0(1) < 1 \\ \dfrac{1}{H_D(1)}\left[H_D'(1) + H_M'(1) + (\nu-1)H_0'(1)\right] \\ \ldots \text{if } H_0(1) = 1 \end{cases} \tag{1.156b}$$

where the primed quantities denote differentiation with respect to z, i.e., $H'(1) = d/dz\, H(z)|_{z=1}$, and

$$P_{ACQ} \triangleq P_{ACQ}(\infty) = U(1) = \sum_{i=0}^{\infty} p_i \tag{1.157}$$

i.e., the probability of acquiring after any number of dwells (see (1.98)). Furthermore, note that in the case $H_0(1) = 1$, (1.154) and (1.157) combine to yield

$$P_{ACQ} = \frac{H_D(1)}{1 - H_M(1)} = 1 \tag{1.158}$$

since it is always true from Figure 1.23 that $H_D(1) + H_M(1) = 1$. Hence the case $H_0(1) = 1$ effectively corresponds to the existence of only one absorbing state, namely ACQ.

Table 1.1
Branch gains for single and multiple dwell systems.

Gain	Single Dwell	Multiple (N) Dwell
$H_p(z)$	z^K	z_N^K
$H_D(z)$	$P_D z$	$\prod_{i=1}^{N} P_{Di\|i-1} z_i = P_D \prod_{i=1}^{N} z_i$
$H_M(z)$	$(1 - P_D)z$	$\sum_{j=2}^{N} \left(\prod_{i=1}^{j-1} P_{Di\|i-1} z_i \right) (1 - P_{Dj\|j-1}) z_j + (1 - P_{D1\|0}) z_1$
$H_{FA}(z)$	$P_{FA} z$	$\prod_{i=1}^{N} P_{FAi\|i-1} z_i = P_{FA} \prod_{i=1}^{N} z_i$
$H_{NFA}(z)$	$(1 - P_{FA})z$	$\sum_{j=2}^{N} \left(\prod_{i=1}^{j-1} P_{FAi\|i-1} z_i \right) (1 - P_{FAj\|j-1}) z_j + (1 - P_{FA1\|0}) z_1$

As simple examples of the application of the unified approach just described, we cite the single and multiple dwell serial search acquisition systems for which the branch gains are shown in Table 1.1.[26] Taking the derivative(s) of these gains as required in (1.56a) and evaluating them with their argument(s) equated to unity produces results identical to (1.3) and (1.112) with $\nu = q$ (i.e., H_1 contains only one cell). Alternately, for the single dwell system with worst case *a priori* probability distribution, we get the additional result

$$\underset{\text{(worse case)}}{\overline{T}_{ACQ}} = \frac{1}{P_D}\left[1 + (q-1)(1 + KP_{FA})\right]\tau_d \tag{1.159}$$

where again we have set $\nu = q$.

As previously mentioned, ν will almost always exceed q in accordance with either (1.152a) or (1.152b). Thus, we now enter into a brief discussion of how to modify the flow graph to account for the fact that the H_1 region actually contains $2q/N_u$ [or $(2q/N_u) - 1$] cells rather than just the single (ν-th) cell shown in Figure 1.23. For example, consider a single dwell system with half-chip search update ($q/N_u = 2$) and let Q_1, Q_2, Q_3, Q_4 denote the four (possibly only three) cells corresponding to the four possible values of relative code misalignment with magnitude less than a chip (i.e., within the triangular correlation curve). Then, the H_1 region of the flow graph expands as in Figure 1.24, where $P_D(Q_i)$; $i = 1, 2, 3, 4$ denotes the detection prob-

[26] For the multiple dwell case, the gains $H(z)$ should actually be written as $H(\mathbf{z})$ where $\mathbf{z}$ is the vector $[z_1, z_2, \ldots, z_N]$. Also, the prime notation in (1.156) now refers to an N-dimensional partial differentiation with respect to the N complements of $\mathbf{z}$ with each component set equal to unity.

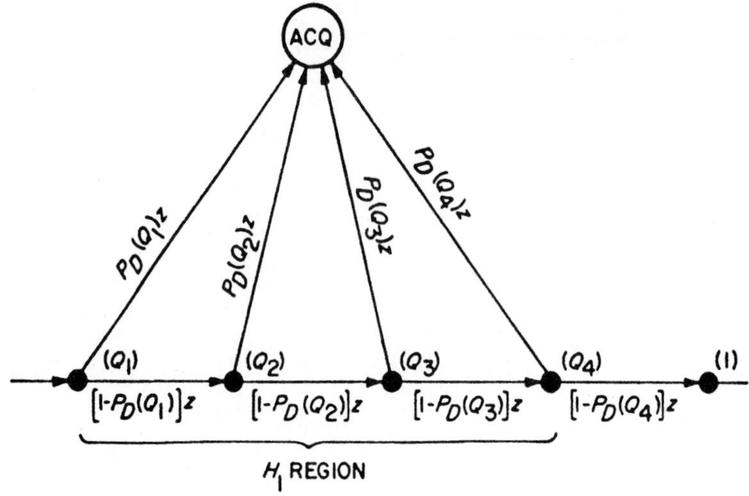

Figure 1.24. Expansion of the H_1 region for a single dwell serial search system indicating the effect of multiple cells with non-zero correlation.

ability evaluated via (1.71) or (1.80) at the relative code misalignment corresponding to Q_i. Thus, instead of the simple entries of $H_D(z)$ and $H_M(z)$ as in Table 1.1, we now have

$$H_D(z) = \sum_{j=1}^{4} \left(\prod_{i=1}^{j-1} (1 - P_D(Q_i)) P_D(Q_j) \right) z^j \tag{1.160}$$

and

$$\begin{aligned} H_M(z) &= \prod_{j=1}^{4} (1 - P_D(Q_j)) z \\ &= \left[\prod_{j=1}^{4} (1 - P_D(Q_j)) \right] z^4. \end{aligned} \tag{1.161}$$

As promised, we conclude this section with a discussion of how to apply the flow graph model to the limited acquisition time case. We recall from the introduction that this case is characterized by the requirement to achieve acquisition (with a given probability) within a finite time, say T_s. Thus, the appropriate performance measure to use here is the probability that the acquisition time T_{ACQ} is less than T_s, which can be calculated by evaluating the cumulative distribution function of T_{ACQ} at T_s. Alternately, if T_s corresponds to J dwells, then we are interested in the probability $P_{ACQ}(J)$

of acquisition in J or fewer dwells as given by a relation analogous to (1.98), which can be evaluated by finding the generating function corresponding to this cumulative probability distribution. Such a generating function is defined by

$$V(z) \triangleq \sum_{j=0}^{\infty}\left(\sum_{i=0}^{j} p_j\right) z^j, \tag{1.162}$$

which can be written in the form

$$\begin{aligned} V(z) &= \sum_{j=0}^{\infty} p_j \sum_{i=j}^{\infty} z^i \\ &= \sum_{j=0}^{\infty} p_j z^j \sum_{i=0}^{\infty} z^i \\ &= \frac{1}{1-z}\sum_{j=0}^{\infty} p_j z^j. \end{aligned} \tag{1.163}$$

Comparing (1.163) with (1.94), we observe that

$$V(z) = \frac{1}{1-z} U(z). \tag{1.164}$$

Since $P_{ACQ}(J)$ is the coefficient of z^J in the power series of (1.162), we can evaluate it with a contour integral analogous to that used to evaluate inverse z transforms, i.e.,

$$\begin{aligned} P_{ACQ}(J) &= \frac{1}{2\pi j}\oint_{\Gamma}\frac{V(z)}{z^{J+1}}\,dz \\ &= \frac{1}{2\pi j}\oint_{\Gamma}\frac{U(z)}{(1-z)z^{J+1}}\,dz \end{aligned} \tag{1.165}$$

where $U(z)$ is given by (1.154) and Γ is a counterclockwise closed contour in the region of convergence of $V(z)$ that encircles the origin.

1.5 RAPID ACQUISITION USING MATCHED FILTER TECHNIQUES

Until now, we have considered only DS acquisition techniques in which the measure of PN correlation was produced by an *active* correlation of the received signal with a locally generated PN reference. For example, in the single dwell serial search system, the received PN signal plus noise was multiplied by the local PN reference and subsequently (after square-law envelope detection to remove the unknown information modulation and unknown carrier phase) integrated for τ_d seconds, the result of which was used to make an acquisition decision by comparison with a threshold. Such a *multiply-and-integrate* type of correlation/detector structure is typified by the fact that the local PN generator is running continuously, and hence, a completely *new* set of $M = \tau_d/T_c$ chips of the received signal is used for each successive threshold test. This poses a basic limitation on the search speed since the local PN reference phase can be updated (slewed) only at τ_d-second intervals (assuming the threshold test fails). Thus, if the search is conducted in $1/N$-chip increments, the search rate $\mathscr{R}_{1D}$ of the single dwell serial search technique is

$$\mathscr{R}_{1D} = 1/\tau_d \quad 1/N\text{-chip positions per second.} \tag{1.166}$$

The search rate of a DS acquisition scheme can be significantly increased by replacing the multiply-and-integrate operation with a *passive* correlator device such as a matched filter (MF). This device can be implemented either as a continuous time or discrete time operation, and with such candidate state-of-the-art technologies as charge coupled devices (CCD's), surface acoustic wave (SAW) convolvers, and discrete time correlators [34], [36], [37].

In the continuous time case, the received PN waveform plus noise is convolved with a fixed finite segment of the PN waveform corresponding to, say, M chips and the continuous time output is tested against a threshold to determine when acquisition has occurred. In this configuration, the input continuously slides past the stationary (not running in time) stored PN waveform replica until the two are in synchronism, at which point the threshold ideally would be exceeded and the local PN generator enabled. Since, as discussed in the introduction, in DS/SS systems the PN spreading waveform is typically biphase modulated on a carrier whose phase is as yet unknown at the receiver, the matched filter acquisition system must be implemented either in a band-pass version (Figure 1.25a) or an equivalent low-pass version (Figure 1.25b). In the former case, a band-pass matched filter is used whose maximum output is detected by a square-law envelope detector. In the latter case, inphase and quadrature carriers with arbitrary phase but known or estimated frequency are used to demodulate the received signal followed by baseband matched filtering of each demodulated signal. The matched filter outputs are then non-coherently combined to produce the desired correlation measure for threshold testing.

Conceptually, the implementation of a matched filter for a finite length PN waveform is most easily visualized in the form of a tapped delay line followed by a passive filter matched to a *single* PN chip waveform (Figure 1.26). To see how this comes about, we recall that a matched filter is generically a passive device that maximizes the signal-to-noise ratio at its output when the signal at its input is imbedded in additive white Gaussian noise. Mathematically speaking, for an input signal $s(t)$ of duration T_o seconds, the impulse response $h(t)$ of the matched filter is given by the reverse of $s(t)$ in its T_o-second time slot, i.e.,

$$h(t) = \begin{cases} s(T_o - t); & 0 \le t \le T_o \\ 0; & \text{otherwise} \end{cases} \tag{1.167}$$

Figure 1.25a. A band-pass version of a matched filter acquisition system.

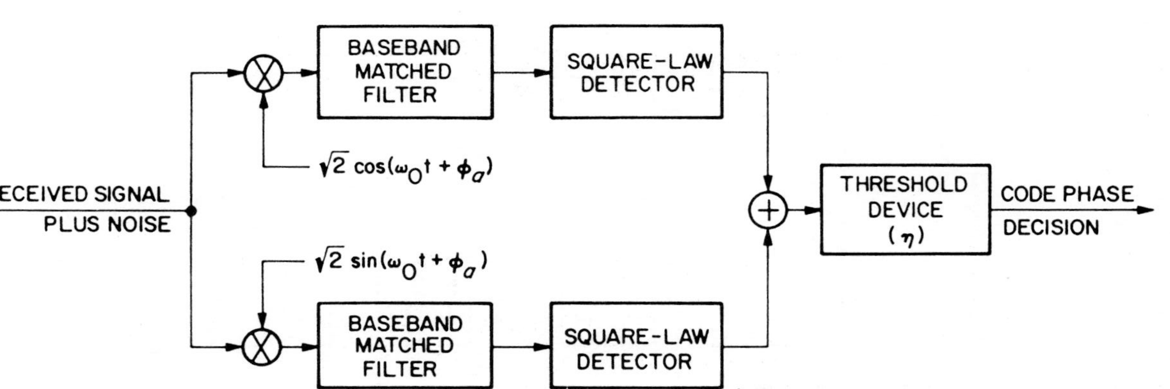

Figure 1.25b. A low-pass version of a matched filter acquisition system.

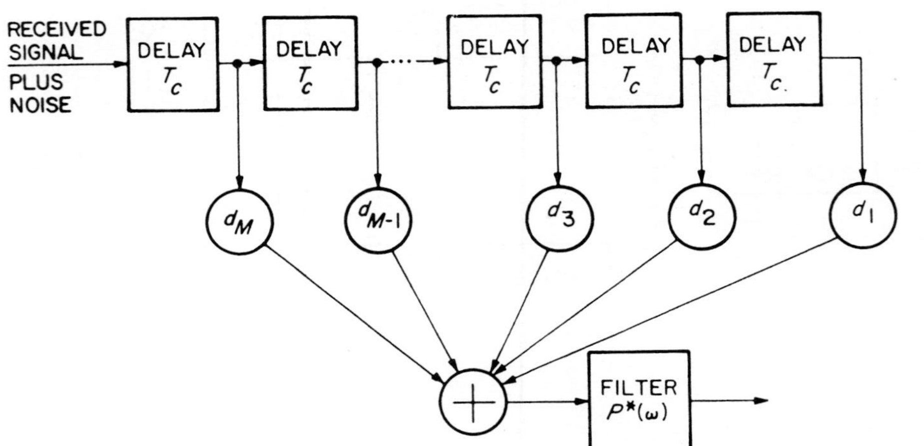

Figure 1.26. A tapped delay line implementation of a matched filter for an M-chip PN sequence.

or in terms of Fourier transforms

$$H(\omega) = S^*(\omega) e^{-j\omega T_o}. \tag{1.168}$$

Suppose now that $s(t)$ corresponds to an M-chip segment of a PN waveform, i.e., $T_o = MT_c$. Then,

$$s(t) = \sum_{n=1}^{M} d_n p[t-(n-1)T_c] \tag{1.169}$$

where d_n is the polarity (± 1) of the n-th chip and $p(t)$ is the basic chip pulse shape. For a baseband matched filter, we would have

$$p(t) = \begin{cases} 1; & 0 \le t \le T_c \\ 0; & \text{otherwise} \end{cases} \tag{1.170}$$

whereas for a band-pass matched filter,

$$p(t) = \begin{cases} \sqrt{2}\cos\omega_0 t; & 0 \le t \le T_c \\ 0; & \text{otherwise.} \end{cases} \tag{1.171}$$

Taking the Fourier transform of (1.169) and substituting its complex conjugate into (1.168) results in

$$H(\omega) = P^*(\omega) \sum_{n=1}^{M} d_n e^{-j\omega(M-n+1)T_c}, \tag{1.172}$$

which has the implementation illustrated in Figure 1.26 as previously stated.

As a prelude to our discussion of the discrete time version of the matched filter acquisition system, consider the output $\tilde{x}(t)$ of the baseband matched filter for an input $x(t)$, i.e.,

$$\begin{aligned} \tilde{x}(t) &= \int_0^{\infty} x(t-\tau) h(\tau)\, d\tau \\ &= \int_0^{T_o} x(t-\tau) s(T_o - \tau)\, d\tau \\ &= \int_0^{T_o} x(t+\zeta-T_o) s(\zeta)\, d\zeta. \end{aligned} \tag{1.173}$$

Of course, for $x(t) = s(t)$, $\tilde{x}(t)$ achieves its maximum value at $t = T_o$, namely,

$$\tilde{x}(T_o) = \int_0^{T_o} s^2(\zeta)\, d\zeta. \tag{1.174}$$

For any other $x(t)$, e.g., a time shift of $s(t)$, and $s(t)$ as in (1.169), we can write (1.173) as

$$\begin{aligned} \tilde{x}(t) &= \int_0^{MT_c} x(t+\zeta-MT_c) \sum_{n=1}^{M} d_n p(\zeta-(n-1)T_c)\, d\zeta \\ &= \sum_{n=1}^{M} d_n \int_{(n-1)T_c}^{nT_c} x(t+\zeta-MT_c)\, d\zeta. \end{aligned} \tag{1.175}$$

Suppose now that we sample $\tilde{x}(t)$ at time instants $t = (M + k/N)T_c$; $k = 0, 1, 2, \ldots$, i.e., at a multiple N of the chip rate. Then

$$\begin{aligned}\tilde{x}\left(\left(M + \frac{k}{N}\right)T_c\right) \triangleq \tilde{x}_k &= \sum_{n=1}^{M} d_n \int_{(n-1)T_c}^{nT_c} x\left(\frac{k}{N}T_c + \zeta\right) d\zeta \\ &= \sum_{n=1}^{M} d_n \sum_{i=1}^{N} \int_{((n-1)N+i-1)\frac{T_c}{N}}^{((n-1)N+i)\frac{T_c}{N}} x\left(\frac{k}{N}T_c + \zeta\right) d\zeta \\ &= \sum_{i=1}^{NM} \mathscr{D}_i X_{i+k} \end{aligned} \tag{1.176}$$

where

$$X_j = \int_{(j-1)\frac{T_c}{N}}^{j\frac{T_c}{N}} x(\xi)\, d\xi \tag{1.177}$$

and $\mathscr{D}_j$ is the j-th *sub*chip polarity which is related to the n-th chip polarity d_n by

$$\mathscr{D}_{(n-1)N+i} = d_n; \quad \begin{array}{l} i = 1, 2, \ldots, N \\ n = 1, 2, \ldots, M. \end{array} \tag{1.178}$$

Equation (1.176) is in the form of a discrete time correlation that can be implemented either in analog or digital form using a tapped delay line or shift register respectively (see Figures 1.27a and 1.27b). In the latter case, the contents of the shift register which holds the signal samples digitized to one bit and the holding register which permanently contains the fixed segment of the code used for comparison are correlated by comparing them stage by stage, generating a "+1" if the two stages match and a "−1" if they don't, and summing the resulting set of "1's" and "−1's."

Using either the analog or digital correlator of Figure 1.27a or 1.27b as matched filters in Figure 1.25b results in the discrete time version of the matched filter rapid acquisition system. Since for either correlator configuration the outputs occur and are ultimately (after squaring and summing) threshold tested at N times the chip rate, the search rate for this acquisition method is clearly

$$\mathscr{R}_{MF} = N/T_c \quad 1/N\text{-chip positions per second,} \tag{1.179}$$

which is a factor of $N\tau_d/T_c = NM$ faster than that of the serial search technique. This large apparent improvement in search rate, or equivalently, the time to search over the total uncertainty region, is a consequence of the fact that in the MF system, only one *new* fractional $(1/N)$ chip of received signal is used for each correlation test since the prior $NM - 1$ received signal samples are already stored in the tapped delay line or shift register. Because of this fact, however, it would appear that the noise-corrupted correlation values from test to test would be highly correlated because of the $NM - 1$ sample overlap as contrasted to the same test values in the single dwell serial search method which are clearly independent of one another because of the disjoint observations. Nevertheless, it can be shown [14] that, despite the overlap, the underlying acquisition process is still Markov and hence the flow graph model of the unified approach discussed in Section 1.4 can be used to determine its acquisition time performance.

Before proceeding to a discussion of the acquisition time performance, we first complete the description of the system by presenting a method of verification of the threshold crossing event. In particular, the non-coherent correlator/detector structure of Figure 1.25b is followed by a *coincidence*

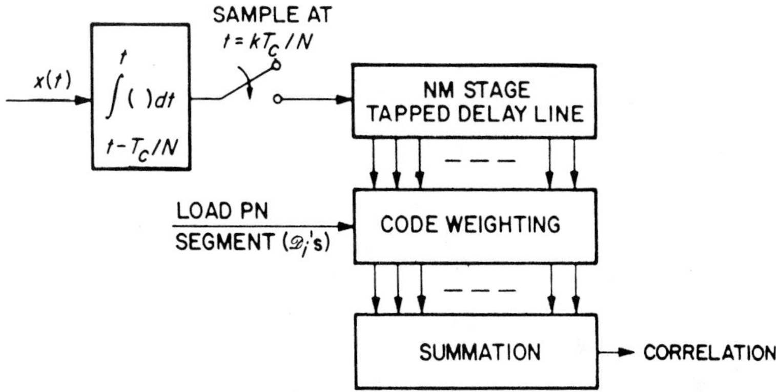

Figure 1.27a. An analog correlator implementation of a matched filter.

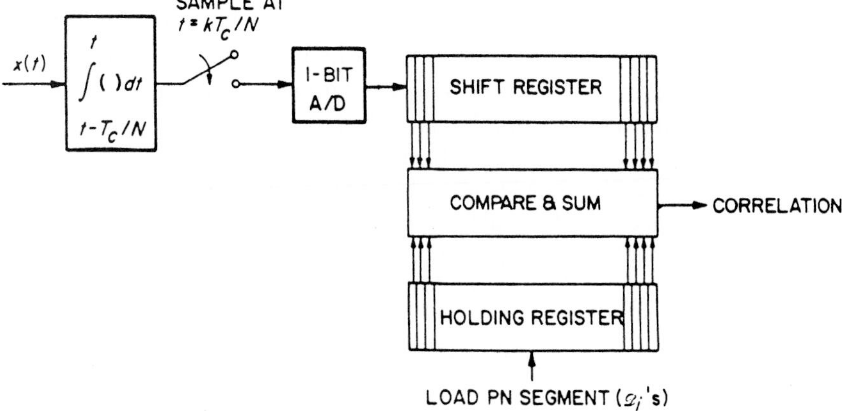

Figure 1.27b. A digital correlator implementation of a matched filter.

detector (CD) whose operation is as follows. Upon a tentative decision of an "in-sync" condition (corresponding to hypothesis H_1), the local PN segment used for code weighting in Figure 1.27a or stored in the holding register of Figure 1.27b is now updated by the local PN generator so that for a specified interval of time, say T_p, the input code and local code segment remain at a fixed relative time offset. During this time interval, the noncoherent correlator/detector continues to make threshold tests; however, to strengthen the reliability of the verification operation performed by the CD these tests are now conducted over disjoint MT_c sec time intervals of the received waveform and are thus statistically independent. If A of these tests are performed in the time interval T_p, i.e., $T_p = AMT_c$, then the rule used by the CD for final acceptance of the H_1 hypothesis is that B out of A of these correspond to threshold crossings. Upon successful completion of this majority logic decision, the tracking loop is activated, whereas upon unsuccessful completion (fewer than B out of A threshold crossings), the local code segment again is held fixed and the search continues.

1.5.1 Markov Chain Acquisition Model and Acquisition Time Performance

The flow diagram for the matched filter acquisition system is a special case of Figure 1.23 where, for the simple case of only one cell leading to the acquisition state ACQ,

$$H_p(z) = 0$$

$$H_0(z) = H_{NFA}(z) = \left[(1 - P_{FA_0}) + P_{FA_0}(1 - P_{FA_1})z^K\right]z$$

$$H_D(z) = P_{D_0}P_{D_1}z^{K+1} = P_D z^{K+1}$$

$$H_M(z) = \left[(1 - P_{D_0}) + P_{D_0}(1 - P_{D_1})z^K\right]z. \tag{1.180}$$

In the above, P_{D_0} and P_{FA_0} denote the detection and false alarm probabilities of the correlation detector (probability of threshold exceedance under H_1 and H_0, respectively) and P_{D_1} and P_{FA_1} are the analogous probabilities of the coincidence detector (probability of B threshold exceedances out of A tests under H_1 and H_0, respectively). Furthermore, since the effective dwell time τ_d (i.e., the time spent in examining each cell under hypothesis H_0 in the absence of a false alarm) in the matched filter system is T_c/N, then equating the false alarm penalty time $T_p = AMT_c$ of the coincidence detector with $K\tau_d = KT_c/N$, gives $K = ANM$.

From (1.180), we observe that $H_0(1) = 1 - P_{FA_0}P_{FA_1} = 1 - P_{FA} < 1$ and thus from (1.154), (1.157), and (1.180),

$$P_{ACQ} = \frac{P_D}{1 - (1 - P_D)(1 - P_{FA})^{\nu-1}} \sum_{i=1}^{\nu} \pi_i (1 - P_{FA})^{\nu-i} < 1, \tag{1.181}$$

which is also implied by the presence here of an absorbing false alarm state. Such an absorbing false alarm state comes about when the correlation detector produces a threshold exceedance under H_0 and the coincidence detector verifies it with a B out of A majority logic decision producing a termination of the search. For the uniform and worst case *a priori* probability distributions, (1.181) reduces to

$$P_{ACQ} = \begin{cases} \left(\dfrac{P_D}{P_{FA}}\right)\dfrac{1-(1-P_{FA})^{\nu}}{1-(1-P_D)(1-P_{FA})^{\nu-1}} & \text{(uniform)} \\ \dfrac{P_D(1-P_{FA})^{\nu-1}}{1-(1-P_D)(1-P_{FA})^{\nu-1}} & \text{(worst case)} \end{cases} \tag{1.182}$$

and the mean acquisition time under these same conditions becomes

$$\overline{T}_{ACQ} = \begin{cases} P_{ACQ}\left\{(K+1) + \dfrac{\nu(1-P_{FA})^{\nu-2}}{1-(1-P_{FA})^{\nu}}\left[\left(\dfrac{P_{ACQ}}{P_D}\right)P_{FA}(1-P_{FA})\overline{T}_M\right.\right. \\ +\overline{T}_0\left[-(1-P_{FA}) + \dfrac{P_{ACQ}}{P_D}\left((1-P_{FA})^{2-\nu} - (1-P_D)(1-P_{FA})\right.\right. \\ \left.\left.\left.+(\nu-1)P_{FA}(1-P_D)\right)\right]\right\}\tau_d & \text{(uniform)} \\ \dfrac{P_{ACQ}}{P_D}\left\{(K+1)P_D + \overline{T}_M P_{ACQ}\right. \\ \left. +(\nu-1)\overline{T}_0\dfrac{P_D + P_{ACQ}(1-P_D)}{1-P_{FA}}\right\}\tau_d & \text{(worst case)} \end{cases} \tag{1.183}$$

where $\overline{T}_0$ and $\overline{T}_M$ are defined as

$$\begin{aligned} \overline{T}_0 &= (1-P_{FA_0}) + (K+1)P_{FA_0}(1-P_{FA_1}) \\ \overline{T}_M &= (1-P_{D_0}) + (K+1)P_{D_0}(1-P_{D_1}). \end{aligned} \tag{1.184}$$

When the H_1 region contains more than one cell, the flow graph of this region expands as in Figure 1.28, which is drawn for the special case of $N = 1$ (two cells, namely Q_1 and Q_2). Under these circumstances, $H_D(z)$ and $H_M(z)$ of (1.180) are modified to become

$$\begin{aligned} H_D(z) = \Big\{P_D(Q_1) + P_D(Q_2)\big[&(1-P_{D_0}(Q_1))z \\ &+P_{D_0}(Q_1)(1-P_{D_1}(Q_1))z^{K+1}\big]\Big\}z^{K+1} \end{aligned} \tag{1.185a}$$

and

$$H_M(z) = \prod_{i=1}^{2}\left[(1-P_{D_0}(Q_i))z + P_{D_0}(Q_i)(1-P_{D_1}(Q_i))z^{K+1}\right]. \tag{1.185b}$$

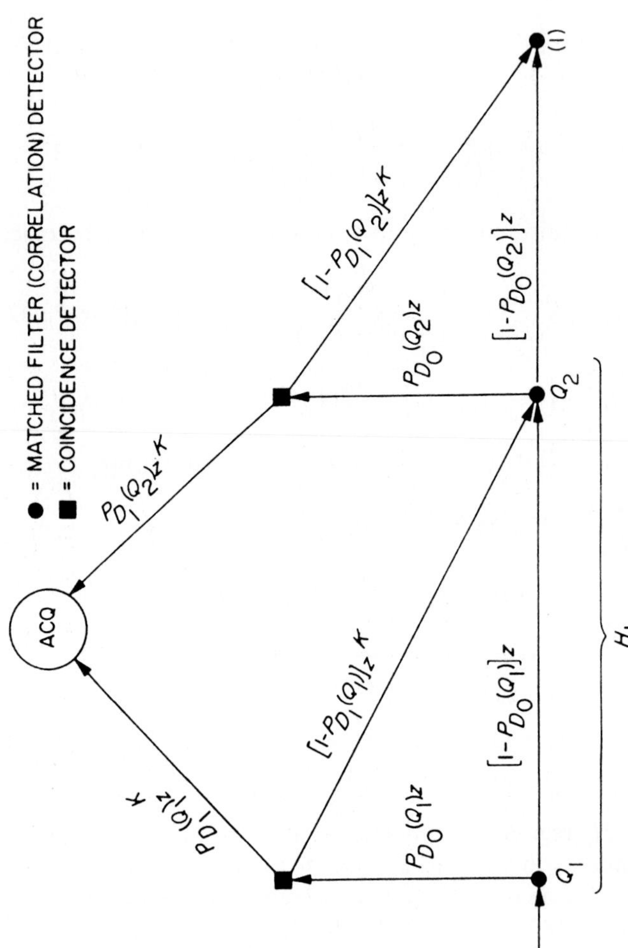

Figure 1.28. Flow graph of the H_1 region for the matched filter acquisition system.

1.5.2 Evaluation of Detection and False Alarm Probabilities for Correlation and Coincidence Detectors

In order to apply the results for P_{ACQ} and $\bar{T}_{ACQ}$ of the rapid acquisition non-coherent receiver as per (1.182) and (1.183), one needs to calculate the detection and false alarm probabilities for both the non-coherent correlation detector (P_{d_0}, P_{FA_0}) and the coincidence detector (P_{d_1}, P_{FA_1}). Computations of this nature were previously performed in Section 1.2.4 for the non-coherent detector associated with the single dwell time acquisition system. While, in principle, the problems are quite similar, we shall soon see that many of the simplifying assumptions made in the previous analysis are not valid here for the matched filter system. Nevertheless, having gone through the details of such an analysis in Section 1.2.4, our presentation here will be brief with emphasis placed on the differences between the two.

First, unlike (1.58), the signal component of the inputs to the square-law detectors in Figure 1.25b is treated as a random variable reflecting the partial correlation effect produced by correlating the input code with the stored reference code over a *finite* time interval which is much less than the code period. In particular, if $\sqrt{2}Ac(t+\tau)$ denotes the input PN code delayed by τ with respect to an arbitrary time reference and $c(t+\hat{\tau})$ denotes the corresponding local reference code, then, when the correlation time MT_c is much less than the code time period pT_c, the correlation

$$C \triangleq \int_0^{MT_c} c(t+\tau)c(t+\hat{\tau})\,dt \tag{1.186}$$

is approximately a Gaussian random variable with mean and variance (conditioned on the hypothesis H_i; $i = 0, 1$) given by [3], [13], [14]

$$E\{C|H_i\} = \begin{cases} MT_c(1-|\varepsilon|); & i=1 \\ 0; & i=0 \end{cases} \tag{1.187a}$$

and

$$\operatorname{var}\{C|H_i\} = MT_c^2 G_i(\varepsilon) = MT_c^2 \begin{cases} \varepsilon^2; & i=1 \\ 1-2|\varepsilon|+2\varepsilon^2; & i=0 \end{cases} \tag{1.187b}$$

In (1.187),

$$\varepsilon = \left(\frac{\tau-\hat{\tau}}{T_c}\right) \pm N_\varepsilon T_c \tag{1.188}$$

denotes the fractional normalized (with respect to a chip) timing offset between the two codes where N_ε is the smallest integer such that ε lies in the interval $(-1, 1)$. Figure 1.29 illustrates the conditional mean and variance of

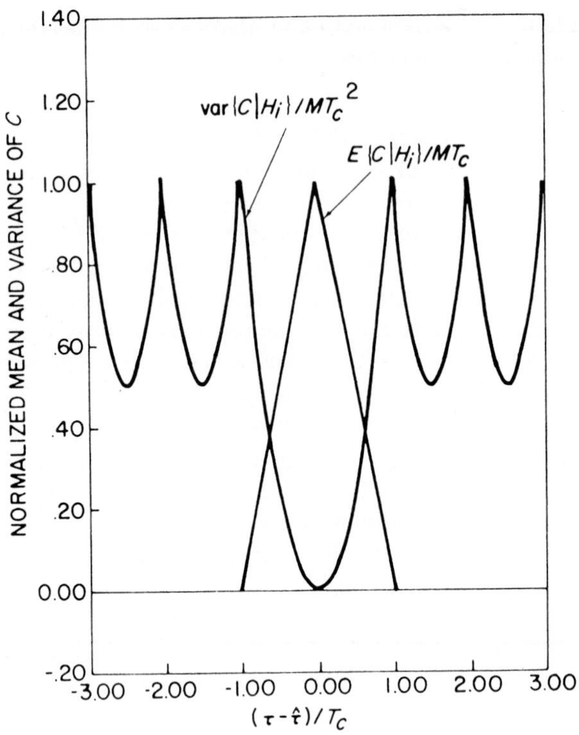

Figure 1.29. The normalized mean and variance of the partial correlation C as a function of the relative timing offset (normalized to the chip interval) between the incoming and local codes.

C for $|(\tau - \hat{\tau})/T_c| \leq 3$. The conditions under which the Gaussian assumption applies to the random variable C have been discussed in Volume II. In short, for $M \ll p$, C behaves like a binomial distribution and the additional constraint $M \gg 1$ causes the binomial distribution to behave like a Gaussian one.

The second difference concerns the validity of the Gaussian approximation to the decision statistic which in the single dwell time system allowed the false alarm and detection probabilities of (1.70) and (1.71) to be replaced by the simpler expressions in (1.79) and (1.80). We recall that the basis for validating this assumption was a central limit theorem argument based on the large values of pre-detection bandwidth–post-detection integration time product $B\tau_d$ typical of the single dwell time system. Since in a fast-decision rate acquisition system, like the matched filter receiver, post-detection integration is not feasible, the central limit argument made previously does not apply here. Instead one must use the exact probability distributions of the decision statistic under hypotheses H_0 and H_1 as determined from the solution to the problem of non-coherently detecting a Gaussian random variable (C) in additive "white" (bandlimited) Gaussian noise. Under certain circumstances, it is possible to simplify matters and obtain results similar to (1.70) and (1.71). Although these simplifications are based on Gaussian approximations to the mixture of two noise processes, one of which is signal dependent [14], it is to be re-emphasized that the assumption of a Gaussian test statistic remains invalid and thus expressions analogous to (1.79) and (1.80) are inappropriate.

1.5.2.1 Exact Results

Defining, analogous to (1.62), the *effective* signal-to-noise ratio γ_i under hypothesis H_i by

$$\gamma_i = \frac{E_c}{N_0} G_i(\varepsilon);\ i = 1, 2 \tag{1.189}$$

where $E_c/N_0 \triangleq A^2 T_c/N_0$ is the chip signal-to-noise ratio and $G_i(\varepsilon)$ is the normalized variance of the partial correlation C as defined in (1.186), then the false alarm probability P_{FA_0} and detection probability P_{D_0} of the matched filter (correlation) detector are given by [14]

$$P_{FA_0} = \sqrt{1 + 2\gamma_0} \int_{\eta^*/\sqrt{1+2\gamma_0}}^{\infty} \exp[-(1 + \gamma_0) y] I_0(\gamma_0 y)\, dy \tag{1.190}$$

and

$$P_{D_0} = \frac{1}{\sqrt{1 + 2\gamma_0}} \exp\left\{-\left(\frac{\gamma_1}{1 + 2\gamma_1}\right)\gamma_{pc}\right\} \sum_{k=0}^{\infty} F_k G_k \tag{1.191}$$

where

$$\eta^* \triangleq \frac{\eta}{N_0 M T_c} \tag{1.192}$$

is a normalization of the actual detection threshold η (see Figure 1.125b),

$$\gamma_{pc} \triangleq \frac{(E\{C|H_1\})^2}{\text{var}\{C|H_1\}} = M\frac{(1 - |\varepsilon|)^2}{G_1(\varepsilon)} \tag{1.193}$$

is the signal-to-noise ratio associated with the partial correlation random variable C, and the coefficients F_k and G_k are evaluated recursively as

$$G_{k+1} = (\eta^*)^{k+1} \exp(-\eta^*) + (k + 1) G_k;\ G_0 = \exp(-\eta^*) \tag{1.194a}$$

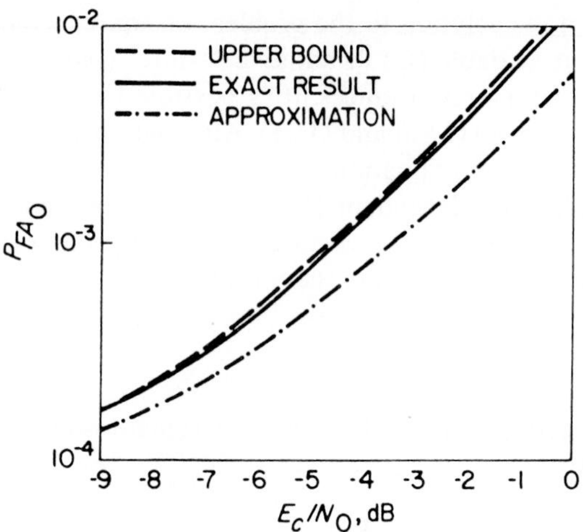

Figure 1.30a. P_{FA_0} versus E_c/N_0 for the matched filter detector with partial correlation ($\varepsilon = 1$, $\eta^* = 10$) (reprinted from [14]).

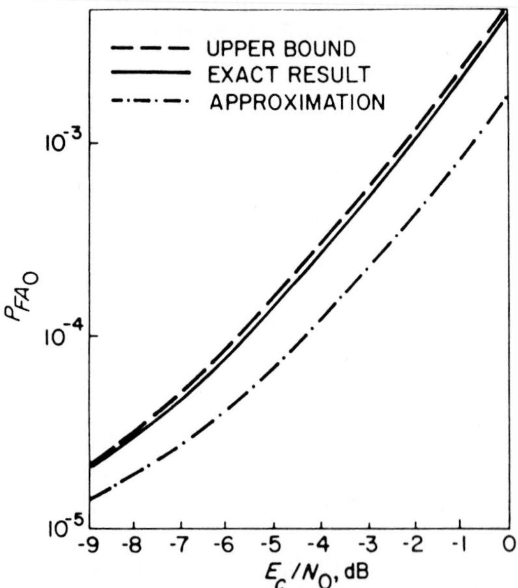

Figure 1.30b. P_{FA_0} versus E_c/N_0 for the matched filter detector with partial correlation ($\varepsilon = 1$, $\eta^* = 12.5$) (reprinted from [14]).

and

$$F_{k+1} = \frac{k+\frac{1}{2}}{(k+1)^2}\left(\frac{2\gamma_1}{1+2\gamma_1}\right)F_k + 2E_1E_{k+1}$$

$$E_{k+1} = \frac{1}{(k+1)^2}\left[\left(\frac{2\gamma_1}{1+2\gamma_1}\right)kE_k + E_1F_k\right]$$

$$F_0 = 1;\ E_1 = \frac{1}{2}\left(\frac{\sqrt{2\gamma_1\gamma_{pc}}}{1+2\gamma_1}\right). \tag{1.194b}$$

Figures 1.30a and 1.30b illustrate P_{FA_0} versus E_c/N_0 for $\varepsilon = 1$ ($\gamma_0 = E_c/N_0$) and normalized threshold values $\eta^* = 10$ and 12.5, respectively. Also shown is an upper bound on P_{FA_0} given by

$$P_{FA_0} \le \sqrt{1+2\gamma_0}\exp\left(-\frac{1+\gamma_0}{1+2\gamma_0}\eta^*\right)I_0\left(\frac{\gamma_0}{1+2\gamma_0}\eta^*\right) \tag{1.195}$$

which over the region of E_c/N_0 illustrated is very tight. Figures 1.31a and 1.31b are the companion illustrations of P_{D_0} versus E_c/N_0 for $\varepsilon = 0, .5$ and $\eta^* = 7.5$, 10, and 12.5. Also, the matched filters are assumed to integrate over 64 chips.

1.5.2.2 Approximate Results

An approximate approach [14] valid for low E_c/N_0, where the partial correlation "noise" is small with respect to the dominant thermal noise, is to model the quadrature total noise components at the matched filter outputs as independent Gaussian random variables with variance

$$\sigma_i^2 = \frac{N_0}{2}\left[1 + \left(\frac{E_c}{N_0}\right)G_i(\varepsilon)\right];\ i = 0, 1, \tag{1.196}$$

which reflects the additive contributions of the thermal noise and partial correlation "noise" under hypothesis H_i. Under this assumption, the false alarm and detection probabilities of the matched filter detector simplify to

$$P_{FA_0} = \exp\left\{-\frac{\eta^*}{1 + \left(\frac{E_c}{N_0}\right)G_0(\varepsilon)}\right\} \tag{1.197}$$

and

$$P_{D_0} = 1 - \int_0^{\beta}\exp\{-(y+\Gamma)\}I_0(2\sqrt{\Gamma y})\,dy \tag{1.198}$$

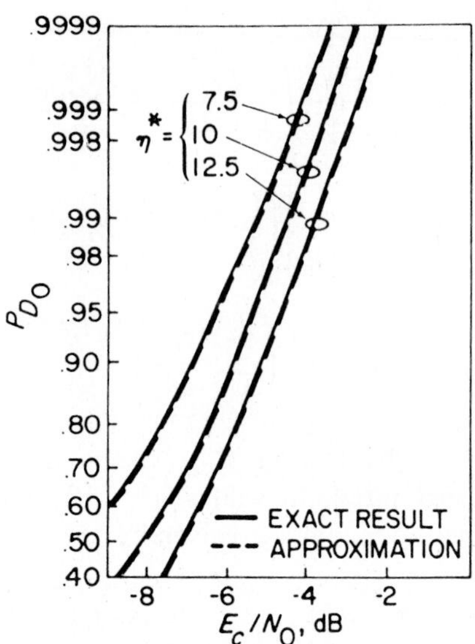

Figure 1.31a. P_{D_0} versus E_c/N_0 for the matched filter detector with partial correlation ($\varepsilon = 0$, $M = 64$) (reprinted from [14]).

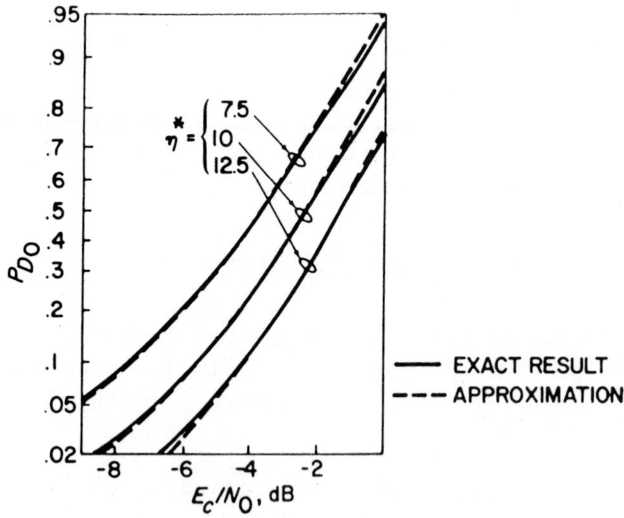

Figure 1.31b. P_{D_0} versus E_c/N_0 for the matched filter detector with partial correlation ($\varepsilon = .5$, $M = 64$) (reprinted from [14]).

where

$$\beta = \frac{\eta^*}{1 + \left(\frac{E_c}{N_0}\right) G_1(\varepsilon)}$$

$$\Gamma = \frac{\gamma_{pc}\left(\frac{E_c}{N_0}\right) G_1(\varepsilon)}{1 + \left(\frac{E_c}{N_0}\right) G_1(\varepsilon)}. \tag{1.199}$$

Equations (1.197) and (1.198), which are in the form of (1.70) and (1.71) respectively with $N_B = 1$, are superimposed (in dotted lines) on the previous exact results in Figures 1.30a, 1.30b and 1.31a, 1.31b. We observe from Figure 1.30 that the approximate analysis of P_{FA_0} is optimistic by about 1 dB, whereas from Figure 1.31 the exact and approximate results for P_{D_0} are in excellent agreement.

It is now a simple matter to compute the false alarm and detection probabilities of the coincidence detector. Since a B out of A majority logic decision with independent testing is governed by a binomial distribution, then

$$P_{FA_1} = \sum_{n=B}^{A} \binom{A}{n} P_{FA_0}^n \left(1 - P_{FA_0}\right)^{A-n}$$

$$P_{D_1} = \sum_{n=B}^{A} \binom{A}{n} P_{D_0}^n \left(1 - P_{D_0}\right)^{A-n}. \tag{1.200}$$

1.5.2.3 Acquisition Time Performance

At this point one has all the tools needed to compute the mean acquisition time performance of the matched filter system. For the worst case *a priori* probability distribution, it is possible to make some significant simplifications. The first step in the procedure would be to rewrite the expression for worst case mean acquisition time in (1.183) (valid for a single cell in H_1) in terms of the system parameters, recalling that $K = ANM$ and $\tau_d = T_c/N = T_u/N_uN$ where N_u is the number of chips searched in one pass and T_u is the corresponding time uncertainty. Then, using the approximations $\nu \simeq q = N_uN \gg 1$, $ANM \gg 1$, and the necessary modifications to allow for a multiple cell H_1 region, it can be shown [13] that

$$\frac{\bar{T}_{ACQ}}{T_u} \cong \frac{1 + ANMP_{FA_0} + f_r}{P'_D}, \tag{1.201}$$

which is a very tight approximation to the exact result in the region $P_{ACQ} > .95$ and $qP_{FA} \ll 1$. In (1.201), P'_D is the *detection probability per run* of the multiple cell H_1 region which from (1.185a) is given by

$$P'_D \triangleq H_D(1) = P_D(Q_1) + P_D(Q_2)(1 - P_D(Q_1)), \qquad (1.202)$$

which can easily be generalized for the case of more than two cells in H_1. Note that if $P_D(Q_1) = P_D(Q_2)$, i.e., the fractional offsets for states Q_1 and Q_2 are $\varepsilon = \pm 1/4$, then $P'_D = 2P_D(Q_1) - (P_D(Q_1))^2$, which is identical, as it should be, with (1.82) for the worst case misalignment with half-chip searching. Furthermore, in arriving at (1.201), allowance has been made for the possibility of a reset penalty time T_r ($f_r \triangleq T_r/T_u$ is then the penalty time normalized by the uncertainty time) associated with the time required to realign the codes to the initial phase offset at the start of the search after an unsuccessful sweep of the entire uncertainty region. Clearly, if the uncertainty region corresponds to the full code period as for short codes or specific acquisition preambles, then realignment is automatic and f_r would be zero.

As numerical examples of the application of the foregoing results, Figures 1.32a, 1.32b, and 1.32c illustrate normalized minimum mean acquisition time $\overline{T}_{ACQ}/T_u$ and optimized[27] normalized detection threshold η^* versus chip signal-to-noise ratio E_c/N_0 in dB with N, the number of cells per chip, and M, the number of chips per matched filter integration as parameters. Other parameters assumed were $P_{ACQ} > .95$, a code rate $\mathcal{R}_c = 1/T_c = 512$ kchips/sec, an uncertainty time $T_u = 64$ msec corresponding to $N_u = T_u\mathcal{R}_c = 32767 = 2^{15} - 1$ uncertainty chips, a reset time $T_r = 5$ msec ($f_r = .078$), and best and worst case values of ε. For all cases considered, it was found that $A = 4$ and $B = 2$ (2 out of 4 majority logic decision) was the optimal choice for the coincidence detector, although the performance was relatively insensitive to the actual A and B values as long as A was roughly two times B. Furthermore, we observe that even for an optimized system, there exists a rather sharp "thresholding" effect in the sense that below a certain value of E_c/N_0 the performance degrades rapidly.

1.6 PN SYNC SEARCH PROCEDURES AND SWEEP STRATEGIES FOR A NON-UNIFORMLY DISTRIBUTED SIGNAL LOCATION

Until now, we have assumed that the *a priori* pdf of the signal location across the uncertainty region was uniform, i.e., the correct cell was equally likely to occur in any of the q cells searched in one complete pass. As such, the acquisition system was designed to make complete passes by sweeping (continuously or in discrete steps) across the entire uncertainty region, once

[27] For any E_c/N_0 and fixed M and N, an optimum threshold exists in the sense of minimum $\overline{T}_{ACQ}$.

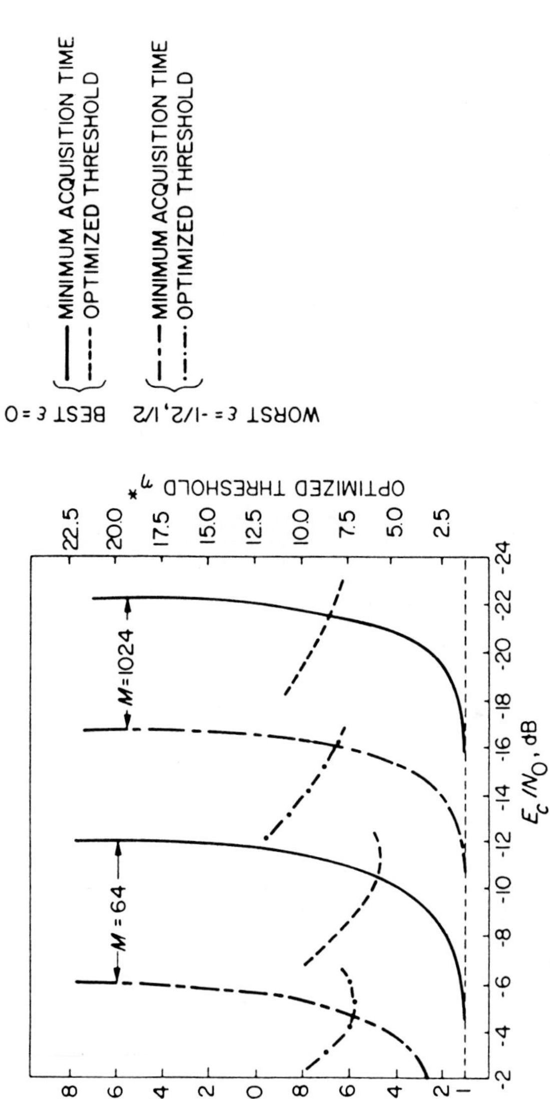

Figure 1.32a. Mean acquisition time versus E_c/N_0; $N = 1$, $A = 4$, $B = 2$, $P_{ACQ} > .95$ (reprinted from [14]).

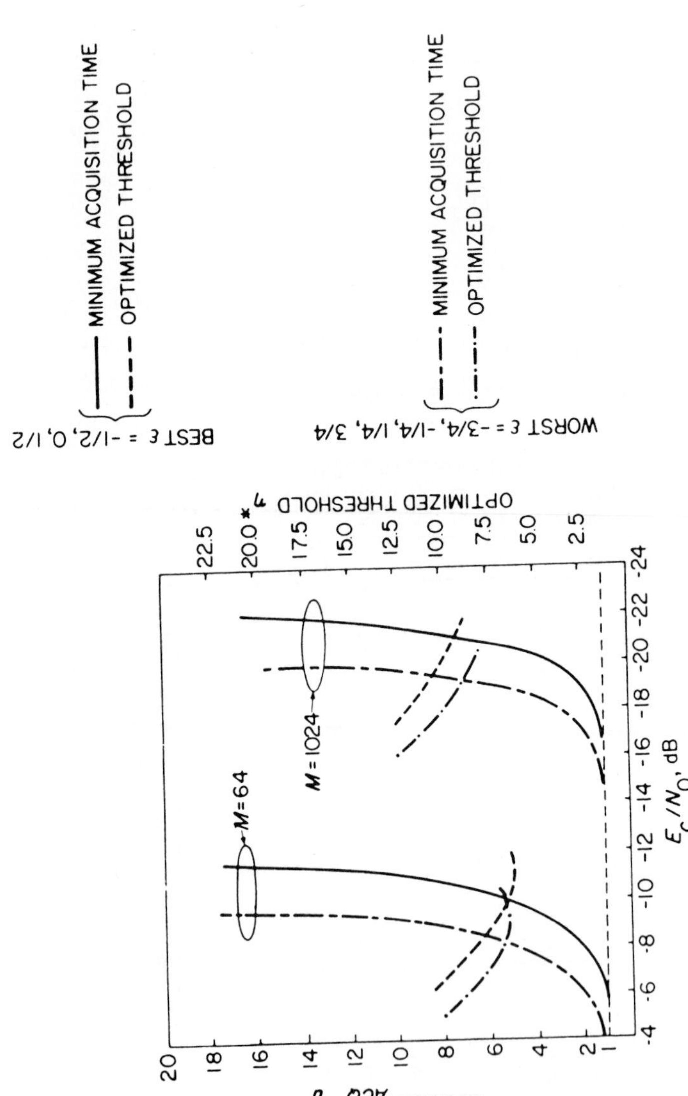

Figure 1.32b. Mean acquisition time versus E_c/N_0; $N = 2$, $A = 4$, $B = 2$, $P_{ACQ} > .95$ (reprinted from [14]).

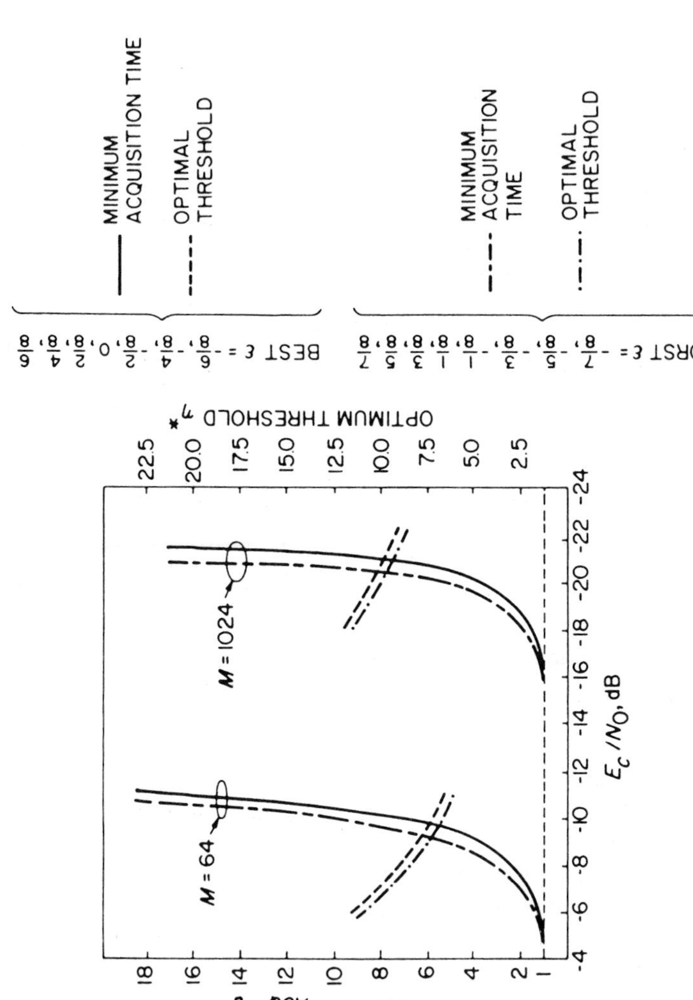

Figure 1.32c. Mean acquisition time versus E_c/N_0; $N = 4$, $A = 4$, $B = 2$, $P_{ACQ} > .95$ (reprinted from [14]).

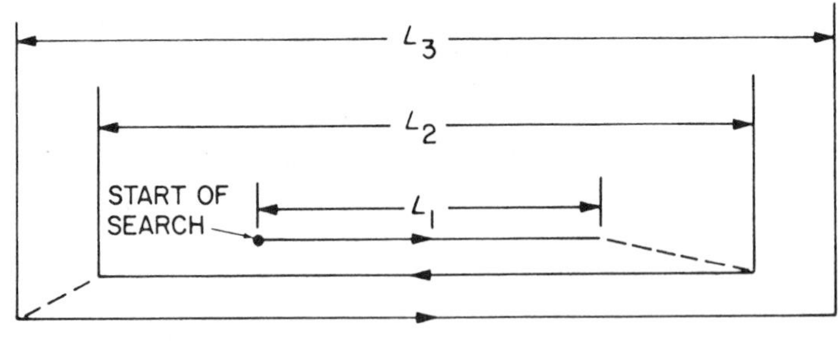

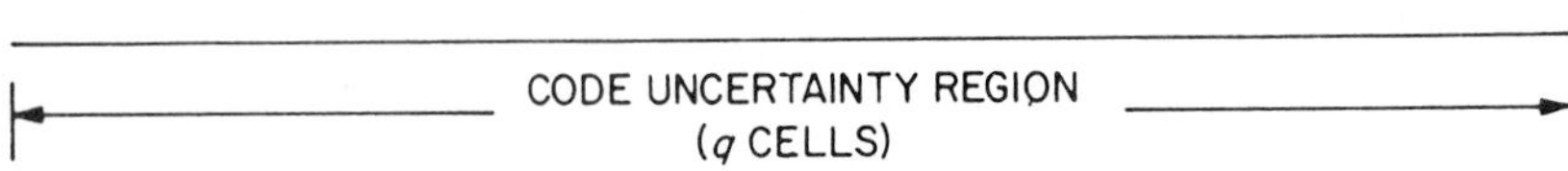

Figure 1.33. A three-window optimized sweep strategy.

per pass, in search of the correct code alignment. When the *a priori* pdf of the signal location is in some sense peaked rather than uniform, then it is more likely to find the correct code phase in the "region" surrounding the peak and one's sweep strategy should be adjusted accordingly. Since, for this situation, full sweeps across the entire uncertainty region would clearly not be the best strategy, one should instead postulate a suitable performance measure, e.g., acquisition time, and proceed to choose a search procedure that optimizes this measure subject to the given system constraints. Indeed, it is intuitively obvious that the number of cells to be searched (and thus the acquisition time) will be reduced by a procedure which begins searching in the region where the likelihood of finding the signal is highest.

1.6.1 An Example—Single Dwell Serial Acquisition with an Optimized Expanding Window Search

As a means of illustration, we shall reduce the scope of the general search problem discussed above by considering first the specific, but practical, case of a single dwell PN acquisition system with a symmetric "expanding window" search centered around the mean of a symmetric, unimodal, *a priori* signal location pdf $\pi_x(x)$ [20]–[24]. An example of such a search strategy for $N_{sw} = 3$ sweeps prior to acquisition is illustrated in Figure 1.33. Let $L_1 \leq L_2 \leq L_3 \leq \cdots \leq L_{N_{sw}}$ denote the lengths (in number of cells) of uncertainty regions to be searched during the N_{sw} sweeps. (We shall set $L_0 = 0$ for convenience). Then if, as before, k (integer) denotes the particular search of the uncertainty region during which the correct cell is *first* detected, then the generalization of (1.8) for the pdf of k is [20]

$$p(k) = P_D \sum_{n=1}^{k} (1 - P_D)^{k-n} [P(L_n) - P(L_{n-1})]; \; k = 1, 2, 3, \ldots \tag{1.203}$$

where $P(L_n)$ is the probability that the signal location x is within the set L_n, i.e.,

$$P(L_n) = \int_{-L_n/2}^{L_n/2} \pi_x(x)\, dx = 2\int_0^{L_n/2} \pi_x(x)\, dx \tag{1.204}$$

with $P(L_0) = 0$ and P_D is still the probability of detection given that the signal is there. Note that for a uniform *a priori* signal location pdf and $L_1 = L_2 = \ldots L_{N_{sw}} = q$ then $P(L_1) = P(L_2) = \ldots P(L_{N_{sw}}) = 1$ and only the $n = 1$ term has a non-zero contribution to the sum in (1.203), whereupon $p(k)$ immediately reduces to the result in (1.8).

Although (1.203) can be formally derived using Bayes' probability rule, it can also be obtained by a simple heuristic argument as follows. Let L_k be divided into k non-overlapping regions, namely, $L_1, L_2 - L_1, L_3 - L_2, \ldots, L_k - L_{k-1}$. Each of these regions represents the additional number of cells searched on a given sweep relative to the previous sweep. By the initiation of the k-th sweep, the region $L_n - L_{n-1}$ has been searched $k - n$ times; $n = 1, 2, \ldots, k - 1$. Thus the *joint* probability of *first* detecting signal in $L_n - L_{n-1}$ and that indeed it was in that region is $P_D(1 - P_D)^{k-n}P(L_n - L_{n-1})$ or, in view of (1.204), $P_D(1 - P_D)^{k-n}[P(L_n) - P(L_{n-1})]$. Since the region $L_k - L_{k-1}$ has not as yet been searched, the joint probability of detecting the signal in this region and that it is indeed there is simply $P_D[P(L_k) - P(L_{k-1})]$. Since the above set of joint probabilities corresponds to mutually exclusive events, (1.203) follows immediately.

To define an optimum symmetric search strategy, we must first define a criterion of optimization along with any additional constraints imposed by the physical system. As suggested earlier, we shall choose as an optimum search strategy that which minimizes the total acquisition time for N_{sw} sweeps where the constraint is to accomplish this minimization subject to a given desired probability of acquiring by the end of these N_{sw} sweeps. Letting $P_{N_{sw}}$ denote this probability, i.e., the probability of acquiring in N_{sw} or fewer sweeps, then since k represents the sweep (search) at which the system is *first* acquired, clearly we would have

$$P_{N_{sw}} = \sum_{k=1}^{N_{sw}} p(k) \tag{1.205}$$

where $p(k)$ is the pdf of k as given in (1.203). Substituting (1.203) into

(1.205) and simplifying yields

$$P_{N_{sw}} = P_D \sum_{k=1}^{N_{sw}} p(L_k)(1 - P_D)^{N_{sw}-k}. \tag{1.206}$$

Analogous to (1.10), the acquisition time for the first N_{sw} sweeps is[28]

$$T_{N_{sw}} = \tau_d \sum_{i=1}^{N_{sw}} L_i \triangleq \tau_d L_T. \tag{1.207}$$

Thus, in mathematical terms, the optimization problem can be stated as: For a given P_D and $\pi_x(x)$, choose the search lengths $L_1, L_2, \ldots, L_{N_{sw}}$ so as to minimize L_T with an acquisition probability equal to $P_{N_{sw}}$.

This type of problem is most easily solved by the method of LaGrange multipliers. In particular, the set $L_1, L_2, \ldots, L_{N_{sw}}$ corresponds to the stationary points of the function

$$F = P_{N_{sw}} - \lambda L_T \tag{1.208}$$

where λ is the LaGrange multiplier (as yet unknown). The stationary points of F correspond to the locations where

$$\frac{\partial F}{\partial L_i} = 0; \; i = 1, 2, \ldots, N_{sw}. \tag{1.209}$$

Thus substituting (1.206) and (1.207) into (1.208) and performing the required partial differentiations gives

$$P_D(1 - P_D)^{N_{sw}-i} \frac{dP(L_i)}{dL_i} - \lambda = 0 \tag{1.210}$$

or in view of (1.204)

$$P_D(1 - P_D)^{N_{sw}-i} \pi_x(L_i/2) = \lambda; \; i = 1, 2, \ldots, N_{sw}. \tag{1.211}$$

For a given $\pi_x(x)$, one can for each i implicitly solve for L_i as a function of λ, say $f_i(\lambda)$. Then λ can, in principle, be eliminated by satisfying the constraint in (1.206), i.e.,

$$P_{N_{sw}} = P_D \sum_{k=1}^{N_{sw}} P(f_k(\lambda))(1 - P_D)^{N_{sw}-k}. \tag{1.212}$$

Typically, for a given P_D, $P_{N_{sw}}$, and form of pdf $\pi_x(x)$, the solution of (1.212) for λ (and thus L_i: $i = 1, 2, \ldots, N_{sw}$) will exist only for certain values of N_{sw}. To show this, lower and upper bounds on N_{sw} can be obtained as follows. Since $P(L_k) \leq 1$ for all $k = 1, 2, \ldots, N_{sw}$, then from

[28] We assume here, for simplicity, a zero false alarm probability or, equivalently, that the penalty time associated with the occurrence of a false alarm is zero. In the next section, we shall include this effect as part of the more general formulation of serial search systems with non-uniform search strategies following the unified approach discussed in Section 1.4.

(1.212) we have

$$P_{N_{sw}} \leq P_D \sum_{k=1}^{N_{sw}} (1 - P_D)^{N_{sw}-k} = 1 - (1 - P_D)^{N_{sw}}. \tag{1.213}$$

Satisfaction of (1.213) with the equality sign gives a lower bound on N_{sw}, namely,

$$N_{sw} \geq \frac{\ln(1 - P_{N_{sw}})}{\ln(1 - P_D)}. \tag{1.214}$$

Similarly, since $L_1 \leq L_2 \leq \cdots \leq L_{N_{sw}}$, then $P(L_1) \leq P(L_2) \leq \cdots \leq P(L_{N_{sw}})$. Hence,

$$P_{N_{sw}} \geq P(L_1)\left[1 - (1 - P_D)^{N_{sw}}\right] \tag{1.215}$$

or

$$N_{sw} \leq \frac{\ln\left[1 - \dfrac{P_{N_{sw}}}{P(L_1)}\right]}{\ln(1 - P_D)}. \tag{1.216}$$

Before presenting a specific example of the application of the previous results and the benefits gained therein by using an optimum search strategy, we must first discuss a measure of improvement which can be used in comparing the optimized scheme to the uniform (full sweeps across the entire uncertainty region) sweep scheme. We recall that for a uniform *a priori* cell location pdf, the probability of first acquiring during the k-th full sweep is given by $p(k)$ of (1.8). Thus, for a given desired probability of acquisition $P_{N_{sw}}$, the number N_F of full sweeps (each having q cells) would be obtained from the solution to

$$\sum_{i=0}^{N_F-1} P_D(1 - P_D)^i \leq P_{N_{sw}} \leq \sum_{i=0}^{N_F} P_D(1 - P_D)^i \tag{1.217}$$

or

$$1 - (1 - P_D)^{N_F} \leq P_{N_{sw}} \leq 1 - (1 - P_D)^{N_F+1}. \tag{1.218}$$

The solution to (1.218) is easily shown to be

$$N_F = \left\lfloor \frac{\ln(1 - P_{N_{sw}})}{\ln(1 - P_D)} \right\rfloor \tag{1.219}$$

where again $\lfloor x \rfloor$ denotes the largest integer less than or equal to x. Since within a given sweep interval, say the k-th, the cumulative probability of acquisition would be a linear interpolation between the upper and lower bounds of (1.218), the total search length L_{TU} (in cells) for the uniform

Table 1.2

Improvement in acquisition time performance of optimized non-uniform sweep relative to uniform sweep.

	Uniform Sweep		Optimized Sweep			% Reduction in Acquisition Time
	N_F	L_{TU}/σ*	L_i/σ	L_T/σ	I	$(1-\frac{1}{I})\times 100$
			$(N_{sw}=3)$			
$P_D=.25$			2.54	8.83	1.66	40
	2	14.67	2.96			
$P_{N_{sw}}=.5$			3.33			
			$(N_{sw}=4)$			
			1.19			
			1.93	8.47	1.73	42
			2.46			
			2.89			
			$(N_{sw}=4)$			
$P_D=.5$			2.63			
			3.53			
	3	20.4	4.24	15.25	1.34	25
			4.85			
			$(N_{sw}=5)$			
$P_{N_{sw}}=.9$			.56			
			2.42	15.22	1.34	25
			3.38			
			4.12			
			4.74			

*For the uniform sweep case, we assume the search region corresponds to $\pm 3\sigma$, i.e., $q=6\sigma$.

sweep strategy is given by

$$L_{TU} = q\left\{ N_F + \frac{P_{N_{sw}} - \left[1 - (1 - P_D)^{N_F}\right]}{1 - (1 - P_D)^{N_F+1} - \left[1 - (1 - P_D)^{N_F}\right]} \right. \tag{1.220}$$

or upon simplification

$$L_{TU} = q\left\{ N_F + \frac{(1 - P_D)^{N_F} - (1 - P_{N_{sw}})}{(1 - P_D)^{N_F} - (1 - P_D)^{N_F+1}} \right\}. \tag{1.221}$$

The improvement factor of the optimized sweep strategy over the uniform sweep strategy is then

$$I = \frac{L_{TU}}{L_T} \tag{1.222}$$

where L_T is determined from the solution of (1.211) using the same P_D and $P_{N_{sw}}$.

As an example, consider a truncated Gaussian *a priori* pdf for $\pi_x(x)$. Then, the solution to (1.211) for the optimized sweep lengths can be expressed in the form [20]

$$L_i = 2\sqrt{2}\,\sigma\sqrt{\ln\left[\frac{P_D(1 - P_D)^{N_{sw}-i}}{\lambda\sqrt{2\pi}\,\sigma}\right]}$$

$$\triangleq f_i(\lambda);\ i = 1, 2, \ldots, N_{sw} \tag{1.223}$$

where σ is the standard deviation of $\pi_x(x)$. Using (1.212) to eliminate λ requires solution of the transcendental equation

$$P_{N_{sw}} = P_D \sum_{k=1}^{N_{sw}} (1 - P_D)^{N_{sw}-k} \left\{ 1 - 2Q\left(\sqrt{2\ln\left[\frac{P_D(1 - P_D)^{N_{sw}-k}}{\lambda\sqrt{2\pi}\,\sigma}\right]} \right) \right\} \tag{1.224}$$

which although impossible analytically can be accomplished numerically on a digital computer for each allowable value of N_{sw}. Several numerical examples were worked out in [20] with the results shown in Table 1.2.

1.6.2 Application of the Circular State Diagram Approach

In Section 1.6.1 we considered the optimization and performance of a particular expanding window serial search strategy as applied to a single dwell acquisition system. This strategy was but one of a class of search strategies that attain improved acquisition performance when *a priori* probabilistic information about the true code sync position is available.

In this section, we generalize these results by allowing for an arbitrary serial search strategy and an arbitrary detector configuration. The approach taken is based upon the circular state diagram method introduced in Section

1.4 as a tool for modelling and analyzing the complete acquisition behavior of straight (uniform) serial search schemes. The advantage of this approach in the application being considered here is that it circumvents complicated combinatorial arguments used in [21]–[23] to characterize the performance of such systems by employing a transform domain description of the stochastic acquisition process. Such a description allows a simple and more systematic evaluation of the generating function of the process using well-known flow graph reduction techniques.

While the method to be described applies to arbitrary serial search strategies, the focus here will be on the two classes of non-uniform strategies depicted in Figure 1.2, namely, the *z-search* and the *expanding window search*. These two classes can be further subdivided into *broken* or *continuous* searches (depending on whether the receiver employs rewinding in order to skip certain cells), and *edge* or *center* searches (depending on where the search and each subsequent sweep are initiated).

Recall from Section 1.4.1 that for a straight serial search, the process can be modelled by a circular state diagram (see Figure 1.23) with $\nu + 2$ states, where $\nu - 1$ of these correspond to out-of-sync cells (hypothesis H_0), one to the collecting state (hypothesis H_1), one to the absorbing correct state (ACQ), and one to the possibly absorbing false alarm state. Along the branches between these various states are found generalized gains $H(z)$ that represent the generating functions of the individual discrete-time detection processes associated with the corresponding paths. Applying standard flow graph reduction techniques to the circular state diagrams then allows evaluation of the moment generating function $U(z)$ of the underlying acquisition process.

To apply this approach to the non-uniform search case, one merely translates the motion of the specific search strategy under consideration into a circular motion along an equivalent circular state diagram analogous to Figure 1.23. To demonstrate how this is accomplished, let us consider first the continuous/center z serial search illustrated in Figure 1.34. Here the search is initiated at the center of the code phase uncertainty region and proceeds following the arrows in the manner shown; i.e., it reverses direction every time the boundaries are reached. Assuming that the location of the true sync state (H_1) is at the shaded cell, the search process will meet it once during each sweep at the dotted positions. We indicate the starting cell by $\nu - k$ where, for the H_1 cell to be in the indicated side, k must satisfy $1 \leq k \leq (\nu - 1)/2$ (for convenience, we assume ν to be odd). Similar diagrams can be drawn for $k = 0$ or $(\nu + 1)/2 \leq k \leq \nu - 1$; however, that will not be necessary due to the symmetry of the problem. Furthermore, we note that since the search is always initiated at the center, π_j should be interpreted as the probability that the central (entrance) cell is not the ν-th (H_1) but the j-th; in other words, π_j stands for the probability that H_1 is actually $\nu - j$ positions to the right (if $j \geq (\nu + 1)/2$) or j positions to the left (if $j \leq (\nu - 1)/2$).

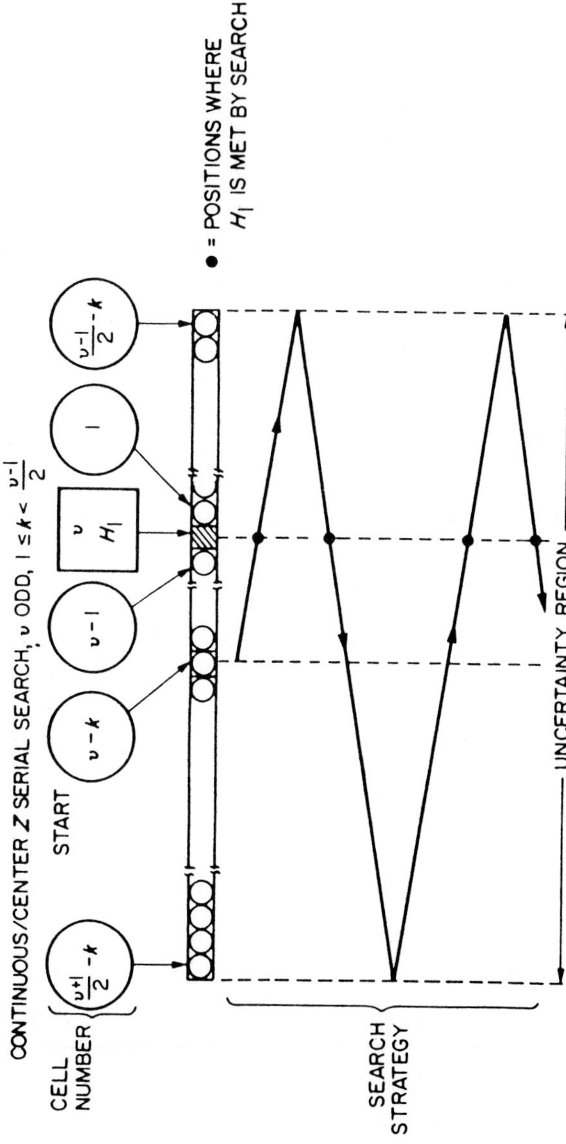

Figure 1.34. Cell numbering for the continuous/center z serial search with $1 \leqq k < (\nu - 1)/2$.

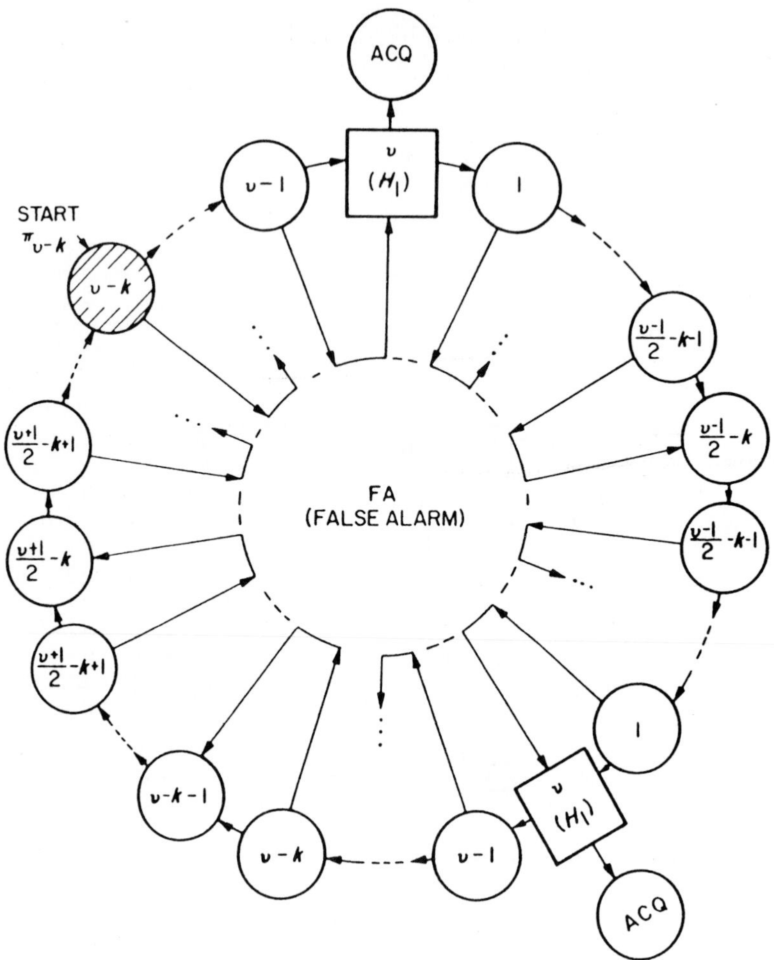

Figure 1.35. Equivalent circular state diagram for the continuous/center z serial search, $1 \leqq k < (\nu - 1)/2$.

Translating the z motion of the search into an equivalent motion along an equivalent circular path leads to the circular state diagram of Figure 1.35, which for purposes of deriving the transfer function $U_{\nu-k,ACQ}(z)$ from state $\nu - k$ to state ACQ can be consolidated into Figure 1.36, which contains two forward paths and one feedback loop. Applying Mason's formula [32] to Figure 1.36 trivially provides the result (for $0 < k < (\nu - 1)/2$)

$$U_{\nu-k,ACQ}(z) = \frac{H_0^k(z)H_D(z)\left[1 + H_M(z)H_0^{\nu-2-2k}(z)\right]}{1 - H_M^2(z)H_0^{2(\nu-2)}(z)}. \quad (1.225)$$

Finally, averaging $U_{\nu-k,ACQ}(z)$ over the *a priori* probability distribution of

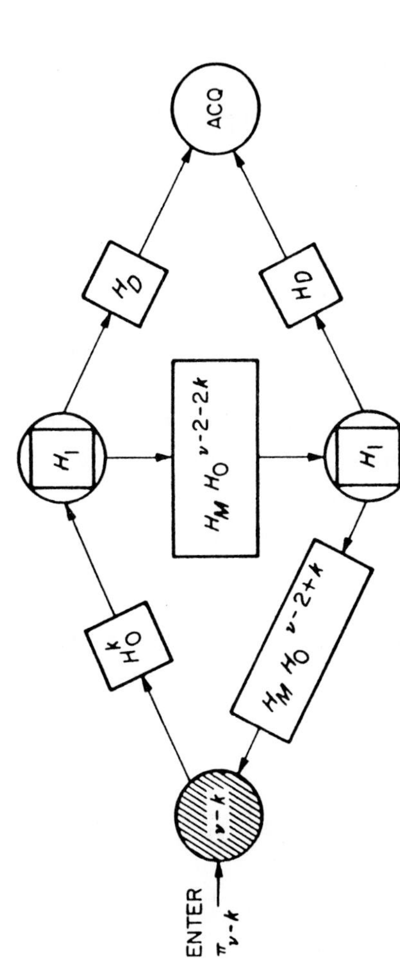

Figure 1.36. Flow graph and corresponding path gains for the continuous/center z serial search entering at node $\nu - k$, $0 < k < (\nu - 1)/2$.

the code phase uncertainty, and taking certain symmetries into account, gives the desired result for the acquisition process generating function $U(z)$, namely,

$$U(z) = \sum_{k=0}^{\nu-1} \pi_k U_{\nu-k,ACQ}(z)$$

$$= H_D(z)\left\{\frac{\sum_{j=1}^{(\nu-3)/2} H_0^j(z)\left[\pi_{\nu-j} + \pi_j H_0^{\nu-1}(z)\right]\left[1 + H_M(z)H_0^{\nu-2-2j}(z)\right]}{1 - H_M^2(z)H_0^{2(\nu-2)}(z)}\right.$$

$$\left. + \frac{H_0^{(\nu-1)/2}(z)\left[\pi_{(\nu+1)/2} + \pi_{(\nu-1)/2}H_0^{\nu-1}(z)\right]}{1 - H_M(z)H_0^{2\nu-3}(z)} + \frac{\pi_\nu}{1 - H_M(z)H_0^{\nu-2}(z)}\right\}. \tag{1.226}$$

Equation (1.226) can be combined with any *a priori* distribution to provide specific results. For example, for the symmetric triangular distribution

$$\pi_j = \begin{cases} \left(\dfrac{2}{\nu-1}\right)\left[1 - \left(\dfrac{2}{\nu-1}\right)j\right] & j = 1,\ldots,\dfrac{\nu-1}{2} \\ \pi_{\nu-j} & j = \dfrac{\nu+1}{2},\ldots,\nu-1 \\ \left(\dfrac{2}{\nu-1}\right) & j = \nu \end{cases} \tag{1.227}$$

which in [22] is used as an approximation to a truncated Gaussian distribution, $U(z)$ of (1.226) becomes

$$U(z) = \left(\frac{2}{\nu-1}\right)\left(\frac{H_D(z)}{1 - H_M^2(z)H_0^{2(\nu-2)}(z)}\right)$$
$$\times\left\{\frac{H_0(z)(1 + H_0^{\nu-1}(z))}{1 - H_0(z)}\left[1 - \frac{2}{\nu-1}\left(\frac{1 - H_0^{(\nu-1)/2}(z)}{1 - H_0(z)}\right)\right.\right.$$
$$\left. - H_0^{\nu-3}(z)H_M(z)\left(1 - \frac{2}{\nu-1}\left(\frac{1 - H_0^{(\nu-1)/2}(z)}{H_0^{(\nu-3)/2}(z)(1 - H_0(z))}\right)\right)\right]$$
$$\left. + 1 + H_M(z)H_0^{\nu-2}(z)\right\}. \tag{1.228}$$

From the generating function $U(z)$ of (1.228), we can obtain the mean acquisition time $\overline{T}_{ACQ}$ by a relation identical to that in (1.3). For example, for a single dwell system, we use the branch gains of Table 1.1 together with the relation of (1.153) in (1.228), whereupon performing the required differentiation and evaluating the result at $z = 1$ gives

$$\overline{T}_{ACQ} = \tau_d\left\{\frac{1}{P_D} + \frac{1 + KP_{FA}}{3P_D(2 - P_D)(\nu - 1)}\left[6\nu^2 - 18\nu + 12 - P_D(6\nu^2 - 15\nu + 9) + P_D^2(2\nu^2 - 4\nu)\right]\right\} \quad (1.229)$$

which for large ν reduces to

$$\overline{T}_{ACQ} = \tau_d\left\{\frac{1}{P_D} + \frac{2(1 + KP_{FA})\nu(3 - 3P_D + P_D^2)}{3P_D(2 - P_D)}\right\}. \quad (1.230)$$

Consider now another variation of the class of z-search strategies, namely, the broken/center z search. This is similar to the continuous/center z, with the exception that the same cells are not searched twice in a row. Instead, when one of the two boundaries is reached, the local code is quickly rewound to the center and the search continues in the opposite direction. Clearly, for *a priori* distributions which are peaked around the center, an improvement in acquisition performance should be expected with respect to the continuous/center z strategy. The magnitude of this improvement will be demonstrated shortly by comparing the mean acquisition time performance of the broken/ and continuous/center z search strategies for the triangular *a priori* distribution. First, however, we present the generating function $U(z)$ for the broken/center z which is obtained from its circular state diagram by steps identical to those used in arriving at (1.226). As in our previous discussions, letting T_r denote the reset penalty time required to rewind the code, $U(z)$ is found to be

$$U(z) = H_D(z)\left\{\frac{\sum_{j=1}^{(\nu-1)/2}\left[\pi_{\nu-j} + \pi_j z^{T_r/\tau_d}H_0^{(\nu+1)/2}(z)\right]H_0^j(z)}{1 - z^{2T_r/\tau_d}H_M(z)H_0^{\nu}(z)} + \frac{\pi_\nu}{1 - z^{T_r/\tau_d}H_M(z)H_0^{(\nu-1)/2}(z)}\right\}. \quad (1.231)$$

For the triangular *a priori* distribution, (1.231) evaluates to

$$U(z) = \left(\frac{2}{\nu - 1}\right)H_D(z)\left\{\frac{1 + z^{T_r/\tau_d}H_0^{(\nu+1)/2}(z)}{1 - z^{2T_r/\tau_d}H_M(z)H_0^{\nu}(z)}\left(\frac{H_0(z)}{1 - H_0(z)}\right) \times\left[1 - \frac{2}{\nu - 1}\left(\frac{1 - H_0^{(\nu-1)/2}(z)}{1 - H_0(z)}\right)\right] + \frac{1}{1 - z^{T_r/\tau_d}H_M(z)H_0^{(\nu-1)/2}(z)}\right\}. \quad (1.232)$$

Once again applying the necessary differentiation to arrive at (1.232) the mean acquisition time of a single dwell system, we obtain from (1.232) the result

$$\overline{T}_{ACQ} = \tau_d \left\{ \frac{1}{P_D} + \frac{T_r}{\tau_d} \frac{\left[\left(\frac{\nu-3}{2}\right)P_D + 2(\nu-2)(1-P_D)\right]}{(\nu-1)P_D} \right.$$

$$\left. + \frac{(1+KP_{FA})}{(\nu-1)P_D}\left[\frac{5}{12}(\nu^2-2\nu-3)P_D + (\nu^2-2\nu-1)(1-P_D)\right]\right\} \tag{1.233}$$

which for large ν reduces to

$$\overline{T}_{ACQ} = \tau_d \left\{ \frac{1}{P_D}\left[1 + \left(\frac{4-3P_D}{2}\right)\frac{T_r}{\tau_d}\right] + \frac{(1+KP_{FA})\nu}{P_D}\left(1 - \frac{7}{12}P_D\right)\right\}. \tag{1.234}$$

To illustrate the improvement in mean acquisition time performance by using a broken/ rather than a continuous/center z search, we can take the ratio of the latter terms in (1.230) and (1.234) since, for large enough ν, the first terms in these equations can be ignored. Thus, to a good approximation

$$\frac{\overline{T}_{ACQ}|_{\text{cont.}}}{\overline{T}_{ACQ}|_{\text{broken}}} = \frac{2(3 - 3P_D + P_D^2)}{3(2-P_D)(1-\frac{7}{12}P_D)}. \tag{1.235}$$

Figure 1.37 is a plot of this mean acquisition time improvement factor versus P_D. We observe that the maximum improvement occurs for $P_D = 1$ (absolute probability of detecting the correct cell once it is reached) in which case (1.235) reduces to

$$\frac{\overline{T}_{ACQ}|_{\text{cont.}}}{\overline{T}_{ACQ}|_{\text{broken}}} = \frac{8}{5} = 1.6 \tag{1.236}$$

i.e., a 37.5 percent saving in acquisition time.

In the more general case where the *a priori* probability distribution of the code phase uncertainty is arbitrary (but symmetric), for $P_D = 1$ and ν large, it is simple to show that[29]

$$\frac{\overline{T}_{ACQ}|_{\text{cont.}}}{\overline{T}_{ACQ}|_{\text{broken}}} = \frac{2\sum_{j=1}^{\nu/2} j\pi_j + \frac{\nu}{2}}{2\sum_{j=1}^{\nu/2} j\pi_j + \frac{\nu}{4}} \tag{1.237}$$

[29] When ν is large, the assumption of ν odd is inconsequential.

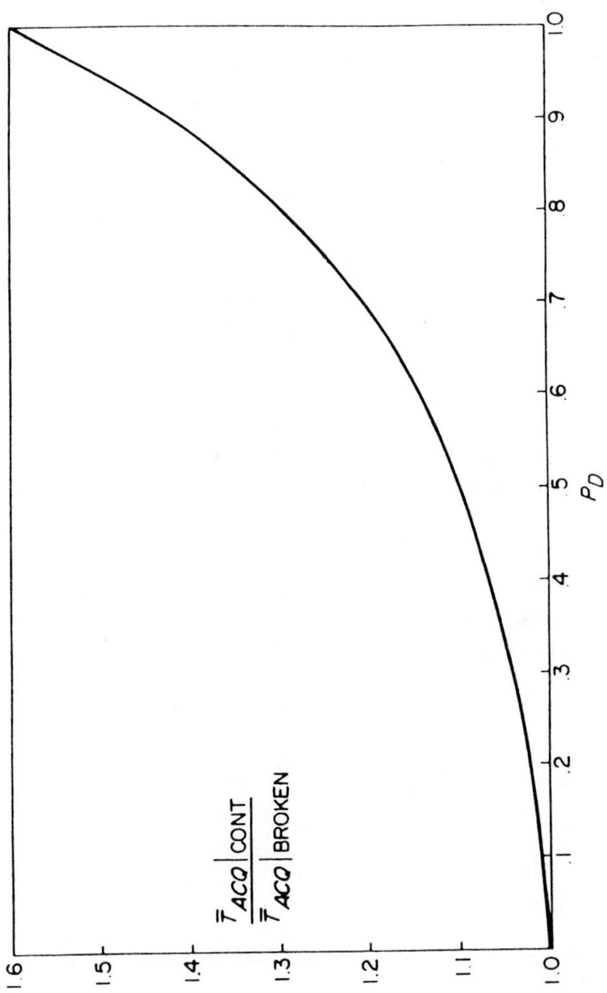

Figure 1.37. Mean acquisition time improvement factor versus detection probability for single dwell acquisition system with triangular *a priori* code phase uncertainty distribution.

which is lower and upper bounded by

$$\frac{6}{5} \leq \frac{\bar{T}_{ACQ}|_{\text{cont.}}}{\bar{T}_{ACQ}|_{\text{broken}}} = 2 \tag{1.238}$$

corresponding to the *a priori* distributions

$$\begin{gathered}\pi_1 = \pi_\nu = \tfrac{1}{2} \\ \pi_j = 0;\ j \neq 1, \nu\end{gathered} \tag{1.239a}$$

and

$$\begin{gathered}\pi_{\nu/2} = \pi_{\nu/2+1} = \tfrac{1}{2} \\ \pi_j = 0;\ j \neq \nu/2, \nu/2 + 1.\end{gathered} \tag{1.239b}$$

Thus, *regardless of the a priori probability distribution of the code phase uncertainty, the broken/center z search potentially offers an improvement of at least* 20 *percent and at most* 100 *percent over the continuous/center z search.* Of course, for $P_D < 1$, these improvements will decrease accordingly.

Finally, we consider the class of expanding window search strategies, two representative cases of which (A and B) are shown in Figure 1.38. The two cases differ in the way the search is continued once the entire uncertainty region has been covered without success. In particular, case A repeats the search starting from the R_1 window,[30] while case B continues by repeating the $R_{N_{sw}}$ window. We note that the strategies analyzed in [21]–[23] constitute slight variations of case B. The equivalent circular state diagrams for the two cases are shown in Figure 1.39. We observe that, after completing the first $R_{N_{sw}}$ sweep, case B is indistinguishable from the continuous/center z search. Furthermore, the diagrams are composed of hexagons with an inscribed R_i; those represent portions of the state diagram which correspond to the partial sweeps R_i; $i = 1, \ldots, N_{sw}$. As seen from Figure 1.38, for each starting cell $\nu - k$ there exists a minimum index j_k such that the first $j_k - 1$ partial windows do not contain the H_1 state, while the remaining $N_{sw} - j_k + 1$ do. This is manifested in Figure 1.39 by the fact that only the hexagons after (and including) the j_k-th can lead to the ACQ state. The portions of the state diagram included in the hexagon R_j can be derived from Figure 1.35 with a proper modification. Typical forms are shown in Figures 1.40a and 1.40b for the two possibilities, i.e., $1 \leq j \leq j_k - 1$ (Figure 1.40a) and $j_k \leq j \leq N_{sw}$ (Figure 1.40b). It has been assumed, without loss of generality, that $1 \leq k \leq (\nu - 1)/2$. Cascading the successive hexagons of Figures 1.40a and 1.40b as per Figure 1.39 will result in the equivalent circular state diagrams for those expanding window search strategies. It is then a matter of systematically following the steps established previously

[30] Note that the radius R_i of the i-th partial window is one-half of the length L_i of the sweep for that window.

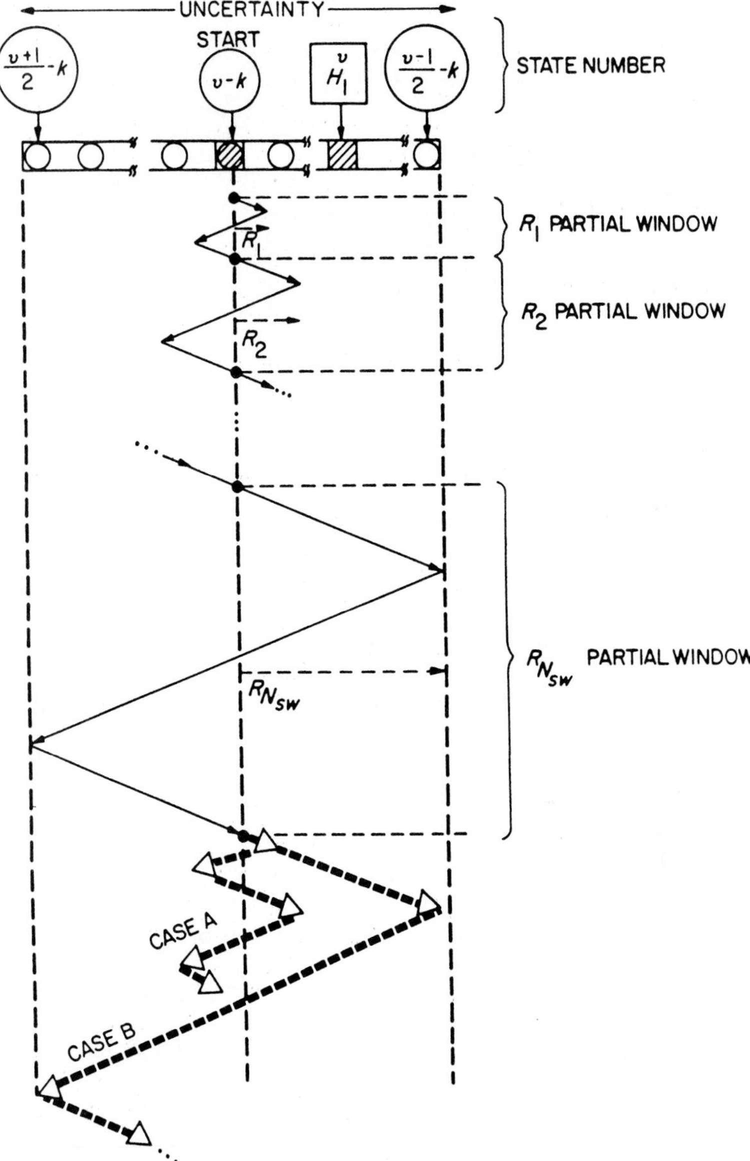

Figure 1.38. Definitions for the expanding window search technique; cases A and B (reprinted from [38]).

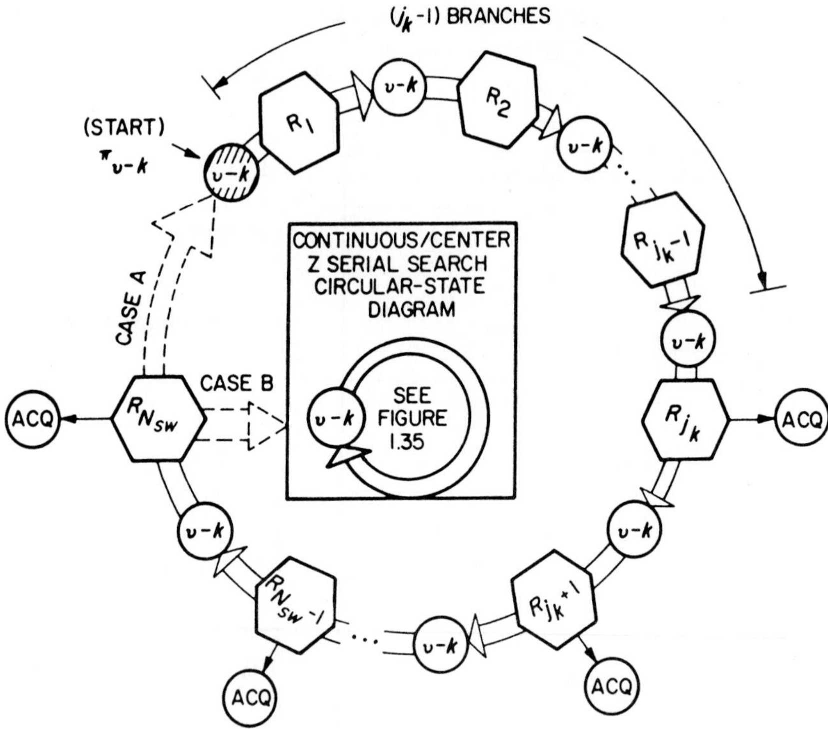

Figure 1.39. Equivalent state diagrams for the two cases A and B of the expanding window serial search of Figure 1.38 (reprinted from [38]).

(i.e., diagram consolidation, gain calculation via Mason's formula, and averaging) in order to arrive at the final expressions of interest. For the two cases A and B, they are given by

$$\text{(Case A)} \quad U(z) = \sum_{i=1}^{N_{sw}} F_1(i) \sum_{j=i}^{N_{sw}} F_2(i, j) \sum_{R_{i-1}+1 \leqq k \leqq R_i} F_3(k, j) \tag{1.240}$$

and

(Case B)

$$U(z) = \left(\frac{H_D(1 + H_0^{\nu}) H_0^{4S(1, N_{sw})}}{1 - H_M^2 H_0^{2\nu}} \right) \sum_{i=1}^{N_{sw}} H_0^{2(N_{sw}-i+1)} \sum_{R_{i-1}+1 \leqq k \leqq R_i} F_3(k, N_{sw})$$

$$+ \sum_{i=1}^{N_{sw}} H_D H_0^{4S(1, i-1)} \sum_{j=i}^{N_{sw}} F_2(i, j) \sum_{R_{i-1}+1 \leqq k \leqq R_i} F_3(k, j) \tag{1.241}$$

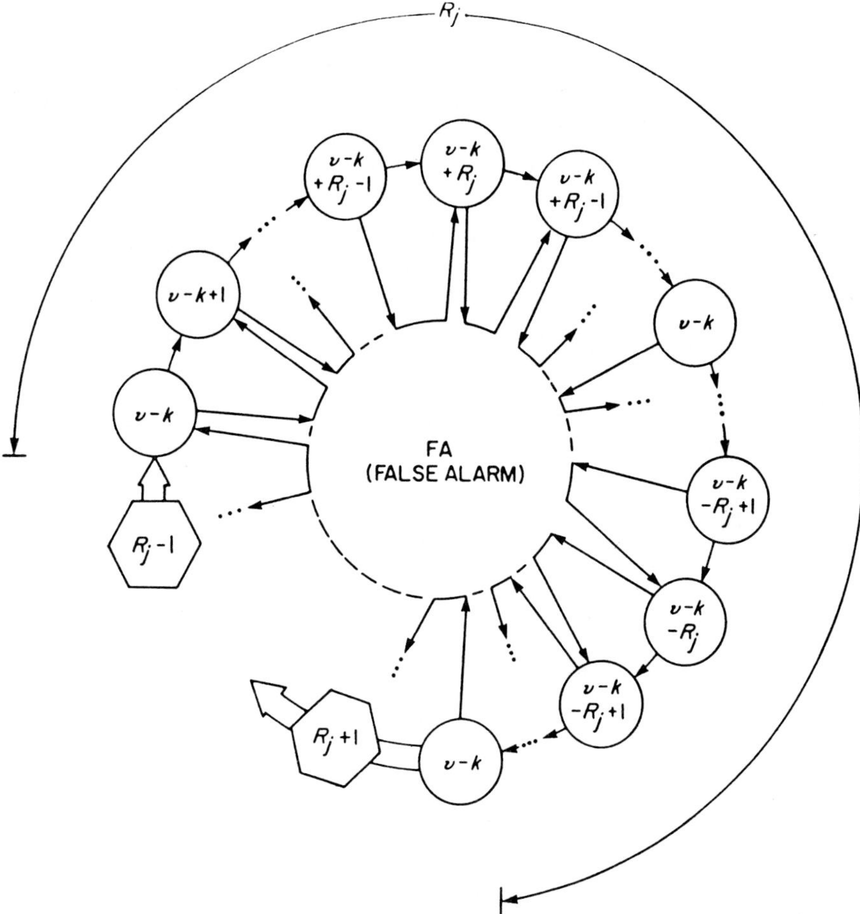

Figure 1.40a. Portion of state diagram corresponding to R_j, expanding window search, $1 \leqq j \leqq j_k - 1$ (reprinted from [38]).

where

$$F_1(i) = \frac{H_D H_0^{4S(1,i-1)}}{1 - H_M^{2(N_{sw}-i+1)} H_0^{4S(1,N_{sw})}} \tag{1.242a}$$

$$F_2(i,j) = H_M^{2(j-i)} H_0^{4S(i,j-1)} \left(1 + H_0^{2R_j}\right) \tag{1.242b}$$

$$F_3(k,j) = \pi_k \left(H_0^k + H_M H_0^{2R_j-k}\right) \tag{1.242c}$$

and

$$S(m,n) = \begin{cases} \sum_{l=m}^{n} R_l, & \text{if } m \leqq n \\ 0, & \text{if } m > n. \end{cases} \tag{1.242d}$$

In deriving the above, the simplifying assumptions were made that the

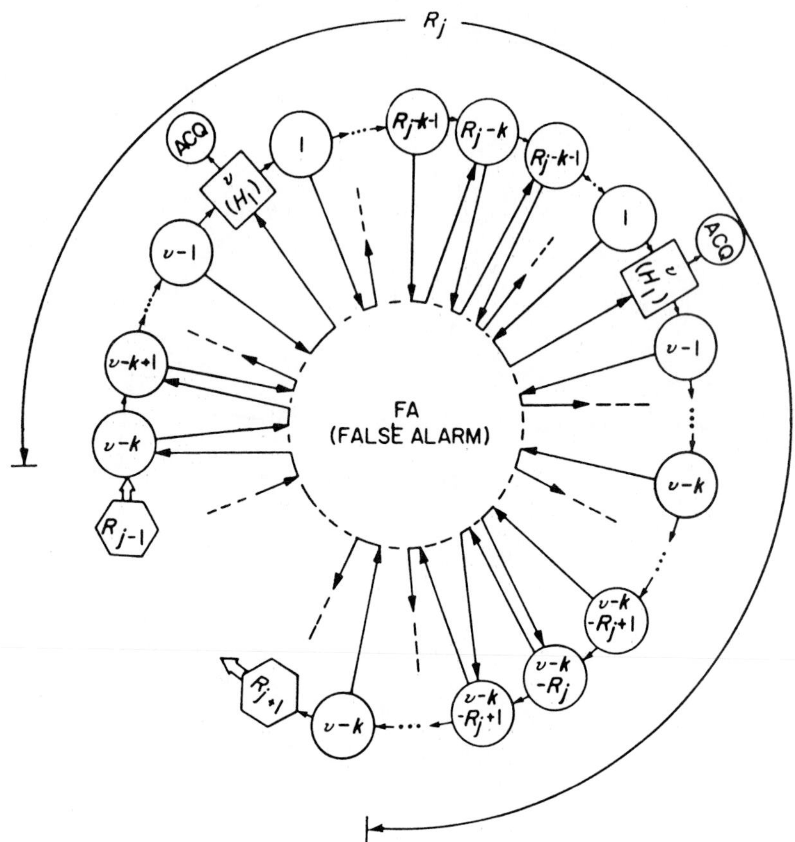

Figure 1.40b. Portion of state diagram corresponding to R_j, expanding window search, $j \geq j_k$ (reprinted from [38]).

a priori distribution is symmetric ($\pi_k = \pi_{\nu-k}$), ν is large, and $R_i \gg N_{sw}$; $i = 1, 2, \ldots, N_{sw}$, all of which are met in practical systems. Also, the dependence of the gains on z has been dropped.

As a particular case of interest, let us consider the "equiexpanding" window search, whereby the radii R_i increase by the same amount of code chips, i.e., $R_i = (\nu/2N_{sw})i$; $i = 1, \ldots, N_{sw}$. Arbitrarily assuming case A, the moment generating function of (1.240) becomes

$$U(z) = H_D \sum_{i=1}^{N_{sw}} \frac{H_0^{i(i-1)\nu/N_{sw}}}{1 - H_M^{2(N_{sw}-i+1)} H_0^{\nu(N_{sw}+1)}} \times \sum_{l=0}^{N_{sw}-i} H_M^{2l} H_0^{l(2i+l-1)\nu/N_{sw}} \left(1 + H_0^{(l+i)\nu/N_{sw}}\right) \times \sum_{R_{i-1}+1 \leq k \leq R_i} \pi_k \left(H_0^k + H_M H_0^{(l+i)\nu/N_{sw}-k}\right) \tag{1.243}$$

and, for the single dwell detector, the corresponding mean acquisition time is given by

$$\overline{T}_{ACQ} = \tau_d \left\{ \frac{1}{P_D} + \frac{2(1 + KP_{FA})\nu}{N_{sw}} \sum_{k=1}^{N_{sw}} \frac{E_1(k, N_{sw})}{1 - (1 - P_D)^{2k}} \right. \\ \left. \times \left[\alpha(k, N_{sw}; P_D) + \beta(k, N_{sw}; P_D) + \gamma(k, N_{sw}; P_D) \right] \right\} \tag{1.244}$$

where

$$\alpha(k, N_{sw}; P_D) = N_{sw}(N_{sw} + 1)(1 - P_D)^{2k} \\ + (N_{sw} - k)(N_{sw} + 1 - k)\left(1 - (1 - P_D)^{2k}\right) \tag{1.245a}$$

$$\beta(k, N_{sw}; P_D) = \frac{1}{2}(N_{sw} + 1 - k)\left(1 - (1 - P_D)^{2k}\right) \\ + \left\{ \frac{1}{2}[4(N_{sw} + 1 - k) - 1] + \frac{1 + (1 - P_D)^2}{1 - (1 - P_D)^2} \right\}(1 - P_D)^2 \\ \times \left[\frac{1 - (1 - P_D)^{2k}}{1 - (1 - P_D)^2} - k(1 - P_D)^{2k-2} \right] \\ - k(k - 1)(1 - P_D)^{2k} \tag{1.245b}$$

$$\gamma(k, N_{sw}; P_D) = \frac{1 - (1 - P_D)^{2k}}{2 - P_D} \\ \times \left\{ (N_{sw} + 1 - k)(1 - P_D) + \frac{N}{\nu} P_D \frac{E_2(k, N_{sw})}{E_1(k, N_{sw})} \right. \\ \left. + (1 - P_D)\left[\frac{(1 - P_D)^2}{1 - (1 - P_D)^2} - k\frac{(1 - P_D)^{2k}}{1 - (1 - P_D)^{2k}} \right] \right\} \tag{1.245c}$$

with

$$E_1(k, N_{sw}) \triangleq \sum_{R_{N_{sw}-k}+1 \le l \le R_{N_{sw}-k+1}} \pi_l; \qquad k = 1, 2, \ldots, N_{sw} \tag{1.246a}$$

$$E_2(k, N_{sw}) \triangleq \sum_{R_{N_{sw}-k}+1 \le l \le R_{N_{sw}-k+1}} l\pi_l; \qquad k = 1, 2, \ldots, N_{sw}. \tag{1.246b}$$

For large ν, it is convenient to replace the discrete *a priori* probability distribution π_k by a continuous distribution corresponding to its envelope $\pi_x(x)$ and evaluate the sums in (1.246) as integrals, namely,

$$E_1(k, N_{sw}) = \int_{(\nu/2)(1-k/N_{sw})}^{(\nu/2)(1-(k-1)/N_{sw})} \pi_x(x)\, dx \tag{1.247a}$$

$$E_2(k, N_{sw}) = \int_{(\nu/2)(1-k/N_{sw})}^{(\nu/2)(1-(k-1)/N_{sw})} x\pi_x(x)\, dx. \tag{1.247b}$$

For the symmetric triangular distribution of (1.227), we have

$$E_1(k, N_{sw}) = \frac{1}{N_{sw}}\left(\frac{2k-1}{2N_{sw}}\right)$$

$$E_2(k, N_{sw}) = \frac{\nu}{4}\left[\frac{3N_{sw}(2k-1) - 2(3k^2 - 3k + 1)}{3N_{sw}^3}\right] \tag{1.248}$$

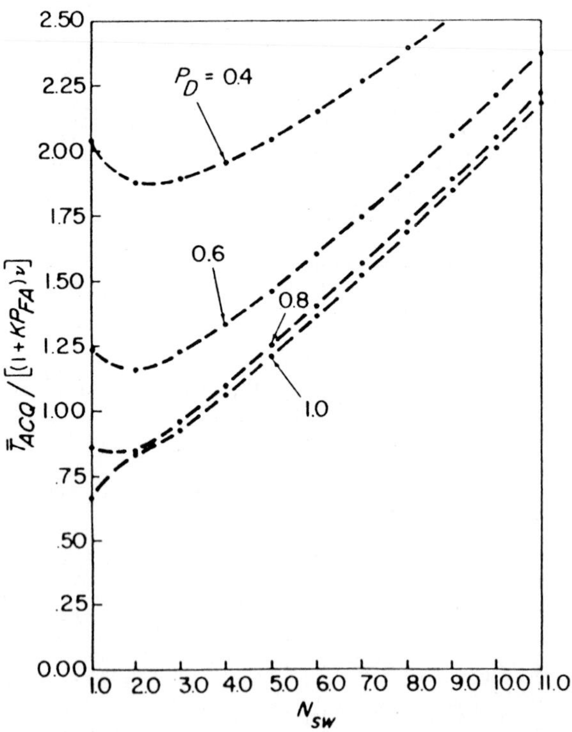

Figure 1.41. Normalized mean acquisition time versus number of partial windows for expanding window search strategy; single dwell system with triangular *a priori* distribution for code phase uncertainty.

whereas for the truncated Gaussian distribution considered in Section 1.6.1

$$E_1(k, N_{sw}) = \frac{Q\left(\frac{\nu}{2\sigma}\left(1 - \frac{k}{N_{sw}}\right)\right) - Q\left(\frac{\nu}{2\sigma}\left(1 - \frac{k-1}{N_{sw}}\right)\right)}{1 - 2Q\left(\frac{\nu}{2\sigma}\right)}$$

$$E_2(k, N_{sw})$$

$$= \sigma\left\{\frac{\exp\left[-\left(\frac{\nu}{2\sqrt{2}\,\sigma}\right)^2\left(1 - \frac{k}{N_{sw}}\right)^2\right] - \exp\left[-\left(\frac{\nu}{2\sqrt{2}\,\sigma}\right)^2\left(1 - \frac{k-1}{N_{sw}}\right)^2\right]}{1 - 2Q\left(\frac{\nu}{2\sigma}\right)}\right\}. \tag{1.249}$$

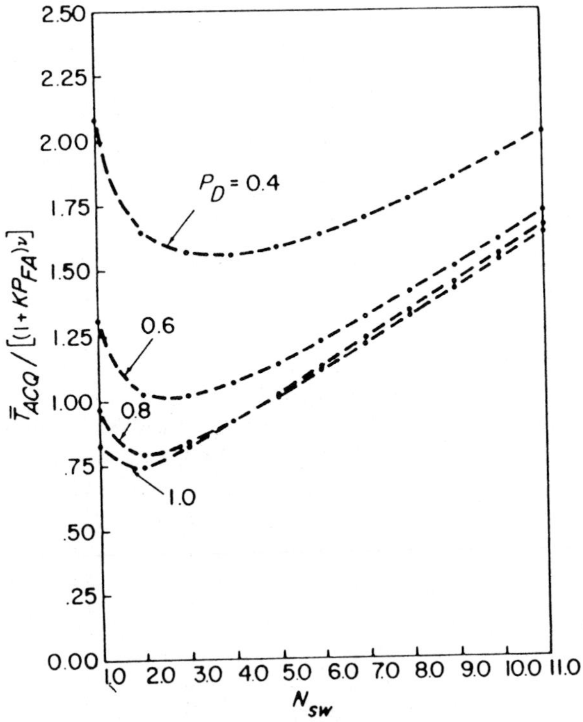

Figure 1.42a. Normalized mean acquisition time versus number of partial windows for expanding window search strategy, single dwell system with Gaussian *a priori* distribution for code phase uncertainty, $\nu/2 = 3\sigma$.

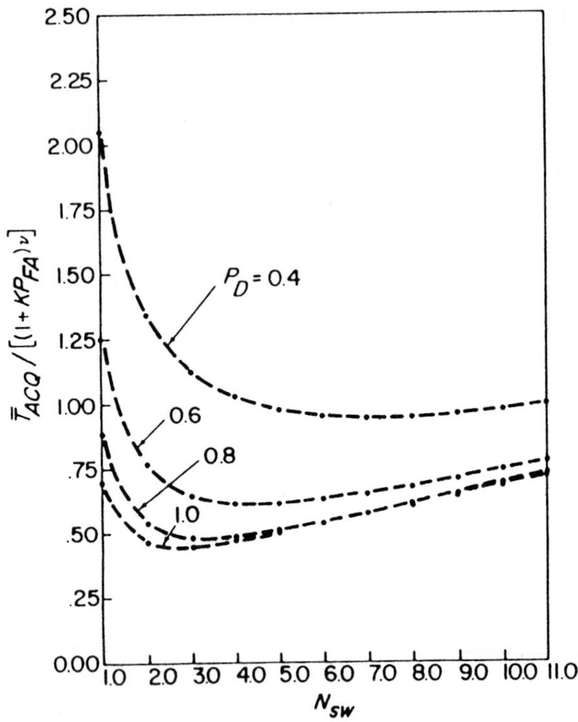

Figure 1.42b. Normalized mean acquisition time versus number of partial windows for expanding window search strategy; single dwell system with Gaussian *a priori* distribution for code phase uncertainty, $\nu/2 = 5\sigma$.

As before, we can ignore the $1/P_D$ term in (1.244) when ν is sufficiently large. Doing so, Figures 1.41 and 1.42a and 1.42b are plots of normalized acquisition time $\overline{T}_{ACQ}/[(1 + KP_{FA})\nu]$ versus the number of sweeps N_{sw} in the uncertainty region with detection probability P_D as a parameter. We observe from these figures that except for $P_D = 1$, there always exists an optimum number of partial windows in the sense of minimizing mean acquisition time. For $P_D = 1$, one window, i.e., a continuous/center z search, is optimum. Furthermore, the more peaked the distribution, e.g., Gaussian rather than triangular, or Gaussian with $\nu/2 = 5\sigma$ rather than Gaussian with $\nu/2 = 3\sigma$, the more there is to be gained by using an expanding window rather than a z-type search. Also, the sensitivity of using more than the optimum number of partial windows decreases as the distribution becomes more peaked.

1.7 PN SYNCHRONIZATION USING SEQUENTIAL DETECTION

We have already made the observation that a single fixed dwell (integration) time PN acquisition system is inefficient from an acquisition time standpoint since its detector spends as much time rejecting a false sync position as it does accepting the correct one. Clearly, if one is to minimize acquisition time, what is needed is a detector that quickly dismisses a false sync position (which occurs in all but one cell per pass through the uncertainty region) but is allowed to integrate over a much longer time interval during the single cell which corresponds to the correct code alignment.

The multiple dwell time system discussed previously was an attempt at accomplishing the above objective wherein the detector integration time was increased in *discrete* steps until the test failed (one output fell below threshold). Thus, for a false sync position, very few steps would be needed (short integration time), whereas for the true sync position, all of the steps would be needed (long integration time).

Another possibility is to allow the integration time to be *continuous* and replace the multiple threshold tests by a continuous test of a single dismissal threshold. Such a variable integration time detector is referred to as a *sequential detector* and the corresponding acquisition system is designed so that the mean time to dismiss the false sync position is much smaller than the integration time of a single dwell system. Thus, since the search spends virtually all of its time dismissing false sync positions, the mean acquisition time of the sequential detection PN acquisition system will be much less than that of the single dwell time system.

To further understand the mechanism by which the above reduction in acquisition time is achieved, we must consider a specific implementation. Consider the serial sequential detection PN acquisition system illustrated in Figure 1.43. Up until the output of the square-law envelope detector, the system operates identically to the single dwell acquisition system of Figure 1.1. Thus, in the absence of the bias voltage b, the output of the continuous time integrator would typically behave as in Figure 1.44a where we have illustrated both the signal plus noise and noise only cases. In particular, the integrator output would follow along the integrated mean of the square-law detector output, which from (1.76) and (1.75) is given by N_0Bt or $N_0B(1 + \gamma)t$, depending upon whether the cell being searched corresponds to a noise only or signal plus noise condition. Equivalently, for both hypotheses, the integrator outputs tend to increase linearly with time but at different slopes. Suppose now that one subtracts a fixed bias voltage b from the signal before integration. Then, if this bias is assigned a value between the means of the square-law detector outputs under the two hypotheses, i.e., $N_0B < b < N_0B(1 + \gamma)$, the integrator output will now tend to *decrease* linearly (with slope $N_0B - b$) when noise only is present, and *increase* linearly (with slope $N_0B(1 + \gamma) - b$) when signal plus noise is present (see Figure 1.44b). If one now chooses a threshold η (of negative value) which causes a dismissal whenever the integrator output falls below it, then the smaller the magnitude of this threshold, the faster the output for the noise only condition will dip below it.

This quick dismissal for the noise only condition is what forms the heart of the sequential detection system and provides the acquisition time ad-

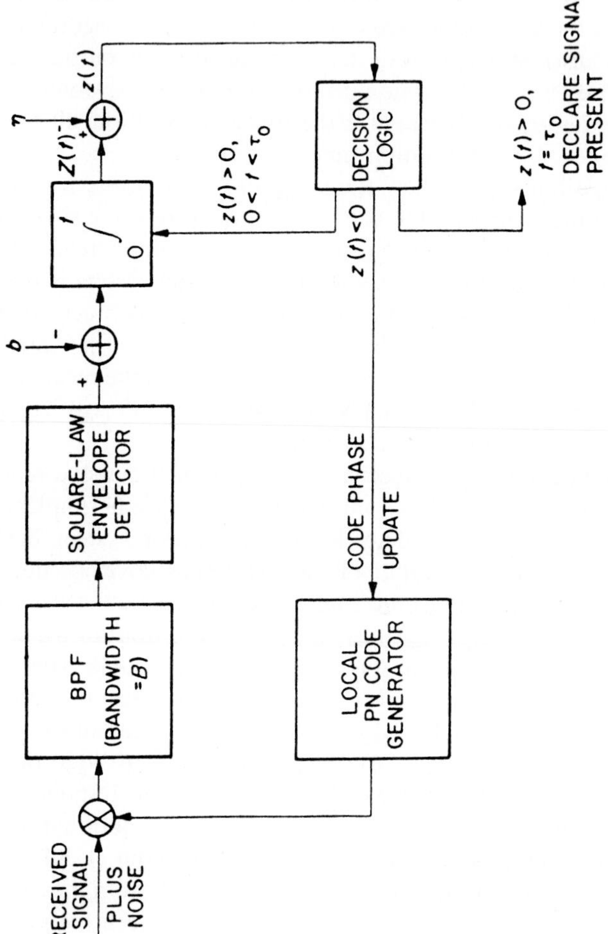

Figure 1.43. A serial sequential detection PN acquisition system with timeout feature.

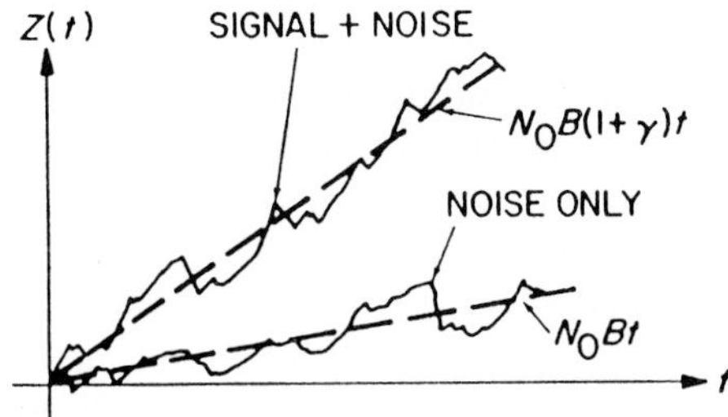

Figure 1.44a. Integrator output with bias voltage absent.

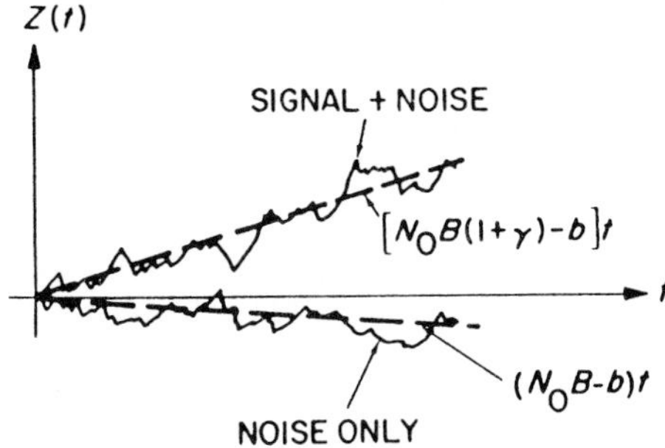

Figure 1.44b. Integrator output with bias voltage present.

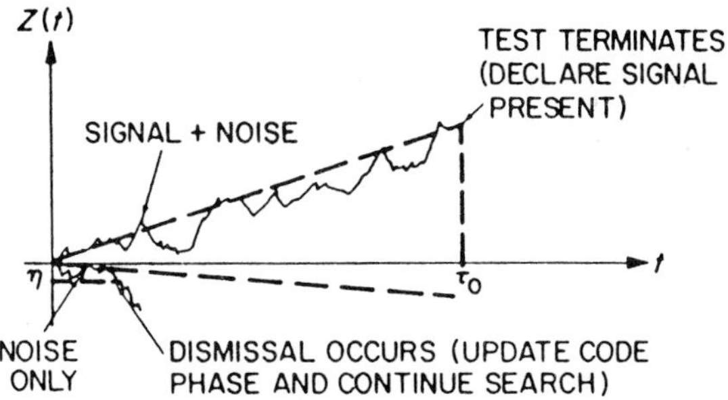

Figure 1.44c. Integrator outputs with threshold dismissal and test truncation.

vantage previously alluded to. Unfortunately, the smaller the magnitude of the threshold, the more likely is the integrator output for the signal plus noise case to also dip below the threshold thus causing a dismissal of the true sync position. Thus, a compromise threshold value must be chosen which allows for a relatively quick dismissal of false sync positions but tends to allow the integrator output for the true sync position to remain above threshold. If this latter event occurs for a designated interval of time, say τ_o, after which the test is terminated (see Figure 1.44c), then the signal is declared present and the cell being searched is declared as the true sync position. The test truncation time τ_o is often referred to as the *time-out* of the sequential detector and in some cases is replaced by a test against a second (positive-valued) threshold. In this instance, the declaration of signal present comes as soon as the integrator output rises above this positive-valued threshold rather than as a result of this output remaining above the lower (negative-valued) threshold for all $0 < t < \tau_o$.

Since the two-threshold sequential detection system is indeed the more classical type in that it represents a direct application of the sequential hypothesis testing originally discussed by Wald [10], we shall discuss its performance first before returning to the sequential detector with the upper threshold replaced by the time-out feature. Another reason for presenting the material in this order is that a good deal more attention (particularly of a theoretical nature) has been paid in the literature to the two-threshold type of system, some of which carries over to the time-out type of system. Unfortunately, both systems are extremely difficult to analyze, and thus, in most applications, one ordinarily relies on simulation results.

1.7.1 A Brief Review of Sequential Hypothesis Testing as Applied to the Non-Coherent Detection of a Sine Wave Signal in Gaussian Noise

Consider the two hypotheses H_0 and H_1 corresponding, respectively, to the application of Gaussian noise only and sine wave signal plus Gaussian noise to a square-law envelope detector as, for example, in Figure 1.45. The equations describing the input $x(t)$ and output $y(t)$ under these conditions are given by (1.58)–(1.60). Furthermore, if $y(t)$ is sampled at a rate $1/B$, then the samples y_k have a probability density function $p_0(y_k')$ given by (1.63) or $p_1(y_k)$ given by (1.61), where the subscript on $p(y_k)$ now corresponds to that on the particular hypothesis being tested.

Define the log-likelihood function

$$\Lambda_k = \ln\frac{p_1(y_k)}{p_0(y_k)} = \ln\left[e^{-\gamma}I_0\left(2\sqrt{\frac{\gamma y_k}{2\sigma^2}}\right)\right]$$
$$= -\gamma + \ln\left[I_0\left(2\sqrt{\frac{\gamma y_k}{2\sigma^2}}\right)\right]. \tag{1.250}$$

Then the sequential *probability ratio* test [27] for the non-coherent detection of a sine wave signal in Gaussian noise sequentially compares the running sum

$$v_i = \sum_{k=1}^{i}\Lambda_k = \sum_{k=1}^{i}\left(-\gamma + \ln\left[I_0\left(2\sqrt{\gamma y_k^*}\right)\right]\right) \tag{1.251}$$

to two thresholds η_1' and η_2' ($\eta_2' < \eta_1'$), where as before it is convenient to talk about the normalized samples $y_k^* \triangleq y_k/2\sigma^2 = y_k/N_0B$. The comparison is made for each $i = 1, 2, \ldots$ until the inequalities $\eta_2' < v_i < \eta_1'$ are not satisfied. Then, if $v_i \le \eta_2'$, it is decided that the signal is not present (dismissal), and if $\eta_1' \le v_i$, it is decided that the signal is present (alarm).

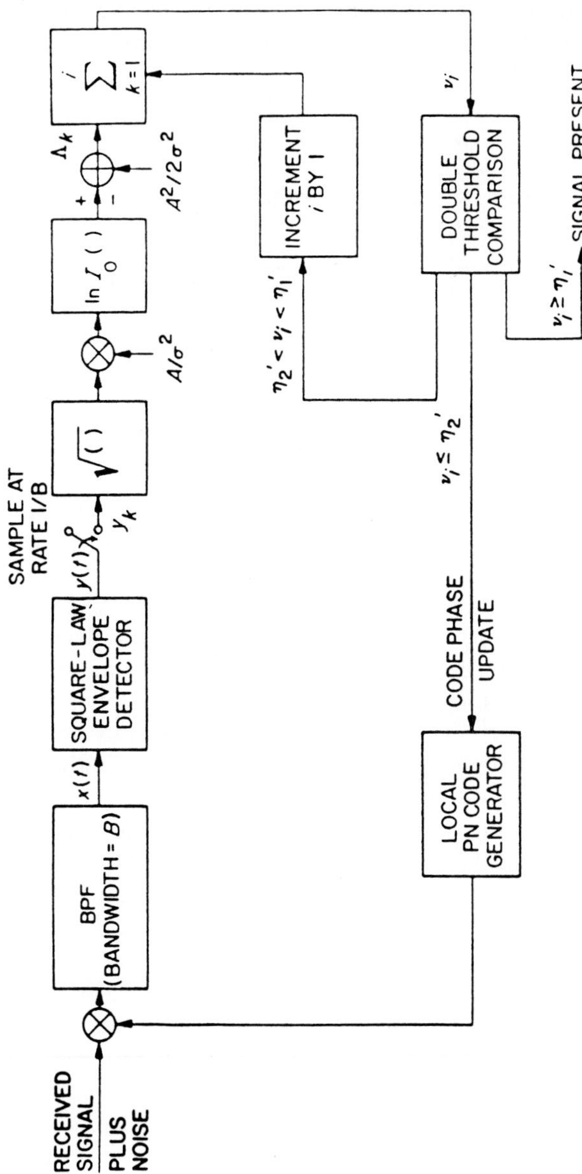

Figure 1.45. Block diagram of a sequential detection PN acquisition system.

Figure 1.45 is a block diagram of the sequential detector with test statistic as in (1.251).

In some discussions of sequential detection, an envelope detector alone is postulated instead of a square-law envelope detector. In this case, the samples of the envelope detector output would have probability density functions

$$p_0(y_k) = \begin{cases} \dfrac{y_k}{\sigma^2}\exp\left(-\dfrac{y_k^2}{2\sigma^2}\right); & y_k \geq 0 \\ 0; & \text{otherwise} \end{cases}$$

$$p_1(y_k) = \begin{cases} \dfrac{y_k}{\sigma^2}\exp\left[-\left(\dfrac{y_k^2}{2\sigma^2} + \gamma\right)\right] I_0\left(2y_k\sqrt{\dfrac{\gamma}{2\sigma^2}}\right); & y_k \geq 0 \\ 0; & \text{otherwise} \end{cases} \tag{1.252}$$

and log-likelihood function

$$\begin{aligned} \Lambda_k &= \ln\left[e^{-\gamma} I_0\left(2y_k\sqrt{\frac{\gamma}{2\sigma^2}}\right)\right] \\ &= -\gamma + \ln\left[I_0\left(2y_k\sqrt{\frac{\gamma}{2\sigma^2}}\right)\right]. \end{aligned} \tag{1.253}$$

Comparing (1.253) with (1.250), we note that the block diagram of Figure 1.45 can be made to apply to the sequential detection system with an envelope detector by simply removing the square root device preceding the multiplication by A/σ^2. This result is intuitively obvious since the tandem combination of square-law and square-root devices following an envelope detector has no effect on its output.

Wald showed [10] that the thresholds η_1' and η_2' are approximately related to the probabilities of false alarm P_{FA} and detection P_D by

$$P_{FA} \cong \frac{1 - \exp(\eta_2')}{\exp(\eta_1') - \exp(\eta_2')} \tag{1.254}$$

and

$$P_D \cong \frac{\exp(\eta_1') - \exp(\eta_1' + \eta_2')}{\exp(\eta_1') - \exp(\eta_2')}. \tag{1.255}$$

Furthermore, the average number of samples $\overline{N}_d$ required to dismiss when signal is not present was shown to be approximately given by the expression

$$\overline{N}_d = \frac{P_{FA}\eta_1' + (1 - P_{FA})\eta_2'}{E\{\Lambda_k\}} = \frac{P_{FA}\ln\left(\dfrac{P_D}{P_{FA}}\right) + (1 - P_{FA})\ln\left(\dfrac{1 - P_D}{1 - P_{FA}}\right)}{E\{\Lambda_k\}} \tag{1.256}$$

where from (1.73) and (1.251)

$$E\{\Lambda_k\} = -\gamma + \int_0^{\infty} \ln\left[I_0\left(2\sqrt{\gamma y_k^*}\right)\right]\exp(-y^*)\,dy^*. \tag{1.257}$$

Evaluation of (1.256) is difficult because of the requirement to accurately compute the expectation in (1.257) for each value of γ of interest. Since the integral cannot be obtained in closed form, one can either evaluate it using numerical integration or first expand the $\ln I_0$ function in a power series and compute as many moments of y_k^* as necessary to achieve the desired degree of accuracy. In the case of the latter, approximation of $\ln I_0(x)$ by only the first few terms in the expansion restricts its validity to small values of x or, equivalently, small values of pre-detection SNR.

Another approach based on the small SNR assumption is to make a similar expansion of $\ln I_0(x)$ *directly in the sequential test statistic* of (1.251) and keep only the first few terms. Doing this has the effect of simplifying the detector implementation, which, except when digital processing allows use of a look-up table for $\ln I_0(x)$, is ordinarily difficult. In the next section, we discuss a small SNR sequential test and the corresponding detector performance corresponding to a two-term approximation of the $\ln I_0$ function.

1.7.2 The Biased Square-Law Sequential Detector

Although (1.251) defines a sequential test for the optimum detector, the important case of small pre-detection SNR allows one to simplify this equation into a similar test for an easier to implement (and analyze) detector as follows. When γ is small, the $\ln I_0$ function can be approximated by the first two terms of its power series, namely,

$$\ln I_0(x) \cong \frac{x^2}{4} - \frac{x^4}{64}. \tag{1.258}$$

Applying (1.258) to (1.251) then gives

$$v_i = \sum_{k=1}^{i}\left(-\gamma + \gamma y_k^* - \frac{1}{4}\gamma^2 y_k^{*2}\right). \tag{1.259}$$

As suggested in [27], the latter term in (1.259) is further approximated by its expected value when no signal is present. Thus, from (1.76)

$$\overline{y_k^{*2}} = \sigma_{y^*}^2 + \left(\overline{y^*}\right)^2 = 2 \tag{1.260}$$

and

$$\begin{aligned} v_i &\cong \sum_{k=1}^{i}\left(-\gamma + \gamma y_k^* - \frac{\gamma^2}{2}\right) \\ &= \sum_{k=1}^{i}\gamma\left[y_k^* - \left(1 + \frac{\gamma}{2}\right)\right] \end{aligned} \tag{1.261}$$

Normalizing v_i by N_0B/γ and recalling the relation between y_k and y_k^* gives the sequential test statistic corresponding to the optimum detector *for small SNR*, namely,

$$Z_i \triangleq \frac{N_0 B}{\gamma} v_i = \sum_{k=1}^{i} (y_k - b) = \sum_{k=1}^{i} Y_k \tag{1.262}$$

where from (1.261) the bias b is given by

$$b = N_0 B\left(1 + \frac{\gamma}{2}\right). \tag{1.263}$$

A block diagram of the small SNR sequential detector is illustrated in Figure 1.46. Identifying (1.262) with Z of (1.64) when $N_B = 1$, one observes that the optimum bias of (1.263) lies halfway between the means of the square-law detector output under the hypotheses H_0 and H_1. Equivalently, for this choice of bias, the integrator output in the presence of the bias voltage will tend to increase linearly when signal plus noise are present at the same rate that it tends to decrease linearly when noise only is present (see Figure 1.44b).

Before proceeding to a discussion of performance, we hasten to point out that for a two-hypothesis test of a sampled random variable, the sequential probability-ratio test is optimum in the sense that, for given P_{FA} and P_D, it requires the minimum average number of samples to produce a decision. For our application, namely, rapid acquisition of a PN sequence in noise, minimizing the average number of samples required is equivalent to minimizing the average dwell time per code phase cell being searched.

Although the sequential probability-ratio test was discovered by Wald in the early 1940's while working on radar detection, an accurate characterization of its performance did not come until many years later. In particular, the integral equation approach of Albert [28][31] was applied by Kendall [29] in 1965 to give exact solutions for the false alarm probability and average test duration of the biased square-law sequential detector in the absence of signal. These results were unique in that they were valid without any restrictions on either the pre-detection SNR or on the thresholds η_1 and η_2. In the next section, we summarize these results beginning with a brief presentation of Albert's integral equation approach.

1.7.3 Probability of False Alarm and Average Test Duration in the Absence of Signal

Let $\{x_i\}$ represent a sequence of observables which form a stationary Markov process with transitions governed by the probability distribution function $F(x_i|x_{i-1})$. Denote by d_i, $i = 1,2$ a pair of decisions which is to

[31]Actually, Albert's work considered a far more general sequential test than the sequential probability-ratio test of Wald. Our interest, however, is only in Wald's test, which is a special case of Albert's results corresponding to stationary increments in the log-likelihood ratio.

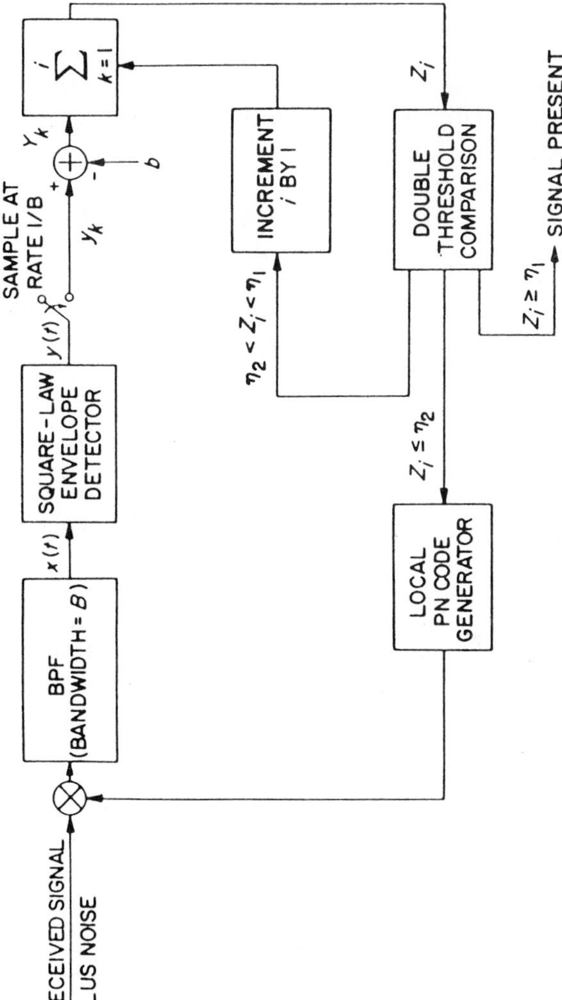

Figure 1.46. Block diagram of a small SNR sequential detection PN acquisition system.

be made about $F(x_i|x_{i-1})$ and d_0 the decision to defer making either d_1 or d_2. The test is conducted by first choosing an arbitrary starting point x_0 (later on we shall set $x_0 = 0$) and making one of the decisions d_i with probabilities $\pi_i(x_0)$, $i = 0, 1, 2$. If either d_1 or d_2 is made the test continues and the element x_1 is drawn using the distribution $F(x_1|x_0)$. Once again one of the decisions is made with the set of probabilities $\pi_i(x_1)$, $i = 0, 1, 2$ and the test either terminates or x_2 is drawn using the distribution $F(x_2|x_1)$. This process is continued until either d_1 or d_2 is made. To guarantee that this occurs with unit probability in a finite number of trials, it must be assumed that there exists an integer M and some $\rho < 1$ such that for all $m \geq M$ the inequality

$$\int_{-\infty}^{\infty}\int_{-\infty}^{\infty}\cdots\int_{-\infty}^{\infty}\prod_{i=1}^{m}\pi_0(x_i)\,dF(x_i|x_{i-1}) \leq \rho \leq 1 \tag{1.264}$$

is satisfied for all x_0.

Using the foregoing model Albert [28] shows that the probability $P_i(x_0)$ that the test ends with decision d_1 or d_2 satisfies the integral equation

$$P_i(x_0) = \pi_i(x_0) + \pi_0(x_0)\int_{-\infty}^{\infty} P_i(y)\,dF(y|x_0) \tag{1.265}$$

and the average test duration (average sample number) $M_1(x_0)$ satisfies the integral equation

$$M_1(x_0) = \pi_0(x_0) + \pi_0(x_0)\int_{-\infty}^{\infty} M_1(y)\,dF(y|x_0). \tag{1.266}$$

For most cases of interest, these integral equations are difficult if not impossible to solve. However, for the non-coherent sequential detection of a sine wave in Gaussian noise using a biased square-law detector, Kendall [29] was able to obtain exact solutions. In particular, the sequence $\{x_i\}$ now corresponds to $\{Z_i\}$ of (1.262), d_1 is the dismissal decision, and d_2 is the alarm decision. Since from (1.262), $Z_i = Z_{i-1} + Y_i = Z_{i-1} + y_i - b$, then, using (1.63),

$$dF(Z_i|Z_{i-1}) = \begin{cases} \dfrac{1}{2\sigma^2}\exp\left[-\left(\dfrac{Z_i - Z_{i-1} + b}{2\sigma^2}\right)\right] dZ_i; & Z_i - Z_{i-1} \geq b \\ 0; & \text{otherwise} \end{cases}. \tag{1.267}$$

Also, the set of decision probabilities $\pi_i(Z_k)$, $i = 0, 1, 2$ is stationary (i.e., independent of k) and given by

$$\pi_0(z) = \begin{cases} 1; & \eta_2 < Z < \eta_1 \\ 0; & \text{otherwise} \end{cases}$$

$$\pi_1(z) = \begin{cases} 1; & Z \leq \eta_2 \\ 0; & \eta_2 < Z \end{cases}$$

$$\pi_2(z) = \begin{cases} 1, & \eta_1 \leq Z \\ 0; & Z < \eta_1 \end{cases}. \tag{1.268}$$

Finally, letting $Z_0 = 0$, then, for $\eta_2 < 0 < \eta_1$,

$$P_{FA} \triangleq P_2(0) = \frac{\exp(-\eta_2'/\gamma)G(-D\eta_2'; Db')}{\exp[(\eta_1' - \eta_2' + b')/\gamma]G[D(\eta_1' - \eta_2' + b'); Db']} \tag{1.269}$$

where we have introduced the normalizations

$$b' \triangleq \frac{\gamma b}{2\sigma^2} = \frac{\gamma b}{N_0 B}$$
$$\eta_i' \triangleq \frac{\gamma \eta_i}{2\sigma^2} = \frac{\gamma \eta_i}{N_0 B}; \; i = 1,2 \tag{1.270}$$

and

$$D \triangleq \frac{1}{\gamma}\exp(-b'/\gamma). \tag{1.271}$$

Also, the function $G(x; c)$ is defined by

$$G(x; c) = 1 + \sum_{n=1}^{N} \frac{(nc - x)^n}{n!} \tag{1.272}$$

where N is an integer chosen to satisfy the inequalities

$$c \leq Nc \leq x \leq (N+1)c. \tag{1.273}$$

By similar methods, Kendall [29] obtains a solution to (1.266) for the average sample number $\overline{N}_d$ which is given by

$$\overline{N}_d \triangleq M_1(0) = \exp(-\eta_2'/\gamma)H[-D\eta_2'; Db'] + P_2(0)\{1 - \exp[(\eta_1' - \eta_2' + b')/\gamma]H[D(\eta_1' - \eta_2' + b'); Db']\} \tag{1.274}$$

where $P_2(0)$ is given by (1.269) and

$$H(x; c) \triangleq (N+1)\exp(-x/\gamma D) - \sum_{n=1}^{N}\sum_{i=0}^{n-1} \frac{(nc - x)^i}{i!(\gamma D)^{i-n}} \tag{1.275}$$

with N still obtained from (1.273). The *average test duration* $\bar{\tau}_d$, for the particular noise only cell under investigation, is simply

$$\bar{\tau}_d = \overline{N}_d / B \tag{1.276}$$

since for the real system the Z_i represent samples taken at a rate $1/B$.

Before presenting numerical illustrations of these results, we point out that with suitable approximations they can be shown to agree with Wald's results [10]. In particular, since Wald's results are approximate in that they neglect the "excess over the bounds," i.e., at the end of the test we have either $Z_i \leq \eta_2$ or $\eta_1 \leq Z_i$, not simply $Z_i = \eta_2$ or $Z_i = \eta_1$, then if the values of the thresholds are such that this effect is negligible, Albert's results simplify to those of Wald. Also, the normalized threshold b' of (1.270) is not required to correspond to the optimum bias of (1.263), i.e.,

$$b' = \gamma\left(1 + \frac{\gamma}{2}\right) = \gamma + \frac{\gamma^2}{2} \tag{1.277}$$

and thus, with Albert's approach, one can study the effect of bias variations on the resulting performance measures. On the other hand, although not previously stated, Wald's result for false alarm probability as applied to the square-law biased detector implies the optimum bias of (1.263) and furthermore is independent of γ [see (1.254)].

Figure 1.47 contains three sets of plots of false alarm probability versus the upper threshold η_1' with pre-detection signal-to-noise ratio γ as a parameter. The first set of plots corresponds to Wald's result of (1.254). The remaining two sets are obtained from Albert's exact result, i.e., (1.269) with two different biases, namely, the optimum choice of (1.277) and $b' = \gamma$. Perhaps the most striking feature of the exact results is their extreme sensitivity to small variations in bias. For example, when $\gamma = .01$, then from (1.277) we would have an optimum bias $b' = .01005$, which only differs from $b' = \gamma = .01$ by an amount equal to .00005. Nevertheless, the false alarm probabilities for these two bias values are markedly different. A similar situation occurs in Figure 1.48 where the average sample number $M_1(0)$ is plotted versus γ with lower threshold η_2' as a parameter and the same three situations as in Figure 1.47. Here, Wald's result for the average sample number of a sequential test corresponds to evaluating (1.256) with the $\ln I_0$ function in (1.257) approximated, as previously discussed, by (1.258). Performing the expectation with the aid of (1.76) gives

$$E\{\Lambda_k\} = -\frac{\gamma^2}{2} \tag{1.278}$$

which when substituted in (1.256) results in

$$M_1(0) = -\frac{P_{FA}\eta_1' + (1 - P_{FA})\eta_2'}{\gamma^2/2} \tag{1.279}$$

where P_{FA} is given by (1.254).

Unfortunately, a similar analysis for the case of signal present is difficult and has not been made available in the open literature. Thus, the relationship among detection probability, pre-detection signal-to-noise ratio, bias, and the two-decision thresholds has not been obtained and, as a result, a complete analytical characterization of the moments of the system acquisition time is not possible.

Another unfortunate situation occurs in regard to the application of Albert's approach to the time-out type of sequential detection system (see Figure 1.43) where the upper threshold is replaced by a maximum time feature. Even in the case of signal absent, there appears to be no valid modification of the basic approach to apply to this situation.

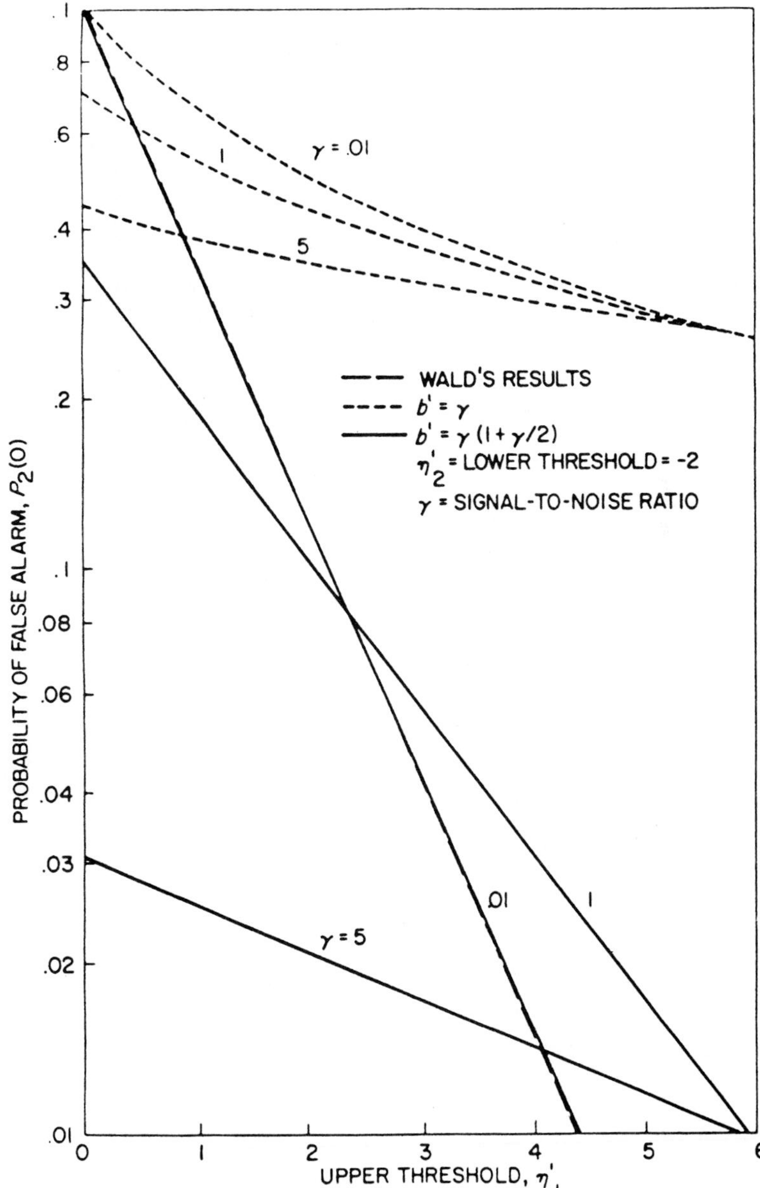

Figure 1.47. Probability of alarm for the biased square-law detector when the signal is not present (reprinted from [29]).

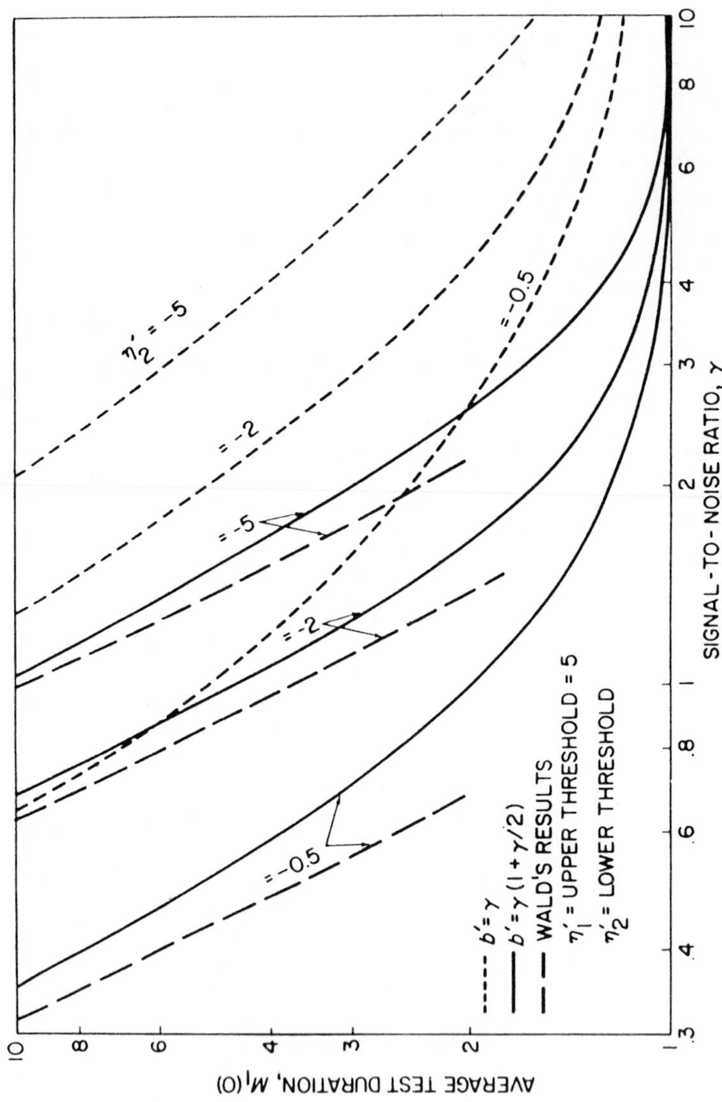

Figure 1.48. Average test duration for the biased square-law detector when the signal is not present (reprinted from [29]).

In view of the foregoing limitations and analytical difficulties, one normally, at this point, turns to a simulation approach. The salient features of such an approach along with typical numerical illustrative results are presented in the next section. Before competely abandoning the analytical approach, however, we recall that Wald's approximate analysis does indeed provide us with a relationship among false alarm probability, detection probability, and the upper and lower detection thresholds [see (1.254) and (1.255)]. Thus, in the region of validity of his approach, i.e., small values of γ and the bias of (1.263), one can combine (1.254) and (1.255) with (1.276) and (1.279) and obtain an expression for the average dismissal time (average test duration for a noise only cell). This relation can then be compared with the fixed dwell time determined from (1.81) for the single dwell system to establish the degree of superiority of the sequential detector.

Thus, we conclude this section with a comparison of the mean search times of the single dwell and sequential detection systems using Wald's approach to analytically characterize the latter. In particular, from (1.254)

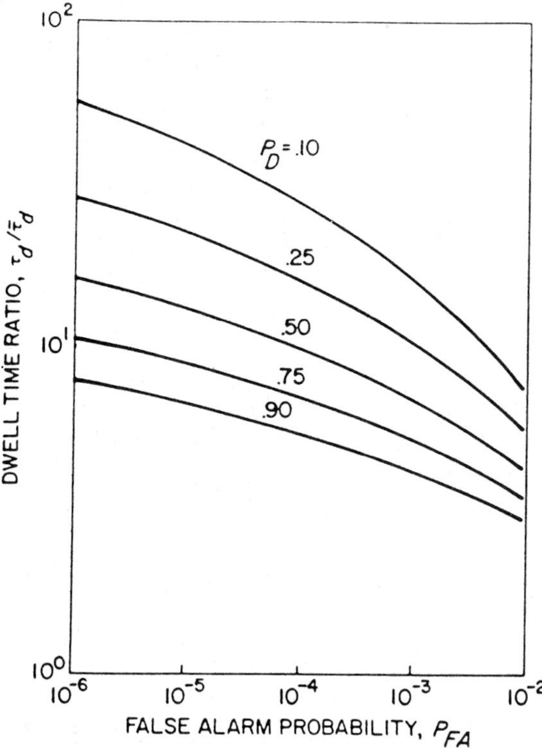

Figure 1.49. A comparison of the average dwell (dismissal) time of a square-law sequential detection system with the dwell time of a fixed single dwell system; $\gamma = -20$ dB.

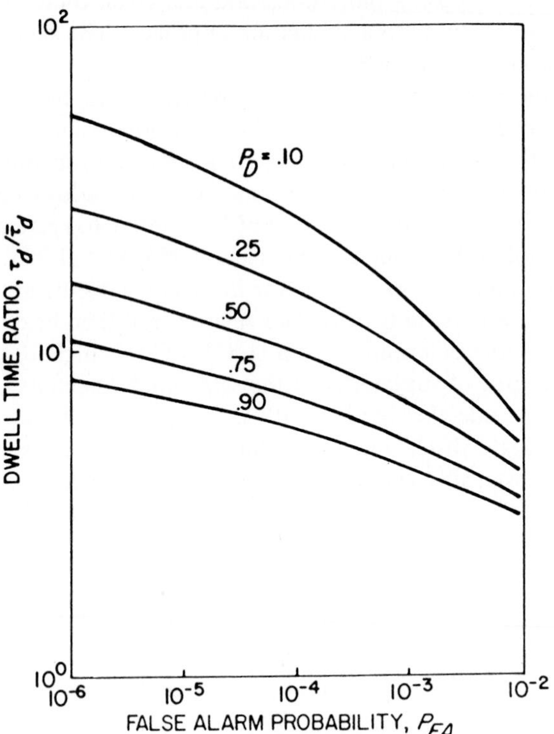

Figure 1.50. A comparison of the average dwell (dismissal) time of a square-law sequential detection system with the dwell time of a fixed single dwell system; $\gamma = -10$ dB.

and (1.255) we obtain

$$\eta_1' = \ln \frac{P_D}{P_{FA}}$$

$$\eta_2' = \ln \frac{1 - P_D}{1 - P_{FA}} \tag{1.280}$$

which when substituted in (1.279) and combined with (1.276) yields

$$B\bar{\tau}_d = -\frac{P_{FA} \ln \dfrac{P_D}{P_{FA}} + (1 - P_{FA}) \ln \dfrac{1 - P_D}{1 - P_{FA}}}{\gamma^2/2}. \tag{1.281}$$

For the single dwell system, solving (1.81) for $B\tau_d$ and, for simplicity, ignoring the prime on γ' gives

$$B\tau_d = \left[\frac{Q^{-1}(P_{FA}) - \sqrt{1 + 2\gamma}\, Q^{-1}(P_D)}{\gamma}\right]^2. \tag{1.282}$$

Figures 1.49 and 1.50 are plots of the ratio $\tau_d/\bar{\tau}_d$ versus P_{FA} with P_D as a parameter and $\gamma = -20$ dB and $\gamma = -10$ dB respectively. A comparison of the two sets of curves reveals their relative insensitivity to the value of pre-detection signal-to-noise ratio γ.

1.7.4 Simulation Results

The final approach for evaluating the performance of a sequential detection system is to simulate the system on a digital computer. Although consuming considerable amounts of computer time, this approach has many advantages over the previously discussed analytical and numerical evaluation techniques. Some of these advantages are as follows:

(1) It allows performance evaluation over a wide range of system parameters, e.g., thresholds, signal-to-noise ratios, false alarm and detection probabilities, etc., merely by changing the program input data.

(2) It is a more "exact" representation of the system behavior. For example, the analytic results presented in the previous two sections originated from consideration of the radar problem where the signal is either "fully on" or not present. In Section 1.2.5 we pointed out that in the spread-spectrum application, the signal may be only "partially on" in that, because of the granularity of the half-chip search step, the signal-present condition occurs at several points along the PN correlation curve. Furthermore, the received PN code is, in general, not synchronous with the local replica so that none of the above signal-present conditions corresponds to fully on; thus, the true signal-to-noise ratio is a random variable that depends on the degree of misalignment between the two codes. Although some approximate analytical modifications were suggested in Section 1.2.5 to try and account for these effects, a simulation can directly model these effects by modelling the code start time as a uniformly distributed random variable between zero and one half of a chip. Simulation results [30] indicate an SNR penalty of about 1 dB due to this random code alignment rather than the pessimistic 2.5 dB suggested in Section 1.2.5 corresponding to a worst case (quarter of a chip) misalignment.

(3) It allows for the consideration of other simplified detector implementations whose performance is either difficult or impossible to evaluate analytically. For example, with a digital implementation, an absolute value detector function might be preferable. Comparison of this implementation with a square-law envelope detector, envelope detector, or the "ideal" detector of Figure 1.45 is then straightforward with a simulation approach.

(4) Finally, the simulation approach is useful in establishing the regions of validity of the various analytical and numerical approximations.

We begin our discussion of simulation results with a comparison of the noise-only behavior of the sequential test for four different detector types. In particular, we examine the variation of false alarm probability and average number of samples to dismiss as a function of bias for:

1. the "ideal" detector (Figure 1.45)
2. the square-law envelope detector (Figure 1.46)

3. the envelope detector (Figure 1.46 with an envelope instead of a square-law envelope detector)
4. the absolute-value envelope detector (Figure 1.46 with an absolute value instead of a square-law envelope detector).

If, for the square-law envelope detector of case (2), the detector output samples y_k are characterized as in (1.60), namely,

$$y_k = (A + n_{ck})^2 + n_{sk}^2 \tag{1.283}$$

where $y_k \triangleq y(kT)$, $n_{ck} \triangleq n_c(kT)$, and $n_{sk} \triangleq n_s(kT)$, then for the envelope detector of case (3) we would have

$$y_k = \sqrt{(A + n_{ck})^2 + n_{sk}^2}\,. \tag{1.284}$$

Similarly, the absolute-value detector model of case (4) would imply

$$y_k = |A + n_{ck}| + |n_{sk}| \tag{1.285}$$

which simulates inphase and quadrature sampling with a large number of quantization levels and the sign bit discarded.

From our previous discussions, it is clear that for all of the above implementations, the sequential test is governed by the choice of three variables, namely, the upper and lower thresholds and the bias. Typically, the upper threshold and bias determine the false alarm probability, P_{FA}, whereas the lower threshold and bias determine the average number of samples to dismiss, $\overline{N}_d$.

Simulation results [30] performed on all four detector types reveal that the false alarm probability is governed by the relation

$$P_{FA} = 0.5\exp(-fT_u) \tag{1.286}$$

where f is a false-alarm rate parameter whose variation with detector type and bias is illustrated in Figure 1.51 and T_u denotes the upper test threshold. The table below relates, for each of the four above cases, the bias and T_u to the analogous parameters previously introduced in this section.

Detector Type	Bias	T_u
Ideal	$\gamma b/2\sigma^2 = b'$	$\gamma\eta_1/2\sigma^2 = \eta_1'$
Square-law	$b/2\sigma^2 = b'/\gamma$	$\eta_1/2\sigma^2 = \eta_1'/\gamma$
Envelope	$b/\sqrt{2}\,\sigma$	$\eta_1/\sqrt{2}\,\sigma$
Absolute-value	$b/\sqrt{2}\,\sigma$	$\eta_1/\sqrt{2}\,\sigma$

From the results in Figure 1.51, we observe that, for the ideal detector, $f = 1$ independent of the bias point, whereas the other detector types have a linear dependence of f on the logarithm of the bias point. This dependence of cases (2), (3), and (4) on bias point could no doubt be removed by a gain normalization of the detector output samples analogous to the A/σ^2 multiplication for the ideal detector (see Figure 1.45). However, the primary purpose of the comparison being to discover the effects of simple implemen-

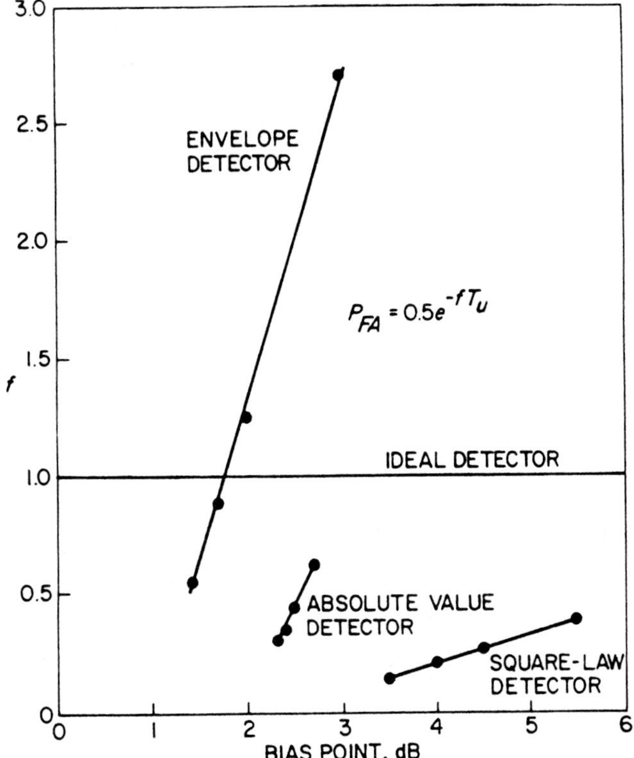

Figure 1.51. Variation in false alarm parameter f with bias point (reprinted from [30]).

tations, such a gain normalization was not introduced into the simulation runs.

Further simulation results [30] performed on the same four detector types produced the following approximate relationship (valid for $\overline{N}_d > 3$) characterizing the average number of samples per dismissal (average sample number):

$$\overline{N}_d = 1.5 - dT_L \tag{1.287}$$

where d is a dismissal parameter whose variation with detector type and bias is illustrated in Figure 1.52 and T_L denotes the lower detection threshold (a negative quantity). Here again T_L is related to η_2 and η_2' in the identical way that T_u was previously related to η_1 and η_1' for the four cases under investigation. Furthermore, the results in Figure 1.52 were generated by setting the bias point to the desired value and then setting T_u to give $P_{FA} = 10^{-6}$ in accordance with (1.286) and the value of f determined from Figure 1.51.

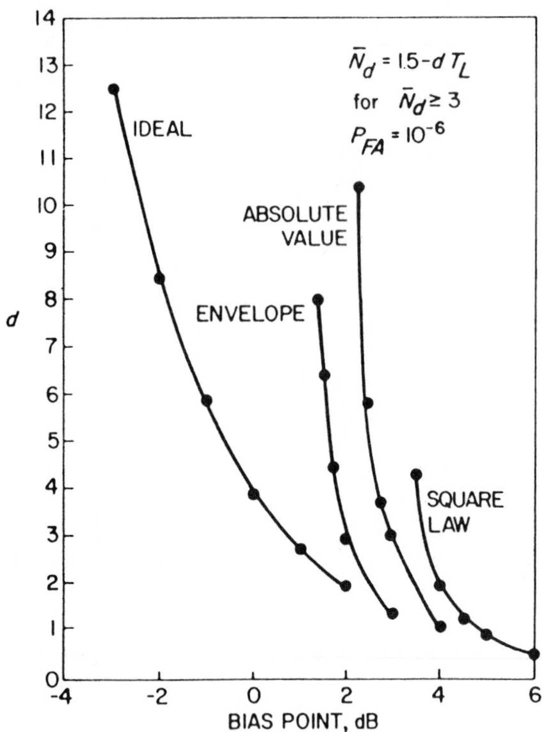

Figure 1.52. Variation of dismissal parameter d with bias point (reprinted from [30]).

In summary, the noise-only simulation results of Figures 1.51 and 1.52 indicate that increasing the bias is effective both in reducing the false alarm probability (except for the ideal detector) and reducing the average number of samples per dismissal.

Simulation results for the signal-plus-noise hypothesis are presented in Figures 1.53 and 1.54, which plot missed detection probability $(1 - P_D)$ versus bias for perfect code phase (operation at the precise peak of the PN code autocorrelation function) and random code phase, respectively. For both sets of plots the pre-detection signal-to-noise ratio γ is chosen equal to 0 dB. Furthermore, for each value of bias point, values of f and d are determined from Figures 1.51 and 1.52, which for $P_{FA} = 10^{-6}$ and $\bar{N}_d = 10.5$ allow calculation of the upper and lower thresholds T_u and T_L from (1.286) and (1.287), respectively. Figure 1.53 reveals the not too surprising result that for each detector implementation there exists an optimum value of bias in the sense of minimum miss probability. Clearly, for the ideal detector with perfect code phase, this optimum bias should theoretically be equal to the pre-detection signal-to-noise ratio, i.e., 0 dB. The simulation results essentially bear this out. What is perhaps surprising, however, is the fact

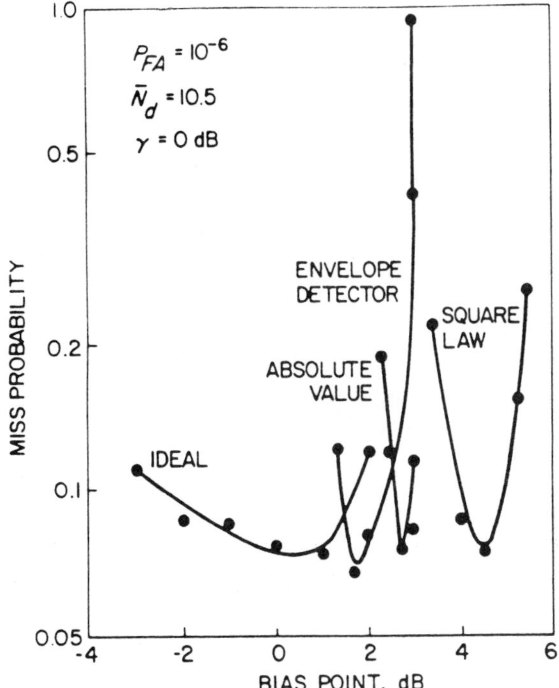

Figure 1.53. Bias points for the various detector types, perfect code phase (reprinted from [30]).

that the ideal detector appears to show no advantage over the other three implementations when all are biased at their respective optimum points. (The fact that the ideal detector minimum appears slightly larger than that for the envelope detector is due to statistical variations in calculating $1 - P_D$ and $\bar{N}_d$).

Another interesting result which may be gleaned from those in both Figure 1.53 and 1.54 is the fact that the ideal detector is much less sensitive to variations about the optimum bias point than the other detectors. This implies more robust performance for the ideal detector in the sense of being more tolerant to parameter variations. This comes as an added bonus to its already optimum behavior in the sense of minimum dismissal time versus miss probability.

A comparison of Figures 1.53 and 1.54 reveals the anticipated results that (1) the optimum bias points are all lower for random code phase, (2) the miss probability is higher for random code phase, and (3) the optimum points are all more sharply defined for random code phase.

Suppose now we assume that the various configurations are designed corresponding to their optimum bias points as determined from Figure 1.54,

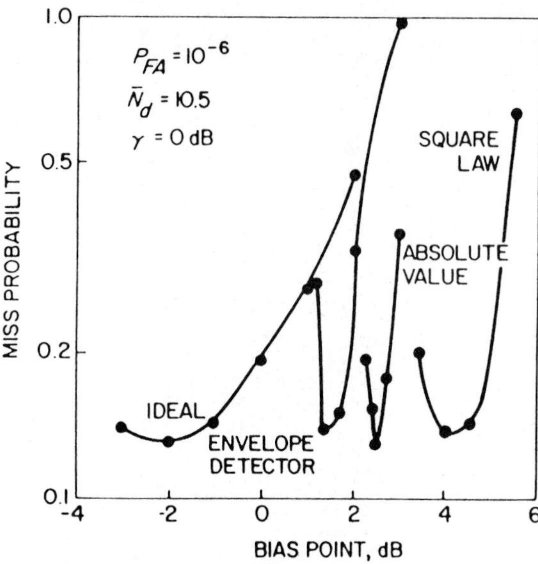

Figure 1.54. Bias points for detectors with random code phase (reprinted from [30]).

namely, -2 dB for the ideal detector, 4.0 dB for the square-law envelope detector, and 2.5 dB for the absolute-value envelope detector. Corresponding to these optimum bias points, upper and lower thresholds can be determined for each configuration from Figures 1.51 and 1.52 and (1.286) and (1.287), assuming P_{FA} and $\bar{N}_d$ are fixed. Then, as the pre-detection signal-to-noise ratio varies about its design point of 0 dB, the miss probability will vary about its design point value (minimum of curves in Figure 1.54) as indicated in Figure 1.55. This portrayal of the variation of miss probability as a function of the predetection signal-to-noise ratio for a fixed design point is often referred to as the "operating characteristic" of the sequential test [11]. To a first-order approximation, the results of Figure 1.55 reveal that the operating characteristic is the same for all four implementations when they are designed with optimized bias.

To wrap up our discussion of simulation results, we now return to the time-out type of sequential detection system introduced earlier in Figure 1.53. Again, this system could be configured with other types of detector implementations as in our discussion of the two-threshold system. However, since the relative performance of these various detector implementations would qualitatively be the same for the acquisition system with the time-out feature as for the two-threshold system, we shall concentrate only on the square-law envelope detector and focus all our attention on whatever behavioral differences occur due to the change in decision logic.

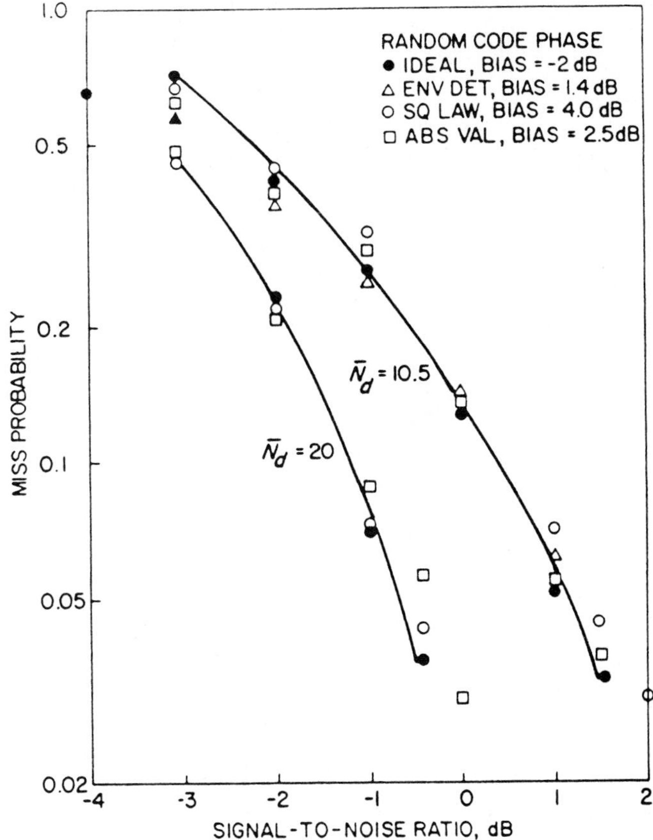

Figure 1.55. Comparison of S/N performance of various detector types at optimum bias point for 0 dB S/N (reprinted from [30]).

Figure 1.56 illustrates the false alarm probability as a function of normalized test truncation time (time-out) $B\tau_o$ for several different values of normalized lower detection threshold η_2/N_0B and normalized bias b/N_0B. The bias values are computed from (1.263) and as such correspond to pre-detection signal-to-noise ratios $\gamma = -17.5$, -15.0, and -12.5 dB. For sufficiently large $B\tau_o$, we observe that P_{FA} decreases exponentially with an exponent whose magnitude increases with increasing bias but is essentially independent of lower threshold. Qualitatively this behavior is analogous to that previously discussed for the two-threshold system with regard to the behavior of false alarm probability versus normalized upper threshold and bias.

Figure 1.57 illustrates the corresponding results for the average sample number $\bar{N}_d$. Again the behavior here is qualitatively similar to that of the

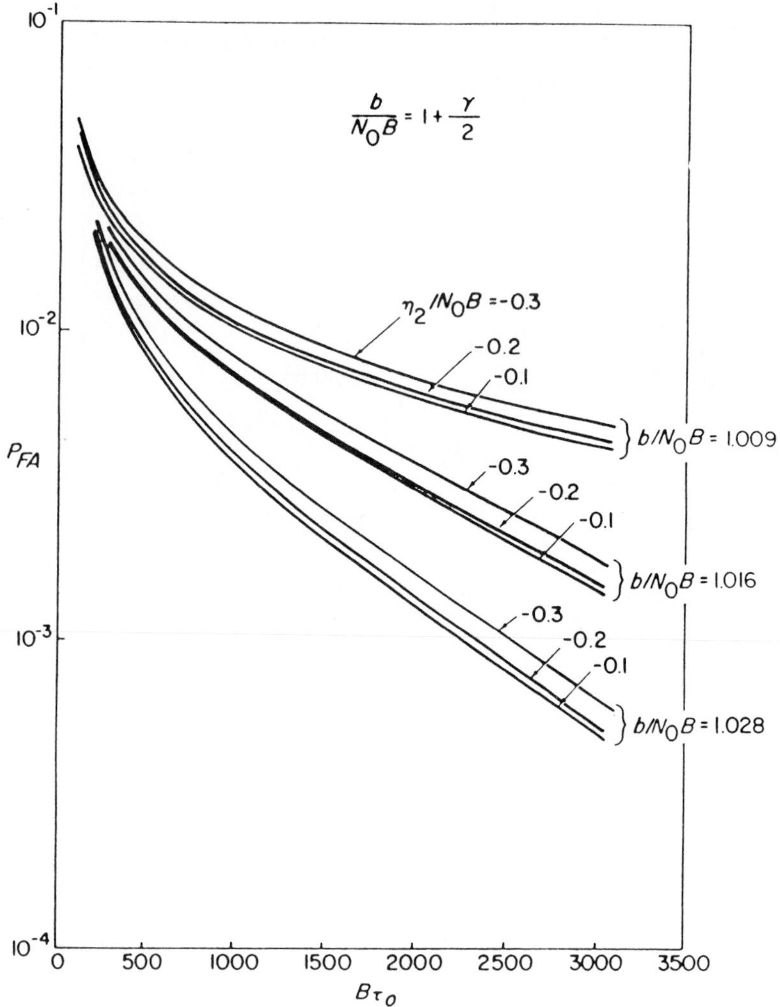

Figure 1.56. False alarm probability versus normalized test truncation time with normalized lower detection threshold and normalized bias as parameters.

two-threshold system in that the average sample number decreases with increasing bias and increasing lower threshold (decreasing $|\eta_2/N_0B|$). Finally, Figure 1.58 illustrates the detection probability versus normalized test truncation time for the same values of normalized lower detection threshold as in Figure 1.56. Here, we observe that detection probability decreases with increasing bias as expected. Furthermore, for small values of $B\tau_o$, detection probability at first decreases but eventually levels off for sufficiently large values of $B\tau_o$. Because of this behavior, it is reasonable to choose the truncation time τ_o to satisfy the requirement on false alarm probability.

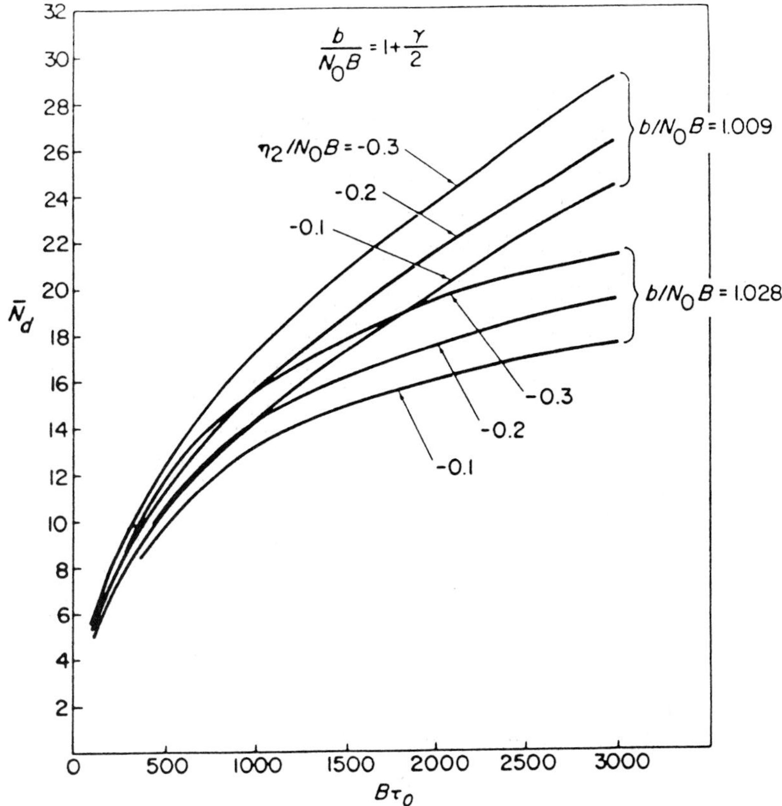

Figure 1.57. Average sample number versus normalized test truncation time with normalized lower detection threshold and normalized bias as parameters.

1.8 SEARCH / LOCK STRATEGIES

In this final section, we discuss the behavior and performance of the receiver's *search/lock strategy* (SLS) whose primary function is to logically control the transition from the *search mode* of operation (coarse PN acquisition) to the *lock mode* of operation (PN tracking). The intermediate state as represented by the above transition from coarse acquisition to tracking is often referred to as *fine PN acquisition*. In effect, it yields a verification of the validity of a "hit" produced by the search algorithm before turning control over to the tracking loop. A secondary function of the SLS is to continuously monitor the receiver while in its lock mode of operation so as to determine when a loss of synchronization has occurred thereby requiring reinitiation of the search mode.

In selecting an SLS, conflicting requirements on the dwell time per test of a code phase cell must be compromised. Since rapid acquisition is desirable,

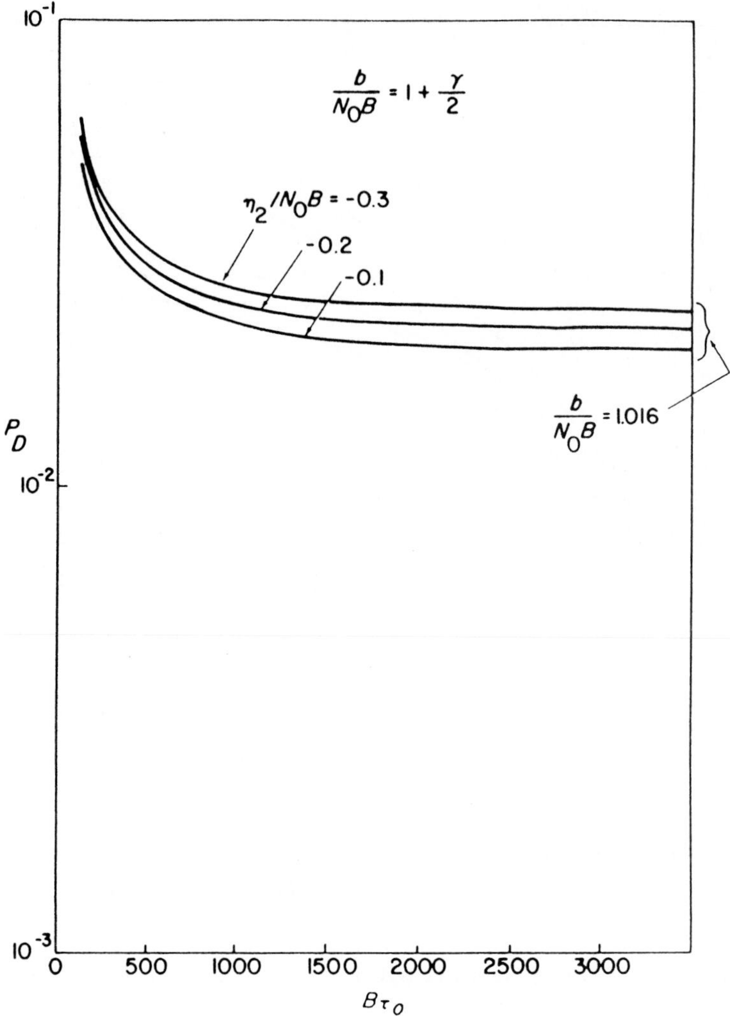

Figure 1.58. Detection probability versus normalized test truncation time with normalized lower detection threshold as a parameter.

the dwell time τ_d per test cell in the search mode should be as small as practical; however, a large τ_d is required to ensure a high probability of detecting the correct cell once it is found. In the lock mode, a very high probability of detection is required to ensure that the detector will not prematurely declare a loss of lock and reinitiate the search, thereby disrupting synchronization. However, since in the lock mode search time is no longer a strong consideration, advantage of this fact can be taken by increasing the post-detection integration (dwell) time to meet the requirement on detection probability. Unfortunately, since the probability of entering the lock mode due to a false alarm is non-zero, the time spent on a false lock while in the lock mode will be substantially increased by the longer integration time. However, if the probability of false alarm is small, then the probability of false lock (falsely entering the lock mode) will likewise be small and hence the mean acquisition time will not be significantly increased. In conclusion, it appears that a salient feature of an SLS should be that the detector parameters are changed upon entering the lock mode from the search mode and vice versa. Furthermore, within each mode, a suitable algorithm should be applied to the "hits" and "misses" (detector threshold crossings or their lack thereof) so as to circumvent the unique relation (see (1.81)) that exists among false alarm probability, detection probability, and dwell time for a single threshold decision, and thus allow the conflicting requirements on τ_d discussed above to be satisfied.

In order to understand in more detail how the above considerations affect acquisition performance, it is convenient to consider a specific SLS and choose a suitable analytical approach for evaluating its behavior. A typical SLS [9] is illustrated in state/transition form in Figure 1.59. This strategy is implicitly assumed to operate in conjunction with the single dwell time PN acquisition system of Figure 1.4. In particular, for the first time a cell is tested (state 1), a miss (failure of the decision variable Z to exceed the detection threshold) results in immediate rejection of the cell and a phase step to the next cell (see Figure 1.4). On the other hand, a hit (Z exceeds the threshold) on the first test of a cell advances the SLS to state 2, whereupon the identical cell is retested. If a second hit occurs, the SLS enters the lock mode. A miss in state 2 causes a return to state 1. Additional hits and misses produce similar transitions between states of the SLS. It is to be emphasized that for the SLS of Figure 1.59, the dwell time τ_{d1} is identical for search states 1 and 2.

Just as a single hit does not put the SLS in the lock mode, three successive misses are required to reinitiate the search mode. Any other combination of hits and misses will maintain the SLS in the lock mode once it has entered that mode. Furthermore, the dwell time τ_{d2} ($> \tau_{d1}$) is assumed to be the same for all three lock mode states.

1.8.1 Mean and Variance of the Acquisition Time

A suitable analytical approach for evaluating the behavior of the SLS is to represent it as a finite Markov chain with absorbing boundaries. Such a Markov chain model for the SLS of Figure 1.59 is illustrated in Figure 1.60. Note that Figure 1.60 is analogous to the generating function flow graph for the single dwell system (Figure 1.5) except that, for convenience, we have omitted the branch parameter z which was previously used to mark time as one proceeded through the graph. Each branch of Figure 1.60, however, is still labelled with the transition probability appropriate for going from one

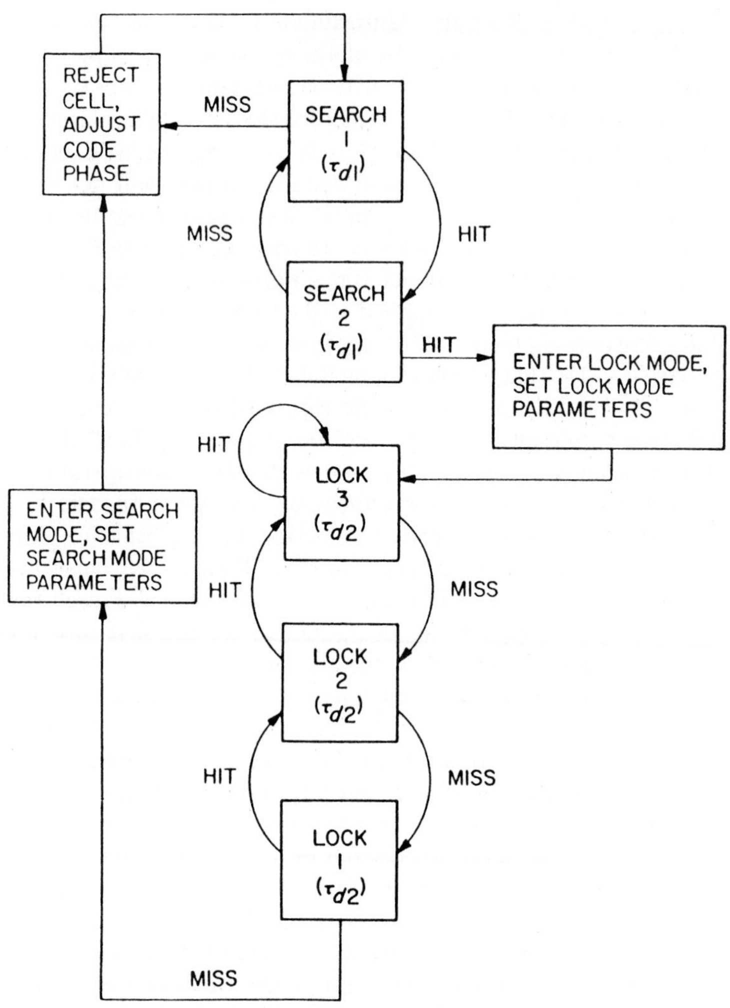

Figure 1.59. A search/lock strategy.

state to the other. Using straightforward techniques for analyzing Markov chains with absorbing boundaries, it can be shown [9] that the mean and variance of the acquisition time of the combination of the single dwell acquisition system of Figure 1.4 and the SLS of Figure 1.59 are given by

$$\bar{T}_{ACQ} = \frac{(2 - P_L) q \bar{\tau}_d}{2 P_L} \tag{1.288}$$

and

$$\sigma_{ACQ}^2 = \bar{\tau}_d^2 q^2 \left(\frac{1}{12} + \frac{1}{P_L^2} - \frac{1}{P_L} \right) \tag{1.289}$$

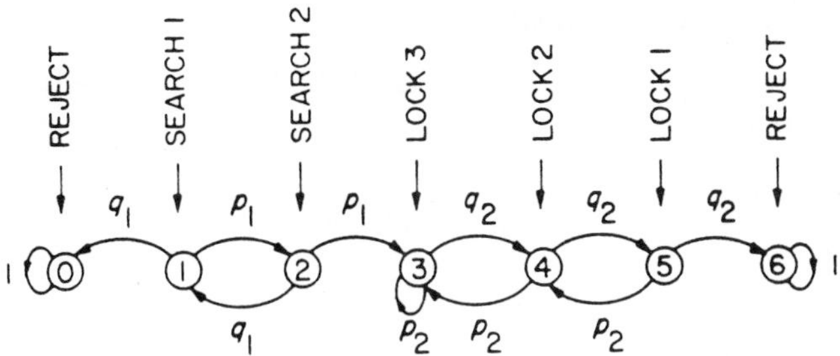

p_0 = P(HIT | SEARCH MODE) $\qquad q_0 = 1 - p_0$

p_1 = P(HIT | LOCK MODE) $\qquad q_1 = 1 - p_1$

Figure 1.60. Markov chain model of search/lock strategy.

where P_L is the probability of lock, i.e., the probability of entering the lock mode assuming the search has reached the correct cell, and $\bar{\tau}_d$ is the mean dwell time for an incorrect cell. In terms of the Markov chain model of Figure 1.60, P_L is simply the probability of going from state 1 to state 3 with $p_1 = P_{D1}$ and $q_1 = 1 - P_{D1}$ where P_{D1} is the detection probability for the search mode. Furthermore, $\bar{\tau}_d$ is the mean time to reach states 0 or 6 (the two absorbing states) from state 1 with $p_1 = P_{FA1}$, $q_1 = 1 - P_{FA1}$, $p_2 = P_{FA2}$, and $q_2 = 1 - P_{FA2}$ where P_{FA1} and P_{FA2} are, respectively, the false alarm probabilities in the search and lock modes.

Before proceeding to an evaluation of P_L and $\bar{\tau}_d$ for the SLS of Figure 1.59, we draw attention to the similarity of (1.288) and (1.4), the latter being the mean acquisition time for the single dwell acquisition acting alone (i.e., in the absence of the SLS). Clearly without any hit verification, the probability of lock would simply be equal to the detection probability of the detector in the search mode of operation, i.e.,

$$P_L = P_D. \tag{1.290}$$

Furthermore, the average dwell time for an incorrect cell without an SLS is the average of the dwell time for a miss (which occurs with probability $1 - P_{FA}$) and the dwell time for a hit (which occurs with probability P_{FA}) including the penalty of K dwell time units to discover the false alarm. Thus,

$$\begin{aligned}\bar{\tau}_d &= \tau_d(1 - P_{FA}) + (\tau_d + K\tau_d)P_{FA} \\ &= \tau_d(1 + KP_{FA}).\end{aligned} \tag{1.291}$$

Finally, substituting (1.290) and (1.291) in (1.288) results in (1.4), as it naturally should.

1.8.1.1 Evaluation of Probability of Lock

The events contributing to an entering of the lock mode starting in search state 1 are as follows:

hit-hit

hit-miss-hit-hit

hit-miss-hit-miss-hit-hit

⋮

$$\underbrace{\text{hit-miss-hit-miss} \ldots \text{hit-miss}}_{n \text{ hits, } n \text{ misses}}\text{-hit-hit.}$$

Since the above events are mutually exclusive, the probability of lock is simply the sum of the probabilities of these events, i.e.,

$$\begin{aligned} P_L &= p_1^2 + p_1 q_1 p_1^2 + (p_1 q_1)^2 p_1^2 + \cdots (p_1 q_1)^n p_1^2 + \cdots \\ &= p_1^2 \sum_{n=0}^{\infty} (p_1 q_1)^n = \frac{p_1^2}{1 - p_1 q_1} = \frac{p_1^2}{1 - p_1 + p_1^2} \end{aligned} \tag{1.292}$$

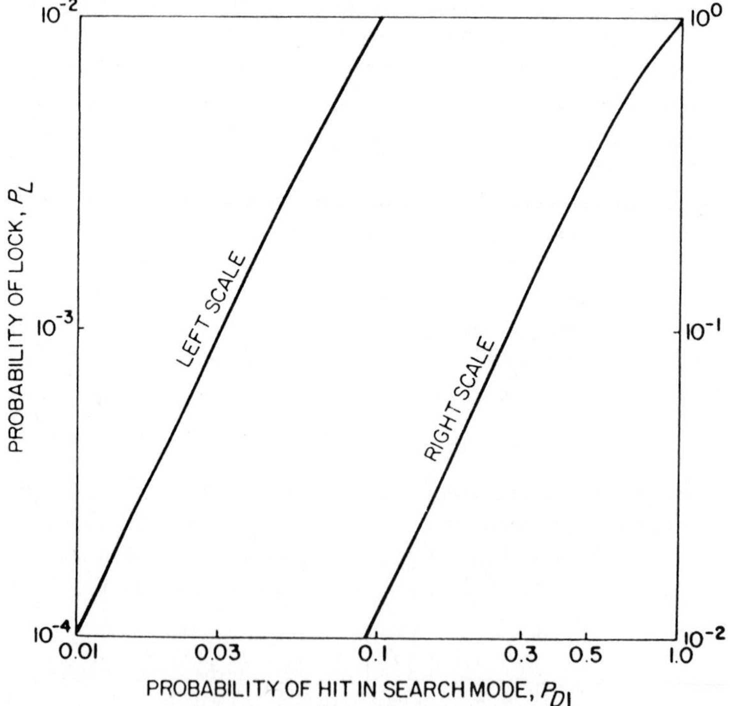

Figure 1.61. Probability of lock versus search mode detection probability (reprinted from [9]).

or in view of the previously mentioned substitution for p_1,

$$P_L = \frac{P_{D1}^2}{1 - P_{D1} + P_{D1}^2}. \tag{1.293}$$

Figure 1.61 is a plot of P_L versus P_{D1}.

1.8.1.2 Evaluation of Mean Dwell Time

The mean dwell time can also easily be computed by first identifying the events contributing to a dismissal of an incorrect cell starting in search state 1, and then assigning the appropriate dwell time and probability of occurrence to each of these events. Considering first those events which dismiss an incorrect cell *without entering the lock mode*, we have the following:

miss
hit-miss-miss
hit-miss-hit-miss-miss
⋮

$$\underbrace{\text{hit-miss-hit-miss}\ldots\text{hit-miss}}_{n\text{ hits, }n\text{ misses}}\text{-miss}$$

Thus, the component of the mean dwell time associated with these events is

$$\begin{aligned}\bar{\tau}_d^{(1)} &= \tau_{d1}(1 - P_{FA1}) + 3\tau_{d1}P_{FA1}(1 - P_{FA1})^2 \\ &\quad + \cdots (2n+1)\tau_{d1}P_{FA1}^n(1 - P_{FA1})^{n+1} + \cdots \\ &= \tau_{d1}(1 - P_{FA1})\sum_{n=0}^{\infty}(2n+1)\left[P_{FA1}(1 - P_{FA1})\right]^n \end{aligned} \tag{1.294}$$

or, since

$$\sum_{n=0}^{\infty}(2n+1)x^n = \frac{1+x}{(1-x)^2}, \tag{1.295}$$

$$\bar{\tau}_d^{(1)} = \tau_{d1}(1 - P_{FA1})\frac{1 + P_{FA1}(1 - P_{FA1})}{\left[1 - P_{FA1}(1 - P_{FA1})\right]^2}. \tag{1.296}$$

Considering next the events which dismiss an incorrect cell by first *entering the lock mode*, we have the following:

hit-hit-lock mode
hit-miss-hit-hit-lock mode
⋮

$$\underbrace{\text{hit-miss-hit-miss}\ldots\text{hit-miss}}_{n\text{ hits, }n\text{ misses}}\text{-hit-hit-lock mode.}$$

⋮

For the moment, we do not identify, in the above, the possible paths through and out of the lock mode. We merely use the words "lock mode" to denote the collection of these paths and associate with them an average penalty time T_p. Shortly, we shall evaluate T_p in terms of the lock mode false alarm probability and dwell time for the specific SLS of Figure 1.59. Also note that previously, when we considered the single dwell acquisition system alone, T_p was chosen equal to $K\tau_d$.

For the events listed above, the contribution to the mean dwell time is given by

$$\begin{aligned}\bar{\tau}_d^{(2)} &= (2\tau_{d1} + T_p)P_{FA1}^2 + (4\tau_{d1} + T_p)P_{FA1}^3(1 - P_{FA1}) \\ &\quad + \cdots ((2n+2)\tau_{d1} + T_p)P_{FA1}^{n+2}(1 - P_{FA1})^n + \cdots \\ &= \tau_{d1}P_{FA1}^2 \sum_{n=0}^{\infty} (2n+2)[P_{FA1}(1 - P_{FA1})]^n \\ &\quad + T_p P_{FA1}^2 \sum_{n=0}^{\infty} [P_{FA1}(1 - P_{FA1})]^n \end{aligned} \tag{1.297}$$

or

$$\bar{\tau}_d^{(2)} = \frac{2\tau_{d1}P_{FA1}^2}{[1 - P_{FA1}(1 - P_{FA1})]^2} + \frac{T_p P_{FA1}^2}{1 - P_{FA1}(1 - P_{FA1})}. \tag{1.298}$$

Adding (1.296) and (1.298), the total mean dwell time is given by

$$\bar{\tau}_d = \frac{(1 + P_{FA1})\tau_{d1} + P_{FA1}^2 T_p}{1 - P_{FA1} + P_{FA1}^2}. \tag{1.299}$$

Using a procedure similar to the above, wherein the dwell time and probability associated with each possible path originating at state 3 and terminating at state 6 of Figure 1.60 is identified, it can be shown that

$$T_p = \left[\frac{3 - 4P_{FA2} + 2P_{FA2}^2}{(1 - P_{FA2})^3}\right]\tau_{d2}. \tag{1.300}$$

Substituting (1.300) in (1.299) gives the desired result for the mean dwell time.

Figure 1.62 is an illustration of the mean dwell time normalized by the search mode dwell time versus the search mode false alarm probability with the lock mode false alarm probability as a parameter. Also the lock mode dwell time is assumed to be five times the search mode dwell time as in the example considered in [9], which has practical application to the Space Shuttle program.

Finally, the mean acquisition time is obtained by substituting (1.293) and (1.299) in (1.288). As a numerical illustration of the result of these substitutions, we continue with the example considered in [9] where the following

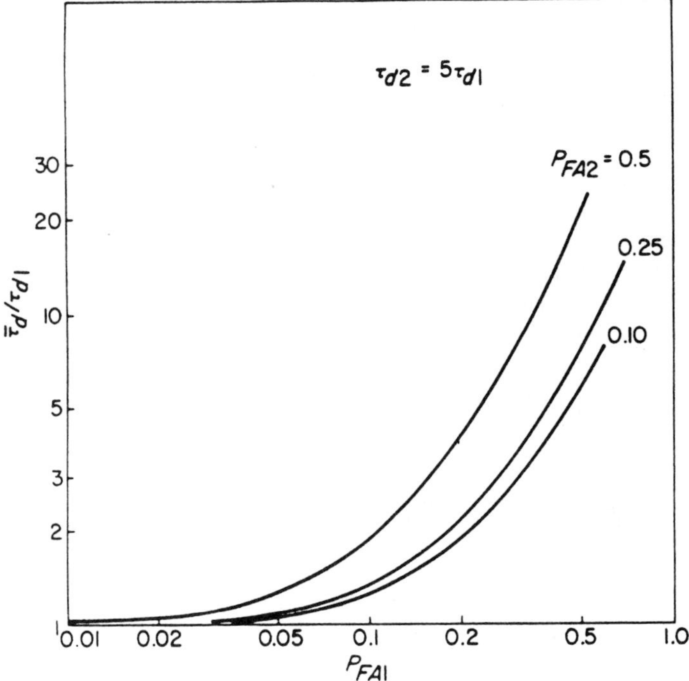

Figure 1.62. Mean dwell time versus search mode false alarm probability (reprinted from [9]).

additional parameter specifications were given:

$$\begin{aligned} \tau_{d1} &= \text{Search Mode Dwell Time} = .91 \text{ ms} \\ \tau_{d2} &= \text{Lock Mode Dwell Time} = 5\tau_{d1} = 4.55 \text{ ms} \\ q &= \text{Number of Search Cells} = 4094 \\ &\quad \text{(PN code of length 2047 chips searched in 1/2 chips increments)} \\ B &= \text{Predetection bandwidth} = 500 \text{ kHz} \\ (P/N_0)_0 &= \text{Nominal signal-to-noise spectral density} = 54.7 \text{ dB-Hz}. \end{aligned} \tag{1.301}$$

Furthermore, a worst case correlation loss $L = .5$ was assumed during the search mode, while during the lock mode L was set equal to .81 to simulate a delay error of .1 chip.

Using the above, we first compute the effective signal-to-noise ratio γ' in the pre-detection filter bandwidth as defined by (1.62) (with $A^2 = P$)

multiplied by L, i.e.,

$$\gamma' = \frac{PL}{N_0 B} = \begin{cases} \dfrac{P}{N_0} \times 10^{-6} \text{ (search mode)} \\ \dfrac{P}{N_0} \times 1.62 \times 10^{-6} \text{ (lock mode)} \end{cases} \tag{1.302}$$

Then, using γ' of (1.302) for A^2/N_0B in (1.81), this equation can be applied to find P_{D1} when $P_{FA1} = .01$ and $B\tau_{d1} = 455$, and P_{D2} when $P_{FA2} = 0.5$ and $B\tau_{d2} = 2275$. The results of these computations are illustrated in Figure 1.63. Combining the results of Figure 1.63 for P_{D1} versus P/N_0 and those of Figure 1.61 for P_L versus P_{D1} enables one to determine P_L as a function of P/N_0. For a lock mode false alarm probability $P_{FA2} = 0.5$ and search

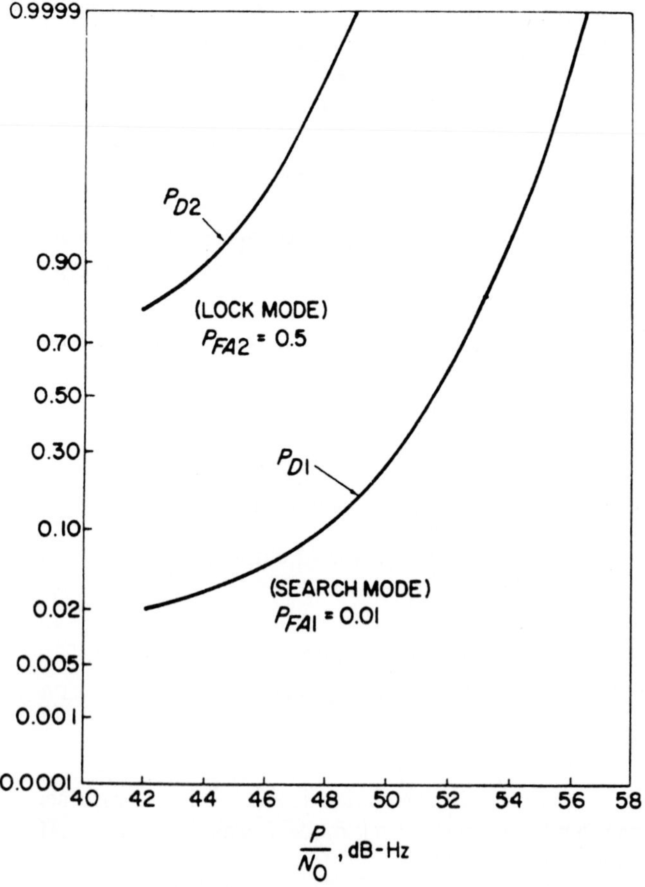

Figure 1.63. Detection performance (reprinted from [9]).

mode false alarm probabilities $P_{FA1} = .001, .01, .03$, and 0.1, we obtain from (1.300) and (1.299) the corresponding values of mean dwell time $\bar{\tau}_d = .912$, .934, 1.016, and 1.7 ms *which are independent of* P/N_0. Finally, using the above-determined functional relationship between P_L and P/N_0 together with the values of $\bar{\tau}_d$ in (1.288) gives the mean acquisition time of the system, which is illustrated versus P/N_0 in Figure 1.64. Note that, for smaller values of P_{FA1}, $\overline{T}_{ACQ}$ increases faster with decreasing P/N_0 than is the case for larger P_{FA1}. The effect is primarily due to the increased P_{D1} which results from increased P_{FA1}.

We hasten to add that all of the results of this section have assumed the absence of code Doppler or its derivatives. To include these effects, one

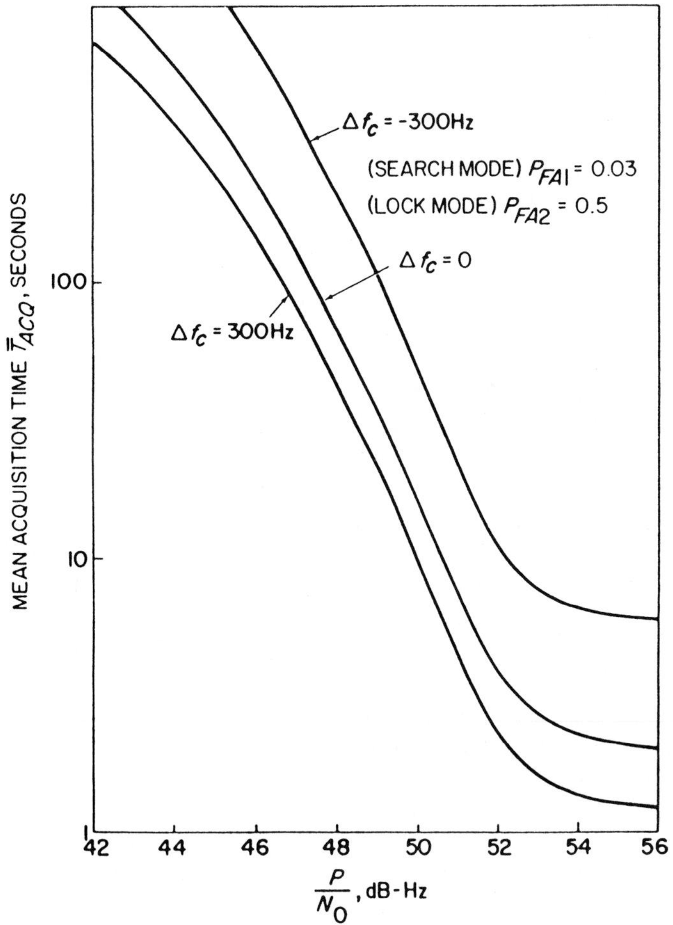

Figure 1.64. Mean acquisition time performance; ±300 Hz frequency error (reprinted from [9]).

would simply apply the modifications discussed in Sections 1.2.3 and 1.2.8 to (1.288) and (1.289). For example, the relation for mean acquisition time in the presence of code Doppler analogous to (1.48a) would now be (see (1.288))

$$\bar{T}_{ACQ} = \frac{\left(\dfrac{2 - P_L}{2P_L}\right) q'\bar{\tau}_d}{1 + \dfrac{q'}{N_u}\Delta f_c \bar{\tau}_d} = \frac{\bar{T}_{ACQ}\big|_{\text{no code Doppler}}}{1 + \dfrac{q'}{N_u}\Delta f_c \bar{\tau}_d} \tag{1.303}$$

where again N_u/q' represents the search update in the absence of Doppler, e.g., one-half of a chip, and $\Delta f_c \bar{\tau}_d$ is the code phase shift due to Doppler during the mean dwell time. As a numerical illustration of the application of (1.303), Figure 1.64 plots $\bar{T}_{ACQ}$ versus P/N_0 for the previous example with now $\Delta f_c = -300$ Hz or $\Delta f_c = +300$ Hz and $N_u/q' = 1/2$.

1.8.2 Another Search / Lock Strategy

Another approach [1] to providing an SLS incorporates a search mode which is modelled after the multiple dwell time acquisition procedure discussed in Section 1.3. In particular, the search mode again consists of two states; however, unlike Figure 1.59, the integration (dwell) times are different for the two states. Furthermore, a miss on state 2 does not return the SLS to state 1 but rather immediately dismisses the cell as being incorrect (see Figure 1.65). The basic philosophy behind the above strategy is to assign a small dwell time τ_{d1} to the first search state so as to search the code phases quickly and a larger dwell time τ_{d2} to the second search state to provide a better estimate (higher probability of detection and lower false alarm probability) of whether the correct cell has been found. In this way, some of the false alarm protection is apportioned in the first integration and the remaining (usually greater) protection is placed in the second integration. Finally, the lock mode portion of the SLS uses a third integration time τ_{d3} (in practice it could be the same as τ_{d2}) with the same algorithm as in Figure 1.59, i.e., a reinitiation of the search requires three consecutive misses.

Before proceeding with the performance analysis of the SLS in Figure 1.65, we point out its similarity with the multiple (here double) dwell time acquisition system alluded to above. In particular, the double dwell time system which incorporates the search mode of the SLS in Figure 1.65 employs *independent* (non-overlapping) integration intervals for its two dwells, whereas a two-dwell version of the multiple dwell time procedure discussed in Section 1.3 uses overlapping integration intervals.

Since the SLS of Figure 1.65 can also be modelled by a Markov chain, the mean and variance of the acquisition time are still given by (1.288) and (1.289), however, with different relationships for P_L and $\bar{\tau}_d$. Clearly, since

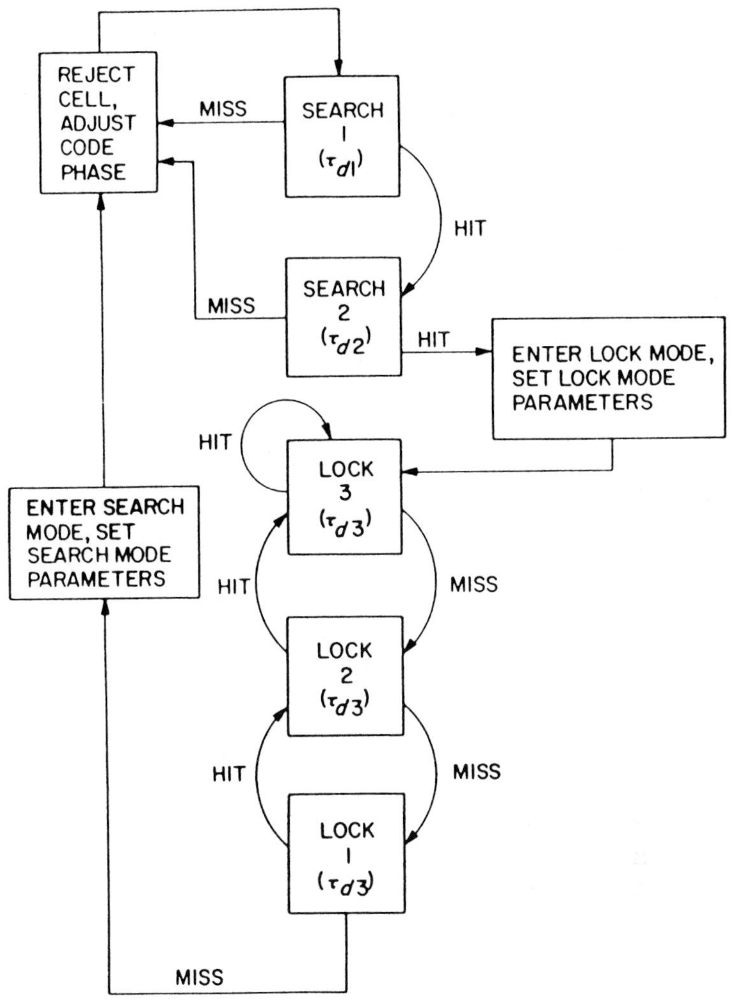

Figure 1.65. Another search/lock strategy.

the only event which causes an entering of the lock mode starting in search state 1 is hit-hit, the probability of lock is now given by

$$P_L = P_{D1}P_{D2} \tag{1.304}$$

where P_{D1} and P_{D2} are, respectively, the detection probabilities for search states 1 and 2. To compute the mean dwell time we again separate the events into those that cause a cell dismissal without entering the lock mode and those that do likewise by passing through the lock mode. In the case of the former, we observe from Figure 1.65 that there are only two appropriate events, namely, miss and hit-miss. Thus, the corresponding component of the mean dwell time is

$$\bar{\tau}_d^{(1)} = \tau_{d1}(1 - P_{FA1}) + (\tau_{d1} + \tau_{d2})P_{FA1}(1 - P_{FA2}) \qquad (1.305)$$

where P_{FA1} and P_{FA2} are, respectively, the false alarm probabilities for search states 1 and 2. For the latter case, we have already observed that only two successive hits cause an entering of the lock mode, which is accompanied by a penalty of T_p sec before rejecting the cell. Thus, this corresponding component of the mean dwell time is

$$\bar{\tau}_d^{(2)} = (\tau_{d1} + \tau_{d2} + T_p)P_{FA1}P_{FA2}. \qquad (1.306)$$

Finally, adding (1.305) and (1.306) gives the mean dwell time as

$$\bar{\tau}_d = \tau_{d1} + \tau_{d2}P_{FA1} + T_pP_{FA1}P_{FA2}. \qquad (1.307)$$

Note that by letting $T_p = K\tau_{d2}$ and substituting (1.304) and (1.307) in (1.288) and (1.289), we obtain the results for the mean and variance of the acquisition time given in [1], which have also been modified as per our previous discussions to include the effects of code Doppler. Using the actual lock mode of the SLS in Figure 1.65, T_p would in reality be given by (1.300) with, in general, P_{FA2} replaced by P_{FA3} and τ_{d2} by τ_{d3}.

We conclude our discussion of this strategy by pointing out that measured values of acquisition time taken on an actual implementation of Figure 1.65 in the code acquisition portion of the Space Shuttle Orbiter system were accurate to within 1 dB of the theoretical results as predicted by the above equations.

1.9 FURTHER DISCUSSION

Throughout this chapter our discussion has focussed on rapid acquisition serial search techniques wherein a single code phase at a time is examined for possible alignment. A natural extension of these techniques would be to use two or more paths to simultaneously search more than one code phase at a time with the hope that by increasing complexity, the acquisition time might decrease in direct relation to the number of paths used. To this end we present here a brief discussion of the possibilities obtainable with a parallel search operation. Specifically, we consider a system where the entire q cell uncertainty region is subdivided into say $N_P(\geq 2)$ equal components each containing q/N_P cells with each of N_P paths responsible for searching one component in parallel with the remaining $N_P - 1$ paths. Furthermore, since the N_P searches progress in parallel under a common control, at any point along the way, all N_P alignment examinations must be dismissed before the search can proceed.

Referring to these joint events as "global" events, if each parallel path is characterized by a detector with false alarm probability P_{FA} and missed detection probability $\beta = 1 - P_D$, the global false alarm probability P_{FAg}

and global missed detection probability $\beta_g \triangleq 1 - P_{Dg}$ are given by

$$P_{FAg} = 1 - (1 - P_{FA})^{N_P}$$
$$\beta_g = \beta(1 - P_{FA})^{N_P - 1}. \tag{1.308}$$

For small P_{FA}, (1.308) simplifies to

$$P_{FAg} \cong N_P P_{FA}$$
$$\beta_g \cong \beta[1 - (N_P - 1)P_{FA}]. \tag{1.309}$$

As an example of the application of the above, we consider the fixed single dwell serial PN acquisition system discussed in Section 1.2 implemented now with N_P parallel search paths. For N_P and q such that q/N_P is still much greater than one, then to a good approximation (1.4) and (1.7) can be used to characterize the moments of the acquisition time of the parallel search system if q is replaced by q/N_P, P_D by P_{Dg}, and P_{FA} by P_{FAg}. For example, using the approximate relations of (1.309), the mean acquisition time would become

$$\bar{T}_{ACQ} = \frac{(1 + \beta_g)(1 + KP_{FAg})}{2(1 - \beta_g)}\left(\frac{q}{N_P}\tau_d\right)$$
$$= \frac{2 - P_D - (1 - P_D)(N_p - 1)P_{FA}}{2[P_D + (1 - P_D)(N_P - 1)P_{FA}]}\frac{(1 + KN_pP_{FA})}{N_P}(q\tau_d). \tag{1.310}$$

Clearly, for small N_P and small false alarm penalty time, the acquisition time varies approximately as an inverse linear function of the number of paths. Eventually, as N_P gets large enough where the false alarm penalty dominates, no further improvement in mean acquisition time will result.

The parallel search idea is obviously applicable to other forms of serial code search such as sequential detection where the improvement in performance would be obtained by similar replacements of q, P_D, and P_{FA} by q/N_P, P_{Dg}, and P_{FAg}, respectively, in the appropriate performance expressions.

1.10 REFERENCES

[1] J. K. Holmes and C. C. Chen, "Acquisition time performance of PN spread-spectrum systems," *IEEE Trans. Commun.*, COM-25, pp. 778–783, August 1977.

[2] W. K. Alem, "Advanced techniques for direct sequence spread spectrum acquisition," Ph.D. Dissertation, Department of Electrical Engineering, University of Southern California, February 1977.

[3] W. K. Alem and C. L. Weber, "Acquisition techniques of PN sequences," *1977 NTC Conference Record*, vol. II, pp. 35:2-1–35:2-4, December 5–7, 1977, Los Angeles, CA.

[4] R. B. Ward, "Acquisition of pseudonoise signals by sequential estimation," *IEEE Trans. Commun.*, COM-13, pp. 475–483, December 1965.

[5] R. B. Ward and K. P. Yiu, "Acquisition of pseudonoise signals by recursion aided sequential estimation," *IEEE Trans. Commun.*, COM-25, pp. 784–794, August 1977. Also see *1977 NTC Conference Record*, vol. II, pp. 35:1-1–35:1-13, December 5–7, Los Angeles, CA.

[6] D. M. DiCarlo and C. L. Weber, "Statistical performance of single dwell serial synchronization systems," *IEEE Trans. Commun.*, COM-28, No. 8, pp. 1382–1388, August 1980.

[7] D. M. DiCarlo, "Multiple dwell serial synchronization of pseudonoise signals," Ph.D. Dissertation, Department of Electrical Engineering, University of Southern California, May 1979. Also see *ICC '81 Conference Record*, pp. 34.4.1–34.4.5, June 14–18, 1981, Denver, CO.

[8] D. M. DiCarlo and C. L. Weber, "Multiple dwell serial search: Performance and application to direct sequence code acquisition," *IEEE Trans. Commun.*, COM-31, No. 5, pp. 650–659, May 1983.

[9] P. M. Hopkins, "A unified analysis of pseudonoise synchronization by envelope correlation," *IEEE Trans. Commun.*, COM-25, pp. 770–777, August 1977.

[10] A. Wald, *Sequential Analysis*, New York: John Wiley, 1947.

[11] J. V. DiFranco and W. L. Rubin, *Radar Detection*, Englewood Cliffs, NJ: Prentice-Hall, 1968, Chapter 16.

[12] C. R. Cahn, N. G. Davies, L. A. Gerhardt, G. F. Gott, and R. L. Harris, AGARD-NATO Lecture Series No. 58 on "Spread Spectrum Communications," May 28–June 6, 1973.

[13] A. Polydoros and C. L. Weber, "Rapid acquisition techniques for direct-sequence spread spectrum systems using an analog detector," *NTC '81 Conference Record*, pp. A7.1.1–A7.1.5, November 29–December 3, 1981, New Orleans, LA.

[14] A. Polydoros and C. L. Weber, "A unified approach to serial search spread-spectrum code acquisition," *IEEE Trans. Commun.*, COM-32, No. 5, pp. 542–560, May 1984.

[15] C. C. Kilgus, "Pseudonoise code acquisition using majority logic decoding," *IEEE Trans. Commun.*, COM-21, No. 6, pp. 772–774, June 1973.

[16] H. M. Pearce and M. P. Ristenblatt, "The threshold decoding estimator for synchronization with binary linear recursive sequences," *ICC '71 Conference Record*, pp. 43-25–43-30, June 12–14, 1971, Montreal, Canada.

[17] G. F. Sage, "Serial Synchronization of Pseudonoise Systems," *IEEE Trans. Commun.*, COM-12, pp. 123–127, December 1964.

[18] P. W. Baier and M. Pandit, "Non-coherent pulse detection with a large predetection bandwidth," *IEEE Trans. Commun.*, COM-26, pp. 1298–1301, August 1978.

[19] M. Pandit, "Mean acquisition time of active- and passive-correlation acquisition systems for spread spectrum communication systems," *Proc. IEEE*, vol. 128, Part F, No. 4, pp. 211–214, August 1981.

[20] J. K. Holmes and K. T. Woo, "An optimum PN code search technique for a given a priori signal location density," *NTC '78 Conference Record*, pp. 18.6.1–18.6.5, December 3–6, 1978, Birmingham, AL.

[21] W. R. Braun, "Performance analysis for the expanding search PN acquisition algorithm," *IEEE Trans. Commun.*, COM-30, pp. 424–435, March 1982.

[22] A. Weinberg, "Search strategy effects on PN acquisition performance," *NTC '81 Conference Record*, pp. F1.5.1–F1.5.5, November 29–December 3, 1981, New Orleans, LA.

[23] A. Weinberg, "Generalized analysis for the evaluation of search strategy effects on PN acquisition performance," *IEEE Trans. Commun.*, COM-31, pp. 37–49, January 1983.

[24] A. Polydoros, "Generalized serial search code acquisition: The equivalent circular state diagram approach," *MILCOM '83 Conference Record*, Washington, D.C., October 1983.

[25] W. K. Alem, G. K. Huth, J. K. Holmes, and S. Udalov, "Spread spectrum acquisition and tracking performance for shuttle communication links," *IEEE Trans. Commun.*, COM-26, pp. 1689–1702, November 1978.

[26] C. Gumacos, "Analysis of an optimum sync search procedure," *IEEE Trans. Commun.*, pp. 89–99, March 1963.

[27] J. J. Bussgang and D. Middleton, "Optimum sequential detection of signals in noise," *IEEE Trans. Inform. Theory*, IT-1, pp. 5–18, December 1955.

[28] G. E. Albert, "On the computation of the sampling characteristics of a general class of sequential decision problems," *Annals of Mathematical Statistics*, vol. 25, pp. 340–356, 1954.

[29] W. B. Kendall, "Performance of the biased square-law sequential detector in the absence of signal," *IEEE Trans. Inform. Theory*, IT-11, pp. 83–90, January 1965.

[30] R. F. Cobb and A. D. Darby, "Acquisition performance of simplified implementations of the sequential detection algorithm," *1978 NTC Conference Record*, pp. 43.4.1–43.4.7, December 4–6, 1978, Birmingham, AL.

[31] W. H. Huggins, "Signal-flow graphs and random signals," *Proc. IRE*, vol. 45, pp. 74–86, January 1957.

[32] S. J. Mason, "Feedback theory–Some properties of signal flow graphs," *Proc. IRE*, vol. 41, pp. 1144–1156, September 1953.

[33] S. J. Mason, "Feedback theory—Further properties of signal flow graphs," *Proc. IRE*, vol. 44, pp. 920–926, July 1956.

[34] M. J. Bouvier, Jr., H. E. Walls, and R. W. Boyd, "Rapid acquisition of spread spectrum signals," Army Research Office, Research Triangle Park, NC, Final Report under Contract No. DAAG29-80-C-0005, December 1980.

[35] J. I. Marcum, "A statistical theory of target detection by pulsed radar: Mathematical appendix," the RAND Corporation Report ASTIA AD101882, July 1, 1948.

[36] D. P. Morgan, J. M. Hannah, and J. H. Collins, "Spread-spectrum synchronizer using a SAW convolver and recirculation loop," *Proc. IEEE*, vol. 64, no. 5, pp. 751–753, May 1976.

[37] L. B. Milstein and P. K. Das, "Spread spectrum receiver using surface acoustic wave technology," *IEEE Trans. Commun.*, COM-25, No. 8, pp. 841–847, August 1977.

[38] A. Polydoros, "On the synchronization aspects of direct-sequence spread spectrum systems," Ph.D. Dissertation, Department of Electrical Engineering, University of Southern California, August 1982.

[39] A. Polydoros, and M. K. Simon, "Generalized serial search code acquisition: The equivalent circular state diagram approach," *IEEE Trans. Commun.*, COM-32, pp. 1260–1268, December 1984.

Chapter 2

PSEUDONOISE CODE TRACKING IN DIRECT-SEQUENCE RECEIVERS

In the previous chapter, we discussed techniques for acquiring a pseudonoise (PN) code in direct-sequence (DS) spread-spectrum (SS) receivers. Although PN acquisition is an extremely important problem, e.g., the code must customarily be acquired in as short a time as possible, the development of closed loop techniques for accurate PN tracking plays an equally important role in supporting the acquisition process once the code has been acquired. As such, the optimum design and true assessment of the performance of the PN tracking loop is an essential component of the overall receiver design.

In searching the literature, one finds that over the years there have been predominantly two PN tracking loop configurations that have been proposed and analyzed, namely, the *delay-locked loop* (DLL) [1]–[5] and the *tau-dither loop* (TDL) or *time-shared loop* [5]–[7]. Either of these configurations can be operated in a coherent or non-coherent mode depending on the system application. Furthermore, both of them fall within the class of so-called *early-late gate* type loops in that the received PN code is correlated either simultaneously or alternately with delayed and advanced versions of the receiver local code PN generator output to produce the timing error correcting characteristic. More recently, modifications of the basic TDL and DLL, namely, the *double dither loop* (DDL) [8], the *product of sum and difference DLL* ($\Sigma\Delta$ DLL) [9], and the *modified code tracking loop* (MCTL) [10], [11] have been proposed which attempt to mitigate the disadvantages of each configuration when compared with the other. Another variation, referred to as the complex sums DLL [12], has been suggested for application in environments characterized by severe dynamic range variation where reception is subject to fast fading and scintillation.

In this chapter, we focus our attention on the class of non-coherent PN tracking loops that are of interest in SS communication receivers where PN acquisition and tracking (despreading) is performed prior to carrier synchronization. Indeed, this is the more common situation in present and past SS communication systems in contrast to the other uses of PN modulation where the code is acquired and coherently tracked as a baseband modulation, e.g., ranging. Although both linear and non-linear loop analyses are possible, we shall concentrate primarily on the steady state tracking performance results obtained from the linear theory since in most situations the equivalent loop signal-to-noise ratio is sufficiently high as to justify this assumption. Following the presentation of these results, we shall discuss the acquisition (transient) behavior [4] and slip time (mean time to lose lock) performance [13] of the DLL and TDL, which, by necessity, must both be derived from consideration of the non-linear theory. Finally, the chapter concludes with a discussion of quadriphase PN tracking and a summary of other recent contributions.

2.1 THE DELAY-LOCKED LOOP

Consider the non-coherent delay-locked loop (DLL) illustrated in Figure 2.1. The input signal $x(t)$ is cross-correlated with advanced and retarded versions of the local PN code generator sequence. The results of these cross-correlation operations are then band-pass filtered, square-law envelope detected, and differenced to produce an error (discriminator) characteristic. The loop is closed by applying this differenced output to a loop filter and voltage controlled clock (VCC) that drives the PN code generator from which the PN reference sequence is obtained.

The advance (and retard) interval δ or, equivalently, the correlator spacing is restricted to a range of $\delta \leq T_c$ where T_c denotes the length (in seconds) of a PN code chip. More conveniently, we shall define δ equal to T_c/N where N is any integer larger than unity. Thus, the advanced and retarded PN signals are $2T_c/N$ apart and a loop such as this is said to have T_c/N of correlator spacing [14]. When the advance (and retard) interval is equal to one-half of a PN code chip, i.e., $N = 2$, the loop is commonly referred to as a "one-delta" loop.

2.1.1 Mathematical Loop Model and Equation of Operation

In mathematical terms, the above statements are expressed as follows. The received signal $x(t)$ is the sum of signal $s(t)$ plus additive noise $n_i(t)$ where[1]

$$s(t) = \sqrt{2S}\, c(t - \tau_t) m(t - \tau_t) \cos[\omega_0 t + \theta(t)] \tag{2.1}$$

and $n_i(t)$ has the band-pass representation

$$n_i(t) = \sqrt{2}\,\{N_c(t)\cos[\omega_0 t + \theta(t)] - N_s(t)\sin[\omega_0 t + \theta(t)]\}. \tag{2.2}$$

In (2.1) S denotes the average signal power, $c(t - \tau_t)$ is the received PN

[1]At this point, we shall only consider the case of a biphase data modulation on the carrier. Later on, we shall discuss PN spread receivers for various forms of quadriphase modulation.

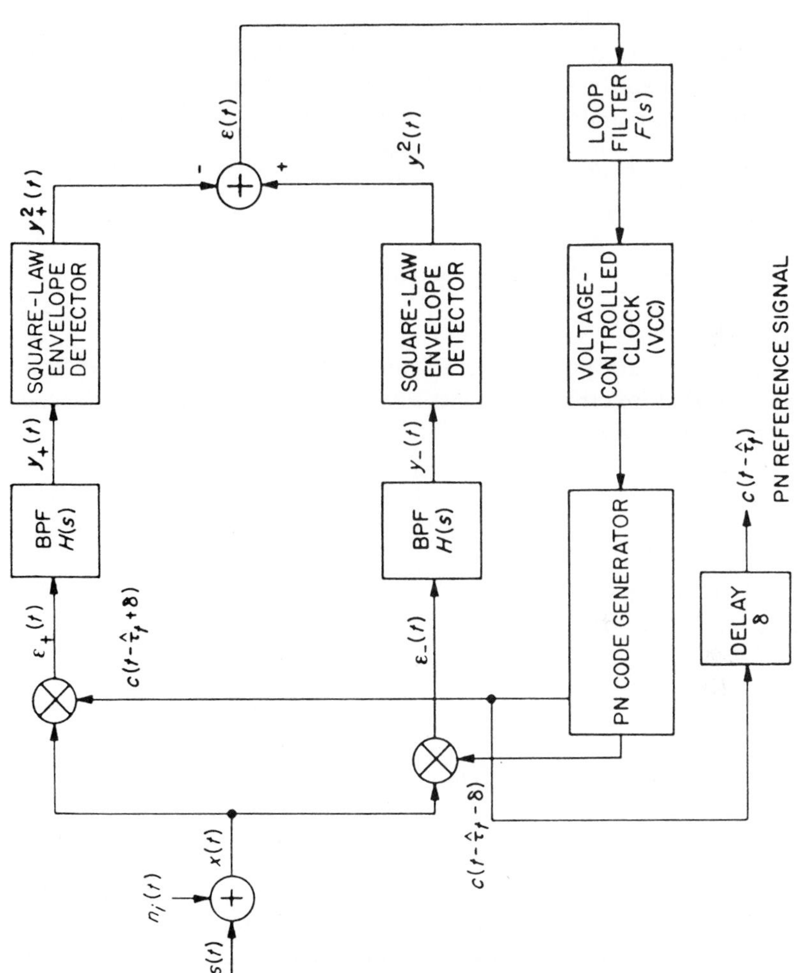

Figure 2.1. A non-coherent delay-locked loop.

signal with transmission delay τ_t, $m(t-\tau_t)$ is the data modulation in the presence of the same delay, ω_0 is the carrier radian frequency, and $\theta(t) \triangleq \theta_0 + \Omega_0 t$ is the unknown carrier phase consisting of a constant term and a term proportional to Doppler. The noise processes $N_c(t)$ and $N_s(t)$ are approximately statistically independent, stationary, low-pass white Gaussian noise processes with single-sided noise spectral density N_0 w/Hz (see [15] or [16]) and one-sided bandwidth $B_N \ll \omega_0/2\pi$.

If the advanced and retarded PN reference signals are respectively given by $c(t-\hat{\tau}_t+\delta)$ and $c(t-\hat{\tau}_t-\delta)$ where $\hat{\tau}_t$ denotes the DLL's estimate of τ_t, then the corresponding cross-correlator (phase detector) outputs become

$$\begin{aligned}\varepsilon_{\pm}(t) = {} & \sqrt{2S}\,K_m m(t-\tau_t)\overline{c(t-\tau_t)c(t-\hat{\tau}_t\pm\delta)}\cos[\omega_0 t+\theta(t)] \\ & +\sqrt{2S}\,K_m m(t-\tau)\big[c(t-\tau_t)c(t-\hat{\tau}_t\pm\delta) \\ & -\overline{c(t-\tau_t)c(t-\hat{\tau}_t\pm\delta)}\big]\cos[\omega_0 t+\theta(t)] \\ & +K_m c(t-\hat{\tau}_t\pm\delta)n_i(t)\end{aligned} \tag{2.3}$$

with K_m denoting the phase detector gain assumed to be identical for both[2] and the overbar referring to statistical expectation. For large PN code period p, we have that

$$R_{PN_+}(\varepsilon_t) \triangleq \overline{c(t-\tau_t)c(t-\hat{\tau}_t+\delta)} = \begin{cases} 0; & \varepsilon_t \le -\dfrac{1}{N}-1 \\ 1+\dfrac{1}{N}+\varepsilon_t; & -1-\dfrac{1}{N} \le \varepsilon_t \le -\dfrac{1}{N} \\ 1-\dfrac{1}{N}-\varepsilon_t; & -\dfrac{1}{N} < \varepsilon_t \le 1-\dfrac{1}{N} \\ 0; & \varepsilon_t > 1-\dfrac{1}{N} \end{cases}$$

$$\begin{aligned}R_{PN_-}(\varepsilon_t) &\triangleq \overline{c(t-\tau_t)c(t-\hat{\tau}_t-\delta)} = R_{PN_+}\left(\varepsilon_t-\frac{2}{N}\right) \\ R_{PN_\pm}(\varepsilon_t) &= R_{PN_\pm}(\varepsilon_t+np);\ n=\pm1,\pm2,\pm3,\ldots\end{aligned} \tag{2.4}$$

where $\varepsilon_t \triangleq (\tau_t-\hat{\tau}_t)/T_c$ denotes the normalized transmission delay error. Figure 2.2 illustrates these two autocorrelation functions.

Letting $H_\ell(s)$ denote the low-pass equivalent of the band-pass filter transfer function $H(s)$, and

$$\begin{aligned}s_{c_\pm}(t-\tau_t,\varepsilon_t) \triangleq {} & c(t-\tau_t)c(t-\hat{\tau}_t\pm\varepsilon_t) \\ & -\overline{c(t-\tau_t)c(t-\hat{\tau}_t\pm\varepsilon_t)}\end{aligned}$$

[2] In practice, the two phase detectors may not have identical gains, which obviates the point that the DLL is sensitive to gain imbalance.

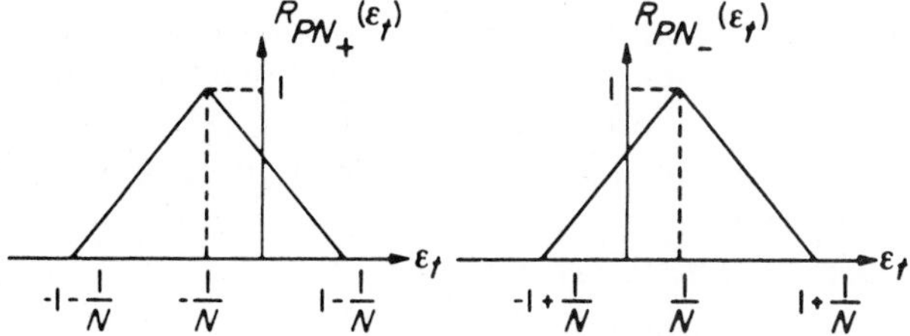

Figure 2.2. Autocorrelation functions of the advanced and retarded PN code.

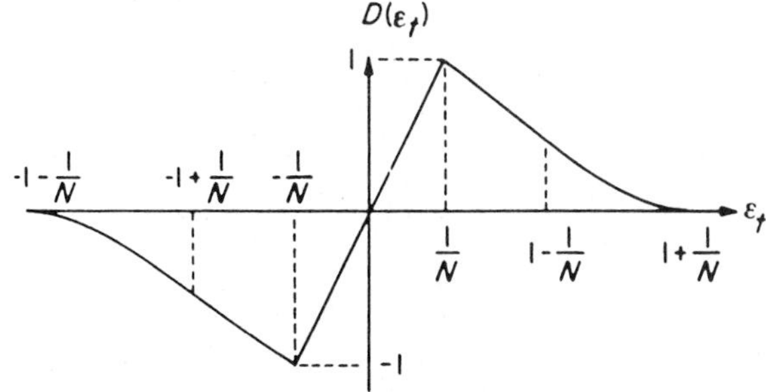

Figure 2.3. Discriminator characteristic.

denote the *PN code self-noise* processes, then combining (2.2) and (2.3) we get (see Figure 2.1)

$$\begin{aligned} y_{\pm}(t) = {} & \sqrt{2S}\,K_m \hat{m}(t-\tau_t) R_{PN_{\pm}}(\varepsilon_t)\cos[\omega_0 t + \theta(t)] \\ & + \sqrt{2S}\,K_m \hat{s}_{c_{\pm}}(t-\tau_t, \varepsilon_t)\cos[\omega_0 t + \theta(t)] \\ & + \sqrt{2}\,K_m \hat{N}_{c_{\pm}}(t)\cos[\omega_0 t + \theta(t)] \\ & - \sqrt{2}\,K_m \hat{N}_{s_{\pm}}(t)\sin[\omega_0 t + \theta(t)] \end{aligned} \tag{2.5}$$

where[3]

$$\begin{aligned} \hat{m}(t) &= H_\ell(p)m(t) \\ \hat{s}_{c_{\pm}}(t,\varepsilon_t) &= H_\ell(p)\left[m(t)s_{c_{\pm}}(t,\varepsilon_t)\right] \\ \hat{N}_{c_{\pm}}(t) &= H_\ell(p)\left[c(t-\tau_t \pm \varepsilon_t)N_c(t)\right] \\ \hat{N}_{s_{\pm}}(t) &= H_\ell(p)\left[c(t-\tau_t \pm \varepsilon_t)N_s(t)\right]. \end{aligned} \tag{2.6}$$

[3] In what follows we shall write differential equations in compact form by introducing the Heaviside operator $p \triangleq d/dt$.

When the single-sided loop bandwidth B_L is much less than the PN code chip rate $1/T_c$ (most cases of practical interest), then, the effect of the PN code self-noise on loop performance can, to a first approximation, be neglected. Thus, ignoring the self-noise term in (2.5) and the second harmonic terms produced by the square-law envelope detectors, we find that the input to the loop filter is given by

$$e(t) \triangleq y_-^2(t) - y_+^2(t) = SK_m^2 \hat{m}^2(t - \tau_t) D(\varepsilon_t) + K_m^2 n_e(t, \varepsilon_t) \quad (2.7)$$

where

$$D(\varepsilon_t) \triangleq R_{PN_-}^2(\varepsilon_t) - R_{PN_+}^2(\varepsilon_t) = \begin{cases} 0; \ \varepsilon_t \le -1 - \frac{1}{N} \\ -\left(1 + \frac{1}{N} + \varepsilon_t\right)^2; \ -1 - \frac{1}{N} < \varepsilon_t \le -1 + \frac{1}{N} \\ -\frac{4}{N}(1 + \varepsilon_t); \ -1 + \frac{1}{N} < \varepsilon_t < -\frac{1}{N} \\ 4\varepsilon_t\left(1 - \frac{1}{N}\right); \ |\varepsilon_t| \le \frac{1}{N} \\ \frac{4}{N}(1 - \varepsilon_t); \ \frac{1}{N} < \varepsilon_t \le 1 - \frac{1}{N} \\ \left(1 + \frac{1}{N} - \varepsilon_t\right)^2; 1 - \frac{1}{N} < \varepsilon_t \le 1 + \frac{1}{N} \\ 0; \ \varepsilon_t > 1 + \frac{1}{N} \end{cases}$$

$$D(\varepsilon_t) = D(\varepsilon_t + np); \ n = \pm 1, \pm 2, \pm 3, \ldots . \quad (2.8)$$

is the loop S-curve or *discriminator characteristic* (see Figure 2.3) and $n_e(t, \varepsilon_t)$ is the equivalent additive noise defined by

$$n_e(t, \varepsilon_t) = \hat{N}_{c_-}^2(t) - \hat{N}_{c_+}^2(t) + \hat{N}_{s_-}^2(t) - \hat{N}_{s_+}^2(t) + 2\sqrt{S}\,\hat{m}(t - \tau_t)\{R_{PN_-}(\varepsilon_t)\hat{N}_{c_-}(t) - R_{PN_+}(\varepsilon_t)\hat{N}_{c_+}(t)\}. \quad (2.9)$$

The instantaneous (normalized) delay estimate $\hat{\tau}_t/T_c$ of the PN code generator output is related (in operator form) to $e(t)$ by

$$\frac{\hat{\tau}_t}{T_c} = \frac{K_{VCC}F(p)}{p} e(t) \quad (2.10)$$

where $F(s)$ is the loop filter transfer function and K_{VCC} is the gain of the voltage controlled clock which drives the PN code generator. Thus, combining (2.7) and (2.10) and letting $K \triangleq K_m^2 K_{VCC}$ denote the loop gain, the stochastic integro-differential equation of operation of Figure 2.1 becomes

$$\frac{\hat{\tau}_t}{T_c} = \frac{KF(p)}{p}\left[S\hat{m}^2(t - \tau_t)D(\varepsilon_t) + n_e(t, \varepsilon_t)\right] \quad (2.11)$$

or

$$\varepsilon_t = \frac{\tau_t}{T_c} - \frac{KF(p)}{p}\left[S\hat{m}^2(t-\tau_t)D(\varepsilon_t) + n_e(t,\varepsilon_t)\right]. \tag{2.12}$$

Consider now decomposing $\hat{m}^2(t-\tau_t)D(\varepsilon_t)$ into its mean value[4] plus a *modulation self-noise* term, viz.,

$$\begin{aligned}\hat{m}^2(t-\tau_t)D(\varepsilon_t) &= \overline{\langle \hat{m}^2(t-\tau_t)\rangle}D(\varepsilon_t)\\ &\quad + \left[\hat{m}^2(t-\tau_t) - \overline{\langle \hat{m}^2(t-\tau_t)\rangle}\right]D(\varepsilon_t)\end{aligned} \tag{2.13}$$

where $\langle\ \ \rangle$ denotes time average, and

$$\overline{\langle \hat{m}^2(t-\tau_t)\rangle} \triangleq M_2 = \int_{-\infty}^{\infty} S_m(f)|H_\ell(j2\pi f)|^2\,df \tag{2.14}$$

with $S_m(f)$ the power spectral density of the data modulation. It has been previously shown [15] in a similar situation that if the loop bandwidth B_L is much less than the data symbol rate $R_s = 1/T_s$ then the modulation self-noise term can be ignored with negligible error. Thus, (2.12) simplifies to

$$\dot{\varepsilon}_t = \frac{\dot{\tau}_t}{T_c} KF(p)\eta SM_2\left[D_n(\varepsilon_t) + \frac{n_e(t,\varepsilon_t)}{\eta SM_2}\right] \tag{2.15}$$

where $D_n(\varepsilon_t) \triangleq (1/\eta)D(\varepsilon_t)$ is the normalized discriminator characteristic with unit slope at the origin, the dot denotes differentiation with respect to time, and

$$\eta \triangleq \frac{4(N-1)}{N}. \tag{2.16}$$

2.1.2 Statistical Characterization of the Equivalent Additive Noise

It is of interest in what follows to determine the autocorrelation function $R_e(\tau)$ of the equivalent additive noise $n_e(t,\varepsilon_t)$. Thus, defining

$$R_e(\tau,\varepsilon_t) \triangleq \overline{n_e(t,\varepsilon_t)n_e(t+\tau,\varepsilon_t)} \tag{2.17}$$

with $n_e(t,\varepsilon_t)$ defined in (2.9), we obtain after considerable algebraic manipulation

$$R_e(\tau,\varepsilon_t) = 8R^2_{\hat{N}}(\tau) + 4SR_{\hat{m}}(\tau)R_{\hat{N}}(\tau)f(\varepsilon_t) \tag{2.18}$$

[4]Note that since $\hat{m}^2(t)$ is a cyclostationary process, both statistical and time averages are required to determine its mean value.

where

$$R_{\hat{N}}(\tau) = \frac{N_0}{2}\int_{-\infty}^{\infty} |H_\ell(j2\pi f)|^2 e^{j2\pi f\tau}\, df$$

$$R_{\hat{m}}(\tau) = \frac{N_0}{2}\int_{-\infty}^{\infty} S_m(f)|H_\ell(j2\pi f)|^2 e^{j2\pi f\tau}\, df$$

$$f(\varepsilon_t) \triangleq R^2_{PN_+}(\varepsilon_t) + R^2_{PN_-}(\varepsilon_t) = \begin{cases} 0; \ \varepsilon_t \le -1 - \dfrac{1}{N} \\ \left(1 + \dfrac{1}{N} + \varepsilon_t\right)^2; \ -1 - \dfrac{1}{N} < \varepsilon_t \le -1 + \dfrac{1}{N} \\ 2\left[\dfrac{1}{N^2} + (1+\varepsilon_t)^2\right]; \ -1 + \dfrac{1}{N} < \varepsilon_t < -\dfrac{1}{N} \\ 2\left[\left(1 - \dfrac{1}{N}\right)^2 + \varepsilon_t^2\right]; \ |\varepsilon_t| \le \dfrac{1}{N} \\ 2\left[\dfrac{1}{N^2} + (1-\varepsilon_t)^2\right]; \ \dfrac{1}{N} < \varepsilon_t \le 1 - \dfrac{1}{N} \\ \left(1 + \dfrac{1}{N} - \varepsilon_t\right)^2; \ 1 - \dfrac{1}{N} < \varepsilon_t \le 1 + \dfrac{1}{N} \\ 0; \ \varepsilon_t > 1 + \dfrac{1}{N}. \end{cases} \tag{2.19}$$

Since the DLL bandwidth is ordinarily designed to be narrow with respect to the equivalent noise bandwidth of $n_e(t, \varepsilon_t)$, we can approximate $n_e(t, \varepsilon_t)$ as a delta correlated process with equivalent single-sided noise spectral density

$$N_e(\varepsilon_t) = 2\int_{-\infty}^{\infty} R_e(\tau, \varepsilon_t)\, d\tau. \tag{2.20}$$

Substituting (2.18) together with (2.19) into (2.20) and simplifying yields

$$N_e(\varepsilon_t) = 4N_0^2\int_{-\infty}^{\infty} |H_\ell(j2\pi f)|^4\, df + 4SN_0 f(\varepsilon_t)\int_{-\infty}^{\infty} S_m(f)|H_\ell(j2\pi f)|^4\, df \tag{2.21}$$

or, alternately,

$$N_e(\varepsilon_t) = 2SN_0\left[2M_4 f(\varepsilon_t) + 2\frac{K_L}{\rho_H}\right] \tag{2.22}$$

where in addition

$$K_L \triangleq \frac{\int_{-\infty}^{\infty} |H_\ell(j2\pi f)|^4\, df}{\int_{-\infty}^{\infty} |H_\ell(j2\pi f)|^2\, df}$$

$$M_4 \triangleq \int_{-\infty}^{\infty} S_m(f)|H_\ell(j2\pi f)|^4\, df \tag{2.23}$$

and B_H denotes the two-sided noise bandwidth of the equivalent low-pass filter $H_\ell(s)$, i.e.,

$$B_H = \int_{-\infty}^{\infty} |H_\ell(j2\pi f)|^2 \, df \tag{2.24}$$

or equivalently the band-pass noise bandwidth of $H(s)$. Also, in (2.22)

$$\rho_H = \frac{S}{N_0 B_H} \tag{2.25}$$

denotes the signal-to-noise ratio in this bandwidth.

2.1.3 Linear Analysis of DLL Tracking Performance

When the equivalent loop signal-to-noise ratio is large, the tracking performance of the DLL can be determined from (2.15) with $D_n(\varepsilon_t)$ replaced by simply ε_t. Under this assumption and further assuming that $\dot{\tau}_t = 0$, one can write down, by inspection of (2.15), an expression for the mean-squared tracking jitter, viz.,

$$\sigma_\varepsilon^2 = \overline{\varepsilon_t^2} = \frac{\overline{N_e(\varepsilon_t)} B_L}{(\eta S M_2)^2}. \tag{2.26}$$

Substituting (2.19) and (2.22) in (2.26) yields

$$\sigma_\varepsilon^2 = \frac{N_0 B_L}{2S} \left[\frac{M_4 \left[1 + \dfrac{16}{\eta^2} \sigma_\varepsilon^2 \right] + \dfrac{8K_L}{\rho_H \eta^2}}{M_2^2} \right] \tag{2.27}$$

or solving for σ_ε^2

$$\sigma_\varepsilon^2 = \frac{1}{2\rho} \left\{ \frac{M_4 + \dfrac{8K_L}{\rho_H \eta^2}}{M_2^2 \left[1 - \dfrac{8}{\eta^2 \rho} \left(\dfrac{M_4}{M_2^2} \right) \right]} \right\} \tag{2.28}$$

where $\rho \triangleq S/N_0 B_L$. Since for the linear analysis case ρ is assumed to be large, then to a first approximation (2.28) can be simplified to

$$\sigma_\varepsilon^2 = \frac{1}{2\rho} \left\{ \frac{M_4 + \dfrac{8K_L}{\rho_H \eta^2}}{M_2^2} \right\} \triangleq \frac{1}{2\rho \mathcal{S}_L} \tag{2.29}$$

where $\mathcal{S}_L$ is the "squaring loss" of the DLL i.e., the ratio of signal $\times$ signal to signal $\times$ noise plus noise $\times$ noise distortions. Alternately in terms of the data symbol signal-to-noise ratio $E_s/N_0 \triangleq ST_s/N_0$ and the ratio of

Table 2.1
Evaluation of M_2 for one- and two-pole Butterworth filters.

	(Signal × Signal Distortion)$^{1/2}$, M_2; $\|H_\ell(j2\pi f)\|^2 = \dfrac{1}{1+\left(\dfrac{f}{f_c}\right)^{2n}}$
	NRZ; $S_m(f) = T_s \dfrac{\sin^2 \pi f T_s}{(\pi f T_s)^2}$
$n = 1$	$1 - \dfrac{1}{2B_H/R_s}[1 - \exp(-2B_H/R_s)]$
$n = 2$	$1 - \dfrac{1}{4B_H/R_s}\{1 - \exp(-2B_H/R_s)[\cos(2B_H/R_s) - \sin(2B_H/R_s)]\}$
	Manchester Code; $S_m(f) = T_s \dfrac{\sin^4 \pi f T_s/2}{(\pi f T_s/2)^2}$
$n = 1$	$1 - \dfrac{1}{2B_H/R_s}[3 - 4\exp(-B_H/R_s) + \exp(-2B_H/R_s)]$
$n = 2$	$1 - \dfrac{1}{4B_H/R_s}\{3 - 4\exp(-B_H/R_s)[\cos(B_H/R_s) - \sin(B_H/R_s)]$ $+\exp(-2B_H/R_s)[\cos(2B_H/R_s) - \sin(2B_H/R_s)]\}$

band-pass filter bandwidth B_H to data rate R_s, we can write

$$\mathscr{S}_L = \frac{S \times S}{S \times N + N \times N} = \frac{M_2^2}{M_4 + K_L \dfrac{B_H/R_s}{2E_s/N_0}\left(\dfrac{N}{N-1}\right)^2} \tag{2.30}$$

where we have also made use of the definition of η in (2.16). It should be noted that (2.30) is quite similar to the expression for squaring loss of a Costas loop used for carrier synchronization of a BPSK signal (see Equation (46) of [17]). Furthermore, one can conclude from (2.30) that the squaring loss of a DLL with a correlator spacing $\delta = T_c/N$ is equal to the squaring loss of a DLL with a correlator spacing of $T_c/2$ (a "one-delta" loop) and a data rate of $4[(N-1)/N]^2 R_s$. Equivalently, then, one need only plot curves of squaring loss for the "one-delta" loop whereupon all other cases can be derived from these curves by appropriately modifying the data rate R_s.

Tables 2.1 and 2.2 present closed form results for M_2 and M_4, corresponding to one- and two-pole Butterworth filters and NRZ or Manchester coded data [18]. Also for an n-pole Butterworth filter [17],

$$K_L = \frac{n-1}{n} \tag{2.31}$$

and

$$B_H = 2f_c \left[\frac{\dfrac{\pi}{2n}}{\sin \dfrac{\pi}{2n}} \right] \tag{2.32}$$

Table 2.2
Evaluation of M_4 for one- and two-pole Butterworth filters.

	Signal × Noise Distortion, M_4; $\lvert H_\ell(j2\pi f)\rvert^2 = \dfrac{1}{1+\left(\dfrac{f}{f_c}\right)^{2n}}$
	NRZ
$n = 1$	$1 - \dfrac{3-(3+2B_H/R_s)\exp(-2B_H/R_s)}{4B_H/R_s}$
$n = 2$	$1 - \dfrac{5-\{4B_H/R_s\cos(2B_H/R_s)+5[\cos(2B_H/R_s)-\sin(2B_H/R_s)]\}\exp(-2B_H/R_s)}{16B_H/R_s}$
	Manchester Code
$n = 1$	$1 - \dfrac{9-4(3+B_H/R_s)\exp(-B_H/R_s)+(3+2B_H/R_s)\exp(-2B_H/R_s)}{4B_H/R_s}$
$n = 2$	$1 - \dfrac{15-\{8B_H/R_s\cos(B_H/R_s)+20[\cos(B_H/R_s)-\sin(B_H/R_s)]\}\exp(-B_H/R_s)}{16B_H/R_s}$ $- \dfrac{\{4B_H/R_s\cos(2B_H/R_s)+5[\cos(2B_H/R_s)-\sin(2B_H/R_s)]\}\exp(-2B_H/R_s)}{16B_H/R_s}$

where f_c is the 3 dB cutoff frequency of the equivalent low-pass filter $H_\ell(j2\pi f)$.

Figures 2.4 to 2.6 plot $\mathscr{S}_L$ of (2.30) in dB versus B_H/R_s with E_s/N_0 as a parameter for $N = 2$, the case of Manchester coded data and one-, two-, and infinite-pole (ideal) Butterworth filters for $H_\ell(s)$ respectively. We observe that at each value of E_s/N_0, there exists an optimum filter band-

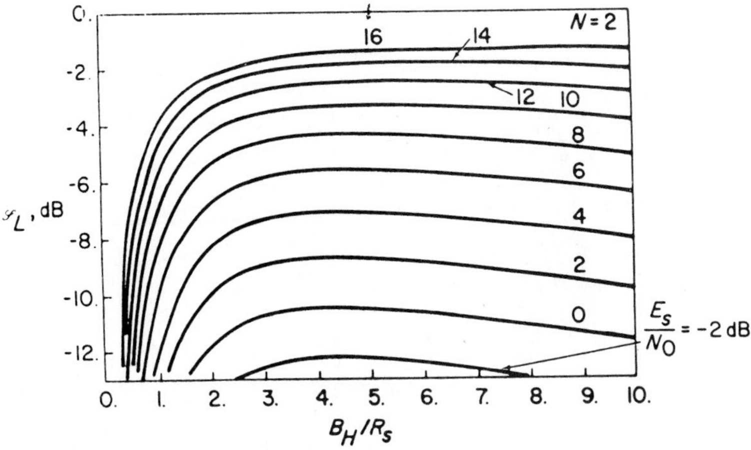

Figure 2.4. Squaring loss variations versus B_H/R_s for various values of E_s/N_0; one-pole Butterworth filter, Manchester coding.

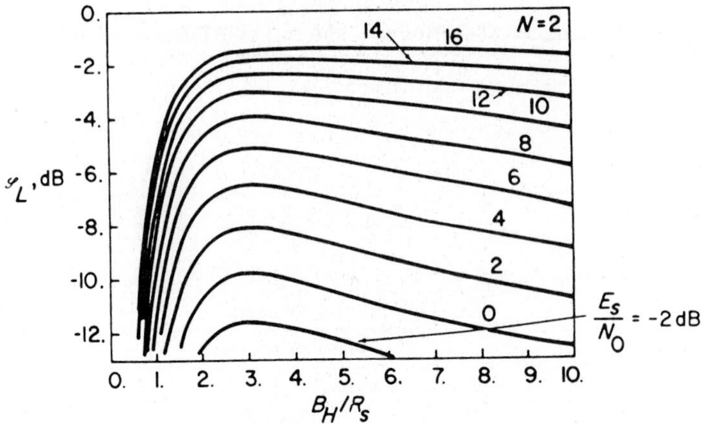

Figure 2.5. Squaring loss variations versus B_H/R_s for various values of E_s/N_0; two-pole Butterworth filter, Manchester coding.

width in the sense of minimizing the loop's squaring loss. From (2.29), such optimization of $\mathscr{S}_L$ is equivalent to minimizing the loop's tracking jitter. Similar optimization behavior of squaring loss as a function of B_H/R_s can also be observed for NRZ data.

As examples, Figures 2.7 and 2.8 illustrate $\sigma_{\varepsilon_{\min}}$ versus E_s/N_0 with $\delta_s \triangleq 1/B_L T_s$ (the ratio of data rate to loop bandwidth) as a parameter for

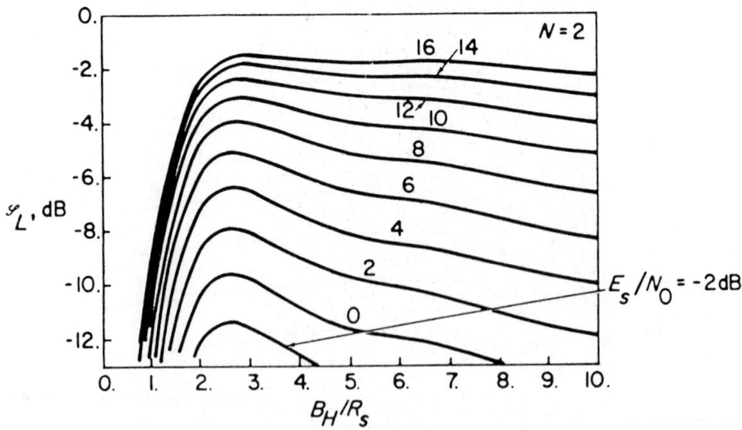

Figure 2.6. Squaring loss variations versus B_H/R_s for various values of E_s/N_0; ideal filter, Manchester coding.

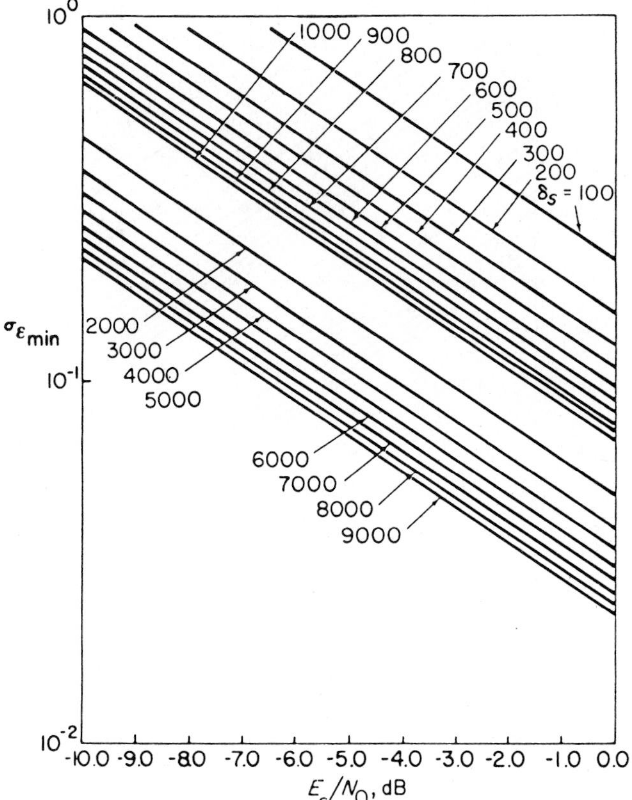

Figure 2.7. Linear tracking jitter performance of non-coherent DLL; two-pole Butterworth filter.

two-pole Butterworth and ideal filters and Manchester coded data. In arriving at these results, we have made the substitution

$$\rho \triangleq \frac{S}{N_0 B_L} = \frac{E_s}{N_0}\delta_s. \tag{2.33}$$

2.2 THE TAU-DITHER LOOP

Consider the non-coherent tau-dither loop (TDL) illustrated in Figure 2.9 whose operation is described as follows. The received signal plus noise is alternately (as opposed to simultaneously) correlated with the advanced and retarded versions of the locally generated PN code (thus the name "dither" loop) to produce an error signal, which, when band-pass filtered, envelope

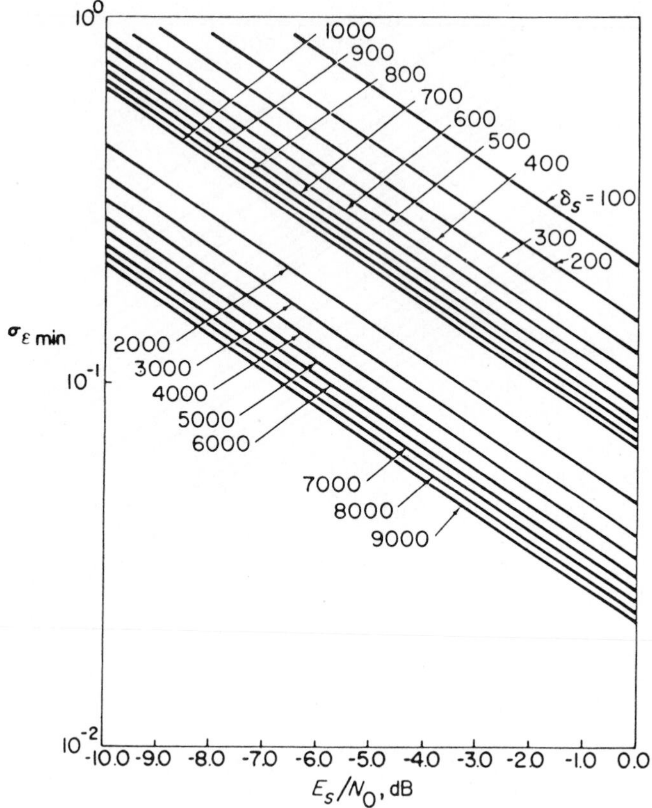

Figure 2.8. Linear tracking jitter performance of non-coherent DLL; ideal filter.

detected, and alternately inverted by the binary signal $q(t)$, drives the voltage controlled clock (VCC) through the loop filter $F(s)$. One obvious advantage of the TDL over the DLL is the fact that only a single input correlator is required, thus eliminating the problems of gain imbalance and other mismatches that are present in a two-channel loop such as the DLL.

2.2.1 Mathematical Loop Model and Equation of Operation

In deriving the loop model and discussing its performance, we shall draw heavily on the notation and results already presented for the DLL. For the purpose of analysis, one can show [6] that when the dither frequency f_d is low relative to the noise bandwidth B_H of the band-pass filter (the usual case of interest), the TDL has the equivalent loop model illustrated in Figure 2.10. Starting then with $y_+(t)$ and $y_-(t)$ as defined in (2.5), the

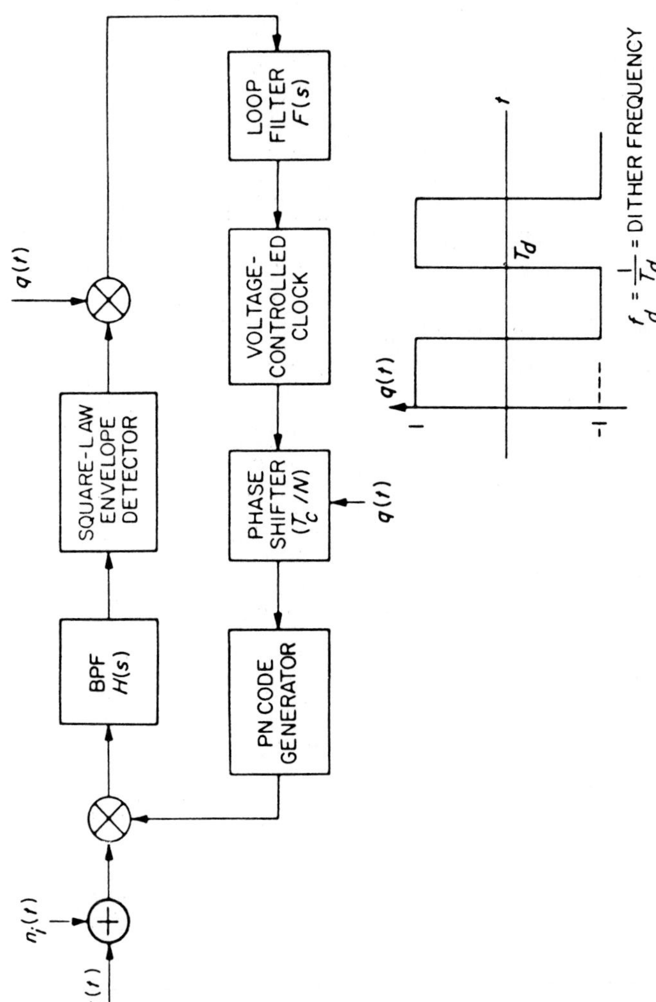

Figure 2.9. A non-coherent tau-dither loop.

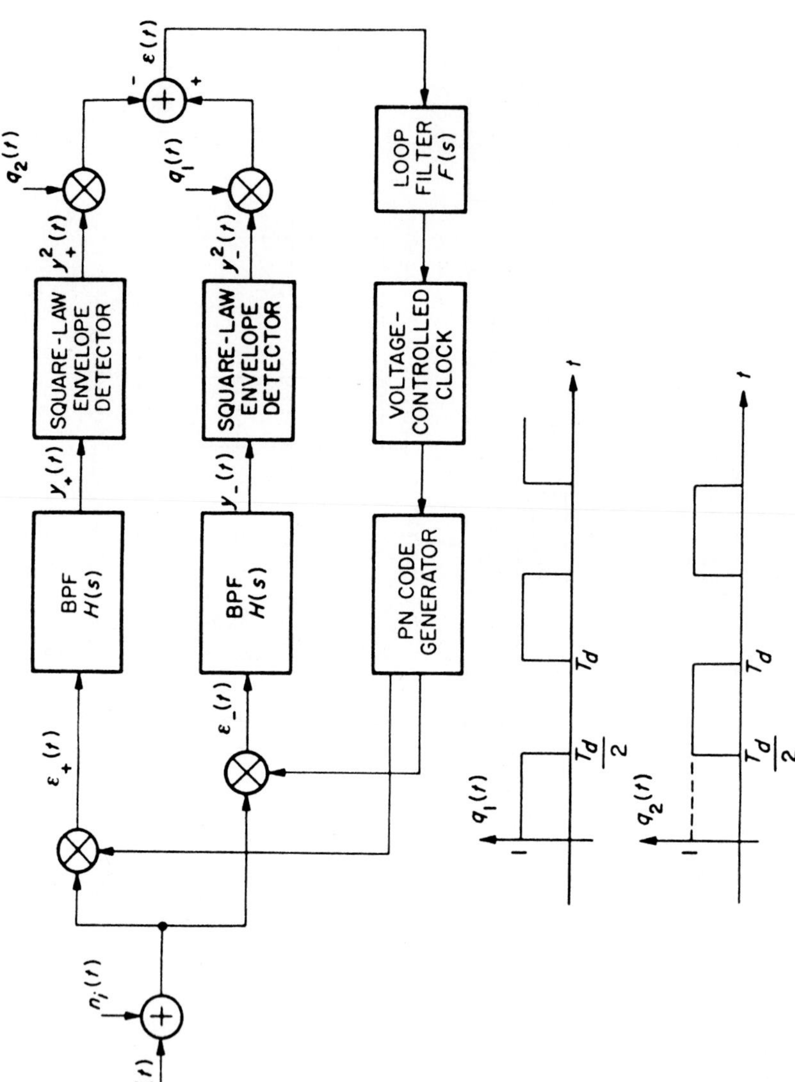

Figure 2.10. An equivalent loop model for the tau-dither loop.

input to the loop filter is now given by

$$\begin{aligned} e(t) &\triangleq y_-^2(t) q_1(t) - y_+^2(t) q_2(t) \\ &= SK_m^2 \hat{m}^2(t-\tau_t)\left[q_1(t) R_{PN_-}^2(\varepsilon_t) - q_2(t) R_{PN_+}^2(\varepsilon_t)\right] \\ &\quad + K_m^2 n_e'(t, \varepsilon_t) \end{aligned} \tag{2.34}$$

where

$$\begin{aligned} n_e'(t, \varepsilon_t) &= q_1(t)\left[\hat{N}_{c_-}^2(t) + \hat{N}_{s_-}^2(t)\right] - q_2(t)\left[\hat{N}_{c_+}^2(t) + \hat{N}_{s_+}^2(t)\right] \\ &\quad + 2\sqrt{S}\,\hat{m}(t-\tau_t)\left\{q_1(t) R_{PN_-}(\varepsilon_t)\hat{N}_{c_-}(t)\right. \\ &\quad \left. - q_2(t) R_{PN_+}(\varepsilon_t)\hat{N}_{c_+}(t)\right\}. \end{aligned} \tag{2.35}$$

Recognizing that $q_1(t) - q_2(t) = q(t)$ and $q_1(t) + q_2(t) = 1$, we see that (2.34) simplifies to

$$e(t) = SK_m^2 \hat{m}^2(t-\tau_t) D'(t, \varepsilon_t) + K_m^2 n_e'(t, \varepsilon_t) \tag{2.36}$$

where

$$D'(t, \varepsilon_t) \triangleq q_1(t) R_{PN_-}^2(\varepsilon_t) - q_2(t) R_{PN_+}^2(\varepsilon_t)$$

$$= \begin{cases} 0; \ \varepsilon_t \le -1 - \dfrac{1}{N} \\ -q_2(t)\left[1 + \dfrac{1}{N} + \varepsilon_t\right]^2; \ -1 - \dfrac{1}{N} < \varepsilon_t \le -1 + \dfrac{1}{N} \\ q(t)\left[(1+\varepsilon_t)^2 + \left(\dfrac{1}{N}\right)^2\right] - \dfrac{2}{N}(1+\varepsilon_t); \ -1 + \dfrac{1}{N} < \varepsilon_t < -\dfrac{1}{N} \\ q(t)\left[\left(1 - \dfrac{1}{N}\right)^2 + \varepsilon_t^2\right] + 2\left(1 - \dfrac{1}{N}\right)\varepsilon_t; \ |\varepsilon_t| \le \dfrac{1}{N} \\ q(t)\left[(1-\varepsilon_t)^2 + \left(\dfrac{1}{N}\right)^2\right] + \dfrac{2}{N}(1-\varepsilon_t); \ \dfrac{1}{N} < \varepsilon_t \le 1 - \dfrac{1}{N} \\ q_1(t)\left[1 + \dfrac{1}{N} - \varepsilon_t\right]^2; \ 1 - \dfrac{1}{N} < \varepsilon_t \le 1 + \dfrac{1}{N} \\ 0; \ \varepsilon_t > 1 + \dfrac{1}{N} \end{cases} \tag{2.37}$$

$$D'(t, \varepsilon_t) = D'(t, \varepsilon_t + np); \qquad n = \pm 1, \pm 2, \pm 3, \ldots. \tag{2.38}$$

As in the DLL case, since the loop bandwidth is narrow with respect to the data rate and here also with respect to the dither frequency, $f_d = 1/T_d$, we can replace $\hat{m}^2(t-\tau_t) D'(t, \varepsilon_t)$ by

$$\overline{\langle \hat{m}^2(t-\tau_t) D'(t, \varepsilon_t)\rangle} = \overline{\langle \hat{m}^2(t-\tau_t)\rangle}\langle D'(t, \varepsilon_t)\rangle. \tag{2.39}$$

Thus, since $\langle q(t)\rangle = 0$ and $\langle q_1(t)\rangle = \langle q_2(t)\rangle = 1/2$, we get

$$D'(\varepsilon_t) \triangleq \langle D'(t,\varepsilon_t)\rangle = \begin{cases} 0; & \varepsilon_t \le -1 - \frac{1}{N} \\ -\frac{1}{2}\left(1 + \frac{1}{N} + \varepsilon_t\right)^2; & -1 - \frac{1}{N} < \varepsilon_t \le -1 + \frac{1}{N} \\ -\frac{2}{N}(1 + \varepsilon_t); & -1 + \frac{1}{N} < \varepsilon_t < -\frac{1}{N} \\ 2\varepsilon_t\left(1 - \frac{1}{N}\right); & |\varepsilon_t| \le \frac{1}{N} \\ \frac{2}{N}(1 - \varepsilon_t); & \frac{1}{N} < \varepsilon_t \le 1 - \frac{1}{N} \\ \frac{1}{2}\left(1 + \frac{1}{N} - \varepsilon_t\right)^2; & 1 - \frac{1}{N} < \varepsilon_t \le 1 + \frac{1}{N} \\ 0; & \varepsilon_t > 1 + \frac{1}{N} \end{cases} \tag{2.40}$$

and (2.36) further simplifies to

$$e(t) = SK_m^2 M_2 D'(\varepsilon_t) + K_m^2 n_e'(t,\varepsilon_t) \tag{2.41}$$

where M_2 is defined in (2.14). Comparing $D'(\varepsilon_t)$ of (2.40) with $D(\varepsilon_t)$ of (2.8), we observe that the TDL suffers an effective reduction in signal power of 3 dB relative to the DLL. Using (2.10) and the assumptions leading up to (2.15), we obtain the stochastic differential equation which characterizes the TDL, viz.,

$$\dot{\varepsilon}_t = \frac{\dot{\tau}_t}{T_c} - \frac{1}{2}KF(p)\eta SM_2\left[D_n(\varepsilon_t) + \frac{n_e'(t,\varepsilon_t)}{\frac{1}{2}\eta SM_2}\right] \tag{2.42}$$

where $D_n(\varepsilon_t) \triangleq (2/\eta)D'(\varepsilon_t)$ is identical to the normalized discriminator characteristic for the DLL.

2.2.2 Statistical Characterization of the Equivalent Additive Noise

What remains is to determine the power spectral density $N_e'(\varepsilon_t)$ of the delta-correlated process $n_e'(t,\varepsilon_t)$, i.e.,

$$N_e'(\varepsilon_t) = 2\int_{-\infty}^{\infty} R_e'(\tau,\varepsilon_t)\, d\tau \tag{2.43}$$

where

$$R_e'(\tau,\varepsilon_t) \triangleq \overline{n_e'(t,\varepsilon_t)n_e'(t+\tau,\varepsilon_t)}. \tag{2.44}$$

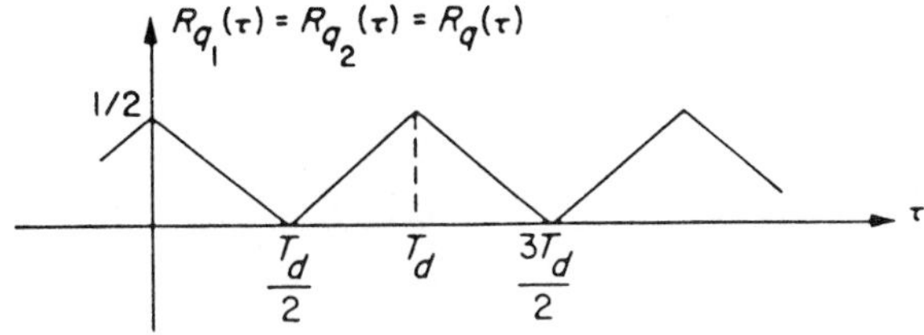

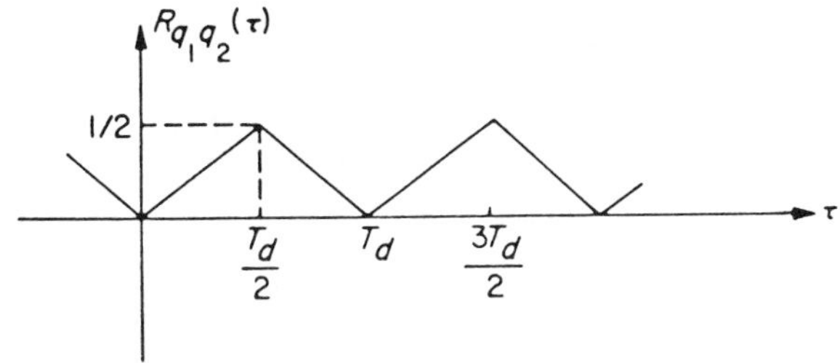

Figure 2.11. Autocorrelation functions of $q_1(t)$ and $q_2(t)$ and cross-correlation function of $q_1(t)$ and $q_2(t)$.

Denoting the autocorrelation and cross-correlation functions of the switching waveforms by

$$R_{q_1}(\tau) \triangleq \langle q_1(t)q_1(t+\tau)\rangle$$
$$R_{q_2}(\tau) \triangleq \langle q_2(t)q_2(t+\tau)\rangle$$
$$R_{q_1q_2}(\tau) \triangleq \langle q_1(t)q_2(t+\tau)\rangle \tag{2.45}$$

we find that

$$R_{q_1}(\tau) = R_{q_2}(\tau) = \tfrac{1}{2} - R_{q_1q_2}(\tau) \triangleq R_q(\tau) \tag{2.46}$$

where $R_q(\tau)$ is illustrated in Figure 2.11. Substituting (2.35) into (2.44) and making use of (2.46), we find after considerable algebraic manipulation that

$$R'_e(\tau, \varepsilon_t) = 8R^2_{\hat{N}}(\tau)R_q(\tau) + 8R^2_{\hat{N}}(0)\left[2R_q(\tau) - \tfrac{1}{2}\right]$$
$$+4SR_{\hat{m}}(\tau)R_{\hat{N}}(\tau)R_q(\tau)f(\varepsilon_t) \tag{2.47}$$

where $R_{\hat{N}}(\tau)$, $R_{\hat{m}}(\tau)$, and $f(\varepsilon_t)$ are all defined in (2.19). Integration of (2.47) as required in (2.43) can alternately be accomplished in the frequency domain, viz.,

$$N'_e(\varepsilon_t) = 16\int_{-\infty}^{\infty} \left[S_{\hat{N}}(f) * S_{\hat{N}}(f)\right]S_q(-f)\,df$$
$$+8Sf(\varepsilon_t)\int_{-\infty}^{\infty} \left[S_{\hat{m}}(f) * S_{\hat{m}}(f)\right]S_q(-f)\,df \tag{2.48}$$

where the asterisk denotes convolution, and

$$S_{\hat{N}}(f) = \mathcal{F}\{R_{\hat{N}}(\tau)\} = \frac{N_0}{2}|H_\ell(j2\pi f)|^2$$

$$S_{\hat{m}}(f) = \mathcal{F}\{R_{\hat{m}}(\tau)\} = S_m(f)|H_\ell(j2\pi f)|^2$$

$$S_q(f) = \mathcal{F}\{R_q(\tau)\} = \frac{1}{4}\delta(f) + \frac{1}{4}\sum_{\substack{n=-\infty \\ n \text{ odd}}}^{\infty}\left(\frac{2}{n\pi}\right)^2\delta\left(f - \frac{n}{T_d}\right). \tag{2.49}$$

Substituting (2.49) into (2.48), we obtain, after much simplification, an expression analogous to (2.22), i.e.,

$$N_e'(\varepsilon_t) = \frac{SN_0}{2}\left[2M_4'f(\varepsilon_t) + 2\frac{K_L'}{\rho_H}\right] \tag{2.50}$$

where

$$M_4' = M_4 + 2\sum_{n=1,3,5\ldots}^{\infty}\left(\frac{2}{n\pi}\right)^2 M_{4n}$$

$$K_L' = K_L + 2\sum_{n=1,3,5\ldots}^{\infty}\left(\frac{2}{n\pi}\right)^2 K_{L_n}$$

$$M_{4n} \triangleq \int_{-\infty}^{\infty} S_m(f)|H_\ell(j2\pi f)|^2\left|H_\ell\left[j2\pi\left(\frac{n}{T_d} - f\right)\right]\right|^2 df$$

$$K_{L_n} = \frac{\int_{-\infty}^{\infty}|H_\ell(j2\pi f)|^2\left|H_\ell\left[j2\pi\left(\frac{n}{T_d} - f\right)\right]\right|^2 df}{\int_{-\infty}^{\infty}|H_\ell(j2\pi f)|^2\,df} \tag{2.51}$$

and K_L and M_4 are defined in (2.23) and ρ_H is defined in (2.25).

2.2.3 Linear Analysis of TDL Tracking Performance

As for the DLL, we can write down, by inspection of (2.42), an expression for the mean-squared tracking jitter for the case $\dot{\tau}_t = 0$, viz.,

$$\sigma_\varepsilon'^2 = \frac{\overline{N_e'(\varepsilon_t)}B_L}{\left(\frac{1}{2}\eta SM_2\right)^2} \tag{2.52}$$

which upon substitution of (2.50) and (2.19) becomes

$$\sigma_\varepsilon'^2 = \frac{1}{2\rho}\left\{\frac{M_4' + \dfrac{8K_L'}{\rho_H\eta^2}}{M_2^2\left[1 - \dfrac{8}{\eta^2\rho}\left(\dfrac{M_4'}{M_2^2}\right)\right]}\right\} \tag{2.53}$$

or, to a first approximation

$$\sigma_\varepsilon'^2 = \frac{1}{2\rho}\left\{\frac{M_4' + \dfrac{8K_L'}{\rho_H\eta^2}}{M_2^2}\right\} = \frac{1}{2\rho\mathscr{S}_L'} \tag{2.54}$$

where $\mathscr{S}_L'$ is the "squaring loss" of the TDL which is given by (2.30) with M_4 and K_L replaced by M_4' and K_L'. A comparison of the linear tracking jitter performances of the DLL and TDL depends then simply on the ratio of $\mathscr{S}_L'$ to $\mathscr{S}_L$, namely,

$$\frac{\mathscr{S}_L}{\mathscr{S}_L'} = \frac{M_4 + \dfrac{8K_L}{\rho_H\eta^2}}{M_4' + \dfrac{8K_L'}{\rho_H\eta^2}}. \tag{2.55}$$

Clearly, from the definitions of M_{4n} and K_{L_n} as given in (2.51), we see that $M_{4n} < M_4$ and $K_{L_n} < K_L$ for any n, in particular, n odd, and T_d finite. Thus, from (2.51)

$$\begin{aligned} M_4' &< M_4 + \frac{8}{\pi^2}\sum_{n=1,3,5\ldots}^{\infty}\frac{1}{n^2}M_4 = 2M_4 \\ K_L' &< K_L + \frac{8}{\pi^2}\sum_{n=1,3,5\ldots}^{\infty}\frac{1}{n^2}K_L = 2K_L. \end{aligned} \tag{2.56}$$

Substituting the bounds of (2.56) into (2.55), we find that

$$\frac{\mathscr{S}_L'}{\mathscr{S}_L} > \frac{1}{2} \tag{2.57}$$

or equivalently, *the linear theory mean-squared timing error for the TDL is less than 3 dB worse than that of the DLL.*

Although the integrals in (2.51) are in general difficult to evaluate in closed form, the case where $H_\ell(s)$ is an ideal filter allows some simplification. In particular,

$$K_{L_n} = \frac{\displaystyle\int_{-B_H/2+n/T_d}^{B_H/2} df}{\displaystyle\int_{-B_H/2}^{B_H/2} df} = \begin{cases} 1 - \dfrac{n}{B_H T_d}; & n \le \lfloor B_H T_d \rfloor \triangleq n_0 \\ 0; & n > n_0 \end{cases} \tag{2.58}$$

where the notation $\lfloor x \rfloor$ denotes the largest integer less than or equal to x. Thus, from (2.51),

$$K_L' = 1 + \frac{8}{\pi^2}\sum_{n=1,3,5,\ldots}^{n_0}\frac{1}{n^2} - \frac{8}{\pi^2 B_H T_d}\sum_{n=1,3,5,\ldots}^{n_0}\frac{1}{n}. \tag{2.59}$$

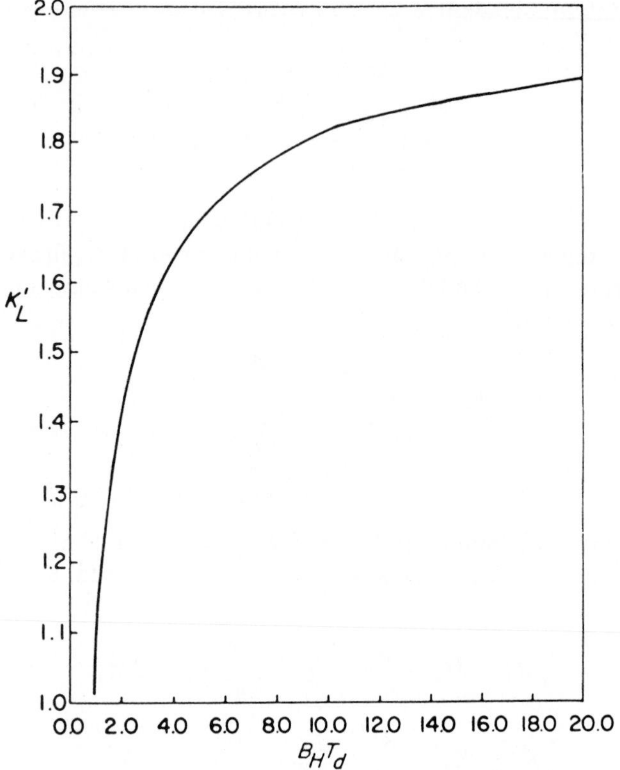

Figure 2.12. A plot of K_L' versus $B_H T_d$; ideal filter.

Figure 2.12 plots K_L' versus $B_H T_d$. Similarly, for the case of Manchester-coded data of rate $R_s = 1/T_s$,

$$M_{4n} = \int_{-B_H/2+n/T_d}^{B_H/2} \frac{\sin^4 \dfrac{\pi f T_s}{2}}{\left(\dfrac{\pi f T_s}{2}\right)^2} df = \int_{-B_H T_s/4}^{B_H T_s/4} \frac{\sin^4 \pi x}{(\pi x)^2} dx$$

$$- \int_{-B_H T_s/4}^{-B_H T_s/4 + nT_s/2T_d} \frac{\sin^4 \pi x}{(\pi x)^2} dx \tag{2.60}$$

and

$$M_4' = \left[1 + \frac{8}{\pi^2} \sum_{n=1,3,5,\ldots}^{n_0} \frac{1}{n^2}\right] \int_{-B_H T_s/4}^{B_H T_s/4} \frac{\sin^4 \pi x}{(\pi x)^2} dx - \frac{8}{\pi^2} \sum_{n=1,3,5,\ldots}^{n_0} \frac{1}{n^2}$$

$$\times \int_{(B_H T_s/4)[1-2n/B_H T_d]}^{B_H T_s/4} \frac{\sin^4 \pi x}{(\pi x)^2} dx \tag{2.61}$$

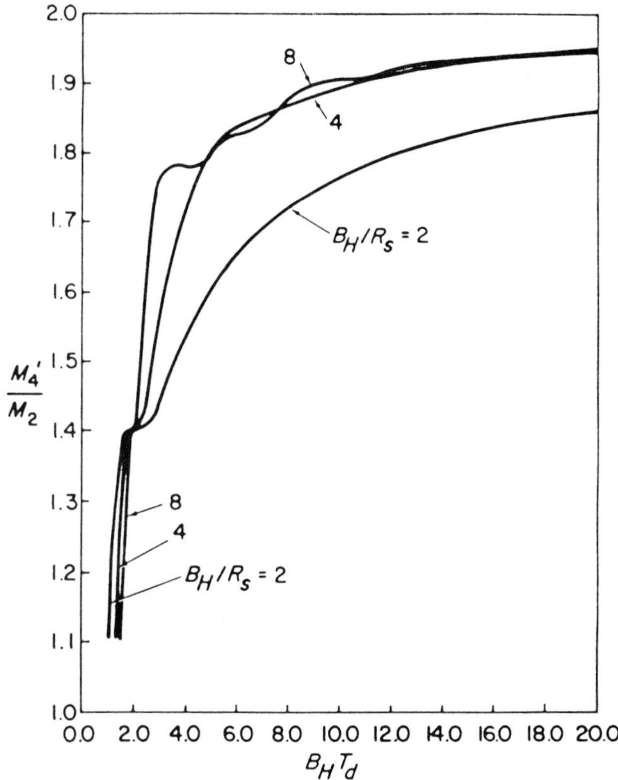

Figure 2.13. Plots of M_4'/M_2 versus $B_H T_d$ with B_H/R_s as a parameter; ideal filter, Manchester coding.

where the first integral in (2.61) is in reality $M_2 = M_4$. Figure 2.13 plots M_4' (normalized by M_2) versus $B_H T_d$ for various values of the ratio of filter bandwidth to data rate, B_H/R_s.

At this point, it is reasonable to expect that if one were to plot $\mathscr{S}_L'$ versus B_H/R_s with E_s/N_0 as a parameter, then at each value of E_s/N_0, there would exist an optimum filter bandwidth in the sense of minimizing the loop's squaring loss. Figure 2.14 illustrates the validity of this statement for the case of an ideal filter with $\mathscr{S}_L'$ as determined from (2.54) together with (2.14), (2.59), and (2.61). The corresponding minimum tracking jitter performance as described by (2.54) is illustrated in Figure 2.15. In both of these figures, the value of $B_H T_d$ was chosen equal to four. Comparing Figure 2.15 with Figure 2.8, we observe that over the entire range of parameter variations chosen, the TDL is approximately 1.06 dB poorer than the DLL.[5]

[5] The comparison here is made on the basis of equal $\sigma_{\epsilon_{\min}}$ and the signal-to-noise ratio penalty of 1.06 dB is obtained directly from the computational data rather than the curves themselves.

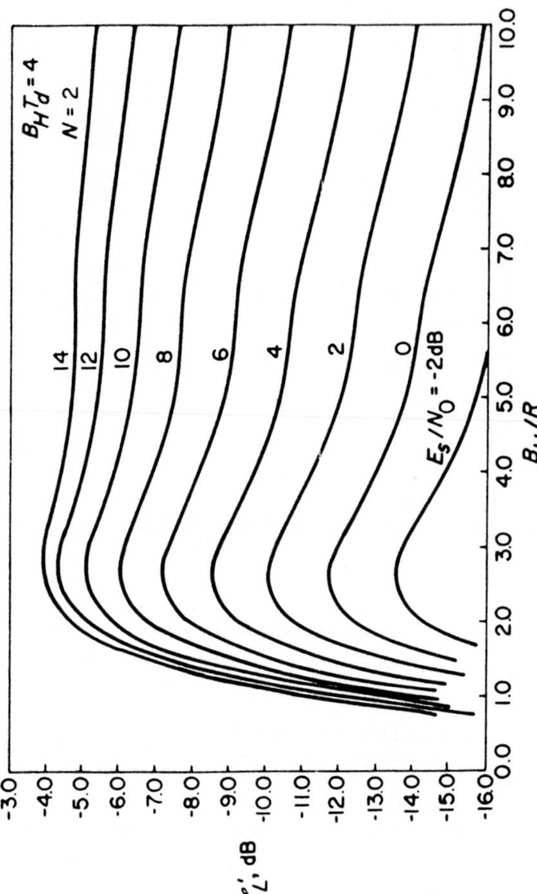

Figure 2.14. Squaring loss variations versus B_H/R_s for various values of E_s/N_0; ideal filter, Manchester coding.

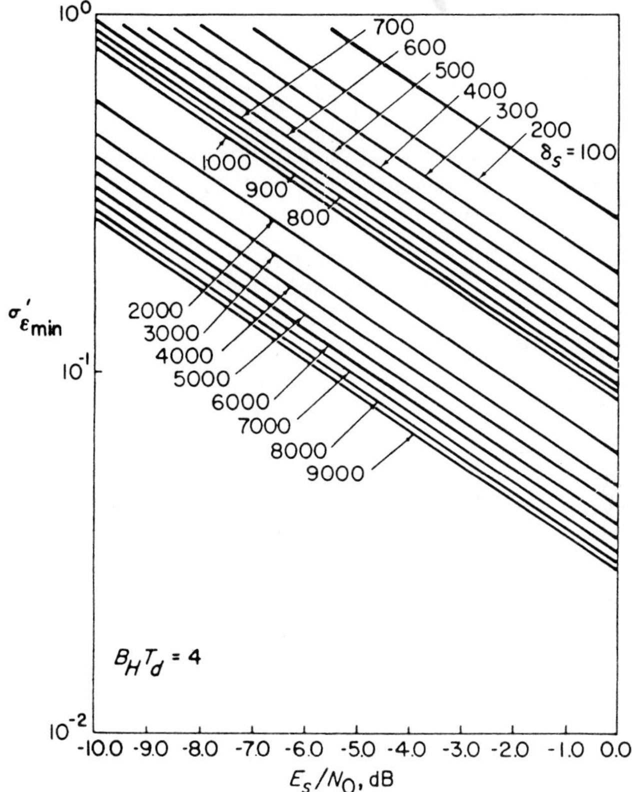

Figure 2.15. Linear tracking jitter performance of non-coherent TDL; ideal filter.

As $B_H T_d$ is increased (typically by lowering the dither frequency relative to the arm filter bandwidth), the performance penalty also increases approaching 1.5 dB in the limit as $B_H T_d$ approaches infinity. Clearly, this situation is never reached in practice, nor in theory, since the assumption made in the analysis that the dither frequency be large relative to the loop bandwidth breaks down.

It is perhaps interesting to see how the optimized performance results presented in this chapter compare with the early results of Gill [3] and Hartmann [6]. In particular, both these authors performed their analyses neglecting the band-limiting effect of the arm filters. Thus, if one sets $K_L = M_2 = M_4 = 1$ in (2.29), and substitutes $(E_s/N_0)/(B_H/R_s)$ for ρ_H one arrives at Gill's result[6] for the normalized mean-squared tracking error of

[6]Actually, Gill and Hartmann considered only the "one-delta" loop, i.e., $N = 2$.

the DLL, namely

$$\sigma_\varepsilon^2 = \frac{1}{2\rho}\left[1 + \frac{2B_H/R_s}{E_s/N_0}\right]. \tag{2.62}$$

A similar analysis to Gill's was performed by Hartmann for the TDL. His result for the normalized mean-squared tracking error (analogous to (2.54)) is

$$\sigma_\varepsilon'^2 = \frac{1}{\rho}\left[0.905 + \frac{4B_H/R_s}{E_s/N_0}\left(0.453 - \frac{0.2}{B_H T_d}\right)\right] \tag{2.63}$$

which for $B_H T_d = 4$ becomes

$$\sigma_\varepsilon'^2 = \frac{1}{\rho}\left[0.905 + \frac{1.612 B_H/R_s}{E_s/N_0}\right]. \tag{2.64}$$

Numerical comparison of (2.62) and (2.64) with the results in Figures 2.8 and 2.15 reveals that both Gill's and Hartmann's simple results are optimistic by about .9 dB [7].

One should also note that if arm filter band-limiting effects were totally ignored for the TDL, then again $K_L = M_2 = M_4 = 1$ and M_4' and K_L' would achieve their upper bounds as in (2.56), in which case, (2.54) would simplify (for $N = 2$) to

$$\sigma_\varepsilon'^2 = \frac{1}{\rho}\left[1 + \frac{2B_H/R_s}{E_s/N_0}\right]. \tag{2.65}$$

Comparing (2.65) with (2.62), we observe the often-quoted (although incorrect) result that the TDL suffers a 3 dB degradation in signal-to-noise performance relative to the DLL.

Finally, we point out that increasing N (decreasing the advance (retard) interval) decreases the mean-squared tracking jitter for both the DLL and TDL. This observation is easily concluded from (2.29) and (2.54) together with (2.16). However, increasing N also decreases the linear tracking region of the discriminator characteristic (see Figure 2.3) and thus increases the loop's tendency to lose lock. This tradeoff between decreasing mean-squared tracking jitter at the expense of increased sensitivity to loss of lock is characteristic of all early-late gate types of loops [15, Chapter 9].

2.3 ACQUISITION (TRANSIENT) BEHAVIOR OF THE DLL AND TDL

In this section, we discuss the transient response of the DLL and TDL with particular emphasis on their acquisition behavior in the presence of an initial code rate offset of the incoming PN code relative to that of the clock that generates the local PN code replica at the receiver. When discussing the transient response behavior of a DLL or TDL, or for that matter any PN code tracking loop, there are primarily two questions of interest:

1. What is the maximum relative code rate offset (due to code Doppler, clock instabilities, etc.) between the received and locally generated PN codes so that the received signal can still be acquired? Equivalently, what is the maximum search rate (velocity) to achieve acquisition?
2. How long do the transients last, i.e., how long does it take to acquire?

The answer to the first question may be obtained (in a noise-free environment) by examination of the phase-plane trajectories. These trajectories are plots of normalized code delay error rate $\dot{\varepsilon}_t$ versus normalized code delay error ε_t with normalized time as a parameter along the curve. To obtain these trajectories for the DLL, we begin by rewriting the system equation of noise-free operation, as given by (2.15), in the normalized form

$$p_0(y - x) = GF_0(p_0)D_n(x) \tag{2.66}$$

where

$$\tau \triangleq \omega_n t$$

$$p_0 \triangleq \frac{d}{d\tau} = \left(\frac{1}{\omega_n}\right)\frac{d}{dt} = \frac{p}{\omega_n}$$

$$x \triangleq \frac{\tau}{T_c}$$

$$y \triangleq \varepsilon_t$$

$$G \triangleq \eta SKM_2/\omega_n$$

$$F_0(p_0) = F_0\left(\frac{p}{\omega_n}\right) \triangleq F(p) \tag{2.67}$$

with ω_n the *radian natural frequency* of the loop.

For a second-order loop with linear closed loop transfer function [16]

$$\begin{aligned} H(s) &= \frac{1 + 2\zeta s/\omega_n}{1 + (1/G + 2\zeta)(s/\omega_n) + (s/\omega_n)^2} \\ &= \frac{\omega_n GF(s)}{s + \omega_n GF(s)} \end{aligned} \tag{2.68}$$

the product of the loop gain G and the filter transfer function $F(s)$ becomes

$$GF(s) = \frac{1 + 2\zeta s/\omega_n}{1/G + s/\omega_n} \tag{2.69}$$

or

$$GF_0(p_0) = \frac{1 + 2\zeta p_0}{1/G + p_0} \tag{2.70}$$

where ζ is the loop's *damping factor*. For a critically damped loop ($\zeta =$

$1/\sqrt{2}$), (2.70) simplifies to

$$GF_0(p_0) = \frac{1 + \sqrt{2}\, p_0}{1/G + p_0}, \tag{2.71}$$

which, upon substitution into (2.66), yields

$$\dot{y}/G + \ddot{y} = \dot{x}/G + \ddot{x} + D_n(x) + \sqrt{2}\, D_n'(x)\dot{x}. \tag{2.72}$$

The dot now denotes the derivative with respect to normalized time (τ) and the prime denotes the derivative with respect to the normalized transmission delay (x). The solution of the second-order partial differential equation in (2.66) for the phase-plane trajectories is facilitated by defining $\gamma \triangleq \ddot{x}/\dot{x} = d\dot{x}/dx$, which results in

$$\gamma = -\frac{D_n(x) + \left[\sqrt{2}\, D_n'(x) + 1/G\right]\dot{x} - \dot{y}/G - \ddot{y}}{\dot{x}}. \tag{2.73}$$

For a constant search velocity, $\ddot{y} = 0$ and the above equation simplifies to

$$\gamma = \frac{D_n(x) + \left[\sqrt{2}\, D_n'(x) + 1/G\right]\dot{x} - \dot{y}/G}{\dot{x}}. \tag{2.74}$$

Statistical methods (e.g., Newton's method [19]) of solving differential equations can now be applied to (2.74) to compute the trajectories in the $(\dot{x}, x)$ plane for given initial conditions. One then looks for the maximum $\dot{y}$ for which the phase-plane trajectories will eventually reach the $(0, \dot{y}/G)$ point, i.e., the DLL will phase and frequency lock.

The acquisition trajectories for $G = 10$, $\zeta = 1/\sqrt{2}$, $N = 2$ and $N = 4$ are shown in Figures 2.16 and 2.17, respectively [4], [14].[7] It is found that the maximum normalized search rate for $N = 2$ is $\dot{y} = 1.0$, while for $N = 4$, the maximum normalized search rate is $\dot{y} = 0.5$. Furthermore, the open loop gain has little effect on the trajectories for $G > 10$ [14].

The second question raised above can be dealt with by using the definition of γ as a starting point and computing the acquisition transients as a function of time and then finding the acquisition time. Figure 2.18 shows the transient response of the DLL for $G = 100$, $\zeta = 1/\sqrt{2}$, $N = 2$ and $N = 4$. The search rate is chosen to be $\dot{y} = 0.9$ for the first case and $\dot{y} = 0.45$ for the second case, respectively. The graphs show that the acquisition time (time required for the transient to subside within $|x| = 0.1$) for $N = 2$ is shorter than that for $N = 4$. The actual acquisition time can be computed from the definition of the normalized time given in (2.67) and the relation between the single-sided loop bandwidth B_L and the loop radian

[7]Historically acquisition trajectories were first found in [1] and [3] but were later shown to be in error [4].

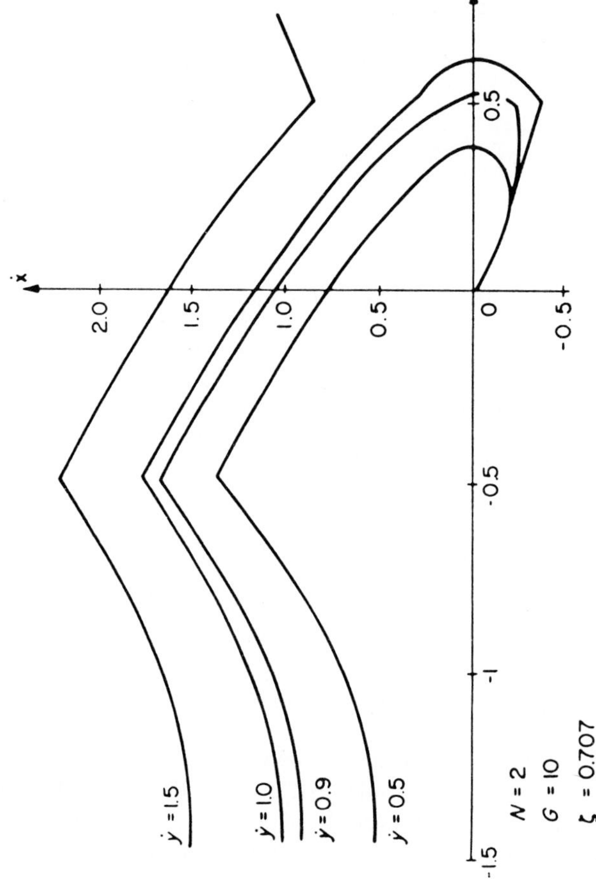

Figure 2.16. Acquisition trajectories for $N = 2$ (reprinted from [14]).

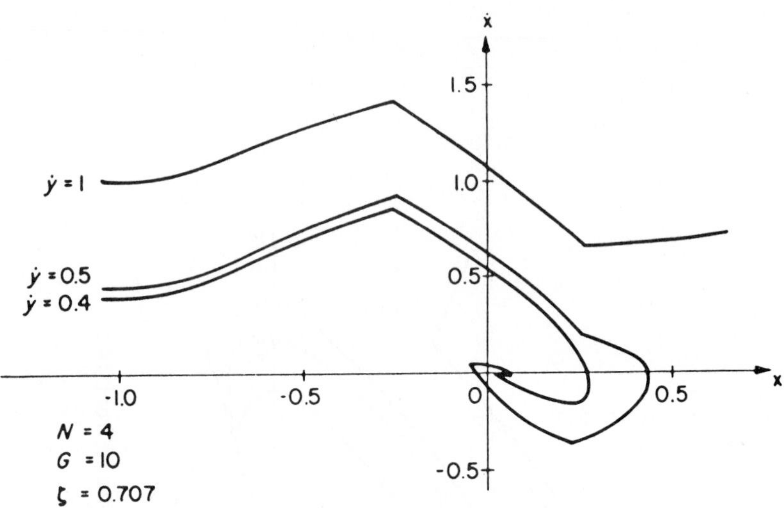

Figure 2.17. Acquisition trajectories for $N = 4$ (reprinted from [14]).

natural frequency ω_n. Since from [16]

$$\omega_n = \left(\frac{8\zeta}{4\zeta^2 + 1}\right) B_L \tag{2.75}$$

then for critically damped loops $\omega_n = B_L/.5303$ and

$$t_{\text{ACQ}} = \frac{.5303\tau_{ACQ}}{B_L}. \tag{2.76}$$

Table 2.3 summarizes the results for several different values of loop bandwidth.

Finally, the actual maximum search velocity in chips/sec (which can be interpreted as the maximum allowable drift in the code) can be found from the definition of the normalized search velocity $\dot{y}$. As a function of the single-sided loop noise bandwidth B_L, the search velocity (v_s) is

$$v_s = \left(\frac{8\zeta}{4\zeta^2 + 1}\right) \dot{y} B_L \text{ chips/sec} \tag{2.77}$$

which for critically damped loops becomes

$$v_s = 1.8857 \dot{y} B_L \text{ chips/sec.} \tag{2.78}$$

Although all our attention has focussed on the DLL, a comparison of (2.15) and (2.42) in the absence of noise reveals that except for a factor of two in the equivalent gain G, the TDL and DLL have identical acquisition performance.

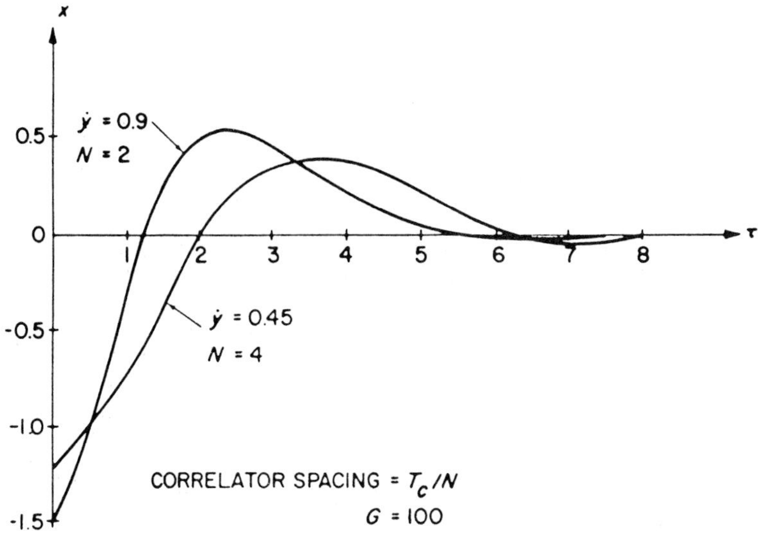

Figure 2.18. Transient response of delay lock loop (reprinted from [14]).

Table 2.3
Acquisition time (sec).

B_L (Hz)	100	200	300	400	
$N = 2$	0.0244	0.0122	0.0081	0.0061	$\dot{y} = 0.9$
$N = 4$	0.0292	0.0146	0.0097	0.0073	$\dot{y} = 0.45$

2.4 MEAN TIME TO LOSS-OF-LOCK FOR THE DLL AND TDL

The ability of the code tracking loop to maintain lock is an important consideration in assessing the overall performance of a DS/SS receiver. One measure of this ability, which is undoubtedly the most informative, is the probability of remaining in lock for a given interval of time. Unfortunately, analytical evaluation of this measure is difficult, and thus an alternate but still informative measure often used is the mean time to lose lock. Although for a carrier tracking loop such as a phase-locked loop (PLL) this performance measure is well defined [16], its definition for a PN code tracking loop requires some clarification. For our purpose, we shall define out-of-lock to occur when the loop error signal goes beyond its uncorrelated value, or equivalently, the delay error exceeds the range of the discriminator characteristic around the lock point, i.e., $\pm T_c(N + 1)/N$.

The mean time to loss-of-lock is a special case of the more general problem of finding the n-th moment of the first passage time of the error process in a synchronous control system (SCS). The solutions to problems of this nature are typically obtained by assuming that the noise process driving the system is wideband compared to the system bandwidth, in which case the error process can be assumed to be Markovian and its probability density function is a solution to the Fokker-Planck equation. Without belaboring the details, one can show that by applying the appropriate boundary conditions to the time-dependent solution of the one-dimensional Fokker-Planck equation, the first moment of the first passage time (mean time to lose lock) of the error process $x(t)$ in a first-order SCS with symmetrical boundaries $\pm b$ and symmetrical restoring force $h(x)$ [i.e., $h(x) = h(-x)$] is given by [16]

$$\overline{T} = \frac{1}{K_2}\int_0^b \int_0^b \exp[U(y) - U(x)]\, dy\, dx \tag{2.79}$$

where $U(x)$ is the system potential function which is related to the restoring force by

$$U(x) \triangleq -\int^x h(y)\, dy \tag{2.80}$$

and K_2 is the second-order intensity coefficient in the Fokker-Planck equation.

For the DLL, the error process x is the normalized delay error ε_t and $h(x)$ is linearly related to the normalized discriminator characteristic by

$$h(x) = -\rho_L D_n(x);\ \rho_L \triangleq 2\rho\mathscr{S}_L = \sigma_\varepsilon^{-2} \tag{2.81}$$

Thus,

$$U(x) = \rho_L \int^x D_n(y)\, dy \triangleq \rho_L \mathscr{D}_n(x) \tag{2.82}$$

Furthermore, $b = (N + 1)/N$ and K_2 evaluates to

$$K_2 = \frac{2\eta^2 B_L}{\rho_L}. \tag{2.83}$$

Finally, then substituting (2.82) and (2.83) in (2.79) gives the desired result for the mean time to loss-of-lock (normalized by the loop bandwidth) of the DLL, namely,

$$B_L\overline{T} = \frac{\rho_L}{2\eta^2}\int_0^{(N+1)/N}\int_0^{(N+1)/N} \exp\{\rho_L[\mathscr{D}(y) - \mathscr{D}(x)]\}\, dy\, dx. \tag{2.84}$$

Comparing (2.15) with (2.42), it is easily seen that (2.84) also applies to a first-order TDL if ρ_L is replaced by

$$\rho_L' \triangleq 2\rho\mathscr{S}_L'. \tag{2.85}$$

Figure 2.19 illustrates $10\log_{10}(B_L\overline{T})$ as computed from (2.84) versus $\sigma_L = 1/\sqrt{\rho_L}$ for $N = 2$, 4, and 8. Clearly, the mean time to lose lock decreases with increasing N in agreement with our previous observation concerning the width of the linear tracking region.

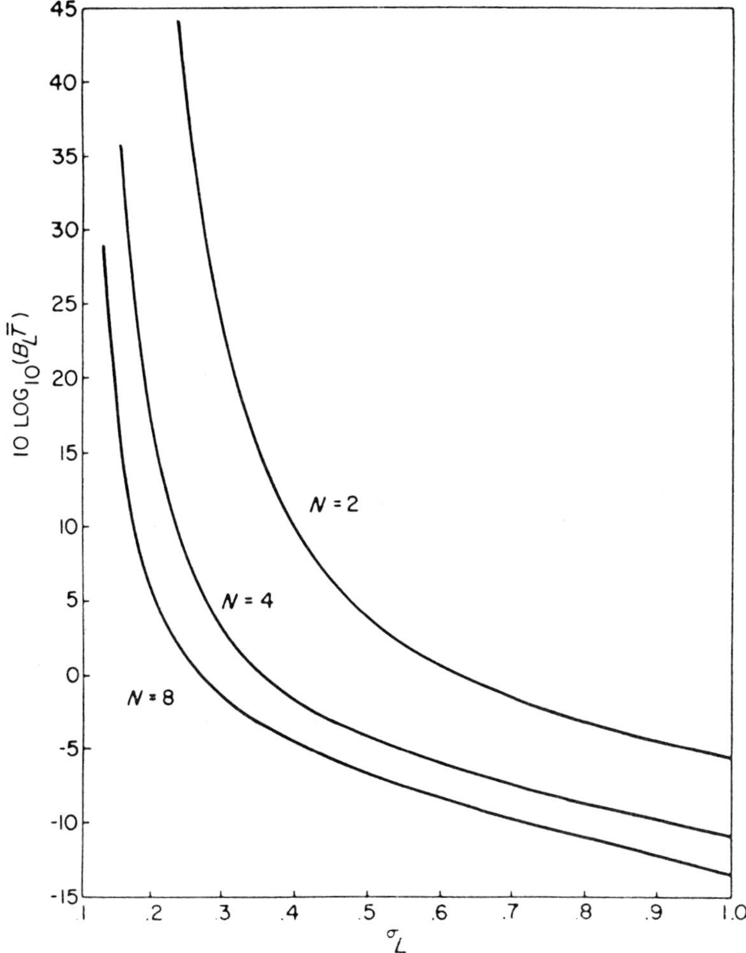

Figure 2.19. Mean time to loss-of-lock performance of delay-locked loop.

2.5 THE DOUBLE DITHER LOOP

The double dither loop (DDL) [8] is a PN code tracking loop that combines the desirable features of the DLL and TDL, i.e., the effects of detector imbalance are eliminated at no significant cost in noise performance. To understand better how this is accomplished, it is convenient to first redraw Figure 2.9 in its conceptually equivalent form illustrated in Figure 2.20. Here a single pair of time-synchronous dither switches is used to accomplish the alternation between early and late codes at the input phase detector and the post-detection multiplication by the square wave $q(t)$. The salient feature of the DDL is that it employs two sets of time synchronous dither

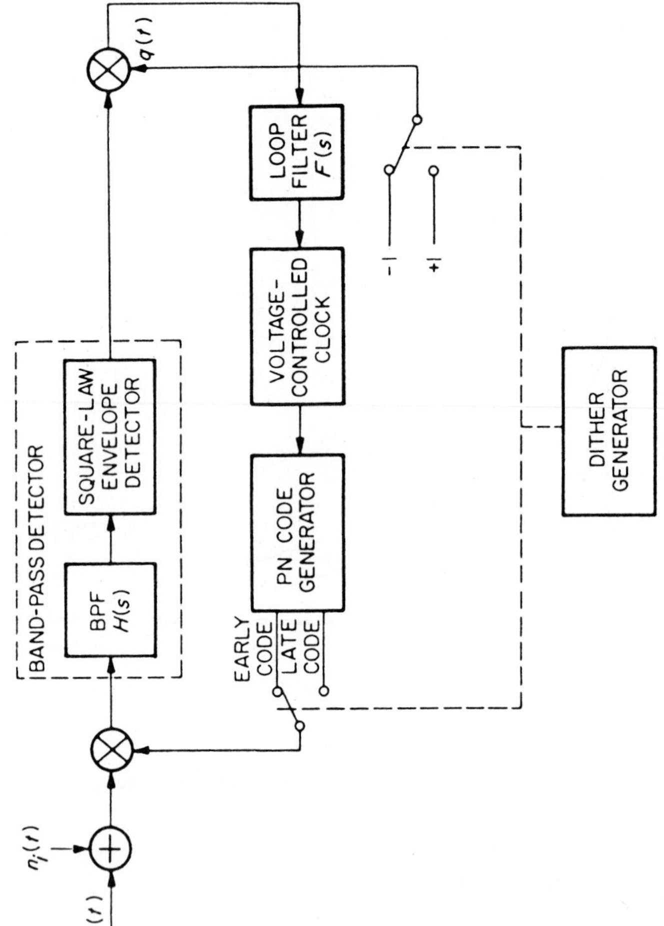

Figure 2.20. A conceptually equivalent version of Figure 2.9.

switches that time share two square-law envelope detectors alternately between the two correlators (see Figure 2.21). From an implementation point of view, the two switched post-multipliers and summer can be replaced by a single switched differencer as in Figure 2.22.

An equivalent loop model for Figure 2.21, which is valid for analysis purposes, is (analogous to Figure 2.10) illustrated in Figure 2.23. The input to the loop filter is given by

$$\begin{aligned} e(t) &= \left(y_{-1}^2(t) - y_{+2}^2(t)\right)q_1(t) + \left(y_{-2}^2(t) - y_{+1}^2(t)\right)q_2(t) \\ &= y_{-1}^2(t)q_1(t) - y_{+1}^2(t)q_2(t) \\ &\quad - \left(y_{+2}^2(t)q_1(t) - y_{-2}^2(t)q_2(t)\right). \end{aligned} \tag{2.86}$$

If both band-pass detectors of the DDL are identical, then in Figure 2.23, $y_{+1}(t) = y_{+2}(t) = y_+(t)$ and $y_{-1}(t) = y_{-2}(t) = y_-(t)$ in which case (2.86) simplifies to

$$e(t) = y_{-1}^2(t) - y_+^2(t) \tag{2.87}$$

since again $q_1(t) + q_2(t) = 1$. Note that (2.87) is identical to (2.7) and thus *under ideal balanced conditions, the DDL has the same performance as the DLL*. This conclusion can also be obtained by interpreting Figure 2.21 in the following manner. Note that while the TDL of Figure 2.9 *time shares* the early and late PN codes over a single channel (thus the loop error signal contains only the correlation of the input PN code with *either* the early or late local PN code), the DDL, by using two channels, allows *both* the early and late codes to be present for correlation in each half dither interval. Thus, in effect, the DDL error signal can be thought of as being generated by alternately switching between two DLLs which differ only in that the band-pass detectors in the two channels of one loop are in the reversed position in the other loop. Clearly, if both channels of each loop contain identical band-pass detectors, then the reversal produces no change and the effective alternate switching between the two error signals has no effect. On the other hand, if the band-pass detectors of the DDL are not identical (perhaps different gains and dc offsets), then the effective switching between the two hypothetical DLLs causes the dc offsets to cancel in the resulting time-averaged error signal. Also this error signal will have a gain proportional to the average of the two channel gains in the DDL.

2.6 THE PRODUCT OF SUM AND DIFFERENCE DLL

The product of sum and difference DLL ($\Sigma\Delta$ DLL) [9] is another configuration that purports to combat the gain imbalance problem of the DLL without sacrificing its tracking performance. The vehicle by which this is accomplished is the replacement of the "difference of squares" operation of the DLL with a "sum and difference product." In particular, the DLL

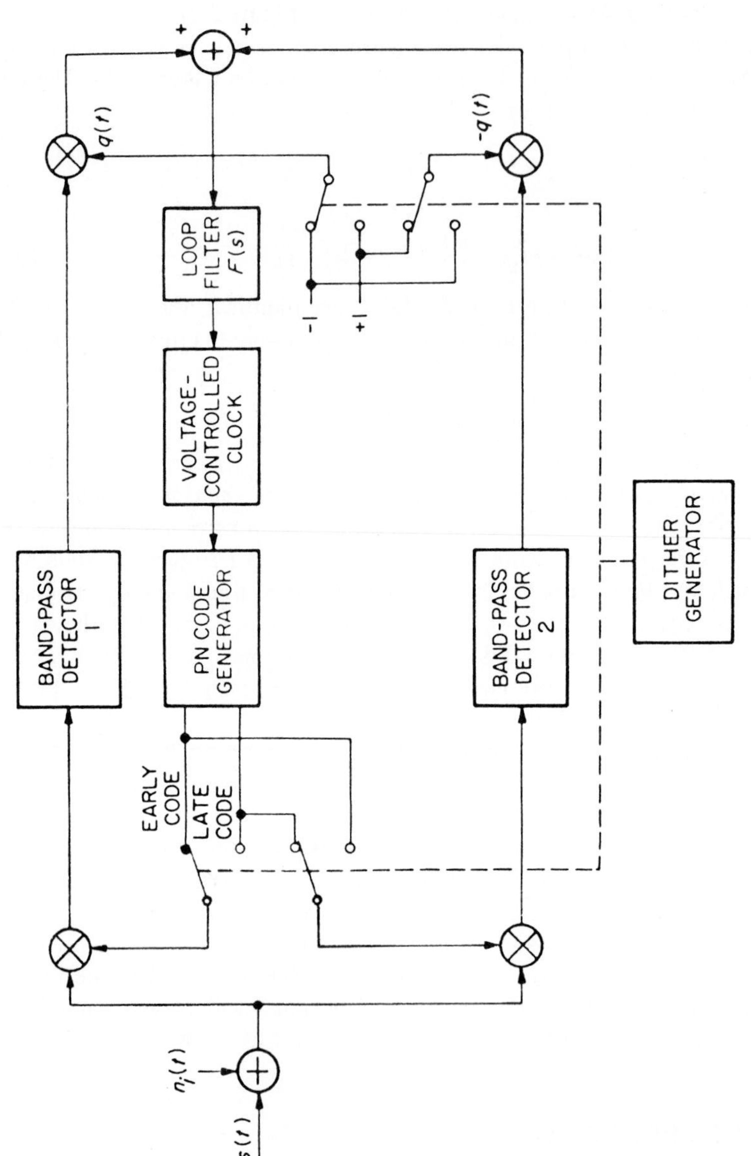

Figure 2.21. A non-coherent double dither loop.

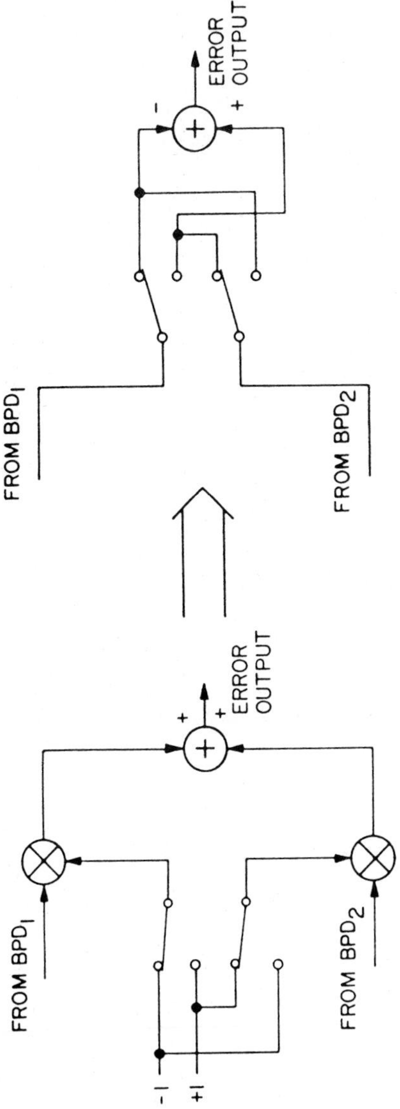

Figure 2.22. A simplification of the implementation in Figure 2.21.

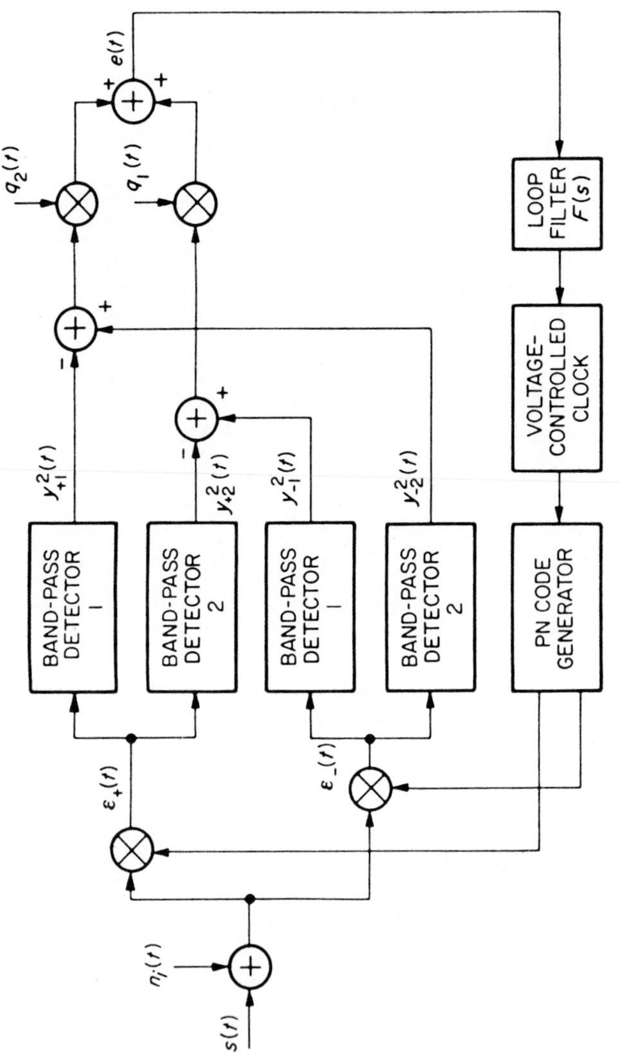

Figure 2.23. An equivalent loop model for the double dither loop.

computes as its error signal[8]

$$\begin{aligned} e(t) &= \left[K_{m_-} H(p) \varepsilon'_-(t)\right]^2 - \left[K_{m_+} H(p) \varepsilon'_+(t)\right]^2 \\ &= K_{m_-}^2 y_-'^2(t) - K_{m_+}^2 y_+'^2(t) \end{aligned} \tag{2.88}$$

where $\varepsilon'_\pm(t)$ and $y'_\pm(t)$ are normalized versions of their counterpart definitions in (2.3) and (2.5), respectively, e.g.,

$$\varepsilon'_\pm(t) \triangleq x(t) c(t - \hat{\tau}_t \pm \delta) = \varepsilon_\pm(t)/K_m \tag{2.89}$$

and similarly for $y'_\pm(t)$. On the other hand, the ΣΔ DLL (Figure 2.24) computes as its error signal

$$\begin{aligned} e(t) &= \left[K_{m_+} H(p)\left(\varepsilon'_-(t) + \varepsilon'_+(t)\right)\right]\left[K_{m_-} H(p)\left(\varepsilon'_-(t) - \varepsilon'_+(t)\right)\right] \\ &= K_{m_+} K_{m_-}\left(y'_-(t) + y'_+(t)\right)\left(y'_-(t) - y'_+(t)\right) \\ &= K_{m_+} K_{m_-}\left(y_-'^2(t) - y_+'^2(t)\right). \end{aligned} \tag{2.90}$$

Clearly, from (2.88), any unbalance in the arm gains, i.e., $K_{m_-} \neq K_{m_+}$, will produce an undesirable loop dc offset, whereas (2.90) is insensitive to this effect. Certainly, if $K_{m_-} = K_{m_+}$ the two loops will have identical theoretical performance. Any further merits of the ΣΔ DLL over the conventional DLL are a matter of practical implementation and a detailed discussion of these considerations is beyond the scope of our presentation here. The interested reader is referred to [9].

2.7 THE MODIFIED CODE TRACKING LOOP

Still another PN code tracking loop configuration that attempts to combat the gain imbalance problem of the DLL without sacrificing tracking performance, but now with hardware simplicity rivalling the TDL, is the modified code tracking loop (MCTL) [10], [11] illustrated in Figure 2.25. The principal idea of this configuration is to replace the sum channel signal of the ΣΔ DLL with a reference signal derived from the on-time PN code, the primary advantage being the elimination of an entire processing channel. The secondary advantage is that since the on-time channel experiences less noise power than the sum channel of Figure 2.24 does, it should serve as a better demodulation reference for the difference channel signal. In fact, in view of this, the mean-squared tracking jitter of Figure 2.25 should ideally be smaller than that of the traditional DLL of Figure 2.1 or the ΣΔ DLL of Figure 2.24.

[8] Here we allow the two phase detectors to have different gains, which we shall further assume represent all the contributors to gain in the two DLL arms.

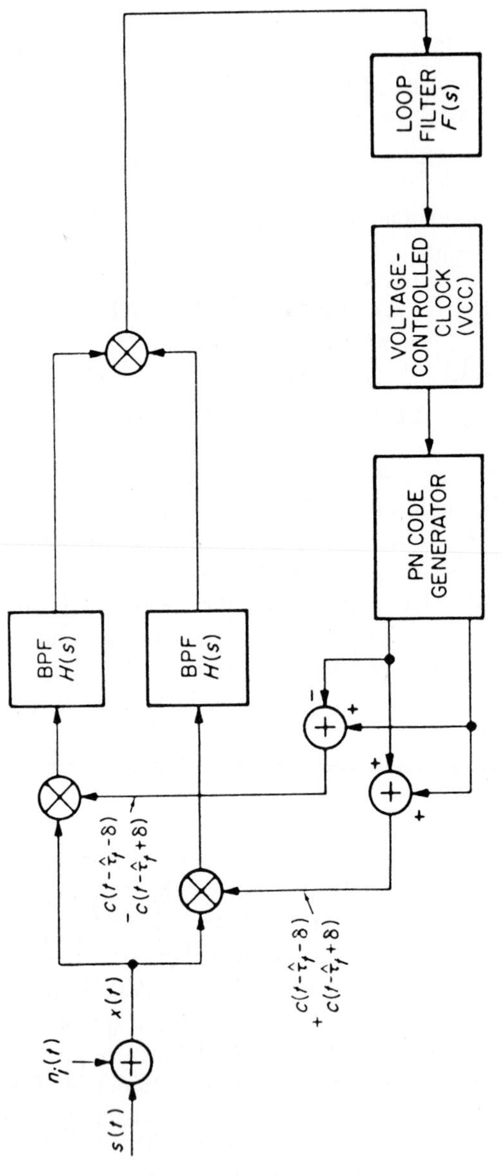

Figure 2.24. A non-coherent ΣΔ DLL.

Indeed the above turns out to be the case, as will be quantitatively demonstrated shortly. Before doing so, however, and also before discussing other behavioral characteristics of the MCTL and its shortcomings, we point out that the implementation of Figure 2.25 can be reconfigured to more closely resemble that of Figure 2.24 and thereby achieve a further reduction in hardware required. In particular, the difference channel signal can be generated as per the dashed lines in Figure 2.25, thus eliminating one mixer. Note, however, that in this alternate mechanization, the reference signal formed from the difference of the early and late PN codes is not a constant envelope waveform which therefore places strict linearity requirements on the single remaining mixer. This constraint also applies to the ΣΔ DLL of Figure 2.24, which conceptually could also be implemented, analogous to Figure 2.25, by forming the sum and difference signals after the input mixers.

Having derived the loop model and discussed the performance of the DLL in great detail, we shall be extremely brief in the analogous presentation for the MCTL, merely presenting the key results in summary form. In fact, to highlight the similarities between the two code tracking loops and allow easy comparison of their differences, we shall use the same equation numbers as in Section 2.1 (with a prime superscript) where appropriate.

Again assuming an input as in (2.1) and (2.2), and making similar assumptions to those leading up to (2.7), the input to the loop filter of the MCTL can be shown [11] to be given by[9]

$$e(t) = y_o(t)\,y_\Delta(t) = SK_m^2\hat{m}^2(t-\tau_t)\tilde{D}(\varepsilon_t) + K_m^2\tilde{n}_e(t,\varepsilon_t) \tag{2.7'}$$

where

$$\tilde{D}(\varepsilon_t) \triangleq R_{PN}(\varepsilon_t)\{R_{PN_-}(\varepsilon_t) - R_{PN_+}(\varepsilon_t)\}$$

$$= \begin{cases} 0; & \varepsilon_t \le -1 \\ -\frac{3}{2} - \frac{5}{2}\varepsilon_t - \varepsilon_t^2; & -1 < \varepsilon_t \le -\frac{1}{2} \\ 2\varepsilon_t - 2\varepsilon_t^2; & -\frac{1}{2} < \varepsilon_t \le \frac{1}{2} \\ \frac{3}{2} - \frac{5}{2}\varepsilon_t + \varepsilon_t^2; & \frac{1}{2} < \varepsilon_t \le 1 \\ 0; & \varepsilon_t > 1 \end{cases}$$

$$\tilde{D}(\varepsilon_t) = \tilde{D}(\varepsilon_t + np); \qquad n = \pm 1, \pm 2, \pm 3, \ldots \tag{2.8'}$$

is the loop discriminator characteristic and $\tilde{n}_e(t,\varepsilon_t)$ is the equivalent

[9] For simplicity of presentation, we shall pursue only the "one-delta" loop wherein $N = 2$.

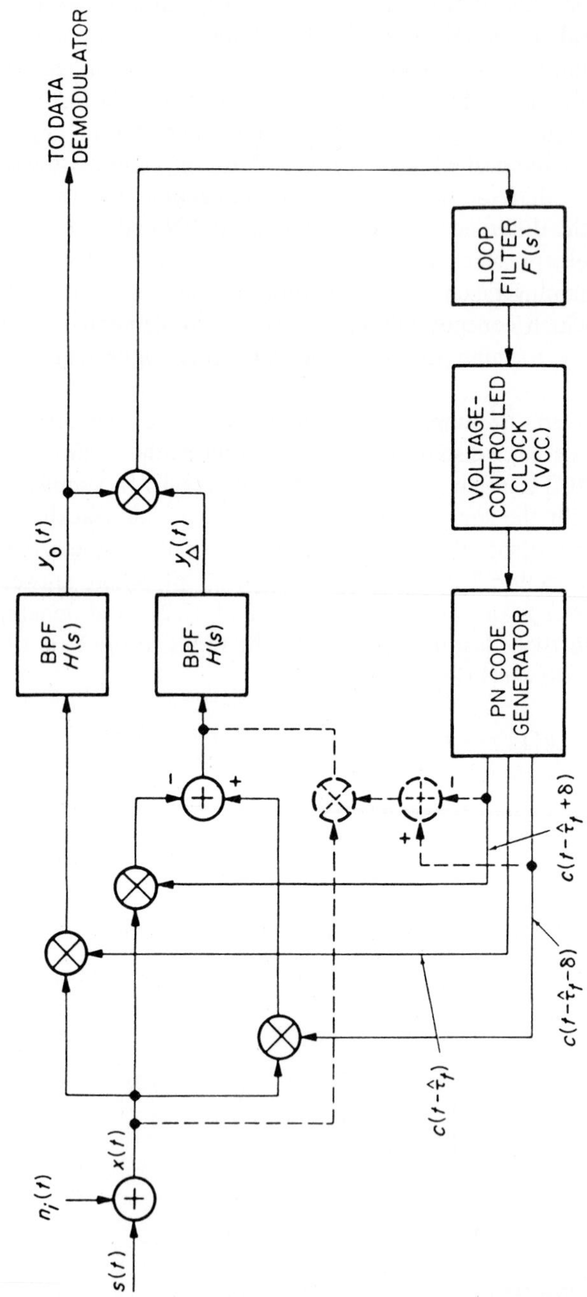

Figure 2.25. The modified code tracking loop (MCTL).

additive noise defined by

$$\begin{aligned}\tilde{n}_e(t,\varepsilon_t) = {} & \hat{N}_{co}(t)\hat{N}_{c\Delta}(t) + \hat{N}_{so}(t)\hat{N}_{s\Delta}(t) \\ & + \sqrt{S}\,\hat{m}(t-\tau_t) \\ & \times\Big\{R_{PN}(\varepsilon_t)\hat{N}_{c\Delta}(t) + \big[R_{PN_-}(\varepsilon_t) \\ & - R_{PN_+}(\varepsilon_t)\big]\hat{N}_{co}(t)\Big\} \end{aligned} \tag{2.9$'$}$$

with

$$\begin{aligned} \hat{N}_{co}(t) &= H_\ell(p)\big[c(t-\hat{\tau}_t)N_c(t)\big] \\ \hat{N}_{so}(t) &= H_\ell(p)\big[c(t-\hat{\tau}_t)N_s(t)\big] \\ \hat{N}_{c\Delta}(t) &= H_\ell(p)\big[\{c(t-\hat{\tau}_t+\delta) - c(t-\hat{\tau}_t-\delta)\}N_c(t)\big] \\ \hat{N}_{s\Delta}(t) &= H_\ell(p)\big[\{c(t-\hat{\tau}_t+\delta) - c(t-\hat{\tau}_t-\delta)\}N_s(t)\big]. \end{aligned} \tag{2.6$'$}$$

Figure 2.26 is a comparative illustration of the discriminator characteristics of the DLL and the MCTL. We immediately observe that the non-zero region of the MCTL characteristic is only 2/3 that of the DLL and thus the modified loop has a 1/3 less pull-in capability. Furthermore, although the two discriminator characteristics have identical slopes at $\varepsilon_t = 0$, the DLL always creates a larger error voltage for any value of timing error.

Despite these disadvantages, when compared with the DLL, the MCTL does have an improved noise performance as previously mentioned. Specifi-

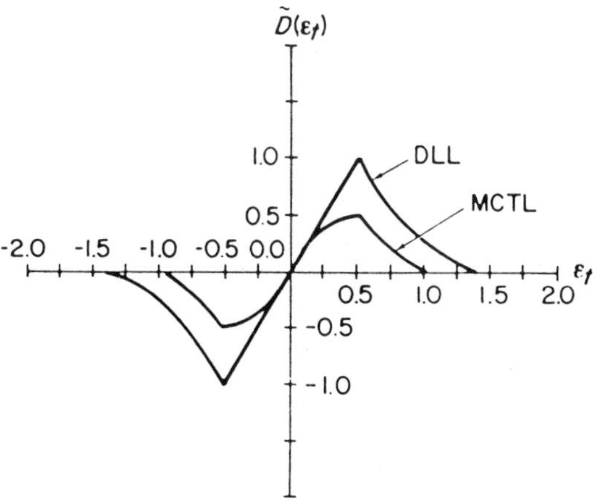

Figure 2.26. One-delta loop discriminator characteristics for the DLL and MCTL (reprinted from [11]).

cally, the equivalent noise spectral density $\tilde{N}_e(\varepsilon_t)$ of $\tilde{n}_e(t, \varepsilon_t)$ is given by [11]:

$$\tilde{N}_e(\varepsilon_t) = 2SN_0\left[M_4\left\{R_{PN}^2(\varepsilon_t) + \tfrac{1}{2}\left[R_{PN_+}(\varepsilon_t) - R_{PN_-}(\varepsilon_t)\right]^2\right\} + \frac{K_L}{\rho_H}\right] \tag{2.22'}$$

with K_L and M_4 defined in (2.23) and ρ_H in (2.25). Following steps similar to those leading up to (2.29), we find that the normalized mean-squared timing error for the MCTL is given by

$$\tilde{\sigma}_\varepsilon^2 = \frac{1}{2\rho\tilde{\mathscr{S}}_L} \tag{2.29'}$$

where the squaring loss $\tilde{\mathscr{S}}_L$ is now

$$\tilde{\mathscr{S}}_L = \frac{M_2^2}{M_4 + K_L \dfrac{B_H/R_s}{E_s/N_0}}. \tag{2.30'}$$

Comparing (2.30′) with (2.30) for $N = 2$, we observe that the $N \times N$ power of the MCTL is one-half that of the DLL, thus producing an associated reduction in mean-squared tracking jitter. To demonstrate the magnitude of

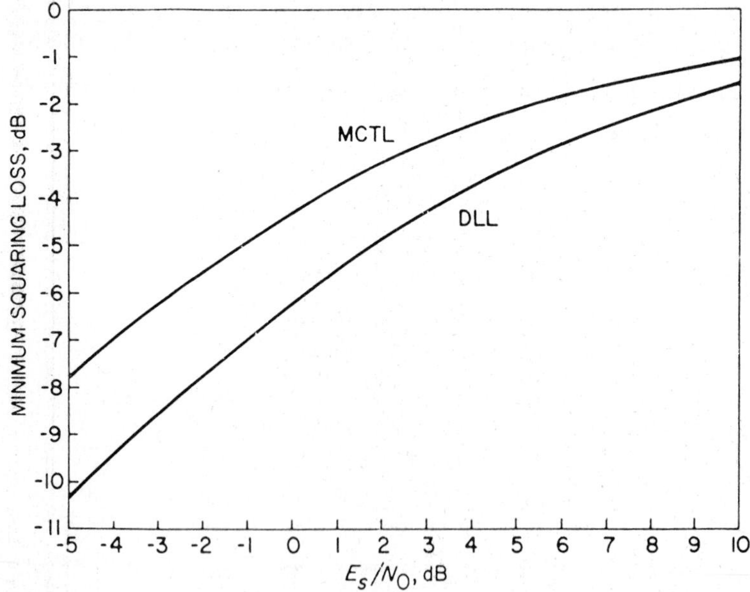

Figure 2.27. Minimum squaring loss comparison for NRZ data modulation (reprinted from [11]).

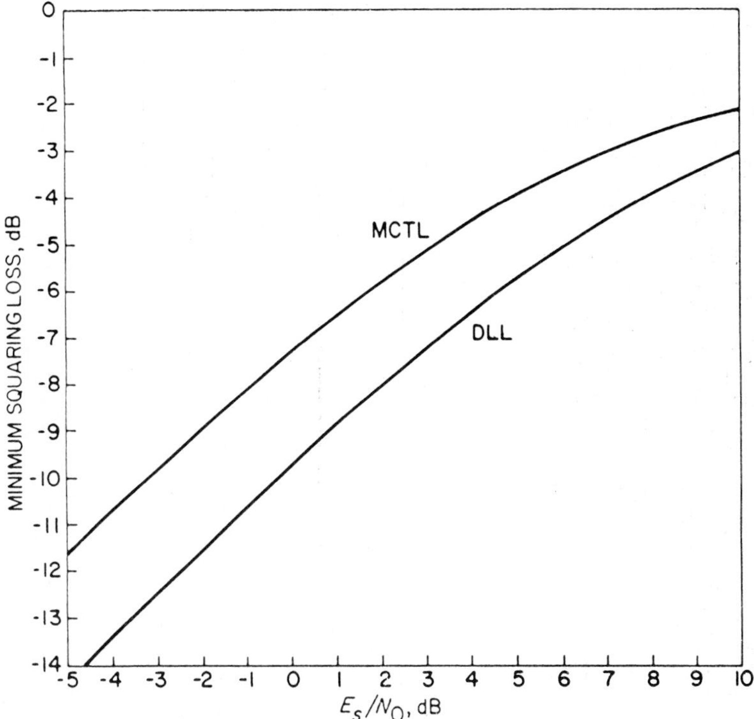

Figure 2.28. Minimum squaring loss comparison for Manchester data modulation (reprinted from [11]).

this reduction, it is sufficient to numerically compare the minimum squaring loss of (2.30) with that of (2.30′) as is done in Figures 2.27 and 2.28 for the case of NRZ or Manchester data and two-pole Butterworth band-pass filters. The appropriate expressions for K_L, M_2, and M_4 are obtained from Tables 2.1 and 2.2.

With regard to the acquisition behavior of the MCTL, it has been shown [11] that for equal rms tracking jitters, i.e., $\sigma_{\text{MCTL}} = \sigma_{\text{DLL}}$, the maximum normalized search rate is given by

$$\dot{y} = .6\frac{\mathscr{S}_L|_{\text{MCTL}}}{\mathscr{S}_L|_{\text{DLL}}} = .6\frac{M_4 + K_L\dfrac{2B_H/R_s}{E_s/N_0}}{M_4 + K_L\dfrac{B_H/R_s}{E_s/N_0}} \tag{2.91}$$

as compared with the previously found $\dot{y} = 1$ for the "one-delta" DLL. Figure 2.29 illustrates $\dot{y}$ as a function of E_s/N_0 for NRZ and Manchester data types, and two-pole Butterworth band-pass filters. Also shown is the

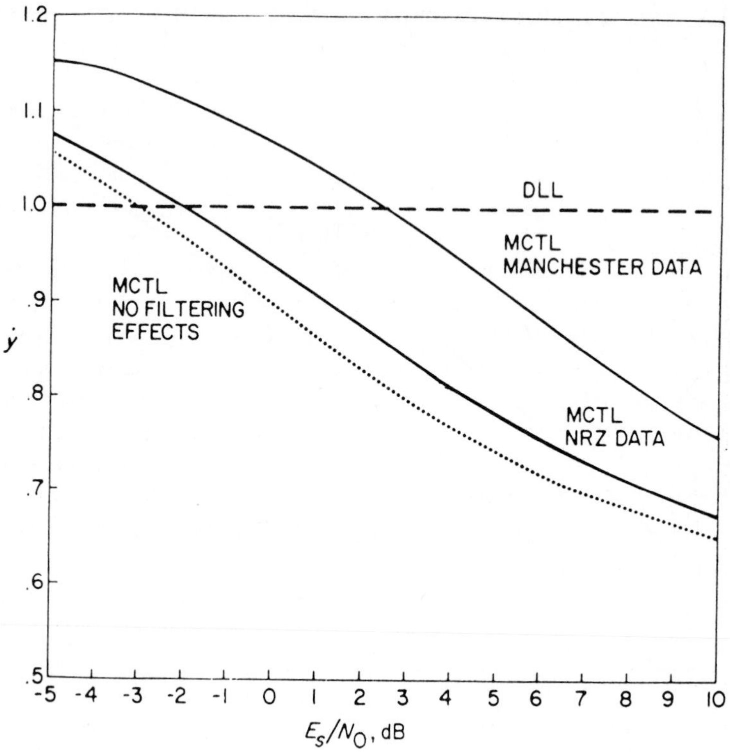

Figure 2.29. Normalized search rate comparison (reprinted from [11]).

curve corresponding to ignoring the arm filter band-limiting effects, i.e., $M_2 = M_4 = K_L = 1$ and $B_H = R_s$. We observe that for small values of E_s/N_0, the MCTL indeed has a higher search rate capability than the DLL, whereas for large values of E_s/N_0, it asymptotically approaches a maximum decrease of 40% in search rate capability.

Finally, when compared with the $\Sigma\Delta$ DLL, the MCTL has the advantage of being significantly less sensitive to gain imbalances at low values of pre-detection signal-to-noise ratio ρ_H resulting in lower tracking bias errors. At high ρ_H's, the gain imbalance sensitivities of the two configurations are nearly equivalent, both being of course much less sensitive than the traditional DLL.

2.8 THE COMPLEX SUMS LOOP (A PHASE-SENSING DLL)

The complex sums loop [12] is by far the least conventional of all the loops discussed thus far in that its operation requires a spread-spectrum signal format wherein the PN code is *phase* modulated on the transmitted carrier rather than the usual amplitude modulation case. In this sense, the complex sums loop may be regarded as the phase modulation analog of the amplitude-sensing ΣΔ DLL discussed previously. Indeed, the input signal plus noise is correlated with the sum and difference of quadrature carriers, *phase* modulated respectively by the advanced and retarded versions of the locally generated PN code (see Figure 2.30). The resultant correlations are first band-pass filtered and then band-pass limited (BPL) to remove the amplitude modulation. The relative phase between the two BPL outputs then represents a measure of the PN code delay error.

Since in virtually all DS/SS systems in use today the PN code is amplitude modulated on the transmitted carrier, particularly when the data modulation is also amplitude modulated on the carrier, we shall discontinue any further discussion of this loop, having included its mention merely for the sake of completeness. This is not to say that the complex sums loop is not capable of performance comparable with the DLL; indeed, it has been theoretically shown [12] to offer a factor of 4 improvement in rms tracking error and a factor of 2.67 improvement in maximum search velocity when compared with amplitude sensing correlation receivers such as the DLL. Rather, its lack of widespread acceptance in the design of current DS/SS receivers precludes our giving it extensive coverage.

2.9 QUADRIPHASE PN TRACKING

Until now we have assumed that the PN spreading code is superimposed on a suppressed carrier binary data modulation. It is our intent in this section to investigate the applicability of the previous PN tracking techniques to various forms of quadriphase PN modulation (QPN).

The simplest form of QPN is obtained by spreading a quadriphase-shift-keyed (QPSK) modulation with a single PN code. In this case, the transmission-delayed signal analogous to (2.1) becomes

$$s(t) = \sqrt{S}\,c(t-\tau_t)\{m_1(t-\tau_t)\sin[\omega_0 t + \theta(t)] + m_2(t-\tau_t)\cos[\omega_0 t + \theta(t)]\} \tag{2.92}$$

where $m_1(t)$ and $m_2(t)$ are unit power statistically independent binary data modulations of the same data rate and the remaining nomenclature is as previously provided. If one uses the DLL of Figure 2.1 to PN track the sum of $s(t)$ of (2.92) and $n_i(t)$ of (2.2), then, without belaboring the details, it can be shown that, analogous to (2.7), the error signal $e(t)$ becomes

$$e(t) = \tfrac{1}{2}SK_m^2[\hat{m}_1^2(t-\tau_t) + \hat{m}_2^2(t-\tau_t)] + K_m^2 n_e(t,\varepsilon_t) \tag{2.93}$$

where the equivalent noise $n_e(t,\varepsilon_t)$ is now given by

$$\begin{aligned} n_e(t,\varepsilon_t) &= \hat{N}_{c_-}^2(t) - \hat{N}_{c_+}^2(t) + \hat{N}_{s_-}^2(t) - \hat{N}_{s_+}^2(t) \\ &\quad + \sqrt{2S}\,\hat{m}_2(t-\tau_t)\{R_{PN_-}(\varepsilon_t)\hat{N}_{c_-}(t) - R_{PN_+}(\varepsilon_t)\hat{N}_{c_+}(t)\} \\ &\quad - \sqrt{2S}\,\hat{m}_1(t-\tau_t)\{R_{PN_-}(\varepsilon_t)\hat{N}_{s_-}(t) - R_{PN_+}(\varepsilon_t)\hat{N}_{s_+}(t)\}. \end{aligned} \tag{2.94}$$

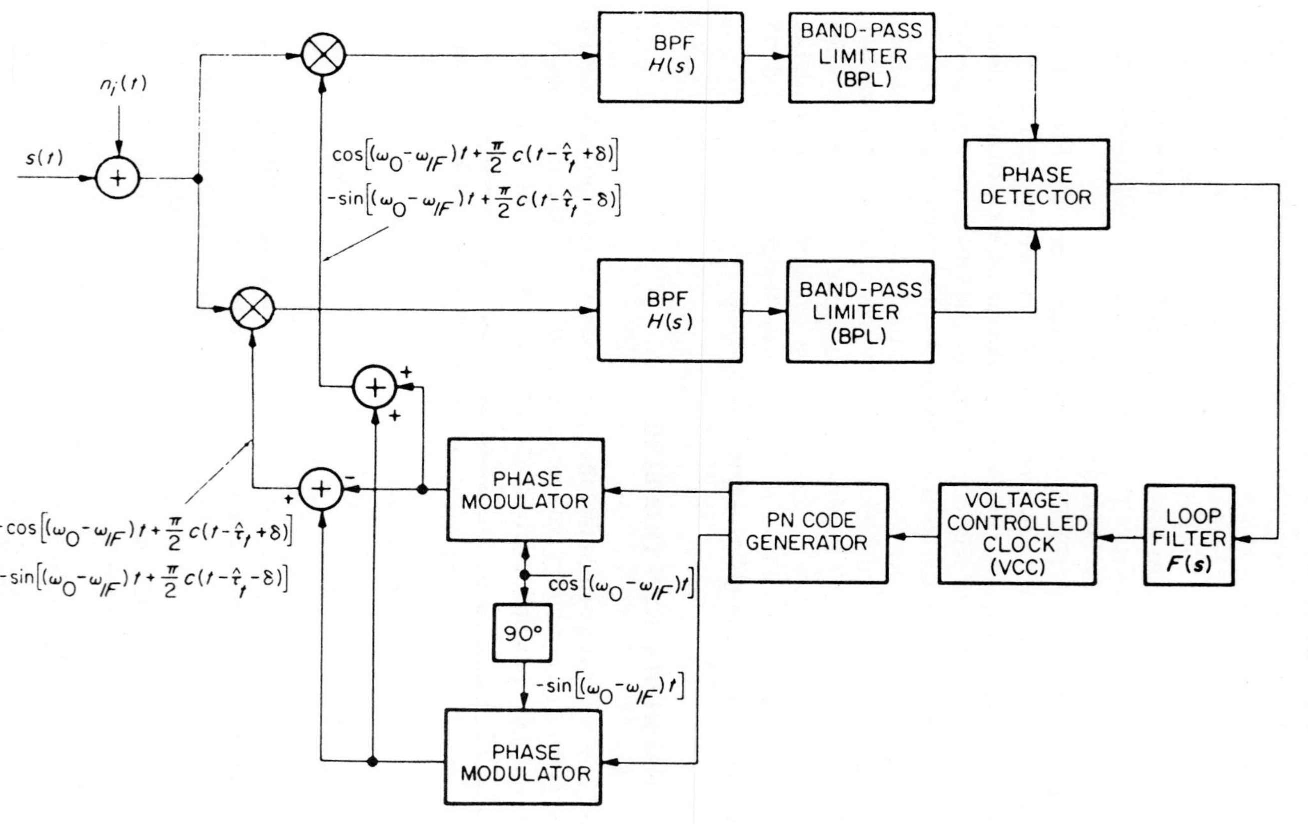

Figure 2.30. The complex sums PN tracking loop.

Now, since

$$\overline{\langle \hat{m}_1^2(t-\tau_t) \rangle} = \overline{\langle \hat{m}_2^2(t-\tau_t) \rangle} = M_2 \tag{2.95}$$

with M_2 defined in (2.14) and, because $m_1(t)$ and $m_2(t)$ are independent, the auto-correlation function of (2.94) is again given by (2.18). Thus, we observe that the equation of operation remains unchanged from (2.15). In conclusion, *the tracking and acquisition performance of the DLL with a QPN input as in* (2.92) *is identical to that with the biphase PN input of* (2.1).

Another form of QPN is obtained by spreading inphase and quadrature biphase modulated carriers with *independent* PN codes. Such a situation is typical of applications where separate addressing of each channel is required, as for example, in a multiple-access type system. Here the received signal (in the absence of noise) has the form

$$\begin{aligned} s(t) &= \sqrt{S}\, c_1(t-\tau_t) m_1(t-\tau_t) \sin[\omega_0 t + \theta(t)] \\ &\quad + \sqrt{S}\, c_2(t-\tau_t-\tau_\Delta) m_2(t-\tau_t) \cos[\omega_0 t + \theta(t)]. \end{aligned} \tag{2.96}$$

If the two codes have identical chip rates, they are often staggered relative to one another by half a chip, i.e., $\tau_\Delta = T_c/2$. This form of QPN is referred to as staggered quadriphase PN (SQPN) and is particularly used on non-linear satellite channels to reduce regeneration of sidelobes removed by transmitter filtering prior to transmission over the channel. Furthermore, from a practical implementation standpoint, $c_2(t)$ is often generated as a time-shifted version of $c_1(t)$ where the time shift corresponds to a large number of code chips, often as many as half the code period.

Consider once again using the DLL of Figure 2.1 to PN track the sum of $s(t)$ of (2.96) and $n_i(t)$ of (2.2). If the PN generator of the DLL is arbitrarily selected to match $c_1(t)$, then, since, by the assumption of code independence,

$$\overline{c_2(t-\tau_t-\tau_\Delta) c_1(t-\hat{\tau}_t \pm \delta)} = 0 \tag{2.97}$$

and the fact that the inphase and quadrature self-noise processes can be neglected, we obtain a loop error signal identical to (2.7) except that S is replaced by $S/2$ in both its signal and noise components. Stated another way, the DLL tracks the channel corresponding to $c_1(t-\tau_t)$ (which contains half the total power) as if the other channel were absent. As such, a 3 dB signal-to-noise ratio penalty is paid relative to that for a PN spread binary data modulation as in (2.1). This 3 dB penalty in signal-to-noise ratio does not, however, directly translate into a 3 dB increase in mean-squared tracking jitter due to the non-linear dependence of the loop squaring loss on S/N_0 (see (2.29) and (2.30)). Once having obtained proper code alignment for $c_1(t-\tau_t)$, the despreading code for $c_2(t-\tau_t-\tau_\Delta)$ can be derived by an appropriate shift of the local PN generator provided that the two codes were generated as suggested above. If indeed the two codes are totally unrelated, i.e., they were generated by separate PN generators with, in general, completely different tap connections and code periods, then two separate DLLs must be employed in the receiver, each having a local PN generator matched to one of the two codes. Again, the performance of each DLL would behave as per the above discussion.

Finally, if the two codes have different chip rates in addition to different code structure, one must again employ separate DLLs for each code where now, in addition to having different local PN generators, the two loops would also have different voltage-controlled clocks, each matched to the appropriate chip rate of the code being tracked.

Before concluding this section, we also point out that quadriphase PN is not limited only to balanced QPSK but indeed can also be applied to unbalanced QPSK data modulation by a simple generalization of (2.96), namely,

$$
\begin{aligned}
s(t) = {} & \sqrt{2S_1}\, c_1(t-\tau_t)m_1(t-\tau_t)\sin[\omega_0 t + \theta(t)] \\
& + \sqrt{2S_2}\, c_2(t-\tau_t-\tau_\Delta)m_2(t-\tau_t)\cos[\omega_0 t + \theta(t)]
\end{aligned}
\tag{2.98}
$$

Here, S_1, the power in channel 1, is, in general, unequal to S_2, the power in channel 2, and the data rates $1/T_1, 1/T_2$ of $m_1(t)$ and $m_2(t)$, respectively, are no longer restricted to be equal. Examples of such PN spread signals are typical of many of the transmission modes of the Tracking and Data Relay Satellite System (TDRSS) [20]. Once again, depending on the relation between the two PN codes, either one or two DLLs are required to provide the necessary PN tracking as per the discussion for balanced QPSK.

2.10 FURTHER DISCUSSION

To conclude this chapter, we briefly summarize some of the most recent contributions to the subject of PN tracking. The primary intent here is to acquaint the reader with the current status of effort in the area without going into the level of detail characteristic of the previous sections of this chapter. It is not intended that the reader come away with the idea that the contributions discussed here are therefore of lesser importance; rather, they should be looked upon as evidence of continued interest in the subject and a springboard for future endeavors.

One idea for improvement in PN tracking loop performance is offered by Wakabayashi, Nakagawa, and Tsunogae [21], who suggest an improved delay-locked loop (IDLL) with an effective increased number of correlators, thus allowing one to shape the loop discriminator characteristic in such a way as to expand the loop's correlation range without affecting its lock range. Although the specific results in [21] are described for a coherent DLL, the concept is readily applicable to a non-coherent DLL. As an example, consider the non-coherent IDLL illustrated in Figure 2.31, which for $N = 2$ represents a slight modification of the loop in Figure 2.1. The

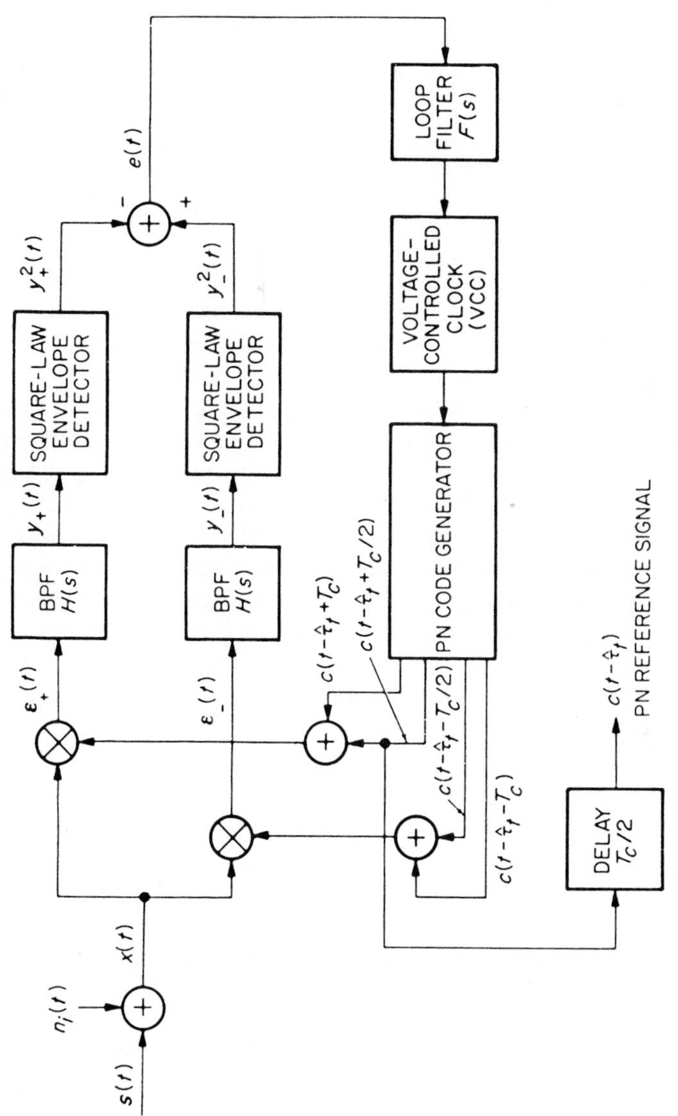

Figure 2.31. A non-coherent improved delay-locked loop (IDLL).

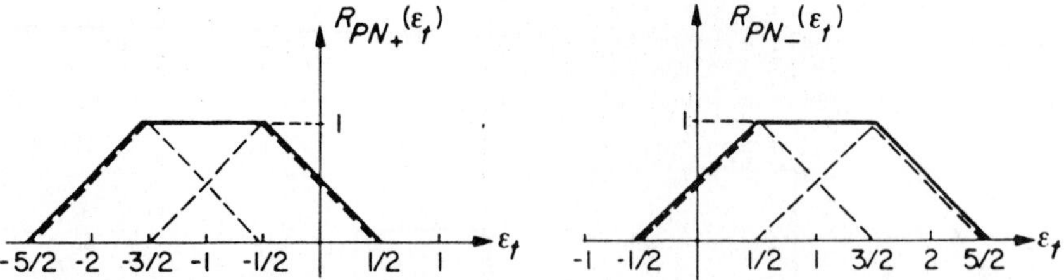

Figure 2.32. Autocorrelation functions of the advanced and retarded correlator outputs for a non-coherent IDLL.

particular modification that distinguishes Figure 2.31 from Figure 2.1 is the effective addition of two correlations of the input signal with two new phase-shifted PN reference signals which are advanced and retarded, respectively, by a full chip relative to the on-time PN reference signal. Although conceptually four correlations are now being formed, the two advanced and two delayed reference signals are first summed so that for implementation only two correlators are needed. Figure 2.32 illustrates the component and resultant advanced and delayed correlation functions analogous to Figure 2.2. Figure 2.33 shows the corresponding discriminator characteristic analogous to Figure 2.3. Note that, as previously mentioned, the lock range of the loop ($\pm T_c/2$) and its gain (positive slope of the discriminator characteristic) are unaffected by the modification, whereas the correlation range has been extended from $\pm 3T_c/2$ to $\pm 5T_c/2$. Clearly, the addition of additional correlations with more phase-shifted PN reference signals can increase the correlation region even further.

All of our discussions of PN tracking thus far have assumed a transmission channel devoid of propagation disturbances. Bogusch, Guigliano, Knepp, and Michelet [22] consider the effects of frequency-selective scintil-

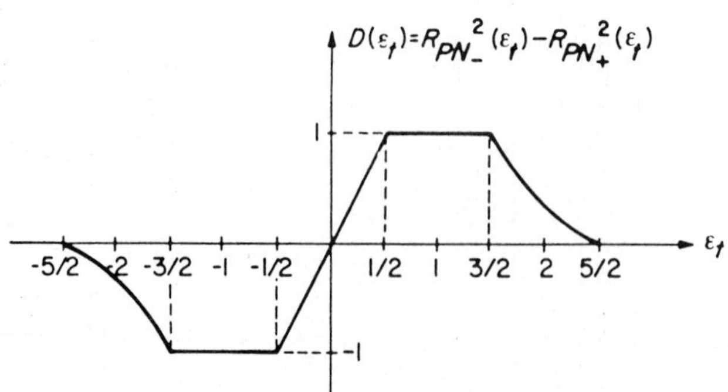

Figure 2.33. Discriminator characteristic.

lation (fading), such as that produced by an ionospheric channel whose coherence bandwidth is less than the signalling bandwidth, on the PN code correlation and tracking functions in a DS/SS system. Consideration was given to both coherent and non-coherent DLLs or TDLs. Also, since the results were obtained using a simulation model of the receiver, several other different loop configurations were programmed in as design options in addition to allowing such parameters as bandwidth and order of the tracking loop to be varied at will. For example, the possibility of having the PN tracking loop Doppler-aided from the carrier tracking loop [23] was included. This type of accommodation of channel dynamics involves using the Doppler estimate formed in the carrier tracking loop, e.g., a composite AFC/Costas loop [24], appropriately scaled by the ratio of PN code chip rate to carrier frequency, to rate-aid the PN tracking loop. Another variation included in the simulation was the option of *time sharing* the single code loop for PN receivers that are required to simultaneously track signals from several satellites.

The objective of the investigation was to identify and evaluate those design configurations out of the above class that would provide robust performance in a frequency-selective scintillation environment. In this regard, the following qualitative conclusions were reached:

1. A non-coherent code loop is less susceptible to losing lock than the equivalent coherent one since the former does not depend on carrier phase lock which is difficult to maintain in scintillation conditions.
2. A dedicated (non-time-shared) loop is more robust than a time-shared loop simply because the former samples the code correlator output more frequently and thus does not suffer a loss of effective signal level produced by the reduced measurement rate of a time-shared loop.

Last, but by no means least, is the work of Meyr [25]–[27], who applies the theory of renewal (regenerative) Markov processes to the non-linear analysis of correlative tracking systems. The method, which is applicable to systems with periodic non-linearities (such as the PLL) as well as those with non-periodic non-linearities (such as the DLL), allows a proper characterization of the cycle-slipping phenomenon of the former and the loss-of-lock phenomenon of the latter. The "periodic extension solution" [16] that has traditionally been applied in such situations is shown to be identical to the "renewal process solution" only for a first-order loop. Most significantly, the "intrinsic" or "self" noise of the DLL, which is always (even in the absence of the additive Gaussian noise) present in the loop, and which depends on the loop tracking error, is accounted for in the renewal process approach. In many applications, this intrinsic noise is dominant and cannot be neglected. We hasten to add that Meyr's work was originally motivated by the necessity of performing precise velocity and distance measurements for modern mass transportation systems [28], [29] and as such his discussions are primarily concerned with the coherent DLL as originally discussed in [1]. More recently, this work was extended to the non-coherent DLL by Polydoros [30].

2.11 REFERENCES

[1] J. J. Spilker, Jr., "Delay-lock tracking of binary signals," *IEEE Trans. Space Electr. and Telem.*, vol. SET-9, No. 1, pp. 1–8, March 1963.

[2] J. J. Spilker, Jr., and D. T. Magill, "The delay-lock discriminator—an optimum tracking device," *Proc. IRE*, vol. 49, No. 9, pp. 1403–1416, September 1961.

[3] W. J. Gill, "A comparison of binary delay-lock loop implementations," *IEEE Trans. Aerosp. and Electr. Syst.*, vol. AES-2, pp. 415–424, July 1966.

[4] P. T. Nielsen, "On the acquisition behavior of binary delay-lock loops," *IEEE Trans. Aerosp. and Electr. Syst.*, vol. AES-11, pp. 415–418, May 1975.

[5] M. K. Simon, "Noncoherent pseudonoise code tracking performance of spread spectrum receivers," *IEEE Trans. Commun.*, COM-25, No. 3, pp. 327–345, March 1977.

[6] H. P. Hartmann, "Analysis of a dithering loop for PN code tracking," *IEEE Trans. Aerosp. and Electr. Syst.*, vol. AES-10, No. 1, pp. 2–9, January 1974.

[7] T. C. Huang and J. K. Holmes, "Performance of noncoherent time-shared PN code tracking loops," *1976 NTC Record*, pp. 45.4-1–45.4-5, November 29–December 1, 1976, Dallas, TX.

[8] P. M. Hopkins, "Double dither loop for pseudonoise code tracking," *IEEE Trans. Aerosp. and Electr. Syst.*, vol. AES-13, No. 6, pp. 644–650, November 1977.

[9] D. T. LaFlame, "A delay-lock loop implementation which is insensitive to arm gain imbalance," *IEEE Trans. Commun.*, COM-27, No. 10, pp. 1632–1633, October 1979.

[10] R. A. Yost and R. W. Boyd, "A modified PN code tracking loop: Its performance and implementation sensitivities," *1980 NTC Record*, 1980, pp. 61.5.1–61.5.5, Houston, TX.

[11] R. A. Yost and R. W. Boyd, "A modified PN code tracking loop: Its performance analysis and comparative evaluation," *IEEE Trans. Commun.*, COM-30, No. 5, pp. 1027–1036, May 1982.

[12] E. F. Osborne and T. A. Schonhoff, "Delay-locked receivers with phase sensing of the correlation (error) function," *1973 NTC Conference Record*, vol. II, pp. 26B-1–26B-6, November 26–28, 1973, Atlanta, GA.

[13] J. K. Holmes and L. Biederman, "Delay-lock-loop mean time to lose lock," *IEEE Trans. Commun.*, COM-26, No. 11 (Part 1), pp. 1549–1557, November, 1978. Also see *1977 NTC Conference Record*, vol. II, pp. 34:2-1–34:2-6, December 5–7, 1977, Los Angeles, CA.

[14] W. K. Alem, G. K. Huth, and S. Udalov, *Integrated Source and Channel Encoded Digital Communication System Design Study*, Final Report, Contract No. NAS 9-13467, Exhibit E, April 13, 1977, Appendices B, C, D, Axiomatix Corp., Marina del Rey, CA.

[15] W. C. Lindsey and M. K. Simon, *Telecommunication Systems Engineering*, Englewood Cliffs, NJ: Prentice-Hall, 1973.

[16] W. C. Lindsey, *Synchronization Systems in Communication and Control*, Englewood Cliffs, NJ: Prentice-Hall, 1972.

[17] M. K. Simon and W. C. Lindsey, "Optimum performance of suppressed carrier receivers with Costas loop tracking," *IEEE Trans. Commun.*, COM-25, No. 2, pp. 215–227, February 1977.

[18] M. K. Simon, "On the calculation of squaring loss in Costas loops with arbitrary arm filters," *IEEE Trans. Commun.*, COM-26, No. 1, pp. 179–184, January 1978.

[19] I. S. Sokolnikoff and R. M. Redheffer, *Mathematics of Physics and Modern Engineering*, New York: McGraw-Hill, 1958.

[20] "Performance specification for services via the tracking and data relay satellite system," S-805-1, Goddard Space Flight Center, Greenbelt, MD, November 1976.

[21] K. Wakabayashi, M. Nakagawa, and T. Tsunogae, "Tracking performance of improved delay-locked loop," *1980 NTC Record*, pp. 24.3.1–24.3.5, 1980, Houston, TX.

[22] R. L. Bogusch, F. W. Guigliano, D. L. Knepp, and A. H. Michelet, "Frequency selective propagation effects on spread-spectrum receiver tracking," *Proc. IEEE*, vol. 69, No. 7, pp. 787–796, July 1981.

[23] C. R. Cahn, D. K. Leimer, C. L. Marsh, F. J. Huntowski, and G. D. La Rue, "Software implementation of a PN spread spectrum receiver to accommodate dynamics," *IEEE Trans. Commun.*, COM-25, No. 8, pp. 832–840, August 1977.

[24] C. R. Cahn, "Improved frequency acquisition of a Costas loop," *IEEE Trans. Commun.*, COM-25, No. 12, pp. 1453–1459, December 1977.

[25] H. Meyr, "Nonlinear analysis of correlative tracking systems using renewal process theory," *IEEE Trans. Commun.*, COM-23, No. 2, pp. 192–203, February 1975.

[26] H. Meyr, "Delay-lock tracking of stochastic signals," *IEEE Trans. Commun.*, COM-24, No. 3, pp. 331–339, March 1976.

[27] W. C. Lindsey and H. Meyr, "Complete statistical description of the phase-error process generated by correlative tracking systems," *IEEE Trans. Inform. Theory*, IT-23, No. 2, pp. 194–202, March 1977.

[28] F. Mesch et al., "Geschwindigkeitsmessung mit Korrelationsverfahren," *Messtechnik*, vol. 7, pp. 152–157, 1971; also vol. 8, pp. 163–168, 1971.

[29] H. Meyr, "Untersuchung Korrelativer Trackingsysteme mit Hilfe der Fokker-Planck Methode," Ph.D. Dissertation, Swiss Federal Institute of Technology, Zurich, Switzerland, 1973.

[30] A. Polydoros, "On the synchronization aspects of direct-sequence spread spectrum systems," Ph.D. Dissertation, Department of Electrical Engineering, University of Southern California, August 1982.

Chapter 3

TIME AND FREQUENCY SYNCHRONIZATION OF FREQUENCY-HOPPED RECEIVERS

Until now, all our discussions of FH/MFSK communication systems have assumed "ideal" synchronization conditions in the sense that the dehopper in the receiver was assumed to have perfect knowledge of the set of received hop frequencies and the instants in time at which the hop modulation changed state. In practice, such ideal conditions are almost never met. This is the lack of perfect knowledge of the phase and Doppler shift produced by the transmission channel; as such, the receiver must provide suitable means for obtaining and maintaining bona fide estimates of these synchronization state parameters. The accuracy with which this can be accomplished ultimately affects the overall error probability performance of the system.

Not unlike the synchronization problem in direct-sequence (DS) spread-spectrum (SS) systems discussed in the previous two chapters, the process of synchronizing the local hop generator with the received sequence of hop tones is ordinarily accomplished in two stages, namely, FH acquisition (coarse synchronization) and FH tracking (fine synchronization). We begin this chapter with a discussion of FH acquisition techniques, the most common of which, as we shall see shortly, have a direct resemblance to similar techniques previously discussed for PN code acquisition.

Once having explained how to coarsely align the local and received hop sequences, we offer next a discussion of a fine synchronization technique for estimation of FH timing [1]. By "fine synchronization," we mean relative timing errors between transmitter and receiver hop generators of less than a hop duration. In presenting the details and mathematical analysis of the time synchronization estimation technique, we shall first make the idealistic assumption that the transmitter and receiver hop generators are perfectly synchronized in frequency. Following this, we consider the behavior and performance of a similar estimation technique for fine frequency synchronization [2], i.e., relative frequency errors between transmitter and receiver hop generators of less than one-half the frequency spacing of the MFSK tones. Here, in calculating the degrading effect on overall system error probability performance because of the residual frequency error produced by the fine frequency estimation technique, the additional degradation due to imperfect fine time synchronization is taken into account. Finally, when both fine time and fine frequency estimators are assumed to augment each other, we are able to obtain the overall performance degradation due to the combination of both residual synchronization errors.

The interference environment in which the time and frequency estimators are assumed to operate is that of the noise (partial- or full-band) jammer. Thus, the overall performance degradation referred to above will be a function of the partial-band fraction, the noise jamming level, and the number of hops used in forming the FH timing and frequency estimates. The performance of these estimators in other narrowband interference environments such as partial-band multitone jamming can be obtained in a straightforward manner using the analytical approach in Chapter 2, Part 2.

3.1 FH ACQUISITION TECHNIQUES

Coarse frequency synchronization is the process by which the local generated hop sequence is aligned with the received hop sequence to within a fraction of a hop interval. This acquisition process is normally thought of as being accomplished in two steps. First, the degree of alignment is determined, typically, by obtaining a measure of correlation (active or passive) between the two hop sequences. Second, the correlation measure is processed by a suitable detector and decision/search algorithm to decide whether or not to continue the search. If, at any point, the search terminates, then coarse frequency acquisition is assumed to have occurred.

3.1.1 Serial Search Techniques with Active Correlation

Although our primary interest in this chapter is with slow or fast FH/MFSK, it is perhaps more instructive to first discuss the most basic non-coherent FH acquisition configuration, which, although best suited to analog information transmitted as an amplitude modulation, or no information modulation at all, nevertheless represents the simplest illustration of the abovementioned acquisition process dichotomy. As such, consider the single (fixed) dwell time serial search acquisition system illustrated in Figure 3.1. In this scheme, the received FH signal plus noise is correlated in a wideband mixer with the local hop sequence produced by an FH synthesizer driven by a PN generator whose epoch is controlled in accordance with the decision to continue the search. The result of this correlation is passed through an IF

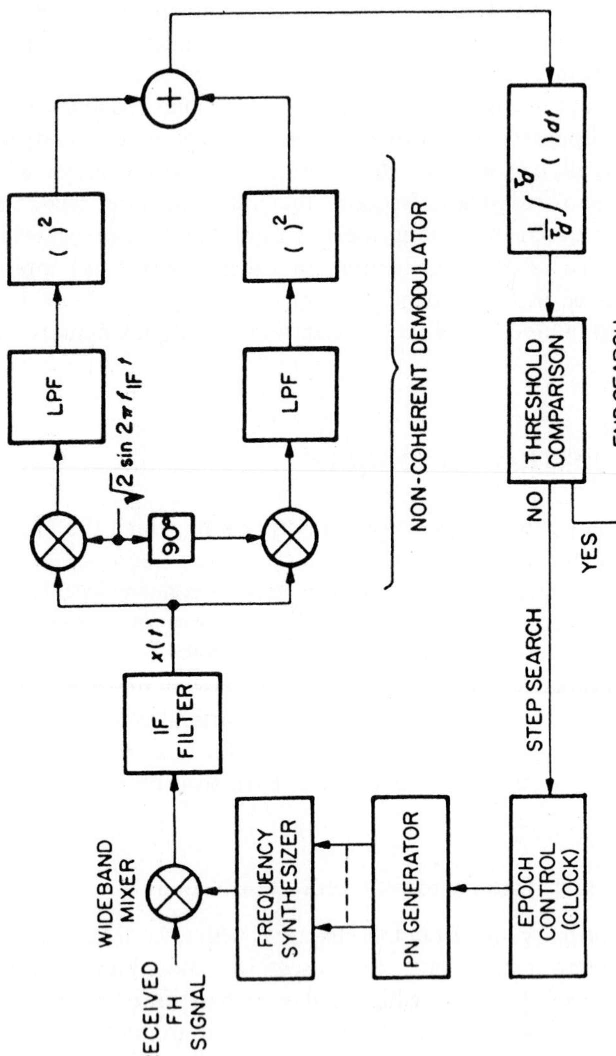

Figure 3.1. A single dwell time serial search FH acquisition system.

filter followed by an energy detector implemented here as a baseband non-coherent demodulator.[1] (The bandwidths of the IF filter and demodulator low-pass filters are chosen based upon considerations to be discussed shortly). Post-detection integration of the energy detector output produces a signal whose mean value is nominally zero when the two hop sequences are misaligned and non-zero when they are either partially or fully aligned. Thus, comparing this signal with a preset threshold allows a decision to be made as to whether or not FH acquisition has been achieved, or equivalently whether or not to step the PN code epoch and continue the search.

A similar serial search technique for acquiring PN sequences was discussed in great detail in Chapter 1. Thus, our discussion here will be, by comparison, brief and merely serve to highlight the essential differences between the two systems.

To begin, first suppose that the received FH signal and the locally generated hop signal out of the mixer will appear as in Figure 3.2a.[2] Now, if the bandwidth of the IF filter is chosen to be less than twice the hop frequency spacing, then all of the frequency components of the mixer difference signal will be outside this bandwidth, resulting in a zero correlation voltage at the demodulator input. Now suppose that the received sequence and synthesizer sequence are partially aligned, i.e., misaligned by less than a single hop interval. Then, the mixer difference signal, as illustrated in Figure 3.2b, will contain frequency components within the IF bandwidth (assuming a composite frequency error δf less than the hop spacing) which are effective for correlation detection. These "bursts" of sinusoids at a frequency $f_{IF} - \delta f$ have random phases relative to one another resulting in an IF filter output $x(t)$ which does not have a discrete spectral component at this frequency. In fact, for a given timing offset τ with magnitude less than a hop interval T_h, we can write $x(t)$ as

$$x(t) = \sqrt{2S}\sum_i \mathrm{rect}_\tau(t - iT_h)\cos[2\pi(f_{IF} - \delta f)t + \psi_i]$$

$$\mathrm{rect}_\tau(t) = \begin{cases} 0; & 0 \le t \le \tau \quad (\tau > 0) \\ & T_h - |\tau| \le t \le T_h \quad (\tau < 0) \\ 1; & \tau \le t \le T_h \quad (\tau > 0) \\ & 0 \le t \le T_h - |\tau| \quad (\tau < 0) \end{cases} \tag{3.1}$$

[1]Alternately, the baseband non-coherent demodulator could be replaced by a band-pass square-law envelope detector, as in our previous discussions of serial search acquisition of PN sequences in Chapter 1.

[2]For simplicity of this discussion, we shall for the time being ignore the information modulation and the additive noise.

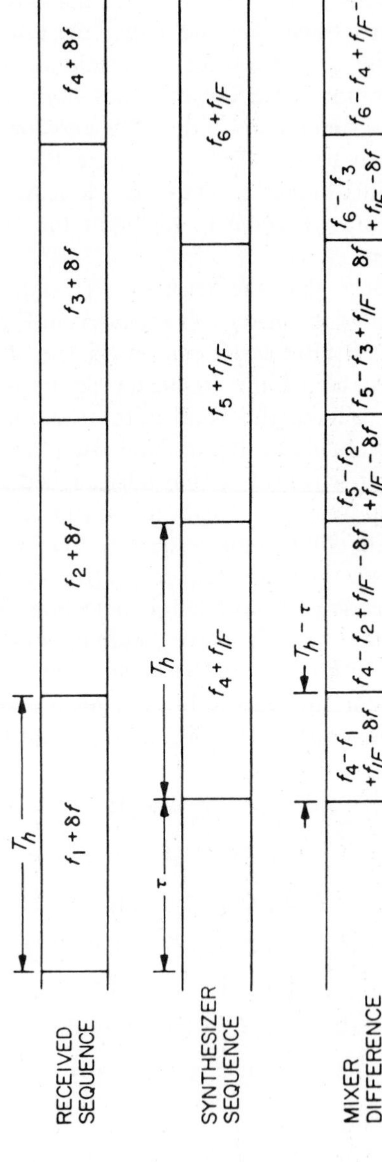

Figure 3.2a. Received FH signal and local hop signal misaligned by more than a single hop interval.

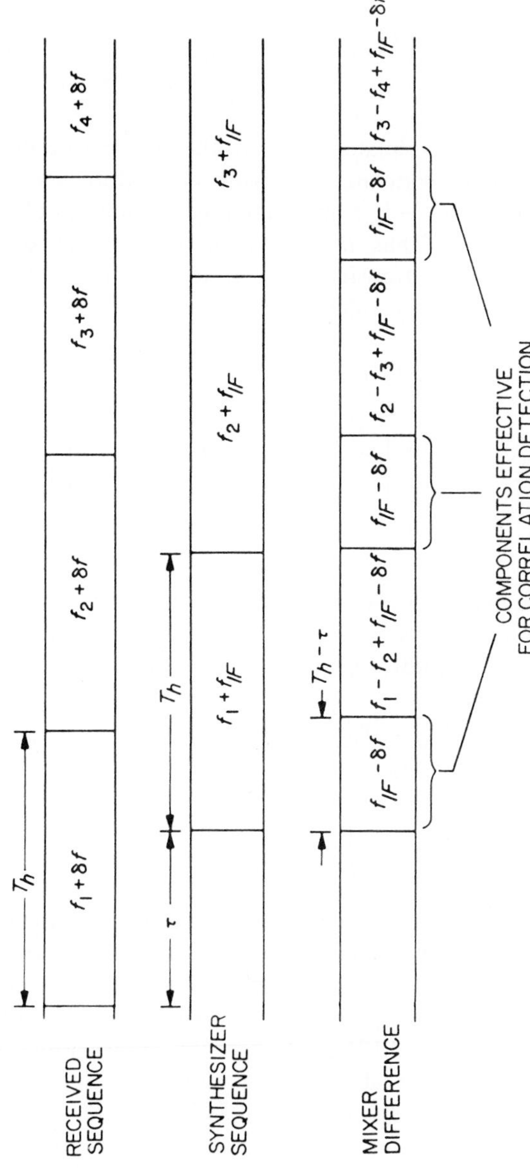

Figure 3.2b. Received FH signal and local hop signal misaligned by less than a single hop interval.

which has the power spectral density

$$S_x(f;\tau) = \frac{1}{T_h}|\mathscr{F}\{x(t)\}|^2$$

$$= \frac{S(T_h - |\tau|)^2}{T_h}\left[\frac{\sin\{\pi[f-(f_{IF}-\delta f)](T_h-|\tau|)\}}{\pi[f-(f_{IF}-\delta f)](T_h-|\tau|)}\right]^2. \quad (3.2)$$

The non-coherent demodulator forms a filtered measure of the average power in $x(t)$ by demodulating it with quadrature reference signals $\sqrt{2}\cos 2\pi f_{IF}t$ and $\sqrt{2}\sin 2\pi f_{IF}t$ and summing the squares of the resultant filtered low-pass signals. Thus, if $|H(j2\pi f)|^2$ denotes the squared magnitude of the low-pass filter transfer function, then the non-coherent demodulator output has an average value

$$R(\tau) = \int_{-\infty}^{\infty} S_x(f+f_{IF};\tau)|H(j2\pi f)|^2\, df$$

$$= \frac{S(T_h-|\tau|)^2}{T_h}\int_{-\infty}^{\infty}\left[\frac{\sin\{\pi(f+\delta f)(T_h-|\tau|)\}}{\pi(f+\delta f)(T_h-|\tau|)}\right]^2 |H(j2\pi f)|^2\, df. \quad (3.3)$$

Assuming first that the bandwidth of the demodulator low-pass filters is much larger than the hop rate $1/T_h$, and, in addition, the frequency error is small (relative to this bandwidth), then (3.3) simplifies to

$$R(\tau) = \frac{S(T_h-|\tau|)^2}{T_h}\int_{-\infty}^{\infty}\left[\frac{\sin \pi f'(T_h-|\tau|)}{\pi f'(T_h-|\tau|)}\right]^2 df'$$

$$= S\left(1-\frac{|\tau|}{T_h}\right) \quad (3.4)$$

i.e., a triangular correlation curve of width $2T_h$. In general, the non-coherent demodulator low-pass filter bandwidth must be chosen large enough to accommodate the information modulation bandwidth, the maximum system frequency error, and the hop frequency modulating spectrum. Thus, for slow frequency hopping (SFH), wherein the information symbol rate dominates this choice, the above assumption of a large low-pass filter bandwidth relative to the hop rate is valid and hence no significant filtering of the correlation curve occurs in accordance with (3.4). For fast frequency hopping (FFH) where the low-pass filter bandwidth is chosen on the order of the hop rate, significant filtering occurs and the correlation curve must be computed from (3.3). As an example of the filtering distortion of the triangular correlation function, consider the case of single-pole low-pass filters with single-sided noise bandwidth B. Then evaluation of (3.3) with

$\delta f = 0$ yields

$$R(\tau) = S\left(1 - \frac{|\tau|}{T_h}\right)\left[1 - \frac{1 - \exp\left\{-4BT_h\left(1 - \frac{|\tau|}{T_h}\right)\right\}}{4BT_h\left(1 - \frac{|\tau|}{T_h}\right)}\right] \tag{3.5}$$

which is plotted against τ/T_h in Figure 3.3 with BT_h as a parameter. We observe from this figure that in the neighborhood of $\tau = 0$, the predominant effect of the filtering is a reduction of the correlation peak by an amount approximately given by $1/4BT_h$ and a corresponding broadening of the triangular shape.

When additive noise and possibly interference signals are present, the design of the demodulator low-pass filters will be governed by considerations additional to minimum correlation function degradation, which, as we noted above, requires their bandwidth to be large. In particular, minimization of the demodulator square-law noise output requires that these same bandwidths be chosen small. Thus, as is characteristic of square-law demodulation systems, a tradeoff exists between signal $\times$ signal and signal $\times$ noise plus noise $\times$ noise degradations.

In summary, then, for SFH of an information-bearing carrier, the low-pass filter bandwidths must be commensurate with the information modulation bandwidth and therefore the demodulator output signal-to-noise ratio will be set by this bandwidth. For FFH of the same information-modulated carrier, the low-pass filter bandwidths must be large enough to accommo-

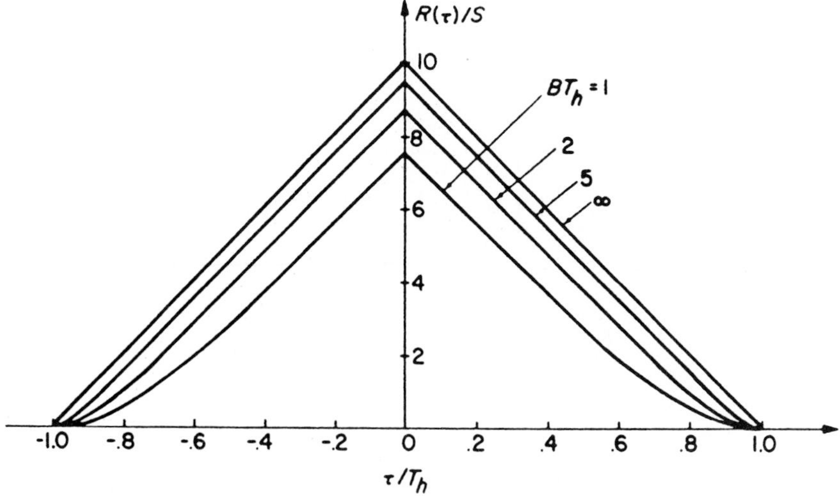

Figure 3.3. Filtering effects on the FH correlation function.

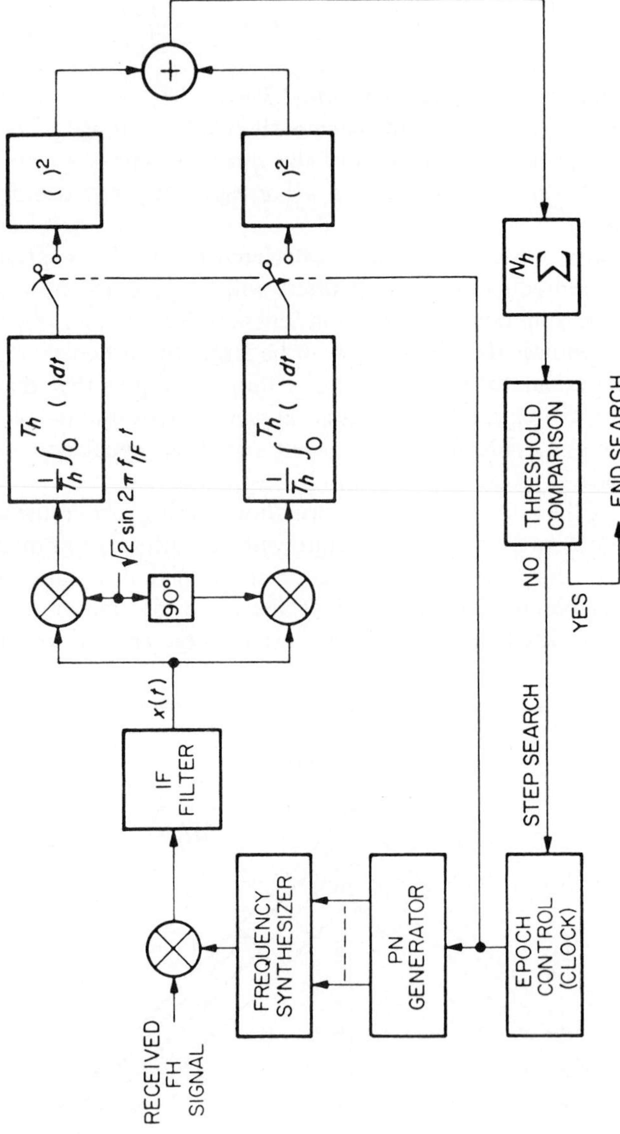

Figure 3.4. A serial search FH acquisition system with integrate-and-dump-type demodulator.

date the hop rate (which is larger than the modulation bandwidth) and can therefore be set to maximize the demodulator output signal-to-noise ratio.

One way of avoiding the degradation of the correlation curve peak in the FFH case is to replace the low-pass filters in the non-coherent demodulator with integrate-and-dump circuits as in Figure 3.4. Since for the rectangular bursts of signal correlation appearing at the demodulator input, the integrate-and-dumps act as matched filters, then the demodulator output samples have an average value

$$R(\tau) = S\frac{\sin^2 \pi\delta f(T_h - |\tau|)}{(\pi\delta f T_h)^2} \tag{3.6}$$

or for $\delta f = 0$,

$$R(\tau) = S\left(1 - \frac{|\tau|}{T_h}\right)^2. \tag{3.7}$$

It is interesting at this point to note that this very same function of time and frequency offset as expressed by (3.6) will again be significant later on in the chapter when we study the effects of time and frequency errors on fine synchronization performance.

With the previous discussion as background, we now return our attention to the case of primary interest in this chapter, namely, coarse acquisition of fast or slow FH/MFSK. A basic serial search acquisition configuration for FFH/MFSK is illustrated in Figure 3.5. For the case when the received and local hop signals are misaligned by less than a single hop interval, the bottom line of Figure 3.6 is the sequence of frequencies characterizing the mixer difference signal. If, as before, the IF filter bandwidth is chosen narrow enough to eliminate the difference of two adjacent hop frequencies, but wide enough now to pass the entire MFSK signalling frequency band, then only the frequency components corresponding to the non-crosshatched areas in Figure 3.6 will pass through this filter and be available for correlation detection. Thus, we observe that in each symbol interval T_s, which is synchronous with the local FH synthesizer, the signal component of the IF filter output will consist of $m = T_s/T_h$ bursts of sinusoid of duration $T_h - |\tau|$. These m bursts are all at the same frequency (corresponding to the particular MFSK tone transmitted in that symbol interval) but have random phases which are independent of one another. A measure of the lack of coarse time synchronization can therefore be obtained by separately combining the energies detected in each hop interval at each of the M possible MFSK frequencies $\{f_{si}; i = 1, 2, \ldots, M\}$ and then choosing the largest of these m-fold diversity combinations. Since this selection is made only once per symbol interval, post-detection accumulation (over say N_{FFH} symbols) is required, the result of which is compared with a preset threshold to determine whether or not to continue the search.

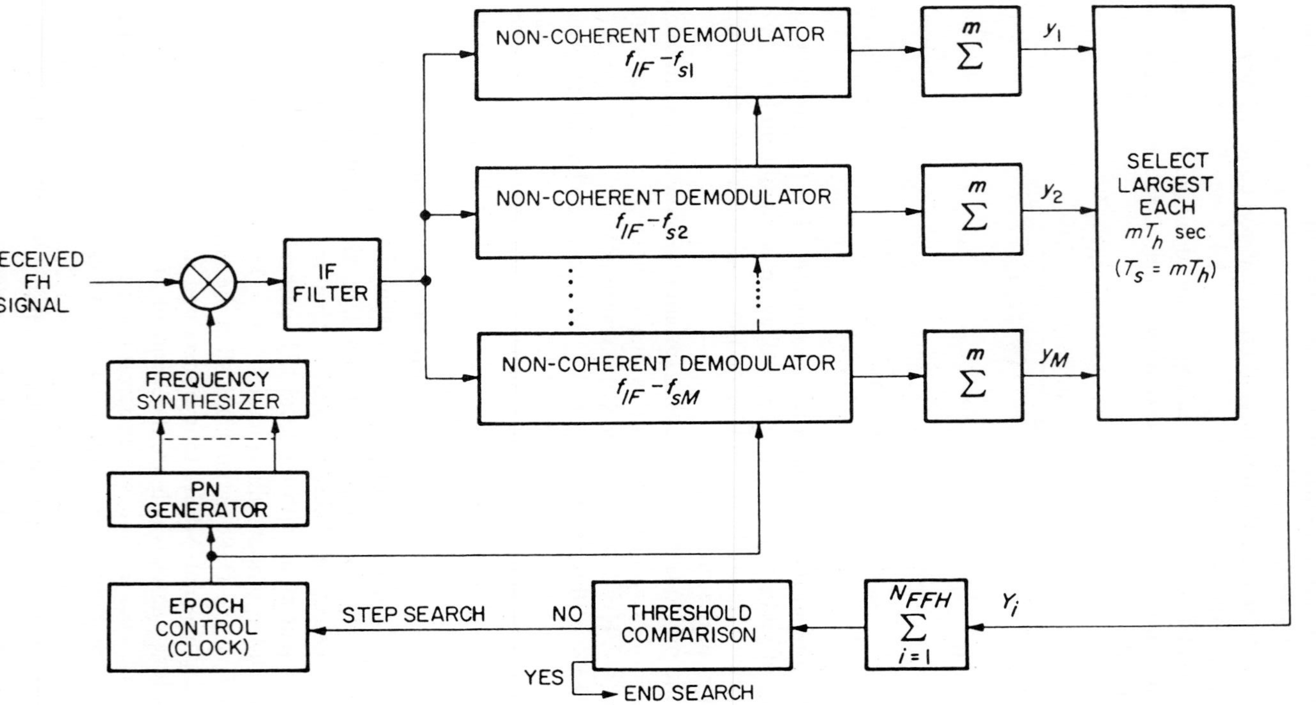

Figure 3.5. A serial search acquisition system for FFH/MFSK.

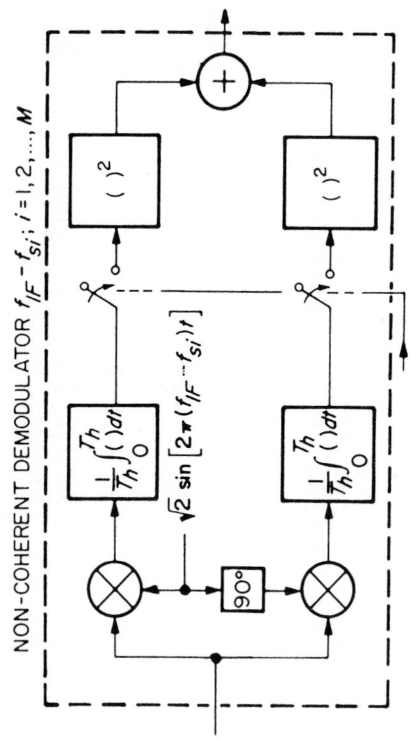

Figure 3.5 (continued)

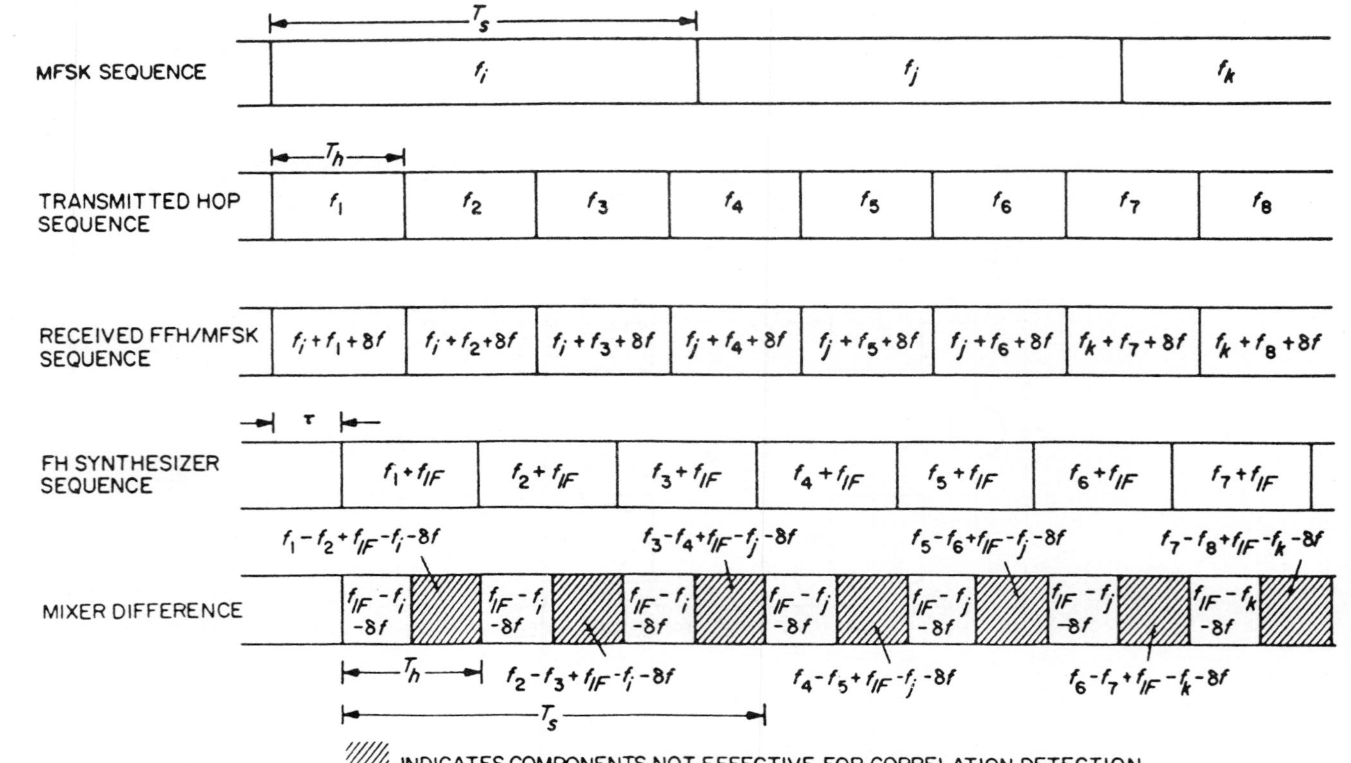

Figure 3.6. Received FFH/MFSK signal and local hop signal misaligned by less than a single hop interval.

In the absence of noise, for the symbol interval during which f_i was the frequency of the transmitted MFSK tone, the m-fold accumulated output samples of the M non-coherent demodulators are given by

$$R_k(\tau) = mS\frac{\sin^2\{\pi[\delta f - (f_{sk} - f_i)](T_h - |\tau|)\}}{\{\pi[\delta f - (f_{sk} - f_i)]T_h\}^2};$$

$$k = 1, 2, \ldots, M. \tag{3.8}$$

Thus if δf is small compared with the spacing between adjacent MFSK tones, then the largest $R_k(\tau)$ will occur for the value of k for which $f_i = f_{sk}$. Since this occurrence will be true independent of which symbol we examine, the input to the post-detection accumulator will be given by $R(\tau)$ of (3.6) multiplied by m.

For ordinary (without diversity) SFH/MFSK, the appropriate serial search acquisition system analogous to Figure 3.5 is illustrated in Figure 3.7 with a corresponding time-frequency diagram in Figure 3.8. Since in each hop interval, the mixer difference signal contains sinusoidal bursts at different frequencies corresponding to the MFSK tones transmitted in that hop, then in contrast with Figure 3.5, no non-coherent combining occurs at the outputs of the M non-coherent demodulators. Rather, the largest of these M outputs is selected each symbol interval. Post-detection accumulation (over say N_{SFH} symbols) of these selections and comparison with a preset threshold again determines whether or not to continue the search.

Another characteristic of the acquisition system in Figure 3.7 is that the set of M non-coherent demodulator outputs does not necessarily remain unchanged as one passes from symbol to symbol within a given hop. For example, if the timing error τ is less than a symbol interval T_s (as is the case illustrated in Figure 3.8), then for all symbols except the last in a given hop interval, the sets of M outputs will be identical, although not necessarily ordered the same way within a given set. Since a maximum is sought in each symbol interval, the ordering is unimportant and thus in each case a decision is made among M energy detections corresponding to an input of $T_s - \tau$ sec of a given MFSK tone and τ sec of the adjacent transmitted tone. For the last symbol of that hop, however, only $T_s - \tau$ sec of the corresponding MFSK tone is available for energy detection, the remaining τ sec corresponding to noise only. As τ increases beyond T_s sec, fewer and fewer symbol decisions will be based upon a full T_s sec of input signal. Finally, when $\tau = T_h$, the entire mixer difference signal will contain noise only.

For SFH/MFSK with diversity m, the appropriate serial search acquisition system reverts back to one resembling Figure 3.5, where the outputs of the M non-coherent demodulators are now individually summed over the m chips (one per hop) corresponding to a given symbol. As such, the integrate-and-dumps in each non-coherent demodulator operate over a chip interval

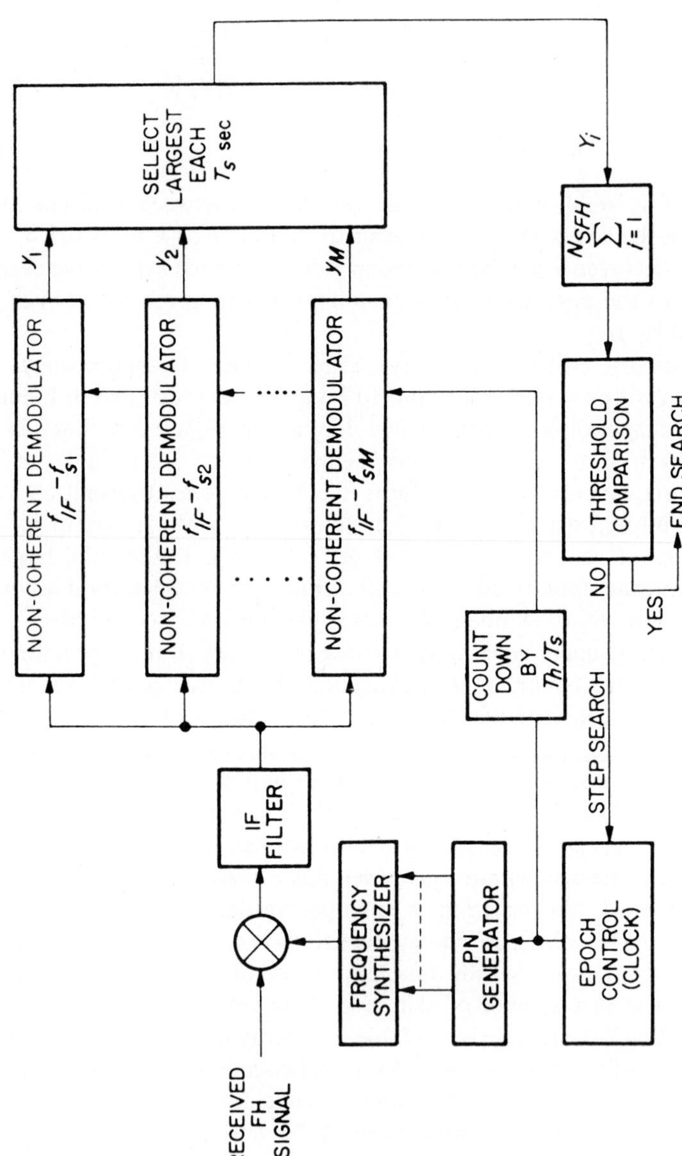

Figure 3.7. A serial search acquisition system for SFH/MFSK.

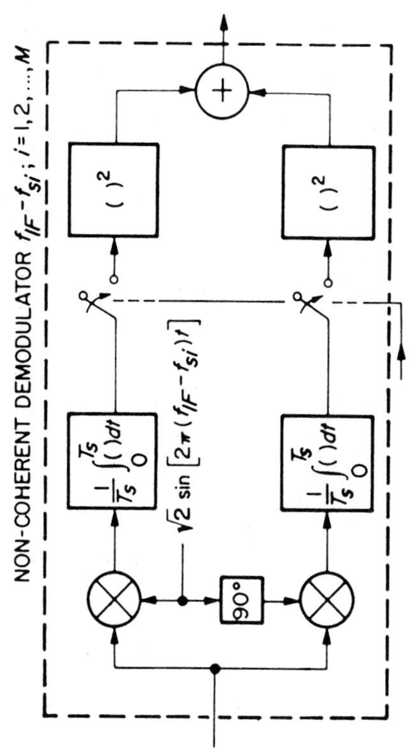

Figure 3.7 (continued)

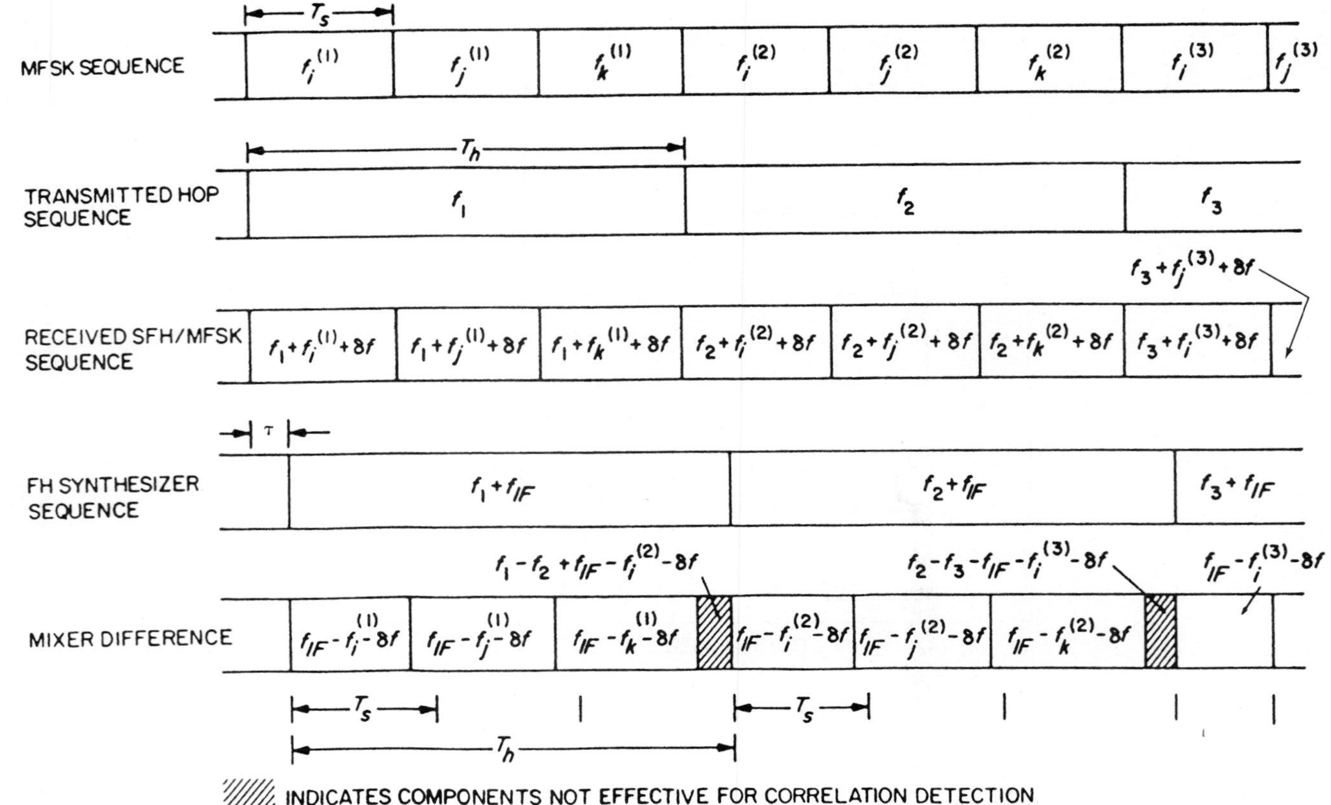

Figure 3.8. Received SFH/MFSK signal and local hop signal misaligned by less than a single hop interval.

corresponding to T_s/m and the demodulator outputs must be delayed by intervals of T_h sec before accumulation.

To evaluate the performance of the various serial search FH/MFSK acquisition systems in the presence of noise, we must determine their operating characteristic, i.e., the relation among false alarm probability P_{FA}, detection probability P_D, and dwell time τ_d. To determine this relation, we shall assume that the post-detection accumulation size N_h (actually N_{FFH} or N_{SFH}) is large so that the statistics at the input to the threshold comparison in Figure 3.5 and 3.7 may be assumed Gaussian. A similar assumption was made in Chapter 1 in connection with our discussion of serial search PN code acquisition. Because of this simplifying assumption, it is sufficient to find only the mean and variance of the signal at the post-detection accumulator input in both the in-sync and out-of-sync conditions.

To illustrate the procedure, we consider first the case of no diversity and equal symbol and hop rates. Thus, with $m = 1$ and $T_s = T_h$, Figures 3.5 and 3.7 are identical. Assuming first the out-of-sync condition ($\tau \geq T_h$), then the mixer output is noise only and the M non-coherent demodulator (normalized) outputs all have the same probability density function (pdf) given by (see (1.73) of Chapter 1)

$$p_N\left(y_k^*\right) = \begin{cases} e^{-y_k^*}; & y_k^* \geq 0 \\ 0; & \text{otherwise} \end{cases} \qquad k = 1, 2, \ldots, M. \quad (3.9)$$

On the other hand, for the "ideal" in-sync condition ($\tau = \delta f = 0$) and orthogonal MFSK tone spacing (i.e., an integer multiple of the symbol rate), then $M - 1$ of the demodulator outputs will be characterized by (3.9), while the remaining output corresponding to the transmitted tone (say f_{sl}) has the pdf (see (1.72) of Chapter 1)

$$p_{S+N}\left(y_l^*\right) = \begin{cases} e^{-(y_l^* + \gamma_h)} I_0\left(2\sqrt{\gamma_h y_l^*}\right); & y_l^* \geq 0 \\ 0; & \text{otherwise} \end{cases} \quad (3.10)$$

where $\gamma_h \triangleq ST_h/N_0$ is the hop signal-to-noise ratio, or, in this case, also the symbol signal-to-noise ratio.

Letting Y_i^* denote the random variable corresponding to the largest of the M non-coherent demodulator normalized outputs at the i-th sampling (once per hop) instant, then the probability density function of Y_i^* is given by

$$q_N\left(Y_i^*\right) = \frac{d}{dY_i^*}\left[P_N\left(Y_i^*\right)\right]^M = Mp_N\left(Y_i^*\right)\left[P_N\left(Y_i^*\right)\right]^{M-1} \quad (3.11)$$

for the out-of-sync condition and

$$\begin{aligned} q_{S+N}(Y_i^*) &= \frac{d}{dY_i^*}\left\{P_{S+N}(Y_i^*)[P_N(Y_i^*)]^{M-1}\right\} \\ &= p_{S+N}(Y_i^*)[P_N(Y_i^*)]^{M-1} \\ &\quad + (M-1)p_N(Y_i^*)P_{S+N}(Y_i^*)[P_N(Y_i^*)]^{M-2} \end{aligned} \tag{3.12}$$

for the in-sync condition where $P_N(Y^*)$ and $P_{S+N}(Y^*)$ are, respectively, the probability *distribution* functions corresponding to the pdf's $p_N(y^*)$ and $p_{S+N}(y^*)$ of (3.9) and (3.10), i.e.,

$$\begin{aligned} P_N(Y^*) &= \int_{-\infty}^{Y^*} p_N(y^*)\,dy^* \\ P_{S+N}(Y^*) &= \int_{-\infty}^{Y^*} p_{S+N}(y^*)\,dy^*. \end{aligned} \tag{3.13}$$

Substituting (3.9) and (3.10) into (3.13) and the results of these integral evaluations into (3.12) gives for the in-sync condition

$$q_{S+N}(Y_i^*) = \begin{cases} \exp[-(Y_i^* + \gamma_h)]\,I_0\left(2\sqrt{\gamma_h Y_i^*}\right)[1-\exp(-Y_i^*)]^{M-1} \\ \qquad + (M-1)\exp(-Y_i^*)[1-\exp(-Y_i^*)]^{M-2} \\ \qquad \times \int_0^{Y_i^*}\exp[-(Y+\gamma_h)]\,I_0\left(2\sqrt{\gamma_h Y}\right)dY;\ Y \geq 0 \\ 0;\ \text{otherwise.} \end{cases} \tag{3.14}$$

The corresponding result for the out-of-sync condition is obtained by letting $\gamma_h = 0$ in (3.14), i.e.,

$$q_N(Y_i^*) = \begin{cases} M\exp(-Y_i^*)[1-\exp(-Y_i^*)]^{M-1};\ Y_i^* \geq 0 \\ 0;\ \text{otherwise.} \end{cases} \tag{3.15}$$

As previously mentioned, we need to determine the first two central moments of Y_i^* in order to evaluate the operating characteristic of the acquisition system. From (3.14), we can determine the mean of Y_i^* for the perfectly in-sync condition as

$$\begin{aligned} \mu_{S+N} &\triangleq \int_{-\infty}^{\infty} Y_i^* q_{S+N}(Y_i^*)\,dY_i^* \\ &= 1 + \gamma_h + (M-1)\sum_{k=0}^{M-2}\frac{(-1)^k}{(k+2)(k+1)^2}\binom{M-2}{k}\exp\left[-\left(\frac{k+1}{k+2}\right)\gamma_h\right] \end{aligned} \tag{3.16}$$

and for the out-of-sync condition,

$$\mu_N = 1 + (M-1)\sum_{k=0}^{M-2} \frac{(-1)^k}{(k+2)(k+1)^2}\binom{M-2}{k}. \tag{3.17}$$

Note that the leading terms of (3.16) and (3.17) correspond to the means of y^* as determined from $p_{S+N}(y^*)$ and $p_N(y^*)$ in (3.10) and (3.9), respectively (see (1.75) and (1.76) of Chapter 1). Similarly, the mean-squared value of Y_i^* under the two sync conditions is determined as

$$\overline{(Y_i^*)^2_{S+N}} = 2 + 4\gamma_h + \gamma_h^2 + 2(M-1)\sum_{k=0}^{M-2} \frac{(-1)^k}{(k+2)(k+1)^2}\binom{M-2}{k} \times \left[\left(\frac{1}{k+2}\right)\left(\frac{\gamma_h}{k+2}+1\right) + \frac{1}{k+1}\right]\exp\left[-\left(\frac{k+1}{k+2}\right)\gamma_h\right] \tag{3.18}$$

and

$$\overline{(Y_i^*)^2_{N}} = 2 + 2(M-1)\sum_{k=0}^{M-2} \frac{(-1)^k}{(k+2)(k+1)^2}\binom{M-2}{k}\left[\frac{1}{k+2} + \frac{1}{k+1}\right]. \tag{3.19}$$

Thus, the in-sync and out-of-sync variances of Y_i^* are given by

$$\sigma^2_{S+N} = \overline{(Y_i^*)^2_{S+N}} - \mu^2_{S+N}$$
$$\sigma^2_N = \overline{(Y_i^*)^2_N} - \mu^2_N \tag{3.20}$$

where once again the leading terms will correspond to the variances of y^* (see (1.75) and (1.76) of Chapter 1).

Post-detection accumulation of Y_i^* produces the approximately Gaussian (N_h large) random variable

$$Z^* = \sum_{i=1}^{N_h} Y_i^* \tag{3.21}$$

which when compared with the normalized threshold η^* gives rise to a false alarm probability (exceeding the threshold when in the out-of-sync condition)

$$P_{FA} = \int_{\eta^*}^{\infty} \frac{1}{\sqrt{2\pi N_h\sigma_N^2}}\exp\left[-\frac{(Z^* - N_h\mu_N)^2}{2N_h\sigma_N^2}\right]dZ^*$$
$$= Q\left(\frac{\eta^* - N_h\mu_N}{\sqrt{N_h\sigma_N^2}}\right) \triangleq Q(\beta) \tag{3.22}$$

and a detection probability (exceeding the threshold when in the in-sync condition)

$$P_D = Q\left(\frac{\eta^* - N_h\mu_{S+N}}{\sqrt{N_h\sigma_{S+N}^2}}\right) = Q\left(\frac{\eta^* - N_h\mu_N - N_h(\mu_{S+N} - \mu_N)}{\sqrt{N_h\sigma_N^2}\,(\sigma_{S+N}/\sigma_N)}\right)$$

$$= Q\left(\frac{\beta - \sqrt{\dfrac{N_h}{\sigma_N^2}}\,(\mu_{S+N} - \mu_N)}{\sigma_{S+N}/\sigma_N}\right) \tag{3.23}$$

where, as in previous chapters, $Q(x)$ is the Gaussian probability integral. Eliminating β between (3.22) and (3.23) produces the desired system operating characteristic

$$P_D = Q\left(\frac{Q^{-1}(P_{FA}) - (\mu_{S+N} - \mu_N)\sqrt{\dfrac{N_h}{\sigma_N^2}}}{\sigma_{S+N}/\sigma_N}\right) \tag{3.24}$$

where μ_{S+N}, μ_N, σ_{S+N}^2, and σ_N^2 are determined from (3.16)–(3.20) and are all functions of the signalling alphabet size M and hop signal-to-noise ratio γ_h. Alternately, since the dwell time τ_d of the system is related to the accumulation size N_h by

$$N_h = \frac{\tau_d}{T_h}, \tag{3.25}$$

then (3.24) can be expressed in terms of the dwell time-hop rate product, which produces a relation analogous to (1.81) of Chapter 1. Figures 3.9 and 3.10 are plots of false alarm probability P_{FA} versus normalized dwell time τ_d/T_h with detection probability P_D as a parameter for $\gamma_h = -20$ dB and either 2-ary or 8-ary FSK, respectively. Clearly, as the number of signalling levels M increases, the required post-detection accumulation increases proportionally.

When m-diversity is employed, then the appropriate pdf's analogous to (3.9) and (3.10) become

$$p_N(y_k^*) = \begin{cases} \dfrac{(y_k^*)^{m-1}}{(m-1)!}\exp(-y_k^*); \; y_k^* \geq 0 \\ 0; \text{ otherwise} \end{cases} \tag{3.26}$$

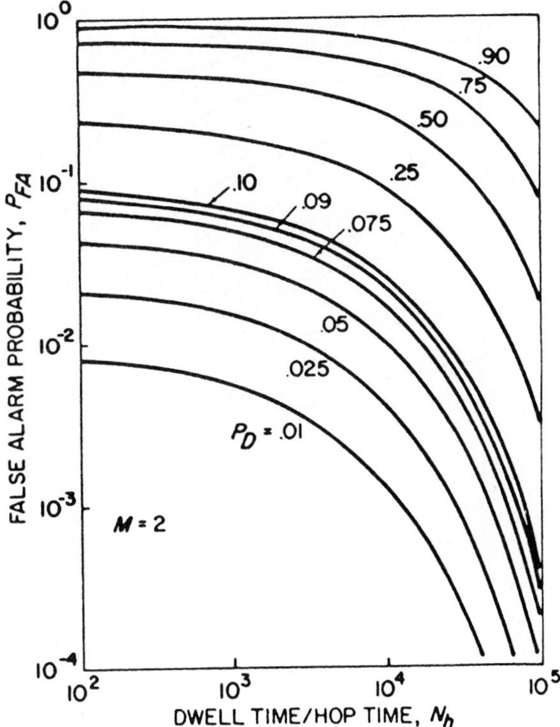

Figure 3.9. False alarm and detection probability performance of serial search FH/MFSK acquisition system; $\gamma_h = -20$ dB.

and

$$p_{S+N}(y_k^*) = \begin{cases} \left(\dfrac{y_k^*}{m\gamma_h}\right)^{(m-1)/2} \exp[-(y_k^* + m\gamma_h)]\, I_{m-1}\left(\sqrt{4m\gamma_h y_k^*}\right); \; y_k^* \geq 0 \\ 0; \text{ otherwise.} \end{cases} \tag{3.27}$$

Similarly the out-of-sync and in-sync pdf's for the largest of the M non-coherently combined normalized demodulator outputs are given respectively by

$$q_N(Y_i^*) = \begin{cases} \dfrac{M(Y_i^*)^{m-1}}{(m-1)!} \exp(-Y_i^*)\left[1 - \displaystyle\sum_{k=0}^{m-1} \frac{(Y_i^*)^k}{k!} \exp(-Y_i^*)\right]^{M-1}; & Y_i^* \geq 0 \\ 0; \text{ otherwise} \end{cases} \tag{3.28}$$

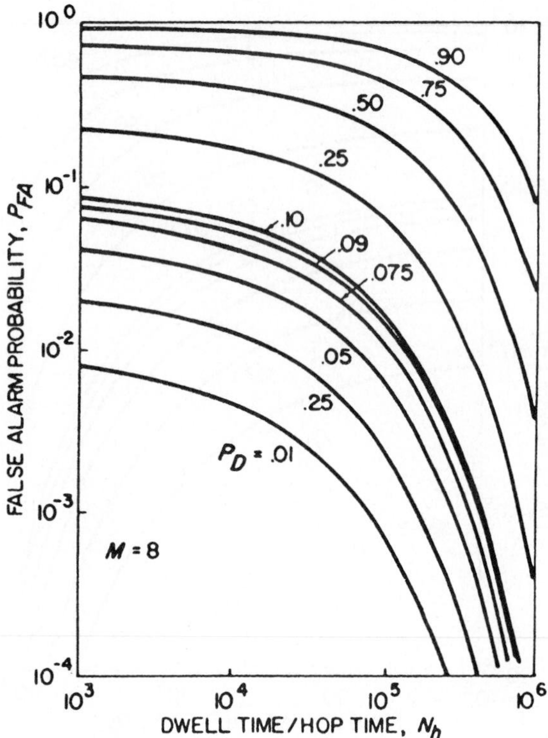

Figure 3.10. False alarm and detection probability performance of serial search FH/MFSK acquisition system; $\gamma_h = -20$ dB.

and

$$q_{S+N}(Y_i^*) = \begin{cases} \left(\dfrac{Y_i^*}{m\gamma_h}\right)^{(m-1)/2} \exp\left[-(Y_i^* + m\gamma_h)\right] I_{m-1}\left(\sqrt{4m\gamma_h Y_i^*}\right) \\ \times\left[1 - \sum_{k=0}^{m-1} \dfrac{(Y_i^*)^k}{k!}\exp(-Y_i^*)\right]^{M-1} \\ +(M-1)\dfrac{(Y_i^*)^{m-1}}{(m-1)!}\exp(-Y_i^*) \\ \times\left[1 - \sum_{k=0}^{m-1} \dfrac{(Y_i^*)^k}{k!}\exp(-Y_i^*)\right]^{M-2} \displaystyle\int_0^{Y_i^*}\left(\dfrac{Y}{m\gamma_h}\right)^{(m-1)/2} \\ \times\exp\left[-(Y + m\gamma_h)\right] I_{m-1}\left(\sqrt{4m\gamma_h Y}\right) dY;\ Y_i^* \geq 0 \\ 0;\ \text{otherwise} \end{cases} \tag{3.29}$$

with first two moments

$$\overline{\left(Y_i^*\right)_{S+N}^n} = \left[m(1+\gamma_h)\right]^n + (n-1)m(1+2\gamma_h)$$
$$+(M-1)\sum_{k=0}^{M-2}\binom{M-2}{k}(-1)^k \exp\left[-\left(\frac{k+1}{k+2}\right)m\gamma_h\right]$$
$$\times \frac{1}{(k+1)^n(k+2)^m}\left\{\sum_{j=0}^{k(m-1)} C_{kj}\frac{(m+j+n-1)!}{(m-1)!(k+1)^{m+j}}\right.$$
$$\times \sum_{l=0}^{m+j+n-1}\left(\frac{k+1}{k+2}\right)^l L_l^{(m-1)}\left(-\frac{m\gamma_h}{k+2}\right)$$
$$\left. - \sum_{j=0}^{(k+1)(m-1)} C_{k+1,j}\frac{(j+n)!}{(k+2)^{j+n}} L_{j+n}^{(m-1)}\left(-\frac{m\gamma_h}{k+2}\right)\right\}$$
$$\overline{\left(Y_i^*\right)_N^n} = \left.\overline{\left(Y_i^*\right)_{S+N}^n}\right|_{\gamma_h=0};\ n = 1,2 \tag{3.30}$$

where $L_k^{(m-1)}(x)$ is the k-th generalized Laguerre polynomial of order $m-1$ [3] and C_{kj} are multinomial coefficients which satisfy the recursion relationship

$$C_{kj} = \begin{cases} 1; & j=0 \\ \dfrac{1}{j}\displaystyle\sum_{l=1}^{\min(j,m-1)}\frac{kl+l-j}{l!}C_{k,j-l} & j = 1,2,\ldots,k(m-1). \end{cases} \tag{3.31}$$

Thus, recognizing that μ_{S+N} and μ_N correspond to (3.30) with $n=1$, and further obtaining σ_{S+N} and σ_N from (3.20) using (3.30) evaluated for $n=2$, one uses (3.24) to obtain the system operating characteristic for the m-diversity case.

We mention in passing that for acquisition in noise, but in the absence of information modulation (see Figure 3.4 for the appropriate system), one merely sets $M=1$ in (3.16)–(3.20), which, when substituted into (3.24), gives the simple result

$$P_D = Q\left[\frac{Q^{-1}(P_{FA}) - \sqrt{N_h}\gamma_h}{\sqrt{1+2\gamma_h}}\right]. \tag{3.32}$$

Note that if the acquisition system of Figure 3.1 were used in place of that in Figure 3.4, then (1.32) would still be appropriate with γ_h replaced by $S/2N_0B$ where B is again the single-sided low-pass filter noise bandwidth. Under these conditions, (3.32) becomes analogous to (1.81) of Chapter 1. In fact, the same substitution is appropriate to all of the previous results for acquisition with MFSK modulation if the integrate-and-dumps in Figures 3.5 and 3.7 are replaced by low-pass filters with noise bandwidth B.

To modify the previous results to allow for a non-ideal in-sync condition, we proceed as follows. Assuming that the MFSK tones are orthogonally spaced, e.g., for FFH we could have $f_{sj} - f_{s,j-1} = k/T_h$ since $1/T_h$ is the minimum tone separation for orthogonality, then in the absence of frequency error ($\delta f = 0$), the m-fold accumulated output samples of the M non-coherent demodulators would in the absence of noise be given by (see (3.8))

$$R_i(\tau) = mS\left(1 - \frac{|\tau|}{T_h}\right)^2 \triangleq mS(1 - |\varepsilon|)^2$$

$$R_l(\tau) = 0; l = 1, 2, \ldots, M; l \neq i \tag{3.33}$$

where f_i is the transmitted tone. Thus, multiplying γ_h by the loss factor $L \triangleq (1 - |\varepsilon|)^2$ in (3.30) is sufficient to account for this degrading effect. A similar result was obtained in connection with our previous discussion of PN code acquisition (see (1.86) of Chapter 1).

When, in addition, frequency error is present, then, even for the above orthogonal tone spacing, the m-fold accumulated output samples of the M non-coherent demodulations will in the absence of noise *all* contain non-zero signal components. Further, this set of output signal components will depend on which MFSK tone was indeed transmitted; i.e.,

$$R_i(\tau) = mS\frac{\sin^2[\pi\delta f(T_h - |\tau|)]}{(\pi\delta f T_h)^2} = mS\frac{\sin^2[\pi\delta f T_h(1 - |\varepsilon|)]}{(\pi\delta f T_h)^2}$$

$$R_l(\tau) = mS\frac{\sin^2\{[\pi\delta f T_h - (l - i)k](1 - |\varepsilon|)\}}{[\pi\delta f T_h - (l - i)k]^2}; \quad l = 1, 2, \cdots, M; l \neq i. \tag{3.34}$$

As a result, all of the normalized output samples y_k^* have pdf's of the form in (3.27) with $m\gamma_h$ replaced by $mR_l(\tau)T_h/N_0$; $l = 1, 2, \ldots, M$. Although formally the procedure is straightforward, the computation of acquisition performance for this case is tedious and is not presented here. However, a similar problem will be considered in detail later on in the chapter relative to the computation of error probability performance in the presence of residual time and frequency tracking errors.

It should be obvious by now that once the system operating characteristic is determined as in (3.24), the specification of acquisition performance in terms of such measures as mean and variance of the acquisition time or probability of acquisition follows directly from the results given in Chapter 1 for serial search PN acquisition. For example, the mean acquisition time $\overline{T}_{ACQ}$ of the serial search FFH/MFSK system of Figure 3.5 is given by (1.34) of Chapter 1 with P_D and P_{FA} related as in (3.24) using μ_{S+N}, μ_N, σ^2_{S+N}, and σ^2_N of (3.16)–(3.20). This parallelism between serial search PN and FH acquisition systems follows from the fact that the basic Markov behavior of the search stepping procedure is the same in both cases. Further parallels between serial search PN and FH acquisition systems along the lines of sequential-type detectors, multiple dwell time detectors, optimum search procedures, etc., can also be drawn, with the details omitted here for the sake of brevity.

3.1.2 Serial Search Techniques with Passive Correlation

Analogous to the matched filter techniques discussed in Chapter 1 for pseudonoise acquisition in DS/SS receivers, the rapid search capability provided by a serial search scheme with passive correlation can also be realized in FH receivers. For the simplest case of rapid acquisition of an FH sequence in the absence of any information modulation, Figure 3.11 illustrates the appropriate structure. A sequence of M consecutive frequencies $f_1, f_2, \ldots, f_M$ within the overall hop sequence is chosen as the sync pattern to which the receiver attempts to match itself. To accomplish this, the received FH signal is simultaneously mixed with these M frequencies (shifted to IF) and the result of each mixture is passed through a non-coherent demodulator (band-pass filter and square-law envelope detector). The demodulator outputs are appropriately delayed so that the sum of these outputs corresponding to the energy in M successive hop interval correlations can be formed and tested against a threshold. Clearly, when the input sequence $f_1, f_2, \ldots, f_M$ has just passed through the receiver matched filter, the above sum will have its maximum value. One hop later, each of the M correlations will have zero contribution to the sum since the corresponding mixer outputs do not pass through the band-pass filters.

A discrete time version of the matched filter receiver of Figure 3.11 can be had by replacing each of the M band-pass non-coherent demodulators by their equivalent low-pass version using integrate-and-dump filters as in Figure 3.4. Here, a threshold decision is made at discrete time instants separated by a hop time and thus the search proceeds at the hop rate.

The performance of the discrete time matched filter FH acquisition system follows directly from the detailed discussions given in Chapter 1 for the analogous PN acquisition system. Thus, other than to point out the obvious parallel between PN code chip time there and hop time here, we shall leave it to the reader to make the remaining necessary associations between the parameters of the two systems.

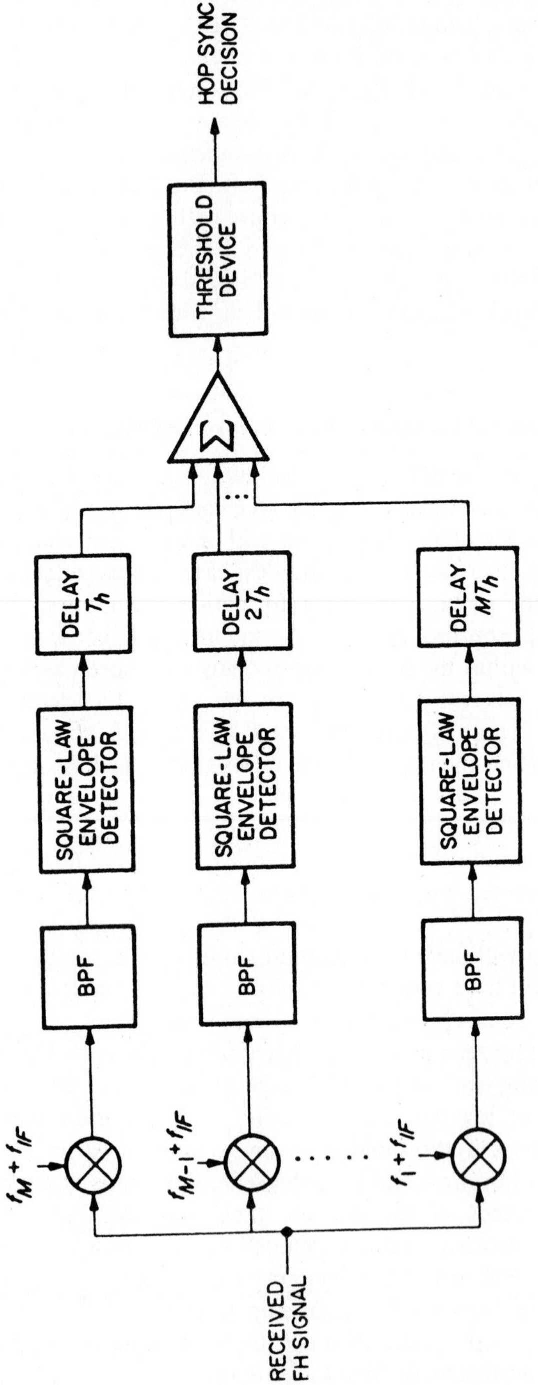

Figure 3.11. A matched filter type of FH acquisition system.

3.1.3 Other FH Acquisition Techniques

A scheme that combines the rapid search capability of passive correlation with the decision reliability of active correlation (over long time intervals) was suggested in [3] and later compared with the more conventional FH acquisition techniques in [4]. The application for which such a two-level acquisition scheme was proposed was a ground mobile radio environment where the users operate in a "push-to-talk" mode and thus the communication among them is intermittent and characterized by frequent and possibly long periods of silence. At the onset of a transmission, prior to message communication, the user sends a leader consisting of several repetitions of the hopped carrier patterns. It is on this leader sequence that the two-level synchronization scheme must acquire and, hence, the length of the leader represents the maximum time (in hops) that the receiver has for FH acquisition. The way in which the acquisition is accomplished is as follows. Each of the hop patterns begins with a specific short segment (say m hops long) referred to as a *sync prefix*. A passive correlator (m-stage matched filter) is used to detect this short m-hop sync prefix and generate a code start signal for those intervals in which its detection threshold is exceeded (see Figure 3.12). The code start signals as they occur each engage any (one) active correlator from the total bank of correlators provided and cause it to cycle through the remaining (say $k \gg m$) hops in the pattern. Non-coherent detection and post-detection integration over these k hop intervals produces an output which is compared against a second threshold. If this threshold is exceeded the test terminates and sync acquisition is declared. Otherwise, the active correlator is again made available to the common bank. If all active correlators are engaged (none are idle) when a code start signal occurs, then this signal is ignored.

Since typically the size (say C) of the bank of active correlators shared among arriving code start signals can be chosen much less than k, then a significant reduction in hardware is potentially possible compared to a full $(m + k)$ parallel correlator structure. Clearly depending on the relative choices of m, k, and bank size C, and the number (say n) of repetitions of the hopped carrier pattern in the leader, a variety of performance tradeoffs are possible between the two extremes of the traditional single-level active and single-level passive correlation schemes.

The notion of estimating from the received signal the state of the linear feedback shift register (LFSR) that generates the local PN code in DS/SS systems (see the discussion of rapid acquisition by sequential estimation in Chapter 1) can also be applied in FH/SS systems. Recall that in the DS/SS system the estimation of the PN sequence that biphase modulates the carrier is accomplished by low-pass filtering the received signal with a filter whose cutoff frequency equals the clock rate of the LFSR followed by hard-limiting. Furthermore, the recursion relation for the PN sequence can be used to improve the accuracy of the initial state estimate (resulting in recursion-aided

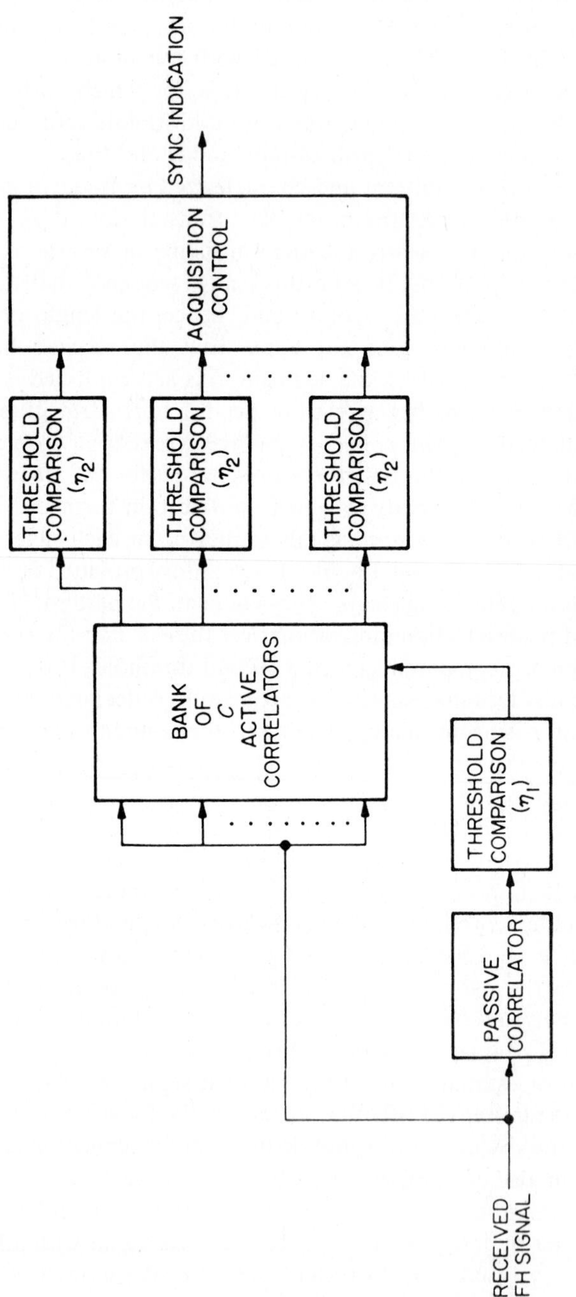

Figure 3.12. A two-level scheme for FH acquisition.

rapid acquisition by sequential estimation) and/or to determine whether the estimate is likely to be error free, thereby reducing acquisition time. In the FH/SS application, the above approach translates to estimating the received frequency over say n_1 successive hop intervals, thus requiring a form of sequential *spectral* estimation. Note that whereas in DS/SS systems an estimate based on observation of the received signal over a single chip interval provides information about only one stage of the LFSR (i.e., we need n successive chip interval estimates to load the contents of an n-stage LFSR), in FH/SS systems an estimate of the frequency in a single hop interval provides information about the entire state of the LFSR. Thus, depending on the order of the model used for the received signal, one can use either the frequency estimate in each hop interval to identify only the most significant bit (MSB) of the corresponding PN codeword, in which case we would have $n_1 = n$, or several significant bits of the LFSR ($n_1 < n$), thus further reducing the acquisition time.

Based on the above discussion, Figure 3.13 illustrates an autoregressive spectral estimation acquisition technique (ASEAT) [5, 6] that is directly analogous to the RASE technique for the DS/SS system (see Figure 3.4 of Chapter 1). The word "autoregressive" refers to the fact that the sampled received signal plus noise (after down conversion) is modelled as an autoregressive (AR) process, thus allowing identification of the instantaneous frequency of this signal by an algorithm developed by El-Ghouroury and Gupta [7].[3] This algorithm, which is incorporated in the frequency identification processor of Figure 3.13, inputs the received signal samples to a linear adaptive filter whose coefficients are updated each sample by a stochastic gradient technique [10] in accordance with the changing statistics of the input signal. The remainder of the frequency identification processor is the frequency identification algorithm [7] which determines the frequency estimate from the signal spectrum, which in turn is related to the filter coefficients through an all-pole model [10].

Note, unlike its PN counterpart (the RASE technique), the ASEAT seeks to achieve acquisition times on the order of the number of stages (n_1) of the LFSR as opposed to the length of the code ($2^{n_1} - 1$) which is characteristic of active correlation serial search techniques. The ability to accomplish this depends quite heavily on the input signal-to-noise ratio, which in turn depends on the nature of the noise interference. Typically, the ASEAT works well in a broadband Gaussian noise environment even for signal-to-noise ratios down to -15 dB [6]; but, like the RASE technique, it is highly vulnerable to narrowband interference. Here the worst case offender is a

[3] In [8], an ASEAT is proposed where the frequency identification processor employs a modification of the spectral estimation algorithms of [9] which uses partial-correlation coefficients to identify the received signal frequency in each hop interval.

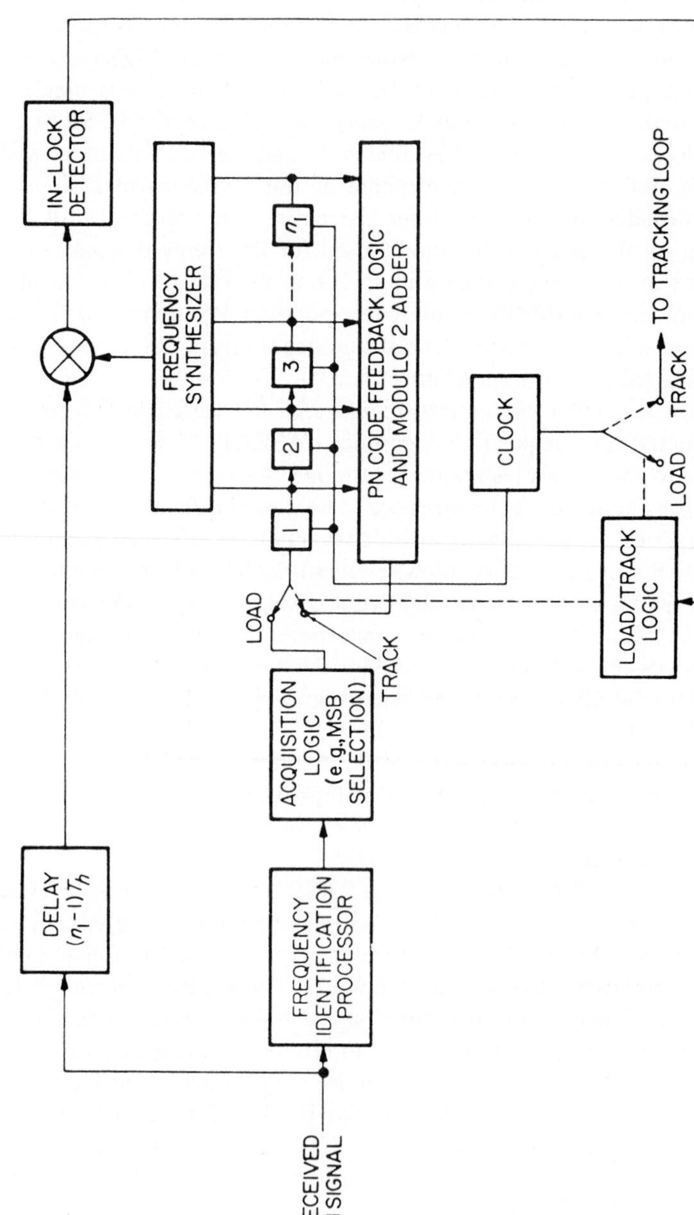

Figure 3.13. An autoregressive spectral estimation acquisition technique (ASEAT).

multitone jammer whose presence in only one of a sequence of n_1 hops might be sufficient to cause the failure of that specific acquisition trial. (Each time this occurs the process must repeat the acquisition trial until a clean record of n_1 successive hops is received without a single jammed tone.) The reason for this vulnerability again stems from the fact that the spectral estimation process is performed on a hop-by-hop basis, thus making no use of the interference rejection capability associated with the FH despreading process. Finally, we point out that the ASEAT is also applicable to hybrid SS systems such as FH/TH and FH/DS [6].

3.2 TIME SYNCHRONIZATION OF NON-COHERENT FH / MFSK SYSTEMS

Time synchronization of a conventional (non-spread) non-coherent MFSK receiver, with additive white Gaussian noise (AWGN) as the only source of disturbance, is typically achieved by transmitting a known synchronization sequence (say frequency f_1 followed by f_2) which is repeated as often as necessary until the desired degree of time synchronization accuracy is obtained. In the presence of this sequence, spectral estimates are formed from discrete (fast) Fourier transforms of the received signal plus noise over one data symbol interval and evaluated at the two frequencies, f_1 and f_2. The ratio of the difference of these two spectral estimates to twice their sum is then the maximum-likelihood estimator of the time of transition from f_1 to f_2 relative to the receiver's present time origin [11], [12]. It is emphasized that it is the *transitions* in the data from f_1 to f_2, and vice versa, that allow the determination of time synchronization by the above approach.

In a non-coherent FH/MFSK receiver, it is sufficient to transmit a *single* frequency tone corresponding to a specific data symbol and allow the frequency hopping to cause the necessary frequency transitions for estimation of time synchronization. As such, the timing estimate is once again obtained in the absence of and prior to true data transmission and, thus, the synchronization process is of a gated nature, being interleaved within the data sequence often enough to provide the desired degree of timing accuracy. The specific manner in which the FH timing estimate is formed may be understood by considering the simplified fine time synchronization of an FH/MFSK system such as that illustrated in Figure 3.14. The transmitted FH signal is successively advanced and delayed *in time* relative to its nominal synchronization position. The received FH signal plus jamming noise is cross-correlated with the local frequency hop generator. Alternately, the local frequency hop generator could be advanced and then delayed in time while the transmitter hop generator remains fixed in its nominal synchronization position. Since the *relative* timing offset between transmitter and receiver hop generators is all that is effectual in producing the timing estimate, either implementation will conceptually produce the same

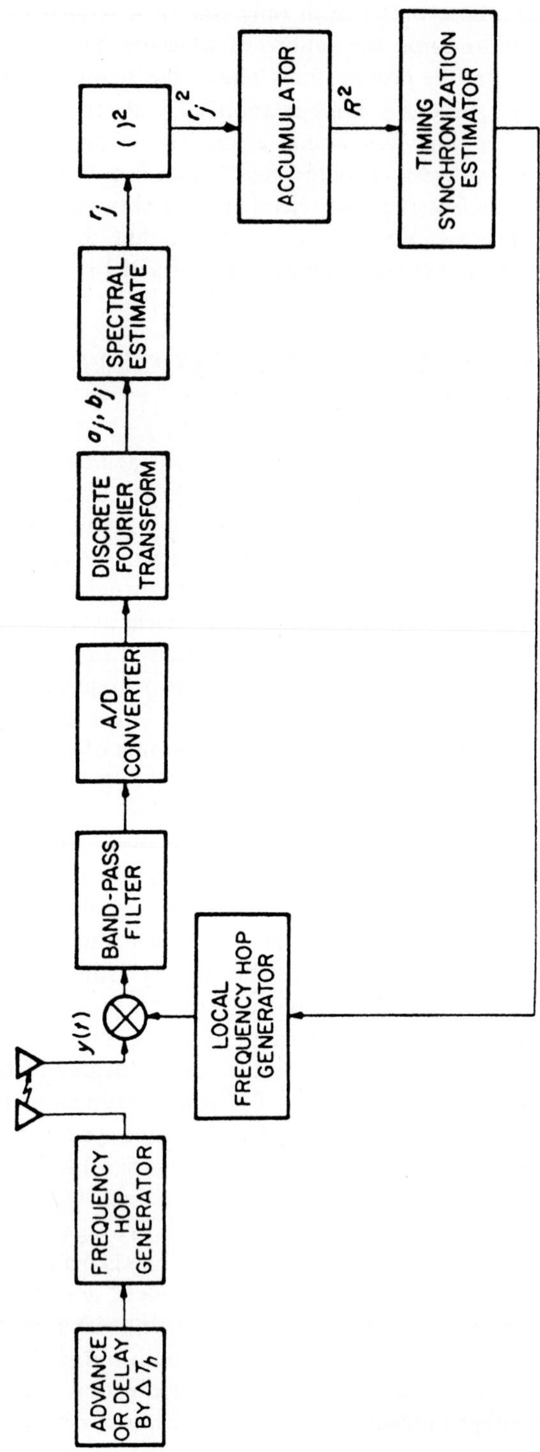

Figure 3.14. Simplified time synchronization of an FH system with on-board processing.

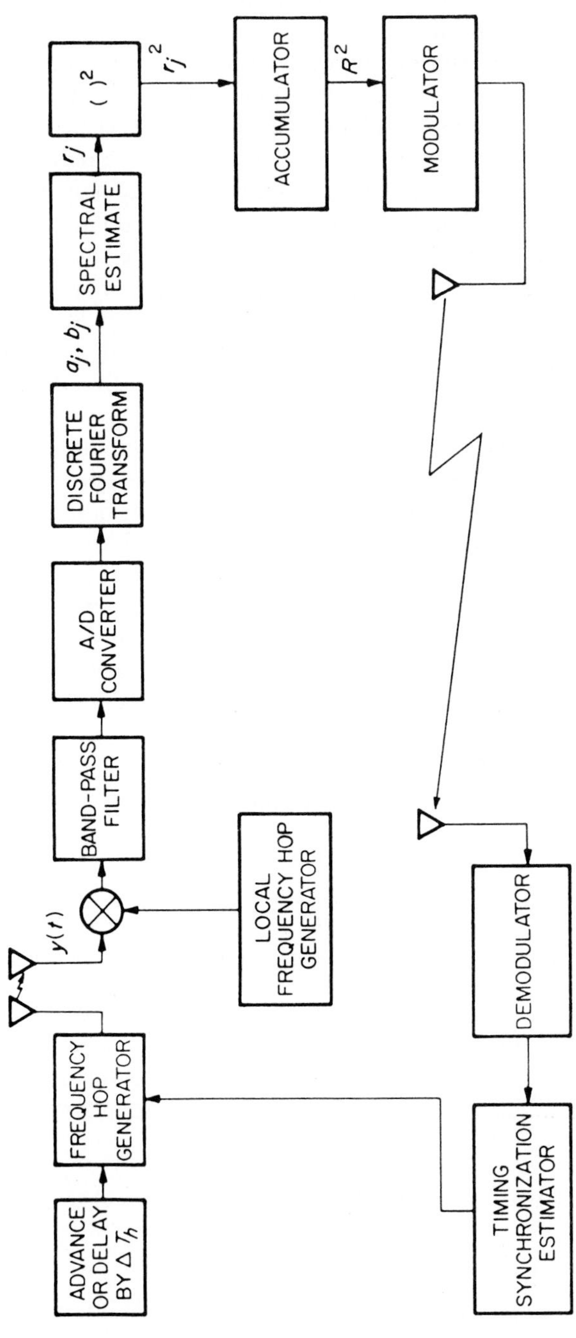

Figure 3.15. Simplified time synchronization of an FH system with a passive processor.

performance with the choice governed by the particular system application. Typically, the former implementation is preferable from the standpoint of reducing receiver complexity.

Assuming that the spacing between successive frequency hops is far outside the bandwidth of the band-pass filter, then in the absence of perfect time synchronization, only a fraction of the total signal energy available in a single hop interval will pass through this filter since the remaining fraction of the hop interval will contain noise only. The output of the band-pass filter is passed through an A/D converter and the resultant signal samples are discrete Fourier transformed to produce spectral estimates corresponding to the advanced and delayed transmitted frequency hop. The squares of these estimates are then accumulated over many hop intervals and the square roots of these accumulated values are then used in much the same fashion as described for the conventional MFSK receiver to form a time synchronization estimate [11], [12]. Finally, this estimate, which is formed in the receiver, is directly used to update the current timing position of the local hop generator. Alternately, in the case of a passive processor such as a satellite, the accumulated estimates could be transmitted back to the originating terminal, where the timing estimate would be formed and used to correct the transmitted hop timing (see Figure 3.15). Once again the specific details and mathematical analysis of the above time synchronization estimation technique are essentially immune to the activity or passivity of the processor. Hence, in the sections that follow we shall pursue the simplified system of Figure 3.14 with the understanding that the results apply to either implementation.

3.2.1 The Case of Full-Band Noise Jamming

3.2.1.1 Signal Model and Spectral Computations

The transmitted signal $s^{(j)}(t)$ in the j-th hop interval is of the form

$$s^{(j)}(t) = \sqrt{2S}\sin 2\pi(f_s + f_j)t;\ (j-1)T_h \le t \le jT_h \tag{3.35}$$

where S is the average power, f_s is the frequency corresponding to the transmitted data symbol, and f_j is the j-th hop frequency. Assuming first that the additive Gaussian distributed jamming noise $J(t)$ is spread across the entire hop frequency band, then in the same hop interval, the received signal is given by

$$y(t) = \sqrt{2S}\sin\left[2\pi(f_s + f_j)t - \phi_j\right] + J(t);\ (j-1)T_h \le t \le jT_h \tag{3.36}$$

where ϕ_j is the unknown received signal phase in this interval, assumed to be uniformly distributed on $(0, 2\pi)$, and $J(t)$ is assumed to have a flat spectral density N_J and band-pass expansion about the sum of f_s and the

j-th hop frequency given by

$$J(t) \triangleq \sqrt{2}\,J_{c1}(t)\cos 2\pi(f_s + f_j)t \\ -\sqrt{2}\,J_{s1}(t)\sin 2\pi(f_s + f_j)t. \tag{3.37}$$

Letting τ denote the time synchronization error between the received signal and the local frequency hop generator, then in its normal (not delayed or advanced) synchronization position, the output of this generator can be expressed as

$$r(t) = 2\sin\left[2\pi(f_s + f_j + f_{IF})t\right]; \\ (j-1)T_h - \tau \le t \le jT_h - \tau \tag{3.38}$$

where f_{IF} is the IF center frequency of the band-pass filter. Cross-correlating $y(t)$ with $r(t)$ and assuming, as previously mentioned, that the hop frequency difference is outside the bandwidth of the IF filter, then the output $x(t)$ of this filter is given by

$$x(t) \triangleq y(t)r(t) \\ = \begin{cases} J'(t); & \text{or} \begin{array}{l} (j-1)T_h - \tau \le t \le (j-1)T_h \quad (\tau \ge 0) \\ jT_h \le t \le jT_h - \tau \quad (\tau < 0) \end{array} \\ \sqrt{2S}\cos(2\pi f_{IF}t - \phi_j) + J'(t); & \text{or} \begin{array}{l} (j-1)T_h \le t \le jT_h - \tau \quad (\tau \ge 0) \\ (j-1)T_h - \tau \le t \le jT_h (\tau < 0) \end{array} \end{cases} \tag{3.39}$$

where

$$J'(t) \triangleq \sqrt{2}\,J_{c2}(t)\cos[2\pi f_{IF}t] \\ -\sqrt{2}\,J_{s2}(t)\sin[2\pi f_{IF}t]. \tag{3.40}$$

If the band-pass filter output is now sampled at the Nyquist rate, then there will be $N_s = 2B_{IF}T_h$ samples in each hop interval where B_{IF} denotes the IF noise bandwidth of the band-pass filter. Letting $x_{ij} = x(iT_h/N_s + (j-1)T_h)$ denote the i-th sample $(i = 0, 1, \ldots, N_s - 1)$, in the j-th hop interval, then these samples are statistically independent Gaussian random variables with variance $\sigma_x^2 = N_J B_{IF} = N_J(N_s/2T_h)$.

Taking the sine and cosine discrete Fourier transforms of these samples and evaluating them at $f = f_{IF}$, one has, in the j-th hop interval,

$$a_j \triangleq \sum_{i=0}^{N_s-1} x_{ij}\cos\left(2\pi f_{IF}\frac{i}{N_s}T_h\right) \\ b_j \triangleq \sum_{i=0}^{N_s-1} x_{ij}\sin\left(2\pi f_{IF}\frac{i}{N_s}T_h\right) \tag{3.41}$$

from which the spectral estimate

$$r_j \triangleq \sqrt{a_j^2 + b_j^2} \tag{3.42}$$

is obtained. Letting $t = iT_h/N_s + (j-1)T_h$ in (3.39) and substituting in (3.41), we arrive at the following results (for large N_s) for the first two statistical moments of a_j and b_j, i.e.,

$$\bar{a}_j \triangleq E\{a_j\} = \begin{cases} \dfrac{\sqrt{2S}\,N_s(1-|\varepsilon|)}{2}\cos\varphi_j; & |\varepsilon| \le 1 \\ 0; & |\varepsilon| > 1 \end{cases}$$

$$\bar{b}_j \triangleq E\{b_j\} = \begin{cases} \dfrac{\sqrt{2S}\,N_s(1-|\varepsilon|)}{2}\sin\varphi_j; & |\varepsilon| \le 1 \\ 0; & |\varepsilon| > 1 \end{cases}$$

$$\sigma_a^2 \triangleq E\left\{\left(a_j - \bar{a}_j\right)^2\right\} \triangleq \sigma^2 = \frac{N_J}{4T_h}N_s^2$$

$$\sigma_b^2 \triangleq E\left\{\left(b_j - \bar{b}_j\right)^2\right\} \triangleq \sigma^2 = \frac{N_J}{4T_h}N_s^2 \tag{3.43}$$

where $\varepsilon \triangleq \tau/T_h$ is the time synchronization error normalized to the hop interval and $\varphi_j = \phi_j - 2\pi(j-1)f_{IF}T_h$. Also, a_j and b_j are Gaussian random variables with conditional pdf's (for $|\varepsilon| \le 1$)

$$p(a_j|\phi_j) = \frac{1}{\sqrt{2\pi\sigma^2}}\exp\left\{-\frac{1}{2\sigma^2}\left[a_j - \xi(1-|\varepsilon|)\cos\phi_j\right]^2\right\}$$

$$p(b_j|\phi_j) = \frac{1}{\sqrt{2\pi\sigma^2}}\exp\left\{-\frac{1}{2\sigma^2}\left[b_j - \xi(1-|\varepsilon|)\sin\phi_j\right]^2\right\} \tag{3.44}$$

where we have introduced the notation

$$\xi \triangleq \frac{\sqrt{2S}\,N_s}{2}. \tag{3.45}$$

Further, letting γ_h denote the ratio of signal energy per hop-to-jamming noise spectral density, i.e.,

$$\gamma_h \triangleq \frac{ST_h}{N_J} = \frac{\xi^2}{2\sigma^2} \tag{3.46}$$

then r_j is a Rician-distributed random variable with pdf (conditioned on ε with $|\varepsilon| \le 1$)

$$p(r_j|\varepsilon) = \begin{cases} \dfrac{r_j}{\sigma^2}\exp\left\{-\left[\dfrac{r_j^2}{2\sigma^2} + \gamma_h(1-|\varepsilon|)^2\right]\right\} I_0\left[\sqrt{2\gamma_h}\,\dfrac{r_j}{\sigma}(1-|\varepsilon|)\right]; 0 \le r_j \le \infty \\ 0; \text{ elsewhere.} \end{cases} \tag{3.47}$$

If the transmitter hop frequency generator is now advanced and delayed by $\Delta T_h (0 \le \Delta \le 1/2)$ from its nominal synchronization position and the corresponding spectral estimates denoted by r_{j+} and r_{j-}, then an appropriate estimator of time synchronization is

$$\hat{\varepsilon} = \frac{r_{j+} - r_{j-}}{K_\Delta (r_{j+} + r_{j-})}, \tag{3.48}$$

where K_Δ is a constant whose value is chosen relative to that of the normalized advance-delay fraction Δ. In the absence of jammer noise, we have that

$$\hat{\varepsilon} = \begin{cases} \dfrac{2\varepsilon}{K_\Delta(2 - 2\Delta)}; & |\varepsilon| \le \Delta \\[2ex] \dfrac{2\Delta}{K_\Delta(2 - 2|\varepsilon|)}; & \Delta \le |\varepsilon| \le 1/2. \end{cases} \tag{3.49}$$

Thus, the maximum region over which $\hat{\varepsilon}$ is a linear function of ε would occur for $\Delta = 1/2$ in which case K_Δ would be chosen equal to 2, so that over this interval $\hat{\varepsilon} = \varepsilon$. In what follows, we shall assume these values for Δ and K_Δ, or equivalently from (3.48),

$$\hat{\varepsilon} = \frac{r_{j+} - r_{j-}}{2(r_{j+} + r_{j-})}. \tag{3.50}$$

Furthermore, since the advance and delay of the transmitter hop generator does not affect the variance of the discrete Fourier transform components, then from (3.43) and (3.47), we have for $|\varepsilon| \le \Delta = 1/2$,

$$p(r_{j\pm}|\varepsilon) = \begin{cases} \dfrac{r_{j\pm}}{\sigma^2} \exp\left\{ - \left[\dfrac{r_{j\pm}^2}{2\sigma^2} + \gamma_h \left(\dfrac{1}{2} \pm \varepsilon \right)^2 \right] \right\} I_0 \left[\sqrt{2\gamma_h} \dfrac{r_{j\pm}}{\sigma} \left(\dfrac{1}{2} \pm \varepsilon \right) \right]; \\ 0; \text{ elsewhere} \quad 0 \le r_{j\pm} \le \infty. \end{cases} \tag{3.51}$$

If it wasn't for the presence of the additive jamming noise, (3.50) would be a perfect estimator of time synchronization. However, in the presence of noise, $\hat{\varepsilon}$ of (3.50), which is computed on the basis of spectral estimates from a *single* hop interval, would possess a large variance. Thus, to produce an estimator with small variance, we must first accumulate the spectral estimates over many hop intervals, say N_h, before forming our estimate of ε in the manner of (3.50). In particular, letting

$$R_{\pm} = \sqrt{\frac{1}{N_h} \sum_{j=1}^{N_h} r_{j\pm}^2}, \tag{3.52}$$

then we define our estimator of time synchronization by

$$\hat{\varepsilon} = \frac{R_+ - R_-}{2(R_+ + R_-)}. \tag{3.53}$$

In order to calculate the variance of the estimator $\hat{\varepsilon}$, we must first compute its pdf (conditioned on ε). From (3.51) and (3.52), one can show that

$$p(R_\pm|\varepsilon) = \begin{cases} \dfrac{N_h R_\pm}{\sigma^2}\left(\dfrac{R_\pm^2}{2\sigma^2\gamma_h\left(\frac{1}{2}\pm\varepsilon\right)^2}\right)^{(N_h-1)/2} \\ \times\exp\left\{-N_h\left[\dfrac{R_\pm^2}{2\sigma^2}+\gamma_h\left(\dfrac{1}{2}\pm\varepsilon\right)^2\right]\right\} \\ \times I_{N_h-1}\left[\sqrt{2\gamma_h}N_h\left(\dfrac{1}{2}\pm\varepsilon\right)\dfrac{R_\pm}{\sigma}\right];\ R_\pm \geq 0,\ |\varepsilon| \leq \dfrac{1}{2} \\ 0;\ \text{elsewhere.} \end{cases} \tag{3.54}$$

Then, by a straightforward transformation of variables and the fact that R_+ and R_- are statistically independent (conditioned on ε), we obtain the desired result, namely,

$$p(\hat{\varepsilon}|\varepsilon) = \begin{cases} N_h^2\left(\dfrac{1}{4}-\hat{\varepsilon}^2\right)\exp\left[-N_h\gamma_h\left(\dfrac{1}{2}+2\varepsilon^2\right)\right] \\ \times\displaystyle\int_0^\infty y^3\left[\dfrac{y^2\left(\frac{1}{4}-\hat{\varepsilon}^2\right)}{2\gamma_h\left(\frac{1}{4}-\varepsilon^2\right)}\right]^{N_h-1}\exp\left\{-\dfrac{N_h y^2}{2}\left(\dfrac{1}{2}+2\hat{\varepsilon}^2\right)\right\} \\ \times I_{N_h-1}\left[\sqrt{2\gamma_h}N_h\left(\dfrac{1}{2}+\varepsilon\right)\left(\dfrac{1}{2}+\hat{\varepsilon}\right)y\right] \\ \times I_{N_h-1}\left[\sqrt{2\gamma_h}N_h\left(\dfrac{1}{2}-\varepsilon\right)\left(\dfrac{1}{2}-\hat{\varepsilon}\right)y\right]dy;\ |\hat{\varepsilon}| \leq \dfrac{1}{2}, \\ 0;\ \text{elsewhere} \end{cases} \tag{3.55}$$

from which the conditional variance of the estimator $\hat{\varepsilon}$ is given by

$$\sigma_{\hat{\varepsilon}|\varepsilon}^2 = \int_{-1/2}^{1/2}(\hat{\varepsilon}-\mu_{\hat{\varepsilon}|\varepsilon})^2 p(\hat{\varepsilon}|\varepsilon)\,d\hat{\varepsilon}, \tag{3.56}$$

where

$$\mu_{\hat{\varepsilon}|\varepsilon} \triangleq E\{\hat{\varepsilon}|\varepsilon\} = \int_{-1/2}^{1/2}\hat{\varepsilon}p(\hat{\varepsilon}|\varepsilon)\,d\hat{\varepsilon}. \tag{3.57}$$

3.2.1.2 Results for Large N_h

The general result of (3.55) can also be simplified when N_h, the number of hop intervals over which the spectral estimates are accumulated, is large. More specifically, for large N_h, we can apply the central limit theorem to (3.52) from which $Z_\pm \triangleq R_\pm^2$ are Gaussian random variables with

$$\mu_\pm(\varepsilon) \triangleq E\{Z_\pm|\varepsilon\} = 2\sigma^2\left[1 + \gamma_h\left(\frac{1}{2} \pm \varepsilon\right)^2\right]$$

$$\sigma_\pm^2(\varepsilon) \triangleq E\left\{(Z_\pm - \mu_\pm)^2|\varepsilon\right\} = \frac{(2\sigma^2)^2}{N_h}\left[1 + 2\gamma_h\left(\frac{1}{2} \pm \varepsilon\right)^2\right]. \quad (3.58)$$

Thus, the conditional pdf's of R_+ and R_- are

$$p(R_\pm|\varepsilon) = \begin{cases} \dfrac{2R_\pm}{\sqrt{2\pi\sigma_\pm^2(\varepsilon)}}\exp\left\{-\dfrac{\left(R_\pm^2 - \mu_\pm(\varepsilon)\right)^2}{2\sigma_\pm^2(\varepsilon)}\right\}; R_\pm \geq 0 \\ 0;\ \text{elsewhere.} \end{cases} \quad (3.59)$$

Using methods similar to those employed in arriving at (3.55), we obtain,

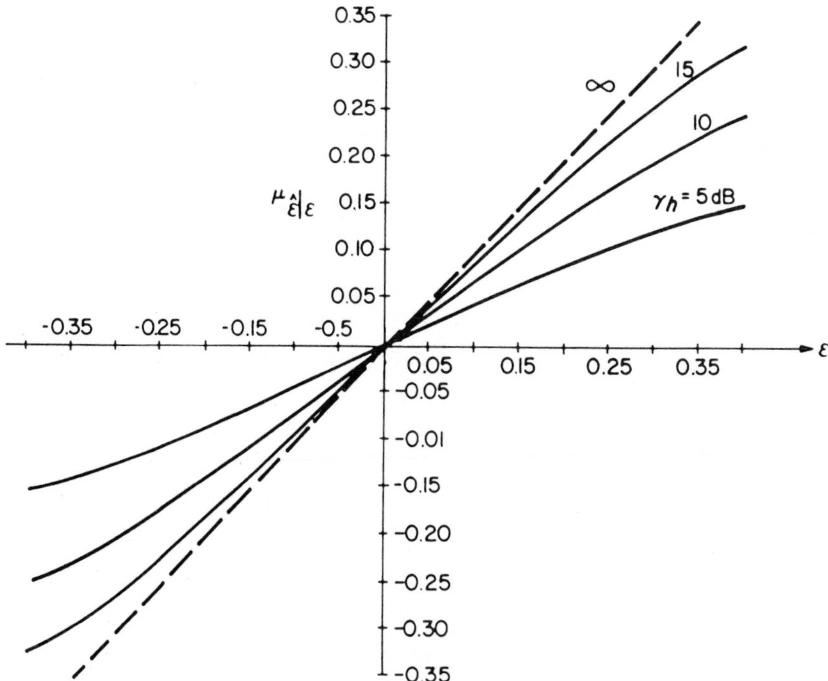

Figure 3.16. Conditional mean $\mu_{\hat{\varepsilon}|\varepsilon}$ versus ε with γ_h as a parameter; $N_h = 10$.

after much simplification,

$$p(\hat{\varepsilon}|\varepsilon)=\begin{cases}\dfrac{N_h\left(\dfrac{1}{4}-\hat{\varepsilon}^2\right)\sigma_T^2}{\pi\sqrt{\left[1+2\gamma_h\left(\dfrac{1}{2}+\varepsilon\right)^2\right]\left[1+2\gamma_h\left(\dfrac{1}{2}-\varepsilon\right)^2\right]}}\\ \times\left\{\exp\left(-\dfrac{\overline{x}_1^2}{2\sigma_1^2}-\dfrac{\overline{x}_2^2}{2\sigma_2^2}\right)+\sqrt{2\pi}\,\sigma_T\left(\dfrac{\overline{x}_1}{\sigma_1^2}+\dfrac{\overline{x}_2}{\sigma_2^2}\right)\exp\left(-\dfrac{(\overline{x}_1-\overline{x}_2)^2}{2(\sigma_1^2+\sigma_2^2)}\right)\right.\\ \left.\times\left[1-Q\left(\sigma_T\left(\dfrac{\overline{x}_1}{\sigma_1^2}+\dfrac{\overline{x}_2}{\sigma_2^2}\right)\right)\right]\right\};\ |\hat{\varepsilon}|\le\dfrac{1}{2}\\ 0;\ \text{elsewhere}\end{cases}\tag{3.60}$$

where

$$\overline{x}_1=\frac{\mu_+}{\left(\dfrac{1}{2}+\hat{\varepsilon}\right)^2 2\sigma^2}=\frac{1+\gamma_h\left(\dfrac{1}{2}+\varepsilon\right)^2}{\left(\dfrac{1}{2}+\hat{\varepsilon}\right)^2}\sigma_1^2=\frac{\sigma_+^2}{\left[2\sigma^2\left(\dfrac{1}{2}+\hat{\varepsilon}\right)^2\right]^2}$$

$$=\frac{1+2\gamma_h\left(\dfrac{1}{2}+\varepsilon\right)^2}{N_h\left(\dfrac{1}{2}+\hat{\varepsilon}\right)^4}$$

$$\overline{x}_2=\frac{\mu_-}{\left(\dfrac{1}{2}-\hat{\varepsilon}\right)^2 2\sigma^2}=\frac{1+\gamma_h\left(\dfrac{1}{2}-\varepsilon\right)^2}{\left(\dfrac{1}{2}-\hat{\varepsilon}\right)^2}\sigma_2^2=\frac{\sigma_-^2}{\left[2\sigma^2\left(\dfrac{1}{2}-\hat{\varepsilon}\right)^2\right]^2}$$

$$=\frac{1+2\gamma_h\left(\dfrac{1}{2}-\varepsilon\right)^2}{N_h\left(\dfrac{1}{2}-\hat{\varepsilon}\right)^4}\tag{3.61}$$

and

$$\sigma_T^2\triangleq\frac{\sigma_1^2\sigma_2^2}{\sigma_1^2+\sigma_2^2}.\tag{3.62}$$

The conditional mean and variance of $\hat{\varepsilon}$ are still determined from (3.57) and (3.56) with $p(\hat{\varepsilon}|\varepsilon)$ as given in (3.60). Figure 3.16 is a plot of this conditional

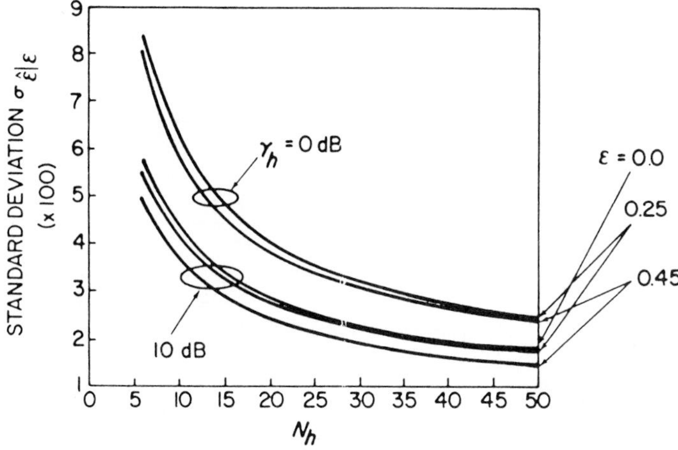

Figure 3.17. Conditional standard deviation $\sigma_{\hat{\varepsilon}|\varepsilon}$ versus N_h with γ_h and ε as parameters.

mean versus ε with $N_h = 10$ and γ_h as a parameter. Figure 3.17 is the corresponding plot of the conditional standard deviation of $\hat{\varepsilon}$ versus N_h with ε and γ_h as parameters.

3.2.2 The Case of Partial-Band Noise Jamming

When the additive jamming noise is not spread over the total hop frequency band, then the previous results can be modified to account for this fact as follows. Let N_h still be the total number of hop intervals per time synchronization estimate, of which ρN_h are now contaminated by jamming noise of power spectral density N_J/ρ and $(1-\rho)N_h$ are noise free.[4] As in our previous discussions of partial-band noise jamming, ρ denotes the fraction of the total hop frequency band that is jammed. Then analogous to (3.52), we have that

$$R_{\pm} = \sqrt{\frac{1}{N_h}\sum_{j=1}^{\rho N_h} r_{j\pm}^2 + (1-\rho)\xi^2\left(\tfrac{1}{2} \pm \varepsilon\right)^2} \qquad (3.63)$$

[4] For values of ρ such that ρN_h and $(1-\rho)N_h$ are not integer, we take the nearest integers, respectively, to these quantities.

with pdf's

$$p(R_{\pm}|\varepsilon) = \begin{cases} \dfrac{\rho N_h R_{\pm}}{\sigma^2}\left(\dfrac{R_{\pm}^2-(1-\rho)\xi^2\left(\frac{1}{2}\pm\varepsilon\right)^2}{2\sigma^2\rho\gamma_h\left(\frac{1}{2}\pm\varepsilon\right)^2}\right)^{(\rho N_h-1)/2} \\ \times\exp\left\{-\rho N_h\left[\dfrac{R_{\pm}^2-(1-\rho)\xi^2\left(\frac{1}{2}\pm\varepsilon\right)^2}{2\sigma^2}+\rho\gamma_h\left(\frac{1}{2}\pm\varepsilon\right)^2\right]\right\} \\ \times I_{\rho N_h-1}\left[\rho N_h\sqrt{2\rho\gamma_h}\left(\frac{1}{2}\pm\varepsilon\right)\sqrt{\dfrac{R_{\pm}^2-(1-\rho)\xi^2\left(\frac{1}{2}\pm\varepsilon\right)^2}{\sigma^2}}\right]; \\ R_{\pm}\geq 0 \\ 0;\ \text{elsewhere.} \end{cases} \tag{3.64}$$

Then, analogous to (3.55), we have that

$$p(\hat{\varepsilon}|\varepsilon) = \begin{cases} (\rho N_h)^2\left(\frac{1}{4}-\hat{\varepsilon}^2\right)\exp\left[-\rho^2 N_h\gamma_h\left(\frac{1}{2}+2\varepsilon^2\right)\right] \\ \times\displaystyle\int_0^\infty y^3\left[\dfrac{y_+y_-\left(\frac{1}{4}-\hat{\varepsilon}^2\right)}{2\rho\gamma_h\left(\frac{1}{4}-\varepsilon^2\right)}\right]^{\rho N_h-1} \\ \times\exp\left\{-\dfrac{\rho N_h}{2}\left[y_+^2\left(\frac{1}{2}+\hat{\varepsilon}\right)^2+y_-^2\left(\frac{1}{2}-\hat{\varepsilon}\right)^2\right]\right\} \\ \times I_{\rho N_h-1}\left[\rho N_h\sqrt{2\rho\gamma_h}\left(\frac{1}{2}+\varepsilon\right)\left(\frac{1}{2}+\hat{\varepsilon}\right)y_+\right] \\ \times I_{\rho N_h-1}\left[\rho N_h\sqrt{2\rho\gamma_h}\left(\frac{1}{2}-\varepsilon\right)\left(\frac{1}{2}-\hat{\varepsilon}\right)y_-\right]dy; \\ |\hat{\varepsilon}|\leq\frac{1}{2} \\ 0;\ \text{elsewhere} \end{cases} \tag{3.65}$$

where

$$y_{\pm}^2 \triangleq y^2-2(1-\rho)\gamma_h\frac{\left(\frac{1}{2}\pm\varepsilon\right)^2}{\left(\frac{1}{2}\pm\hat{\varepsilon}\right)^2}. \tag{3.66}$$

Note that when $\rho = 1$, i.e., jamming over the total hop frequency band, then $y_+ = y_- = y$, and (3.65) reduces to (3.55) as it should.

3.2.2.1 *Results for Large* ρN_h

As was true for (3.55), the general result of (3.65) can be simplified now when ρN_h is large. Once again, $Z_{\pm} \triangleq R_{\pm}^2$, with $R_{\pm}$ now defined in (3.63), becomes a Gaussian random variable with

$$\mu_{\pm}(\varepsilon) \triangleq E\{Z_{\pm}|\varepsilon\} = 2\frac{\sigma^2}{\rho}\left\{(1-\rho)\rho\gamma_h\left(\tfrac{1}{2}\pm\varepsilon\right)^2 + \rho\left[1+\rho\gamma_h\left(\tfrac{1}{2}\pm\varepsilon\right)^2\right]\right\}$$

$$= 2\sigma^2\left[1+\gamma_h\left(\tfrac{1}{2}\pm\varepsilon\right)^2\right]$$

$$\sigma_{\pm}^2(\varepsilon) \triangleq E\left\{(Z_{\pm}-\mu_{\pm})^2|\varepsilon\right\} = \frac{\rho^2\left(2\frac{\sigma^2}{\rho}\right)^2}{\rho N_h}\left[1+2\rho\gamma_h\left(\tfrac{1}{2}\pm\varepsilon\right)^2\right]$$

$$= \frac{(2\sigma^2)^2}{\rho N_h}\left[1+2\rho\gamma_h\left(\tfrac{1}{2}\pm\varepsilon\right)^2\right]. \tag{3.67}$$

Note that $\mu_{\pm}(\varepsilon)$ are independent of ρ but $\sigma_{\pm}^2(\varepsilon)$ are not. Thus, the conditional pdf's of R_+ and R_- are still given by (3.59) with $\mu_+(\varepsilon)$, $\sigma_+^2(\varepsilon)$, $\mu_-(\varepsilon)$, and $\sigma_-^2(\varepsilon)$, now defined by (3.67), and similarly $p(\hat{\varepsilon}|\varepsilon)$ is given by (3.60) with γ_h and N_h replaced by $\rho\gamma_h$ and ρN_h, respectively, $\bar{x}_1$ and $\bar{x}_2$ given by (3.61), and

$$\sigma_1^2 = \frac{\left[1+2\rho\gamma_h\left(\tfrac{1}{2}+\varepsilon\right)^2\right]}{\rho N_h\left(\tfrac{1}{2}+\hat{\varepsilon}\right)^4}; \quad \sigma_2^2 = \frac{\left[1+2\rho\gamma_h\left(\tfrac{1}{2}-\varepsilon\right)^2\right]}{\rho N_h\left(\tfrac{1}{2}-\hat{\varepsilon}\right)^4} \tag{3.68}$$

with σ_T^2 still defined in (3.62) using now σ_1^2 and σ_2^2 of (3.68).

3.2.3 The Effects of Time Synchronization Error on FH/MFSK Error Probability Performance

The presence of a time synchronization error in an FH/MFSK receiver causes a degradation in system error probability performance that is attributable to the following two factors. First, the signal component of the receiver correlator corresponding to the true transmitted frequency is attenuated. Second, a spillover of transmitted signal energy occurs in each of the adjacent $M-1$ correlator outputs where, ordinarily (perfect time sync), only noise appears. This second contribution to the performance degradation, namely, the presence of signal components in the incorrect frequency correlator outputs, is referred to as a loss of orthogonality [13]. Clearly, then, the first step in assessing the impact of a time synchronization error ε on the performance of the FH/MFSK receiver is to evaluate the *signal attenuation* and *loss of orthogonality* degradations in terms of the synchronization error and then use these results to arrive at an expression for the ε-conditional error probability of the system.

To illustrate the procedure we shall first discuss the case of FH/MFSK with no diversity, i.e., one data symbol per hop. Following this we shall extend these results to the case of FH/MFSK with m chips per symbol diversity and non-coherent combining at the receiver. The performances of these SS techniques have previously been discussed in Chapter 2, Volume II, for a perfectly synchronized system and thus our purpose here is to show how they are modified to account for a time synchronization error.

3.2.3.1 Conditional Error Probability Performance—No Diversity

Based on the spectral computations performed in Section 3.2.1.1, it is clear that the spectral estimate r_j corresponding to the actual transmitted frequency in the j-th hop interval is characterized by (3.42) and has the ε-conditional pdf $p(r_j|\varepsilon)$ given by (3.47). Thus, from (3.47), the signal energy attenuation caused by the lack of perfect time synchronization is represented by the factor

$$D_j(\varepsilon) = (1 - |\varepsilon|)^2. \tag{3.69}$$

Assuming now that the MFSK tones are orthogonally spaced by k/T_h ($1/T_h$ is the minimum tone separation for orthogonality), then the spectral estimate r_{jn} for an incorrect correlator spaced in frequency by nk/T_h from the correct one is obtained by evaluating the discrete Fourier transform operations of (3.41) at the frequency $f = f_{IF} + nk/T_h$ rather than $f = f_{IF}$. If a_{jn} and b_{jn}, respectively, denote the results of these operations, then it can be shown that the loss of orthogonality degradation $D_{jn}(\varepsilon)$ is given by

$$D_{jn}(\varepsilon) \triangleq \frac{\bar{a}_{jn}^2 + \bar{b}_{jn}^2}{\xi^2} = \frac{\sin^2[\pi nk(1 - |\varepsilon|)]}{N_s^2 \sin^2 \dfrac{\pi nk}{N_s}} \tag{3.70}$$

where ξ is defined in (3.45). For large N_s, (3.70) simplifies to

$$D_{jn}(\varepsilon) = (1 - |\varepsilon|)^2 \left[\frac{\sin \pi nk(1 - |\varepsilon|)}{\pi nk(1 - |\varepsilon|)}\right]^2. \tag{3.71}$$

Note that for $\varepsilon = 0$ and $n \neq 0$, $D_{jn} = 0$, i.e., in the perfectly synchronized system, the incorrect correlator outputs consist of noise alone.

Now, since

$$r_{jn} = \sqrt{a_{jn}^2 + b_{jn}^2} \tag{3.72}$$

then, analogous to (3.47), the ε-conditional pdf of r_{jn} is given by

$$p(r_{jn}|\varepsilon) = \begin{cases} \dfrac{r_{jn}}{\sigma^2} \exp\left\{-\left[\dfrac{r_{jn}^2}{2\sigma^2} + \gamma_h D_{jn}(\varepsilon)\right]\right\} I_0\left[\sqrt{2\gamma_h D_{jn}(\varepsilon)}\, \dfrac{r_{jn}}{\sigma}\right]; & 0 \le r_{jn} \le \infty \\ 0; \text{ otherwise.} \end{cases} \tag{3.73}$$

To compute the ε-conditional error probability, it is convenient to order the spectral estimates as $r^{(1)}, r^{(2)}, \ldots, r^{(M)}$ where $r^{(1)}$ corresponds to the lowest frequency MFSK tone and $r^{(M)}$ corresponds to the highest frequency

MFSK tone. Then, if, in the j-th hop interval, the l-th tone in the set is transmitted, the conditional probability of symbol error for that transmission, denoted by $P_s(l|\varepsilon)$ is described by the probability

$$P_s(l|\varepsilon) = 1 - \mathrm{Prob}\{r^{(l)} = \max r^{(i)};\ i = 1, 2, \ldots, M\}$$

$$= 1 - \int_0^\infty p(r^{(l)}|\varepsilon) \int_0^{r^{(l)}} \cdots \int_0^{r(l)} \prod_{\substack{i=1 \\ i \neq l}}^{M} p(r^{(i)}|\varepsilon)\, dr^{(i)}. \tag{3.74}$$

Since $p(r^{(l)}|\varepsilon)$ is given by (3.47) and $p(r^{(l+n)}|\varepsilon)$ equals $p(r_{jn}|\varepsilon)$ of (3.73), then after some simplification (3.74) becomes

$$P_s(l|\varepsilon) = 1 - \int_0^\infty y \exp\left\{-\left[\frac{y^2}{2} + \gamma_h D_j(\varepsilon)\right]\right\} I_0\left[\sqrt{2\gamma_h D_j(\varepsilon)}\, y\right]$$

$$\times \prod_{\substack{n=1-l \\ n \neq 0}}^{M-l} \left[1 - Q\left(\sqrt{2\gamma_h D_{jn}(\varepsilon)}, y\right)\right] dy \tag{3.75}$$

where $Q(\alpha, \beta)$ is Marcum's Q-function [14] and as such

$$1 - Q(\alpha, \beta) = \int_0^\beta x \exp\left(-\frac{x^2 + \alpha^2}{2}\right) I_0(\alpha x)\, dx. \tag{3.76}$$

Finally, the average ε-conditional symbol error probability is given by

$$P_s(\varepsilon) = \frac{1}{M} \sum_{l=1}^{M} P_s(l|\varepsilon) \tag{3.77}$$

and the corresponding ε-conditional bit error probability $P_b(\varepsilon)$ is related to (3.77) by

$$P_b(\varepsilon) = \frac{M}{2(M-1)} P_s(\varepsilon). \tag{3.78}$$

Also, since for no diversity the hop signal-to-noise ratio γ_h is equal to the MFSK symbol energy-to-jammer-noise spectral density ratio E_s/N_J, then the bit energy-to-jammer noise spectral density ratio E_b/N_J is simply given by

$$\frac{E_b}{N_J} = \frac{\gamma_h}{\log_2 M}. \tag{3.79}$$

Using (3.77)–(3.79) together with (3.71) and (3.75), Figure 3.18 is an illustration of $P_b(\varepsilon)$ versus E_b/N_J in dB with ε as a parameter for 4-ary FSK and the minimum orthogonal tone spacing, i.e., $M = 4$ and $k = 1$. The performance degradation, namely, the additional E_b/N_J required at a given value of ε relative to that required at $\varepsilon = 0$, is plotted in Figure 3.19 versus timing error for $P_b(\varepsilon) = 10^{-2}$. Also shown is the composition of the performance degradation in terms of its signal attenuation and loss of orthogonality components. We note that for small timing errors signal

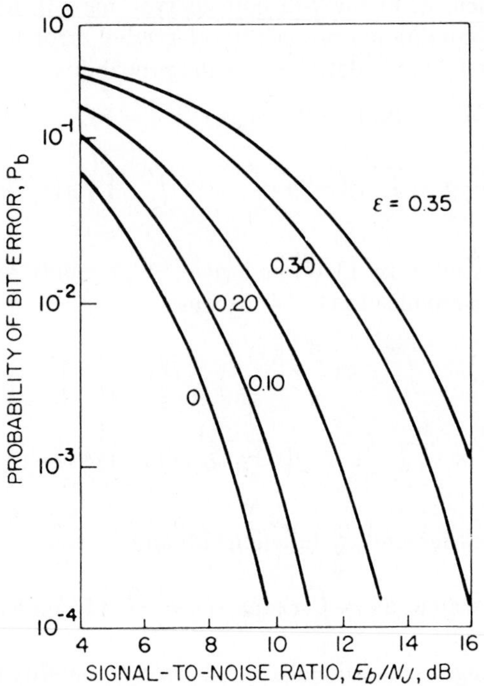

Figure 3.18. 4-ary FSK with timing error (minimum orthogonal tone spacing) (reprinted from [13]).

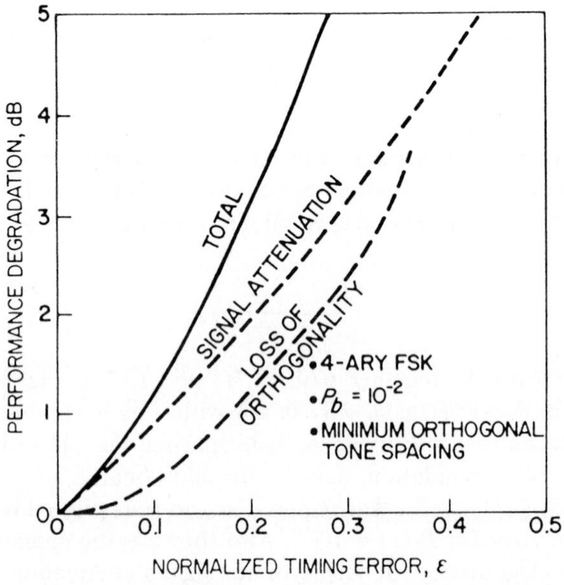

Figure 3.19. Performance degradation due to timing error (reprinted from [13]).

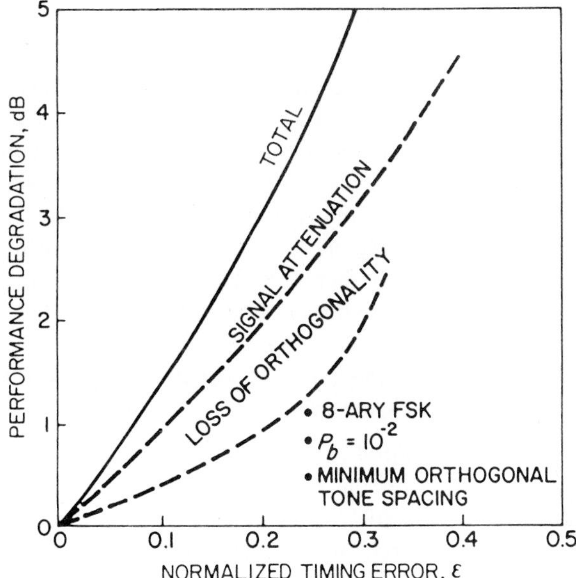

Figure 3.20. 8-ary FSK performance degradation due to timing error (reprinted from [13]).

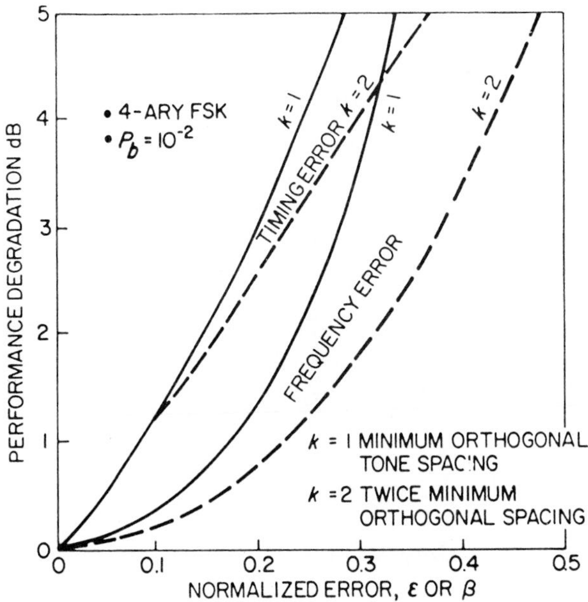

Figure 3.21. Performance degradation due to synchronization errors for different tone spacings (reprinted from [13]).

attenuation is the dominant cause of degradation, whereas for large timing errors the loss of the orthogonality component plays an equally, if not more, important role. Figure 3.20 illustrates similar performance degradation results for 8-ary FSK. These results, when compared with the corresponding 4-ary FSK performance results of Figure 3.19, indicate that increasing the number of tones M decreases the performance degradation due to the timing synchronization error. Finally, Figure 3.21 demonstrates the effect of increasing the MFSK tone spacing to twice its minimum orthogonal value. The additional results shown there for frequency error will be explained later on in the chapter when we discuss that subject.

3.2.3.2 Conditional Error Probability Performance—m-Diversity with Non-Coherent Combining

When the same MFSK symbol is transmitted on m different hops, and the symbol decision is based on the non-coherent combining of the m corresponding detector outputs for that tone, then, assuming all m chips are jammed, the conditional pdf for the spectral estimates formed in the receiver is given by

$$p(r|\varepsilon) = \begin{cases} \dfrac{r}{\sigma^2}\left(\dfrac{r^2}{2\sigma^2 m\gamma_h'}\right)^{(m-1)/2} \exp\left[-\left(\dfrac{r^2}{2\sigma^2} + m\gamma_h'\right)\right] I_{m-1}\left(\sqrt{2m\gamma_h'}\,\dfrac{r}{\sigma}\right); & r \geq 0 \\ 0; \text{ otherwise} \end{cases} \tag{3.80}$$

where for the correct tone, r corresponds to r_j, and

$$\gamma_h' = \gamma_h D_j(\varepsilon) \tag{3.81}$$

with $D_j(\varepsilon)$ defined in (3.69). For the $M-1$ incorrect tones, r corresponds to r_{jn}, and

$$\gamma_h' = \gamma_h D_{jn}(\varepsilon) \tag{3.82}$$

with $D_{jn}(\varepsilon)$ defined in (3.70) or (3.71). Thus, following the steps leading to the evaluation of (3.75), we can immediately write down the corresponding result for FH/MFSK with m-diversity and non-coherent combining, namely,

$$\begin{aligned} P_s(l|\varepsilon) = 1 - \int_0^\infty y\left(\frac{y^2}{2m\gamma_h D_j(\varepsilon)}\right)^{(m-1)/2} \exp\left\{-\left[\frac{y^2}{2} + m\gamma_h D_j(\varepsilon)\right]\right\} \\ \times I_{m-1}\left[\sqrt{2m\gamma_h D_j(\varepsilon)}\, y\right] \\ \times \prod_{\substack{n=1-l \\ n\neq 0}}^{M-l}\left[1 - Q_m\left(\sqrt{2m\gamma_h D_{jn}(\varepsilon)}\,, y\right)\right] dy \end{aligned} \tag{3.83}$$

where $Q_M(\alpha, \beta)$ is the generalized Q-function and as such

$$1 - Q_M(\alpha, \beta) = \int_0^\beta x\left(\frac{x}{\alpha}\right)^{M-1} \exp\left(-\frac{x^2+\alpha^2}{2}\right) I_{M-1}(\alpha x)\, dx. \quad (3.84)$$

The E_b/N_J performance degradation at $P_b = 10^{-2}$ as a function of timing error is illustrated in Figure 3.22 for 4-ary FSK with minimum orthogonal tone spacing and three values of m. Increasing m clearly reduces the degradation since non-coherent combining reduces the effect of loss of orthogonality. Non-coherent combining, however, does not affect the signal attenuation loss component and thus this loss, as shown in the figure, represents a lower bound on the total degradation as m increases.

Thus far in this section we have implicitly assumed a full-band jammer. For the worst case partial-band noise jammer of a perfectly synchronized FH/MFSK system as discussed in Chapter 2, Part 2, $P_s(l|\varepsilon)$ of (3.75) would become

$$\begin{aligned} P_s(l|\varepsilon) &= \frac{K_\rho}{E_b/N_J}\left\{1 - \int_0^\infty y \exp\left\{-\left[\frac{y^2}{2} + K_\rho(\log_2 M) D_j(\varepsilon)\right]\right\}\right. \\ &\quad \times I_0\left[\sqrt{2K_\rho(\log_2 M) D_j(\varepsilon)}\, y\right] \\ &\quad \left. \times \prod_{\substack{n=1-l \\ n\neq 0}}^{M-l} \left[1 - Q\left(\sqrt{2K_\rho(\log_2 M) D_{jn}(\varepsilon)}, y\right)\right] dy\right\} \\ &= \frac{K_\rho f(\varepsilon; K_\rho)}{E_b/N_j} \end{aligned} \quad (3.85)$$

where, for a given M, K_ρ is determined by the worst case partial-band fraction

$$\rho_{wc} = \begin{cases} \dfrac{K_\rho}{E_b/N_J}; & E_b/N_J > K_\rho \\ 1; & E_b/N_J \le K_\rho \end{cases} \quad (3.86)$$

and is tabulated as γ (in dB) in Table 2.1 of Chapter 2, Part 2, for various values of $K = \log_2 M$. Note that $f(\varepsilon; K_\rho)$ is not a function of E_b/N_J and thus for a given ε, the degradation in error probability performance is constant. Also, using (3.78),

$$P_b(l|\varepsilon) = \frac{MK_\rho f(\varepsilon; K_\rho)}{2(M-1)E_b/N_J} \quad (3.87)$$

and for $\varepsilon = 0$,

$$\begin{aligned} P_b(l|0) &= \frac{MK_\rho f(0; K_\rho)}{2(M-1)E_b/N_J} \\ &= \frac{A}{E_b/N_J} \end{aligned} \quad (3.88)$$

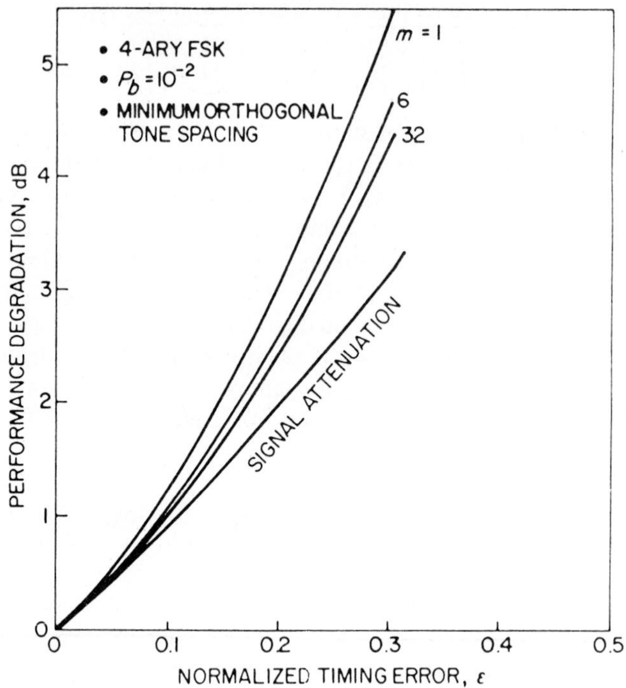

Figure 3.22. Performing degradation due to timing error with chip combining (reprinted from [13]).

where A is tabulated as β in Table 2.1 of Chapter 2, Part 2, for various values of $K = \log_2 M$.

For the worst case partial-band noise jammer of an m-diversity FH/MFSK system with non-coherent combining at the receiver, the conditional symbol error probability $P_s(l|\varepsilon)$ of (3.83) is modified to become

$$P_s(l|\varepsilon) = \rho_{\text{wc}}\left\{1 - \int_0^\infty y\left(\frac{y^2}{2m^*\rho_{\text{wc}}\gamma_h D_j(\varepsilon)}\right)^{(m^*-1)/2}\right.$$

$$\times \exp\left\{-\left[\frac{y^2}{2} + m^*\rho_{\text{wc}}\gamma_h D_j(\varepsilon)\right]\right\}$$

$$\times I_{m^*-1}\left[\sqrt{2m^*\rho_{\text{wc}}\gamma_h D_j(\varepsilon)}\, y\right]$$

$$\left.\times \prod_{\substack{n=1-l \\ n\neq 0}}^{M-l}\left[1 - Q_m\left(\sqrt{2m^*\rho_{\text{wc}}\gamma_h D_{jn}(\varepsilon)},\, y\right)\right] dy\right\} \tag{3.89}$$

where

$$\rho_{wc} = \tfrac{3}{4}; \; m^* = \left(\frac{\log_2 M}{4}\right)\frac{E_b}{N_J} \tag{3.90a}$$

are the worst case partial-band fraction and optimum diversity for the perfectly synchronized system (see Chapter 2, Part 2), and analogous to (3.78), γ_h is related to E_b/N_J by

$$\frac{E_b}{N_J} = \frac{m^* \gamma_h}{\log_2 M}. \tag{3.90b}$$

Actually, the quantities in (3.90a) are derived from a minimax solution of a Chernoff bound on the error probability. Nevertheless, it is convenient to use them in the exact expression for error probability of (3.89).

3.2.3.3 *Average Error Probability Performance in the Presence of Time Synchronization Error Estimation*

If the estimator $\hat{\varepsilon}$ of (3.53) is used for FH time synchronization of the non-coherent receiver, then a residual time offset $\eta(\varepsilon) \triangleq \varepsilon - \hat{\varepsilon}$ arises which affects system performance in the same manner as just discussed for an uncompensated time error ε. In particular, it is clear that in the presence of the residual offset, a signal attenuation degradation occurs that is given by

$$D_j(\eta) = (1 - |\varepsilon - \hat{\varepsilon}|)^2 = (1 - |\eta(\varepsilon)|)^2; \; \eta(\varepsilon) \triangleq \varepsilon - \hat{\varepsilon}. \tag{3.91}$$

Likewise, a loss of orthogonality degradation analogous to (3.71) occurs that is given by

$$D_{jn}(\eta) = (1 - |\eta(\varepsilon)|)^2 \left[\frac{\sin \pi n k (1 - |\eta(\varepsilon)|)}{\pi n k (1 - |\eta(\varepsilon)|)}\right]^2. \tag{3.92}$$

Thus, if $p_{\eta|\varepsilon}(\eta|\varepsilon)$ denotes the ε-conditional probability density function of the residual offset $\eta(\varepsilon)$, and is given by

$$p_{\eta|\varepsilon}(\eta|\varepsilon) = p_{\hat{\varepsilon}|\varepsilon}(\varepsilon - \eta|\varepsilon) \tag{3.93}$$

where the right-hand side of (3.93) is given by either (3.55), (3.60), or (3.65), it then follows that the average bit error probability P_b is

$$P_b = 2\int_0^{1/2} d\varepsilon \int_{\varepsilon - 1/2}^{\varepsilon + 1/2} P_b(\eta)\, p_{\hat{\varepsilon}|\varepsilon}(\varepsilon - \eta|\varepsilon)\, d\eta. \tag{3.94}$$

In (3.94), $P_b(\eta)$ is the η-conditional bit error probability obtained from (3.78) together with (3.77) and (3.75) or (3.83) with ε replaced by η.

Substitution of (3.78) and (3.93) in (3.94) requires evaluation of a double integral to obtain numerical results for P_b. To somewhat simplify matters, we observe from Figure 3.17 that, for the range of values of interest, $\sigma_{\hat{\varepsilon}|\varepsilon}$ is comparatively small so that $\hat{\varepsilon}$ is very close to its conditional mean $\mu_{\hat{\varepsilon}|\varepsilon}$ with high probability. Equivalently, $p_{\eta|\varepsilon}(\eta|\varepsilon)$ may be approximated by a delta function located at $\varepsilon - \mu_{\hat{\varepsilon}|\varepsilon}$ or from (3.93)

$$p_{\hat{\varepsilon}|\varepsilon}(\varepsilon - \eta|\varepsilon) = \delta\left(\eta - \left(\varepsilon - \mu_{\hat{\varepsilon}|\varepsilon}\right)\right). \tag{3.95}$$

Substituting (3.95) into (3.94) gives the much simplified result

$$P_b = 2\int_0^{1/2} P_b\left(\varepsilon - \mu_{\hat{\varepsilon}|\varepsilon}\right) d\varepsilon. \tag{3.96}$$

To evaluate (3.96) (assuming large N_h), we first compute $\mu_{\hat{\varepsilon}|\varepsilon}$ from (3.57) using $p(\hat{\varepsilon}|\varepsilon)$ from (3.60) with γ_h replaced by $(\log_2 M)E_b/N_J$ as in (3.79).

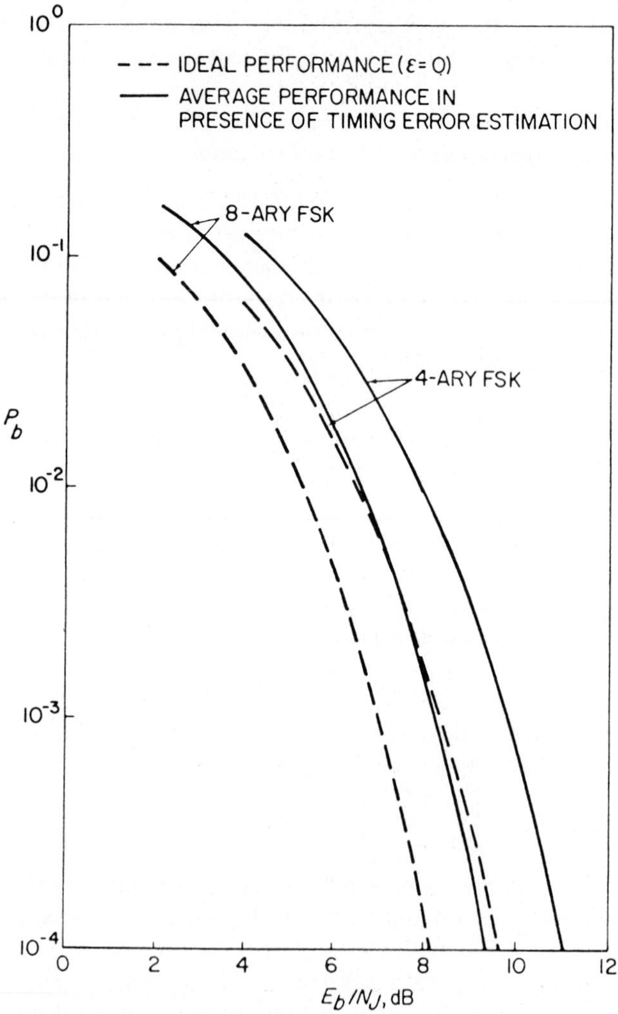

Figure 3.23. Average bit error probability performance in the presence of timing error estimation; $N_h = 10$.

Figure 3.23 is an illustration of the average bit error probability performance of (3.62) for 4-ary and 8-ary FSK with $N_h = 10$. In computing these results, (3.78) together with (3.75) and (3.77) were used for the conditional bit error probability.

3.3 FREQUENCY SYNCHRONIZATION OF NON-COHERENT FH / MFSK SYSTEMS

Frequency synchronization of a conventional (non-spread) non-coherent MFSK receiver has been typically achieved by transmitting a single known MFSK frequency, which is repeated as often as necessary within the true data stream, until the desired degree of frequency synchronization accuracy is obtained. Spectral estimates in the form of discrete Fourier transforms of the receiver signal are formed with those adjacent to the transmitted MFSK frequency used to form the frequency error estimator. For example, Chadwick and Springett [12] used the ratio of the difference of these two adjacent spectral estimates to twice the spectral estimate of the transmitted frequency as an approximation to the maximum likelihood estimator of frequency error. The advantage of this estimator, or, for that matter, any estimator formed from spectral estimates of the standard MFSK tones, is that frequency error estimation could be used during the true data transmission for frequency tracking. Unfortunately, however, using the standard MFSK frequencies forms a very poor estimator since it can be shown (see Appendix 3A) that, for any function of the standard MFSK frequencies, the slope of the conditional mean of the estimator is zero for zero frequency error.

A more suitable approach, which, we shall see shortly, also applies in the SS application, is to transmit a single known frequency chosen halfway between two standard MFSK frequencies. By using the spectral estimates evaluated at these two standard MFSK frequencies, a frequency error estimator can now be formed which, in the absence of noise, will be a linear function of frequency error.

To see how the above approach can be applied to an FH/MFSK communication system, consider the simplified frequency synchronization system illustrated in Figure 3.24. Letting $f_o \pm m/2T_h$; $m = 1, 2, \ldots, M/2$ denote the standard MFSK frequencies used for data transmission, then during fine frequency synchronization, we generate the single data symbol frequency equal to f_o, which is halfway between the two center (innermost) standard frequencies. This data frequency is frequency-hopped over the SS bandwidth. As in the case of the time synchronization system, the received signal plus jamming noise is first cross-correlated with the local hop generator, which has a *frequency* error relative to the transmitted signal equal to λ Hz. Also, we assume here that only coarse time synchronization has been obtained, and thus the local hop generator is also in *time* error

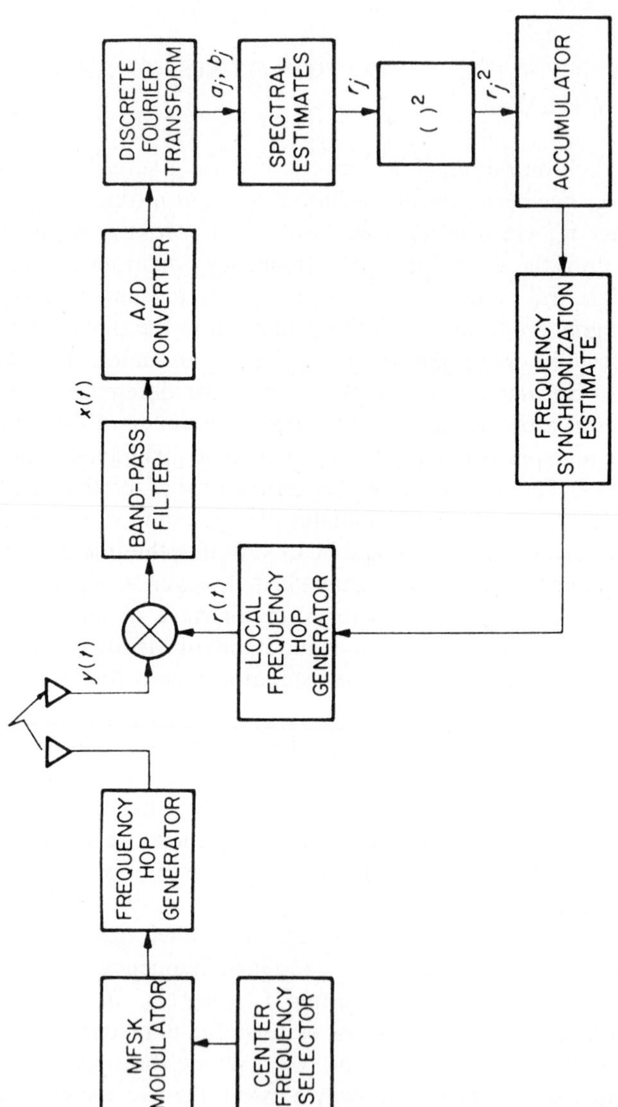

Figure 3.24. Simplified frequency synchronization of a frequency-hopped system with on-board processing.

relative to the transmitted signal by an amount equal to τ seconds, where, as before, τ is less than a hop duration. The cross-correlation is band-pass filtered and the output of this filter is passed through an A/D converter. The resultant signal samples are discrete Fourier transformed to produce spectral estimates corresponding to the MFSK frequencies for each frequency hop. The squares of these estimates are then accumulated over many hop intervals and the square roots of these accumulated values are then used to form the frequency synchronization estimate. Finally, this estimate, which is formed in the receiver, is directly used to update the current frequency position of the local hop generator. Alternately, as for the time synchronization only case, the system in Figure 3.24 can be modified in the same manner that the system in Figure 3.14 was changed to Figure 3.15 to allow for a system whose receiver is a passive processor.

3.3.1 The Case of Full-Band Noise Jamming

3.3.1.1 Signal Model and Spectral Computations

The transmitted signal in the j-th hop interval is still characterized by (3.35) with, however, f_s replaced by f_o. Using similar replacements in (3.36) and (3.37), the received signal $y(t)$ and jammer noise $J(t)$ are still, respectively, given by these equations. The output of the local FH generator in the presence of a timing error τ and frequency error λ can be expressed as

$$r(t) = 2\sin\left[2\pi(f_o + f_j + \lambda + f_{IF})t\right]; \quad (j-1)T_h - \tau \le t \le jT_h - \tau. \tag{3.97}$$

Cross-correlating $y(t)$ with $r(t)$, the output $x(t)$ of the band-pass filter gives

$$x(t) \triangleq \begin{cases} J'(t) & (j-1)T_h - \tau \le t \le (j-1)T_h \quad (\tau \ge 0) \\ & \text{or} \\ & jT_h \le t \le jT_h - \tau \quad (\tau < 0) \\ \sqrt{2S}\cos\left[2\pi(f_{IF} + \lambda)t - \phi_j\right] + J'(t) & \\ & (j-1)T_h \le t \le jT_h - \tau \quad (\tau \ge 0) \\ & \text{or} \\ & (j-1)T_h - \tau \le t \le jT_h \quad (\tau < 0) \end{cases} \tag{3.98}$$

where $J'(t)$ is still given by (3.40). Sampling $x(t)$ at the Nyquist rate and taking the sine and cosine discrete Fourier transforms of these samples evaluated at the two center standard MFSK frequencies $f = f_{IF} \pm 1/2T_h$, one has, in the j-th hop interval,

$$a_{j\pm} \triangleq \sum_{i=0}^{N_s-1} x_{ij}\cos\left[2\pi\left(f_{IF} \pm \frac{1}{2T_h}\right)\frac{i}{N_s}T_h\right]$$

$$b_{j\pm} \triangleq \sum_{i=0}^{N_s-1} x_{ij}\sin\left[2\pi\left(f_{IF} \pm \frac{1}{2T_h}\right)\frac{i}{N_s}T_h\right] \tag{3.99}$$

from which the spectral estimates

$$r_{j\pm} \triangleq \sqrt{a_{j\pm}^2 + b_{j\pm}^2} \tag{3.100}$$

are obtained. Letting $t = iT_h/N_s + (j-1)T_h$ in (3.98) and substituting into (3.99), we arrive at the following results (for large N_s) for the first two statistical moments of $a_{j\pm}$ and $b_{j\pm}$, that is,

$$\bar{a}_{j\pm} \triangleq E\{a_{j\pm}\} = \begin{cases} \dfrac{\sqrt{2S}\,N_s}{2}\operatorname{sinc}[\pi(1/2 \mp \beta),(1-|\varepsilon|)]\cos\varphi_{j\pm}; & |\varepsilon| \le 1 \\ 0; & |\varepsilon| > 1 \end{cases}$$

$$\bar{b}_{j\pm} \triangleq E\{b_{j\pm}\} = \begin{cases} \dfrac{\sqrt{2S}\,N_s}{2}\operatorname{sinc}[\pi(1/2 \mp \beta),(1-|\varepsilon|)]\sin\varphi_{j\pm}; & |\varepsilon| \le 1 \\ 0; & |\varepsilon| > 1 \end{cases}$$

$$\sigma_a^2 \triangleq E\left\{\left(a_{j\pm} - \bar{a}_{j\pm}\right)^2\right\} = \sigma^2 = \frac{N_J}{4T_h}N_s^2$$

$$\sigma_b^2 \triangleq E\left\{\left(b_{j\pm} - \bar{b}_{j\pm}\right)^2\right\} = \sigma^2 = \frac{N_J}{4T_h}N_s^2 \tag{3.101}$$

where

$$\varphi_{j\pm} \triangleq \pi(\pm 1/2 - \beta)(1 - |\varepsilon|) + \phi_j - 2\pi(j-1)f_{IF}T_h, \tag{3.102}$$

$$\operatorname{sinc}[x, y] \triangleq \sin(xy)/x, \tag{3.103}$$

and $\beta \triangleq \lambda T_h$ is the frequency synchronization error normalized by the hop rate (also, the MFSK frequency spacing). Noting again that $a_{j\pm}$ and $b_{j\pm}$ are conditionally Gaussian random variables, then the random variables $r_{j\pm}$ are Rician-distributed with pdf's (conditioned on ε and β with $|\varepsilon| \le 1$ and $|\beta| \le 1/2$)

$$p(r_{j\pm}|\varepsilon,\beta) = \begin{cases} \dfrac{r_{j\pm}}{\sigma^2}\exp\left\{-\left[\dfrac{r_{j\pm}^2}{2\sigma^2} + \gamma_\pm\right]\right\} & \\ \times I_0\left[\sqrt{2\gamma_\pm}\,\dfrac{r_{j\pm}}{\sigma}\right]; & 0 \le r_{j\pm} \le \infty \\ 0; \text{ elsewhere} & \end{cases} \tag{3.104}$$

where

$$\gamma_{\pm} \triangleq \gamma_h(\text{sinc}[\pi(1/2 \mp \beta), (1 - |\varepsilon|)])^2 \tag{3.105}$$

and γ_h is as defined in (3.46).

To produce an estimator with small variance, the spectral estimates must again be accumulated over many hop intervals, say, N_h, before forming the estimate $\hat{\beta}$. In particular, letting $R_{\pm}$ be defined identical to (3.52) using, however, $r_{j\pm}$ of (3.100), then, analogous to (3.53), the estimator of frequency synchronization is given by

$$\hat{\beta} = \frac{R_{+} - R_{-}}{2(R_{+} - R_{-})} \tag{3.106}$$

whose first two statistical moments are

$$\mu_{\hat{\beta}|\beta} \triangleq E\{\hat{\beta}|\beta\} = \int_{-1/2}^{1/2} \hat{\beta} p(\hat{\beta}|\beta)\, d\hat{\beta} \tag{3.107}$$

$$\sigma^2_{\hat{\beta}|\beta} = \int_{-1/2}^{1/2} (\hat{\beta} - E\{\hat{\beta}|\beta\})^2 p(\hat{\beta}|\beta)\, d\hat{\beta} \tag{3.108}$$

where $p(\hat{\beta}|\beta)$ is the β-conditional pdf of $\hat{\beta}$. Proceeding directly to the results for large N_h, we again apply the central-limit theorem to (3.52) from which $z_{\pm} = R^2_{\pm}$ are Gaussian random variables whose first two statistical moments are given by

$$\begin{aligned} \mu_{\pm}(\beta) &\triangleq E\{z_{\pm}|\beta\} = 2\sigma^2[1 + \gamma_{\pm}] \\ \sigma^2_{\pm}(\beta) &\triangleq E\{(z_{\pm} - \mu_{\pm})^2|\beta\} = \frac{(2\sigma^2)^2}{N_h}[1 + 2\gamma_{\pm}]. \end{aligned} \tag{3.109}$$

Using the Gaussian conditional pdf's for R_{+} and R_{-} together with (3.106), the pdf of $\hat{\beta}$ conditioned on β is given by

$$p(\hat{\beta}|\beta) = \begin{cases} \dfrac{N_h\left(\frac{1}{4} - \hat{\beta}^2\right)\sigma_T^2}{\pi\sqrt{(1 + 2\gamma_{+})(1 + 2\gamma_{-})}} \left\{ \exp\left\{ -\dfrac{\bar{x}_1^2}{2\sigma_1^2} - \dfrac{\bar{x}_2^2}{2\sigma_2^2} \right\} \right. \\ \quad + \sqrt{2\pi}\,\sigma_T\left(\dfrac{\bar{x}_1}{\sigma_1^2} + \dfrac{\bar{x}_2}{\sigma_2^2}\right)\exp\left\{ -\dfrac{(\bar{x}_1 - \bar{x}_2)^2}{2(\sigma_1^2 + \sigma_2^2)} \right\} \\ \quad \left. \times\left[1 - Q\left(\sigma_T\left(\dfrac{\bar{x}_1}{\sigma_1^2} + \dfrac{\bar{x}_2}{\sigma_2^2}\right)\right)\right]\right\}; \quad |\hat{\beta}| \le \dfrac{1}{2} \\ 0; \quad \text{elsewhere} \end{cases} \tag{3.110}$$

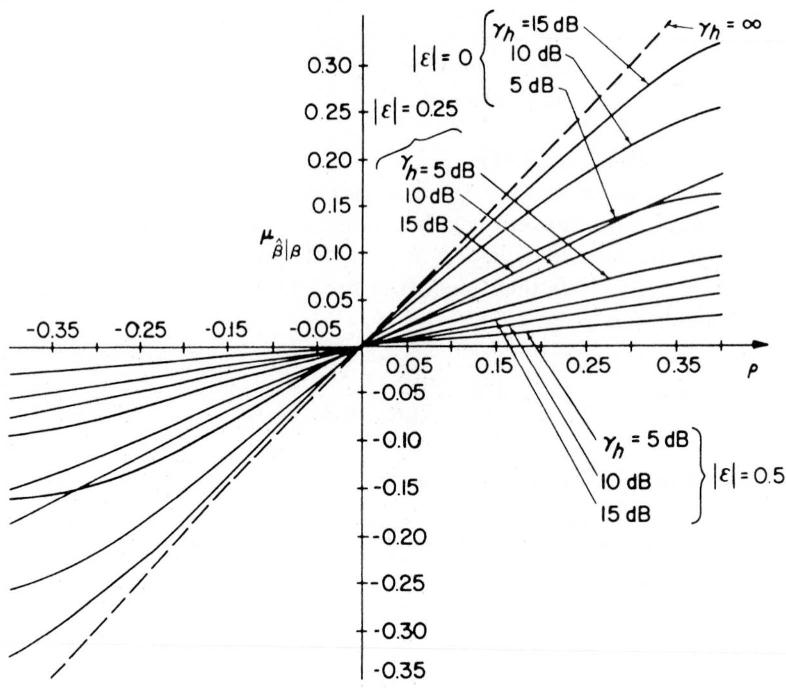

Figure 3.25. Conditional mean $\mu_{\hat{\beta}|\beta}$ versus β with γ_h and ε as parameters; $N_h = 10$.

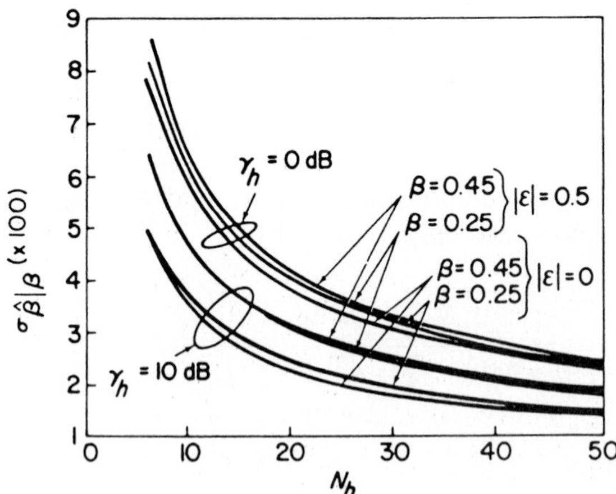

Figure 3.26. Conditional standard deviation $\sigma_{\hat{\beta}|\beta}$ versus N_h with γ_h, β and ε as parameters.

where

$$\bar{x}_1 = \frac{\mu_+}{(\frac{1}{2} + \hat{\beta})^2 2\sigma^2}; \ \bar{x}_2 = \frac{\mu_-}{(\frac{1}{2} - \hat{\beta})^2 2\sigma^2}$$

$$\sigma_1^2 = \frac{\sigma_+^2}{\left[2\sigma^2(\frac{1}{2} + \hat{\beta})^2\right]^2}; \ \sigma_2^2 = \frac{\sigma_-^2}{\left[2\sigma^2(\frac{1}{2} - \hat{\beta})^2\right]^2};$$

$$\sigma_T^2 = \frac{\sigma_1^2\sigma_2^2}{\sigma_1^2 + \sigma_2^2}. \tag{3.111}$$

The conditional mean $\mu_{\hat{\beta}|\beta}$ from (3.107) and the conditional standard deviation $\sigma_{\hat{\beta}|\beta}$ from (3.108) are presented in Figures 3.25 and 3.26, respectively. It is seen from Figure 3.25 that the slope of $\mu_{\hat{\beta}|\beta}$ is non-zero at the origin but decreases significantly as the absolute value of the normalized time synchronization error $|\varepsilon|$ is increased. Figure 3.26 shows that, for the range of parameter values of interest, $\sigma_{\hat{\beta}|\beta}$ is comparatively small so that the random variable $\hat{\beta}$ is very close to the mean $\mu_{\hat{\beta}|\beta}$ with high probability.

3.3.2 The Case of Partial-Band Noise Jamming

Analogous to (3.63), the square root of the accumulated spectral estimates is now

$$R_{\pm} = \sqrt{\frac{1}{N_h}\sum_{j=1}^{\rho N_h} r_{j\pm}^2 + (1-\rho)\xi^2(\text{sinc}[\pi(1/2 \mp \beta), (1-|\varepsilon|)])^2}. \tag{3.112}$$

For large ρN_h, the central-limit theorem can be applied to (3.112). Once again, $z_{\pm} = R_{\pm}^2$ are Gaussian random variables with the first two statistical moments given by

$$\mu_{\pm}(\beta) \triangleq E\{z_{\pm}|\beta\} = 2\sigma^2[1 + \gamma_{\pm}]$$

$$\sigma_{\pm}^2(\beta) \triangleq E\left\{(z_{\pm} - \mu_{\pm})^2|\beta\right\} = \frac{(2\sigma^2)^2}{\rho N_h}[1 + 2\rho\gamma_{\pm}] \tag{3.113}$$

and, hence, $p(\hat{\beta}|\beta)$ is given by (3.110) with N_h replaced by ρN_h, $\gamma_{\pm}$ of (3.105) with γ_h replaced by $\rho\gamma_h$, and $\bar{x}_1$, $\bar{x}_2$, σ_1^2, and σ_2^2 as defined in (3.111) but evaluated using $\mu_{\pm}$ and $\sigma_{\pm}^2$ of (3.113).

3.3.3 The Effects of Frequency Synchronization Error on FH / MFSK Error Probability Performance

The presence of a frequency synchronization error in an FH/MFSK receiver causes a degradation in system error probability performance due to factors not unlike those produced by a timing synchronization error. In fact, both signal attenuation and loss of orthogonality degradations once again exist; however, the functional dependence of these degradation components on the frequency error is quite different from the corresponding relationships for a timing error. Nevertheless, once these differences are identified, the remaining task of relating the above degradations to their impact on system error probability performance is straightforward in view of our previous detailed discussion for the effects of time synchronization errors. Thus, our discussion here will be brief and, wherever possible, draw heavily upon the results given in Section 3.2.3.

Starting first with the simple case of FH/MFSK with no diversity and orthogonal tones spaced by k/T_h, then if, for example, the transmitted MFSK symbol in the j-th hop interval is given by

$$s^{(j)}(t) = \sqrt{2S}\,\sin\left[2\pi\left(f_o + f_j + \frac{1}{2T_h}\right)t\right]; \quad (j-1)T_h \le t \le jT_h \tag{3.114}$$

then following the development in (3.97)–(3.103), and taking the sine and cosine Fourier transforms at $f = f_{IF} + 1/2T_h$, the spectral estimate r_j corresponding to the transmitted MFSK symbol has the conditional pdf

$$p(r_j|\varepsilon,\beta) = \begin{cases} \dfrac{r_j}{\sigma^2}\exp\left\{-\left[\dfrac{r_j^2}{2\sigma^2} + \gamma_h D_j(\varepsilon,\beta)\right]\right\} I_0\left[\sqrt{2\gamma_h D_j(\varepsilon,\beta)}\,\dfrac{r_j}{\sigma}\right]; & 0 \le r_j \le \infty \\ 0;\ \text{otherwise} \end{cases} \tag{3.115}$$

where

$$D_j(\varepsilon,\beta) = \operatorname{sinc}^2[\pi\beta, 1-|\varepsilon|]. \tag{3.116}$$

Similarly, the spectral estimate r_{jn} for an incorrect correlator spaced in frequency by nk/T_h from the correct one has the pdf of (3.115) with $D_j(\varepsilon,\beta)$ replaced by

$$D_{jn}(\varepsilon,\beta) = \operatorname{sinc}^2[\pi(nk+\beta), 1-|\varepsilon|]. \tag{3.117}$$

Note that for $\beta = 0$, $D_j(\varepsilon,\beta)$ of (3.116) and $D_{jn}(\varepsilon,\beta)$ of (3.117) reduce, respectively, to $D_j(\varepsilon)$ of (3.69) and $D_{jn}(\varepsilon)$ of (3.71).

Comparing (3.115) with (3.73), it is clear that the bit error probability performance conditioned on fixed frequency and time synchronization errors is given by (3.78) together with (3.75) and (3.77) where $D_j(\varepsilon,\beta)$ and $D_{jn}(\varepsilon,\beta)$ are used in place of $D_j(\varepsilon)$ and $D_{jn}(\varepsilon)$ in (3.75).

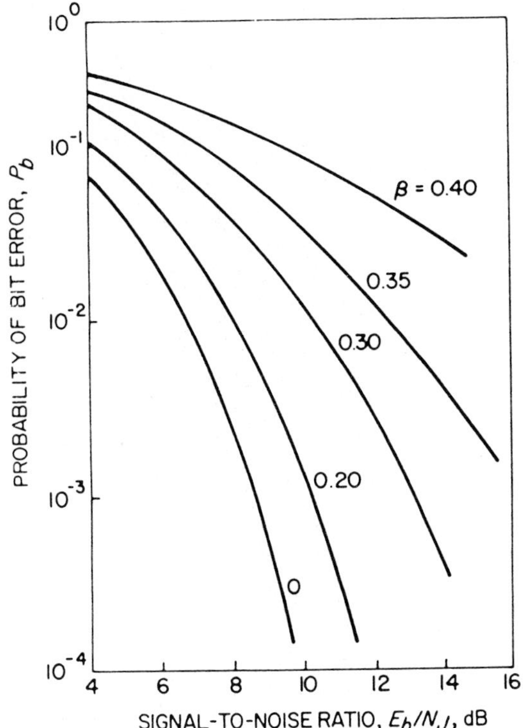

Figure 3.27. 4-ary FSK with frequency error (minimum orthogonal tone spacing) (reprinted from [13]).

Figures 3.27, 3.28, and 3.29 are the analogous results for performance in the presence of frequency error alone to those in Figures 3.18, 3.19, and 3.20, which depict performance in the presence of timing error alone. Comparing Figure 3.28 with Figure 3.19, for example, we observe that in the case of frequency error, the loss of orthogonality is the dominant degradation component for all β, whereas, as previously mentioned, for time synchronization error, loss of orthogonality dominates only for large error values.

Returning to Figure 3.21, we observe that increasing the MFSK tone spacing to twice its minimum orthogonal value has a more pronounced effect on the performance improvement achieved in the presence of frequency error alone than that when timing error alone is present, particularly when the synchronization errors are large. When both time and frequency errors exist simultaneously, Figure 3.30 illustrates a set of curves that represent contours of constant E_b/N_J degradation for a fixed bit error probability. Both 4-ary and 8-ary FSK results are provided.

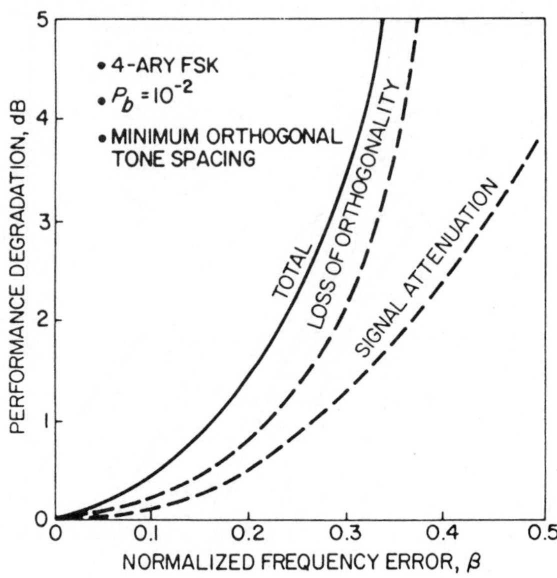

Figure 3.28. Performance degradation due to frequency error (reprinted from [13]).

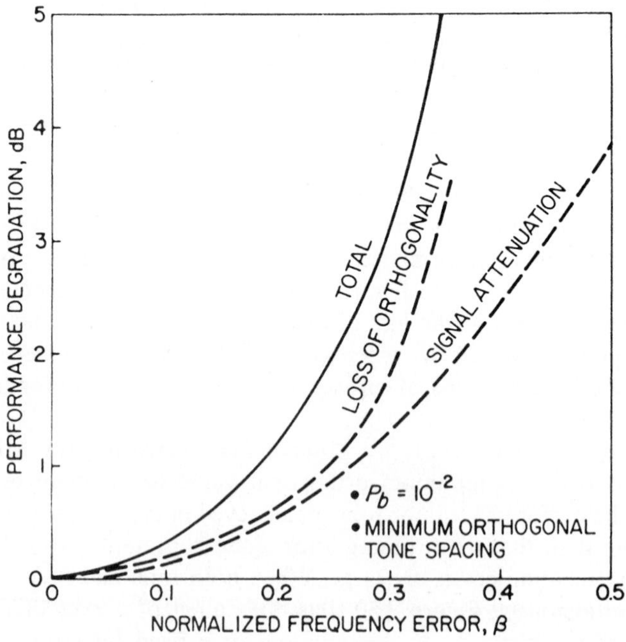

Figure 3.29. 8-ary FSK performance degradation due to frequency error (reprinted from [13]).

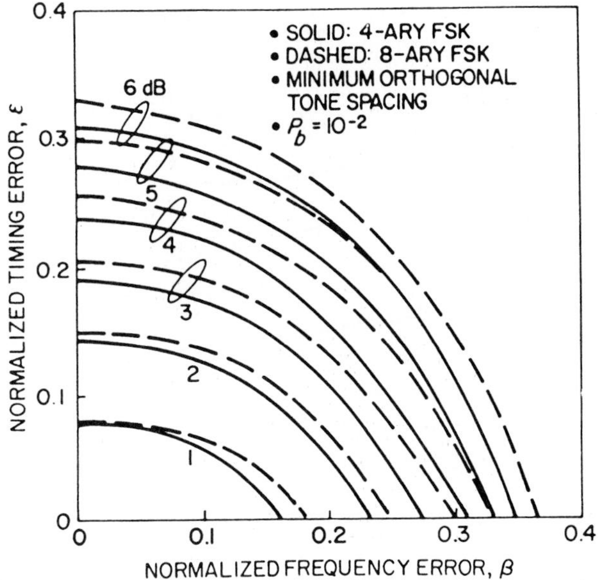

Figure 3.30. Performance degradation due to time and frequency synchronization errors (reprinted from [13]).

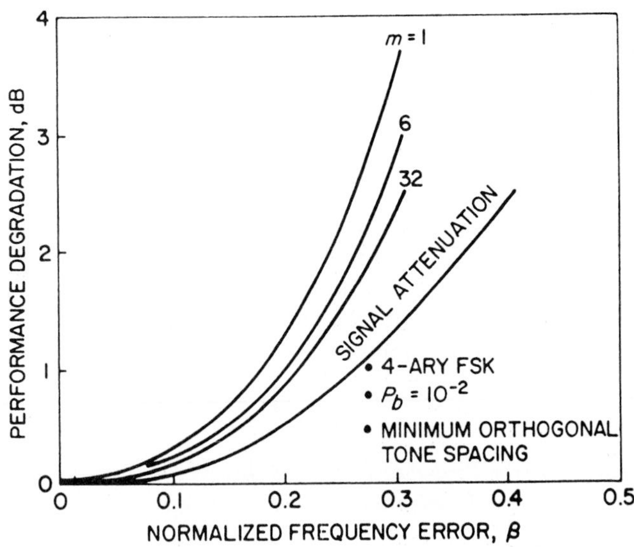

Figure 3.31. Performance degradation due to frequency error with chip combining (reprinted from [13]).

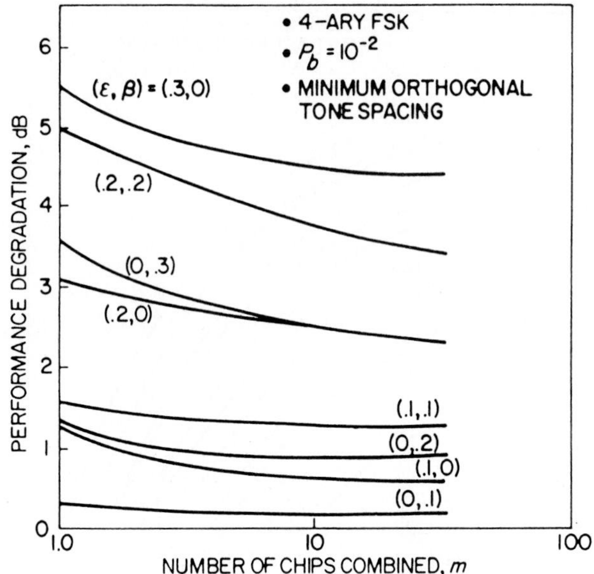

Figure 3.32. Effect of chip combining on degradation due to synchronization errors (reprinted from [13]).

Finally, when m-diversity and non-coherent combining are superimposed on the basic FH/MFSK system of above, then again all of the results of Section 3.2.3.2 apply after making the same replacements of $D_j(\varepsilon, \beta)$ and $D_{jn}(\varepsilon, \beta)$ for $D_j(\varepsilon)$ and $D_{jn}(\varepsilon)$. In this regard, Figure 3.31 provides, for frequency error alone, the analogous results to Figure 3.22. Again we observe that increasing m improves performance; however, a comparison of the two figures reveals that the reduction of loss of orthogonality by non-coherent combining plays a more prominent role with frequency errors than with timing errors. When both time and frequency errors are present and fixed, Figure 3.32 illustrates the performance degradation as a function of m, the number of chips combined.

3.3.3.1 Average Error Probability Performance in the Presence of Frequency Synchronization Error Estimation

If the estimator $\hat{\beta}$ of (3.106) is used for FH frequency synchronization and ε is the fixed normalized time synchronization error, then a residual frequency offset $\nu(\beta) \triangleq \beta - \hat{\beta}$ arises, which, as in our previous discussions, affects system performance by reducing the signal energy available for the non-coherent detection of the transmitted MFSK symbol and spreading signal energy into adjacent MFSK frequency detectors. In particular, it is clear that in the presence of the residual offset, a signal attenuation degradation occurs that is given by

$$\begin{aligned} D_j(\varepsilon, \nu) &= \operatorname{sinc}^2[\pi(\beta - \hat{\beta}), 1 - |\varepsilon|] \\ &= \operatorname{sinc}^2[\pi\nu(\beta), 1 - |\varepsilon|] \end{aligned} \tag{3.118}$$

and a loss of orthogonality also occurs that is given by

$$D_{jn}(\varepsilon, \nu) = \operatorname{sinc}^2[\pi(nk + \nu(\beta)), 1 - |\varepsilon|]. \tag{3.119}$$

Thus, if $p_{\nu|\beta}(\nu|\beta)$ denotes the β-conditional pdf of the residual error $\nu(\beta)$, then analogous to (3.93)

$$p_{\nu|\beta}(\nu|\beta) = p_{\hat{\beta}|\beta}(\beta - \nu|\beta). \tag{3.120}$$

It then follows that conditioned on ε, the average bit error probability $P_b(\varepsilon)$ is

$$P_b(\varepsilon) = 2\int_0^{1/2} d\beta \int_{\beta-1/2}^{\beta+1/2} P_b(\varepsilon, \nu)\, p_{\hat{\beta}|\beta}(\beta - \nu|\beta)\, d\nu \tag{3.121}$$

where $P_b(\varepsilon, \nu)$ is obtained from (3.78) together with (3.77) and (3.75) with $D_j(\varepsilon, \nu)$ and $D_{jn}(\varepsilon, \nu)$ used in place of $D_j(\varepsilon)$ and $D_{jn}(\varepsilon)$.

Since, as previously noted, $\sigma_{\hat{\beta}|\beta}$ is comparatively small, we may make a simplifying assumption analogous to (3.95), namely,

$$p_{\hat{\beta}|\beta}(\beta - \nu|\beta) = \delta(\nu - (\beta - \mu_{\hat{\beta}|\beta})) \tag{3.122}$$

in which case (3.121) simplifies to

$$P_b(\varepsilon) = 2\int_0^{1/2} P_b(\varepsilon, \beta - \mu_{\hat{\beta}|\beta})\, d\beta. \tag{3.123}$$

Analogous to Figure 3.23, Figure 3.33 is an illustration of the average bit error probability performance of (3.123) for 4-ary and 8-ary FSK with no timing error ($\varepsilon = 0$) and $N_h = 10$. Comparing these two figures, we observe that the average bit error probability is considerably less degraded by a residual frequency error than by a residual timing error.

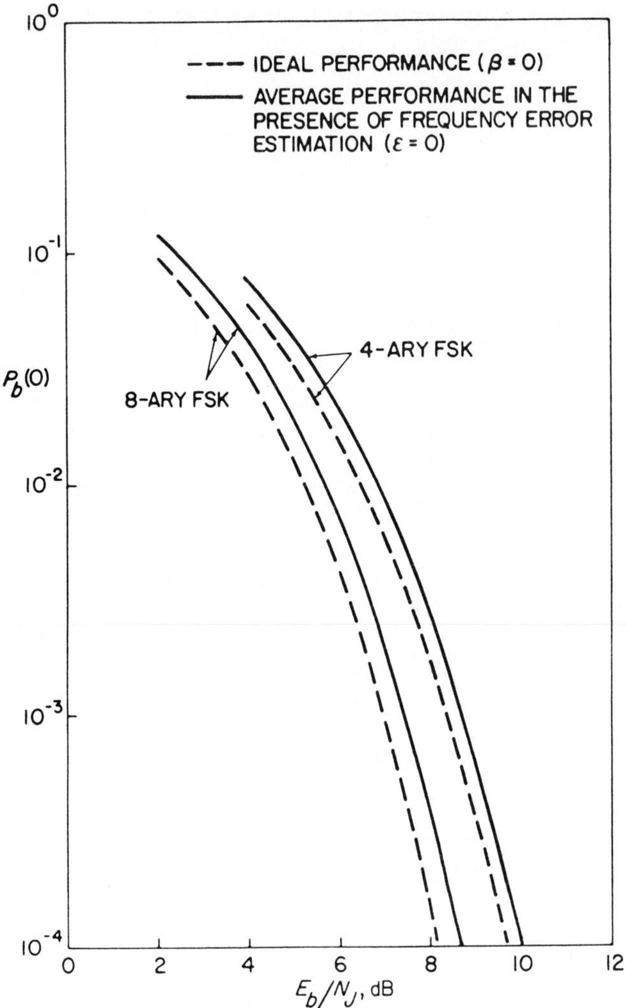

Figure 3.33. Average bit error probability performance in the presence of frequency error estimation; $\varepsilon = 0$, $N_h = 10$.

Finally, if both the fine time and fine frequency estimators of (3.53) and (3.106), respectively, are employed, then the overall error probability performance in the presence of the combination of the two residual synchronization errors can be computed from

$$P_b = 4\int_0^{1/2} d\varepsilon \int_0^{1/2} d\beta \int_{\varepsilon-1/2}^{\varepsilon+1/2} \int_{\beta-1/2}^{\beta+1/2} P_b(\varepsilon, \nu)\, p_{\hat{\beta}|\beta}(\beta - \nu|\beta)$$

$$\times p_{\hat{\varepsilon}|\varepsilon}(\varepsilon - \eta|\varepsilon)\, d\nu\, d\eta \qquad (3.124)$$

or from the approximate simplified expression

$$P_b = 4\int_0^{1/2}\int_0^{1/2} P_b(\varepsilon - \mu_{\hat{\varepsilon}|\varepsilon}, \rho - \mu_{\hat{\beta}|\beta})\, d\beta\, d\varepsilon. \tag{3.125}$$

3.4 REFERENCES

[1] M. K. Simon, A. Polydoros, and G. K. Huth, "Time synchronization of a frequency-hopped MFSK communication system," *ICC'81 Conference Record*, June 1981, pp. 76.1.1–76.1.5, Denver, CO.

[2] G. K. Huth, A. Polydoros, and M. K. Simon, "Frequency synchronization of a frequency-hopped MFSK communication system," *ICC'81 Conference Record*, June 1981, pp. 34.1.1–34.1.5, Denver, CO.

[3] S. S. Rappaport and D. L. Schilling, "A two level coarse code acquisition scheme for spread spectrum radio," *NTC'79 Conference Record*, November 1979, pp. 54.6.1–54.6.6, Birmingham, AL.

[4] C. A. Putnam, S. S. Rappaport, and D. L. Schilling, "A comparison of schemes for coarse acquisition of frequency hopped spread spectrum signals," *NTC'81 Conference Record*, December 1981, pp. 34.2.1–34.2.5, New Orleans, LA. Also see *IEEE Trans. Commun.*, COM-31, No. 2, pp. 183–189, February 1983.

[5] G. S. Takhar, A. K. Elhakeem, and S. C. Gupta, "Frequency hopping acquisition by autoregressive spectral estimation," *ICC'78 Conference Record*, June 1978, pp. 16.4.1–16.4.5, Toronto, Canada.

[6] A. K. Elhakeem, G. S. Takhar, and S. C. Gupta, "New code acquisition techniques in spread spectrum communication," *IEEE Trans. Commun.*, COM-28, no. 2, pp. 249–257, February 1980.

[7] H. S. El-Ghouroury and S. C. Gupta, "Algorithmic measurement of digital instantaneous frequency," *IEEE Trans. Commun.*, COM-24, no. 10, pp. 1115–1122, October 1976.

[8] J. A. Ponnusamy and M. D. Srinath, "Acquisition of pseudonoise codes in FH systems," *IEEE Trans. Aerospace and Electronic Systems*, AES-17, no. 3, pp. 335–341, May 1981.

[9] M. D. Srinath and M. M. Viswanathan, "Sequential algorithm for identification of parameters of an autoregressive process," *IEEE Trans. Automatic Control*," AC-20, pp. 542–546, August 1975.

[10] L. J. Griffiths, "Rapid measurements of digital instantaneous frequency," *IEEE Trans. Acoustics, Speech, and Signal Processing*, ASSP-25, pp. 510–519, December 1977.

[11] W. C. Lindsey and M. K. Simon, *Telecommunication Systems Engineering*, Englewood Cliffs, NJ: Prentice-Hall, 1973, Chapter 10.

[12] H. D. Chadwick and J. C. Springett, "The design of a low data rate MFSK communication system," *IEEE Trans. Commun. Tech.*, COM-18, no. 6, pp. 740–750, December 1970.

[13] F. S. Nakamoto, R. W. Middlestead, and C. R. Wolfson, "Impact of time and frequency errors on processing satellites with MFSK modulation," *ICC'81 Conference Record*, June 14-18, 1981, pp. 37.3.1–37.3.5, Denver, CO.

[14] J. I. Marcum, *Table of Q Functions*, ASTIA Document No. AD116551, January 1, 1950, RAND Corporation, Santa Monica, CA.

APPENDIX 3A: TO PROVE THAT A FREQUENCY ESTIMATOR BASED UPON ADJACENT SPECTRAL ESTIMATES TAKEN AT INTEGER MULTIPLES OF 1/*T* CANNOT BE UNBIASED

Let k/T denote the observed frequency and j/T the nominal signal frequency. Then $i/T \triangleq (k-j)/T$ represents the frequency spacing of the observed frequency relative to the nominal signal frequency. In the presence of a normalized frequency error $\beta = \lambda T$, the pdf of the spectral estimates r_i is given by

$$p(r_i) = \begin{cases} \dfrac{r_i}{\sigma^2}\exp\left\{-\dfrac{1}{2\sigma^2}\left[r_i^2 + \xi^2 \operatorname{sinc}^2 \pi(i-\beta)\right]\right\} I_0\left[\dfrac{r_i \xi |\operatorname{sinc} \pi(i-\beta)|}{\beta}\right]; \\ \qquad\qquad\qquad\qquad\qquad\qquad\qquad\qquad 0 \le r_i \le \infty \\ 0; \text{ otherwise} \end{cases} \tag{3A.1a}$$

where

$$\frac{\xi^2}{2\sigma^2} = \gamma; \quad \operatorname{sinc} x \triangleq \frac{\sin x}{x}. \tag{3A.1b}$$

Suppose we consider constructing an estimator $\hat{\beta}$ of β which is only a function of the spectral estimates at the nominal signal frequency and the two adjacent ones, i.e., r_0, r_{+1}, and r_{-1}. Thus, we propose that

$$\hat{\beta} = g\left[r_0(\beta), r_{+1}(\beta), r_{-1}(\beta)\right] \tag{3A.2}$$

where g is an arbitrary function and we have shown the dependence of the spectral estimates on the normalized frequency error β. We wish to prove that $\partial E\{\hat{\beta}|\beta\}/\partial\beta|_{\beta=0} \neq \beta$, i.e., $\hat{\beta}$ as given by (3A.2) is biased. We do this by proving something stronger, namely that

$$\left.\frac{\partial E\{\hat{\beta}|\beta\}}{\partial \beta}\right|_{\beta=0} = 0 \tag{3A.3}$$

where

$$E\{\hat{\beta}|\beta\} \triangleq \int_{-1/2}^{1/2} p(\hat{\beta}|\beta)\hat{\beta}\, d\hat{\beta}. \tag{3A.4}$$

To prove (3A.3) we must first find the conditional pdf $p(\hat{\beta}|\beta)$. If $\hat{\beta}$ is given by (3A.3), then there exists some other function f such that

$$r_0(\beta) = f\left[\hat{\beta}, r_{+1}(\beta), r_{-1}(\beta)\right]. \tag{3A.5}$$

Define

$$r_{+1}(\beta) = u$$

$$r_{-1}(\beta) = v$$

$$r_0(\beta) = f(\hat{\beta}, u, v). \tag{3A.6}$$

Then, the Jacobian of the transformation is given by

$$J\left(\frac{r_{-i}, r_0, r_{+1}}{\hat{\beta}, u, v}\right) = \frac{\partial f(\hat{\beta}, u, v)}{\partial \hat{\beta}}. \tag{3A.7}$$

Now

$$p(\hat{\beta}|\beta) = \int_0^\infty \int_0^\infty p(\hat{\beta}, u, v|\beta)\, du\, dv$$

$$= \int_0^\infty \int_0^\infty \left| J\left(\frac{r_{-1}, r_0, r_{+1}}{\hat{\beta}, u, v}\right)\right| p(r_{-1}, r_0, r_{+1})\, du\, dv. \tag{3A.8}$$

Since r_{+1}, r_{-1} and r_0 are independent random variables, then from (3A.8) we get

$$p(\hat{\beta}|\beta) = \int_0^\infty \int_0^\infty \left| \frac{\partial f(\hat{\beta}, u, v)}{\partial \hat{\beta}} \right| p(u) p(v) p(f(\hat{\beta}, u, v))\, du\, dv. \tag{3A.9}$$

Substituting (3A.1) into (3A.9) and making use of (3A.4) and (3A.6) gives

$$\begin{aligned} E\{\hat{\beta}|\beta\} = {} & \int_0^\infty \int_0^\infty u'v' \exp\{-\tfrac{1}{2}(u'^2 + v'^2)\} \\ & \times \int_{-1/2}^{1/2} \hat{\beta} f(\hat{\beta}, u', v') \left| \frac{\partial f(\hat{\beta}, u', v')}{\partial \hat{\beta}} \right| \\ & \times \exp\{-\tfrac{1}{2} f^2(\hat{\beta}, u', v')\} \exp\left\{-\gamma \sum_{i=-1}^{1} \operatorname{sinc}^2 \pi(i - \beta)\right\} \\ & \times I_0\left(\sqrt{2\gamma}\, u' |\operatorname{sinc} \pi(1 - \beta)|\right) \\ & \times I_0\left(\sqrt{2\gamma}\, v' |\operatorname{sinc} \pi(1 + \beta)|\right) \\ & \times I_0\left(\sqrt{2\gamma}\, f(\hat{\beta}, u', v') |\operatorname{sinc} \pi\beta|\right) d\hat{\beta}\, du'\, dv' \end{aligned} \tag{3A.10}$$

where

$$u' = u/\sigma$$
$$v' = v/\sigma \tag{3A.11}$$

and γ has previously been defined in (3A.1b).

Taking the partial derivative of (3A.10) with respect to β and evaluating at $\beta = 0$ gives

$$\left.\frac{\partial E\{\hat{\beta}|\beta\}}{\partial\beta}\right|_{\beta=0} = \int_0^\infty\int_0^\infty u'v' \exp\{-\tfrac{1}{2}(u'^2 + v'^2)\}$$
$$\times \int_{-1/2}^{1/2} \hat{\beta} f(\hat{\beta}, u', v') \left|\frac{\partial f(\hat{\beta}, u', v')}{\partial\hat{\beta}}\right| \exp\{-\tfrac{1}{2} f^2(\hat{\beta}, u', v')\}$$
$$\times \Bigg[\exp(-\gamma) \frac{\partial}{\partial\beta}\{ I_0(\sqrt{2\gamma}\, u' |\mathrm{sinc}\, \pi(1-\beta)|)$$
$$\times I_0(\sqrt{2\gamma}\, v' |\mathrm{sinc}\, \pi(1+\beta)|) I_0(\sqrt{2\gamma}\, f(\hat{\beta}, u', v') |\mathrm{sinc}\, \pi\beta|)\}\big|_{\beta=0}$$
$$+ \exp(-\gamma) \left[-\gamma \frac{\partial}{\partial\beta} \left\{ \sum_{i=-1}^{1} \mathrm{sinc}^2 \pi(i-\beta) \right\}\Bigg|_{\beta=0} \right]$$
$$\times I_0(\sqrt{2\gamma}\, f(\hat{\beta}, u', v')) \Bigg] d\hat{\beta}\, du'\, dv'. \tag{3A.12}$$

Now

$$\frac{\partial}{\partial\beta} \mathrm{sinc}^2 \pi(i-\beta) = 2\, \mathrm{sinc}\, \pi(i-\beta) \left[\frac{\partial}{\partial\beta} \mathrm{sinc}\, \pi(i-\beta) \right]. \tag{3A.13}$$

At $\beta = 0$,

$$\mathrm{sinc}\, \pi(i-\beta) = 0 \text{ for } i = \pm 1$$
$$\frac{\partial}{\partial\beta} \mathrm{sinc}\, \pi(i-\beta) = 0 \text{ for } i = 0. \tag{3A.14}$$

Thus

$$\left.\frac{\partial}{\partial\beta} \mathrm{sinc}^2 \pi(i-\beta)\right|_{\beta=0} = 0 \text{ for } i = -1, 0, +1 \tag{3A.15}$$

or

$$\left.\frac{\partial}{\partial\beta}\left[\sum_{i=-1}^{1} \mathrm{sinc}^2 \pi(i-\beta) \right]\right|_{\beta=0} = 0. \tag{3A.16}$$

This takes care of the second partial derivative in (3A.12). For the first partial derivative, we observe that

$$
\begin{aligned}
&\frac{\partial}{\partial\beta}\Big\{ I_0\big(\sqrt{2\gamma}\,u'|\mathrm{sinc}\,\pi(1-\beta)|\big) I_0\big(\sqrt{2\gamma}\,v'|\mathrm{sinc}\,\pi(1+\beta)|\big) \\
&\qquad \times I_0\big(\sqrt{2\gamma}\,f(\hat{\beta},u',v')\,|\mathrm{sinc}\,\pi\beta|\big)\Big|_{\beta=0} \\
&= I_1\big(\sqrt{2\gamma}\,f(\hat{\beta},u',v')\big)\left|\cancelto{0}{\frac{\partial|\mathrm{sinc}\,\pi\beta|}{\partial\beta}}\right|_{\beta=0} \\
&\qquad + I_0\big(\sqrt{2\gamma}\,f(\hat{\beta},u',v')\big)\left\{\left|\frac{\partial I_0\big(\sqrt{2\gamma}\,u'|\mathrm{sinc}\,\pi(1-\beta)|\big)}{\partial\beta}\right|_{\beta=0}\right. \\
&\qquad \left. + \left|\frac{\partial I_0\big(\sqrt{2\gamma}\,v'|\mathrm{sinc}\,\pi(1+\beta)|\big)}{\partial\beta}\right|_{\beta=0}\right\} \\
&= I_0\big(\sqrt{2\gamma}\,f(\hat{\beta},u',v')\big)\Big\{ I_1\big(\sqrt{2\gamma}\,u'|\mathrm{sinc}\,\pi(1-\beta)|\big)\big(\sqrt{2\gamma}\,u'\big) \\
&\qquad \times \left|\cancelto{0}{\frac{\partial|\mathrm{sinc}\,\pi(1-\beta)|}{\partial\beta}}\right|_{\beta=0} \\
&\qquad + I_1\big(\sqrt{2\gamma}\,v'|\mathrm{sinc}\,\pi(1+\beta)|\big) \\
&\qquad \times \big(\sqrt{2\gamma}\,v'\big)\left|\cancelto{0}{\frac{\partial|\mathrm{sinc}\,\pi(1+\beta)|}{\partial\beta}}\right|_{\beta=0}\Big\} \\
&= 0.
\end{aligned}
\tag{3A.17}
$$

Substituting (3A.16) and (3A.17) into (3A.12) gives the desired result, i.e.

$$
\left.\frac{\partial E\{\hat{\beta}|\beta\}}{\partial\beta}\right|_{\beta=0} = 0. \tag{3A.18}
$$

Part 5

SPECIAL TOPICS

Chapter 4

LOW PROBABILITY OF INTERCEPT COMMUNICATIONS

The design of a communication link to have low probability of intercept (LPI) capability is predicated on the requirement for it to operate in a hostile environment wherein the enemy tries to detect the presence of the communicator's transmission. A typical scenario might consist of an underwater or surface vehicle (the communicator) attempting to correspond with a satellite (the receiver) via transmission of a short message, and an enemy search aircraft (the interceptor) whose mission it is to detect the presence of RF energy corresponding to this communicated message. The key words in the last sentence are *detect* and *energy* since typically the interceptor's performance is judged by his ability to determine (detect) that the communicator has initiated a transmission (energy) and not by what might occur following this accomplishment, e.g., location of the communicator, decoding of the message, etc. To further emphasize this point, the interceptor is ordinarily acquainted only with such communicator information as his frequency band, modulation format, and those spread-spectrum (SS) modulation characteristics such as bandwidth and code (hop) rate, which are insufficient by themselves to allow for decoding of the message. Thus, in the absence of information related to the time of message initiation and the secure codes used to generate the SS modulation, the interceptor's detection strategy is limited to employing some form of energy detector.

A large part of this chapter shall be devoted to discussing and comparing the merits of several different interceptor detector topologies which are important either because of their simplicity of implementation or because of their theoretically optimum performance capability. Such ability to employ a reasonably sophisticated signal feature detector, as opposed to, say, a simple wideband radiometer, is a technique the interceptor is assumed to have at his disposal for improving his detectability. This is not to say that the enemy will necessarily employ this option since, in many cases, little or nothing is gained both from a performance and cost standpoint by using other than the simplest energy detector. In fact, in those situations, it may be sufficient for the interceptor to jam the link between communicator and receiver so as to force the communicator to increase his transmitted power above the level normally required for reliable reception, thereby raising his chance of being detected. The subject of enemy jamming of a communicator's transmission, with emphasis on the various system design tradeoffs possible between the two adversaries, has been adequately treated in many of the chapters in Parts 1 to 3. Thus, we shall not repeat such discussions here in this chapter except in summary form in the final section.

As is true for any scenario posed for a communication system design, the extent to which the interceptor can employ any or all of the above methods for improving his detectability is determined by factors involving both cost and complexity. Some mention of these factors will be included in our discussion later on.

Having briefly mentioned the various options available to the interceptor, we complete our introductory picture by discussing the conditions and associated technologies which, when utilized by the communicator, greatly enhance his LPI position. For convenience of discussion we shall use as our model scenario the underwater or surface vehicle to satellite communication link. However, much of what follows is directly applicable to other scenarios such as communication between an airborne command post and a satellite or surface ships communicating to airborne relays.

First and foremost, the communicator must maintain as low a visual profile as possible, even when not communicating, to the extreme of completely concealing his location. Second, when transmitting, the communicator should reduce his radio detectability by minimizing his radiated power. The techniques available for accomplishing such include (1) specially designed low sidelobe antennas, (2) maximum use of channel coding to minimize the transmitter power necessary for proper message detection, (3) an optimum performance receiving system and, (4) low message bit rates and the shortest possible message lengths. Each of these are attainable to various degrees and the extent to which any of them may be employed depends upon the available implementation technologies and costs. Finally, the communicator should employ SS modulation techniques to provide anti-jam (AJ) protection against the interceptor. At this juncture, it is also worth pointing out that the communication receiver may itself attempt to jam the interceptor's receivers or otherwise confuse the interceptor by various decoy methods. Thus, the interceptor must be aware of this possibility and, if possible, guard against its occurrence.

While all of the above factors individually contribute to a maximum LPI state for the communicator, it is possible that all may not be realizable simultaneously. The reason for this is that some factors are both time and spatial dependent and the communicator may have little control over these when it becomes necessary to transmit. Variables of this nature might include (1) the transmitting antenna elevation angle when pointed to the communication receiver (which depends upon the relative transmitter and receiver positions at the time), (2) whether the satellite is receiving by means of a spot (high gain) antenna or an earth-coverage (moderate gain) antenna, and (3) the weather conditions along the surface to satellite line-of-sight communication path, which might be different for the link between the communicator and receiver than that between the communicator and interceptor. A high elevation angle generally means lower sidelobe radiation into the altitudes that the search aircraft fly as well as obviating main beam intercept at far range, while the use of the satellite spot antenna and clear weather conditions are synonymous with minimum radiated power.

The remainder of this chapter deals with the issues and answers pertaining to the tradeoffs among the various modulation, coding, and synchronization techniques used by the communicator and the sophistication of the detection technique employed by the interceptor in carrying out their respective missions. In keeping with the philosophy adopted in previous chapters, we shall intentionally omit discussion of all issues related to antenna design. This is not to say by any means that such issues are neither performance nor cost effective. In fact, one of the viable options available to the interceptor to improve its detectability is to employ multiple narrow-coverage antenna/receiver combinations that accrue gain by individually covering fractional portions of the total search area. Nevertheless, we shall focus our attention only on those issues that have a direct bearing on the previously mentioned system design considerations.

4.1 SIGNAL MODULATION FORMS

The various signal modulation forms that might be used by the communicator are no different from those already discussed in great detail in previous chapters. Thus, in this chapter we shall merely review their intrinsic form with emphasis on the LPI application.

The underlying modulation technique for data communication in many LPI systems reported upon thus far is MFSK. For such a modulation, the form of the transmitted signal in the i-th transmission interval $iT_s \le t \le (i+1)T_s$ is

$$s(t) = \sqrt{2S}\sin[2\pi(f_0 + d_i\Delta f)t + \phi_i] \tag{4.1}$$

where S is the transmitted power, f_0 is the carrier frequency, ϕ_i is the random phase associated with the i-th transmitted tone, $\Delta f = kT_s$ (k integer) is the frequency spacing between tones in the M-ary set, and d_i is the value of the i-th data symbol chosen from the set of integers $\{1, 2, \ldots, M\}$. To reduce the chance of the interceptor detecting his message and also to combat jamming, the communicator will employ an SS modulation which typically takes on the form of frequency hopping (FH) or a combination (hybrid) of FH with time hopping (TH) and/or direct-sequence pseudonoise (PN). Thus, the four basic SS modulations employed in most LPI systems transmitting MFSK data modulation are FH, FH/PN, FH/TH, and FH/PN/TH. The intrinsic forms of the transmitted signals corresponding to the first two of these SS modulations are[1]

FH

$$s(t) = \sqrt{2S}\sin\left[2\pi\left(f_0 + \frac{n_i + \frac{1}{2}}{T_h}\right)t + \phi_i\right]; \qquad \begin{array}{c} iT_h \le t \le (i+1)T_h \\ n_i \,\varepsilon\{0,1,2,\ldots,N_T - 1\} \end{array}$$

T_h = hop time interval

N_T = total number of hops in SS bandwidth (4.2)

FH/PN

$$s(t) = \sqrt{2S}\,c(t)\sin\left[2\pi\left(f_0 + \frac{n_i + \frac{1}{2}}{T_c}\right)t + \phi_i\right] \qquad \begin{array}{c} iT_h \le t \le (i+1)T_h \\ n_i \,\varepsilon\{0,1,2,\ldots,N_T - 1\} \end{array}$$

$c(t)$ = PN modulation

T_c = PN chip time interval. (4.3)

(Note that here the hop frequency spacing is $1/T_c$, a factor of T_h/T_c larger than for pure FH, to accommodate the bandwidth of the PN modulation.) Although the time-hopped SS modulation types are of interest, we shall focus our attention on the two more commonly found in LPI applications, namely, FH and FH/PN, occasionally making reference to the hybrid TH forms whenever appropriate.

4.2 INTERCEPTION DETECTORS

A great amount of effort has been expended over the past decade on the subject of the properties, configurations, performance, and implementation of intercept detectors and many reports and papers are available which delineate basic detector topology and optimum configurations and methods for performance analysis [1]–[6]. The results produced lay the necessary foundations and provide bounding criteria for detectability as a function of the principal parameters: detection SNR (S/N_0), total message time (T_M) or hop time (T_h), and spread-spectrum bandwidth (W_{ss}) or hop frequency spacing (W_h). (The reason for the choice between T_M or T_h and W_{ss} or W_h is tied to the choice between the two basic approaches to detecting hopped signals, as will become apparent shortly.) Section 4.2.1 presents the most

[1] For simplicity, we have not included the MFSK data modulation in (4.2) or (4.3) since it does not affect the basic form of these expressions or alter their spectral properties.

pertinent aspects of these endeavors and weighs the merits of the basic detector configurations against some practical considerations.

In Section 4.2.2, the suboptimum performance of the detector types is evaluated against the substantial problems of time and frequency synchronization. The results show how little real advantage is likely to be gained by sophisticated channelized detectors over the wideband radiometer type detector.

Finally, Section 4.2.3 begins with a discussion of some implementation considerations associated with wideband single-channel detectors and concludes with a presentation of some potential alternative detection methods, along with an assessment of conditions required for their probable use.

4.2.1 Ideal and Realizable Detectors

In the following subsections, perfect frequency and time synchronization to the received signal structure is assumed. However, no presumption is made with respect to knowledge about the pseudorandomness of the signal's SS states.

4.2.1.1 Detectability Criteria

The interceptor's task is to detect the presence of the communicator's transmission and attempt to identify the communicator's location within a specified geographic area. Since the communicator's message or transmission is not time-continuous and occupies only a brief interval, the interceptor desires a reasonably high probability that such a short message will, in fact, be detected if he is anywhere within detectable range. Thus, the detection probability, P_D, should be close to unity.

On the other hand, the interceptor does not want his equipment to indicate a state of signal detection when no actual signal is present. Such a state of false alarm caused by system noise should have a very low probability P_{FA} of occurrence, perhaps on the order of one false alarm per sortie or per day. Typical values of P_D and P_{FA} might be $P_D = 0.9$ and $P_{FA} = 10^{-6}$.

4.2.1.2 Maximum or Bounding Performance of Fundamental Detector Types

Extensive literature exists on the subject of interceptor detection techniques and performance. All of the various methods for detecting hopped signals fall into two basic types of approach: employing a wideband radiometer matched in bandwidth to the transmission (i.e., W_{ss}) and integrating energy over the entire transmission (i.e., T_M) or using multiple narrowband radiometers whose filter bandwidths and detector integration times are matched, to the bandwidth (W_h) and duration (T_h) of the hop pulse. The second of these two approaches implies, in its generic form, a requirement for a filter at each of the possible hop frequencies. Structures which ease this requirement have also been considered. The basic difference between the various structures realizable under the second approach centers on the decision procedure used to convert the hop pulse detection data into decisions about the presence of a transmission. The following is a summary of the applicable detector types and their relative practical value:

	Detector Type	*Relative Practical Value*
(1)	Wideband Energy Detector (Wideband Radiometer)	Very functional and in general use
(2)	Optimum Multichannel FH Pulse-Matched Detector	Academic—provides an optimum performance bound
(3)	Maximum Channel Filter Bank Combiner (FBC)	Suboptimum version of (2)
(4)	Optimum Partial-Band FH Pulse-Matched Detector	Realizable but complex subconfiguration of (2) [not discussed in this chapter]
(5)	Partial-Band FBC (PB-FBC)	Realizable subconfiguration of (3)

As will be seen from the following discussions, detector types (1) and (5) are those of most utilitarian value to the interceptor. The analyses in the following subsections consider only pure FH signals. In Section 4.2.1.3, the merits of other SS signal forms in terms of detector performance are discussed.

(1) Wideband Energy Detector (Radiometer)

By far the most elementary and easy to implement detector is the wideband energy detector or *radiometer*,[2] shown functionally in Figure 4.1. The wideband detector consists of a bandpass filter (BPF) of center frequency f_0 and bandwidth W (equal to the total FH spread-spectrum bandwidth W_{ss}), a square-law operation followed by a T-second integrator (reset at the end of each successive T-second period), and a comparator that weighs the integrator output against a threshold value in order to decide if a signal is received for each T-second segment. The size of T is generally dictated by the communicator's message duration T_M. When T_M is short and discontinuous, usually T is set equal to T_M for highest performance.

[2]The generic term "radiometer" refers to a square-law measurement device covering an RF band of interest. Techniques for receivers employing such devices evolved primarily to satisfy the need to measure the extremely weak, broadband non-coherent RF energy radiated by astronomical objects.

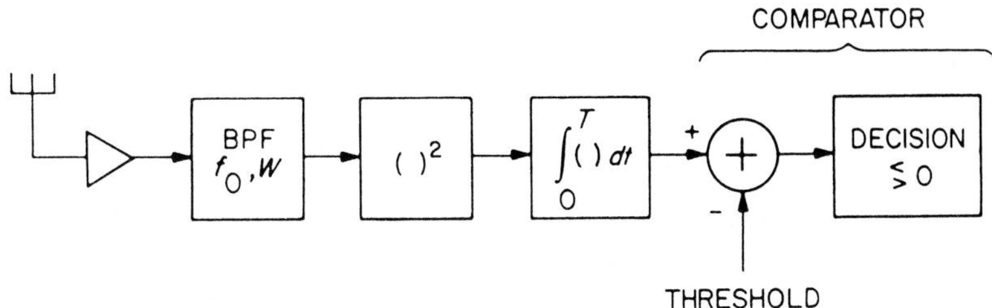

Figure 4.1. Functional wideband energy detector (radiometer).

For large $TW = T_M W_{ss}$ products (large being greater than 1,000 for the typical values of P_D and P_{FA} previously given), the wideband radiometer performance may be calculated using the equations

$$S/N_0 = d\sqrt{W_{ss}/T_M} = W_{ss} d\sqrt{1/W_{ss}T_M} \tag{4.4}$$

and

$$d = Q^{-1}(P_{FA}) - Q^{-1}(P_D) \tag{4.5}$$

where $Q^{-1}(\cdot)$ is the inverse of the Gaussian probability integral. Recognizing the similarity between Figure 4.1 and the detection portions of the single dwell serial search PN and FH acquisition schemes discussed in Chapters 1 and 3, respectively, then (4.4) together with (4.5) is identical[3] to (1.81) with the appropriate substitutions of notation, i.e., $A^2 \to S$, $\tau_d \to T_M$, and $B \to W_{ss}$. Figure 4.2 is a plot of P_D versus d in dB with P_{FA} as a parameter. For the sample typical values of $P_D = .9$ and $P_{FA} = 10^{-6}$, we obtain $d = 6$ (7.8 dB), which for given values of SS bandwidth and total message time enables computation, from (4.4), of the minimum value of S/N_0 above which the communicator is detectable.

Before leaving this subsection, we point out that using a continuous integrator (over a T-sec interval) rather than an I & D as indicated in Figure 4.1, in general, yields significantly better performance since it ensures alignment in time with the signal. However, calculations based on I & D detection and the assumption of perfect alignment of sampling times with signal occurrences will provide close estimates of the detection performance of continuous integration [5]. Thus, we have justified the ease of analysis afforded by the assumption of I & D detection with perfect message alignment. More will be said later on regarding the degradation due to imperfect alignment.

[3] One other simplifying assumption is made in arriving at (4.4) and (4.5) from (1.81), namely that $S/N_0W \ll 1$ and thus $\sqrt{1 + 2S/N_0W} \cong 1$. This is equivalent to assuming equal variances for the integrator output under signal-plus-noise-and noise-only conditions.

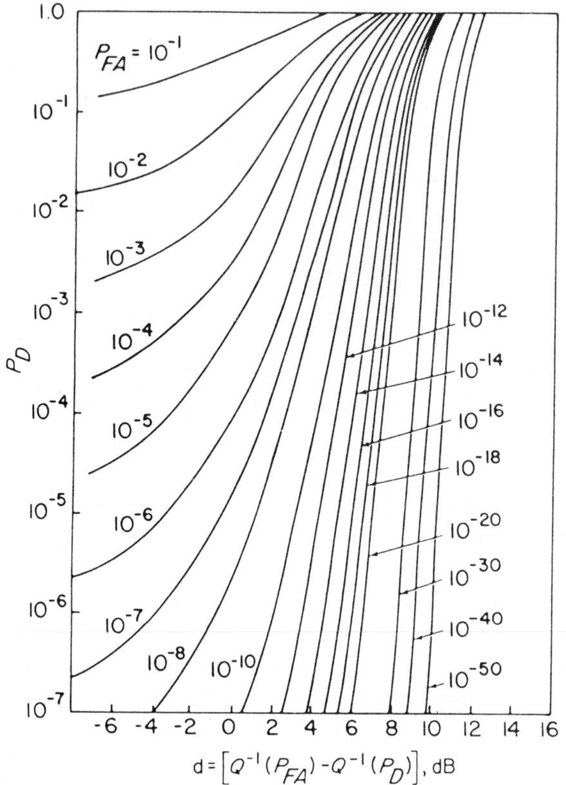

Figure 4.2. Radiometer probability of detection P_D and probability of false alarm P_{FA} versus parameter $d = [Q^{-1}(P_{FA}) - Q^{-1}(P_D)]$ (reprinted from [4]).

(2) Optimum Multichannel FH Pulse-Matched Energy Detector

From (4.4), it may be seen that the wideband detector's performance in terms of S/N_0 is proportional to the square root of the spread-spectrum total bandwidth, W_{ss}. Actually, all basic square-law detectors behave in proportion to the square root of the input bandwidth. Thus, if it is somehow possible to effectively reduce W_{ss}, greater S/N_0 sensitivity will be obtained.

The only realistic way to effectively reduce W_{ss} is to subdivide the total bandwidth into, say, K sub-bands or channels, each having bandwidth $W_K = W_{ss}/K$. Each channel then forms the basis of a separate energy detector and the outputs of the K channels are further processed to render the overall detection decision. Figure 4.3 shows the functional configuration wherein each channel has bandwidth W_{ss}/K and is contiguous with respect to those adjacent.

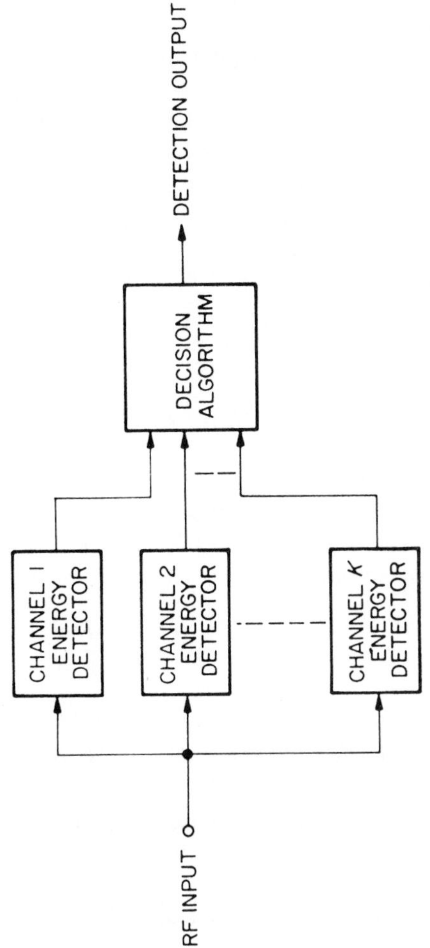

Figure 4.3. Topology of the multiple-channel detector.

It can be shown (see Appendix 4A) that an arbitrary choice of K without regard to the FH frequency cell bandwidth, W_h, and the FH hop period T_h, will lead to performance inferior to that of the wideband detector. The key to superior operation is that the individual channels be matched to the individual hop pulses in both bandwidth and time. Thus, $W_K = W_h$ and $T = T_h$.

An optimum multichannel detector is one having N_T channels (N_T is the total number of hop cells in W_{ss}) and utilizing a likelihood ratio decision algorithm. Figure 4.4 indicates the essential elements. Each channel consists of an energy detector (BPF, squarer, and integrator), followed by scaling. The channel outputs are summed at the end of each hop period and the sums from all N_h hops in the message are multiplied, with the result being compared to a threshold, l, in order to decide if a signal is present at the detector input.

The generalized performance expression for the optimum multichannel detector cannot be obtained due to an inability to specify the output probability distribution functions. When N_h is large (e.g., $N_h > 100$), however, it is possible to closely approximate the true answer by using Gaussian statistics, with the result that S/N_0 is given by [4]:

$$\frac{S}{N_0} = \frac{W_h}{2} I_0^{-1}\left[1 - N_T + N_T \exp\left(d^2/N_h\right)\right] \tag{4.6}$$

where I_0^{-1} is the inverse of the zero-order modified Bessel function of the first kind, and d is given as per (4.5). Since $N_T = W_{ss}/W_h$ and $T_M = N_h T_h$, then letting $W_h T_h = 1$ (as is typical for FH), we arrive at $N_T = W_{ss} T_M / N_h$, which, when substituted in (4.6) results in the alternate expression

$$\frac{S}{N_0} = \frac{W_{ss}}{2N_T} I_0^{-1}\left[1 - N_T + N_T \exp\left(\frac{d^2 N_T}{W_{ss} T_M}\right)\right]. \tag{4.7}$$

Figure 4.5 is a plot of the ratio (in dB) of S/N_0 as determined from (4.4) to S/N_0 of (4.7) versus $W_{ss}T_M$ with the total number of hops N_T in the SS bandwidth as a parameter.[4] For a given $W_{ss}T_M$ and N_T these results illustrate the increase in detectability obtained by the interceptor by using an optimum multichannel detector rather than a wideband radiometer. For example, if $W_{ss}T_M = 8 \times 10^9$, then for $N_T = 10^6$, the optimum detector has an 11.1 dB advantage.[5] If this could be fully realized, it would allow an almost fourfold increase in the detection range over that possible with the wideband radiometer. Clearly, the price for the optimum detector's superior performance is complexity, both in terms of functional operations and the

[4]Note that in comparing the required S/N_0's of the two detectors, it is not necessary to know either the SS bandwidth W_{ss} or the hop rate $R_h = 1/T_h$. Rather the *product* of W_{ss} and the message time T_M, and the total number of hops N_T in W_{ss}, are all that enter the calculation.

[5]This value of $W_{ss}T_M$ is used in [4].

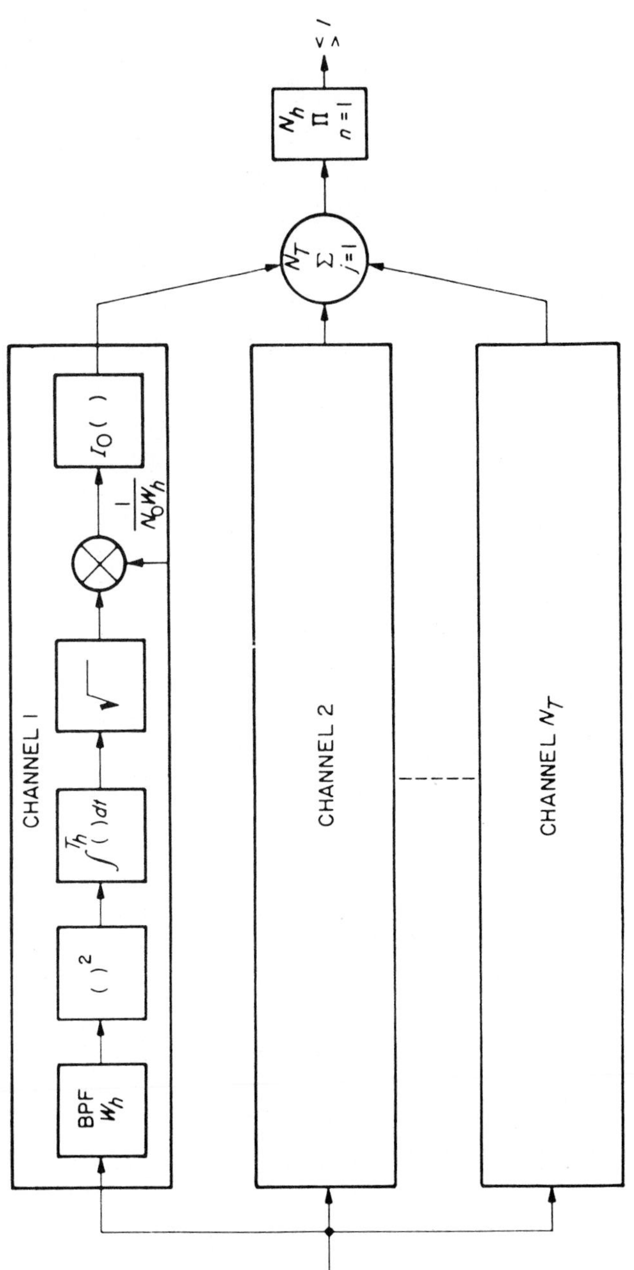

Figure 4.4. Optimum detector for frequency-hopped signals.

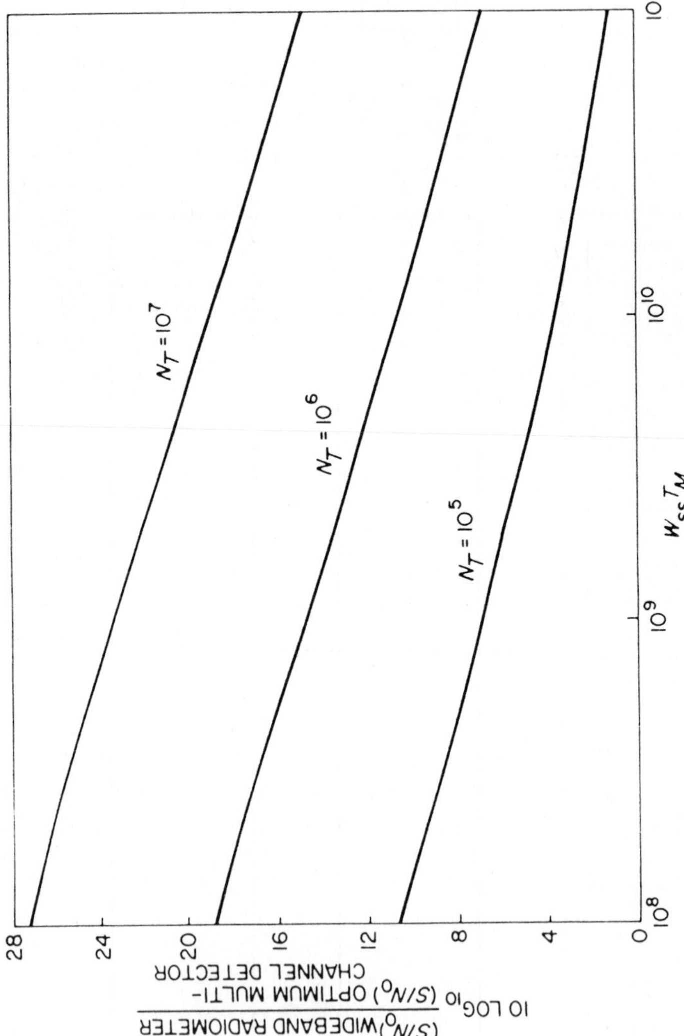

Figure 4.5. S/N_0 performance gain of optimum multichannel detector over wideband radiometer.

number of channels required; for the example above, the detector must have one million channels! Since this seems prohibitive in terms of size, power, and cost (even in the MIC and LSI era), the optimum detector is deemed unfeasible. A more realistic approach is that of the partial-band filter bank combiner. First, we discuss the full-band filter bank combiner in terms of its differences with respect to the optimum multichannel detector.

(3) Filter Bank Combiner (FBC) Detector

Figure 4.6 shows the basic FBC. A comparison with the optimum detector of Figure 4.4 reveals that the energy detector portions are the same but that a decision in each channel relative to a threshold k has replaced the scaling operations. Thus, each channel is allowed to detect the presence or absence of a hop pulse each T_h seconds, with the output of the decision circuit being a logic 1 or 0, respectively. All decisions are subsequently OR'd (i.e., the output of the OR gate is a logic 1 if any of the individual channel decisions are logic 1), and the number of OR output logic 1 states is accumulated over the number of hops in the message duration, i.e., $N_h = T_M/T_h$. The result is finally compared with the threshold l to determine if a message has been detected.

The obvious advantage of the FBC over the optimum multichannel detector is its simpler decision structure obtained for a cost of higher required S/N_0 for the same P_D and P_{FA} performance. Calculation of the FBC S/N_0 requirement cannot be found directly due again to the non-Gaussian nature of the variables, coupled with the fact that the FBC has two decision thresholds, k and l. Computer simulations [3] have found that the "best performance" value of l lies somewhere between five and twenty-five, depending on the values of the other parameters (P_D, P_{FA}, T_h and W_h). A somewhat pessimistic performance bound for the FBC can be obtained by letting $l = 1$, the result being between about 1–2 dB higher in S/N_0 [4]. With $l = 1$, the problem simply reduces to determining the probability of detection and false alarm as a function of the other parameters on a per-channel basis. With the overall message detection and false alarm probabilities being designated as P_D and P_{FA}, respectively, the individual channel probabilities are given by

$$P_{DI} \cong P_D/N_h = P_D N_T/(W_{ss}T_M) \tag{4.8a}$$

$$P_{FAI} \cong P_{FA}/(N_h N_T) = P_{FA}/(W_{ss}T_M) \tag{4.8b}$$

provided that N_T and N_h are sufficiently large. The required S/N_0 may then be calculated using the relationships

$$S/N_0 = \eta d_I \sqrt{W_h/T_h} = \frac{W_{ss}}{N_T}\eta d_I \sqrt{\frac{1}{W_h T_h}} = \frac{W_{ss}}{N_T}\eta d_I \tag{4.9a}$$

$$d_I = Q^{-1}(P_{FAI}) - Q^{-1}(P_{DI}) \tag{4.9b}$$

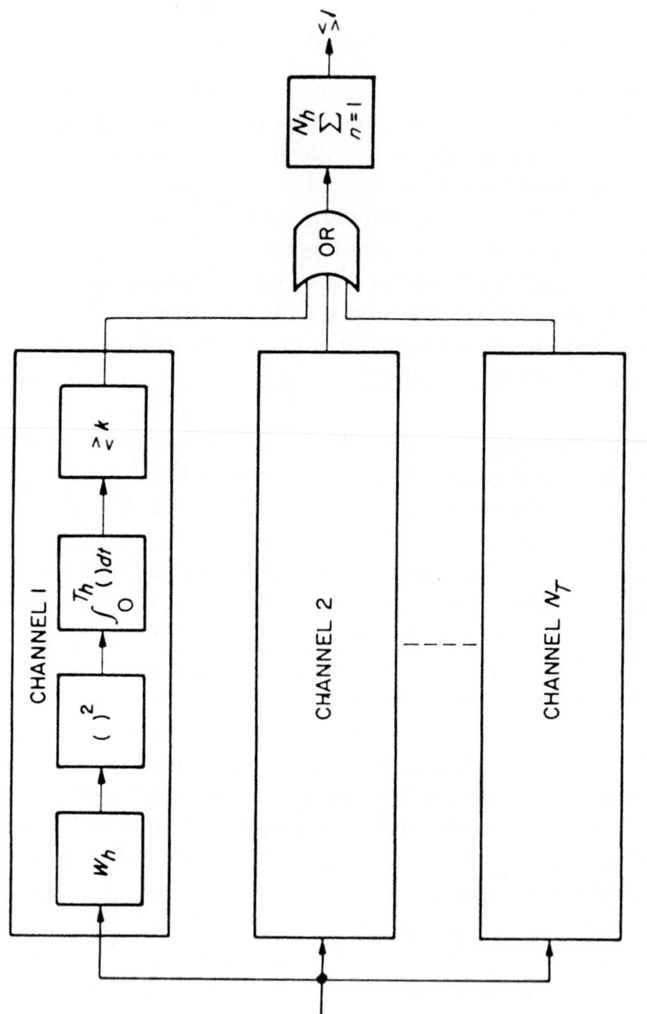

Figure 4.6. Filter bank combiner.

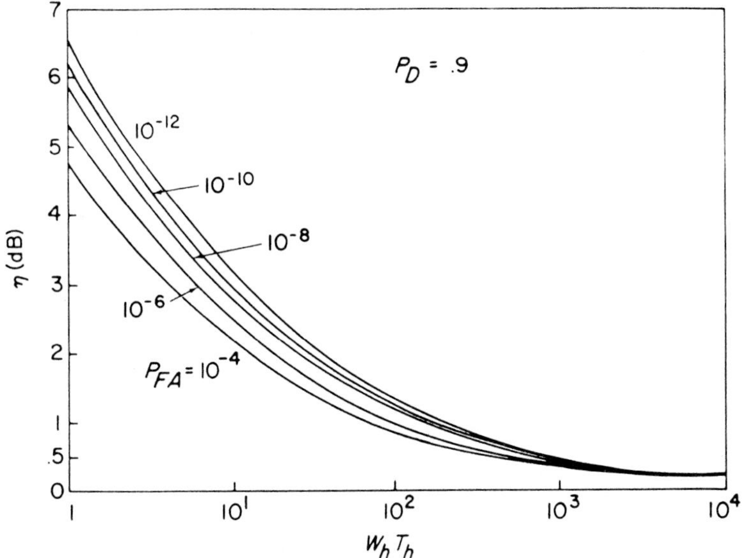

Figure 4.7a. Correction factor η for Gaussian approximation as a function of time-bandwidth product ($P_D = .9$) (reprinted from [4]).

where η is a chi-square correction factor[6] applied to the Gaussian-assumed d_I of (4.9b). Curves of η as a function of P_{DI}, P_{FAI}, and $W_h T_h$ are given in Figure 4.7.

Returning now to the continuing example parameters ($P_D = .9$, $P_{FA} = 10^{-6}$), the $l = 1$ FBC performance as given by (4.9) relative to that of the optimum multichannel detector (4.7) is 3.2 dB worse for $W_{ss} T_M = 8 \times 10^9$ and $N_T = 10^6$. For $N_T = 10^5$ and 10^7, the corresponding performance degradations are 5.1 dB and 2.8 dB respectively. A complete set of curves analogous to Figure 4.5 for the ratio of S/N_0 given by (4.9a) to S/N_0 of (4.7) is hard to come by due to the difficulty in interpolating between the individual graphs in Figure 4.7a–f for different values of P_{DI}. Nevertheless, a coarse examination of the behavior of this S/N_0 ratio over a decade variation in $W_{ss} T_M$ above and below the above sample value reveals a rather insensitive behavior (approximately a $\pm$ 1 dB variation in the ratio for each of these values of N_T). Finally, if l is optimized (somewhere between 5 and 25) with the corresponding adjustments being made for P_{DI} and P_{FAI}, it is

[6] Note that, when $W_h T_h$ is small ($W_h T_h = 1$ in the case at hand), the output of the energy detector cannot be approximated by Gaussian statistics. Use of the Gaussian approximation to the chi-square distribution will yield results which are generally pessimistic in the predicted covertness of the waveform (i.e., the calculated S/N_0 will be less than the true value).

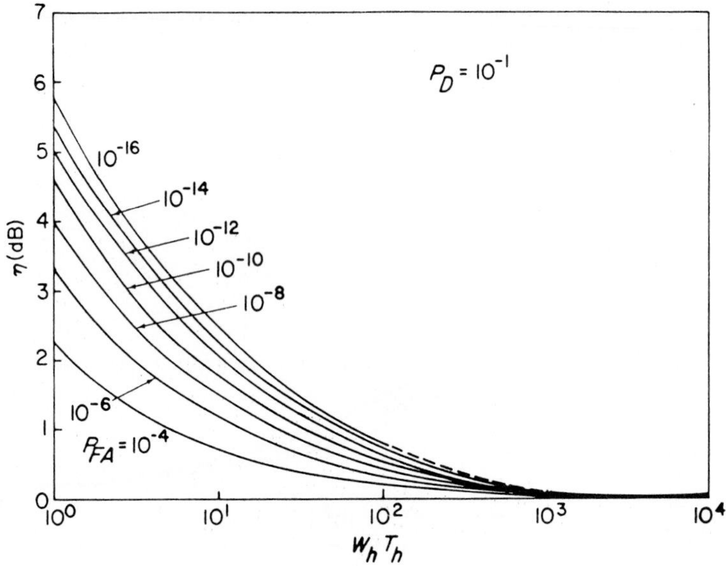

Figure 4.7b. Correction factor η for Gaussian approximation as a function of time-bandwidth product ($P_D = 10^{-1}$) (reprinted from [4]).

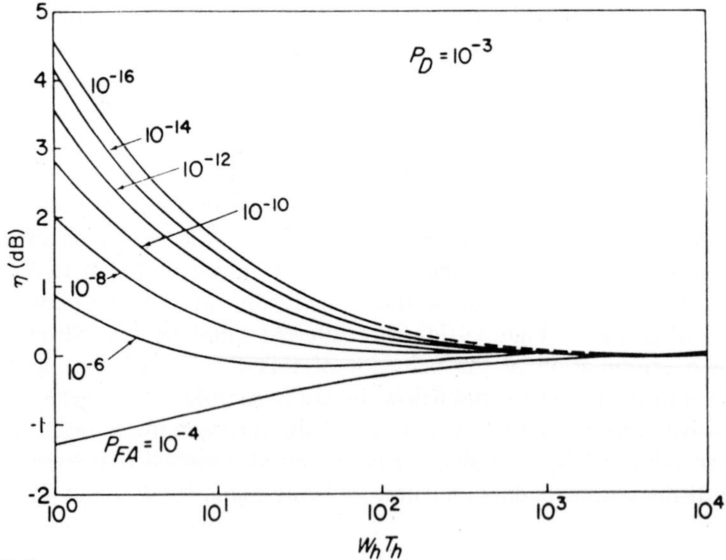

Figure 4.7c. Correction factor η for Gaussian approximation as a function of time-bandwidth product ($P_D = 10^{-3}$) (reprinted from [4]).

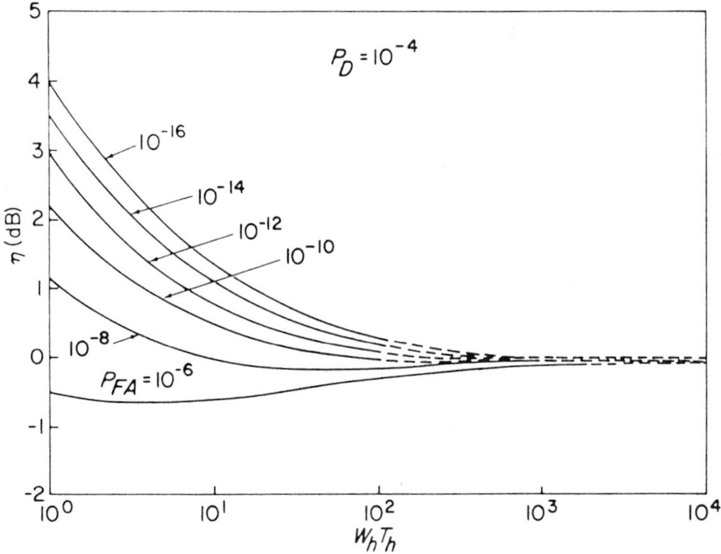

Figure 4.7d. Correction factor η for Gaussian approximation as a function of time-bandwidth product ($P_D = 10^{-4}$) (reprinted from [4]).

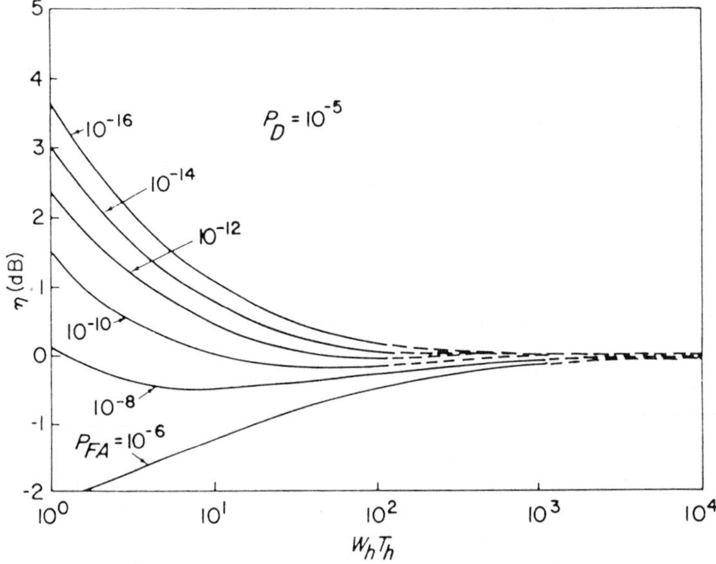

Figure 4.7e. Correction factor η for Gaussian approximation as a function of time-bandwidth product ($P_D = 10^{-5}$) (reprinted from [4]).

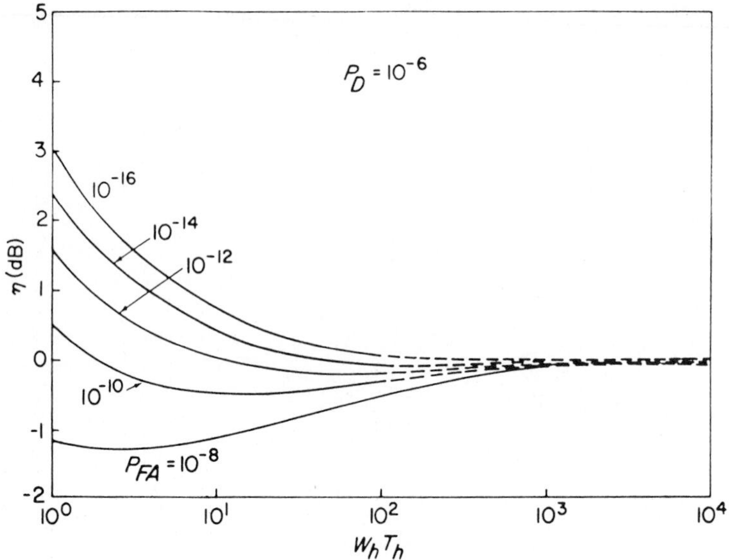

Figure 4.7f. Correction factor η for Gaussian approximation as a function of time-bandwidth product ($P_D = 10^{-6}$) (reprinted from [4]).

expected that the FBC performance may be on the order of only 1.7 dB worse than the optimum detector (1.5 dB better than the $l = 1$ FBC).

At the modest cost of about 1.7 dB of S/N_0 required, it is therefore seen that the reduced complexity FBC is a more practical topology for a multichannel detector. However, even though the individual channels and their output combiner is simplified, one million channels are still required to achieve the above performance. One million less-complex channels, practically speaking, still remains untenable.

(4) Partial-Band Filter Bank Combiner (PB-FBC)

The PB-FBC is simply an FBC with less than the optimum or maximum number of channels. Suppose that $N_T' < N_T$ channels are used, each channel still matched to one of the candidate FH frequencies. The channel reduction factor is defined as $f = N_T'/N_T$.

A new consideration now enters the detector performance. When all N_T channels are implemented, a hop frequency must appear at any given time in one of the channel filters. If only N_T' channels are employed, then, on a per-hop basis, a specific hop frequency will not be covered by the filter bank if it corresponds to a deleted channel. Thus, from hop to hop, it becomes a probabilistic matter as to whether or not the PB-FBC will have a signal within one of its filters. When a signal is present within one of the channels, this condition is known as a "hit." The probability of a hit, assuming that one of the N_T possible hop frequencies may, with equal likelihood, be transmitted on any given hop interval, is $P_{\text{hit}} = f$.

One view of the performance penalty paid for a partial-band detector is to consider what happens to the per-channel detection probabilities P_{DI} and P_{FAI}. If the transmitted message is sufficiently long (for the moment, assume that it is infinite in duration or continuous), then, on the average, the effective per-hop detection probability is $P'_{DI} = P_{DI}P_{\text{hit}}$. The per-channel false alarm probability, however, is unchanged, as it always depends on the absence of a hit. Now, since P_D and P_{FA} are the real measures of performance, using relationships akin to (4.8), the following results are obtained:

$$P'_D = N_h P'_{DI} = (N_h P_{DI}) P_{\text{hit}} \tag{4.10a}$$

$$P'_{FA} = N_h N'_T P_{FAI} = (N_h N_T P_{FAI}) f. \tag{4.10b}$$

But, because $P_{\text{hit}} = f$, it is readily seen that $P'_D = P_D f$ and $P'_{FA} = P_{FA} f$, i.e., the original probabilities are reduced by the channel reduction factor, f. There are only two ways to restore the desired performance: (1) increase the per-channel P_{DI} and P_{FAI} values by $1/f$, which requires a higher S/N_0 relative to the full-band FBC, or (2) increase N_h by $1/f$. This latter fix implies that the communicator's message must therefore be longer by a factor of $1/f$ (which is no problem if the message is continuous) but, since the interceptor has absolutely no control over the message duration, increasing N_h represents an untenable solution.

Use of the PB-FBC should be predicated on its performance being equivalent to the full-band FBC for all conditions except that of a larger S/N_0 requirement. On very short messages, however, the considerations are a bit more complex. What must be factored into the performance criteria is the probability of a given number of hits, n, per message, this being determined by the binomial distribution, viz.,

$$P(n) = \frac{N_h!}{n!(N_h - n)!}(P_{\text{hit}})^n (1 - P_{\text{hit}})^{N_h - n}. \tag{4.11}$$

Defining P^*_{DI} and P^*_{FAI} as the per-channel detection and false alarm probabilities needed to achieve the PB-FBC short message detection and false alarm probabilities, P_D and P_{FA}, the actual P_D conditioned on n is given by

$$P_D(n) = 1 - (1 - P^*_{DI})^n (1 - P^*_{FAI})^{N_h - n} \tag{4.12}$$

whereupon the message detection probability, P_D, is obtained by averaging (4.12) over the probability distribution of (4.11), namely,

$$P_D = \sum_{n=1}^{N_h} P_D(n) P(n). \tag{4.13}$$

Equation (4.13) cannot be easily calculated without the use of a computer;

however, with N_h large and P^*_{FAI} very small, the approximation

$$P_D \cong P_D(\bar{n}) \tag{4.14}$$

is valid, where $\bar{n}$ is the mean of the distribution in (4.11), namely,

$$\bar{n} = \sum_{n=1}^{N_h} nP(n) = N_h f. \tag{4.15}$$

Substituting (4.15) into (4.12) and ignoring the $(1 - P^*_{FAI})^{N_h - n}$ factor gives

$$P_D \cong 1 - \left(1 - P^*_{DI}\right)^{N_h f}. \tag{4.16}$$

Solving for P^*_{DI} yields the desired result

$$\begin{aligned} P^*_{DI} &= 1 - (1 - P_D)^{1/N_h f} \\ &= 1 - \left(1 - P_D\right)^{N_T/(W_{ss}T_M f)}. \end{aligned} \tag{4.17}$$

The companion relationship for P^*_{FAI} is

$$\begin{aligned} P^*_{FAI} &= P_{FA}/(N_T N_h f) \\ &= P_{FA}/(W_{ss}T_M f). \end{aligned} \tag{4.18}$$

Equations (4.17) and (4.18) are therefore used in lieu of (4.8a) and (4.8b), respectively, for computing the performance of the PB-FBC as per (4.9).

The preceding gives the average or expected performance of the PB-FBC for a single message having N_h hops. It is instructive to examine the conditional detection probability in order to gain an understanding of the true statistical nature of per-message detection using a PB-FBC. For this purpose, it is necessary to return to the numerical example. A recapitulation of the parameter values is:

$$\begin{aligned} P_D &= 0.9 \\ P_{FA} &= 10^{-6} \\ N_T &= 10^6 \\ W_{ss}T_M &= 8 \times 10^9 \\ N_h &= 8000. \end{aligned}$$

Suppose that it is decided that an $N'_T = 1000$-channel PB-FBC is practical (rather than the one-million-channel FBC), then $f = P_{\text{hit}} = N'_T/N_T = 10^{-3}$. The per-channel probabilities calculated using (4.17) and (4.18) become $P^*_{DI} = 0.25$ and $P^*_{FAI} = 1.25 \times 10^{-13}$. (Contrast these numbers with $P_{DI} = 1.25 \times 10^{-4}$ and $P_{FAI} = 1.25 \times 10^{-16}$ for the one-million-channel FBC). Also note that $\bar{n} = N_h f = 8$, i.e., this is the average number of hits per message.

Table 4.1 lists $P(N)$, $P_D(N)$, and the cumulative probability, $\Pr\{n \le N\}$ as functions of N. The interpretation is that, for any given message of 8000 hops, there could be N hits with probability $P(N)$ and the

Table 4.1
Binomial distribution detection probabilities, $P_D = P_D(\bar{n}) = 0.9$.

N	$P(N)$	$P_D(N)$	$\Pr\{n \leq N\} = \sum_{n=0}^{N} P(n)$
0	0.000334	0	0.000334
1	0.002675	0.250	0.003009
2	0.010712	0.438	0.013722
3	0.028587	0.578	0.042308
4	0.057209	0.684	0.099519
5	0.091581	0.763	0.191098
6	0.122153	0.822	0.313252
7	0.139639	0.867	0.452890
8	0.139656	0.900	0.592547
9	0.124139	0.925	0.716686
10	0.099298	0.944	0.815985
11	0.072199	0.958	0.881843
12	0.048115	0.968	0.936299
13	0.029594	0.976	0.965893
14	0.016900	0.982	0.982793

corresponding conditional probability of detection $P_D(N)$. Note that eight or more hits per message are required to raise $P_D(N)$ to the point where it equals or exceeds the desired $P_D = 0.9$. The probability of this happening is only $\Pr\{n \geq 8\} = 0.55$. (For the full-band FBC, there is no hit conditional statistic so that $P_D = 0.9$ can be expected with unit probability.) The inference, then, is that, if P_D is to be quite close to 0.9 in a single-message basis, a further modification of P_{DI}^* is in order. Say it is desired to equal or exceed $P_D = 0.9$, with a corresponding hit-related probability of 0.9. This requires $P_D(N) \geq 0.9$, which, from Table 4.1 demands that $N \geq 5$. Using these values in (4.12) results in $P_{DI}^* = 0.37$ (rather than 0.25, as above).

Suppose, now, that the PB-FBC is reduced to a single channel. The per-hop hit probability becomes $P_{\text{hit}} = 10^{-6}$ and the probability of one or more hits in the 8000-hop message sequence would be only 7.9×10^{-3}. Clearly, since at least one hit is required for detection, these are very unfavorable odds, and the interceptor would not use a single-channel FBC no matter how high S/N_0 might be. What, then, is a reasonable lower limit on the number of channels, i.e., how small can f be allowed to become? As a minimum, at least one hit per message is needed. In [3], it is suggested that f must be greater than or equal to $1/N_h$. Taking $f = P_{\text{hit}} = 1/N_h$, the probability of one or more hits per message is $1 - (1 - 1/N_h)^{N_h}$. For very large N_h, it can be easily shown that this quantity approaches $1 - e^{-1} = 0.632$. This figure may be only marginally acceptable, as explained previously. If the probability of one or more hits per message is to be, say, 0.9, then P_{hit} will have to be increased from 10^{-6} to 2.87×10^{-4} and the minimum f becomes $f = 2.3/N_h$. Further, on the basis that a single hit is to

Table 4.2
PB-FBC $\Delta S/N_0$ requirements; $P_D = 0.9$, $P_{FA} = 10^{-6}$

f	Number of Channels	$P_{DI}^{*\#}$	$\Delta S/N_0$ Relative to the Full-Band FBC^{+}
1	1,000,000	1.125×10^4	0 dB
10^{-2}	10,000	0.045	+2.8 dB
10^{-3}	1,000	0.37	+3.8 dB
5×10^{-4}	500	0.536	+4.5 dB
2.88×10^{-4}	288	0.90	+5.6 dB
1.25×10^{-4}	125	0.90@	+5.4 dB

Based on a hit-related probability of 0.9 (see text)
+ The second detection threshold $l = 1$ in all cases
@Hit-related probability is 0.63 (see text)

be adequate for detection, the per-hop channel detection probability must be made equal to the overall detection probability, i.e., $P_{DI}^{*} = P_D$. Thus, a detection probability of 0.9 will be achieved if a hit occurs, while the probability of no hits per message will be 0.368 for a 125-channel absolute minimum channel PB-FBC, and 0.1 for a PB-FBC that has 288 channels.

Table 4.2 summarizes the $\Delta S/N_0$ requirements for the PB-FBC relative to the full-band FBC as a function of f. As can be seen, the cost is significant, especially for the 1000 or less channel PB-FBC, which represents the range of practical detectors.

A summary of the relative performance of the various detector configurations discussed to this point appears in Table 4.3. What should be deduced is the gross complexity (as measured by the number of channels) versus the

Table 4.3
Performance comparison of detector types using wideband radiometer as reference.

Detector Type	Number of Channels	Required $\Delta S/N_0$	Implementation Notes
Optimum Multichannel	10^6	−11.1 dB	Impractical because of large number of channels
Full-Band Filter Bank Combiner	10^6	−7.9 dB	Impractical because of large number of channels
Partial-Band Filter Bank Combiner	1000 500 125	−4.1 dB −3.4 dB −2.5 dB	Practical but quite complex and costly to build using analog mechanization of the channels
Wideband Energy	1	0 dB	Simplest and least costly of all types to build

performance tradeoff. Taking, for example, the 500-channel PB-FBC as representative of the realizable multichannel class, it can be seen that its S/N_0 performance is 7.7 dB inferior to the optimum detector and only 3.4 dB superior to the wideband detector. In fact, as will be shown in Section 4.2.2.2, even the 3.4 dB advantage virtually disappears when the practical problem of frequency synchronization is considered. Obviously, since the PB-FBC will cost significantly more than the wideband energy detector (see Section 4.2.3), its slight performance advantage is judged insufficient to justify its general use.

4.2.1.3 Signal Structure and Modulation Considerations

In the preceding subsections, the performance of the various detector types was viewed solely from the perspective of pure FH modulation. The effects of using PN and TH modulation in conjunction with FH will now be examined. We begin by briefly examining the effects on the impractical optimum multichannel detector.

When PN modulation is used in conjunction with frequency hopping as in (4.3), the bandwidth of each hop is increased to the PN chip rate $R_c = 1/T_c$. Thus the time-bandwidth product of each hop becomes

$$N \triangleq W_h T_h = T_h R_c > 1. \tag{4.19}$$

The optimum multichannel detector in this case has a structure identical to Figure 4.4 with the operation $I_0(\cdot)$ replaced by $K_N(\cdot)$ where

$$K_N(x) \triangleq \left[\frac{I_{N-1}(Nx)}{(Nx)^{N-1}}\right] 2^{N-1}\Gamma(N). \tag{4.20}$$

The performance of this detector is similarly given by (4.7) with $I_0^{-1}(\cdot)$ replaced by $K_N^{-1}(\cdot)$, i.e.,

$$\frac{S}{N_0} = \frac{W_{ss}}{2N_T} K_N^{-1}\left[1 - N_T + N_T \exp\left(\frac{d^2 N_T}{W_{ss} T_M}\right)\right]. \tag{4.21}$$

For convenience, the function $\frac{1}{2}K_N^{-1}(y)$ (in dB) is plotted against y in dB in Figure 4.8, with N as a parameter. For large values of N, a good approximation to $\frac{1}{2}K_N^{-1}(y)$ is [4]

$$\frac{1}{2} K_N^{-1}(y) \cong \sqrt{\frac{\ln y}{N}} \tag{4.22}$$

which is quite accurate for $\frac{1}{2}K_N^{-1}(y) < \frac{1}{4}(-6 \text{ dB})$ which corresponds to $N \gtrsim 200$ for the range of y plotted in Figure 4.8. Thus, using (4.22) in (4.21) gives the simplified relation

$$\frac{S}{N_0} = \frac{W_{ss}}{N_T}\left\{\frac{1}{N}\ln\left[1 - N_T + N_T \exp\left(\frac{d^2 N_T}{W_{ss} T_M}\right)\right]\right\}^{1/2}; N > 200. \tag{4.23}$$

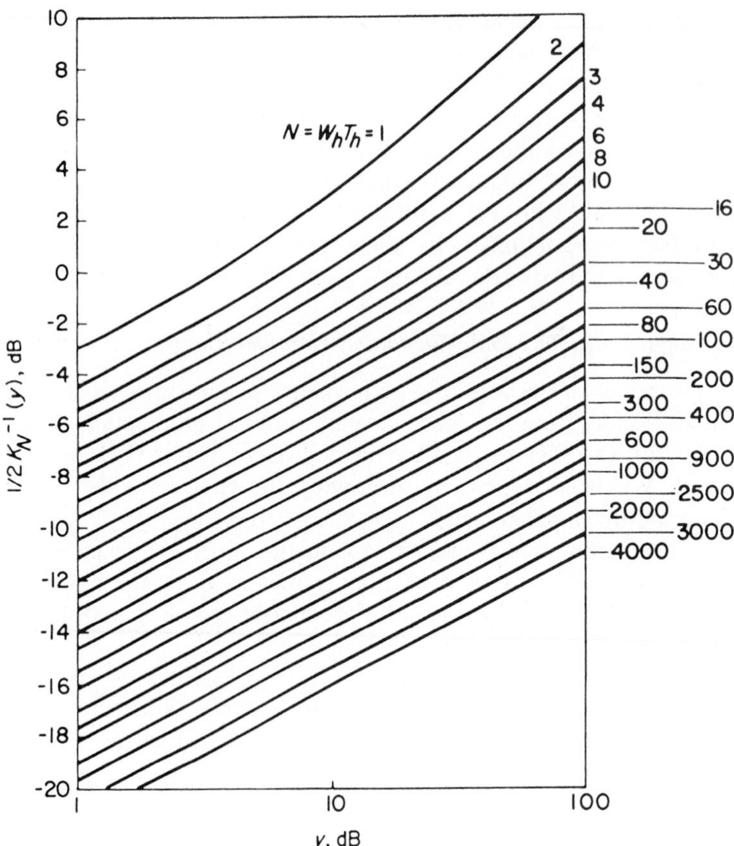

Figure 4.8. Optimum receiver channel weighting factor for several bandwidth-time products (reprinted from [4]).

For the more important practical detector types, namely, the wideband energy detector and the partial-band filter bank combiner, it has previously been seen that the underlying equation of performance is of the form

$$S/N_0 = (\eta d)\sqrt{W_x/T_x} \tag{4.24}$$

where ηd is a function of the desired P_D and P_{FA} together with the statistical (non-Gaussian) nature of the decision quantities, W_x is the detection channel bandwidth, and T_x is the detection integration interval. A wideband detector requires $W_x = W_{ss}$ (total hop bandwidth) and $T_x = T_M$ (total message duration) while, for the PB-FBC, $W_x = W_h$ (hop pulse bandwidth) and $T_x = T_h$ (hop pulse duration). The communicator therefore has three parameters which he may change or influence in some fashion to make detection more difficult for the interceptor, namely, his transmitter power, which directly affects S/N_0, W_x, and T_x.

For the wideband detector, it is clear that restructuring the signal per-hop bandwidth within a fixed total bandwidth of W_{ss} (assumed to be at its maximum value already due to RF channel allocation regulations) has no impact on wideband detector performance. One option of the communicator is to lower his bit or symbol rate by a factor of $\lambda < 1$. This implies that his transmitter power may also be lowered by this same λ factor (ignoring, for the present, the likely increase in non-coherent combining loss in the receiver), meaning that the interceptor's received S/N_0 is also reduced by λ. Now, since $T_x = T_M$ is increased by $1/\lambda$ (the number of bits per message is fixed), the net effective S/N_0 loss to the interceptor is proportional to $\sqrt{\lambda}$, as can be seen by referring to (4.24). It is clear that not quite all of this advantage will be gained if the communicator's non-coherent combining losses are accounted for, but some increase in covertness can be expected from this strategy.

The other option of the communicator as regards the wideband detector is to time hop the message, i.e., to transmit the bits or hop pulses in a time-pseudorandom and non-continuous fashion. Thus, the message transmitter is pulsed on and off in a sequence known only to the communicator. If the transmission is therefore effectively spread in time from T_M to δT_M, $\delta > 1$, the interceptor has no choice but to make his $T_x = \delta T_M$ while, at the same time, his average S/N_0 decreases by $1/\delta$.

Against the wideband detector, then, the communicator may effectively employ a joint strategy of low data rate and TH to the point where he is no longer willing to stretch the total message transmission time beyond some limit (likely dictated by some other operational considerations). The communicator is also frequency hopping over the entire RF band, W_{ss}, but employing further pulse spreading by direct-sequence PN modulation of the instantaneous hop frequencies has no performance effect on the wideband detector.

As concerns the FBC, lowering the communicator's transmitter power as a result of decreasing the data rate (but without altering the hop parameters) can be seen from (4.24) to effectively lower the intercept per-hop detection S/N_0 by λ. On the other hand, the use of TH by the communicator causes the interceptor to raise his ηd because N_h increases, requiring a smaller P^*_{FAI} in order to maintain the specified per-message P_{FA}. However, since ηd is not very sensitive to the increase, the overall effectiveness of this technique is slight. The proper strategy, therefore, is to lower the data rate and corresponding transmitter power as much as possible, again subject to some total transmission time constraint.

Since the PB-FBC operates on the per-hop parameters, the performance being dependent on $\sqrt{W_h/T_h}$, anything the communicator does to increase this quantity directly affects the required intercept S/N_0, forcing it closer to that needed for the wideband detector and discouraging PB-FBC use (especially because of its much higher cost). Now, with pure FH, the per-pulse bandwidth is fixed at $W_h = 1/T_h$. If, for a given T_h, a wider hop pulse bandwidth is desired, it must be brought about by means of additional modulation, namely, PN spreading of the instantaneous hop frequency in accordance with (4.19). Thus the interceptor's S/N_0 requirement appears to increase by $\sqrt{N}$. But it must be remembered that N_T decreases with increasing per-channel bandwidth to $N_{PN} = N_T/N$. This decrease means that the P_{FAI}^* as given by (4.18) is allowed to increase by N. By means of a numerical example, the net effect can be judged. Postulating the 125-channel PB-FBC found in Tables 4.2 and 4.3, suppose that $N = 10$. The required S/N_0 is found to be 2 dB *higher* than that required by the wideband energy detector! (As a point of reference, replacing N_T by $N_{PN} = 10^5$ in (4.21), then making use of Figure 4.8, the optimum multichannel detector still requires 10.1 dB less S/N_0 than the wideband radiometer.)

A general conclusion drawn from this single example is misleading, however. A second example will illustrate that PN spreading of the individual hop frequencies could decrease rather than increase covertness. Suppose that, relative to the ongoing example, the hop rate R_h is reduced by a factor of 20 with all other parameters remaining the same. Then the pertinent system parameters established by the communication are now:

$$W_{ss}T_M = 8 \times 10^9$$

$$N_T = 2 \times 10^7$$

$$N_h = 400 \text{ hops.}$$

The communicator now has two options in terms of signal design: pure FH or FH/PN.

With pure FH, if the interceptor wishes to build a minimum channel PB-FBC, he will have to implement $N_T/N_h = 50{,}000$ channels. Such is probably unjustifiable, so the interceptor opts for the wideband energy detector, which requires the same S/N_0 as before.

Alternatively, assume that the communicator selects FH/PN with a PN code rate such that $N = 10^4$. Then, $N_{PN} = 2000$, meaning that the interceptor could either implement a 2000-channel full-band FBC or a 5-channel minimum-channel PB-FBC (certainly affordable!) The S/N_0 requirements for these two FBCs are, respectively, 5.3 dB and 2.7 dB *below* that of the wideband energy detector. Thus, the interceptor, by virtue of either choice (or any between), is able to better his performance over that of the wideband energy detector. So, for this example, the communicator is seen to lose covertness by selecting FH/PN over pure FH. Of course, it must be conceded that the communicator could be forced to the FH/PN position simply because of the very practical problem of building frequency synthesizers able to produce 2×10^7 frequencies of the required spacing with the necessary accuracy and stability. Nevertheless, the example serves to show that FH/PN is not necessarily superior to pure FH from a sophisticated detector point of view.

As a final point, it should be stated at this juncture that, although the use of PN spreading appears, under appropriate conditions, to doom the PB-FBC to a position of virtual uselessness, the PB-FBC actually attains this distinction on its own when the effects of imperfect frequency synchronization are included in its performance (as discussed in the next section). Thus, the addition of PN spreading will only act to "add icing to the cake." The real value of the PN coding, if it is to have some effective purpose, is to combat jamming of the receiver so that the communicator does not have to increase his transmitter power to overcome the jamming to the same limit as that required when no PN modulation is employed.

4.2.2 Non-Idealistic Detector Performance

4.2.2.1 The Problem of Time Synchronization

The detector performance discussed to this point has been computed on the basis of ideal conditions in that the interceptor has been assumed to have information necessary for perfect time and frequency synchronization. In the case of the former, this is equivalent to saying that the interceptor has exact knowledge of both the time at which a single message transmission originates and the epochs of the individual hop pulses.

In this section, the penalty paid (in increased S/N_0 required) by the interceptor for total lack of time synchronization information is determined. For this more practical or realistic condition, it will be necessary to consider adjunct capabilities to the detectors of Section 4.2.1. Only the wideband energy detector and the FBC will be investigated as they represent the most viable types of detectors useful to the interceptor.

The only continuing assumption will be that the interceptor knows the message duration (T_M) and the hop time interval (T_h). Epochs for the message and its constituent hops are presumed to be unknown. It is also assumed that the interceptor has no means of "learning" so that timing information gleaned from one message transmission will aid in synchronization and detection of a subsequent message (should it occur).

(1) Wideband Detector with Overlapping I & Ds, Each of Duration Equal to that of the Message

Consider, first, a simple modification of the wideband (single-channel) detector wherein the square-law detector output now feeds two T_M-sec integrate and dumps (I & Ds) which overlap $T_M/2$ sec (see Figure 4.9). For this interceptor detector, a signal or noise-only decision will be made every $T_M/2$ seconds.

Assuming with noise only present at the input, an output from either threshold device (corresponding to an I & D output that exceeds the

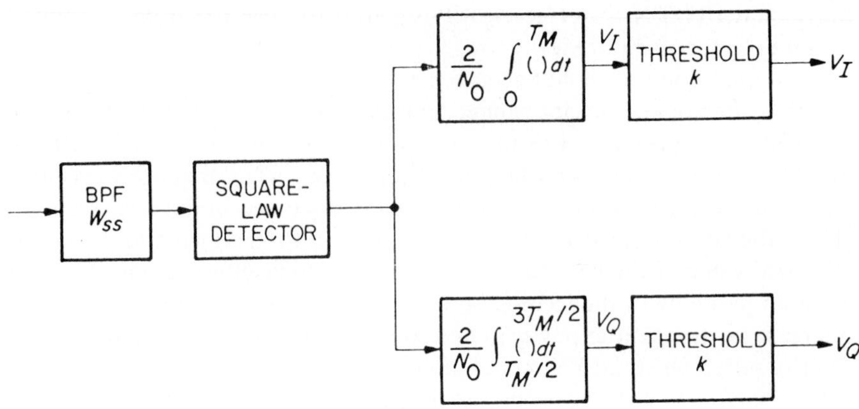

Figure 4.9. Overlapping I & D detector.

threshold k) constitutes a false alarm. The false alarm rate (FAR) is the product of the decision rate $2/T_M$ and the false alarm probability per decision P_{FA}, i.e.,

$$\text{FAR} = \frac{2}{T_M} P_{FA} \tag{4.25}$$

where, as before, for large $W_{ss}T_M$,

$$P_{FA} \cong Q\left[\frac{k - 2W_{ss}T_M}{2\sqrt{W_{ss}T_M}}\right]. \tag{4.26}$$

Thus, to achieve the same false alarm rate as for the basic non-overlapping I & D case, the false alarm probability of (4.26) must be one-half its previous value.

To determine the probability of detection P_D, it is assumed that, with signal-plus-noise present at the input, an output from either threshold device constitutes a true decision, i.e., message detection. When the I & Ds are overlapped as in Figure 4.9, then, in the worst case, three-quarters of the signal energy will be covered by one I & D and three-quarters by the other (assuming that the signal energy is uniformly distributed). This situation is depicted in Figure 4.10.

The above statements can be put into mathematical terms as follows:

$$\begin{aligned} P_D &= \Pr\{V_I > k \text{ or } V_Q > k\} \\ &= 1 - \Pr\{V_I < k \text{ and } V_Q < k\} \end{aligned} \tag{4.27}$$

where, for large $W_{ss}T_M$, V_I and V_Q are jointly Gaussian random variables. For the worst case situation of Figure 4.10, their joint probability density

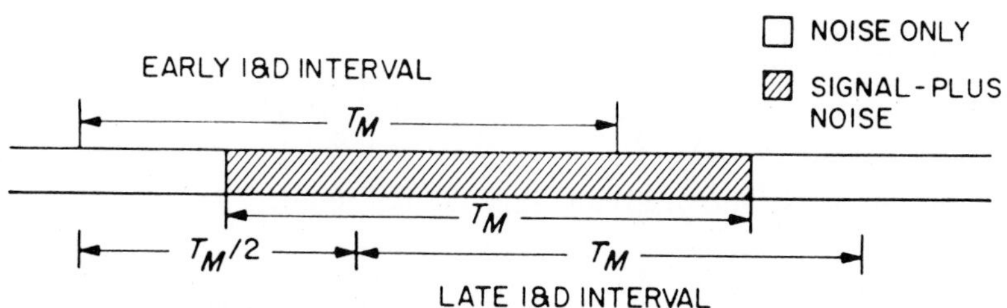

Figure 4.10. Worst case signal misalignment.

function is given by

$$p(V_I, V_Q) = \frac{1}{2\pi\sigma^2\sqrt{1-\rho^2}} \exp\left\{ -\frac{1}{2(1-\rho^2)} \left[\left(\frac{V_I - \mu}{\sigma} \right)^2 + \left(\frac{V_Q - \mu}{\sigma} \right)^2 - 2\rho \frac{(V_I - \mu)(V_Q - \mu)}{\sigma^2} \right] \right\} \tag{4.28}$$

with

$$\rho = \frac{1}{2}\left(\frac{1 + 2\gamma}{1 + \frac{3}{2}\gamma} \right)$$
$$\mu = 2W_{ss}T_M\left(1 + \frac{3\gamma}{4}\right)$$
$$\sigma^2 = 4W_{ss}T_M\left[1 + \frac{3\gamma}{2}\right] \tag{4.29}$$

and

$$\gamma \triangleq \frac{S}{N_0 W_{ss}}. \tag{4.30}$$

The parameter γ in (4.30) represents the signal-to-noise ratio in the input bandwidth.

Using (4.28) the detection probability of (4.27) can be expressed as

$$P_D = 1 - \int_{-\infty}^{k} \int_{-\infty}^{k} p(V_I, V_Q)\, dV_I\, dV_Q \tag{4.31}$$

which unfortunately cannot be obtained in closed form. Nevertheless, P_D can be upper (union) and lower bounded as follows:

$$\begin{matrix} \int_k^\infty p(V_I)\, dV_I \\ \text{or} \\ \int_k^\infty p(V_Q)\, dV_Q \end{matrix} < P_D < \int_k^\infty p(V_I)\, dV_I + \int_k^\infty p(V_Q)\, dV_Q \tag{4.32}$$

or, equivalently,

$$Q\left(\frac{k-\mu}{\sigma}\right) < P_D < 2Q\left(\frac{k-\mu}{\sigma}\right). \tag{4.33}$$

Substituting (4.29) into (4.33) gives the desired result:

$$Q\left(\frac{k - 2W_{ss}T_M\left(1+\frac{3\gamma}{4}\right)}{2\sqrt{W_{ss}T_M\left(1+\frac{3\gamma}{2}\right)}}\right) < P_D < 2Q\left(\frac{k - 2W_{ss}T_M\left(1+\frac{3\gamma}{4}\right)}{2\sqrt{W_{ss}T_M\left(1+\frac{3\gamma}{2}\right)}}\right) \tag{4.34}$$

To determine the S/N_0 required by an interceptor using the overlapped I & D detector of Figure 4.9, for a basis of comparison, the same false alarm rate and detection probability as would be required for a non-overlapped single I & D detector with perfect time synchronization is assumed. Since the overlapped I & D does not have an explicit closed-form expression for P_D, it will be equated to both of the two bounds in (4.34) and thereby a bounding range of values for the required S/N_0 will be obtained.

Proceeding as above, the right-hand side of (4.26) is equated to $P_{FA}/2$, and the threshold k is eliminated between the resulting expression and either the upper or lower bound of (4.34) with the result

$$P_D = C_D Q\left[\frac{Q^{-1}\left(\frac{P_{FA}}{2}\right) - \frac{3}{4}\left(\frac{\lambda}{2\sqrt{W_{ss}T_M}}\right)}{\sqrt{1+\frac{3}{4}\left(\frac{\lambda}{W_{ss}T_M}\right)}}\right] \tag{4.35}$$

where $C_D = 1$ or 2, and

$$\lambda = \frac{2ST_M}{N_0}. \tag{4.36}$$

Since, typically $\lambda \ll W_{ss}T_M$, the square root in (4.35) simplifies to unity. Finally, solving for S/N_0 and substituting the values of 1 or 2 for C_D gives the desired result:

$$\frac{4}{3}\sqrt{\frac{W_{ss}}{T_M}}\left\{Q^{-1}\left(\frac{P_{FA}}{2}\right) - Q^{-1}\left(\frac{P_D}{2}\right)\right\}$$

$$< \left(\frac{S}{N_0}\right) < \frac{4}{3}\sqrt{\frac{W_{ss}}{T_M}}\left\{Q^{-1}\left(\frac{P_{FA}}{2}\right) - Q^{-1}(P_D)\right\}. \tag{4.37}$$

Recall that the equivalent result for the detector with a single non-overlapping I & D (and perfect synchronization) is given by (4.4) together with (4.5).

As an example of the application of (4.37), consider the parameters of the continuing example of Section 4.2.1 ($W_{ss}T_M = 8 \times 10^9$). For the performance criteria of $P_D = 0.9$ and $P_{FA} = 10^{-6}$, the lower and upper bounds on the S/N_0 requirement for the overlapping I & D detector as found from (4.37) are then, respectively, 0.3 dB and 1.2 dB greater than the S/N_0 requirement for the perfectly synchronized wideband energy detector. Alternately stated, for the above performance parameters and the detector of Figure 4.9, the penalty paid by the interceptor for lack of message time synchronization is between 0.3 and 1.2 dB.

(2) *Wideband Detector with Single (Non-Overlapping) I & D of Duration Equal to Half the Message Duration*

A simpler configuration than that of Figure 4.9 is to maintain the identity of the ideal wideband (single channel) detector but reduce the post-detection I & D interval by a factor of two. Thus, by consecutively integrating over only half the message duration, the interceptor is guaranteed to have one interval which contains signal-plus-noise over its entire duration regardless of his initial epoch. Of course, since the integration interval is now only half as long as before, then, relative to the ideal wideband detector with integration over the full message duration and perfect time synchronization, an S/N_0 penalty of approximately a factor of $\sqrt{2}$ (1.5 dB) will be paid.

In the following, a more exact mathematical formulation of the above conclusion will be developed. The worst case situation from the interceptor's viewpoint occurs when one integration interval (the 0-th) sees full signal and the two adjacent intervals (−1-st and 1-st) each contains signals in only half the interval, as shown in Figure 4.11.

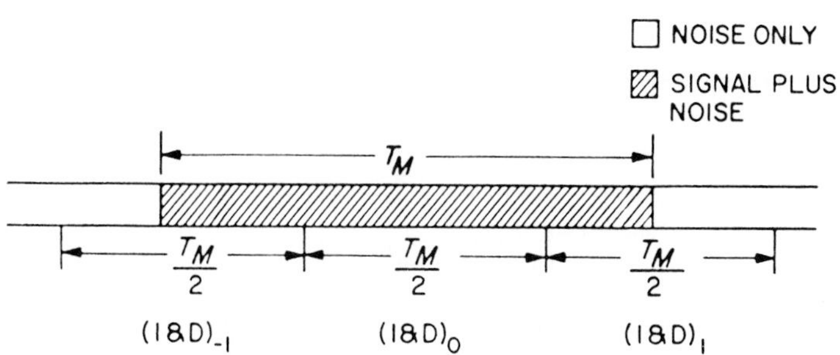

Figure 4.11. Worst case signal condition.

For this case, the probability of detection is

$$P_D = 1 - \Pr\{V_{I_{-1}} < k \text{ and } V_{I_0} < k \text{ and } V_{I_1} < k\}$$

$$= 1 - Q\left(\frac{-k+\mu_{-1}}{\sigma_{-1}}\right) Q\left(\frac{-k+\mu_0}{\sigma_0}\right) Q\left(\frac{-k+\mu_1}{\sigma_1}\right)$$

$$> 1 - Q\left(\frac{-k+\mu_0}{\sigma_0}\right) = Q\left(\frac{k-\mu_0}{\sigma_0}\right) \tag{4.38}$$

where (for large $W_{ss}T_M$)

$$\mu_{-1} = \mu_1 = W_{ss}T_M\left(1 + \frac{1}{2}\gamma\right)$$

$$\mu_0 = 2W_{ss}T_M(1+\gamma)$$

$$\sigma_{-1}^2 = \sigma_1^2 = W_{ss}T_M(1+\gamma)$$

$$\sigma_0^2 = 2W_{ss}T_M(1+2\gamma). \tag{4.39}$$

Since the false alarm probability is still given by (4.26) with, however, T_M replaced by $T_M/2$, then using the lower bound of (4.38) on P_D, together with (4.39), a simple upper bound is obtained on the required interceptor S/N_0, namely,

$$\left(\frac{S}{N_0}\right) < \sqrt{\frac{2W_{ss}}{T_M}}\left\{Q^{-1}(P_{FA}) - Q^{-1}(P_D)\right\}. \tag{4.40}$$

Comparing (4.40) with (4.4) together with (4.5), it is readily observed that the maximum penalty (inferred above) is $\sqrt{2}$ (1.5 dB). Thus, the required S/N_0 falls on the average, between that given by (4.4) and (4.40).

(3) Wideband Detector with a Continuous Integration Post-Detection RC Filter

Perhaps the simplest alternative of all consists of a square-law (envelope) detector followed by an RC filter which acts as a continuous integrator, as shown in Figure 4.12.

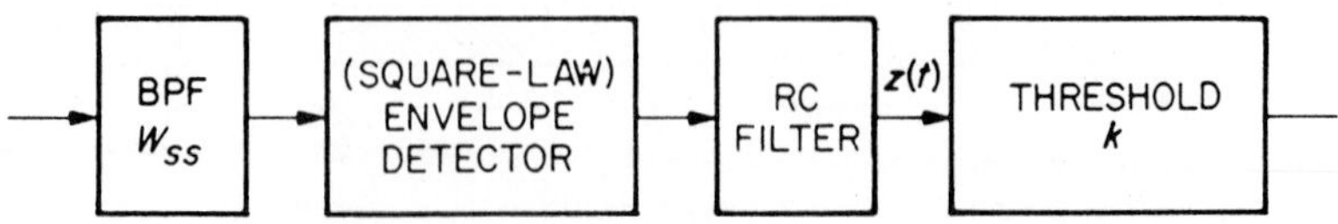

Figure 4.12. Continuous integration detector.

A similar configuration using digital integration is considered in [6]. When noise only is present, the RC filter output is a random process whose instantaneous mean and variance are theoretically constant (independent of time).[7] Furthermore, the instantaneous signal-to-noise ratio (mean-to-standard deviation ratio) is only a function of the ratio of the pre-detection filter bandwidth W_{ss} to the RC filter 3 dB cutoff frequency f_c.

When signal-plus-noise is present, the RC filter output mean and variance become functions of time over the message duration. Furthermore, the mean-to-standard deviation ratio is again a function of W_{ss}/f_c, plus, now, the pre-detection bandwidth signal-to-noise power.

If the noise bandwidth B_N of the RC filter is chosen equal to that of the integrate-and-dump with integration interval equal to the message duration, namely,

$$B_N = \frac{\pi f_c}{2} = \frac{1}{2T_M} \tag{4.41}$$

or, equivalently,

$$\frac{W_{ss}}{f_c} = \pi W_{ss} T_M \tag{4.42}$$

then, for large $W_{ss}T_M$, the RC filter output mean-to-standard deviation ratio becomes

$$\frac{\overline{z(t)}}{\sigma_z} = \begin{cases} \sqrt{W_{ss}T_M}\,; -\infty \le t \le t_1 & \text{(noise only)} \\ \sqrt{\dfrac{W_{ss}T_M}{1 + 2\gamma\left(1 - \exp\left[-\dfrac{4}{T_M}(t - t_1)\right]\right)}} \\ \times\left[1 + \gamma\left(1 - \exp\left[-\dfrac{2}{T_M}(t - t_1)\right]\right)\right]; \\ t_1 \le t \le t_1 + T_M & \text{(signal-plus-noise).} \end{cases} \tag{4.43}$$

In (4.43) the parameter t_1 represents the time epoch of the single message duration T_M.

If any threshold crossing by the RC filter output $z(t)$ constitutes an alarm, then for large W_{ss}/f_c (or, equivalently, large $W_{ss}T_M$), it may be assumed that $z(t)$ is a Gaussian process and the false alarm and detection

[7]From a practical standpoint, it is necessary only to assume that the RC filter has been integrating on noise for a period of time which is long relative to the filter time constant.

probabilities are given by

$$P_{FA} \cong Q\left[\frac{k' - 2W_{ss}T_M}{2\sqrt{W_{ss}T_M}}\right]$$

$$P_D(t) = Q\left[\frac{k' - 2W_{ss}T_M\left[1 + \gamma\left(1 - \exp\left[-\frac{2}{T_M}(t - t_1)\right]\right)\right]}{2\sqrt{W_{ss}T_M\left[1 + 2\gamma\left(1 - \exp\left[-\frac{4}{T_M}(t - t_1)\right]\right)\right]}}\right] \quad (4.44)$$

where the normalized threshold k' is related to the threshold k of Figure 4.12 by

$$k' = \frac{2T_M}{N_0}k. \quad (4.45)$$

The normalization in (4.45) is chosen to make (4.33) analogous to the relations derived for the previous I & D detector configurations.

Letting $t = t_1 + T_M$ in (4.44) (the detection probability is maximized if the RC filter output crosses the threshold at the termination of the message), then eliminating k' between P_{FA} and P_D (as before) gives a relationship for the S/N_0 required by the interceptor, namely,

$$\left(\frac{S}{N_0}\right) = \frac{\sqrt{\frac{W_{ss}}{T_M}}\,\{Q^{-1}(P_{FA}) - Q^{-1}(P_D)\}}{1 - e^{-2}}. \quad (4.46)$$

Comparing (4.46) with (4.4) together with (4.5) it is observed that, for given values of W_{ss}, T_M, P_{FA}, and P_D, the interceptor pays a "synchronization penalty" of $10\log_{10}(1 - e^{-2}) = 0.63$ dB relative to the ideal wideband detector.

Summing up the expected performance of the wideband energy detector for the condition of unknown message epoch, it is seen that the average S/N_0 performance penalty paid for any one of the three proposed "fixes" amounts to about 0.7 dB, and the maximum penalty does not exceed 1.5 dB. Which of the three approaches should be used by the interceptor will likely be dependent on cost and other operational factors.

(4) Filter Bank Combiner with Overlapping I & Ds, Each of Hop Interval Duration

Analogous to the modification of the wideband detector discussed in (1) of Section 4.2.2.1 and illustrated in Figure 4.9, it is proposed that a filter bank combiner make use of quadrature overlapping I & Ds, each of hop interval duration, as shown in Figure 4.13. In the most general case, channel threshold decisions made on the N_T in-phase I & D outputs are logically

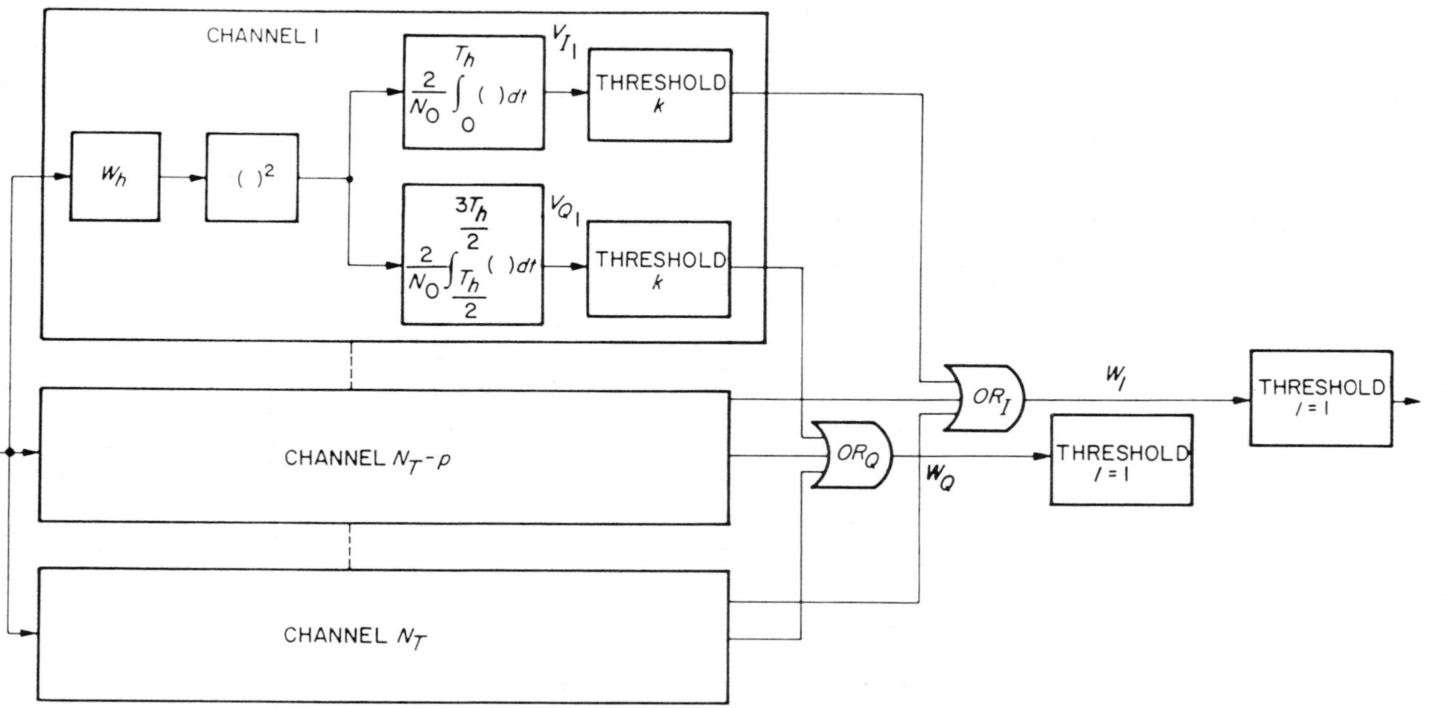

Figure 4.13. Filter bank combiner (unity output threshold) with overlapping I & D detectors.

OR'd, accumulated over a message duration, and compared with an integer threshold, k. A similar situation takes place for the N_T quadrature I & D outputs. If, as has been previously done, one assumes that $l = 1$ for simplicity of analysis, then the accumulators which would normally precede these threshold devices can be eliminated with no loss in generality. This has been done in Figure 4.13.

When noise-only is present, an output from any of the N_T inphase I & Ds which exceeds the channel threshold k will produce an output from the in-phase logical OR and a corresponding output from the in-phase ($l = 1$) threshold device. This constitutes a false alarm and can occur at any integer multiple of the hop time, T_h. Similarly, an output from any of the quadrature I & Ds which exceeds the channel threshold k will produce a false alarm which can occur at any odd multiple of half the hop time. Since potential false alarm decisions are now being made every half-hop interval ($T_h/2$), the false alarm rate is again the product of the decision rate ($2/T_h$) and the false alarm probability per decision, P_{FA}. Letting P_{FAI} denote the per-channel, per-hop false alarm probability, i.e., the probability that an individual I & D output exceeds the channel threshold k, then, clearly, P_{FA} and P_{FAI} are related by the familiar binomial equation

$$P_{FA} = 1 - (1 - P_{FAI})^{N_T} \tag{4.47}$$

and the corresponding false alarm rate is given by

$$\text{FAR} = \frac{2}{T_h} P_{FA} = \frac{2}{T_p}\left[1 - (1 - P_{FAI})^{N_T}\right] \tag{4.48}$$

which, for $P_{FAI} \ll 1$, becomes approximately

$$\text{FAR} = \frac{2}{T_h} P_{FAI}. \tag{4.49}$$

To achieve a false alarm rate equal to that of the wideband detector with overlapping I & Ds, (4.49) is equated with (4.25). Then,

$$\frac{2}{T_M} P_{FA} = \frac{2}{T_h} N_T P_{FAI} = \frac{2}{T_M} N_h N_T P_{FAI} \tag{4.50}$$

or

$$P_{FAI} = \frac{P_{FA}}{N_h N_T} = Q\left(\frac{k - 2W_h T_h}{2\sqrt{W_h T_h}}\right). \tag{4.51}$$

Note that (4.51) is the identical equation which relates P_{FA} and P_{FAI} for the "ideal" filter bank combiner (see (4.8b)).

Alternatively, for Figure 4.13 to achieve the same false alarm rate as the "ideal" FBC, the false alarm probability P_{FA} or the per-channel false alarm probability P_{FAI} must be reduced to half its previous value.

To determine the overall probability of detection P_D, it is again assumed that, with signal-plus-noise present at the input, an output from either (unit level) threshold device constitutes a true alarm, i.e., message detection. However, to relate P_D to the per-channel, per-hop detection probability, P_{DI}, namely, the probability that an individual I & D output exceeds the threshold k, is, in general, a difficult task due to the continuing overlap of the inphase and quadrature I & Ds throughout the duration of the message. Nevertheless, through continued application of union bound techniques, upper and lower bounds on P_D are derived assuming a worst case out-of-synchronization condition of 1/4 of a hop interval. In particular, after many simplifying but practical assumptions, it is shown that

$$N_h Q\left(\frac{k - 2W_hT_h\left(1 + \frac{3\gamma_h}{4}\right)}{2\sqrt{W_hT_h\left(1 + \frac{3\gamma_h}{2}\right)}}\right) < P_D < 2N_h Q\left(\frac{k - 2W_hT_h\left(1 + \frac{3\gamma_h}{4}\right)}{2\sqrt{W_hT_h\left(1 + \frac{3\gamma_h}{2}\right)}}\right) \tag{4.52}$$

where

$$\gamma_h = \frac{S}{N_0 W_h}. \tag{4.53}$$

To determine the required S/N_0 using the detector of Figure 4.13 assume for a basis of comparison the same false alarm rate and detection probability as would be required for the ideal filter bank combiner with perfect time synchronization. Since again there is no explicit closed form expression for P_D, it will be equated to either of the two bounds in (4.52) and thereby a range of values of the required S/N_0 will be obtained. Proceeding as before, equating the right-hand side of (4.51) to $P_{FA}/2N_hN_T = P_{FAI}/2$ and eliminating the threshold k between the resulting expression and either the upper or lower bound of (4.52) gives

$$P_D = C_D N_h Q\left[\frac{Q^{-1}\left(\frac{P_{FA}}{2N_hN_T}\right) - \frac{3}{4}\left(\frac{\lambda_h}{2\sqrt{W_hT_h}}\right)}{\sqrt{1 + \frac{3}{4}\left(\frac{\lambda_h}{W_hT_h}\right)}}\right] \tag{4.54}$$

where $C_D = 1$ or 2 and

$$\lambda_h = \frac{2ST_h}{N_0}. \tag{4.55}$$

Since, typically, $\lambda_h \ll W_hT_h$, then simplifying the square root in (4.54) to unity, and solving for S/N_0 by substituting the values of either 1 or 2 for

C_D gives the desired result:[8]

$$\frac{4}{3}\eta_2\sqrt{\frac{W_h}{T_h}}\left\{Q^{-1}\left(\frac{P_{FA}}{2N_hN_T}\right)_. - Q^{-1}\left(\frac{P_D}{2N_h}\right)\right\}$$

$$< \frac{S}{N_0} < \frac{4}{3}\eta_1\sqrt{\frac{W_h}{T_h}}\left\{Q^{-1}\left(\frac{P_{FA}}{2N_hN_T}\right) - Q^{-1}\left(\frac{P_D}{N_h}\right)\right\}. \tag{4.56}$$

Recall that the equivalent result for the ideal filter bank combiner with perfect time synchronization is given by (4.9).

Calculating the upper and lower bounds on the S/N_0 requirement for the FBC with overlapping I & Ds (recall that $N_hN_T = W_{ss}T_M$ or $N_h = W_{ss}T_M/N_T$, and $W_hT_h = 1$) and comparing these results with the S/N_0 requirement of a 125-channel partial-band FBC with perfect time synchronization (see Table 4.2), it is concluded that for the parameters of the continuing example, time synchronization loss ranges between 0.3 and 1.4 dB. Note that this result is essentially the same as that obtained for the wideband detector in (1) of Section 4.2.2.1.

4.2.2.2 The Problem of Frequency Synchronization

(1) Doppler Effects

For LPI scenarios in which the interceptor assumes the position of an enemy search aircraft, very significant Doppler shifts over the SS bandwidth can occur due to his velocity. The largest shifts occur for the lowest aircraft altitudes as the aircraft velocity component in the direction of the radiating source is nearly equal to the aircraft velocity. Since typically the interceptor is unable to know his velocity and altitude precisely, and certainly not his range, it should be easily appreciated that a PB-FBC having 125 channels randomly scattered across the frequency band will not have the channel center frequencies coincident with the received hop frequencies. In fact, if a hit occurs, the frequency error can, in many circumstances, be considered to be more or less any value across the filter passband with a uniform probability of occurrence.

(2) Performance of the FBC with Frequency Error

First it should be noted that the performance equation (4.9) for the FBC does not take into account the hop pulse energy lost due to the channel filter. Thus, the effective signal power at the input to the square-law detector

[8] Note that, as in the case of the ideal filter bank combiner, the (S/N_0) result must be multiplied by η, which represents a correction factor from a Gaussian assumption to chi-squared statistics.

following the filter will be reduced by the factor

$$\gamma_0 = \int_{-\infty}^{\infty} |H(f)|^2 T_h \left(\frac{\sin \pi f T_h}{\pi f T_h} \right)^2 df \tag{4.57}$$

where $H(f)$ is the equivalent lowpass transfer function of the bandpass filter.

If, for simplicity, an ideal rectangular-shaped filter characteristic is assumed, viz.,

$$|H(f)| = \begin{cases} 1; & |f| \leq \dfrac{1}{2T_h}, \\ 0; & \text{otherwise} \end{cases} \tag{4.58}$$

then (4.57) simplifies to

$$\gamma_0 = \int_{-1/2T_h}^{1/2T_h} T_h \left(\frac{\sin \pi f T_h}{\pi f T_h} \right)^2 df = \frac{1}{\pi} \int_{-\pi/2}^{\pi/2} \left(\frac{\sin x}{x} \right)^2 dx$$

$$= 0.7737 = -1.1\ dB. \tag{4.59}$$

Because the channel or filter which coincides with a given hop pulse does not pass all of the pulse power, adjacent channels must contain proportional amounts of the "spillover." In particular, the i-th adjacent channel, $i = \pm 1, \pm 2, \pm 3, \ldots$, will contain a signal component with power proportional to

$$\gamma_i = \int_{-(i+1/2)/T_h}^{-(i-1/2)/T_h} T_h \left(\frac{\sin \pi f T_h}{\pi f T_h} \right)^2 df = \frac{1}{\pi} \int_{-(i+1/2)\pi}^{-(i-1/2)\pi} \left(\frac{\sin x}{x} \right)^2 dx. \tag{4.60}$$

Thus, a more exact characterization of the FBC performance than that given in (4.8) and (4.9) is the following.

The per-hop (frame) detection and false alarm probabilities P_{Df} and P_{FAf} (i.e., the probabilities of a one out of the OR circuit in Figure 4.6 under signal-plus-noise and noise-only conditions) are given by

$$P_{Df} = 1 - \prod_i (1 - P_{DI_i}) \tag{4.61}$$

$$P_{FAf} = 1 - (1 - P_{FAI})^{N_T} \cong N_T P_{FAI}, \tag{4.62}$$

where the product over i in (4.61) goes over the N_T FBC channels and P_{DI_i} denotes the individual channel detection probabilities (no frequency error assumed at this juncture). Note that all P_{DI_i} have the same mathematical form, with the signal-to-noise ratio for each channel proportional to γ_i of (4.60) ($i = 0$ corresponds to the hop pulse channel). If, as was previously assumed, the $(\sin x/x)^2$ dependence of the effective power within the

N_T-channel energy detectors is ignored, (4.61) simplifies to

$$P_{Df} = 1 - (1 - P_{DI})(1 - P_{FAI})^{N_T - 1} \cong P_{DI}, \tag{4.63}$$

where P_{DI} and P_{FAI} are the previously defined individual channel detection and false alarm probabilities.

Now since $P_{DI_0} \gg P_{DI_i}$ for $i \neq 0$, the following simplifying assumption can be made:

$$\prod_i (1 - P_{DI_i}) \cong (1 - P_{DI_0}) \tag{4.64}$$

which, when substituted into (4.61), yields

$$P_{Df} \cong P_{DI_0}. \tag{4.65}$$

Comparing (4.63) and (4.65), it is observed that the per-hop detection probability is degraded approximately (in terms of SNR) by γ_0 relative to its value obtained by ignoring the true $(\sin x/x)^2$ spectral nature. Thus, since, for a unit threshold ($l = 1$ in Figure 4.6), the per-hop and overall message probabilities are related by

$$\begin{aligned} P_D &= N_h P_{Df} \cong N_h P_{DI_0} \\ P_{FA} &= N_h P_{FAf} \cong N_h N_T P_{FAI}, \end{aligned} \tag{4.66}$$

then comparing (4.66) with (4.8), (4.9) may be readily modified to include the effect of the channel filter on the required S/N_0, namely,

$$S/N_0 = \frac{\eta}{\gamma_0} d_I \sqrt{W_h/T_h} \tag{4.67}$$

where now

$$\begin{aligned} d_I &= Q^{-1}(P_{FAI}) - Q^{-1}(P_{DI_0}) \\ &= Q^{-1}(P_{FA}/N_h N_T) - Q^{-1}(P_D/N_h). \end{aligned} \tag{4.68}$$

For the partial-band FBC, the results of (4.64) and (4.65) are even better approximations since the remaining channels are far apart from one another and, thus, there is negligible adjacent channel $(\sin x/x)^2$ spillover.

When a frequency error Δf exists between the hop frequency in a given hop interval and the center frequency of the corresponding BPF, the SNR degradations γ_i of (4.59) and (4.60) are simply replaced by

$$\gamma_0(\Delta f T_h) = \int_{-1/2T_h + \Delta f}^{1/2T_h + \Delta_f} T_h \left(\frac{\sin \pi f T_h}{\pi f T_h} \right)^2 df = \frac{1}{\pi} \int_{-\pi[1/2 + \Delta f T_h]}^{\pi[1/2 + \Delta f T_h]} \left(\frac{\sin x}{x} \right)^2 dx \tag{4.69}$$

and

$$\gamma_i(\Delta f T_h) = \int_{-(i+1/2+\Delta f T_h)/T_h}^{-(i-1/2+\Delta f T_h)/T_h} T_h \left(\frac{\sin \pi f T_h}{\pi f T_h} \right)^2 df$$

$$= \frac{1}{\pi} \int_{-(i+1/2+\Delta f T_h)\pi}^{-(i-1/2+\Delta f T_h)\pi} \left(\frac{\sin x}{x} \right)^2 dx. \tag{4.70}$$

Table 4.4 tabulates $\gamma_0(\Delta f T_h)$ versus $\Delta f T_h$. Clearly, the worst case degradation occurs when $\Delta f T_h = 0.50$. For the full-band (N_T channel) FBC at this value of $\Delta f T_h$, two adjacent channels in each hop interval will have identical signal energy, each degraded by $\gamma_0(0.5) = 0.4514$ relative to the total. In this instance, the per-hop detection probability, ignoring the $(\sin x/x)^2$ spillover into the other channels, is given by

$$P_{DF} = 1 - \left(1 - P_{DI_0}(0.5)\right)^2 = 2P_{DI_0}(0.5) - \left[P_{DI_0}(0.5)\right]^2 \tag{4.71}$$

where, in general, $P_{DI_0}(\Delta f T_h)$ denotes the individual channel detection probability in the presence of a frequency offset Δf.

For the partial-band FBC, in each hop interval, it may be assumed that only one channel has signal-plus-noise with the total signal energy degraded by $\gamma_0(\Delta f T_h)$. Thus, the per-hop detection probability for the PB-FBC becomes

$$P_{DF} = 1 - \left[1 - fP_{DI_0}(\Delta f T_h)\right]\left[1 - P_{FAI}\right]^{fN_T - 1} \cong fP_{DI_0}(\Delta f T_h) \tag{4.72}$$

where f is the channel reduction factor (previously defined) from the PB-FBC. The result is that a frequency error of Δf will require an effective increase in S/N_0 by a factor of $\gamma_0(0)/\gamma_0(\Delta f T_h)$.

In general, as was previously discussed under (1) of Section 4.2.2.2, the Doppler effects render Δf to a random variable status, which may be taken to be uniformly distributed between $-1/2T_h$ and $1/2T_h$. An average S/N_0

Table 4.4
Frequency offset losses.

$\Delta f T_h$	$\gamma_0(\Delta f T_h)$	$\gamma_0(\Delta f T_h)$ in dB
0	0.7737	−1.1143
0.05	0.7697	−1.1371
0.10	0.7576	−1.2054
0.15	0.7380	−1.3196
0.20	0.7112	−1.4799
0.25	0.6781	−1.6871
0.30	0.6395	−1.9417
0.35	0.5964	−2.2446
0.40	0.5499	−2.5968
0.45	0.5012	−2.9996
0.50	0.4517	−3.4543

modifying factor may thus be obtained by averaging $\gamma_0(\Delta f T_h)$ over the uniform distribution in frequency. This factor is computed to be 1.55 or 1.9 dB and comprises the two components $1/\gamma_0(0) = 1.1$ dB and $1/\overline{\gamma_0(\Delta f T_h)} = 0.8$ dB.

4.2.3 Detector Implementation

In this section, some of the problems of realizing the detector types discussed in Section 4.2.1 are addressed. Since this subject alone could generate an entire chapter unto itself, the present scope will be limited to an assessment of the various general functional circuit topologies that may be employed. In addition, some insight will be given to implementation degradations which can further act to diminish the real effectiveness of the more complex detection approaches.

4.2.3.1 Basic Configurations

(1) Wideband Single-Channel Detectors

Many wideband radiometers have been built to operate in the SHF and EHF frequency bands, and have been used extensively for ground, airborne, and spacecraft applications. As a result, the technology needed for this type of detector is fairly well at hand. From a functional standpoint, a most difficult problem is that of setting and maintaining the receiver threshold value. Proper setting of the comparator threshold voltage relative to the output of the integrator is essential to meeting the specified P_D and P_{FA}. If the threshold is too low, an excessive false alarm rate is obtained while, if it is too high, detection of an actual signal may be missed. Even if the threshold is set properly initially, time, temperature, and voltage variations, and other dynamic conditions, will affect the overall receiver gain such that the initial setting will become incorrect. Further, the receiver effective noise temperature will also change with interceptor altitude and attitude (as the receiving antenna is subjected to varying background temperature due to changing angles and field of view). Thus, some precise, automatic, periodically updating method of threshold determination is needed.

Since the signal to be detected and the noise are uncorrelated but have a definite power ratio for a given P_D and P_{FA} at a specified S/N_0 and W_{ss}, it is necessary only to measure the noise level in the absence of signal in order to derive the independent variable which permits threshold calculation or establishment. Although elementary in principle, the implementation of this concept gives rise to a serious problem. The fact that the noise level must be measured in the absence of signal means that whatever time is taken to accomplish this must be taken from the time available to detect the signal. Switched (Dicke)-type receivers [7] work in this manner by providing a precision noise source which is periodically switched into the receiver in place of the antenna signal and multiplexing the calibration noise and actual signal-plus-noise out of the detector between a noise-level measuring integrator and the signal detection integrator. Typically, the performance penalty paid due to a 50 percent signal duty cycle and front-end switch insertion loss is about 4 dB in required S/N_0, which clearly impairs the interceptor's detection capability.

What then are the possible detector and receiving system alternatives which minimize these disadvantages? One solution would be to continuously measure the received system noise in a band immediately outside of W_{ss}, or to measure noise in a narrowband segment of W_{ss} for which P_{hit} is sufficiently small that an occasional signal pulse will have no significant effect on the measurement. This approach overcomes, to some extent, the problems with the switched (Dicke) method but suffers primarily from the fact that the measurement does not truly characterize the external and internal conditions over the whole bandwidth W_{ss}. Therefore, more than acceptable error in setting the threshold is probable.

In order to provide a means of wideband calibration without incurring the basic switched (Dicke) receiver losses, conventional temperature-measuring radiometers often employ switched parallel channels (e.g., Graham's receiver). Unfortunately, this technique, which is basically a differencing-null method, is inappropriate to the very wideband receivers of the type needed for intercept signal detectors because (1) uniform gain and phase-matching of the channels is very difficult, and (2) the form of the detected signal is not suited to separation into the necessary integration and threshold establishment functions.

Another possible technique would make use of phase orthogonal IF components—one embodying the input signal-plus-noise and the other a wideband, locally generated, very stable calibration noise. Just prior to detection, the orthogonal components are phase separated into different detectors. The detector handling the signal-plus-noise component is fed to the integrator and threshold comparator circuits as usual, while the detected calibration noise is used to vary the threshold setting as a function of IF gain changes. Although this technique does not suffer from the 50 percent signal loss of the switched (Dicke) receiver, it still does not account for external, or non-common circuit internal, noise temperature, or gain variations. Maintaining a good quadrature relationship over a very wide IF band may also be quite difficult.

The best approach to threshold determination is based solely on the received signal and noise itself. It must be remembered that, for the general LPI scenario, the communicator's signal is present for only a very short time interval relative to the total intercept search period. Thus, most of the time, a noise-only condition exists against which adaptive statistical measurements may be made to maintain a constant P_{FA} as the statistics slowly change.[9] Since the specified P_{FA} is small (e.g., 10^{-6}), it obviously cannot be

[9] "Slowly" is defined such that the P_{FA}, if uncorrected, would change no more than a factor of 2 upward or a factor of 1/2 downward from one decision period to the next.

measured directly on a short-term basis. However, measurement of the higher order statistical parameters by means of moments or extreme methods, coupled with appropriate predictive formulas, leads to more accurate estimates of P_{FA}. Further, if this is done using reasonably wideband samples, the results can be made virtually insensitive to the presence of signal (whenever such occurs). The result is that the P_{FA} estimates may be directly related to the correct threshold value and the comparator threshold will be continually adjusted to compensate for all external and internal receiver noise temperature and gain changes. Contemporary microprocessor-based algorithms make this method highly viable.

(2) *Channelized Detectors*

In most situations, because of the small practical processing gain achievable at a significant cost over the wideband detector a channelized detector is unlikely to be used. Apart from these considerations, this subsection will investigate channelized detectors from a purely operational topology.

As representative of the considerations involved for channelized detectors, the 125 minimum channel PB-FBC of (4) in Section 4.2.1.2 will be used to illustrate the tradeoffs and problems. Stated explicitly, the task is to receive the total SS band of frequencies and downconvert 125 selected hop frequency positions into W_h-wide channels, each followed by detectors, FH pulse period integrators, and comparators.

The first question that must be answered is: which 125 of the $N_T = 10^6$ possible channels should be selected? If the communicator's FH pattern is essentially random and uniform over the hop frequency set, then it can be rightfully argued that it makes no difference which frequencies are chosen. Whether they are uniformly spaced and contiguous on some 125 W_h-wide sub-band or randomly dispersed across the total SS band should have no effect on the statistical parameter P_{hit}. From an ease of implementation point of view, even without supplying details, it is well conjectured that a receiver built around the contiguous sub-band would be the simplest to realize in terms of downconversion and IF amplification. The uniformly spaced but separated channels would be the second-best choice on the same basis. The communicator also appreciates this and, if he surmises that either approach has been adopted by the interceptor, even if he is not aware of which specific hop channels (uniformly spaced or contiguous) have been chosen, he can likely increase his LPI advantage by structuring the nature of his hop pattern over the *finite* message. Thus, if a contiguous sub-band receiver is being used by the interceptor, the communicator should hop his frequencies over some narrow band (of necessity, still much greater than 125 W_h) or over a small number of non-uniformly separated narrow bands in the hope that none of the frequencies coincide with the interceptor's sub-band. If, on the other hand, the interceptor's receiver is built on the uniformly separated principle, the communicator should hop his frequencies

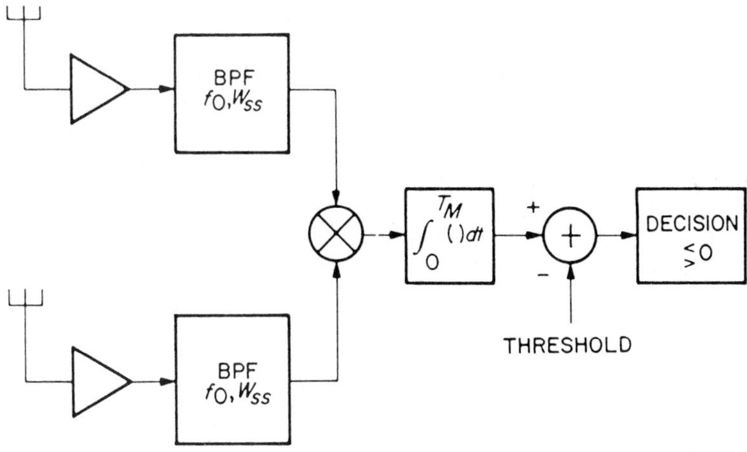

Figure 4.14. Correlation radiometer.

in a pattern that would not allow any frequencies over the message duration to have a separation anywhere near whatever the interceptor's uniform separation distance is expected to be and its multiples.[10] By virtue of such considerations, it appears that the interceptor must employ the randomly dispersed strategy if he is not to give the communicator any *a priori* reason to use some structured hop format over the message duration in order to lower the probability of a hit in the interceptor's channels.

4.2.3.2 Other Possible Feature Detector Configurations

In this section, several additional detector types that have appeared in the literature as applicable to LPI detection are briefly reviewed. One configuration is a variation of the wideband energy detector. Another exploits a specific feature of the communicator's signal in an attempt to detect the FH hop rate. Finally, a method of actually detecting the FH pattern is discussed.

A technique known as the *correlation radiometer* is illustrated in Figure 4.14. This instrument has two independent antennas (that cover the same geometric area) and RF circuits. The result is that, when a signal is present, the signal components from each leg into the multiplier are highly correlated (essentially identical in amplitude and phase) while the noise terms are uncorrelated. Thus, only the cross-correlated signals produce a direct voltage to the integrator. The theoretical advantage of the correlation radiometer over the square-law radiometer is that it requires 3 dB less S/N_0 for the

[10] Large Doppler may modify this strategy somewhat.

same P_D and P_{FA} performance. If two antennas are to be used, however, it is also possible to have each antenna cover one-half of the specified geometric area (3 dB gain increase), which then produces the same S/N_0 performance with two wideband radiometers (operating independently) as that for the correlation radiometer. An advantage of the half-coverage dual-antenna system is that it gives some directional information (say, left versus right) which the correlation radiometer is incapable of since its antennas cover the same overlapping area. The threshold maintenance problem for the correlation receiver is essentially the same as that for the square-law receiver except that the former does not produce a direct voltage which is a function of the noise levels. This slightly simplifies the calculation of the threshold value from the statistical measurements made toward its determination. Overall, the tradeoffs between a correlation receiver and two independent square-law receivers are slight, and system performance and complexity are virtually the same.

One disadvantage of every wideband square-law or correlation type of detector is that it is sensitive to any form of signal, i.e., it will respond equally as well to the communicator's FH signal or to any other extraneous signal irrespective of modulation form and bandwidth (provided that its frequencies fall within (f_0, W_{ss})) as long as it has the same energy content on $(0, T_M)$. For this reason, other types of detectors that are more feature-dependent have been developed. One such configuration is the hop rate detector shown in Figure 4.15. For this receiver, the input band is subdivided into two sub-bands (upper and lower bands), each $W_{ss}/2$ wide. The output of each BPF is square-law detected and the results are differenced. When an FH signal appears at the receiver input, on the average, it spends 50 percent of its time in each sub-band, transitioning randomly at multiples of the hop period. Therefore, the differenced signal appears as (in the absence of noise) a two-level or bipolar waveform. Highpass filtering to remove any direct voltage components and lowpass filtering with a bandwidth on the order of the hop rate yields a narrowband lowpass signal. This signal is delayed by $T_h/2$, and the signal and its delay are multiplied. The result is a process that contains a strong periodic component at the hop rate which, in turn, is detected by, say, a narrowband spectrum analyzer. Although this receiver is capable of making a very accurate measurement of the hop rate, it does so at a large penalty in S/N_0 because it is basically a fourth-law device. (For the widely used system parameters of this section, the S/N_0 would have to be increased by 16 dB in order to achieve an equivalent detectability SNR.) As a result, the FH hop rate detector of Figure 4.15 offers the interceptor no advantage whatsoever in terms of basic detectability. Other rate detection (e.g., PN chip rate or TH rate) receivers may also be realized, but they likewise provide no gain over the wideband energy detector in terms of basic detectability.

Based upon our previous discussion, the implementation of the optimum multichannel receiver of Figure 4.4 is thought to be impractical. There is,

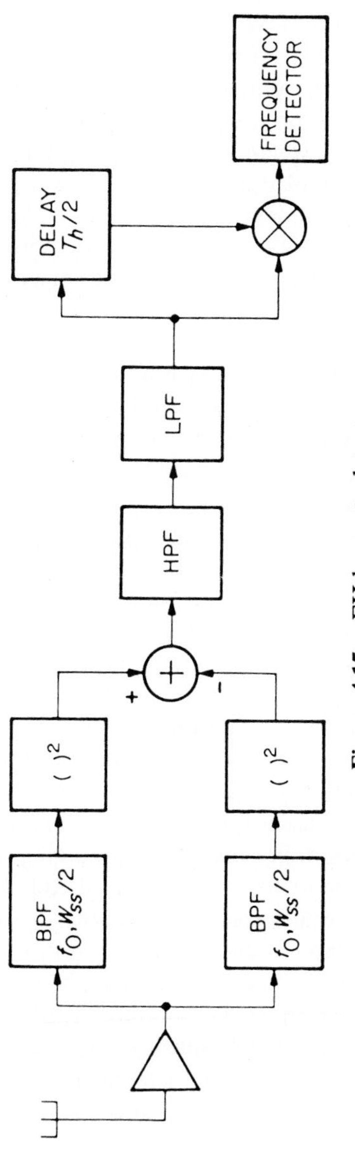

Figure 4.15. FH hop rate detector.

however, a particular mechanization which might make the multichannel detector somewhat more tractable, namely, the *digital spectrum analyzer*.

It may be easily shown that from a detection theoretic point of view, the outputs of a discrete frequency spectrum analyzer at the candidate hop frequencies are equivalent to an optimum non-coherent detection channelized receiver.[11] The spectral values may therefore be compared to appropriate thresholds and detection decisions made akin to the PB-FBC.

Realization of the spectrum analyzer requires that a particular RF frequency band, f_a to f_b, be translated to a lowpass frequency region so that $f_a \to 0$ and $f_b \to f_m$, where $f_m = f_b - f_a$. The lowpass waveform (signal-plus-noise) is then sampled at a rate of $2f_m$ samples/second and for a period of T_h seconds to obtain a sample set of $N_s = 2f_mT_h$ samples. A discrete Fourier transform is then calculated using the sample set for each of the candidate hop frequency locations. The magnitude of the Fourier transform at each frequency is compared with a threshold to determine if its spectral value is sufficiently large to indicate the presence of a signal (a hop pulse). This process is repeated for each hop pulse interval T_h.

Figure 4.16 shows functionally the steps involved in the spectrum analyzer algorithm and the pertinent equations of operation. The translation of the bandpass sub-band into the lowpass range $(0, f_m)$ assumes that the candidate hop frequencies are at $f_1 = W_h$, $f_2 = 2W_h$, $f_3 = 3W_h$, etc., with the total number of frequencies (channels) being f_m/W_h.

Consider now a full-band or N_T-channel spectrum analyzer, with the probability of a correct hop pulse decision being 0.9. (For the sake of the following, a message is assumed to be present.) Since, for a full-band spectrum analyzer $P_{\text{hit}} = 1$, on a per-hop basis, the probability of correctly determining the hop pulse frequency is therefore 0.9. Such a receiver would employ a maximum-likelihood decision process, and the required S/N_0 for $N_T = 10^6$ (plus the other example parameters previously cited) is (perfect time synchronization and no frequency error assumed) about the same as that required by a 500-channel PB-FBC for absolute detection; thus, if detection is possible, hop following is also possible provided a 10^6 channel spectrum analyzer can be realized! But it has already been pointed out that a 10^6 channel receiver of any sort is intractable. It would seem then that, even though FH following is theoretically possible, it cannot reasonably be implemented by a spectrum analyzer. There is, however, a technique which offers the potential of a realizable solution without the need for calculating the spectrum at each FH frequency. The method, first proposed by Kleinrock [8], involves time-domain autocorrelation operations on a T_h segment of received signal-plus-noise, and the principles may be summarized as follows.

---

[11] For perfect time and frequency synchronization, such a receiver performs slightly better than the optimum multichannel FH pulse-matched detector introduced in (2) of Section 4.2.1.2.

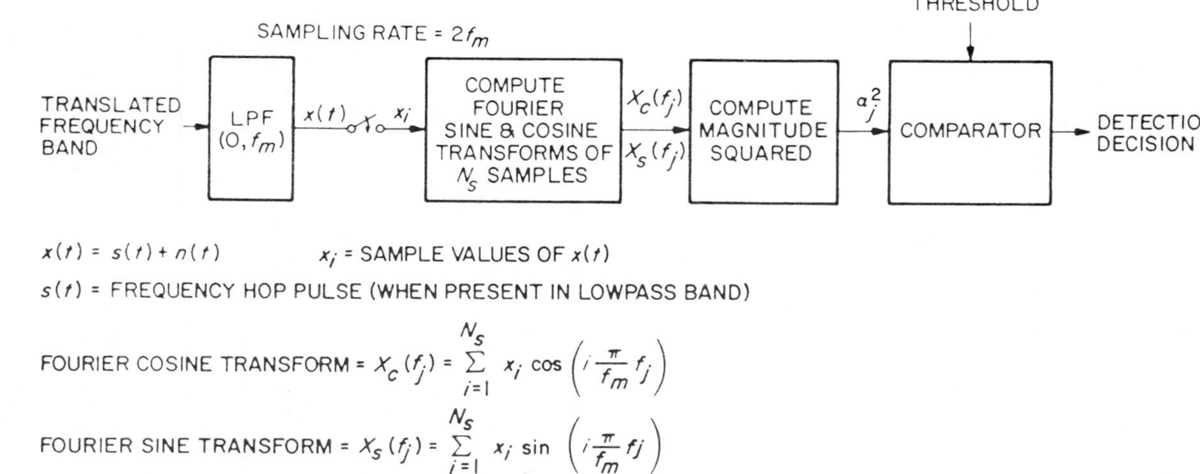

Figure 4.16. Spectrum analyzer operation.

Consider, for the moment, that a finite variance time function $x(t)$ has a power spectrum $S_x(f)$, and that the largest spectral value occurs at a frequency $f = f_{max}$. Define the normalized autocorrelation function of $x(t)$ by the relationship

$$R_0(\tau) = \frac{\int x(t)x(t+\tau)\,dt}{\int x^2(t)\,dt}. \tag{4.73}$$

Next calculate the autocorrelation function of the autocorrelation function, viz.,

$$R_1(\tau) = \frac{\int R_0(\lambda)R_0(\lambda+\tau)\,d\lambda}{\int R_0^2(\lambda)\,d\lambda}, \tag{4.74}$$

and continue this process again and again. The n-th iteration therefore becomes

$$R_n(\tau) = \frac{\int R_{n-1}(\lambda)R_{n-1}(\lambda+\tau)\,d\lambda}{\int R_{n-1}^2(\lambda)\,d\lambda}. \tag{4.75}$$

Now it can be shown as $n \to \infty$ that the following limiting result is obtained:

$$\lim_{n\to\infty} R_n(\tau) \propto \cos[2\pi f_{max}\tau], \tag{4.76}$$

that is, after an infinite number of iterations, a pure cosine function is obtained whose frequency corresponds to the location of the spectral maximum of $x(t)$.

As seen, then, it is possible to calculate the location of the largest spectral value without having to calculate the spectrum itself; this is exactly what needs to be accomplished if an FH follower is to be realized. Now the application of the above property to FH following requires that (1) only a finite T_h-second time segment be considered and, (2) an answer be obtained after only a reasonable number of iterations. As a result, some compromise must be allowed in terms of the accuracy of the estimate. Further, even with a T_h-second segment of signal-plus-noise to begin with, each successive iteration theoretically doubles the storage or memory required to hold the result; i.e., after n iterations, $R_n(\tau)$ is generally non-zero over a τ range of $2^{n+1}T_h$. Thus, in order to keep the storage needed at a reasonable size, truncation of the iterated function must be allowed so that τ_{max} becomes manageable. This will further reduce the accuracy of the result. Nevertheless, for a desired frequency resolution or accuracy, there exists a procedure which will calculate an estimate of f_{max}, namely, $\hat{f}_{max}$, after only n_0 iterations.

The FH following receiver therefore becomes one which subdivides the received signal-plus-noise into contiguous T_h-second periods and applies the autocorrelation iterative estimator to each segment. The successive frequency estimates are then taken as being representative of the nearest true hop frequency, and the FH pattern (including the MFSK data) used by the communicator may be reconstructed with occasional errors that depend upon S/N_0 and the finite processing limitations previously summarized.

Implementation of an autocorrelation iterating receiver for large SS bandwidths (on the order of GHz) is currently nearly as unrealistic as the full-band spectrum analyzer. To be sure, the total band would have to be subdivided and individual processors applied to each sub-band. Frequency estimates for each sub-band would be obtained along with the normalization factors that would be used to determine which frequency corresponds to the largest spectral value. Present hardware capabilities appear to preclude that such a receiver could be cost effectively constructed. With the rapid advances being made in the surface acoustic wave (SAW), the charge-coupled device (CCD), and very high-speed digital technologies, however, economic feasibility may be only a few years hence. Using one-bit (two-level) quantization (at a sacrifice in required S/N_0), it is possible even with today's circuits to construct a processor capable of handling a 10 MHz frequency range. A 100 MHz range is probable by the mid to late 1980s. With such a capability, only a small number of channels is needed to cover the entire SS bandwidth. Clearly, then, the potential is realistic.

4.3 PERFORMANCE AND STRATEGIES ASSESSMENT

In this final section, an attempt is made to summarize and reconcile the issues and tradeoffs that have been detailed in the foregoing sections. The reader is again reminded that, due to the large number of variables involved, specific but typical examples are being used as the basis for extrapolating general conclusions. So as to broaden this basis and hopefully dispel "what if" type questions or uncertainties, some additional parameter and configuration conditions are explored.

4.3.1 Communicator Modulation and Intercept Detectors

Section 4.2 contained a very detailed examination of intercept detector types from both practical (or attainable) performance (as measured by the S/N_0 required) and implementation (assessed by functional and circuit complexity) perspectives. Using a fixed set of system parameters, the relative merits of four well-known detectors (optimum multichannel, full-band filter bank combiner (FB-FBC), partial-band filter bank combiner, wideband energy or radiometer) were compared, and it was observed that only the minimum channel partial-band filter bank combiner (PB-FBC) and the wideband energy detector have utility. Further, the minimum channel PB-FBC would be employed only when its S/N_0 performance advantage over the wideband radiometer justifies its complexity as reflected by the cost of mechanizing the number of channels needed.

To further strengthen these earlier conclusions, the performance of these same detectors will now be calculated for several different hop rates and in addition PN spreading of the hop pulses. The results are tabulated in Table 4.5. To repeat an earlier observation, in comparing the S/N_0 requirements of various intercept detectors, relative to, say, that of the wideband energy detector as a reference, it is not necessary to specify the SS bandwidth W_{ss}, the message duration T_M, or the hop rate $R_h = 1/T_h$. Rather, the product of W_{ss} and T_M, the total number of hops N_T in W_{ss}, and, if a partial-band configuration, the fractional number of channels f used in the implementation are all that are needed to perform the calculations. If PN spreading is used in hybrid with the assumed FH modulation, then one must, in addition, specify the ratio of PN code chip rate R_c to the hop rate. In Table 4.5 the PN code chip rate is held constant as the hop rate is varied over two decades (the effects of varying the chip rate will be discussed toward the end of this section). Thus, the ratio R_c/R_h also varies over two decades.

The central column in Table 4.5 repeats the numbers tabulated in Table 4.3 for FH modulation, with the modification that the time and frequency asynchronous losses derived in Sections 4.2.2.1 and 4.2.2.2, respectively, have been added. All other entries also include losses for lack of time and frequency synchronization. A double crosshatched line has been placed to separate the practical versus impractical detector realizations as measured by the number of channels required. As can be seen, only two entries represent a potential gain over the wideband energy detector; these are further reviewed in the following paragraphs.

For R_h such that $N_T = 10^6$, a 125-channel PB-FBC is capable of achieving a lower S/N_0 threshold than a wideband energy radiometer of a mere 0.5 dB. Considering the complexity of a 125-channel PB-FBC relative to that of the one-channel wideband detector, the gain is clearly not worth the cost. Thus, the interceptor will opt to use the wideband radiometer.

There is another pure-FH entry in Table 4.5 that warrants some review, namely, the minimum channel PB-FBC requiring 12,500 channels with R_h chosen to give $N_T = 10^7$. The 10.2 dB performance advantage over the wideband energy detector is very significant, and some form of implementation is therefore tempting. Postulating that mechanization of 12,500 channels is out of the question, even for a 10.2 dB S/N_0 advantage, it may be logically asked: Is there some implementable realization that can attain some of the gain?

Since it is mandatory that 12,500 channels be equivalently manifest, the only choice is to construct a PB-FBC with fewer real channels, say, by a

Table 4.5

A comparison of detector performance as a function of hop rate and FH versus FH/PN ($W_{ss}T_M = 8 \times 10^9$).

Detector Type		$R_c/R_{h1} = 1000$		$R_c/R_{h2} = 100$		$R_c/R_{h3} = 10$	
		R_{h1} ($N_T = 10^7$)		R_{h2} ($N_T = 10^6$)		R_{h3} ($N_T = 10^5$)	
		No. of Channels	$\Delta S/N_0$ (dB)	No. of Channels	$\Delta S/N_0$ (dB)	No. of Channels	$\Delta S/N_0$ (dB)
Optimum	FH	10^7	−17.5	10^6	−9.1	10^5	−1.9
Multichannel	FH/PH	10^4	−7.3	10^4	−3.7	10^4	+0.2
FB-FBC	FH	10^7	−14.6	10^6	−5.9	10^5	+3.3
	FH/PN	10^4	−5.0	10^4	+0.1	10^4	+5.3
Minimum Channel PB-FBC	FH	12,500	−10.2	125	−0.5	2	+9.0
($f = 1.25 \times 10^{-3}$)	FH/PN	13	−2.1	2	+3.7	1	+10.4
Wideband Energy	FH FH/PN	1	0	1	0	1	0

(Includes Average Time and Frequency Asynchronous Losses)

Table 4.6
Hopped-channel PB-FBC performance.

Detector	$1/K$	No. of Channels	$\Delta S/N_0$ (dB)
PB-FBC	1	12,500	−10.2
PB-FBC	0.1	1,250	−2.4
PB-FBC	0.01	125	+6.1
Wideband Energy	1	1	0

factor of $1/K$, and further reduce the integration time in each channel by the same factor so that the $12{,}500/K$ channels may be "hopped" to different (unique) sub-band locations K times per hop pulse interval. Table 4.6 summarizes the results of such a strategy. As can be seen, a reduction of the number of channels by a factor of 10 (to 1250 channels) decreases the gain from 10.2 dB to 2.4 dB, while another factor of 10 decrease (to 125 channels) causes worse performance than the wideband energy detector by 6.1 dB. Thus, the attempt is in vain. There is just no way the the minimum channel requirement can be ignored. This being the case, the communicator need never fear that the PB-FBC will ever be used by the interceptor as long as the required number of minimum channels is forced (by design) at low hop rates to be above some threshold (say, greater than 100) for which the cost per dB of advantage is untenable.

Turning now to the FH/PN performance entry in Table 4.5 for the minimum channel PB-FBC at R_h corresponding to $N_T = 10^7$, the 2.1 dB advantage over the wideband radiometer requires only 13 channels. This therefore represents a situation where the interceptor might indeed justify the PB-FBC. A good strategy for the communicator should be to avoid designing an FH/PN system with the subject parameters. If such a low hop rate is deemed necessary, the communicator should avoid PN spreading, at least at such a high chip rate. Table 4.7 shows the level of PB-FBC performance which may be expected if a lower chip rate is employed with the above hop rate. Again it can be seen that the tradeoff is a better intercept S/N_0 requirement, but at the expense of a significantly increased number of minimum channels. Thus, although the interceptor might opt to build a 13-channel detector when the PN chip rate is 1000 times the hop rate, he will likely refrain from a 125-channel unit when the chip rate is 100 times the hop rate, in favor of some more economical approach.

Having now reviewed a rather wide range of FH and FH/PN parameters, it appears reasonable to conclude that:

1. For any of the pure FH cases, the interceptor will be forced to the wideband energy detector,
2. PN spreading of the FH pulses is not essential to the prevention of channelized detector usage, nor does it directly add to the state of LPI.

Table 4.7
Performance of a minimum channel PB-FBC for a fixed hop rate and different PN chip rates; $N_T = 10^7$.

Detector	R_c/R_h	No. of Channels	$\Delta S/N_0$ (dB)
PB-FBC	1000	13	−2.1
PB-FBC	100	125	−6.0
PB-FBC	10	1,250	−8.9
Wideband Energy	Any	1	0

Restating, then, the basic strategy that should be employed by the communicator:

1. He should choose FH or FH/PN parameters so that any channelized detector requires larger S/N_0 than that for the wideband radiometer, or
2. He should choose FH or FH/PN parameters so that, if any channelized detector requires lower S/N_0 than that for the wideband radiometer, it is uneconomical to build because of the large minimum number of channels needed.

No channelized detector can be expected to be used against pure FH provided that the hop cell bandwidth is set equal to the hop rate and all possible hop frequencies are employed (i.e., can be synthesized).

4.3.2 Anti-Jam Measures

The basis for good AJ performance was covered in Parts 1 to 3. It was established there that both spread-spectrum modulation and error-correction coding must generally be used jointly in order to maximize jamming immunity. Table 4.8 tabulates for two different hop rates the maximum J/S ratios that may be tolerated for some typical cases of interest.[12] Each J/S entry has been calculated against the most effective jammer type and, therefore, represents the worst case jamming environment. As large a J/S ratio as possible is the desired condition that will, in turn, foster the most favorable LPI state.

Without coding, it is clear that FH/PN at the lower hop rate R_{h1} gives the best results. With coding, either FH or FH/PN at R_{h1} emerges the winner. Since, with error-correction coding, the highest levels of performance are attained for all conceivable jamming situations, it should be preferred. Whether or not PN spreading is employed is unimportant as it gains nothing when the hop rate is low.

[12] The numerical entries for this table may be calculated from the theoretical results presented in Chapter 2, Part 2.

Table 4.8
Maximum J/S ratios as a function of modulation and coding methods.

Modulation Technique / Error Correction Coding Technique	Maximum J/S $= (W_{ss}/R_b)/(E_b/N_0) = (N_T/3R) \times (R_h/R_s)/(E_b/N_0)$ for $P_b = 10^{-4}$			
	FH/8-ary MFSK		FH/PN/8-ary MFSK	
	$N_T = 10^7$; $R_{h1}/R_s = 8$	$N_T = 10^6$; $R_{h2}/R_s = 80$	$N_T = 10^7$; $R_{h1}/R_s = 80$	$N_T = 10^6$; $R_{h2}/R_s = 80$
No Coding ($R = 1$)	59.3 dB $\rho = .085$ PB-MTJ	59.1 dB FB-NJ	62.9 dB $\rho = .59$ PB-NJ	59.1 dB FB-NJ
$R = 1/2$ Convolutional Coding	63.0 dB $\rho = .60$ PB-NJ	59.1 dB FB-NJ	63.0 dB $\rho = .60$ PB-NJ	59.1 dB FB-NJ
Dual-3 Convolutional Coding	65.3 dB FB-NJ	59.7 dB $\rho = .93$ PB-MTJ	65.3 dB FB-NJ	61.8 dB FB-NJ

ρ = Fraction of Total Band Jammed
PB-MTJ = Partial-Band Multitone Jamming
PB-NJ = Partial-Band Noise Jamming
FB-NJ = Full-Band Noise Jamming
R_b = Data Bit Rate
$E_b = ST_b$ = Energy Per Information Bit
$R_s = R_b/3$ = Data Symbol Rate
R_h/R_s = Number of Hops Per Symbol

4.3.3 Optimum LPI Modulation / Coding Conditions

Having now reviewed the intercept detectability and AJ performance of the various modulation and coding methods, a final conclusion may be drawn. The use of FH/PN versus pure FH has been shown to be of no advantage and, since it represents additional communication system complexity, especially in terms of receiver acquisition and tracking functions, FH becomes the recommended SS approach.

The remaining issue is the choice of hop rate. Three criteria may be applied. The first involves a restatement of the conditions which preclude the interceptor's use of a channelized detector; namely, for finite duration messages, it is essential to minimize the number of hop slots per message relative to the total number of possible hop slots $N_T = W_{ss}/R_h$. To satisfy the first criterion:

$$\text{Hop Rate} < (\text{Total FH Slots}) \div (100 \times \text{Message Time}).$$

A second hop rate criterion is dictated by the number of hops per coded symbol that must be employed to obtain good AJ protection, namely:

$$\text{Hop Rate} \geq 4 \times (\text{Symbol Rate}).$$

Thus, the first two criteria, respectively, bound the hop rate to upper and lower values. The third criterion involves minimization of the message receiver non-coherent combining loss. Clearly, the fewer the number of hops per symbol, the lower the non-coherent combining loss and, therefore, the lower the communicator's EIRP. This criterion demands that the lowest possible hop rate be selected. However, since a lower limit is dictated by the second criterion, this limit becomes the optimum hop rate for all considerations.

4.4 FURTHER DISCUSSION

The material presented in this chapter has focussed on providing a systems viewpoint of the tradeoffs required between the communicator/receiver and the interceptor for communication in an LPI environment. Emphasis has been placed on determining the system design parameters necessary for communicating in the presence of *practical* interceptor detectors, nevertheless pointing out their relation to optimal structures.

In the recent literature, several authors [9], [10], [11] have taken a more formal maximum-likelihood approach to the LPI communications problem, both from the standpoint of estimating the unknown synchronization parameters associated with the communicator's modulation (e.g., carrier phase, chip or hop epoch) and determining the optimum interceptor detector structures given none, some, or all of this synchronization knowledge. In particular, Polydoros and Weber [9] determine synchronous and asynchronous (with respect to the chip or hop offset of the spread-spectrum modulation), coherent and non-coherent (with respect to the carrier phase) detectors for both direct sequence and frequency-hopped modulations. All of these structures fall into the category of feature-extraction detectors, since in the absence of all knowledge except carrier frequency, the wideband radiometer is the obvious choice and is in fact an asymptotically optimum device as the predetection SNR decreases to zero. The following represents a summary of the results obtained in [9].

Let $y(t)$ denote the signal received by the interceptor which, when the communicator is transmitting, is the sum of signal plus noise and otherwise consists only of noise. For a direct-sequence spread-spectrum modulation, application of the generalized likelihood ratio test leads to the following decision rules. Assuming both chip timing epoch and carrier phase are known (a very idealistic assumption), then the *generalized coherent synchronous radiometer* is an implementation of the decision rule:

$$\text{if} \sum_{i=1}^{N} \ln\cosh y_i \begin{array}{ll} > \eta, & \text{decide signal present} \\ < \eta, & \text{decide signal absent} \end{array} \tag{4.77}$$

where η is the detection threshold,

$$y_j = \int_{(j-1)T_c}^{jT_c} y(t)\, dt \tag{4.78}$$

and N is the number of chips, each of duration T_c, in the observation time T used to define the likelihood ratio test. If the "ln cosh" non-linearity is approximated by a square-law device as is appropriate at low predetection SNR, then the resulting structure is just a *synchronous coherent energy detector or radiometer.*

Relaxing the assumption of known carrier phase leads to the *optimal non-coherent detector* satisfying the decision rule:

$$\text{if} \sum_{\substack{i=1 \\ i\varepsilon G \text{ or } \bar{G}}}^{2^{N-1}} I_0\left(\frac{2\sqrt{S}}{N_0} R_i\right) \begin{array}{ll} > \eta, & \text{decide signal present} \\ < \eta, & \text{decide signal absent} \end{array} \tag{4.79}$$

where

$$R_i = \sqrt{e_{ci}^2 + e_{si}^2} \tag{4.80}$$

with

$$e_{\left[\begin{smallmatrix} c \\ s \end{smallmatrix}\right] i} = \sum_{j=1}^{N} r_{\left[\begin{smallmatrix} c \\ s \end{smallmatrix}\right] j} c_{ij} \tag{4.81}$$

and

$$r_{\left[\begin{smallmatrix} c \\ s \end{smallmatrix}\right] j} = \int_{(j-1)T_c}^{jT_c} r(t) \begin{bmatrix} \cos\omega_0 t \\ \sin\omega_0 t \end{bmatrix} dt; \quad j = 1, 2, \ldots, N. \tag{4.82}$$

Here ω_0 is the carrier radian frequency and c_{ij} denotes the j-th binary element ($+1$ or -1) of the i-th PN code pattern $c_i(t)$. In general, the index

i ranges over the N-dimensional space corresponding to the 2^N possible patterns (arrangements) of the N binary symbols within the $T = NT_c$-second observation interval. However, it can be shown that insofar as the decision rule is concerned, it is sufficient to divide the above space into two disjoint complementary subsets (G and $\bar{G}$), each having 2^{N-1} elements, and sum only over those elements in either G or $\bar{G}$. The rule for the subdivision is that, for each possible PN code vector $\boldsymbol{c}_i = (c_{i1}, c_{i2}, \ldots, c_{iN})$, its negative (complement) belongs to the other subset. If as before the non-linearity "I_0" is approximated by its low SNR equivalent $I_0(x) = 1 + x^2/4$, then a *synchronous non-coherent energy detector* results.

For detection of frequency-hopped signals, it can be shown that the optimal *synchronous non-coherent detector* is an implementation of the decision rule

$$\text{if } \sum_{n=1}^{N_h} \ln\left(\sum_{m=1}^{N_T} I_0(R_{mn})\right) \begin{matrix} > \eta, & \text{decide signal present} \\ < \eta, & \text{decide signal absent} \end{matrix} \tag{4.83}$$

where, analogous to (4.80), R_{ij} is the envelope of the signal in the j-th hop frequency slot and the i-th hop time interval, N_h is the number of hop frequency slots in the spread-spectrum bandwidth, and N_T is the total number of hop time intervals in the observation. We note that the detector corresponding to (4.83) is equivalent to Figure 4.4 since in deriving (4.83) the log-likelihood ratio test was actually employed. Applying this same test in deriving Figure 4.4 would have resulted in the inclusion of a logarithm non-linearity between the summer and product blocks in this figure. However, since the logarithm of a product is identical to the summation of the logarithms, we obtain the equivalence with (4.83).

While the above results that have been reported in [9] are only for synchronous structures, they are not purely of academic interest since they can be used to derive upper bounds on performance for any practical asynchronous system. Furthermore, as the authors point out, the same maximum-likelihood approach can be used to derive asynchronous optimal and suboptimal detector structures.

In [10], Krasner addresses the general problem of optimum detection of digitally modulated signals (a train of unknown symbols modulated onto a single or quadrature carriers) in the context of the LPI application, i.e., low symbol SNR, unknown symbol epoch, unknown carrier phase. By not restricting the symbol set to be binary and allowing various choices for the correlation properties of the symbol set, e.g., antipodal (balanced), orthogonal, or biorthogonal, the direct-sequence and frequency-hopping spread-spectrum modulations occur as special cases. Again the structures that are developed result from application of the maximum-likelihood theory to testing the hypothesis of signal plus noise against the null hypothesis of noise alone. As such, the presence of information modulation on the signal when present is of no consequence. Analogous to [9], optimal detectors for the coherent and non-coherent carrier cases are derived, here, however, in the presence of unknown symbol epoch (asynchronism). Performance comparisons are made in terms of output SNR between the optimal structures and the classical wideband radiometer.

Also considered in [10] are the effects on the maximum-likelihood structures produced by (1) assuming that the signal of interest is formed by passing the "ideal" digitally modulated signal through a band-pass filter that may severely distort the waveform and (2) assuming the presence of correlation among the symbols in the transmitted sequence. The practical significance of the assumptions in (1) and (2) are that filtering is often intentionally performed on spread-spectrum type signals to make them appear more "noise-like," whereas sequences of correlated symbols naturally come about when modulations such as minimum-shift-keying (MSK) are employed to produce desirable spectral shaping.

While all of the structures that are developed in [10] assume a uniform *a priori* probability distribution on the input symbols, a simple modification, e.g., a non-linear weighting of each of the terms contributing to the sum in (4.79), can be performed to make the results applicable to other distributions.

In [11], Krasner continues his work in [10] by developing maximum-likelihood estimators of carrier phase and symbol epoch for quadriphase modulated signals, again under the assumption that the symbol sequence is unknown and that the presence of data information on these symbols is of no interest to the receiver. As in [10], the case of interest is low-symbol SNR and the resulting maximum-likelihood structures that are derived are further simplified to correspond to this case. The effects of filtering and correlated symbols are also considered.

Finally, we wish to point out the existence of an excellent tutorial style article by Glenn [12] (also presented at MILCOM'82 but not included in the proceedings), which identifies the key system parameters and their interrelation in determining the LPI performance of airborne command post/satellite links operating at super high frequency (SHF) and extremely high frequency (EHF).

4.5 REFERENCES

[1] G. M. Dillard, "A moving-window detector for binary integration," *IEEE Trans. Inform. Theory*, IT-13, no. 1, pp. 2–6, January 1967.

[2] R. A. Dillard, "Vulnerability of low detectability communication to energy detection," Naval Electronic Laboratory Center, San Diego, California, January 26, 1971.

[3] J. D. Edell, "Wideband noncoherent frequency-hopped waveforms and their hybrids in low-probability-of-intercept communications," Naval Research Laboratory, Washington, D.C., Technical Report No. 8025, November 8, 1976.

[4] D. G. Woodring, "Performance of optimum and suboptimum detectors for spread spectrum waveforms," Naval Research Laboratory, Washington, D.C., Technical Report No. 8432, December 1980.
[5] R. A. Dillard, "Detectability of spread spectrum signals," *IEEE Trans. Aerospace and Electronic Systems*, AES-15, no. 5, pp. 526–537, July 1979.
[6] J. E. Ohlson, "Efficiency of radiometers using digital integration," *Radio Science*, vol. 6, no. 3, pp. 341–345, March 1971.
[7] M. Skolnik, ed., *Radar Handbook*, New York: McGraw-Hill, 1970.
[8] L. Kleinrock, "Detection of energy peak of an arbitrary signal," MIT Lincoln Laboratory, Lexington, Mass., Technical Report No. 325, August 23, 1963.
[9] A. Polydoros and C. L. Weber, "Optimal detection considerations for low probability of intercept," *MILCOM'82 Conference Proceedings*, Boston, Mass., pp. 2.1-1–2.1-5, October 17–20, 1982.
[10] N. F. Krasner, "Optimal detection of digitally modulated signals," *IEEE Trans. Commun.*, COM-30, no. 5, pp. 885–895, May 1982.
[11] N. F. Krasner, "Maximum likelihood parameter estimation for LPI signals," *MILCOM'82 Conference Proceedings*, Boston, Mass., pp. 2.3-1–2.3-4, October 17–20, 1982.
[12] A. B. Glenn, "Low probability of intercept," *IEEE Commun. Mag.*, vol. 21, no. 4, pp. 26–33, July 1983.

APPENDIX 4A: CONDITIONS FOR VIABLE MULTICHANNEL DETECTOR PERFORMANCE

Assume that a K-channel detector is to be realized by arbitrarily dividing the total signal bandwidth W_{ss} into K contiguous non-overlapping bands. As such, a hit is guaranteed in one of the K channels for each hop. The required per-channel S/N_0 is given by

$$\left(\frac{S}{N_0}\right)_K = (d_K \eta_K)\sqrt{\frac{W_K}{T_K}}, \tag{4A.1}$$

where the K subscript denotes the per-channel parameters. Now, the term $(d_K \eta_K)$ is a function of the per-channel P_{DI} and P_{FAI} and the Gaussian assumption correction factor,* and $W_K = W_{ss}/K$. This leaves only T_K to be specified.

Clearly, the larger T_K is, the lower the $(S/N_0)_K$ required. The minimum T_K that could be used is $T_K = T_h$, the hop pulse period. However, since the individual channels are, by definition, not matched in bandwidth to that of the hop pulses, this would be a very poor choice. Intuitively, it can be seen that T_K should be "matched" to the presence of hop pulses in each channel; i.e., the channel integrator is enabled (integrates) when a pulse is present and is disabled (holds) when a pulse is absent. But the detector has no idea

*The factor η, which represents a correction from a Gaussian assumption to chi-squared statistics, is discussed in (3) of Section 4.2.1.2.

when the various hits in each channel will occur; thus, the "matched" strategy is totally impractical. There is no recourse, then, but to make $T_K = T_M$. Therefore,

$$\left(\frac{S}{N_0}\right)_K = \frac{1}{\sqrt{K}} d_K \eta_K \sqrt{\frac{W_{ss}}{T_M}} . \tag{4A.2}$$

Now the single-channel wideband radiometer (which occurs if $K = 1$) has its performance given by:

$$\left(\frac{S}{N_0}\right)_{WB} = d_{WB} \eta_{WB} \sqrt{\frac{W_{ss}}{T_M}} . \tag{4A.3}$$

If it is assumed that $W_{ss}T_M \gg 1$ and $W_{ss}T_M/K \gg 1$, then η_{WB} and η_K can both be conveniently taken as unity. Substituting (4A.3) into (4A.2) gives

$$\left(\frac{S}{N_0}\right)_K = \left(\frac{d_K}{d_{WB}}\right)\left[\frac{1}{\sqrt{K}}\left(\frac{S}{N_0}\right)_{WB}\right]. \tag{4A.4}$$

Now, assume for the moment that the (S/N_0) input to the K channel radiometer is exactly $(S/N_0)_{WB}$. On the basis of equal energy division between the K channels, the available $(S/N_0)_K$ is

$$\left(\frac{S}{N_0}\right)_K (\text{available}) = \frac{1}{K}\left(\frac{S}{N_0}\right)_{WB} . \tag{4A.5}$$

Further, taking $d_K = d_{WB}$ (as a bounding worst case assumption), by comparing (4A.5) with (4A.4), it is readily seen that the *available* $(S/N_0)_K$ is a factor of $1/\sqrt{K}$ lower than that *required* by (4A.4). Clearly, then, if parity is to be achieved between the two detectors, it is necessary that $d_K = d_{WB}/\sqrt{K}$. Suppose the per-channel P_{DI} and P_{FAI} of the K-band detector are defined as:

$$P_{DI} = P_D/K \tag{4A.6}$$

$$P_{FAI} = P_{FA}/K. \tag{4A.7}$$

The requirement then becomes:

$$\left[Q^{-1}(P_{FA}/K) - Q^{-1}(P_D/K)\right] \stackrel{?}{=} \left[Q^{-1}(P_{FA}) - Q^{-1}(P_D)\right]/\sqrt{K} \tag{4A.8}$$

Although the validity of (4A.8) cannot be readily established, recourse to Figure 4.2 or to numerical examples, shows that equality will not be obtained and that the inequality

$$[Q^{-1}(P_{FA}/K) - Q^{-1}(P_D/K)] > [Q^{-1}(P_{FA}) - Q^{-1}(P_D)]/\sqrt{K} \tag{4A.9}$$

must hold. [Example: With $P_D = 0.9$, $P_{FA} = 10^{-6}$, and $K = 10$, (4A.9) becomes, specifically, 5.8 dB > 2.8 dB.]

The conclusion, then, is that a K channel detector of the form postulated above requires a higher S/N_0 than the simple single-channel wideband radiometer. A manifest reason for this is that the channels are not matched to the times when signal is present within them. This is a necessary criterion for any detector that is going to outperform the wideband radiometer. (In theory, the partial-band FBC meets this criterion and, as a result, its performance is generally superior.)

Chapter 5

MULTIPLE ACCESS

Spread-spectrum signals[1] examined in this book are designed to combat intentional jamming interference in radio channels. Thus, to any spread-spectrum transmitter/receiver pair that is communicating in a network of radios, other spread-spectrum signals can be collectively regarded as a jamming signal and, provided their numbers are not too large, each such link should be able to achieve reliable communication with this unintentional mutual interference.

This chapter presents a somewhat tutorial discussion of the performance of spread-spectrum communication systems in some generic networks where there are several spread-spectrum signals of the same type occupying the same time and frequency. Specifically, we examine two basic questions concerning multiple access communications:

1. Point-to-Point: How well can a receiver detect and decode a spread-spectrum signal from one radio transmitter when there is interference from several other spread-spectrum radios?
2. Multipoint-to-Point: How well can a receiver simultaneously detect and decode several spread-spectrum signals transmitted from spatially separated radios?

For the point-to-point channel, multiple access is achieved only at baseband using a multiplexer and demultiplexer at the transmitter and receiver, as shown in Figures 5.1 and 5.2. The corresponding multipoint-to-point system is illustrated in Figures 5.3 and 5.4. Here multiple access can be achieved at radio frequencies.

The above questions arise in military digital radio networks. We assume throughout that *in these networks spread-spectrum signals are used primarily to combat intentional jamming*. Since they are designed to combat channel interference of all kinds, they have certain multiple access capabilities as well as some tolerance to mutual interference.

---

[1] In this chapter we examine DS/BPSK and FH/MFSK signals.

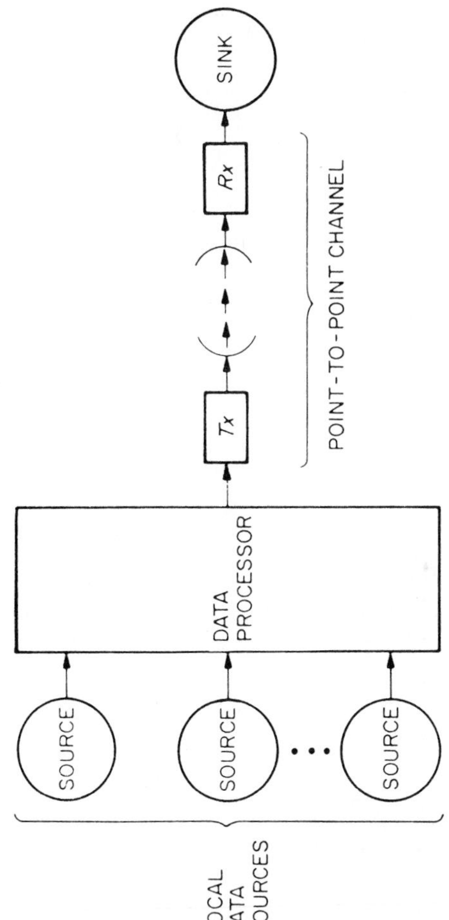

Figure 5.1. The multiplexer channel.

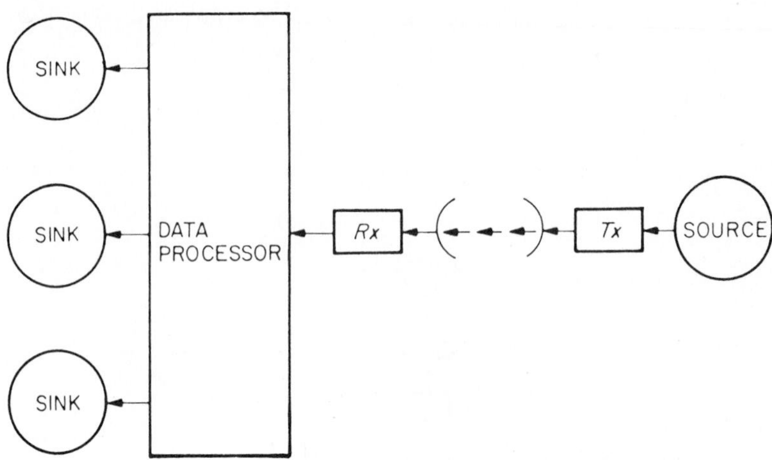

Figure 5.2. The demultiplexer.

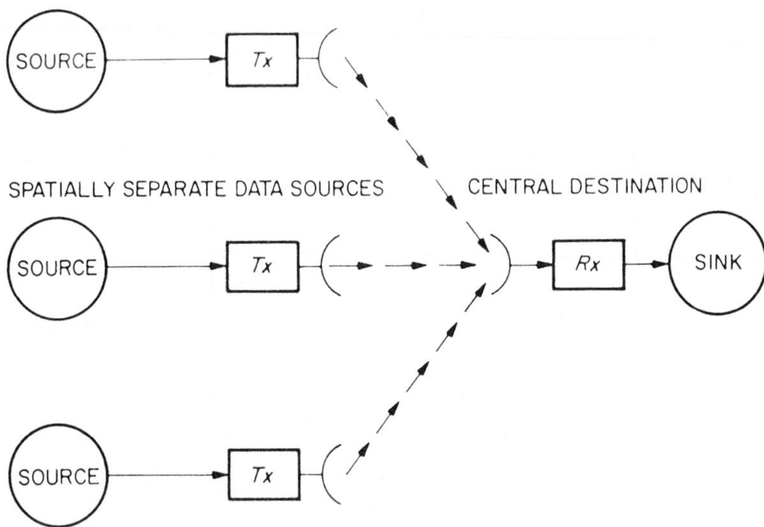

Figure 5.3. Distributed multiple access channel.

Military digital radio network design principles are not as well understood or developed as those for commercial digital networks. For one thing there is a much wider variety of military network types compared with commercial networks. Radios here are often mobile, subject to jamming and physical attack, and must operate in all types of environments [1]–[3]. In addition, to reduce vulnerability terrestrial tactical digital radio networks

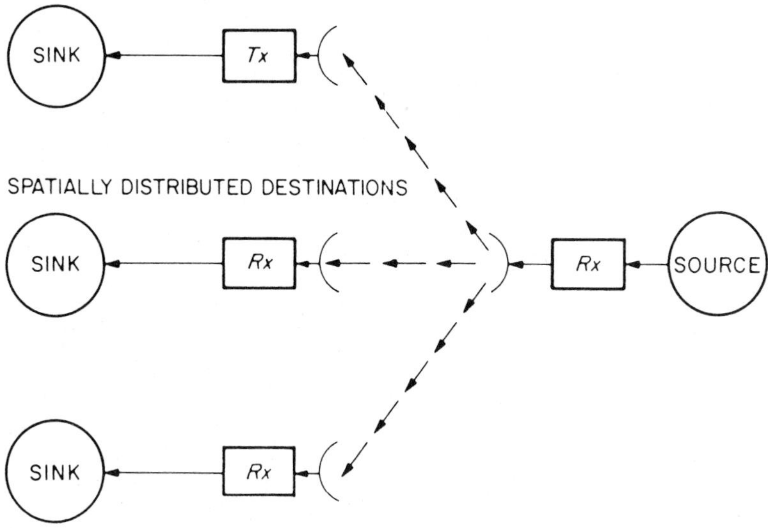

Figure 5.4. Distributed broadcast channel.

often require distributed network control. Other higher level networks, such as a satellite network, may have centralized network control [4]. To motivate the multiple access analysis of this chapter we first briefly describe two generic military digital radio networks. After this we discuss mutual interference and multiple access techniques in general, followed by the examination of the two questions raised above on mutual interference and multiple access with spread-spectrum signals.

5.1 NETWORKS

There are many different types of military communication networks and these are often interconnected to form parts of larger networks resulting in layers of communication networks. To place in some context and to motivate the mutual interference and multiple access problems that we examine in this chapter, consider two generic examples of radio and satellite communication networks where some or all terminals may be mobile.

5.1.1 Decentralized (Point-to-Point) Networks

Consider a collection of mobile radios scattered across some terrain. Assume each radio has an omni-directional antenna with no prior knowledge of the location of other radios. All radios use spread-spectrum signals for combatting intentional jamming where each radio has a unique key that generates a PN sequence assigned to it and can also generate the PN

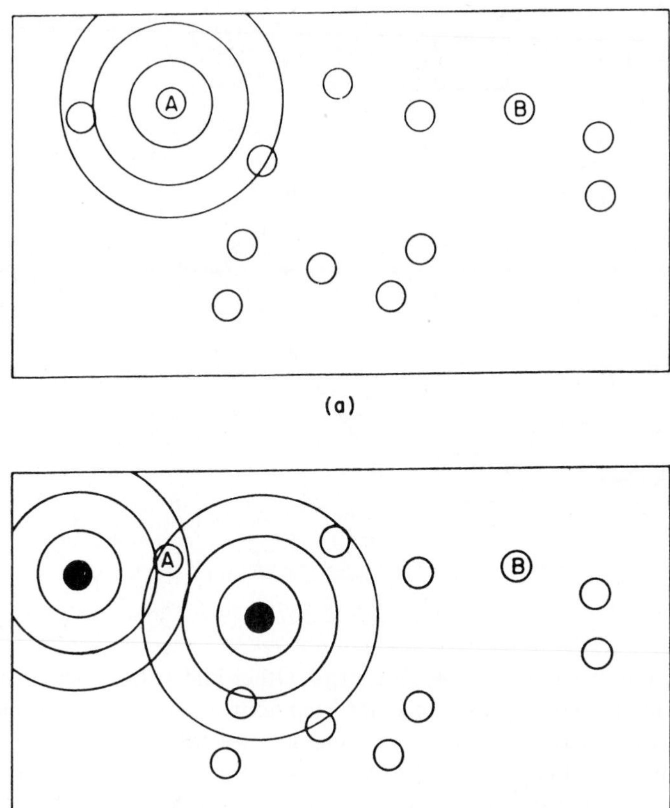

Figure 5.5. Illustration of flooding.

sequence assigned to some of the other radios. Acquisition and synchronization of these PN sequences is assumed throughout this chapter. Also there is enough processing capability and memory in each radio to maintain and update knowledge of the overall network connectivity between radios. Assume there is no central controller and each radio is within range of some subset of all radios in the terrain.

Consider only point-to-point communication between any two radios. Specifically, for the generic mobile digital radio network described, how does one radio communicate digital data to another radio? Since we do not assume full connectivity among radios, this is a multihop communication network. That is, a communication link between two radios in this network typically requires other radios to act as relays.

One brute force method, called "flooding" [3], [5]–[7], is illustrated in Figure 5.5. Suppose Radio A wants to send a message to Radio B but has no knowledge of the location of Radio B or any other radio in the network.

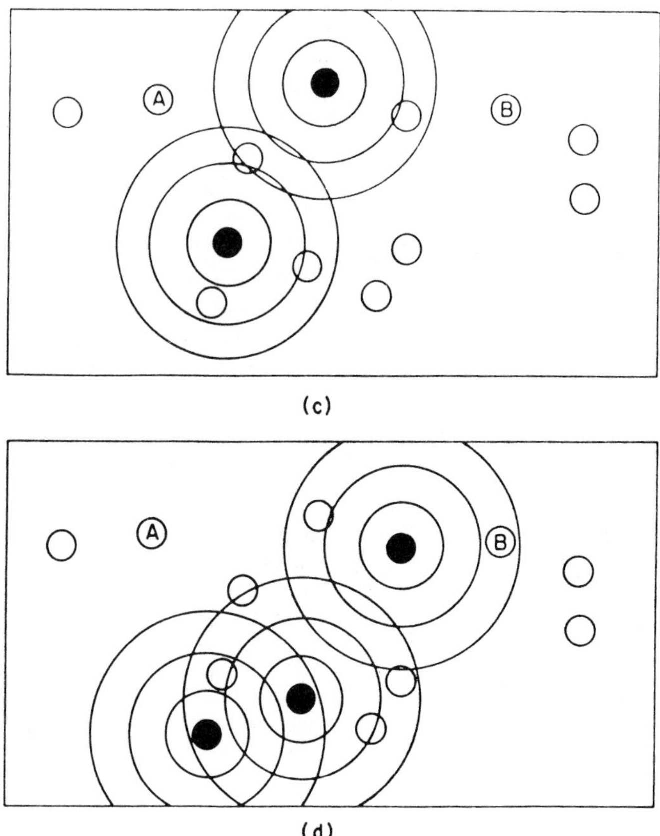

Figure 5.5. (continued)

Assume all other radios have a common key that generates a common pseudorandom sequence used for spread-spectrum signalling. Radio A transmits the message in an omni-directional signal that also identifies the destination Radio B and source Radio A. This signal can be received by all radios within some range, assuming all radios use the common key. The protocol for radios in this network is to retransmit the same message only once right after first receiving it. Hence, as shown in Figure 5.5(a), Radio A first transmits the message. In Figure 5.5(b) only radios marked in dark first receive Radio A's transmission and retransmit the same message. In Figure 5.5(c) radios that received the signal for the first time in the second transmission are shown. These in turn retransmit the same message with the final result that Radio B receives the message as shown in Figure 5.5(d). Retransmissions, however, may continue until each radio has received and transmitted the message once.

In this flooding technique a single radio may receive the same signal simultaneously from several other radios. This is the same as receiving a signal from a single transmitter in a multipath channel. If the relative delays between the different signals are greater than a "chip" time, then the receiver can resolve this difference and detect only one signal. Typically, in mobile digital radio systems real multipath would occur and techniques for handling it are required (see Chapter 1, Part 2).

There are several variations of the flooding scheme [3], [5]–[7]. For instance, each radio may retransmit the same message more than once. However, a maximum number of hops for a flooding signal might be set requiring each retransmission to update a "hop count" which is also transmitted. If a radio receives a signal with a count equal to a predetermined value, it will not retransmit it. Another approach is for each radio that receives a signal to wait a random length of time before retransmission. If it receives another copy of the same signal while it is waiting, it does not retransmit the signal.

The "flooding" technique is clearly an inefficient way for Radio A to send a message to Radio B. It results in excessive transmission by other terminals and few messages can be sent across the network at the same time. However, it may be useful to broadcast a short emergency message to many terminals.

In order for Radio A to more efficiently transmit a message to Radio B, it needs to know the connectivity of radios in the network so that it can route a message through the network. This means that somehow all radios must learn about how the radios in the network are connected to each other. Thus there are two problems:

1. How do radios learn of their connectivity in the network?
2. When network connectivity is known, how should a radio transmitter route messages through the network?

One approach is to assume there is a common network key that is used to generate a common pseudorandom sequence for the purpose of handling network overhead traffic. This sequence is used by the radios to learn how the radio network is connected. Here the flooding technique can be utilized with one radio sending a "route-finding" packet and each other radio adding its own identification to the packet before retransmitting it. Then whenever a radio receives such a signal it learns the sequence of radios that transmitted it. With enough such retransmissions each radio can obtain some knowledge of how the radio network is connected. For a time-varying mobile radio network this route-finding flooding technique is repeated periodically as the network changes.

Given a network connection table stored in memory, a radio can now transmit a message to any other radio by first selecting a route through the network based on this knowledge [8]–[27]. Now rather than use the common network key, the radio can route a message to the next radio in a multihop route by transmitting a spread-spectrum signal with the unique key for that specific radio. To all other radios this signal would appear only as small additional interference since such signals are designed to combat jamming. Only the radio that is receiving signals with its own unique spread-spectrum carrier would receive the transmitted signal and relay it on to the next radio in the designated route. This next hop in the route is again done by transmitting a spread-spectrum signal using the key unique to this next radio. Destination and routing information is assumed to be attached to the message.

It is common practice in communication networks to acknowledge the receipt of messages. The failure to receive an acknowledgment causes a retransmission of the message. In multihop networks, where messages are relayed one or more times, acknowledgments may be used for each relay (hop-by-hop), from the final destination to the source (end-to-end), or both.

The above generic decentralized network might represent terrestrial digital radios in a tactical battlefield environment where radios may drop out of the network due to jamming and/or direct attack. Centralized network control may make such a network system too vulnerable. Hence we have considered here a system with minimal network control and synchronization requirements.

5.1.2 Centralized (Multipoint-to-Point) Networks

Military communication satellites are usually processing satellites that can despread, demodulate, decode, reformat, and route through various downlink antenna beams the uplink spread-spectrum signals from various mobile and stationary terminals [4]. Generally, such a satellite is the central node in a star network as sketched in Figure 5.6 where the satellite serves as the

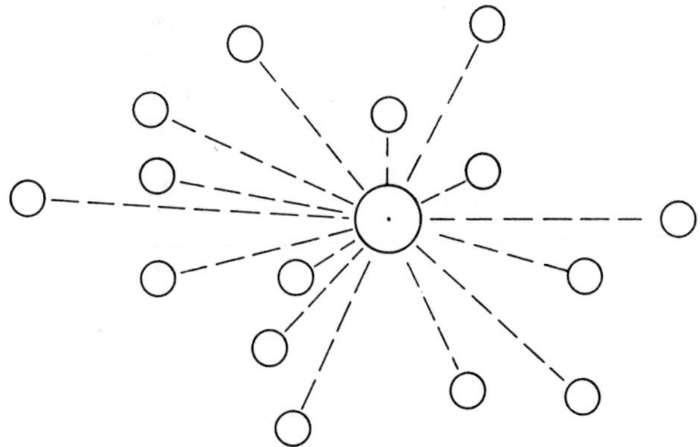

Figure 5.6. Star network.

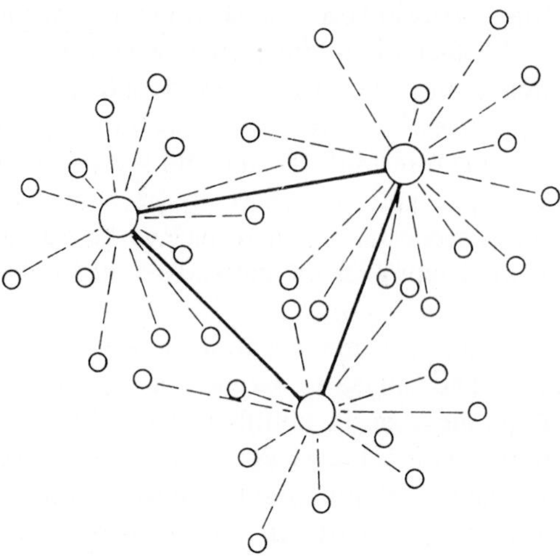

Figure 5.7. Fully connected star networks.

central controller for the network. This type of radio network is the opposite extreme from the terrestrial radio network described in the previous section.

For the star network the central node provides time synchronization[2] for each radio, typically through a feedback loop where each radio terminal adjusts its time reference based on feedback from the central node. Here we can expect some basic time reference available to all radios. For this case we consider the performance of various spread-spectrum multiple access schemes where several coordinated radios transmit signals to the central node. This is a multipoint-to-point system where the central node simultaneously receives signals from many radios.

A generalization of the star network is shown in Figure 5.7. Here there are several star networks with the central nodes forming a fully connected higher order network. This could represent a single processing satellite where each star network can represent a separate antenna beam, a separate frequency band, a separate spread-spectrum carrier, or any combination of these. Each network may also represent separate satellites with cross links that may or may not be fully connected. There is the possibility that any radio terminal will be able to switch from one star network to another.

The star network presents the multiple access problem of how several physically separated radios simultaneously transmit spread-spectrum signals to a single central node. We shall examine various techniques for doing this and evaluate their performance.

[2] The central node's signal may also provide a stable frequency reference.

5.2 SUMMARY OF MULTIPLE ACCESS TECHNIQUES

In a radio communication network where many radios communicate among themselves, there must be some means of sharing the available channel capacity. This means dividing up the overall channel into sub-channels and then assigning these to radios. Typically, there are more radios than available sub-channels but only a fraction of all radios have messages to transmit at any given time. The assignment of sub-channels to radios can be fixed or vary in time according to some policy.

Coordinating the assignment of sub-channels to various radios often requires that network control information flow in the network. This uses some of the available capacity. Ideally, one would like to assign sub-channels to those radios that have a message to transmit. A *fixed assignment* scheme (which can also change in time in a fixed manner) does not require much network capacity for coordination but it does not account for the random time-varying data transmission requirements of each radio. A real-time assignment of sub-channels upon demand by radios, called *demand assignment*, takes more network capacity and is more complex [28]–[36]. Demand assignment schemes require setting aside some channel capacity for transmitting requests and responding to these requests by one or more controllers. This can also be done by having a controller *poll the radios* to see if any one or more of them want to transmit messages [37]–[41]. One approach that takes little network coordination is for each radio to grab a sub-channel whenever it has a message to transmit. This is called *random access* [42]–[51]. Two or more radios, however, may use the same sub-channel at the same time causing "collisions" and these must somehow be resolved [52]–[56].

The simplest way to divide up the total radio channel capacity is to use frequency division multiple access (FDMA) [57]. Here the available frequency band is divided into disjoint sub-bands where any two radios can communicate using a sub-band or frequency. There would be no interference between radio signals whose spectra occupy disjoint parts of the total available frequency band.

If we restrict spread-spectrum signals to a sub-band of the total available frequency band, then the signal's anti-jam capability is reduced. Therefore, FDMA is not a good idea for spread-spectrum signals. Instead of dividing the available channel capacity using FDMA, a natural choice for spread-spectrum signals is to divide the available channel capacity into different spread-spectrum carriers. That is, instead of assigning a frequency to a radio, assign a spread-spectrum carrier which is specified by a pseudorandom sequence. The pseudorandom sequence is in turn determined by a pseudorandom sequence generator key and its initial state. Thus, rather than assign a frequency to a radio we can assign a key to the radio that uses spread-spectrum signals. This is referred to as *spread-spectrum multiple access* (SSMA) [1]–[4], [58]–[62].

Assigning a key to a spread-spectrum radio is analogous to assigning a frequency to a conventional narrowband radio. The primary difference is that signals of different frequencies in an FDMA system are orthogonal functions of time, whereas spread-spectrum signals with different keys in an SSMA system have some time cross-correlation. When regarded as random processes, however, spread-spectrum signals with different keys are often designed to be statistically independent and are orthogonal in the statistical sense of being uncorrelated random processes. This means that the expectation of the time cross-correlation is zero.

It is possible for M signals of bandwidth of W Hz and T seconds to be orthogonal (zero time cross-correlation) for $M \leq 2WT$ (coherent) and $M \leq WT$ (non-coherent). These orthogonal signals can, in fact, be generated using the same waveforms as spread-spectrum signals discussed in previous chapters but with specific assigned chip sequences. For DS/BPSK waveforms, for example, using orthogonal binary sequences as the chip sequences will result in orthogonal signals. For FH/MFSK waveforms hopping sequences can be chosen so that during a chip time (hop time) no two signals hop to the same part of the spread-spectrum frequency level. This is true as long as the chip sequences are time synchronized among all radios.

If we relax the chip synchronization requirement, we can use chip sequence generators specifically designed to yield low time cross-correlations between signals for all relative time delays. Gold sequences and Bent sequences discussed in Chapter 5 of Part 1 result in signals using DS/BPSK waveforms that have low time cross-correlations [63]–[76]. For FH/MFSK waveforms, Reed-Solomon codewords have been proposed [77]–[82] as hopping sequences that yield low time cross-correlation.

Signals with the same form as spread-spectrum signals discussed in earlier chapters but designed to have low time cross-correlation require the use of specific chip sequences to be assigned to radios. When these are used to divide the available channel capacity we refer to this as code division multiple access (CDMA). *We distinguish*[3] *this CDMA technique from SSMA where in SSMA we assume the chip sequences are statistically independent when regarded as random processes*. That is, for SSMA we assume pseudorandom sequences are well modelled as i.i.d. sequences and different keys result in independent pseudorandom sequences. The SSMA system thus uses spread-spectrum signals that are uncorrelated in the statistical sense where the expectation of the time cross-correlation of any two signals is zero. We define CDMA signals as those designed to have low time cross-correlations where the signals are not statistically independent. Generally, CDMA signals with sequences of long periods behave like SSMA signals [65].

[3] To our knowledge this distinction between CDMA and SSMA has not been used before.

Another common way to divide up the total radio channel capacity is to use time-division multiple access (TDMA) [57]. Here time is divided into disjoint slots where any two radios communicate using assigned time slots. This can be done with signals that occupy the entire signal bandwidth or with each sub-band of an FDMA system.

In principle, TDMA is equivalent to FDMA with time rather than frequency being the primary variable that is divided into segments. In practice, however, TDMA systems are more flexible than FDMA systems. TDMA systems require some means of maintaining a common time reference among all radios, which usually means that some network control signal must be used. Flexibility is achieved with TDMA since time slots can be easily changed without requiring hardware changes in the radio system. Also a radio can receive data from many other radios with only one receiver since their transmission time slots do not overlap.

Just as a single frequency in an FDMA system can be used in a TDMA mode, a spread-spectrum carrier can be used in a TDMA mode. That is, several radios can use the same pseudorandom sequence determined by a key but each transmitting a spread-spectrum signal at disjoint assigned time slots. Using disjoint time slots as in a TDMA format, however, is not necessary when using spread-spectrum signals. When two radios use the same spread-spectrum carrier (same pseudorandom sequence specified by the same key) but have a relative delay between them of greater than a chip time T_c, a radio can pick out either one of the two radio transmissions. For DS/BPSK spread-spectrum signals, for example, this is like a multipath channel where (recall from Chapter 1 in Part 2) at the receiver each received multipath signal component can be separated. Essentially, we can have a matched filter[4] with outputs that have separated signal correlation peaks due to the relative time delay of the separate signals. These matched filter output peaks resulting from different signals will not overlap if time delays between signals using the same key are greater than a chip time. Here the receiver must sample the matched filter outputs at times corresponding to one of the transmitted signals. It is interleaved with others but can be separated by selecting appropriate samples. This is illustrated in Figure 5.8.

FH/MFSK spread-spectrum signals using the same key but separated by more than a chip time (hop time) also can be separated at the receiving radio. Here the FH/MFSK radio receiver merely needs to be synchronized with the intended transmitted signal.

For spread-spectrum signals the notion of TDMA has a new form. Here we merely require spread-spectrum signals using the same key to use fixed time delays relative to each other where time delay slots are spaced every

[4] This may be implemented using a pseudorandomly time-varying surface acoustic wave (SAW) matched filter [83]–[86].

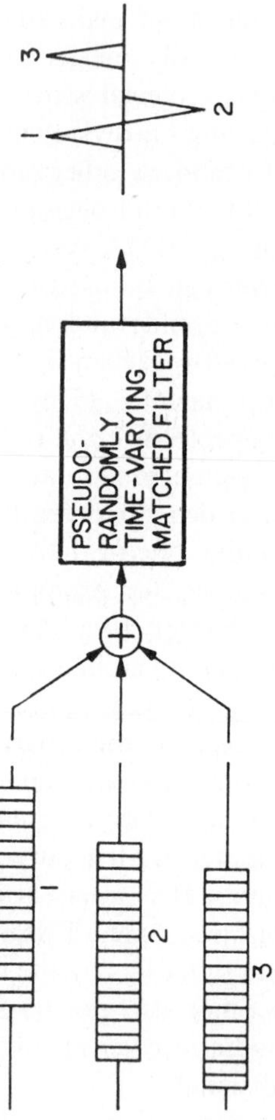

Figure 5.8. Resolving time shifted spread-spectrum signals sharing common PN sequence.

chip time interval. This is due to the fact that despreading the received radio signal at the receiver essentially filters out all signals except the one signal that is synchronized with the receivers. For many terrestrial military radio applications, however, maintaining time accuracy up to a chip time interval may be too difficult. This is especially true of DS/BPSK systems where chip times are usually much smaller than the chip (hop) time of FH/MFSK systems.

Random access is like a TDMA scheme except here each radio transmits a signal whenever it has a message to send without regard for other radios in the network. The Aloha random access scheme [42] is the simplest in that there are no restrictions on when a radio can transmit. In this scheme a radio transmits any time it has a message and listens for an acknowledgment from the receiving radio. If there is no acknowledgment, it retransmits the message after a random delay. Slotted Aloha [45] is a scheme where the random transmissions are restricted to fixed time slots. This implies that all radios must maintain a time reference. In carrier sense multiple access (CSMA) [44] techniques the radio senses the channel before transmitting and delays transmission if it is already being used. There are several variations on the CSMA technique [45]–[51]. The more complex random access techniques allow more efficient utilization of the channel but also require more side information in the form of time synchronization and/or channel measurements.

Since spread-spectrum signals are generally difficult to detect (see Chapter 4, Part 5), CSMA schemes are not useful for most spread-spectrum carriers. Slotted Aloha requires time synchronization among radios which is often difficult to achieve. Also, with spread-spectrum signals the notion of non-overlapping time slots is not useful since these signals do not have "collisions" even when using the same spread-spectrum carriers and the same time interval as long as their relative time delays are greater than the chip time. With pure Aloha random access, two spread-spectrum radio signals can cause a "collision" at a receiving radio only if they both use the same key and transmit with relative delays of less than the chip time. Otherwise, these signals interfere with each other like independent jamming interference. If pure Aloha random access is to be used, this suggests that all radios must transmit with random delays and receiving radios must be able to acquire and synchronize over the range of possible transmission delays. These delays can be small compared with data bit time intervals in DS/BPSK systems.

Finally, note that there are ways to divide up a channel using antenna techniques. Adaptive multiple spot beam antennas are used in satellites [87]–[89], for example, not only to separate uplink and downlink signals[5] but also to null out undesirable interference such as intentional jamming.

---

[5]Signals from terminals that are in different spot beam areas can be separated.

Antennas can also use polarization division where electromagnetic fields can be polarized into separate channels.

5.3 SPREAD-SPECTRUM MULTIPLE ACCESS WITH DS/BPSK WAVEFORMS

When a transmitter and receiver use a DS/BPSK waveform to communicate, all the interference in the channel can be approximated as additive white Gaussian noise. This was shown to be a good approximation in Chapter 1 of Part 2, provided the pseudorandom sequence used is statistically independent of the interference signal. In fact, for many CDMA systems where signals are not independent, the Gaussian approximation is also justified, although the resulting variance may be different [65]. In this section we assume radios in a network where different keys have statistically independent pseudorandom sequences associated with them and that each sequence is modelled as a sequence of independent equal probable binary random variables. We refer to this case as SSMA as opposed to CDMA where different keys correspond to sequences designed to have low cross-correlation properties. Our assumption here is that the primary purpose in using DS/BPSK waveforms is to combat jamming and the multiple access capability is a secondary additional property we can use for multiple access in digital radio networks.

Throughout this section assume that pseudorandom sequence acquisition and synchronization can be easily achieved by the intended receiver. This discussion is limited to the idealized assumption that the receiver for the desired DS/BPSK signal is perfectly synchronized in frequency, phase, chip epoch, and bit epoch. Also assume all radios are asynchronous and there is no network control or common time reference among the radios. As stated earlier for our example distributed radio network each radio has a unique key or pseudorandom sequence assigned to it as well as a common network key shared by all radios. During certain known fixed times the network key is used by all radios. Otherwise, each radio uses its own unique key for receiving DS/BPSK transmissions and each radio can transmit DS/BPSK waveforms with the key corresponding to some other radios. In this context we examine SSMA properties of DS/BPSK waveforms.

5.3.1 Point-to-Point

The analysis of Chapter 1 of Part 2 applies directly to the point-to-point communications system where the interference or jamming signal is due to other users in the radio network. Suppose that while a transmitter and synchronized receiver are communicating, the interference in the channel is due to L other radio transmitters of power

$$J_\ell; \quad \ell = 1, 2, \ldots, L \tag{5.1}$$

at the receiver in question while the intended signal has power S. Then the effective bit energy-to-jammer-noise ratio is

$$\frac{E_b}{N_J} = \frac{PG}{J/S} \tag{5.2}$$

where

$$PG = N \tag{5.3}$$

is the number of chips per data bit and

$$J = \sum_{\ell=1}^{L} J_\ell. \tag{5.4}$$

As an example suppose the $K = 7$ rate $R = 1/2$ convolutional code with soft decision Viterbi decoding is used with the DS/BPSK waveform. To achieve 10^{-6} bit error probability we require the bit energy-to-noise ratio of (see Figure 1.7 of Chapter 1 in Part 2)

$$E_b/N_J = 5 \text{ dB}. \tag{5.5}$$

Also suppose the number of chips per data bit is

$$\begin{aligned} N &= 1000 \\ &= 30 \text{ dB}. \end{aligned} \tag{5.6}$$

This means the point-to-point DS/BPSK radio link in question can communicate effectively as long as the total interference power satisfies

$$\frac{\sum_{\ell=1}^{L} J_\ell}{S} \leq 316.23. \tag{5.7}$$

That is, up to 316 radios of equivalent power (at the receiver) as the intended transmitter signal can be simultaneously transmitting DS/BPSK waveforms. In practice, of course, some radios will be closer[6] than others and the power levels will be unequal at the receiver. This is the "near-far" problem encountered in terrestrial radio networks. Also some of the interference may be due to multipath components of the intended signal. In this example all these interferences must have total power that is no more than 316 times the intended signal power at the receiver.

The analysis here is based on the continuous jammer of power J. In a radio network, interference in any point-to-point link will vary randomly in time. Here assume the maximum interference power is less than the prescribed value. In general a coded or uncoded spread-spectrum DS/BPSK system designed to combat continuous jamming will have the same performance bound (see Section 1.2, Chapter 1, Part 2) as a BPSK signal in

[6] If an interfering radio is very close it can drive the receiver front end to saturation and effectively block all transmissions. The analysis here assumes no saturation has taken place.

white Gaussian noise with bit energy-to-noise ratio given by (5.2). If γ is the bit energy-to-noise ratio that achieves a desired bit error probability, then the total interference in the channel must be bounded by

$$J = \sum_{\ell=1}^{L} J_\ell \leq \left(\frac{N}{\gamma}\right) S. \tag{5.8}$$

Figure 5.9 illustrates the special case where

$$J_\ell = S; \quad \ell = 1, 2, \ldots, L \tag{5.9}$$

plotting the maximum number of equal power interference signals at the receiver that can be tolerated as a function of the number of pseudorandom sequence chips N per information bit, called the processing gain (PG). This is parameterized by the required bit energy-to-noise ratio γ, which varies with the bit error probability requirement, the choice of coding technique, and the decoding metric. Since we assume maximum power for the total interference in giving γ, we can use standard error probability curves for the additive white Gaussian noise channel to determine the required value of γ

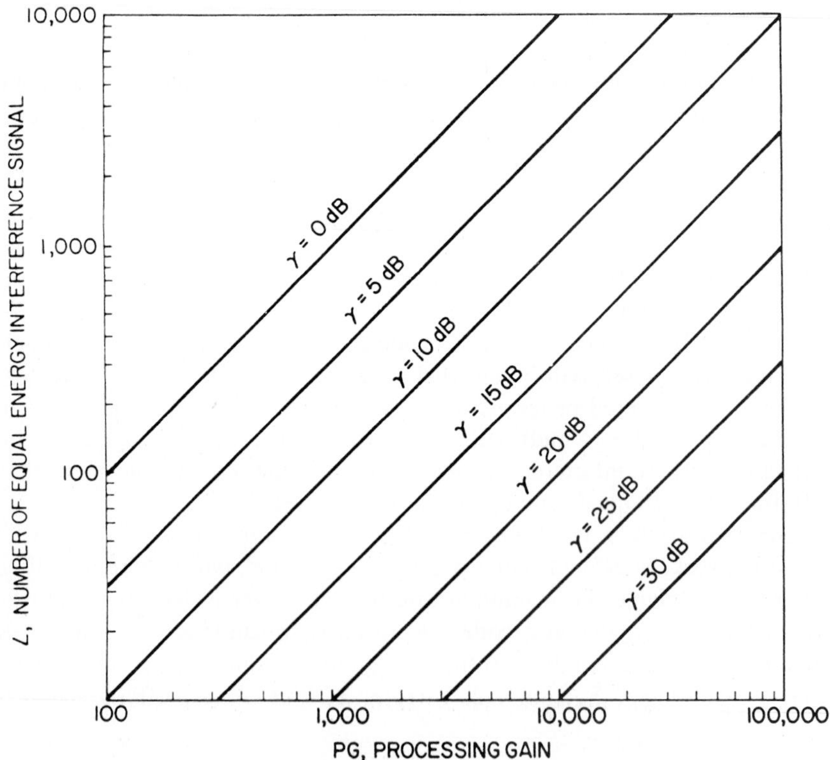

Figure 5.9. Simultaneous transmissions versus process gain.

to achieve a desired coded or uncoded bit error probability. Keep in mind that these results assume no background or receiver noise. This must ultimately be considered for some cases, as described in Chapter 3 of Part 1. Background noise can be added directly to the equivalent interference.

The point-to-point SSMA analysis for DS/BPSK waveforms is the same as that of the continuous jammer case covered in Chapter 1 of Part 2. For CDMA where pseudorandom sequences are designed to have low cross-correlation the multiple access performance will improve somewhat [63]–[76]. For the CDMA case the SSMA results here can be viewed as a bound on performance. Generally, when the number of CDMA signals is large the SSMA results presented here are close [65].

The results here generalize directly to fading channels. With Rayleigh fading the bit energy-to-noise ratio becomes

$$E_b/N_J = \frac{PG}{\bar{J}/\bar{S}} \tag{5.10}$$

where $\bar{J}$ is the average interference power and $\bar{S}$ is the average signal power. The curves used to determine γ, the required bit energy-to-noise ratio for a given bit error probability, would be obtained from analysis assuming Rayleigh fading (see Chapter 1 in Part 2). Otherwise, Figure 5.9 can still be applied. As with pulse jamming, because the real time bit energy-to-noise ratio varies in time, with the use of coding, care must be taken to distinguish between using side information to obtain the maximum-likelihood metric or a simpler non-optimum metric. With suboptimum metrics (no side information about real time bit energy-to-noise ratio) hard decision channel quantization can outperform soft decision channel quantization [90].

5.3.2 Conventional Multipoint-to-Point

Consider the possibility of two or more radios transmitting simultaneously to a single radio terminal in a network. For a conventional FDMA system this would be possible if the transmitting radios use different frequencies and the receiving radio terminal has separate receivers each tuned to one of the transmitting frequencies. For DS/BPSK waveforms the analogous system is where the transmitting radios use different keys and the receiving radio terminal has separate receivers each using a key with a pseudorandom sequence synchronized to the corresponding transmitting radio. Here a key in the SSMA system is similar to a frequency in the FDMA system. This is illustrated in Figure 5.10.

A radio terminal capable of receiving several signals of different frequencies in an FDMA system or DS/BPSK waveforms of different pseudorandom sequences in an SSMA system is often too complex and costly. This is because the receiving radio terminal essentially consists of several separate receivers. Conventional TDMA systems get around this problem since a

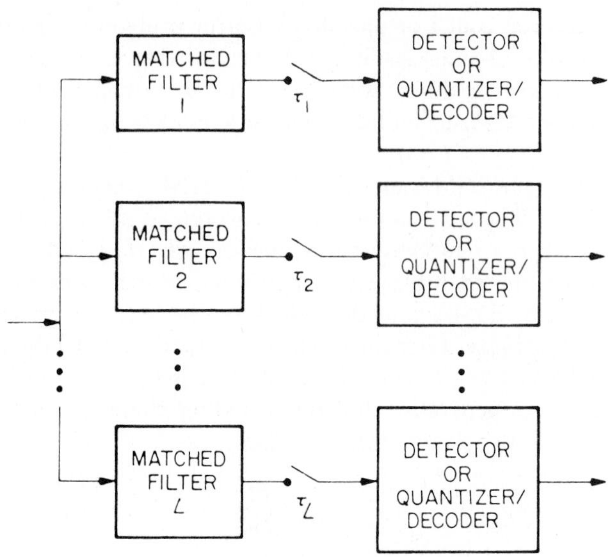

Figure 5.10. Transmissions with different keys.

single radio receiver can sequentially receive each of the transmitted radio signals that occupy non-overlapping time intervals. However, TDMA receivers must operate at higher burst rates to achieve the same overall throughput. In addition, time synchronization must somehow be maintained among the radios in the network. Acquisition and synchronization must also be done by the receiver for each separate radio transmission burst and this reduces the overall efficiency by requiring extra overhead bits in each burst.

Similar to conventional TDMA, a radio terminal in an SSMA system using DS/BPSK waveforms can simultaneously receive transmissions from several radios using a single receiver. Suppose all radios transmitting to the same receiving radio terminal use the unique key associated with this radio. Instead of transmitting in non-overlapping time intervals as in TDMA systems, each transmitting radio introduces a unique time shift in its DS/BPSK transmission which is a multiple of the basic chip time. At the receiving radio terminal these time-shifted DS/BPSK signals all using the same pseudorandom sequence appear like components of a multipath channel output with one radio transmission. If the receiving radio knows the time shifts used by the transmitting radios, then it can correlate delayed versions of the common pseudorandom sequence with the received radio signal to resolve the various transmitted signals (see Section 1.6, Chapter 1, Part 2).

If each coded bit consists of N_C chips then correlation is done for each N_C chip sequence corresponding to a coded transmitted bit of each radio transmitter. The N_C chip correlator can be realized with a time-varying matched filter using a SAW device [83]–[86]. With a matched filter the various transmitted DS/BPSK signals will appear as peaks of energy at the filter output. The peaks are roughly two chip time in width and separated from each other by the relative delays of the radio signal shifts at the receiving radio. This is illustrated in Figure 5.8 where we show one coded bit from three radios and the time-varying matched filter output. Note that there is a unique sample point in every coded bit time interval for each of the transmitting radio signals. These samples correspond to the usual correlator outputs in the DS/BPSK receiver except that with the use of a single matched filter, correlator outputs for all transmitted radio signals can be obtained at once. The sample sequence for each transmitting radio is then decoded separately.

Figure 5.11 illustrates the difference between receiving signals with different keys and a common key. For the uncoded case the detector is a simple hard quantizer. Also here we assume known phase and bit time epoch for each signal.

The receiving radio terminal described here uses one matched filter followed by a sampling circuit and individual decoders for each transmitted signal. We assumed that the relative time shifts of each transmitted signal were known at the receiving radio terminal which samples the match filter output at the correct time. For DS/BPSK waveforms it is usually impracti-

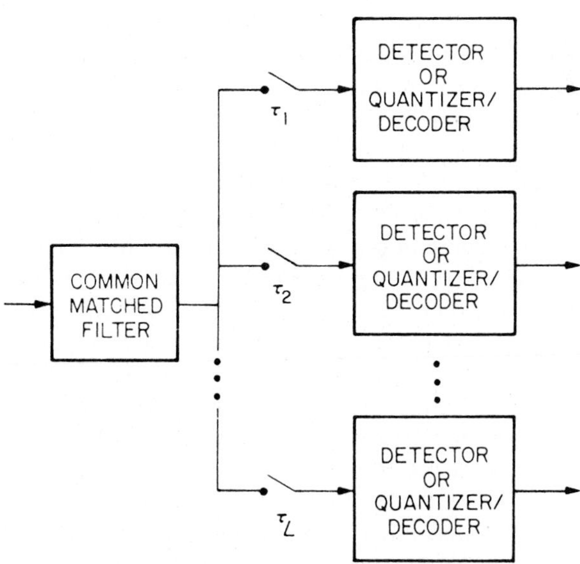

Figure 5.11. Transmissions with a common key.

cal for radio transmitters to accurately time shift their transmissions so that they are within a prescribed chip time at the receiving radio terminal. A more practical approach is to have each radio transmission introduce a random shift within a time interval and have the receiver system estimate appropriate sample times. This requires some sample time estimation scheme at the matched filter output. In addition, this introduces the possibility that two or more transmitting radios will have relative time shifts less than a chip time interval, with the result that their matched filter output sample times will coincide and cause "collisions." The probability of such collisions is determined in a manner analogous to the Aloha random access scheme. It depends on the number of simultaneous transmitting signals and the number of chip time slots in the random time shift interval. Generally, this probability is very small for DS/BPSK signals of interest.

The multipoint-to-point SSMA system described here requires radio terminals to have more digital signal processing capability in order to simultaneously receive from several radio transmitters. However, it requires the use of only one key or pseudorandom sequence in a time-varying matched filter. Without collisions the bit error probability for each transmitted data sequence is the same as in the point-to-point system described in the previous section. Here the interference is due to all other simultaneously transmitted radio signals, including those using the same key.

5.3.3 Optimum Multipoint-to-Point

In this section we present the theoretically optimum multiple access receiver when L radios transmit simultaneously to one radio terminal. Assume each transmitting radio uses a different key for its DS/BPSK waveform and all L radios transmit uncoded data at a rate of one data bit every T_b seconds. As illustrated in Figure 5.3, the distributed multiple access channel has asynchronous spatially separate radios transmitting simultaneously to a single destination radio.

It was first pointed out by Shnidman [91] that intersymbol interference and crosstalk between multiplexed signals are essentially identical phenomena. Kaye and George [92] have worked out this idea by investigating the transmission of multiplexed signals over multiple channel and diversity systems. Savage [93] analyzed such systems using random coding bounds where signal addresses were randomized. Van Etten [94] and Schneider [95] began looking at optimal detector techniques. The optimal multiple access detector for the system presented here was studied by Verdu [96], [97] and is based on earlier work on optimal receivers for channels with intersymbol interference [98]–[104]. We follow the work of Verdu in this section.

During the time interval $[kT_b, (k+1)T_b]$ each of the L radios will begin transmission of its k-th data bit using a DS/BPSK waveform. Since there is no time synchronization among the radios, assume the l-th radio transmits a data bit sequence using a continuous sequence of pulses of the form

$$\begin{aligned} s_l(t; d_k^{(l)}) &= A_l d_k^{(l)} c_l(t - \tau_l)\cos[\omega_0(t - \tau_l) + \theta_l]; \\ kT_b + \tau_l &\le t < (k+1)T_b + \tau_l \\ k &= \cdots -1, 0, 1, 2, \cdots . \end{aligned} \tag{5.11}$$

Here $d_k^{(l)} \varepsilon \{-1, 1\}$ is the k-th data bit of the l-th radio. The pseudorandom sequence waveform is given by $c_l(t - \tau_l)$ (see Chapter 1, Volume II). Parameters A_l, τ_l and θ_l depend on the propagation conditions of the radio channel as well as the radio transmitter.

Figure 5.12 shows a sketch of the k-th pulse $s_l(t; d_k^{(l)})$ of the l-th radio that transmits the k-th data bit $d_k^{(l)}$. This pulse occupies the time interval $[kT_b + \tau_l, (k+1)T_b + \tau_l]$. The actual transmission of this radio is a continuous sequence of such pulses. However, we focus here on the pulse related to the k-th data bit because we are interested in the sum of such pulses from all L radios. This is given by

$$x_k(t; \boldsymbol{d}_k) = \sum_{l=1}^{L} s_l(t; d_k^{(l)}) \tag{5.12}$$

which is sketched in Figure 5.13. Here define

$$\boldsymbol{d}_k = \begin{bmatrix} d_k^{(1)} \\ d_k^{(2)} \\ \vdots \\ d_k^{(L)} \end{bmatrix} \tag{5.13}$$

as the k-th data vector consisting of the k-th bits from all L radios. Note that due to the arbitrary delays $\tau_1, \tau_2, \ldots, \tau_L$ this waveform begins at $kT_b + \min\{\tau_l\}$ and ends at $(k+1)T_b + \max\{\tau_l\}$, which is confined to the interval $[kT_b, (k+2)T_b]$.

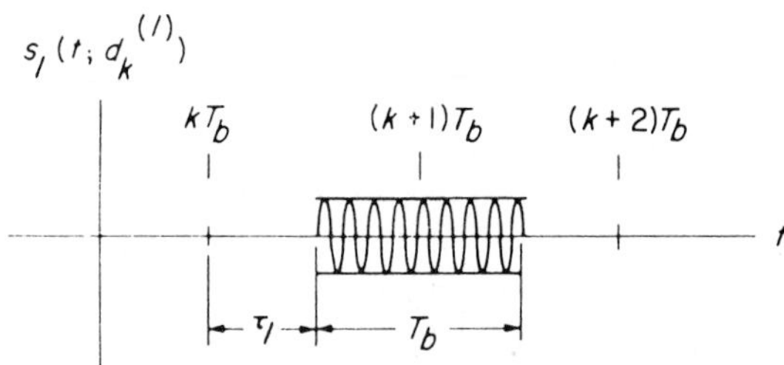

Figure 5.12. Single radio pulse.

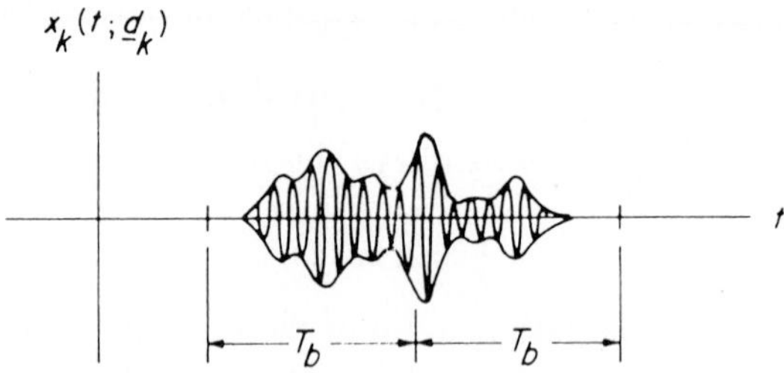

Figure 5.13. L radio pulses.

The composite signal from all L radios consists of a continuous sequence of pulses $x_k(t; \boldsymbol{d}_k)$, denoted

$$x(t) = \sum_k x_k(t; \boldsymbol{d}_k). \tag{5.14}$$

Note that these pulses are spaced T_b seconds apart, whereas each pulse has length greater than T_b seconds but less than $2T_b$ seconds. Transmission of such overlapping pulses is commonly referred to as *intersymbol interference*.

Based on the above discussion now model the set of L asynchronous radios of Figure 5.3 as a set of time synchronous radios followed by arbitrary delays as shown in Figure 5.14. Mathematically the transmitted signals are the same. Now, however, we have the final equivalent model of Figure 5.15 where we start with a vector source that outputs data vector $\boldsymbol{d}_k$ at time kT_b followed by a modulator and an additive white Gaussian noise channel with intersymbol interference. The signal at the receiving radio is

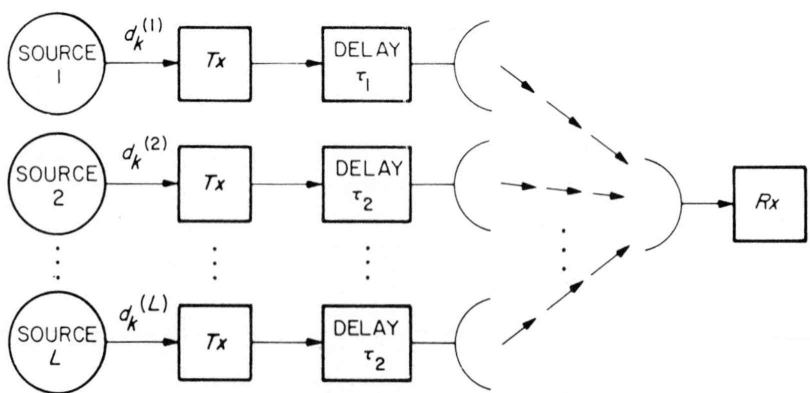

Figure 5.14. Equivalent synchronized radios.

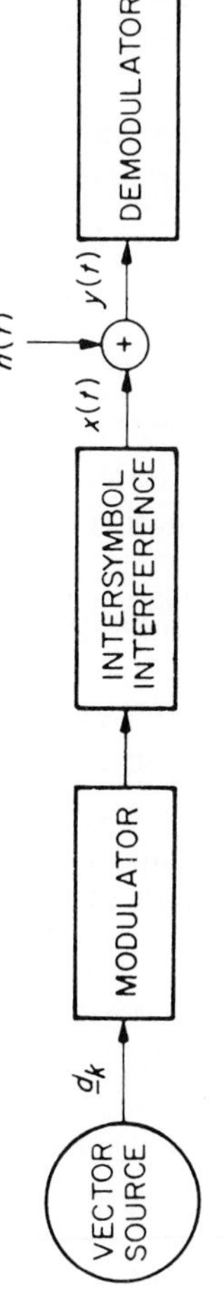

Figure 5.15. Intersymbol interference channel model.

given by

$$y(t) = x(t) + n(t) \tag{5.15}$$

where $n(t)$ is white Gaussian noise of single-sided spectral density N_o. Here we introduce receiver noise in the analysis.

Now consider the optimum receiver or demodulator. Assume that the receiver has acquired and accurately synchronized estimates of the signal parameters $\{A_l\}$, $\{\tau_l\}$, and $\{\theta_l\}$. Thus the receiver has complete knowledge of the transmitted radio signals except for the data vector sequence $\{\boldsymbol{d}_k\}$. The goal of the receiver is to estimate this data vector sequence given the received radio signal $\{y(t), -\infty < t < \infty\}$.

The optimum receiver will examine each data vector sequence such as $\{\hat{\boldsymbol{d}}_k\}$, which has the corresponding signal

$$\begin{aligned}\hat{x}(t) &= \sum_k x_k(t; \hat{\boldsymbol{d}}_k) \\ &= \sum_k \sum_{l=1}^{L} s_l(t; \hat{d}_k^{(l)}),\end{aligned} \tag{5.16}$$

and determine its likelihood as a transmitted data vector sequence. It uses the maximum-likelihood (ML) criterion based on minimizing [103]

$$\int_{-\infty}^{\infty} [y(t) - \hat{x}(t)]^2 \, dt \tag{5.17}$$

or maximizing

$$\int_{-\infty}^{\infty} y(t)\hat{x}(t) \, dt - \tfrac{1}{2}\int_{-\infty}^{\infty} \hat{x}^2(t) \, dt. \tag{5.18}$$

Thus, given the received radio signal $\{y(t), -\infty < t < \infty\}$, the optimum ML receiver chooses the data vector sequence $\{\hat{\boldsymbol{d}}_k\}$ that maximized (5.18).

Note that

$$\begin{aligned}&\int_{-\infty}^{\infty} y(t)\hat{x}(t) \, dt \\ &= \sum_k \sum_{l=1}^{L} \int_{-\infty}^{\infty} y(t) s_l(t; \hat{d}_k^{(l)}) \, dt \\ &= \sum_k \sum_{l=1}^{L} \hat{d}_k^{(l)} \int_{kT_b+\tau_l}^{(k+1)T_b+\tau_l} y(t) A_l c_l(t-\tau_l) \cos[\omega_0(t-\tau_l) + \theta_l] \, dt \\ &= \sum_k \sum_{l=1}^{L} \hat{d}_k^{(l)} y_k^{(l)}\end{aligned} \tag{5.19}$$

where

$$y_k^{(l)} = \int_{kT_b+\tau_l}^{(k+1)T_b+\tau_l} y(t) A_l c_l(t-\tau_l) \cos[\omega_0(t-\tau_l) + \theta_l] \, dt \tag{5.20}$$

is the matched filter output sampled at time $(k+1)T_b + \tau_l$ for the filter matched to the l-th pseudorandom DS/BPSK waveform. Thus the required (sufficient statistics) received radio signal components are the L matched filter output samples.

The energy term

$$\int_{-\infty}^{\infty} \hat{x}^2(t)\,dt \tag{5.21}$$

depends on the cross-correlation properties of the L pseudorandom waveforms and the particular data vector sequence $\{\hat{\boldsymbol{d}}_k\}$ being examined (see Verdu [96]). This results in the overall decision rule based on

$$\int_{-\infty}^{\infty} y(t)\hat{x}(t)\,dt - \tfrac{1}{2}\int_{-\infty}^{\infty} \hat{x}^2(t)\,dt = \sum_k m_k(\,y_k;\hat{\boldsymbol{d}}_k,\hat{\boldsymbol{d}}_{k-1}) \tag{5.22}$$

where $m_k(\,y_k;\hat{\boldsymbol{d}}_k,\hat{\boldsymbol{d}}_{k-1})$ is some metric[7] and

$$y_k = \begin{bmatrix} y_k^{(1)} \\ y_k^{(2)} \\ \vdots \\ y_k^{(L)} \end{bmatrix} \tag{5.23}$$

is the vector of sampled matched filter outputs. The metric at time k depends on $\hat{\boldsymbol{d}}_k$ and $\hat{\boldsymbol{d}}_{k-1}$ because only the pulse $x_{k-1}(t;\hat{\boldsymbol{d}}_{k-1})$ interferes with the transmission during the k-th pulse $x_k(t;\hat{\boldsymbol{d}}_k)$.

By defining $\hat{\boldsymbol{d}}_{k-1}$ as the state at time k we can model the L radio signals as a finite state process described by a trellis diagram where there are 2^L states. The process of finding the data vector sequence $\{\hat{\boldsymbol{d}}_k\}$ that maximizes (5.22) can be implemented using the Viterbi algorithm [103]. This system is illustrated in Figure 5.16.

Verdu [96] took examples and evaluated upper and lower bounds on their bit error probabilities for this optimum maximum-likelihood receiver. These bounds were derived as a function of the L signal parameters $\{A_l\}$, $\{\tau_l\}$, and $\{\theta_l\}$. Then the results were averaged over uniform probability distributions for $\{\theta_l\}$ and $\{\tau_l\}$ and for the worst case choice of the delays $\{\tau_l\}$. Figure 5.17 shows Verdu's example of $L = 2$ equal energy $(A_1 = A_2)$ radios transmitting to a single receiver. The chip sequence here was periodic with a three chip period and $N = 3$ chips per data bit as shown. Except at low values of E_b/N_0, the optimum ML receiver is able to demodulate both signals as well as if there was only one DS/BPSK radio transmitting. The conventional receiver here has the form of Figure 5.10 as compared with the optimum receiver shown in Figure 5.16. This result is similar to the comparison of conventional and maximum-likelihood receivers for channels

[7] This metric may be time varying because of the pseudorandom sequences used.

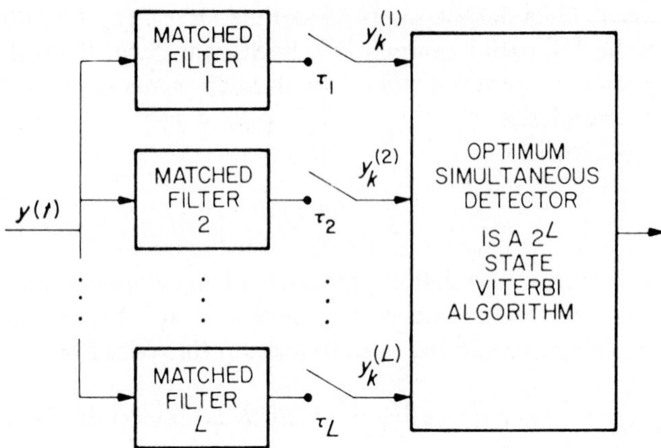

Figure 5.16. Optimum detector.

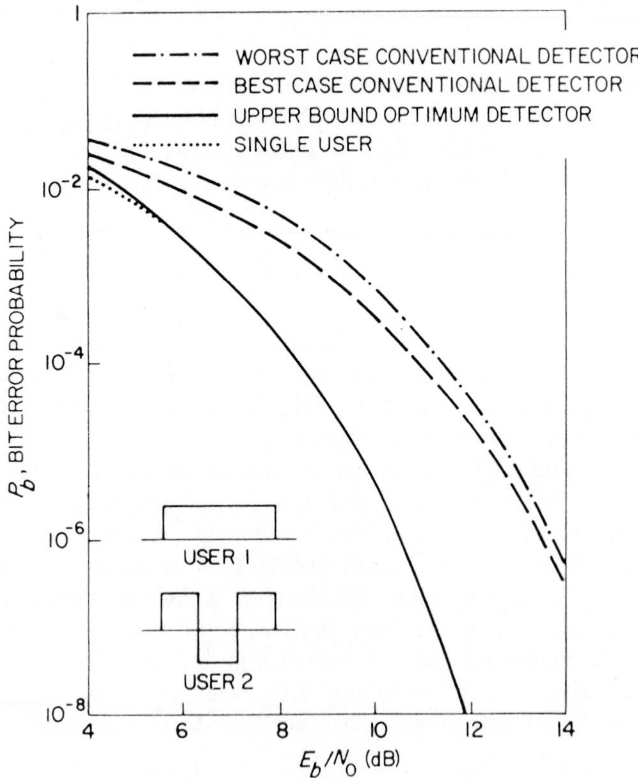

Figure 5.17. $N = 3,\ L = 2$ example.

with intersymbol interference. Other examples considered by Verdu include $L = 3$ equal power radios using $N = 31$ chips per data bit and an $L = 2$ case with unequal signal powers. These examples also show that the optimum maximum-likelihood receiver can achieve the same performance as the single radio transmitter case for high signal-to-noise ratios.

At high signal-to-noise ratios the optimum maximum-likelihood receiver in these examples can reliably determine the transmitted data from all simultaneously transmitting radios. This is not surprising since we assumed complete information about the signal parameters $\{A_l\}$, $\{\tau_l\}$, and $\{\theta_l\}$. Also we assumed no quantization of the matched filter output samples $\{y_k\}$ or of the metrics used in the Viterbi algorithm. In practice some quantized metrics must be used and little or no side information may be available regarding signal parameters. The optimum receiver results presented here serve as a theoretically achievable limit or baseline with which we can compare practical uncoded systems.

5.4 SPREAD-SPECTRUM MULTIPLE ACCESS WITH FH / MFSK WAVEFORMS

SSMA systems using FH/MFSK waveforms can take a wider range of forms compared with systems using DS/BPSK waveforms. This is due to the fact that a wide variety of detector functions and decoder metrics can be used here including metrics that allow for side information regarding the channel conditions (see Chapter 2, Part 2). In addition, with FH/MFSK waveforms, M is a parameter which can be increased until the entire spread-spectrum frequency band consists of one large MFSK signalling band with no hopping.

For point-to-point communication we exploit the fact that interference due to other radio signals resembles multitone jamming. In general worst case multitone jamming with the same total interference power will result in greater performance degradation than this unintentional interference due to other FH/MFSK signals. *Therefore, earlier results on multitone jamming can be used to upper bound bit error probabilities in the FH/MFSK SSMA system.*

For point-to-multipoint SSMA with FH/MFSK waveforms there exists the possibility of considering synchronous radio transmitters. In practice, with FH/MFSK waveforms, hop time intervals are generally much larger than the chip time intervals in DS/BPSK waveforms. Thus we can have some networks with radios transmitting FH/MFSK waveforms where the hopping is synchronized.

5.4.1 Point-to-Point

Consider here the performance of point-to-point communication between two radios using FH/MFSK waveforms in a network of other similar radios. Between the transmitter and receiver assume ideal synchronization where the receiver knows the frequency pattern and hop time epoch of the desired FH/MFSK signal. As usual non-coherent detectors are used. Throughout this discussion the other users may or may not have synchronized hop times. *All hopping patterns are assumed to be independent when different keys are used and each hopping pattern is modelled as a sequence of i.i.d. random frequency variables uniformly distributed over some uniformly spaced set of points across the spread-spectrum frequency band.* This is the SSMA system as opposed to a CDMA system where specific hopping patterns with low mutual interference is used [77]–[82] primarily for multiple access applications. In military networks the primary requirements are to use waveforms with anti-jam (AJ) and low probability of intercept (LPI) capabilities.

Suppose the point-to-point link using an FH/MFSK waveform has interference in the radio channel due to L other radio transmitters of power distribution given by (5.1) at the radio receiver in question while the intended signal has power S. *The L interfering signals appear as multiple tones of different powers randomly hopping across the band much like a multitone jammer. We now upper bound the bit error probability by assuming that a multitone jammer has the same total power J given by* (5.4) *and uses this in a worst case multitone strategy*. Generally, this means the jammer would take equal size tones and distribute them according to some strategy as discussed in Section 2.2, Chapter 2, Part 2.

With the worst case multitone jammer the effective bit energy-to-noise ratio is again given by (5.2), where the processing gain is the total spread-spectrum bandwidth divided by the link data rate in bits per second. Figure 5.9 again illustrates the special case where all L interference signals have the same power at the receiver. The only difference between using Figure 5.9 for the DS/BPSK system and the FH/MFSK system is the choice for the required bit energy-to-noise ratio γ to be used. For DS/BPSK this is based on the additive white Gaussian noise channel, whereas for FH/MFSK systems it is based on the worst case multitone jammer.

The multitone jammer analysis of Chapter 2 in Part 2 assumes ideal jammer state information and conventional chip energy detector outputs. What this means is that during a hop time interval, in the MFSK sub-band of the intended transmitted signal, the receiver has M energy detectors. If a jamming tone is also present along with the transmitted signal in this sub-band, then this fact is used by the receiver when it takes a weighted sum of energy detector outputs to make decisions. If this same type of receiver is used in the radio network with interference due to other radios, the resulting required bit energy-to-noise ratio γ would be less than that for the worst case multitone jammer. The number of users L in Figure 5.9 would then be a lower bound when the required value of γ is taken from the worst case multitone jamming analysis.

With FH/MFSK waveforms many other detectors and metrics are possible. Against intelligent jammers, combining chip energies without jammer state information is not effective. This is because such a pure "soft decision" receiver without jammer state information is vulnerable to a jammer strategy where high jammer power can be concentrated on a small number of symbols of a coded transmission sequence and lead to a large number of decoding errors. One approach to alleviating this problem is to quantize the chip energy detector outputs into a finite number of threshold levels, but the disadvantage of this is that optimum threshold settings require AGC, which is difficult to maintain in a jamming environment.

An example of a detector that does not require AGC is one that makes hard M-ary decisions based on the largest chip energy detector output or that outputs an erasure symbol [105]–[108]. Reed-Solomon codes have been proposed for these systems with M-ary symbols that can correct twice as many erasures as hard decision errors. Various techniques for the detector to select a hard decision or make an erasure decision have been proposed including taking advantage of the fact that for asynchronous radios the interfering tone usually does not overlap completely in time with the intended signal [109], [110].

An alternative approach, called list detection, was discussed in Section 2.7.3 in Chapter 2 of Volume II. With this technique, demodulator energy outputs are ranked in magnitude from the highest to the lowest, and metrics are assigned according to position in the ranking rather than the magnitude. The process of rank-ordering is equivalent to partitioning the M-dimensional observation space of demodulator outputs into regions corresponding to the different ordered lists. In this sense list detection is like soft-decision quantization because it creates a discrete memoryless channel with more outputs than inputs as seen by the encoder/decoder. Note that list detection does not depend on thresholds which are difficult to maintain during jamming.

List detection has been considered previously [111], [112] for the AWGN channel where performance is inferior to threshold quantization. More recently, Viterbi [113] has presented an interference mitigation technique which is a variant of list detection, and results show that robust performance is achieved against tone jamming with simple receiver implementation (see Section 2.7.2, Chapter 2, Part 2). Following the analysis of Section 2.7.3 in Chapter 2 of Part 2, we present results of Crepeau [114] and Crepeau et al. [115] for the evaluation of cutoff rates against worst case multitone jamming using the list detector. The metrics associated with list detector outputs are the maximum-likelihood metrics with or without jammer state information. Here jammer state information is in the form where the receiver knows which of the M frequencies contain some signal or interference energy. In the multiple access context we say that the receiver has "collision compensation" information since this is used to change or compensate the metric assigned to the list detector outputs. Our multiple access results are thus given for the cases with collision compensation (CC) and without collision compensation.

For M-ary alphabets, the cutoff rate R_0 can be defined by[8]

$$R_0 = \log_2 M - \log_2[1 + (M-1)D] \tag{5.24}$$

with the Chernoff parameter, D, given for $\hat{x} \neq x$ by

$$D = \min_{\lambda \geq 0} E\{\exp \lambda\, [m(y,\hat{x}) - m(y,x)] | x \text{ sent}\} \tag{5.25}$$

where $m(y,x)$ is the decision metric evaluated for the channel output y, and the transmitted code symbol x. For MFSK, the channel output is the set of energy detector outputs $y = (e_1, e_2, \dots, e_M)$. The list decision metric is defined by

$$m(y,x) = N_{L_x} \tag{5.26}$$

where L_x is the position on the list where the symbol x placed (symbol with the highest energy places first) and N_ℓ is the "score" awarded to the symbol placing ℓ-th on the list.

For an arbitrary set of scores, $N = (N_1, N_2, \dots, N_M)$, R_0 is evaluated using ($\hat{x} \neq x$),

$$\begin{aligned} D &= \min_{\lambda \geq 0} \sum_{\ell=1}^{M} \sum_{k=1}^{M} e^{\lambda(N_k - N_\ell)} P\{L_x = \ell, L_{\hat{x}} = k | x \text{ sent}\} \\ &= \min_{\lambda \geq 0} \frac{1}{M-1} \sum_{\ell=1}^{M} \left[\sum_{k=1}^{M} e^{\lambda(N_k - N_\ell)} - 1 \right] q_\ell \end{aligned} \tag{5.27}$$

where $q_\ell = P\{L_x = \ell | x \text{ sent}\}$. Here we used the symmetry condition, for $\hat{x} \neq x$,

$$P\{L_{\hat{x}} = k | x \text{ sent}, L_x = \ell\} = (M-1)^{-1}(1 - \delta_{\ell,k}). \tag{5.28}$$

We can simplify the list metric by choosing to rank only the L^* detector outputs with the highest energies. Each of the remaining $M - L^*$ unranked symbols would then be given a common score. This "list-of-L^*" metric specializes to the hard decision metric for $L^* = 1$. By direct differentiation, we obtain conditions for selecting the list scores, N, so as to maximize R_0 for the list-of-L^* metric ($1 \leq L^* \leq M$). The resulting list scores and cutoff rate are [111]

$$N_k = \begin{cases} \log q_k; & k = 1, 2, \dots, L^* \\ \log\left(\dfrac{q_0}{M - L^*}\right); & k = L^* + 1, \dots, M \end{cases} \tag{5.29}$$

[8]A symmetric, memoryless channel is assumed.

and

$$R_0 = \log_2 M - 2\log_2\left(\sum_{l=1}^{L^*}\sqrt{q_l} + \sqrt{(M - L^*)q_0}\right) \tag{5.30}$$

where q_0 is the probability that the transmitted symbol will be off the list of L^*. The ordering distribution $\{q_l\}$ will depend upon E_c/N_J and the jamming format encountered, which we shall examine next.

Suppose that a tone jammer divides his power, J, equally so as to jam a fraction ρ of the total number of hopping frequencies. Furthermore, suppose that the jammer has perfect knowledge of the communicator's frequency slots and positions his tones randomly among these slots. Then, defining β as the signal-to-jamming-tone power ratio, the number of slots that the jammer jams is $N^* = \beta(J/S)$. Denoting[9] the time per bit by T_b, the total number of hopping frequencies is $N_T = W_{ss}T_bR = R(W_{ss}/R_b) = (E_c/N_J)(J/S)$, so that $\beta = \rho(E_c/N_J)$ where $S/J \leq \beta \leq E_c/N_J$. Let $T_{\hat{x}} = 1$ indicate that the symbol $\hat{x}$ was hit by the jammer ($T_{\hat{x}} = 0$ otherwise), then the energy detector outputs for the transmitted symbol, x, and any $\hat{x} \neq x$ are given by

$$e_x = \begin{cases} E_c, & T_x = 0 \\ \left(1 + 2\sqrt{\beta}\cos\theta + \beta\right)\dfrac{E_c}{\beta}, & T_x = 1 \end{cases}$$

$$e_{\hat{x}} = \begin{cases} 0, & T_{\hat{x}} = 0 \\ \dfrac{E_c}{\beta}, & T_{\hat{x}} = 1 \end{cases} \tag{5.31}$$

where θ is the relative phase angle between the information and jamming tones. Letting n_J denote the number of MFSK symbols, other than x, hit by the jammer during a hop, then

$$q_\ell = \sum_{n=0}^{M-1}\binom{M-1}{n}\rho^n(1-\rho)^{M-1-n}\left[(1-\rho)q_\ell(n,0) + \rho q_\ell(n,1)\right] \tag{5.32}$$

where $q_\ell(n_J, T_x) = P\{L_x = \ell | x \text{ sent}, n_J, T_x\}$.

First, consider the case where the information tone is not hit ($T_x = 0$). If $\beta > 1$, then x places first on the list. If $\beta < 1$, then x places $(n_J + 1)$-th. However, sufficiently near $\beta = 1$, the ordering of x and the n_J jammed symbols will be determined by noise sources not modelled here (e.g., receiver noise). Consequently, at $\beta = 1$, we assume that x can place

[9]We define R = code rate in bits per MFSK chip, R_b = data rate in bits per second, $N_J = J/W_{ss}$, and the normalized cutoff rate $r_0 = R_0/\log_2 M$.

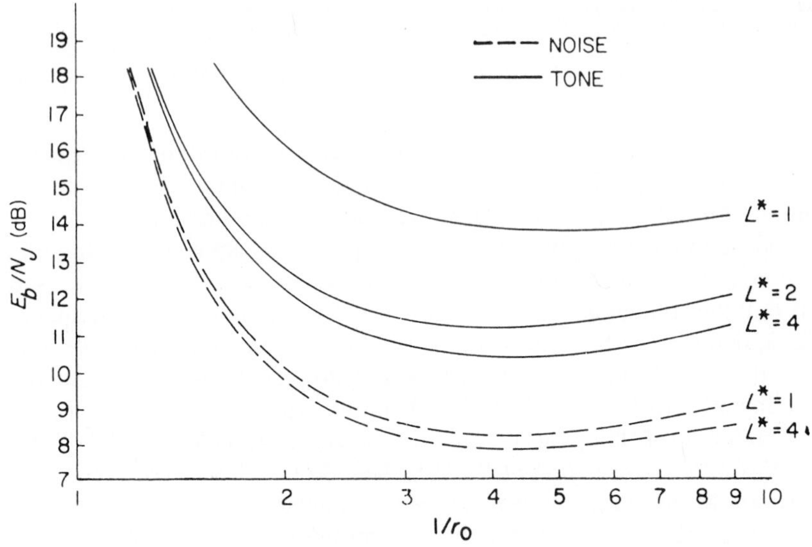

Figure 5.18. Minimum E_b/N_J for list detection (4 FSK).

anywhere among the n_J jammed tones with equal probability so that

$$q_\ell(n,0) = \begin{cases} \delta_{l,n+1}; & \beta < 1 \\ 1/(n+1), \quad 1 \le l \le n+1; & \beta = 1 \\ \delta_{l,1}; & \beta > 1. \end{cases} \tag{5.33}$$

Next, consider the case when x is hit by the jammer ($T_x = 1$). Assume that the relative phase angle, θ, is uniformly distributed over $(-\pi, \pi)$. Notice from (5.33) that when $\beta \ge 4$, x always places first on the list. However, when $\beta < 4$ and $|\theta| > \theta_c = \cos^{-1}(-\sqrt{\beta}/2)$, x places $(n_J + 1)$-th. Thus, averaging over θ we obtain

$$q_\ell(n,1) = \begin{cases} \dfrac{(\pi - \theta_c)}{\pi}\delta_{\ell,n+1} + \dfrac{\theta_c}{\pi}\delta_{\ell,1}; & \beta \le 4 \\ \delta_{\ell,1}; & \beta > 4. \end{cases} \tag{5.34}$$

Worst case tone jamming with no jammer state information results for $4 \le M \le 32$ are given in Figures 5.18 through 5.21 by solid curves. Dashed lines correspond to worst case partial-band noise jamming.

Here the code rate is set at the cutoff rate, $R = R_0$. For $E_c/N_J > 4$ dB, worst case performance results when the jammer places slightly more power in his tones than the communicator's tone (i.e., $\beta = 1^-$) so that x places $(n_J + 1)$-th when $T_x = 0$. For $E_c/N_J \ll 4$ dB, β is small and θ_c near $\pi/2$ so that when $T_x = 1$, x places first or $(n_J + 1)$-th with about equal probability. In this situation, if the jammer were to jam all slots, then x

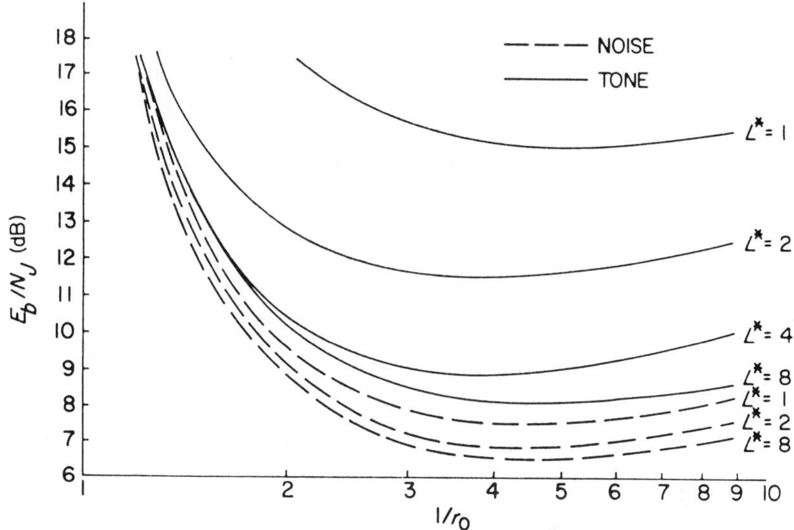

Figure 5.19. Minimum E_b/N_J for list detection (8 FSK).

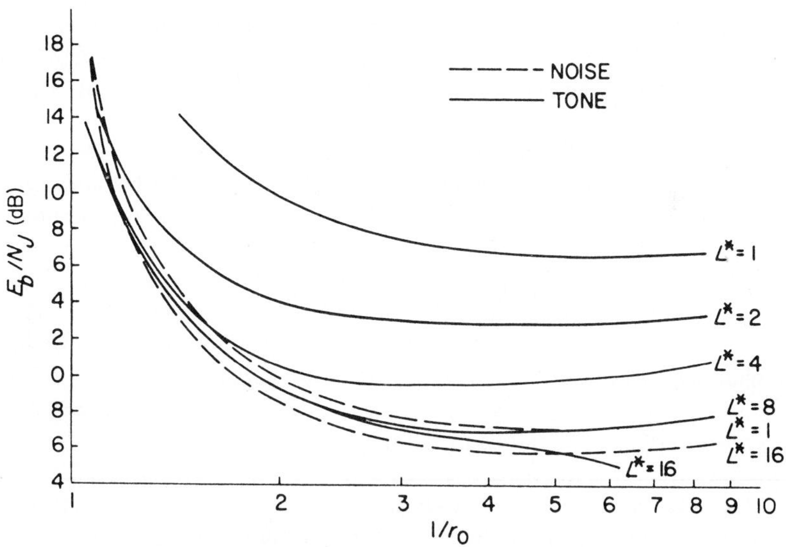

Figure 5.20. Minimum E_b/N_J for list detection (16 FSK).

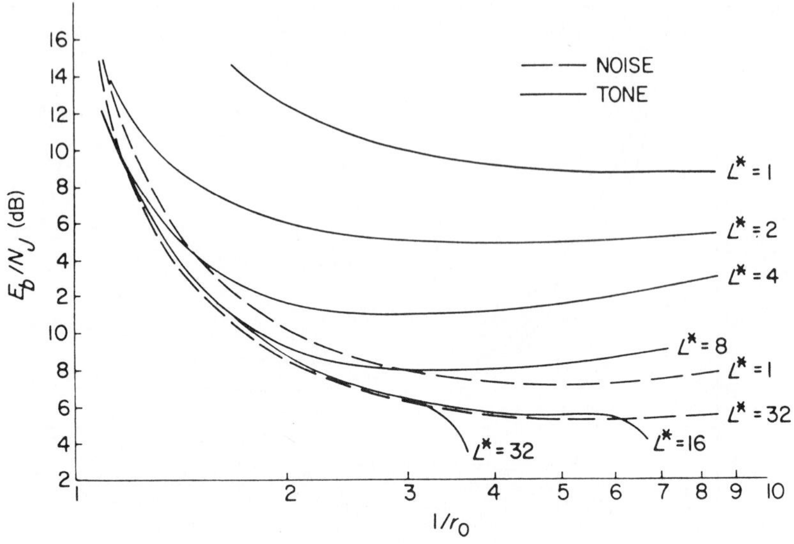

Figure 5.21. Minimum E_b/N_J for list detection (32 FSK).

always places either first or last with about equal probability and $r_0 = 1 - 1/\log_2 M$, which approaches 1 for large M. Consequently, at low E_c/N_J, the best strategy for the tone jammer is in general not full band ($\rho = 1$) jamming, as it was for the noise jammer.

The worst case tone jamming results for list metrics specifies the required bit energy-to-noise ratio for coded systems. Here we can find γ and use this in Figure 5.9 to obtain a lower bound on the maximum number of simultaneous equal energy radio transmitters that can be tolerated in a radio network. In a radio network environment list detectors can be quite effective, especially for large alphabet size M, while being robust against jamming. The metrics used here, however, do depend on some knowledge of the channel statistics in the form of probabilities q_k; $k = 1, 2, \ldots, L^*$. In a network such channel statistics may be available at each radio along with the connectivity of the radios in the network.

Figure 5.22 illustrates the effectiveness of the list metric for larger alphabet size $M = 32$. We compare the full list ($L^* = M = 32$) metric with the energy metric (EM), which is near optimum for the additive white Gaussian noise channel, and the hard decision metric (HDM). The probability q_ℓ that the transmitted signal is ℓ-th on the list is plotted in Figure 5.23 for the worst case partial-band noise jammer when $M = 8$. Note that q_ℓ for $\ell = 2, 3, \ldots, 8$ are not too far apart. This result is contrasted with the worst case tone jammer results shown in Figure 5.24, which show a much wider divergence in the values of q_ℓ for $\ell = 2, 3, \ldots, 8$. Against tone jamming there is more information in the list detector outputs.

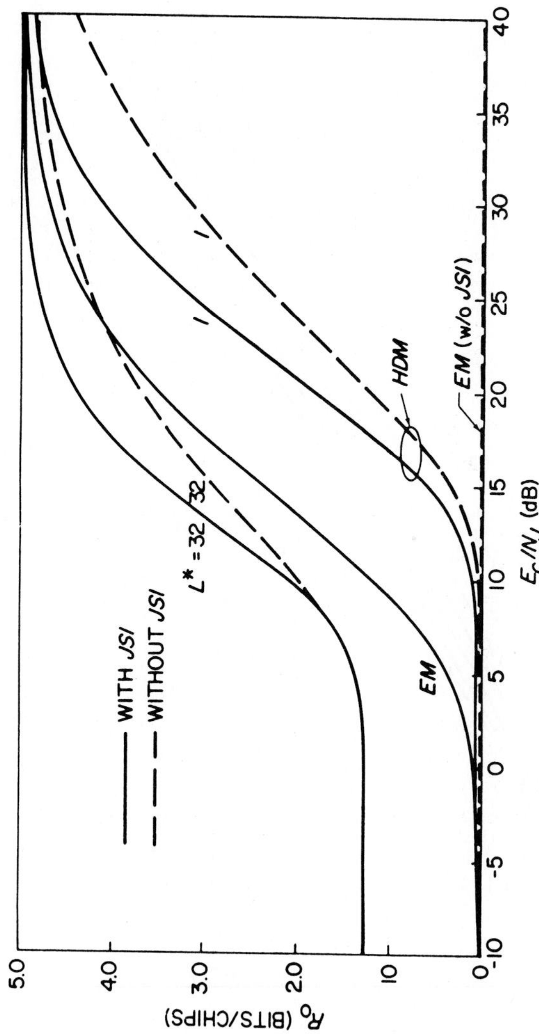

Figure 5.22. R_0 versus E_c/N_J against worst case tone jamming ($M = 32$).

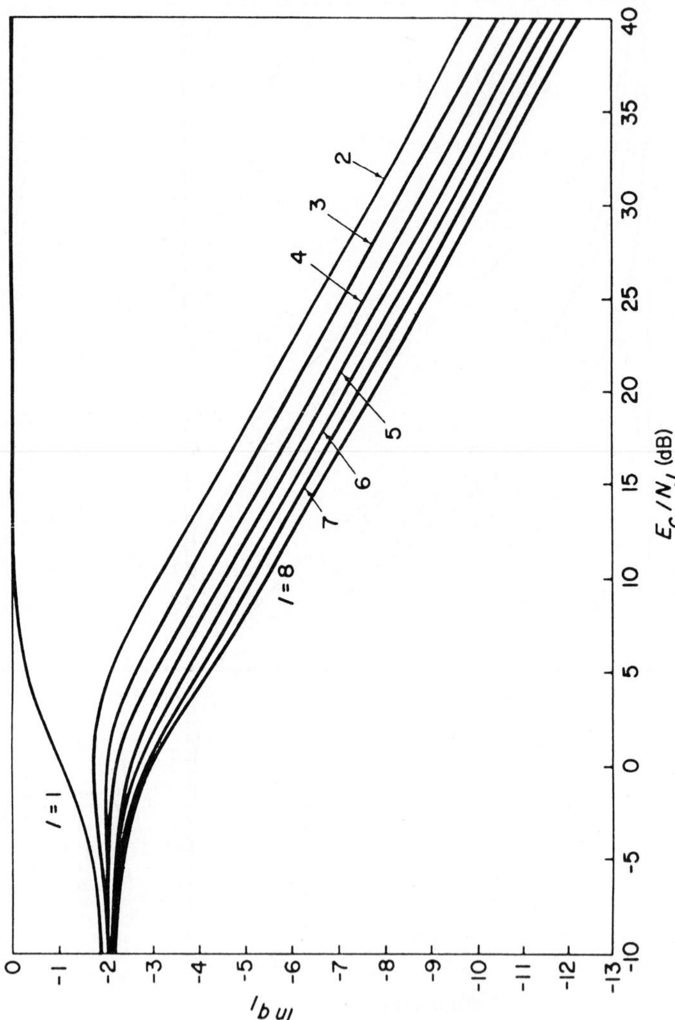

Figure 5.23. ℓnq_{ℓ} versus E_c/N_J against worst case PB noise jamming (M = 8).

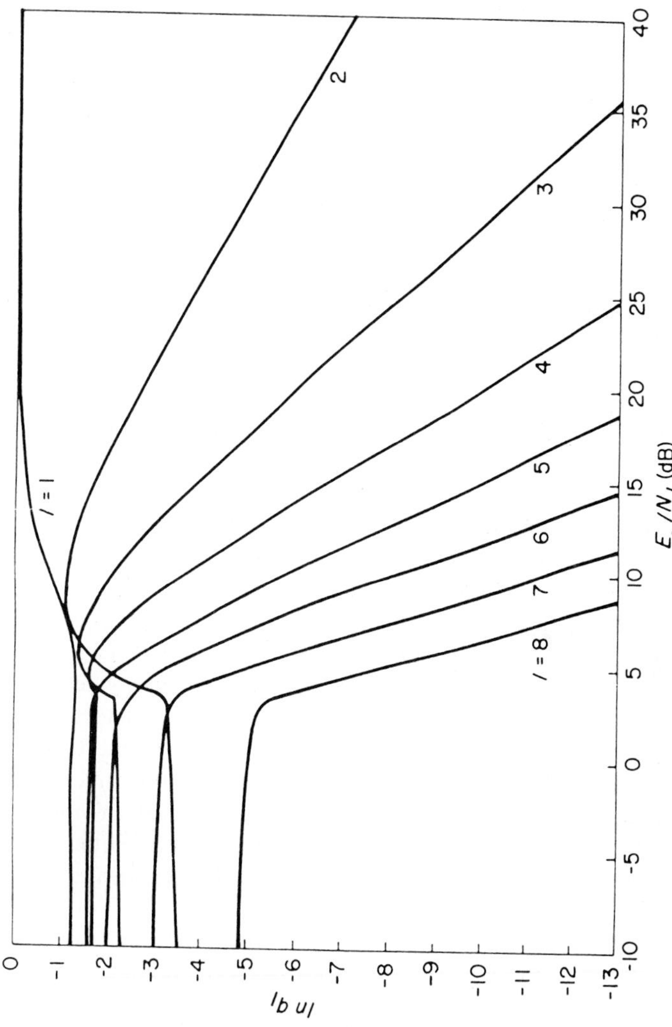

Figure 5.24. $\ell n q_\ell$ versus E_c/N_J against worst case tone jamming ($M = 8$).

Rather than assume the worst case multitone jammer, Creighton [116] studied the list detector with maximum-likelihood metrics when there are L simultaneously transmitting radios with FH/MFSK signals of equal power at the receiver. He assumed the following:

1. All FH/MFSK signals have the same power level at the receiver.
2. Over a chip time interval, the average power of the sum of tones at a given frequency equals the sum of their average powers.
3. All radios are time synchronized and have signals hopping at the same time.
4. All hopping patterns are independent of each other and consist of independent uniformly distributed hop frequencies.
5. The performance is limited by mutual interference and receiver noise can be ignored.

With these assumptions the following parameters were selected:

m = diversity or number of MFSK chips for each M-ary symbol

L^* = list size

L = number of simultaneously transmitting radios

Two types of maximum-likelihood metrics were selected. The first metric assumes only knowledge of the probabilities $\{q_k\}$ and uses the metric defined by (5.29). The second metric assumes that additional side information is available in the form of knowing the number of M chip energy detector outputs that consist of one or more tones.[10] This can vary from chip to chip and is assumed to be measured at the chip energy detectors and provided along with the ordered list of L^* largest energy detector outputs. This side information changes the probabilities $\{q_k\}$ to conditional probabilities which can change from chip to chip. The corresponding maximum-likelihood metric is referred to as the "collision compensation" metric. It is the same as (5.29) with $\{q_k\}$ replaced by conditional probabilities where the condition is on the number of the M chip frequencies with some signal input.

Under these assumptions Creighton [116] first examined the bit error probability with diversity alone, which is given by the bound

$$P_b \leq \frac{M}{2} D^m \tag{5.35}$$

where D is given by (5.27) and the energy per chip is related to the energy

[10] This is equivalent to knowing how many chip energy detectors had no input tones.

Table 5.1

Maximum number of users—PG = 30 dB.

Channel	Metric		List-of-L^* without Collision Compensation					List-of-L^* with Collision Compensation				
		M	2	8		32		2	8		32	
	P_b	m \ L^*	1,2	1	8	1	32	1,2	1	8	1	32
No Fading	10^{-2}	2	32	42	115	33	170	87	72	170	43	180
	10^{-4}	4	16	31	80	31	170	45	47	110	39	190
	10^{-6}	4	6	11	27	12	58	20	22	50	17	68
Fading	10^{-2}	4	14	13	68	6	125	98	35	190	11	220
	10^{-4}	8	7	9	47	5	100	48	22	115	8	155
	10^{-6}	8	3	4	18	3	42	26	11	62	5	82

per bit by

$$mE_c = (\log_2 M) E_b. \tag{5.36}$$

Here the energy-per-bit-to-equivalent-noise ratio is

$$\begin{aligned} \frac{E_b}{N_J} &= \frac{PG}{J/S} \\ &= \frac{PG}{L-1}. \end{aligned} \tag{5.37}$$

Tables 5.1 and 5.2 summarize the number of allowable simultaneously transmitting radio signals under these conditions. Here $L^* = 1$ corresponds to the hard decision M-ary channel. The fading cases are assumed to be Rayleigh fading, which is independent from chip to chip.

As stated throughout this book, when channel interference is unpredictable, as with jamming waveforms, optimum detectors and decoding metrics are not known. The detectors and metrics given here require different amounts of side information regarding the channel. In theory, we could have a perfect system with perfect side information. For example, suppose the receiver knew exactly the intended signal's power level. Then it could distinguish it from all other signals since in practice no two signals will have the same power level at the receiver. Generally, there is a tradeoff between performance, complexity, and amount of side information required. One would like to have detectors and metrics that are robust in the sense that they minimize the degradation due to the worst conditions in the channel and are not sensitive to channel parameters and do not require much side information.

Table 5.2

Maximum number of users—$P_b \leq 10^{-4}$

Channel	Metric		List-of-L^* without Collision Compensation					List-of-L^* with Collision Compensation				
		M	2	8		32		2	8		32	
	PG (dB)	m \ L^*	1, 2	1	8	1	32	1, 2	1	8	1	32
No Fading	20	4	3	4	9	4	17	5	6	12	5	20
	30	4	16	31	80	31	170	45	47	110	39	190
	40	2	30	45	115	37	200	160	150	320	93	350
Fading	20	8	1	1	5	1	12	5	3	11	1	13
	30	8	7	9	47	5	100	48	22	115	8	155
	40	4	13	16	96	10	240	270	98	560	32	590

5.4.2 Conventional Multipoint-to-Point

The point-to-point system covered in the previous section assumed all radios used independent hopping patterns and that during each hop an MFSK chip is transmitted. There the frequency hopping radios may or may not be synchronized. Now suppose L radios use FH/MFSK waveforms to simultaneously transmit data to a single radio terminal.

A brute force approach to the point-to-multipoint design is to have a radio terminal with L separate receiver systems where the ℓ-th system receives the ℓ-th radio transmitter signal using the ℓ-th random frequency hopping pattern. This means there are L frequency synthesizers at the receiving radio terminal where each one is synchronized to one of the L transmitting radios.

One approach to reducing the complexity of the receiving radio's terminal is to require all radios to transmit synchronously such that at the receiving radio terminal all transmitted radio signals hop at the same time. In addition, suppose all L radios use the same hopping pattern but with frequency offset so that after dehopping (using one frequency synthesizer) the L transmitted radio signals appear in non-overlapping MFSK sub-bands. These can then be detected using a conventional FDMA receiver system. This is illustrated in Figure 5.25 where W_{ss} is the total spread-spectrum frequency band and W_{MA} is the frequency range used for the L MFSK signals in an FDMA mode. Here the multiple access band is generally much smaller than the spread-spectrum frequency band

$$W_{MA} \ll W_{ss} \tag{5.38}$$

and it is hopped around once every chip time T_c. Thus, we have here a

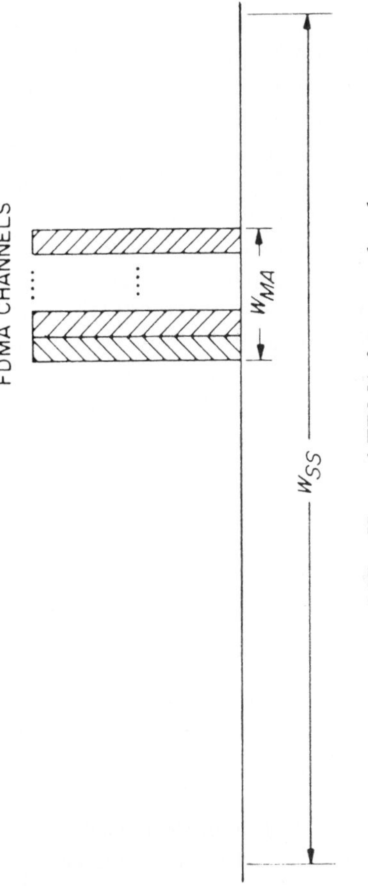

Figure 5.25. Hopped FDMA frequency band.

conventional FDMA system with MFSK waveforms but the frequency band W_{MA} is hopping over a wide frequency range once[11] every chip time T_c.

With L radios transmitting synchronized FH/MFSK waveforms with the same frequency hopping pattern, the receiving radio terminal's front end requires only one frequency synthesizer to dehop all the transmitted signals simultaneously. For the first part of this section we shall assume this type of multipoint-to-point system. We shall, however, examine alternative ways in which the L radios can use the multiple access frequency band of W_{MA} Hz.

Assume for the multiple access frequency band that there are M_o frequency slots where tones of duration T_c are orthogonal. This is roughly $M_o = W_{MA}T_c$ for non-coherent chip waveforms. The simplest approach to dividing up the available capacity of frequency W_{MA} Hz and T_c seconds is to use FDMA as discussed above and sketched in Figure 5.25. If there are more possible transmitting radios than available FDMA slots using MFSK waveforms,[12] then there must be some means of sharing these slots, as discussed earlier in Section 5.2. Demand assignment or polling schemes are possible but these require some central control capabilities. Another approach which requires no control is to allow each user to randomly hop *within* the available non-overlapping MFSK frequency sub-bands in an SSMA mode. These systems will be discussed next.

Goodman, Henry, and Prabhu [117] extended a technique first proposed by Viterbi [118] for multiple access by low rate mobile users employing a satellite transponder. They suggested that each radio be assigned a unique address of m symbols belonging to $\{0, 1, \ldots, M-1\}$ where $M = M_0$, the number of orthogonal tone positions in the frequency band of W_{MA} Hz. An M-ary symbol is transmitted by each radio by sending m MFSK chips using the unique address as follows: Let the ℓ-th radio's m symbol address be

$$R_1^{(\ell)}, R_2^{(\ell)}, \ldots, R_m^{(\ell)} \tag{5.39}$$

where $R_k^{(\ell)} \in \{0, 1, \ldots, M-1\}$ and $M = M_o$. If X is an M-ary data symbol, then the transmitted m chip sequence of the ℓ-th radio is

$$Y_k^{(\ell)} = X + R_k^{(\ell)} \text{ modulo } M. \tag{5.40}$$

This is then sent as an MFSK chip sequence after frequency hopping.[13] After dehopping, the receiver hard quantizes each of the M chip energy detector outputs. That is, at the output of each of the M energy detectors a decision is made as to the presence or absence of a transmitted MFSK chip tone as follows: Any set of chip energy detector outputs $(e_1, e_2, \ldots, e_M)$ is

[11] Slower hopping schemes where several MFSK chips (tones) are transmitted during each hop, are not effective against partial-band or multitone jammers unless interleaving is also used to create independent channel statistics for each chip.

[12] Although there may be many radios, each radio may be transmitting only a small fraction of the time.

[13] For commercial applications frequency hopping may not be used.

hard quantized to $(n_1, n_2, \ldots, n_M)$ where

$$n_k = \begin{cases} 1, & \varepsilon_k \geq \delta \\ 0, & \varepsilon_k < \delta \end{cases} \qquad k = 1, 2, \ldots, M \tag{5.41}$$

for some decision threshold δ. Naturally, with noise and multipath a decision of a tone being present at a frequency may be made when none has been transmitted (false alarm) as well as a decision of no tone being present when in fact a chip tone was transmitted at the frequency (miss).

Each chip time there are M hard quantized bits. The receiver examines the sequence of m such outputs to make decisions as to which symbols were transmitted. The decision rule for the receiver is to choose the data symbol associated with an address pattern as given by (5.40) which has the greatest number of entries or detected tones. For example, suppose $m = 5$ and the address sequence for the ℓ-th radio is

$$0, 1, 2, 3, 4 \tag{5.42}$$

with $M = 8$ as the number of possible tones. If $X = 6$ is the 8-ary data symbol, then the transmitted sequence is (see (5.40))

$$6, 7, 0, 1, 2. \tag{5.43}$$

Suppose the sequence of 5 chip energy detector hard quantized outputs is given by the array

	1st	2nd	3rd	4th	5th
7	0	①	1	0	1
6	①	0	0	1	1
5	0	0	0	0	0
4	1	0	0	0	0
3	0	0	0	1	0
2	1	1	0	0	⓪
1	0	1	0	①	0
0	0	1	①	1	1

The only possible output sequences the ℓ-th radio could transmit are

Symbol		Sequence
0	→	0, 1, 2, 3, 4
1	→	1, 2, 3, 4, 5
2	→	2, 3, 4, 5, 6
3	→	3, 4, 5, 6, 7
4	→	4, 5, 6, 7, 0
5	→	5, 6, 7, 0, 1
6	→	6, 7, 0, 1, 2
7	→	7, 0, 1, 2, 3

(5.44)

By checking the detector output patterns we see that the sequence 6, 7, 0, 1, 2 corresponding to $X = 6$ had the greatest number of entries. This is the circled chip energy detector output sequence shown.

Under this hard quantized detector output with the above pattern decision rule, errors will occur when noise and other users combine to form allowed sequences with more entries than the sequence that was actually transmitted.

The multiple access scheme just described assumes that, given the output pattern of m chip sequence of M hard decision bits, the receiver first checks for the possible sequences of the 1st radio and makes a data symbol decision for it. Then it independently checks the same output pattern for possible sequences of the 2nd radio and makes a data symbol decision for it. It does this L times for the L radios that are transmitting. Here each data symbol decision is independent of each other even though the output pattern of the m chip sequence of M quantized bits for making decisions is the same. This is illustrated in Figure 5.26.

Goodman et al. [117] has shown that for $M = 625$ and $m = 19$ with perfect transmission where the only degradation is mutual interference, an error rate of less than 10^{-3} can be maintained with up to 209 simultaneous transmitting radios. Transmission impairments, consisting of white Gaussian noise and frequency-selective Rayleigh fading with an average signal-to-noise ratio of 25 dB, reduced the number of simultaneous users to about 170. This exceeded the capacity of the original frequency-hopped, phase-shift-keying, spread-spectrum system proposed by Cooper and Nettleton [119]–[121]. Haskell [122] did computer simulations to compare the performance of randomly chosen address sequences with chirp sequences and those found by Einarsson [123]. His results show that the chirp and Einarsson address sequences were equivalent and somewhat better than random address sequences but the differences diminish as the number of symbols $M = M_o$ increases.

The case where each radio transmitter uses a random address sequence is essentially the spread-spectrum example where each transmitter uses the FH/MFSK waveform with diversity of degree m. The only difference here is that we have L radios simultaneously transmitting at all times in the same M-ary sub-band of total bandwidth W_{MA}. The examples here assume that each chip energy detection output is hard quantized. Certainly, more information is maintained for making decisions if the chip energy detector outputs are quantized into more levels. Another possibility is to form an ordered list of the chip energy detector outputs and use it for making decisions. One could then account for the differences in received signal strengths from different radios. Weaker signals will consistently fall lower on the list. Creighton [116] has examined the use of list detectors with various metrics for this SSMA system.

The address sequence is essentially the simplest repeat m coding. With more powerful codes we can achieve somewhat better performance. Greater

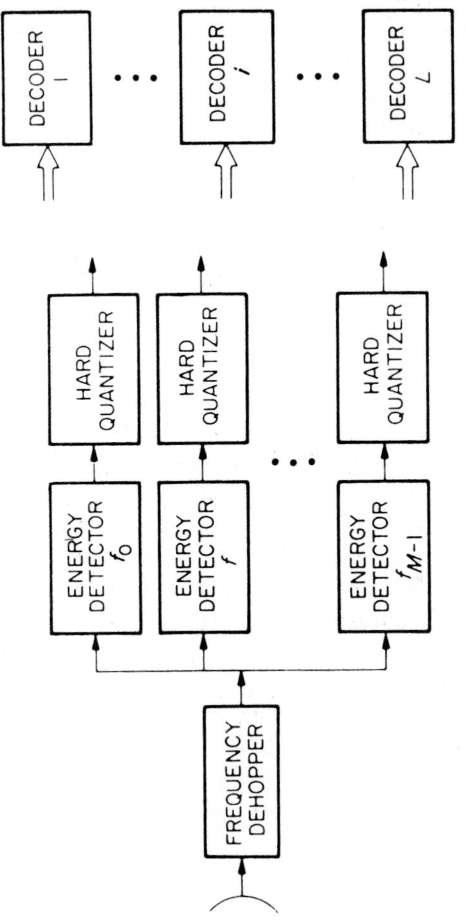

Figure 5.26. Independent decoders.

improvements, however, can be achieved by changing detectors and metrics, and taking advantage of side information in the decoding process.

The system proposed by Goodman et al. [117] certainly is not as efficient as pure FDMA. However, it allows random access with no overall control. With low duty cycle users this means many users can access a single receiving radio terminal with no overall control other than hop synchronization. To make this system more efficient Haskell [122] and Timor [124], [125] have proposed schemes that make use of information derived while decoding the messages of other users to reduce interference of a given transmitted radio signal. For the same example above with 209 simultaneous users Timor's scheme achieves 450 users. In the next section we examine the general question of optimum receivers for multipoint-to-point radios using FH/MFSK waveforms.

5.4.3 Optimum Multipoint-to-Point

We examine the same system as in the previous section where L radios using FH/MFSK waveforms transmit to a single receiving radio terminal. These radios are hop synchronized at the receiving radio and they use the same hopping pattern. Thus the hopping at the transmitters and dehopping at the receiving radio can be ignored since they are transparent to the analysis. Also assume all L radios transmit MFSK waveforms in the same frequency band (after dehopping) and the hard quantized chip energy detectors are the channel outputs upon which decisions are based.

In the previous section the receiver had the form shown in Figure 5.26. Here each transmitted radio signal was decoded independently where the ℓ-th decoder investigated the set of possible sequences of m M-ary symbols that the ℓ-th transmitter could have sent. We now examine what can be done when the decoder decodes all L signals simultaneously.

To illustrate the optimum receiver take the simplest case of $L = 2$ radios each transmitting binary symbols where $M = 2$. Let f_0 and f_1 represent the two possible transmitted frequencies by the two radios. Ignoring hopping and dehopping, the set of possible frequencies and the corresponding hard quantized chip energy detector outputs are:

Inputs Frequency		Detector Outputs	
Radio 1	Radio 2	Output for f_0	Output for f_1
f_0	f_0	1	0
f_0	f_1	1	1
f_1	f_0	1	1
f_1	f_1	0	1

If we take the conventional approach illustrated in Figure 5.26, the second transmitting radio is regarded as channel interference to the link between the first transmitting radio and the receiving radio. To this link the

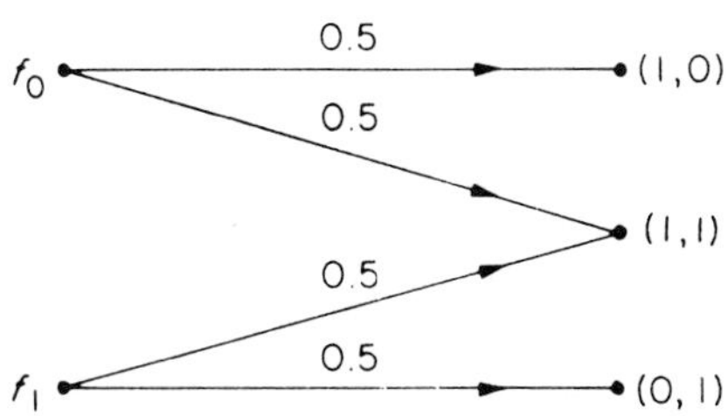

Figure 5.27. Binary erasure channel.

interference channel is as shown in Figure 5.27, where we assume all binary symbols are equally likely to occur. Each time the second radio sends a frequency different from the first radio, which occurs with probability .5, the receiver detector hard quantized output for the two detectors is (1, 1). Essentially, there is no information about what frequency the first radio transmitted when this occurs and we might as well have "erased" the output. This is the binary erasure channel which has channel capacity [103]

$$C_{BEC} = .5 \text{ bits/symbol.} \tag{5.45}$$

This is the maximum data rate possible between the first transmitting radio and the receiving radio. By symmetry this is also the channel between the second transmitting radio and the receiving radio when the first transmitting radio's signal is regarded as interference.

Since the channel capacity of the interference channel in Figure 5.27 is 1/2, codes of this rate, in principle, can achieve any arbitrarily small bit error probability. Suppose the first radio uses such codes and the receiver decodes with no errors. Then the receiver knows exactly the first radio's transmitted coded symbols and can use this to determine exactly the symbols transmitted by the second radio. Thus the second transmitting radio achieves reliable communication without any coding and sends data at rate

$$R_2 = 1.0 \text{ bits/symbol.} \tag{5.46}$$

The rate 1/2 coded first radio sends data at rate

$$R_1 = .5 \text{ bits/symbol.} \tag{5.47}$$

The above example is an illustration of how an optimum decoder simultaneously decodes the signals from both radios. Such multiple access communication systems were first studied by Shannon [127] in 1961. In 1971, Ahlswede [128] determined the capacity regions for the two-user and three-user multiple access channels with independent sources, and van der Meulen [129] put forward a limiting expression and simple inner and outer bounds on the capacity region for the two-user multiple access channel. Liao [130] studied the general L-user multiple access channel with

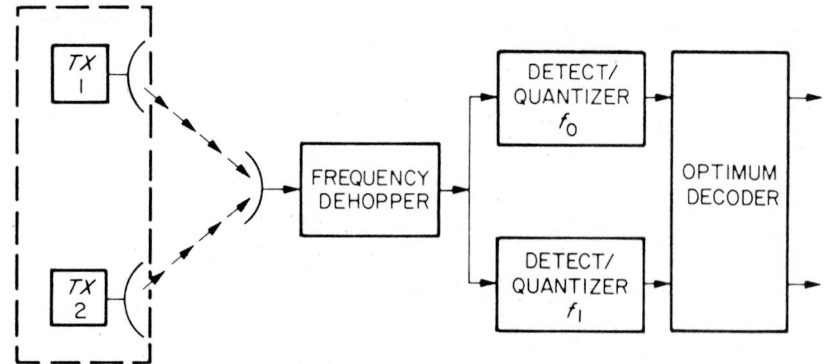

Figure 5.28. Optimum decoder.

independent sources. He formulated the capacity region for this channel and proved the fundamental coding theorem. An extensive survey on the information-theoretic aspects of multiple access channels has been assembled by van der Meulen [131], [132].

As sketched in Figure 5.28, the optimum detector simultaneously decodes both radio signals. It regards the two transmitting radios shown as a single radio with a vector data symbol consisting of two binary data symbols. Thus there are four possible inputs and three possible outputs. The optimum decoder examines all possible sequences of vector data symbols and compares them with the channel output pattern of hard quantized energy detector outputs. The resulting channel is shown in Figure 5.29.

Since the two transmitting radios are spatially separated, the codes used in this channel are restricted. Liao [130], and then Slepian and Wolf [133], gave formulas for the capacity region for this discrete memoryless channel

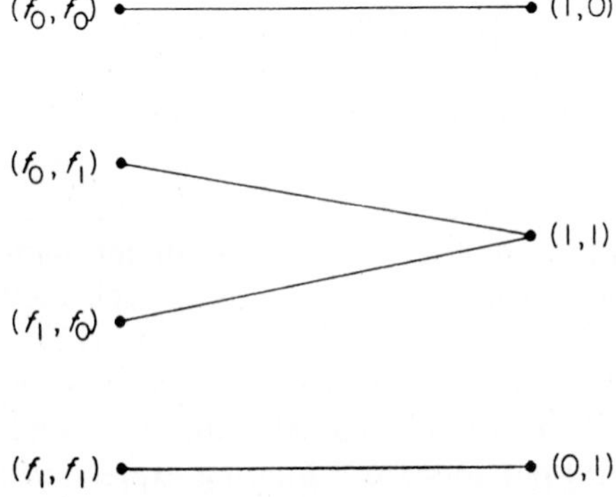

Figure 5.29. Channel for optimum decoder ($M = 2,\ L = 2$).

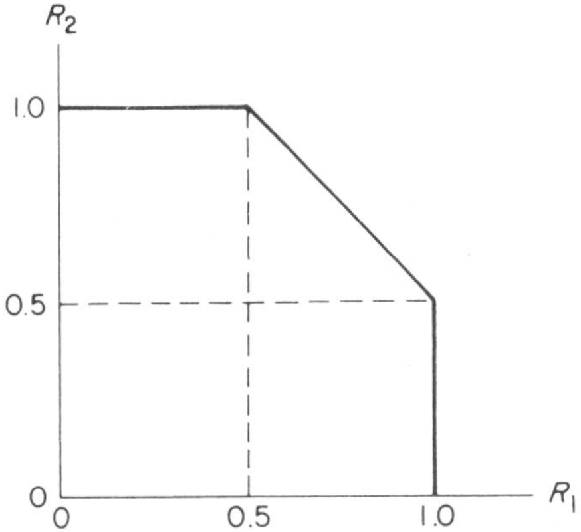

Figure 5.30. Optimum decoder capacity region.

with independent encoding of the two message sources. Their results are shown in Figure 5.30, which gives the data rates of the two transmitting radios that can be simultaneously achieved while maintaining arbitrarily small bit error probabilities. The rates $R_1 = .5$ and $R_2 = 1.0$ illustrated above represent one achievable point in this capacity region.

It is interesting to compare the optimum case of the previous example with pure TDMA. Suppose in a TDMA mode the first radio transmits ρ fraction of the time while the second radio transmits at $1 - \rho$ fraction of the time. Since there would be no interference there are no errors and the average data rates are

$$\begin{aligned} R_1 &= \rho \text{ bits/symbol} \\ R_2 &= 1 - \rho \text{ bits/symbol} \end{aligned} \tag{5.48}$$

or

$$1 = R_1 + R_2. \tag{5.49}$$

This defines the capacity region for pure TDMA and is shown in Figure 5.31. Note that the *simultaneously transmitting radios with optimum decoding can achieve higher data rates than pure TDMA*.

Construction of specific codes for the two-radio channel has been investigated by several authors [134]–[138]. Chang and Weldon [139] and Chang and Wolf [140] extended these results to the general case of L-users and M frequencies. The use of trellis codes for these multiple access channels has also been investigated [141]–[147].

Figures 5.32 to 5.34 show the multiple access channels for $L = 3$, $M = 2$; $L = 2$, $M = 3$; and $L = 2$, $M = 4$. For arbitrary L and M there are M^L inputs and the number of outputs is given by

$$\sum_{k=1}^{\lambda} \binom{M}{k}, \qquad \lambda = \min\{L, M\}. \tag{5.50}$$

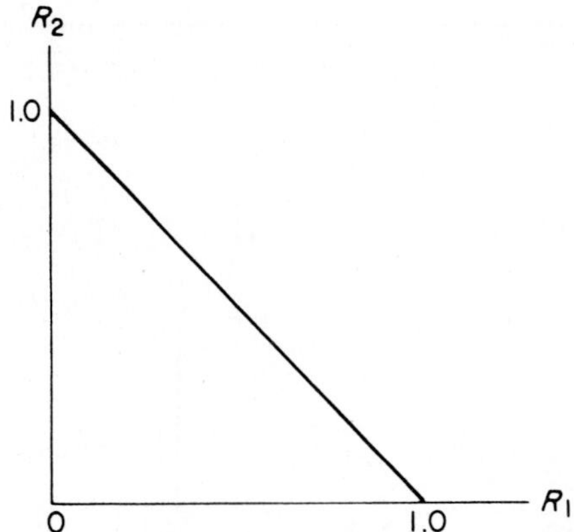

Figure 5.31. Pure TDMA capacity region.

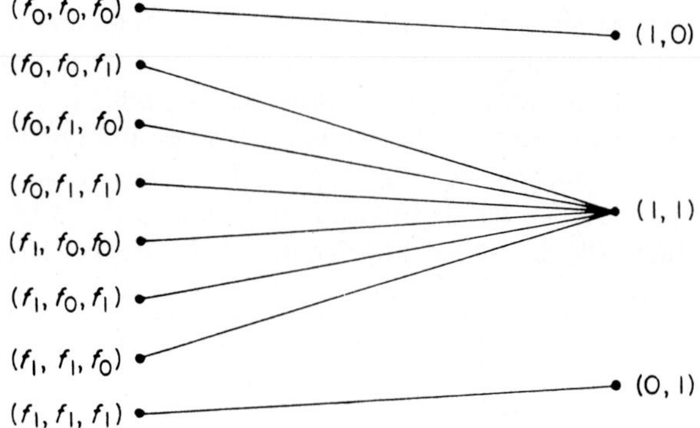

Figure 5.32. Channel for optimum decoder ($M = 2$, $L = 3$).

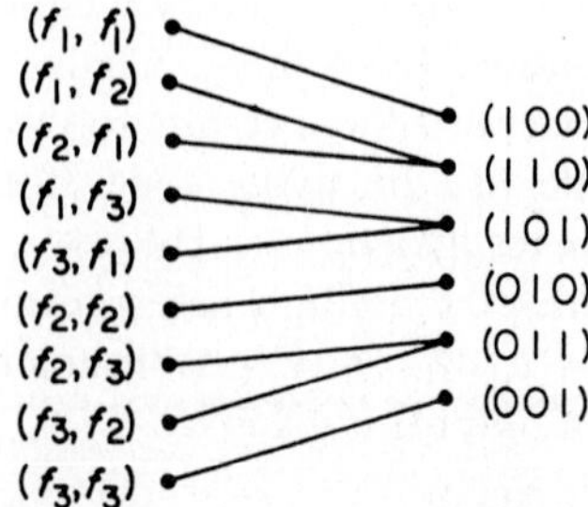

Figure 5.33. Channel for optimum decoder ($M = 3$, $L = 2$).

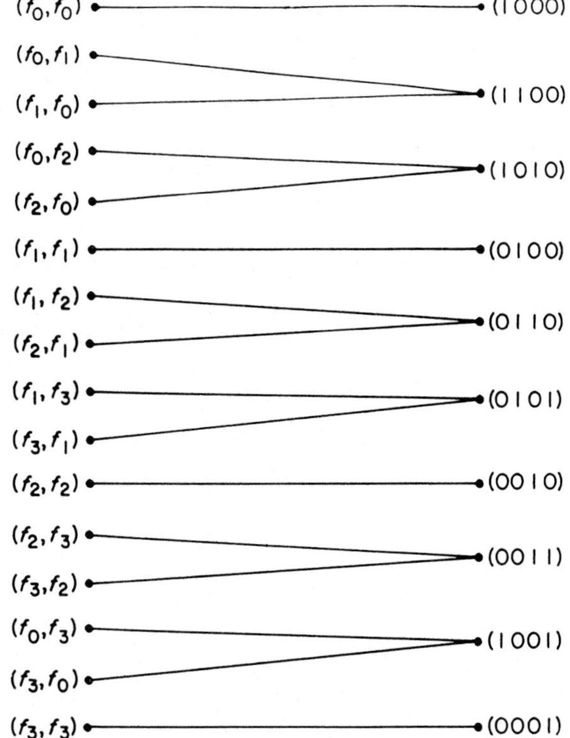

Figure 5.34. Channel for optimum decoder ($M = 4$, $L = 2$).

The overall system, however, is almost the same as that described by Goodman et al. [117] and discussed in the previous section. The major difference here is that all transmitted signals are decoded simultaneously by regarding all L transmitting radios as a single composite multiple frequency tone transmitting radio. The L separate data sources are viewed as a single L dimensional vector source and the optimum receiver compares all possible sequences of these vector data symbols with the channel output sequence. In this case it looks for the vector sequence of greatest agreement with the channel output sequence.

This section examined only the special case where the chip energy detector outputs were quantized to one bit. Generalization to multiple level quantization is possible but will require AGC, which is difficult to maintain in a jamming environment. List detectors with various metrics have been studied by Vo [148] for these multiple access systems. In the list detector, side information regarding the L transmitting radio's signal tone energies at the receiving radio can be incorporated in the decision process. The optimum decoder again treats all L data sources as a single L dimensional vector source and compares all possible transmitted vector data sequences with the total channel output sequence. The metric used for making this comparison depends on the kind of detectors used and the available side information. As an example, consider $L = 8$ identical multiple access transmitters where there are $M = 32$ orthogonal tone frequencies available. Pure FDMA is achieved when each user is given two tones where we have $L = 8$ non-overlapping BFSK signals. Assuming the use of coding, Vo [148] has shown that the overall throughput is higher than FDMA when all $L = 8$ users use all 32 tones (32-FSK) with list detectors and maximum-likelihood metrics. This improvement over pure FDMA is even greater when the multiple access signals have different power levels which are known to the optimum multiple access receiver.

5.5 DISCUSSION

Spread-spectrum techniques are currently being incorporated into most military communication systems. One of the most active areas of research and new developments is in military communication networks [149]–[152]. In this chapter we presented an overview of the possible applications of spread-spectrum waveforms in a network environment with an emphasis on some theoretically optimum systems under ideal conditions. In practice, particularly in a mobile radio environment, there are many practical problems. Turin [153], for example, has examined experimental multipath fading data for mobile radios and developed more complete channel models. His results show that the multipath fading problems can result in worse performance than one expects with the idealized case presented here [154]–[157].

Our purpose here was to examine various types of multiple access systems using spread-spectrum waveforms. The ideal optimum receiver for multipoint-to-point systems in particular may not be practical today but does serve as a baseline with which to compare practical system designs. Also as our ability to do more complex signal processing at higher speeds develops, we can approach the idealized system designs discussed in this chapter. We are just beginning to understand and develop a new generation of spread-spectrum radios for military communication networks.

5.6 REFERENCES

[1] The MITRE Corporation, *Definition of Network Management Problems for Large Ground Data Networks*, MTR-79W00001, Charles F. Swett, Contract No. F19628-81-C-0001, Washington Operations, McLean, VA, February 1979.

[2] The MITRE Corporation, *A Survey of Routing Algorithms for Distributed Digital Radio Networks*, MTR-81W00074, Richard W. Carpenter, Contract No. F19628-81-0001, Washington Operations, McLean, VA, March 1981.

[3] The MITRE Corporation, *Channel Access Methods for Distributed Digital Radio Networks*, MTR-81W00273, Richard W. Carpenter, Contract No. F19628-82-C-0001, Washington Operations, McLean, VA, January 1981.

[4] Session 25, "Advanced space technology for next-generation MILSATCOM system," *MILCOM '82*, Boston, MA, October 1982.

[5] P. Baran, *On Distributed Communications: I. Introduction to Distributed Communications Networks*, The RAND Corporation, RM-3420-PR, August 1964.

[6] B. W. Boehm and R. L. Mobley, "Adaptive routing techniques for distributed communications systems," *IEEE Trans. Commun.*, COM-17, no. 3, pp. 340–349, June 1969.

[7] J. W. S. Liu, "Distributed routing and relay management in mobile packet radio networks," *Proc. Compcon Fall 80*, pp. 235–243, September 1980.

[8] E. W. Dijkstra, "A note on two problems in connection with graphs," *Numerische Mathematik 1*, pp. 269–271, 1959.

[9] L. R. Ford and D. R. Fulkerson, *Flow in Networks*, Princeton, NJ: Princeton University Press, 1962.

[10] R. W. Floyd, "Algorithm 97 shortest path," *Communications of the ACM*, vol. 5, no. 6, p. 345, June 1962.

[11] L. Kleinrock, *Communication Nets: Stochastic Message Flow and Delay*, New York: McGraw-Hill, 1964.

[12] S. E. Dreyfus, *An Appraisal of Some Shortest Path Algorithms*, The RAND Corporation, RM-5433-1-PR, September 1968.

[13] L. Fratta, M. Gerla, and L. Kleinrock, "The flow deviation method: An approach to store-and-forward communication network design," *Networks*, vol. 3, pp. 97–133, 1973.

[14] H. Rudin, *On Routing and "Delta Routing": A Taxonomy of Techniques for Packet-Switched Networks*, IBM Zurich Research Laboratory, RZ 701, June 1975.

[15] W. D. Tajibnapis, *Message-Switching Protocols in Distributed Computer Networks*, Ph.D. Dissertation, The University of Michigan, 1976.

[16] D. B. Johnson, "Efficient algorithms for shortest paths in sparse networks," *Journal of the Association for Computing Machinery*, vol. 24, no. 1, pp. 1–13, January 1977.

[17] R. G. Gallager, "A minimum delay routing algorithm using distributed computation," *IEEE Trans. Commun.*, COM-25, no. 1, pp. 73–85, January 1977.

[18] W. D. Tajibnapis, "A correctness proof of a topology information maintenance protocol for a distributed computer network," *Communications of the ACM*, vol. 20, no. 7, pp. 477–485, July 1977.

[19] T. E. Stern, "A class of decentralized routing algorithms using relaxation," *IEEE Trans. Commun.*, COM-25, no. 10, pp. 1092–1102, October 1977.

[20] J. L. Kennington, "A survey of linear cost multicommodity network flows," *Operations Research*, vol. 26, no. 2, pp. 209–236, March-April 1978.

[21] F. C. Schoute and J. M. McQuillan, "A comparison of information policies for minimum delay routing algorithms," *IEEE Trans. Commun.*, COM-26, no. 8, pp. 1266–1271, August 1978.

[22] J. M. McQuillan, G. Falk, and I. Richer, "A review of the development and performance of the ARPANET routing algorithm," *IEEE Trans. Commun.*, COM-26, no. 12, pp. 1802–1811, December 1978.

[23] R. Dial et al., "A computational analysis of alternative algorithms and labeling techniques for finding shortest path trees," *Networks*, vol. 9, no. 3, pp. 215–248, Fall 1979.

[24] D. R. Shier, "On algorithms for finding the k shortest paths in a network," *Networks*, vol. 9, no. 3, pp. 195–214, Fall 1979.

[25] P. M. Merlin and A. Segall, "A failsafe distributed routing protocol," *IEEE Trans. Commun.*, COM-27, no. 9, pp. 1280–1287, September 1979.

[26] J. M. McQuillan, I. Richer, and E. C. Rosen, "An overview of the new routing algorithm for the ARPANET," *Sixth Data Communications Symposium*, pp. 63–68, November 1979.

[27] Y. W. Ma, "A Shortest Path Algorithm with Average Execution Time $0(\sqrt{n}\log n)$," Ph.D. Dissertation, Department of Electrical Engineering and Computer Sciences, University of California, Berkeley, 1980.

[28] W. K. Crowther, R. Pettbert, D. Walden, S. Ornstein, and F. Heart, "A system for broadcast communication: Reservation-Aloha," in *Proceedings 6th Hawaii International Systems Science Conference*, January 1973.

[29] L. Roberts, "Dynamic allocation of satellite capacity through packets reservation," National Computer Conference, *AFIPS Conference Proceedings*, vol. 42, 1973.

[30] R. Binder, "A dynamic packet-switching system for satellite broadcast channels," *Proc. ICC 1975*, San Francisco, CA, June 1975.

[31] I. Rubin, "Integrated random-access reservation schemes for multi-access communication channels," UCLA-ENG-7752, July 1977.

[32] J. W. Mark, "Global scheduling approach to conflict free multiaccess via a data bus," *IEEE Trans. Commun.*, COM-26, no. 9, pp. 1342–1352, September 1978.

[33] I. M. Jacobs, R. Binder, and E. V. Hoversten, "General purpose packet satellite networks," *Proc. IEEE*, vol. 66, no. 11, pp. 1445–1467, November 1978.

[34] J. E. Wieselthier and A. Ephremides, "A new class of protocols for multiple access in satellite networks," *IEEE Trans. Automatic Control*, vol. Ac-25, pp. 865–879, October 1980.

[35] A. Nilsson and C. J. Graff, "Packet radio communication system architecture in a mixed traffic and dynamic environment," Computer Networking Symposium, IEEE Catalog No. 80CH1586-7, December 10, 1980.

[36] E. P. Greene and A. Ephremides, "Distributed reservation control protocols for random access broadcasting channels," *IEEE Trans. Commun.*, COM-29, no. 5, pp. 726–735, May 1981.

[37] F. A. Tobagi and L. Kleinrock, "Packet switching in radio channels: Part III —Polling and (dynamic) split-channel reservation multiple access," *IEEE Trans. Commun.*, COM-24, no. 8, pp. 832–844, August 1976.

[38] A. K. Agrawala and R. L. Larsen, *Efficient Communication for Local Computer Networks-Coordinated Access Broadcast*, TR-639, NAS5-24092, February 1978.

[39] J. F. Hayes, "An adaptive technique for local distribution," *IEEE Trans. Commun.*, COM-26, no. 8, pp. 1178–1186, August 1978.

[40] I. Chlamtac, W. R. Franta, and K. D. Levin, "BRAM: The broadcast recognizing access method," *IEEE Trans. Commun.*, COM-27, no. 8, pp. 1183–1189, August 1979.

[41] L. Kleinrock and M. O. Scholl, "Packet switching radio channels: New conflict-free multiple access schemes," *IEEE Trans. Commun.*, COM-28, no. 7, pp. 1015–1029, July 1980.

[42] N. Abramson, "The aloha system," in *Computer Networks*, N. Abramson and F. Kuo, Ed., Englewood Cliffs, NJ: Prentice-Hall, 1973, pp. 501–517.

[43] S. S. Lam, *Packet Switching in a Multi-Access Broadcast Channel With Application to Satellite Communication in a Computer Network*, Ph.D. Dissertation, University of California, Los Angeles, CA, UCLA-ENG-7429, April 1974.

[44] F. A. Tobagi, *Random Access Techniques for Data Transmission Over Packet-Switched Radio Networks*, Ph.D. Dissertation, University of California, Los Angeles, CA, UCLA-ENG-7499, December 1974.

[45] L. G. Roberts, "Aloha packet system with and without slots and capture," *Computer Communications Review*, vol. 5, pp. 28–42, April 1975.

[46] L. Kleinrock and S. Lam, "Packet switching in a multi-access broadcast channel: Performance evaluation," *IEEE Trans. Commun.*, COM-23, pp. 410–423, April 1975.

[47] S. S. Lam and L. Kleinrock, "Packet switching in a multi-access broadcast channel: Dynamic control procedures," *IEEE Trans. Commun.*, COM-23, no. 9, pp. 891–904, September 1975.

[48] L. Kleinrock and F. A. Tobagi, "Packet switching in radio channels: Part I—Carrier sense multiple-access modes and their throughput-delay characteristics," *IEEE Trans. Commun.*, COM-23, no. 12, pp. 1400–1416, December 1975.

[49] F. A. Tobagi and L. Kleinrock, "Packet switching in radio channels: Part II—The hidden terminal problem in carrier sense multiple-access and the busy-tone solution," *IEEE Trans. Commun.*, COM-23, no. 12, pp. 1417–1433, December 1975.

[50] G. Fayolle, E. Gelenbe, and J. Labetoulle, "Stability and optimal control of the packet switching broadcast channel," *Journal of the Association for Computing Machinery*, vol. 24, no. 3, pp. 375–386, July 1977.

[51] F. A. Tobagi, "Packet switching in radio channels: Part IV—Stability considerations and dynamic control in carrier sense multiple access," *IEEE Trans. Commun.*, COM-25, no. 10, 1103–1119, October 1977.

[52] J. I. Capetanakis, *The Multiple Access Broadcast Channel: Protocol and Capacity Considerations*, Report ESL-R-806, M.I.T., Cambridge, MA, March 1978.

[53] R. G. Gallager, "Conflict resolution in random access broadcast networks," 1978 AFOSR Workshop in Communication Theory and Applications, Provincetown, MA, pp. 74–76, September 1978.

[54] J. I. Capetanakis, "Tree algorithms for packet broadcast channels," *IEEE Trans. Inform. Theory*, IT-25, no. 5, pp. 505–515, September 1979.

[55] P. A. Humblet and J. Mosely, "Efficient accessing of a multiaccess channel," *IEEE Conference on Decision Control*, Albuquerque, NM, December 1980.

[56] J. L. Massey, "The capacity of the collision channel without feedback," *IEEE Int. Symposium on Information Theory*, Les Ares, France, June 21–25, 1982.

[57] J. L. Spilker, Jr., *Digital Communications by Satellite*, Englewood Cliffs, NJ: Prentice-Hall, 1977.

[58] The MITRE Corporation, *JTIDS Net Access via Distributed Reservation*, J. C. Seaquist, Contract No. F19628-79C-0001, Bedford Operations, Bedford, MA, October 1978.

[59] R. R. Boorstyn and A. Kershenbaum, *Research in Network Management Techniques for Tactical Data Communication Networks*, Polytechnic Institute of New York, NY, October 1979 to September 1980.

[60] R. R. Boorstyn and A. Kershenbaum, "Throughput analysis of multihop packet radio," *ICC 1980 Conference Record*, vol. 1, pp. 1361–1365, 1980.

[61] J. E. Wieselthier, "Spread spectrum multiple access issues in the HF intra task force communication network," *5th MIT/ONR Workshop on C^3 Systems*, Naval Postgraduate School, Monterey, CA, August 1982.

[62] J. E. Wieselthier and A. Ephremides, "A distributed reservation scheme for spread spectrum multiple access channels," GLOBECOM '83, San Diego, CA, November 1983.

[63] M. B. Pursley, "Evaluating performance of codes for spread spectrum multiple-access communications," in *Proc. 12th Annual Allerton Conf. on Circuit and Systems Theory*, pp. 765–774, October 1974.

[64] J. L. Massey, and J. J. Uhran, "Sub-baud coding," *Proc. 13th Annual Allerton Conference on Circuit and Systems Theory*, pp. 539–547, October 1975.

[65] K. Yao, "Error probability of asynchronous spread spectrum multiple-access communication systems," *IEEE Trans. Commun.*, COM-25, pp. 803–809, August 1977.

[66] M. B. Pursley, "Performance evaluation for phase-coded spread spectrum multiple-access—Part I: System analysis." *IEEE Trans. Commun.*, COM-25, pp. 795–799, August 1977.

[67] N. E. Bekir, *Bounds on the Distribution of Partial Correlation for PN and Gold Sequences*, Ph.D. Dissertation, Department of Electrical Engineering, University of Southern California, Los Angeles, CA, January 1978.

[68] N. E. Bekir, R. A. Scholtz, and L. R. Welch, "Partial period correlation properties of PN sequences," in *Proc. Nat. Telecommunications Conf.*, pp. 35.1.1–4, December 1978.

[69] M. B. Pursley and H. F. A. Roefs, "Numerical evaluation of correlation parameters for optimal phases of binary shift-register sequences," *IEEE Trans. Commun.*, COM-27, pp. 1597–1604, October 1979.

[70] D. E. Borth, M. B. Pursley, D. V. Sarwate, and W. E. Stark, "Bounds on error probability for direct-sequence spread spectrum multiple-access communications," in *1979 Midcon Professional Program*, vol. 15: Spread Spectrum Communication System Concepts, November 1979.

[71] D. V. Sarwate and M. B. Pursley, "Cross-correlation properties of pseudorandom and related sequences," *Proc. IEEE*, vol. 68, pp. 593–619, May 1980.

[72] M. B. Pursley, D. V. Sarwate, and W. E. Stark, "On the average probability of error for direct-sequence spread spectrum multiple-access system," in *Proc. 1980 Conf. Information Sciences and Systems*, pp. 320–325, 1980.

[73] K. T. Wu, and D. L. Neuhoff, "Average error probability for DS-SSMA communication system," *Proc. 18th Annual Allerton Conf. on Communication, Control, and Computing*, pp. 359–368, October 1980.

[74] K. T. Wu, "Average error probability for DS-SSMA Communications: The Gram-Charlier expansion approach," *Proc. 19th Annual Allerton Conf. on Communication, Control, and Computing*, pp. 237–246, October 1981.

[75] M. B. Pursley, D. V. Sarwate, and W. E. Stark, "Error probability for direct-sequences spread spectrum multiple-access communication—Part I: Upper and lower bounds," *IEEE Trans. Commun.*, COM-30, pp. 975–984, May 1982.

[76] E. A. Geraniotis and M. B. Pursley, "Error probability for direct-sequences spread spectrum multiple-access communications—Part II: Approximations," *IEEE Trans. Commun.*, COM-30, pp. 985–995, May 1982.

[77] R. C. Singleton, "Maximum distance Q ~ ary codes," *IEEE Trans. Inform. Theory, IT-10, pp. 116–118, April* 1964.

[78] L. I. Bluestein and R. L. Greenspan, "Efficient approximation of orthogonal waveforms," Group Report 1964-48, M.I.T., Lincoln Laboratory, November 3, 1964.

[79] I. S. Reed, "kth order near orthogonal codes," *IEEE Trans. Inform. Theory*, IT-17, pp. 116–117, January 1971.

[80] G. Solomon, "Optimal frequency-hopping sequences for multiple-access," *Proc. 1973 Symposium on Spread-Spectrum Communications*, vol. 1, AD-915, pp. 33–35, 1973.

[81] R. M. Marsareau and T. S. Seay, "Multiple access frequency hopping patterns with low ambiguity" *IEEE Trans. Aerospace and Electronic Systems*, AES-17, no. 4, pp. 571–578, July 1981.

[82] T. S. Seay, "Hopping patterns for bounded mutual interference in frequency hopping multiple access," *MILCOM '82*, Boston, MA, October 1982, paper 22.3.

[83] J. H. Cafarella, "Advanced SAW-based signal processing for packet communications," *MILCOM '82*, Boston, MA, October 1982, paper 10.6.

[84] W. Skudera, W. Novick, and D. Mains, "SAW spread spectrum remote control link," *MILCOM '82*, Boston, MA, October 1982, paper 12.1.

[85] D. M. Grieco and J. K. Gutman, "The SEEK TALK spread spectrum acquisition using a SAW matched filter," *MILCOM '82*, Boston, MA, October 1982, paper 17.3.

[86] T. J. Goblick, W. B. Goggins, D. H. Hurlburt, P. G. McHugh, and N. W. Spencer, "A spread spectrum burst communication system using SAW convolvers," *MILCOM '82*, Boston, MA, October 1982, paper 18.5.

[87] R. E. Conley, "MILSTAR—A military communication system," *MILCOM '82*, Boston, MA, October 1982, paper 31.5.

[88] S. B. Heppe, "Viewpoints on control of military satellite communications, *IEEE Commun. Mag.*, vol. 21, no. 4, July 1983.

[89] TRW Electronic Systems Group, "30/20 GHz low data rate ground terminal design study," Final Report to NASA Lewis Research Center, Document Number 3-6-T-9-F2 on Contract Number NAS3-23341, June 1983.

[90] O. Yue, "Hard-limited versus linear combining for frequency-hopping multiple-access systems in a Rayleigh fading environment," *IEEE Trans. Veh. Technol.*, VT-30, pp. 10–14, March 1981.

[91] D. A. Shnidman, "A generalized Nyquist criterion and optimum linear receiver for a pulse modulation system," *Bell Syst. Tech. J.*, vol. 46, pp. 2163–2177, November 1967.

[92] A. R. Kaye and D. A. George, "Transmission of multiplexed PAM signals over multiple channel and diversity systems," *IEEE Trans. Commun. Technol.*, COM-18, pp. 520–526, October 1970.

[93] J. E. Savage, "Signal detection in the presence of multiple-access noise," *IEEE Trans. Inform. Theory*, IT-20, pp. 42–49, January 1974.

[94] W. Van Etten, "Maximum likelihood receiver for multiple channel transmission systems," *IEEE Trans. Commun.*, COM-24, no. 2, pp. 276–283, February 1976.

[95] K. S. Schneider, "Optimum detection of code division multiplexed signals," *IEEE Trans. Aerospace and Electronic Systems*, AES-15, no. 1, pp. 181–185, January 1979.

[96] S. Verdu, *Minimum Bit-Error-Rate Detection of Asynchronous Multiple-Access Communications*, Coordinated Science Laboratory Technical Report.

[97] S. Verdu, "Optimum sequence detection of asynchronous multiple-access communications," *IEEE 1983 Int. Symposium on Information Theory*, St. Jovite, Canada, September 1983.

[98] J. K. Omura, "Optimal receiver design for convolutional codes and channels with memory via control theoretical concepts," *Information Sciences*, vol. 3, pp. 243–266, 1971.

[99] H. Kobayashi, "Correlative level coding and maximum-likelihood decoding," *IEEE Trans. Inform. Theory*, IT-17, pp. 586–594, January 1971.

[100] G. D. Forney, "Maximum likelihood sequence estimation of digital sequences in the presence of intersymbol interference," *IEEE Trans. Inform. Theory*, IT-18, no. 3, pp. 363–378, May 1972.

[101] L. K. Mackechnie, "Receivers for channels with intersymbol interference," (Abs.) *IEEE 1972 Int. Symposium on Information Theory*, Asilomar, CA, p. 82.

[102] G. D. Forney, "The Viterbi algorithm," *Proc. IEEE*, vol. 61, no. 3, pp. 268–278, March 1973.

[103] A. J. Viterbi and J. K. Omura, *Principles of Digital Communication and Coding*, New York: McGraw-Hill, 1979.

[104] J. K. Omura, "Performance bounds for Viterbi algorithms," *Proc. 1981, IEEE Int. Commun. Conf.*, Denver, CO, pp. 2.2.1–5.

[105] M. B. Pursley, "Coding and diversity for channels with fading and pulsed interference," *Proc. Sixteenth Annual Conference on Information Sciences and Systems*, Princeton University, pp. 413–418, March 1982.

[106] B. Hajek, "Recursive retransmission control—Application to a frequency-hopped spread-spectrum system," *Proc. Sixteenth Annual Conference on Information Sciences and Systems*, Princeton University, pp. 116–120, March 1982.

[107] E. A. Geraniotis and M. B. Pursley, "Error probabilities for slow-frequency-hopped spread-spectrum multiple-access communications over fading channels," *IEEE Trans. Commun.*, COM-30, pp. 996–1009, May 1982.

[108] M. B. Pursley, "Throughput of frequency-hopped spread-spectrum communications for packet radio networks," *Proc. Seventeenth Annual Conference on Information Sciences and Systems*, Johns Hopkins University, pp. 550–556, March 1983.

[109] J. E. Wieselthier and A. Ephremides, "A scheme to increase throughput in frequency hopping multiple access channels," *Proc. Seventeenth Annual Conference on Information Sciences and Systems*, Johns Hopkins University, p. 379, March 1983.

[110] J. E. Wieselthier and A. Ephremides, "Throughput increase in frequency hopped multiple access channels by means of discrimination against partially overlapping interference," Submitted to *IEEE Trans. Commun.*

[111] K. L. Jordan, Jr., "The performance of sequential decoding in conjunction with efficient modulation," *IEEE Trans. Comm. Tech.*, COM-14(3), 283–297, June 1966.

[112] J. M. Wozencraft and R. S. Kennedy, "Modulation and demodulation for probabilistic decoding," *IEEE Trans. Inform. Theory*, IT-12, pp. 291–297, July 1966.

[113] A. J. Viterbi, "A robust ratio-threshold technique to mitigate tone and partial-band jamming in coded MFSK systems," *MILCOM '82*, Boston, MA, October 18–20, 1982.

[114] P. J. Crepeau, "Generalized list detection for coded MFSK/FH signaling on fading and jamming channels," NRL Report 8708, Naval Research Laboratory, Washington, DC, June 1983.

[115] P. J. Crepeau, M. A. Creighton, and J. K. Omura," Performance of FH/MFSK with list metric detection against partial band noise and random tone jamming," *MILCOM '83*, Washington, D.C., October 31–November 2, 1983.

[116] M. A. Creighton, *Analysis of List Decoding Metrics for Jamming and Multiple Access Channels*, Ph.D. Thesis, University of California, Los Angeles, CA, 1985.

[117] D. J. Goodman, P. S. Henry, and V. K. Prabhu, "Frequency-hopped multilevel FSK for mobile radio," *Bell Syst. Tech. J.*, vol. 59, no. 7, September 1980.

[118] A. J. Viterbi, "A processing satellite transponder for multiple access by low-rate mobile users," National Radio Science Meeting, November 6–9, 1978, Boulder, Colorado, Commission C, Session 3.

[119] G. R. Cooper and R. W. Nettleton, "A spread spectrum technique for high capacity mobile communication," *IEEE Trans. Vehic. Tech. J.*, VT-27, pp. 264–275, November 1978.

[120] P. S. Henry, "Spectrum efficiency of a frequency-hopped DPSK mobile radio system," *Proc. IEEE Vehic. Tech.*, VT-28, pp. 327–332, November 1979.

[121] O. Yue, "Frequency-hopping multiple-access, phase-shift-keying systems in a Rayleigh fading environment," *Bell Syst. Tech. J.*, vol. 59, no. 6, pp. 861–879, July–August 1980.

[122] B. G. Haskell, "Computer simulation results on frequency-hopped MFSK mobile radio-noiseless case," *Proc. Nat. Telecommun. Conf.*, Houston, TX, December 1980.

[123] G. Einarsson, "Address assignment for a time frequency-coded spread spectrum system," *Bell Syst. Tech. J.*, vol. 59, no. 7, pp. 1241–1255, September 1980.

[124] U. Timor, "Improved decoding scheme for frequency-hopped multilevel FSK system," *Bell Syst. Tech. J.*, vol. 59, no. 9, pp. 285–296, November 1980.

[125] U. Timor, "Multistage decoding of frequency-hopped FSK system," *Bell Syst. Tech. J.*, vol. 60, no. 4, pp. 471–483, April 1981.

[126] U. Timor, "Multitone frequency-hopped MFSK system for mobile radio," *Bell Syst. Tech. J.*, vol. 61, no. 10, pp. 3007–3017, December 1982.

[127] C. E. Shannon, "Two-way communication channels," *Proc. 4th Berkeley Symp. Math. Stat. Prob.*, vol. 1, pp. 611–644, 1961. Reprinted in *Key Papers in the Development of Information Theory*, D. Slepian, ed., New York: IEEE Press, 1974, pp. 339–372.

[128] R. Ahlswede, "Multi-way communication channels," *Proc. 2nd. Int. Symp. Inform. Theory*, Tsahkadsor, Armenia, USSR, pp. 23–52, 1971.

[129] E. C. van der Meulen, "The discrete memoryless channel with two senders and one receiver," *Proc. 2nd Int. Symp. Inform. Theory*, Tsahkadsor, Armenia, USSR, pp. 103–135, 1971.

[130] H. Liao, "A coding theorem for multiple access communications," presented at Int. Symp. on Inform. Theory, Asilomar, CA, 1972. Also Ph.D. Dissertation, *Multiple Access Channels*, Deptartment of Electrical Engineering, University of Hawaii, 1972.

[131] E. C. van der Meulen, "Advances in multiple-user communication channels," *Proc. 1975 IEEE-USSR Joint Workshop Inform. Theory*, Moscow, USSR, December 1975.

[132] E. C. van der Meulen, "A survey of multi-way channels in information theory: 1961–1976," *IEEE Trans. Inform. Theory*, IT-23, pp. 1–37, January 1977.

[133] D. Slepian and J. K. Wolf, "A coding theorem for multiple access channels with correlated sources," *Bell Syst. Tech. J.*, vol. 52, pp. 1037–1076, September 1973.

[134] T. Kasami and S. Lin, "Coding for a multiple-access channel," *IEEE Trans. Inform. Theory*, IT-22, pp. 129–137, March 1976.

[135] E. J. Weldon, Jr., and K. P. Yiu, "Coding for a multiple access channel," presented at Int. Symp. Inform. Theory, Ronneby, Sweden, 1976.

[136] E. J. Weldon, Jr., "Coding for a multiple access channel," *Inform. Contr.*, vol. 36, no. 3, pp. 256–274, 1978.

[137] T. Kasami and S. Lin, "Bounds on the achievable rates of block coding for a memoryless multiple-access channel," *IEEE Trans. Inform. Theory*, IT-24, pp. 187–197, March 1978.

[138] H. C. A. van Tiborg, "An upper bound for codes in a two-access binary erasure channel," *IEEE Trans. Inform. Theory*, IT-24, pp. 112–116, January 1978.

[139] S. C. Chang and E. J. Weldon, Jr., "Coding for T-user multiple-access channels," *IEEE Trans. Inform. Theory*, IT-25, pp. 684–691, November 1979.

[140] S. C. Chang and J. K. Wolf, "On the T-user M-frequency multiple-access channel with and without intensity information," *IEEE Trans. Inform. Theory*, IT-27, no. 1, pp. 41–48, January 1981.

[141] R. L. Peterson, *Tree, Trellis, and Convolutional Coding for Multiple-Access Channels*, Department of Electrical Engineering, Illinois Institute of Technology, Technical Report EE, 7808-32-02, August 1978.

[142] P. R. Chevillat, *N-User Trellis Coding for a Class of Multiple-Access Channels*, IBM Research Report, Zurich, Switzerland, RZ 928 (#31790), November 1978.

[143] D. J. Costello and R. L. Peterson, "Binary convolutional codes for a multiple-access channel," *IEEE Trans. Inform. Theory*, IT-25, pp. 101–105, January 1979.

[144] R. L. Peterson and D. J. Costello, Jr., "Error probability and free distance bounds for two-user tree codes on multiple-access channels," *IEEE Trans. Inform. Theory*, IT-26, pp. 658–670, November 1980.

[145] P. R. Chevillat, "N-user trellis coding for a class of multiple-access channels," *IEEE Trans. Inform. Theory*, IT-27, pp. 114–120, January 1981.

[146] J. K. Omura and R. Sorace, "Coding for a multiple access channel," 1979 *NTC Record*, 1979, pp. 23.4.1–23.4.7, Washington, DC.

[147] R. Sorace, *Analysis of Noncoherent Multiple Access Communication Channels*, Ph.D. Dissertation, University of California, Los Angeles, CA, 1981.

[148] Q. Vo, *Optimal Detection of Multiple Access Spread Spectrum Signals*, Ph.D. Dissertation, University of California, Los Angeles, CA, 1985.

[149] R. E. Kahn et al., "Advances in packet radio technology," *Proc. IEEE*, vol. 66, pp. 1468–1496, November 1978.

[150] P. Sass, "Army spread-spectrum—Evolution or revolution," MILCOM '82, Boston, MA, October 1982, paper 4.1.

[151] P. Sass, "Why is the army interested in spread spectrum?" *IEEE Commun. Mag.*, vol. 21, no. 4, pp. 23–25, July 1983.

[152] K. Brayer, "Implementation and performance of survivable computer communication with autonomous decentralized control," *IEEE Commun. Mag.*, vol. 21, no. 4, July 1983.

[153] G. Turin, "Introduction to spread spectrum antimultipath techniques and their application to urban digital radio," *Proc. IEEE*, vol. 68, no. 3, March 1980.

[154] G. L. Turin et al., "Urban vehicle monitoring: Technology, economics and public policy," Vol. II: Technical Analysis and Appendices," report prepared under DHUD contract H-1030, October 1970.

[155] G. L. Turin et al., "A statistical model of urban multipath propagation," *IEEE Trans. Veh. Technol.*, VT-21, pp. 1–9, February 1972.

[156] G. L. Turin et al., "Simulation of urban vehicle-monitoring systems," *IEEE Trans. Veh. Technol.*, VT-21, pp. 9–16, February 1972.

[157] G. L. Turin, "Simulation of urban radio propagation and of urban radio communication systems," *Proc. Int. Symp. Antennas and Propagat.*, Sendai, Japan, pp. 543–546, August 1978.

Chapter 6

COMMERCIAL APPLICATIONS

The emphasis of this book has been on the design and analysis of spread-spectrum radios for military applications. In such applications, the goal is to combat intentional jamming by an enemy transmitter. The price for using spread-spectrum radios that provide the desired AJ properties is using large-bandwidth spread-spectrum signals that result in the apparent inefficient use of the radio spectrum. Owing to this apparent bandwidth inefficiency, most people, including at one time the authors of this book, incorrectly assumed that commercial applications of spread-spectrum radios were impractical (see Viterbi [1, 2]). However, in commercial radios, interference typically comes from other similar radios that are part of an overall system, and these, unlike enemy jammers, *can* be controlled. Moreover, the criterion for capacity in many commercial systems is not the number of users per unit bandwidth but, more appropriately, the number of users in a large area.

Since the first publication of *Spread Spectrum Communications* in 1985, a great deal of interest has been shown in spread-spectrum radios for commercial applications and has led to many significant developments. This chapter discusses some of the primary reasons for that interest and presents an overview of commercial spread-spectrum applications.

Cooper and Nettleton [3], in 1978, were the first to recognize that digital spread-spectrum radios had a potentially higher capacity for mobile radio applications than the FM analog radios used at that time. Viterbi's paper on fast frequency hopping [4] was soon followed by the work of Goodman, Henry, and Prabu [5], while Turin [6] examined the use of these radios to overcome multipath for urban digital radios. These researchers were ahead of their time, since neither the technology required to provide low-cost implementations of their ideas nor a market demand for high-capacity mobile radios then existed.

Viterbi's [7] consideration of a multiple-access satellite system for mobile users may have been a precursor of the Qualcomm systems in operation today. Indeed, the earliest commercial applications of spread-spectrum radios were for satellite communications with the small earth terminals used by Equitorial, a company founded by Professor Edwin Parker of Stanford University. This first widespread commercial application of spread-spectrum technology was in Equitorial's C-band receive-only small satellite earth stations [8, 9, 10]. In this application, each broadcast satellite channel required many receive-only earth stations, constituting a powerful economic incentive to make earth stations inexpensive. Also, the satellite transponders were power-limited rather than bandwidth-limited. Equitorial designed an earth station with small antennas that would pick up interfering signals from other geostationary satellites. Direct-sequence spread-spectrum radio signals were used in this design to overcome this interference.

One of the commercial spread-spectrum devices most widely used today is a receive-only satellite terminal called GPS. It is based on the U.S. military global positioning system (GPS) of 24 satellites with non-stationary orbits that transmit broadcast spread-spectrum signals [11]. A GPS receiver can simultaneously receive signals from three satellites and can determine its own position with a high degree of accuracy. Although it was originally intended for military applications, commercial companies have designed a range of GPS products, which are now widely used.

In 1980, Hewlett-Packard engineers designed an experimental spread-spectrum radio for indoor applications [12]. Bell Laboratories engineers also tested a similar direct-sequence spread-spectrum radio for indoor applications [13, 14]. These experimental systems created in research laboratories were not developed into commercial products.

By the late 1980s and early 1990s, the combination of the rapidly growing popularity of mobile radios sparking a demand for more capacity and the availability of the technology needed for low-cost implementation renewed the interest in commercial applications of spread-spectrum mobile radios. During this same period, allowance by the Federal Communications Commission (FCC) of more liberal unlicensed use of spread-spectrum radios prompted the development of a wide variety of commercial spread-spectrum radio applications.

We wish to point out that among the many multiple-access techniques under consideration for cellular telephony, we emphasize digital code division multiple access (CDMA) because it is a spread-spectrum technique, which is in keeping with the subject of this book. By doing so, we do not wish to imply that digital CDMA has been universally adopted as a standard for cellular telephones either in the United States or elsewhere. In fact, the European Community (EC) has already elected to follow digital time division multiple access (TDMA), a non-spread-spectrum approach.

6.1 KEY EVENTS IN THE COMMERCIAL MARKET

In commercial applications, the bandwidth efficiency—with a high number of bits per second per hertz—is often an important criterion. Consequently, it had generally been assumed that spread-spectrum radios had no practical commercial applications. Why is it that today a considerable commercial interest exists in the use of spread-spectrum radios?

The interest is largely the result of two events:

- In 1985, the FCC, in its Part 15 rules, allowed the unlicensed use of spread-spectrum radios in ISM bands for power levels up to 1 watt (W).
- Qualcomm developed a well-publicized spread-spectrum CDMA system for digital mobile cellular phone applications [15]. This digital cellular system provides as much as 20 times the capacity of existing analog cellular radios, which use frequency division multiple access (FDMA). It also has a higher potential capacity than the first U.S. digital cellular standard, IS-54, based on TDMA, using a conventional narrowband *M*-ary phase-shift-keying (MPSK) radio. Qualcomm's effort has led to the adoption of a second U.S. digital cellular standard, IS-95.

In the next sections, we discuss the impact of these two events, which are primarily responsible for the widespread interest in commercial applications of spread-spectrum radios today, and the advantages of spread-spectrum CDMA in multicell voice networks.

6.2 THE FCC PART 15 RULES

Prior to 1985, conventional radios with very low power (less than a milliwatt) were allowed by the FCC to operate in certain bands without licenses. To stimulate innovation, Dr. Michael Marcus of the FCC championed the use of higher power (up to 1 W) unlicensed spread-spectrum radios that have essentially the same power density (power per bandwidth) as unlicensed narrowband radios. Since spread-spectrum radios are less sensitive to interference (antijamming characteristic), it was felt that such signals might not interfere with each other any more than unlicensed narrowband signals with less power. Thanks to Marcus's efforts, in 1985 the FCC ruled to allow higher-power spread-spectrum radios in ISM bands (Table 6.1).

Frequency Hopping

The maximum dwell time during each hop is 0.4 sec, forcing a minimum hop rate of 2.5 hops per second. Differences in the maximum instantaneous

Table 6.1.
FCC Part 15 rules.

Carrier Frequency	Total Bandwidth
902–928 MHz	26 MHz
2.4000–2.4835 GHz	83.5 MHz
5.725–5.850 GHz	125 MHz

bandwidth and minimum number of hop channels for frequency hopping radios in each of the bands include the following:

ISM Band	Maximum Bandwidth	Minimum Number of Hops
902–928 MHz	500 kHz	50
2.4000–2.4835 GHz	1.0 MHz	75
5.725–5.850 GHz	1.0 MHz	75

Direct Sequence

Direct-sequence radios have a minimum spreading bandwidth of 500 kHz, with a minimum processing gain of 10 dB, implying a minimum of 10 chips per data bit.

The Part 15 rule was unusual in that it came from within the FCC rather than as a response to a request from outside the FCC.

With a higher power limit and no FCC licensing required, commercial companies began to introduce a wide range of innovative spread-spectrum radios capable of communicating over greater distances than the earlier low-power narrowband unlicensed radios. Some spread-spectrum wireless applications in these ISM bands are discussed in the following sections.

6.2.1 Indoor Applications

Commercial spread-spectrum radios that took advantage of this FCC Part 15 rule were first used in indoor office applications. These range from simple radios that link office equipment, e.g., several personal computers with a shared printer, to more complex wireless local area networks (WLANs).

Spread-spectrum cordless telephones using this technology are also available for the consumer market, including wireless PBX systems in office applications. These wireless office spread-spectrum telephone systems have the advantage of adequate power levels without requiring FCC licensing and they are robust against interference and multipath.

Wireless point-of-sale (POS) applications also use spread-spectrum radios. These include cash registers, bar-code readers, and menu pads in restaurants, which are, in essence, simple forms of wireless LANs. Also PCMCIA spread-spectrum radia modem cards are available for laptop computers and personal digital assistants (PDAs).

Spread-spectrum radios are ideal for home control systems, providing greater security owing to the different codes used for creating the spread-spectrum signals. Building alarm systems can be made more reliable by attaching to windows and doors small but higher-power unlicensed spread-spectrum radio transmitters that detect unauthorized entry into buildings and send alarm signals to a receiver.

6.2.2 Outdoor Applications

In many situations, the local telephone company is unwilling or unable to provide wired voice or data service in a timely manner. Unlicensed spread-spectrum radios are often used as an alternative, providing quick and easy setup of such links without requiring the user to apply for a radio frequency from the FCC. Sometimes, these "bypass" radios are used as emergency backup to wired lines, but in many cases, they are used as a more economical substitute for digital leased lines.

Among interesting outdoor applications is the Federal Emergency Management Agency's (FEMA) experimental use of spread-spectrum radios over a 60-mi range (with a relay) to transmit digital video at a full-duplex 256 kpbs data rate. In the Galapagos Islands, spread-spectrum radios are used to link remote scientific stations to the main research center without disturbing the environment with wires. A spread-spectrum radio system in Moscow links companies to a satellite earth station to provide direct digital communication with the United States.

In a campus environment (company or university), these radios provide quick and easy linking of wired LANs in different buildings.

Metropolitan area networks (MANs) for electronic mail services are now being designed to allow home computer users access to Internet directly or to their own company computer networks. These require wireless packet network bridge/router functions distributed throughout.

Another outdoor application for spread-spectrum radios is the intelligent vehicle highway system (IVHS) program, which uses radios with data-gathering devices, including digital video. These are now being tested with spread-spectrum radios transmitting data back to a central control hub. In the planning stage are automatic electronic toll booths that will use this technology for radio communication between automobiles and toll booths. Other shorter-range and lower-cost spread-spectrum radios have been designed for utility meter devices and even for electronic parking meters.

For isolated or rural areas where a wired system may be too costly, a wireless telephone local loop using unlicensed spread-spectrum radios is affordable, and in rural areas, the possibility of interference from other unlicensed radios is small.

6.2.3 Direct Sequence versus Frequency Hopping

A comparison of direct-sequence and frequency hopping spread-spectrum radio techniques for commercial applications must take into account many issues, some addressed here.

6.2.3.1 Conversion of Narrowband Radios

Conceptually, frequency hopping is easier to understand than direct-sequence spreading. In addition, most radio manufacturers can easily convert their narrowband radios to spread-spectrum radios in which the center frequency hops around according to a fixed pattern, or code. However, hopping around the transmitting radio carrier frequency is not enough: Now, the receiving radio must be synchronized to the hopping pattern of the transmitting radio. Synchronization is one of the most problematical operations in frequency-hopping radios.

6.2.3.2 Cost of Development and Products

The cost of development and the cost of the final product are important considerations in selecting a spread-spectrum technique. For most commercial applications, a fast frequency-hopping radio is not cost-effective. In fact, hopping rates of commercial radios are generally very slow compared to the data rates, typically having several hundreds of bits or more transmitted during a hop duration. Similarly, direct-sequence implementations for commercial applications with large processing gain require costly high-speed circuits which are generally impractical. Thus, the processing gain for commercial direct-sequence radios is usually limited to less than 20 dB to avoid having to use high-speed circuits.

With lower processing gain (fewer chips per bit), direct-sequence radios for commercial applications can use digital matched fibers instead of serial correlators. Matched filters have the advantage of being able to achieve faster acquisition times than serial correlators or frequency-hopping radios. In general, however, direct-sequence radios with matched filters demand a greater development effort than other types of spread-spectrum radios. The final cost of direct-sequence spread-spectrum radios with digital matched filters, however, is no greater than that for serial correlator type direct-sequence or frequency-hopping radios. In fact, as shown in the currently marketed cordless telephones, this type of direct-sequence spread-spectrum radio with digital matched filters can yield low-cost consumer electronics products.

6.2.3.3 Performance

Without interference from other radios and in free space, both direct-sequence and frequency-hopping spread-spectrum radios would give the same performance—*in theory*. In practice, however, the performance depends on the design of the radio and propagation conditions, and the realized performance varies greatly.

With large multipath delays (delays greater than a chip time), direct-sequence spread-spectrum radios can be more robust since they can better overcome the effects of multipath. Commercial slow frequency-hopping radios behave as narrowband radios. Thus, for higher data rates, the impact of multipath tends to degrade frequency-hopping radios more than direct-sequence radios.

The issue of mutual interference resulting from many spread-spectrum radios independently operating in a given area is very interesting. In a system in which many such spread-spectrum radios co-exist in the same area, it is difficult to compare the performances of these two types of radios, which depend largely on the application.

With frequency-hopping radio, for each hop, radio performance is "good" or "bad," depending on whether any other similar radio signal hops into the same band at the same time. The probability of this occurring depends on the number of hopping radios in the area and the availability of non-overlapping hopping bands.

Multipath conditions are likely to be different in each hopped frequency, even without interference, so performance during each hop can vary greatly, owing to different multipath conditions. Thus, frequency-hopping radios result in a channel that is time-varying, with changes in channel conditions occurring at each hop transition, somewhat like a fading channel in which fades occur at discrete times. As in any fading channel, coding with interleaving can dramatically improve performance (see Part 1, Chapter 3, Sections 3.7 and 3.8). Unfortunately, it is impractical to interleave data when the hop rate is slow, as is true for most commercial frequency-hopping systems.

Thus, the major difference between the two types of spread-spectrum radio is that frequency-hopping radios experience occasional strong bursty errors, while direct-sequence radios experience continuous but lower-level random errors. In direct-sequence radios, errors can be considered to be scattered randomly over time; in frequency hopping, errors are distributed in clusters.

For packetized data systems such as wireless LAN applications, frequency-hopping radios have an advantage. During a hop, frequency-hopping radios may transmit one or more packets. The higher-layer LAN protocol typically checks for errors in a packet, and if they exist, requests retransmission of the packet. In this type of system, the number of errors in a packet is not important—only the fact that an error has occurred is important. Thus, if the average number of packets with errors is the main performance criterion, it is preferable to have errors arrive in clusters, as in frequency-hopping radios.

The receiving slow frequency-hopping radio, however, generally takes longer to synchronize to the transmitting radio than corresponding direct-sequence radios with matched filters. For packetized data, this can be a major problem owing to the time needed for resynchronization for each packet or group of packets.

For all practical purposes, the FCC rules limit frequency-hopping radios to a maximum data rate of 1 Mbps since their instantaneous bandwidth is a maximum of 1 MHz. Direct-sequence radios can have higher data rates when sufficient bandwidth is available. For the 5.7-GHz band, several manufacturers offer commercial direct-sequence spread-spectrum radios capable of a wireless LAN burst rate of at least 5 Mbps and full-duplex operation of 2 Mbps.

Voice applications are more tolerant of errors but require full-duplex operation. In voice applications, the acquisition time is not as critical, but unlike applications with packetized data, strong bursts of errors are more bothersome.

In addition, owing to lower data rates (typically 32 kbps or less) for voice than for most data applications, each direct-sequence radio channel requires less bandwidth. For cordless telephones, e.g., each voice channel typically requires 2 MHz of bandwidth. For the 902–928 MHz ISM band, this means that 13 non-overlapping direct-sequence voice channels are available, with cordless telephones "smart enough" to select the clearest channel among them. This somewhat resembles "intelligent" frequency hopping in that the radio selects the clearest channel, hops to it, and stays there. With frequency hopping, which indiscriminately hops over the total band, the voice channel may be hit with occasional high bursts of errors owing to multipath and interference in different hop bands.

Digital video conferencing has the most demanding requirements in both types of radio, requiring higher data rates and full-duplex operation.

Probably the most important functionality to be compared between direct-sequence and frequency-hopping spread-spectrum radios is the potential overall capacity achievable in areas with many such radios. In Section 6.5, we address this question for a high-density network of many synchronized cells.

6.2.4 Multipath and Diversity

For most mobile applications, multipath often constitutes the most serious limitation on performance. Many studies have been conducted which clearly prove that diversity techniques can dramatically improve performance against multipath, with antenna diversity the most common method. For multipath delays longer than a chip-time interval, direct-sequence spread-spectrum radios can use RAKE processing to take advantage of multipath (see Part 2, Chapter 1, Section 1.7). Coding with interleavers, which has been discussed extensively as a means of combatting jamming, is also ideal for multipath if the interleaver time span covers independent fades.

Antenna diversity is effective against multipath for both direct-sequence and frequency-hopping spread-spectrum radios. Coding and interleaving techniques are effective for frequency hopping if coded bits are taken from different hop bands. With commercial slow frequency-hopping radios, this is generally impractical because the interleaving span (memory) is too large. For direct-sequence radios, the interleaver span must cover a time interval that includes independent fades, which in most practical applications occur only in rapidly moving mobile radios.

For direct-sequence radios using a RAKE processor in the receiver, diversity works on multipath signals that have differential delays greater than the chip-time interval. For indoor environments with lower-data-rate radios, such multipath delays are too small. For such radios, Qualcomm invented a delay-line antenna system which artificially creates multipath of sufficient delays for the RAKE processor to work effectively [16].

Appendix 6A discusses Rayleigh and log normal statistical models for multipath fading, presents some indoor dynamic measurements of fading time variation, and analyzes statistical characteristics of fades with various degrees of diversity.

6.2.5 Results of the Part 15 Rule

In response to the FCC Part 15 ruling allowing unlicensed operation in selected radio bands, many new wireless applications have emerged for spread-spectrum radio. Without licensing, however, there is no protection against interference from other unlicensed users. Nevertheless, spread-spectrum radios inherently possess a certain degree of protection against interference (10 dB is the minimum processing gain). As Dr. Marcus predicted, the FCC Part 15 rule has been a catalyst for innovative wireless applications and has stimulated the development of many new forms of low-cost spread-spectrum radios. Companies can offer wireless products that can be used by purchasers immediately, without their having to wait for a license.

Perhaps the best protection for spread-spectrum radios is their inherent robustness against interference and large multipath delays. Figure 6.1 illustrates this by showing a transmitter and an interfering (jamming) radio in the same band transmitting with the same power. The bit error rate at a receiver depends on the signal-to-jammer ratio S/J, which depends on the location of the receiver relative to the transmitter and the interfering signal. Typically, for a good narrowband radio, acceptable bit error rates can be achieved with a signal-to-jammer ratio, S/J, between 10 and 20 dB, depending on whether voice or data is being transmitted. For a good narrowband radio operating with a minimum S/J of 10 dB, the receiver can operate at the region shown in the shaded area of Figure 6.1.

The FCC requires that direct-sequence spread-spectrum radios have a minimum processing gain of 10 dB. With a 10-dB processing gain, the required $S/J = 10$ dB of a narrowband radio becomes the required $S/J = 0$ for the spread-spectrum radio. Such a spread-spectrum radio can receive signals as shown in the left halfplane of Figure 6.1. With more processing gain, this area of reception can be increased with additional bandwidth.

This figure assumes omnidirectional antennas in free space. Using an antenna with additional gain, the intended receiver will dramatically in-

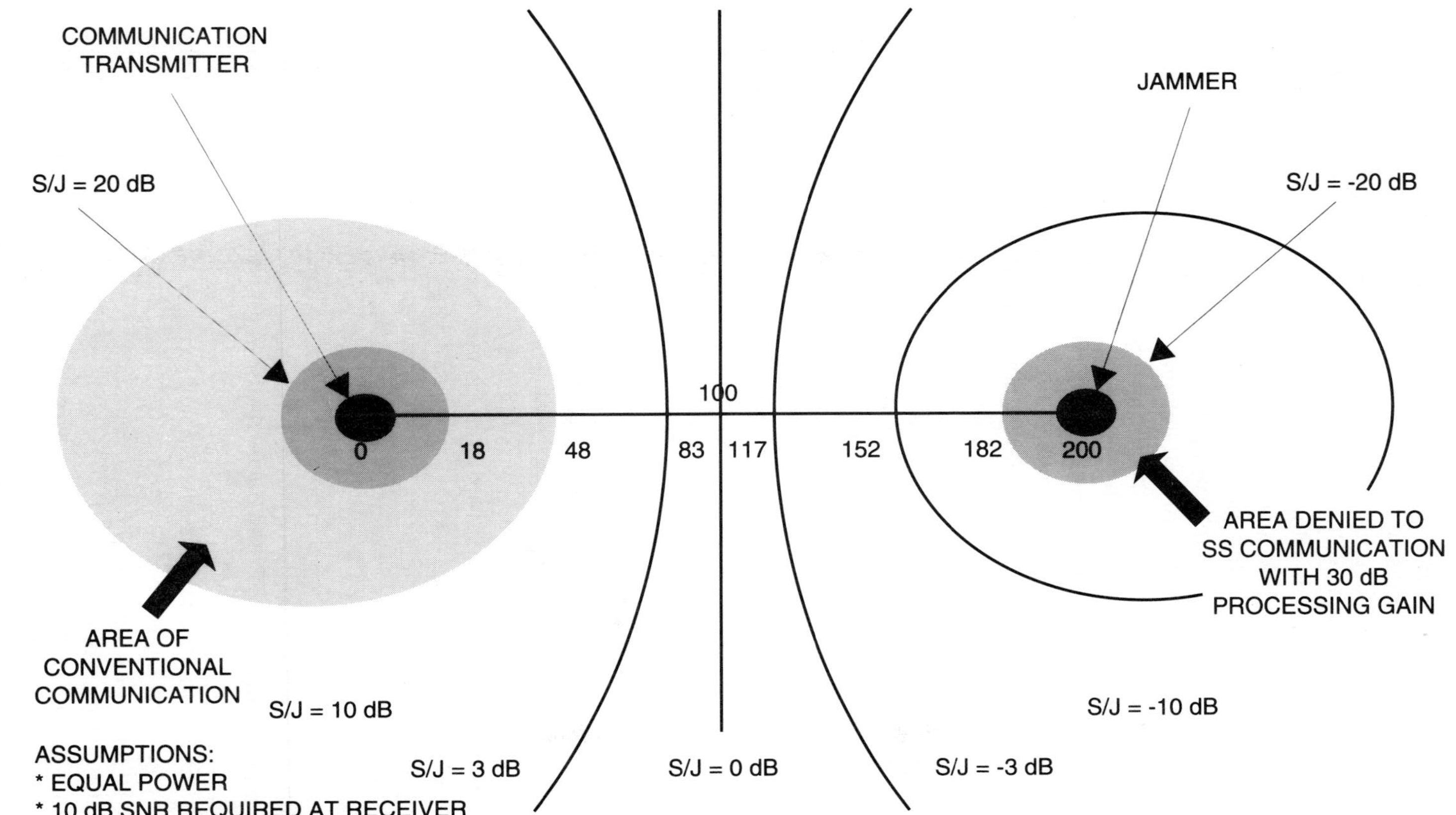

Figure 6.1. Jamming power versus processing gain.

crease the region of operation in this interference environment. The operation region is defined by the S/J measured at the antenna output of the receiver. This S/J depends on the antenna gain in the direction of the transmitter (determines S) and the antenna side lobe attenuation of the receiver antenna in the direction of the jammer (determines J). Here, the region of operation will be a complex region determined by the antenna pattern of the receiver. If the transmitter and jammer also have directional antennas, then this region will be complicated by all three antenna patterns.

For fixed locations for the radios, antenna polarization can be used to separate signals. Normally, for narrowband signals, antenna polarization may not provide adequate isolation when radios are located in the same area. Since spread-spectrum signals have additional protection against interference when different codewords are used, antenna polarization can be used very effectively to increase capacity. Spread-spectrum radios allow for a much more flexible application of antenna techniques for increasing capacity.

It is clear that the determination of the number of radios that can work effectively in a given area is a very complex matter. Spread-spectrum radios are less sensitive to interference and can operate with smaller S/J than conventional narrowband signals. These signals, however, require more bandwidth. Narrowband radios may be able to use this same band by creating many non-interfering frequency channels. Typically, up to 20 percent of this frequency band may be wasted in using guard bands between these narrowband radio channels to ensure non-interference.

In comparisons of the capacity of narrowband radios versus spread-spectrum radios, the same bandwidth must be used. It seems obvious that narrowband radios would provide more overall capacity. Such a judgment, however, considers capacity only as measured by number of users per bandwidth. In fact, in most *practical* applications, the real criterion is the number of users in a given area. We see from our discussion of Figure 6.1 that, with interference, spread-spectrum radios can operate over a wider area than a corresponding narrowband radio. Using the same bandwidth as a spread-spectrum radio, several narrowband radios can operate in different frequency bands. These radios, of course, will have some out-of-band emissions, and their band separation will depend on how effectively this is minimized. In practical applications with complex propagation conditions, it is not clear whether narrowband radios or spread-spectrum radios with a fixed total bandwidth will give the overall highest number of users in a given area.

The FCC Part 15 rule has been adopted in part or completely by many other countries. Generally, North, Central, and South American countries have adopted this same rule. Other countries in which European cellular systems occupy parts of the 902–928 MHz band have adopted modified versions of this rule. Most countries worldwide allow some form of unlicensed spread-spectrum radios for the commercial applications mentioned in this chapter.

6.3 THE DIGITAL CELLULAR CDMA STANDARD

Based partly on its two-way satellite messaging and position reporting system OmniTRACS [16], Qualcomm developed a spread-spectrum radio system for digital cellular phone applications [15, 16, 18]. Unlike traditional multiple-access techniques used with conventional narrowband radio signals, Qualcomm's CDMA system employs spread-spectrum signals. Its development help account for the considerable interest today in spread-spectrum radios for wireless applications.

That spread spectrum and CDMA are the same is a frequent but incorrect assumption. Multiple-access techniques are typically applied in a star network with a hub base station communicating with many remote radio units, as shown in Figure 6.2. FDMA and TDMA techniques can be used with

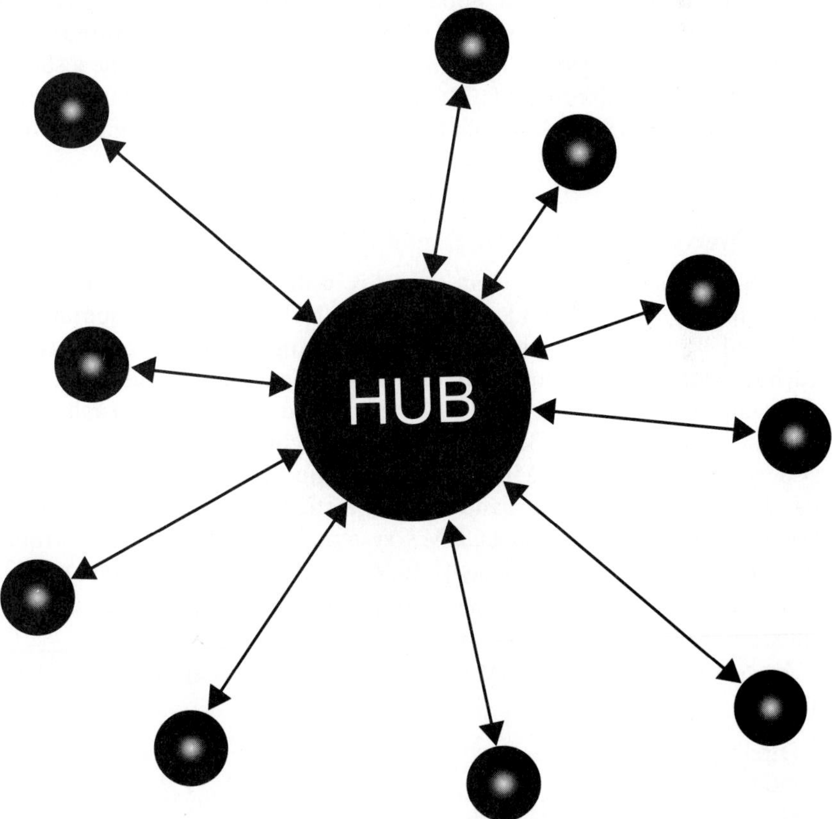

Figure 6.2. Single cell.

any type of modulation, including spread-spectrum signals. However, code division multiple access, as its name implies, applies only to modulation techniques associated with a code, specifically spread-spectrum modulation techniques. Since CDMA is used only with spread-spectrum signals, it is often assumed that spread spectrum, a modulation technique, and CDMA, a multiple-access technique, are the same. However, in general, while spread-spectrum signals can be used with or without CDMA, the employment of CDMA requires spread-spectrum signals. Part 5, Chapter 5, discusses the topic of multiple access in greater detail. (See [19] for further discussion of multiple-access communications.)

Qualcomm's spread-spectrum CDMA system was optimized under existing U.S. mobile cellular system constraints. Its analysis shows that the CDMA system can achieve about 10 to 20 times the capacity of the existing analog FDMA system and about 3 to 7 times that of the new digital TDMA standard system. The key to this increase in capacity is the ability of the CDMA system to reuse the same frequency in all cells, with capacity defined as the total number of active mobile users in a large area with many cells.

Several cellular operators in the United States have committed to installing this CDMA system, beginning in 1993, the year it became a second digital cellular standard, IS-95. The previous U.S. digital cellular standard, IS-45, is based on TDMA, which is similar to the European digital cellular standard referred to as GSM.

6.3.1 Overview of the CDMA Digital Cellular System (IS-95)

The IS-95 digital cellular system operates in the same band as the current U.S. analog cellular band (AMPS) in which full-duplex operation is achieved by using frequency division duplexing (FDD) with 25 MHz in each direction, with an uplink of 869–894 MHz mobile-to-cell band and a downlink of 824–849 MHz cell-to-mobile band. For AMPS, each analog cellular signal occupies 30 kHz in each direction in a standard FDMA system. In IS-95, the 25 MHz in each direction is divided into 20 FDMA bands. In each 1.25-MHz band (each direction), direct-sequence spread-spectrum signals are used in a CDMA system. The implementation strategy is to introduce this higher-capacity IS-95 system one CDMA system (1.25-MHz band) at a time, using the dual-mode (AMPS and CDMA) mobile units.

Among the modulation and coding features of this system are the following:

- Direct-sequence spreading with quadrature phase-shift-keying (QPSK) modulation
- Nominal data rate of 9600 bps
- Chip rate of 1.25 MHz
- Filtered bandwidth of 1.25 MHz

- Convolutional coding with Viterbi decoding
- Interleaving with 20-msec span

Details for the modulation and coding differ for the uplink and downlink channels. Pilot signals transmitted by each cell site aid the mobile radios in acquiring and tracking the cell site downlink signals. The strong coding enables these radios to operate effectively at E_b/N_0 in the 5-dB to 7-dB range.

To minimize mutual interference, this CDMA system uses power control and voice activation circuits. Voice activation occurs in the form of a variable-rate vocoder that operates from a high of 8 kbps down to 4 kbps, 2 kbps, and a minimum of 1 kbps, depending on the level of voice activation. With the decreased data rate, the power control circuits can reduce the transmitter power for the lower data rates to achieve the same bit error rate performance. Tight power control, along with voice activation circuits, is critical for avoiding excessive transmitter signal power, which contributes to the overall interference level in this interference-limited CDMA system. It is estimated that in a typical two-way conversation, the average data rate is 3 kbps, which, with power control, increases the battery life of mobile radios.

To overcome rapid multipath fading and shadowing, a time interleaver with a 20-msec span is used with the error-control coding. The time span used is the same as that in the time frame of the voice compression algorithm. Also a RAKE processor is used in these radios to take advantage of multipath delays greater than 1 μsec, which are common in large cellular networks. (See Part 1, Chapter 2, Section 2.2.8 for historical origins of RAKE and Part 2, Chapter 1, Section 1.7 for technical details of this unique diversity technique.)

Key IS-95 system features for each 1.25-MHz band CDMA system are as follows:

- All signals use an unmodulated "carrier," a direct-sequence binary phase-shift-keying (BPSK) signal using a 15-state pseudorandom (PN) sequence with a 32,768-chip period, with each cell using a different phase (time shift) of this PN sequence. Thus, each cell has its own unique PN carrier, which is used as a common carrier by all radios active in the cell.
- A downlink pilot channel consists of the cell's unique PN carrier, which helps mobile units acquire and track cell-site signals. The mobile unit essentially acquires the strongest unmodulated direct-sequence BPSK signal it finds by ranging over the time shifts of the PN code.
- Each cell also transmits a low-bit-rate, low-power synchronization channel, which allows mobile radios to time-synchronize to the network.
- Each CDMA downlink supports up to 62 paging and traffic channels.

- The downlink channels use orthogonal Walsh codewords assigned uniquely to each mobile unit active in the cell. These codewords, further modulated by coded data bits, are superimposed on the PN carrier for the cell.
- Each active uplink mobile radio signal uses a unique non-orthogonal PN code of 2^{42} chips on top of the PN carrier.
- Taking advantage of the RAKE processor, fake multipath signals transmitted from two cell sites allow mobile radios to conduct "soft handoffs" from one cell site to another.

Although much more complex, this system is inherently more robust than conventional narrowband radios using traditional FDMA and TDMA approaches. Perhaps most important is its robustness against multipath fading. It also allows more flexibility in the application of antennas for sectorization, being able to use fixed and adaptive multibeam antennas to increase capacity dramatically and further reduce radio power requirements.

6.3.2 Comparison of IS-95, IS-54, and GSM

The first U.S. digital cellular standard, IS-54, and the European digital cellular standard, GSM, are both based on narrowband modulations, with TDMA as the basic multiple-accessing technique. The second U.S. digital cellular standard, IS-95, differs fundamentally in its use of direct-sequence spread-spectrum modulation, using CDMA for multiple access. All three systems overlay these basic access systems with further channelization using FDMA. Table 6.2 summarizes the key features of these three digital cellular standards [20].

Like existing analog cellular systems, these digital cellular systems use separate uplink and downlink frequency bands, with frequency division duplexing (FDD) to achieve full-duplex operation. Some level of power

Table 6.2.
Comparison of digital cellular systems

Feature	IS-54	GSM	IS-95
Multiple access	TDMA	TDMA	CDMA
Frequency band	United States	Europe	United States
Uplink (MHz)	869–894	935–960	869–894
Downlink (MHz)	824–849	890–915	824–849
Channel spacing	30 kHz	200 kHz	1.25 MHz
Modulation	DQPSK	GMSK	BPSK/QPSK
Maximum Tx power (mobile handset)	600 mW	1 W	600 mW
Average Tx power	200 mW	125 mW	Variable
Speech rate	8 kbps	13 kbps	1–8 kbps
Number of channels	3	8	Variable
Channel bit rate	48.6 kbps	270.3 kbps	1.25 Mcps

control is used by all three systems, but the IS-95 system uses the tightest dynamic power control since power control plays a more critical role in CDMA systems. Dynamic power control means that the average transmit power of the IS-95 handsets can be less than that in IS-54 and GSM handsets. All three systems also employ convolutional coding with Viterbi decoding. The IS-95 system, however, uses stronger constraint length $K = 9$ convolutional codes, with rate $\frac{1}{2}$ in the cell-to-mobile channel and rate $\frac{1}{3}$ in the mobile-to-cell channel.

All three digital cellular systems require some level of synchronization among all adjacent cells in a given area. The IS-95 system uses GPS receivers to provide master clocks for each cell. GPS is another widely used commercial application of spread-spectrum radios.

Overall capacity is the most important feature of the three digital cellular systems. Owing to so many parameters and other performance issues, it is very difficult to show clearly which system offers the greatest overall capacity. For example, the soft handoff feature of the IS-95 system enhances performance but sacrifices some capacity on the less critical downlink. It is clear, however, that the spread-spectrum CDMA system differs fundamentally from the TDMA systems and possesses three key properties that can greatly increase overall system capacity: 100 percent frequency of reuse, flexible antenna applications, and voice activation. The issue of capacity will be discussed further in the next sections.

6.4 A NEW PARADIGM FOR DESIGNING RADIO NETWORKS

In the military, spread-spectrum radios are primarily used to combat enemy jamming since they tolerate much more interference than conventional radios. Their processing gain, typically defined as the radio of the spread-spectrum signal bandwidth to the conventional signal bandwidth for the same data rate, is a direct measure of how much interference such spread-spectrum radios can tolerate. Since spread-spectrum signals take up a larger bandwidth, they are generally bandwidth-inefficient. That is, if we use the conventional measure of bandwidth efficiency—the number of data bits per signal bandwidth—spread-spectrum radio signals are not very efficient. It came as a surprise, therefore, when Qualcomm first made the claim that its spread-spectrum digital cellular phone system resulted in *higher* overall capacity than any other system.

Yet its claim was true. This spread-spectrum introduced a new paradigm for designing multicell voice networks using CDMA [15, 16]. It is based on the fact that the main criterion for efficiency, or capacity, *should* be this:

FOR A GIVEN TOTAL BANDWIDTH, CAPACITY IS THE MAXIMUM NUMBER OF ACTIVE USERS IN A HIGH-DENSITY NETWORK OF CELLS.

Most earlier works focused on the capacity of a multiple-access system in terms of the number of users per bandwidth or the number of users per isolated cell in a star network. The key point is that in a multicellular system illustrated in Figure 6.3, spatial isolation and voice activation are critical for achieving a high overall capacity as defined above. Spatial isolation owing to the typical terrestrial ultra-high-frequency (UHF) propagation attenuation with the distance to the fourth power, together with the added protection of spread-spectrum techniques, allows for 100 percent frequency of reuse among all cells in a network [15]. This 100 percent reuse is the reason that, in a well-designed spread-spectrum radio network, the overall capacity can be much greater than that with conventional narrowband radio multiple-access techniques.

Note that this is a more global capacity criterion. Capacity does not consider the maximum number of users per bandwidth or the maximum number of users per cell, but is more practically based on the total number of users in the total area covered by multiple cells. Normally, evaluating systems on the basis of users per bandwidth, users per cell, and users per

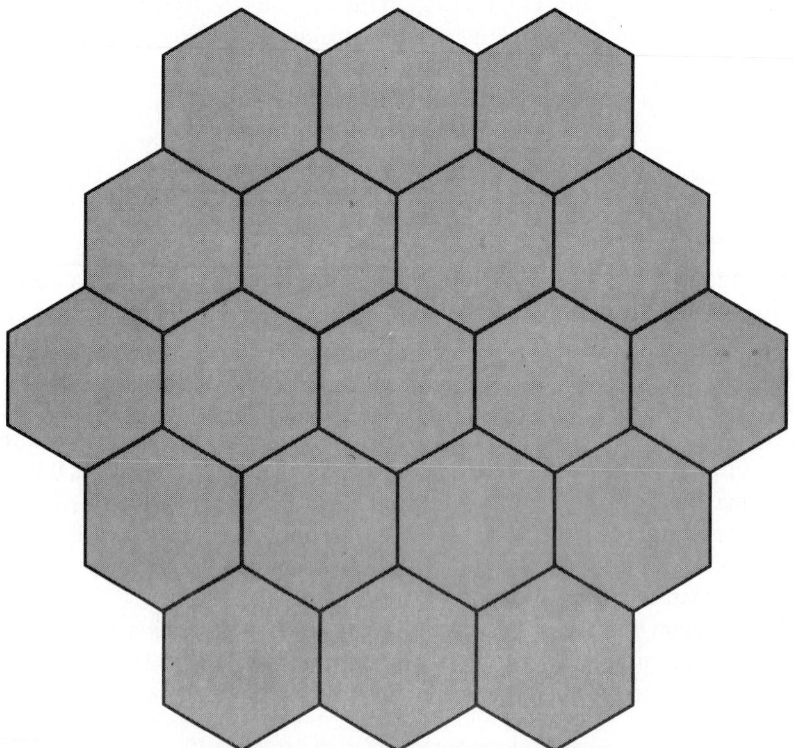

Figure 6.3. High-density network of microcells. For a given bandwidth and size of each microcell, what is the total number of active channels?

area would give the same result. With spread-spectrum radios, however, these are not the same. The key difference lies in the frequency of reuse among cells in the network, which differs for spread-spectrum radios.

The design of networks using spread-spectrum radios can aim to limit mutual interference but cannot necessarily eliminate it completely, as with conventional radio systems. Spread-spectrum radios are designed to tolerate some level of interference, with their overall capacity limited by how well this mutual interference can be controlled. Conventional radios are limited by the number of non-interfering signals achieved by using complete separation with FDMA or TDMA techniques. Thus, the capacity of spread-spectrum radio systems is interference-limited, while the capacity of conventional radio systems is limited by the number of non-interfering coordinates. We restate this important difference as follows:

THE CAPACITY OF SPREAD SPECTRUM RADIOS IS INTERFERENCE-LIMITED, WHILE THE CAPACITY OF NARROWBAND RADIOS IS DIMENSION-LIMITED.

The paradigm for the design of a radio system consisting of a large network of cells changes with the use of spread-spectrum radios. When overall capacity is considered, as measured in the total number of active users in an area of many cells (capacity per square kilometer, e.g.), a well-designed spread-spectrum system can achieve a higher overall capacity than one using conventional narrowband radios. In such interference-limited radio networks, power control is critical to overall capacity. For digital voice networks, the advantage is greater with spread spectrum, because mutual interference can be further reduced (thus increasing capacity) with the use of voice activation. Finally, this type of design puts more pressure on good radio design, in which better performance against interference—which translates to less transmitted power—is critical. Thus, the use of forward error-correction coding can play an important role.

Narrowband signals using FDMA need a frequency guard band to separate the FDMA channels to maintain a low co-channel interference level. Similar guard times are needed for narrowband signals to separate assigned time slots in TDMA systems. Up to 20 percent of the total capacity needed for guard bands (FDMA) or guard times (TDMA) is eliminated in the spread-spectrum CDMA systems, which are designed to perform with some level of interference.

In Part 5, Chapter 5, we make a distinction between SSMA and CDMA. With SSMA, we assume that transmitters are not synchronized in time and that interference from other users is modeled as Gaussian noise. Massey and Mittelholzer [21] have characterized the case in which users are not time-synchronized as "asynchronous code division multiple access" (A-CDMA). Here, one can use the SSMA assumption of Gaussian noise interference or take into account all the random time shifts of the interference signals. Massey and Mittelholzer characterize the case when transmitters are all time-synchronized as "synchronous code division multiple access" (S-CDMA). For S-CDMA systems, specific spread-spectrum spreading codes can enhance performance to a greater degree than in A-CDMA systems.

Although the IS-95 system uses an overall network time reference, the inbound signal (from mobile units to cell site) is treated as an A-CDMA system, and interference can be modeled as Gaussian noise. For large cell sizes with some multipath delays larger than a chip-time interval, mobile unit signals cannot be easily synchronized. In this direction, signals in a cell are not orthogonal. The outbound signal (from cell site to mobile units) is S-CDMA, since all signals originate from one location and can be time-synchronized.

In military spread-spectrum radio applications, interference derives from enemy jammers not under any control by the communication system. For a large network of cells in a commercial application, on the other hand, interference *can* be tightly controlled among all radios, since all are part of the same system. This tight control of mutual interference among spread-spectrum radios within a network of cells is the key to achieving high overall capacity for that network.

6.5 THE POTENTIAL CAPACITY OF DIRECT-SEQUENCE SPREAD-SPECTRUM CDMA IN HIGH-DENSITY NETWORKS

For practical commercial spread-spectrum radios, the potential capacity discussed in the previous section is that achievable with direct-sequence spreading. In principle, frequency-hopping spreading can achieve similar results but requires fast hopping implementation, which is less practical in low-cost commercial applications. Thus, this discussion is limited to direct-sequence spread-spectrum radio systems.

To understand the apparent paradox of achieving higher overall capacity with spread-spectrum radios than with conventional radios, consider a comparison of TDMA versus CDMA for a single-star network as shown in Figure 6.4. Assuming the same fixed total bandwidth available for both TDMA and CDMA, Figure 6.4 shows the number of channels on the horizontal axis and the tolerable level of interference on the vertical axis. Initially, consider the performance of a single radio or multiple radios located at the cell site that receive TDMA or CDMA signals from mobile units surrounding the cell.

TDMA is a time-dimension-limited system in which there can be no additional users when all slots have been assigned. As time slots are filled by increasing numbers of TDMA users, there is no interference caused by one mobile radio to the reception of another mobile radio at the cell site. The number of TDMA users can increase until the number of dimensions (in this case, time slots) is exhausted. It is not possible to increase the

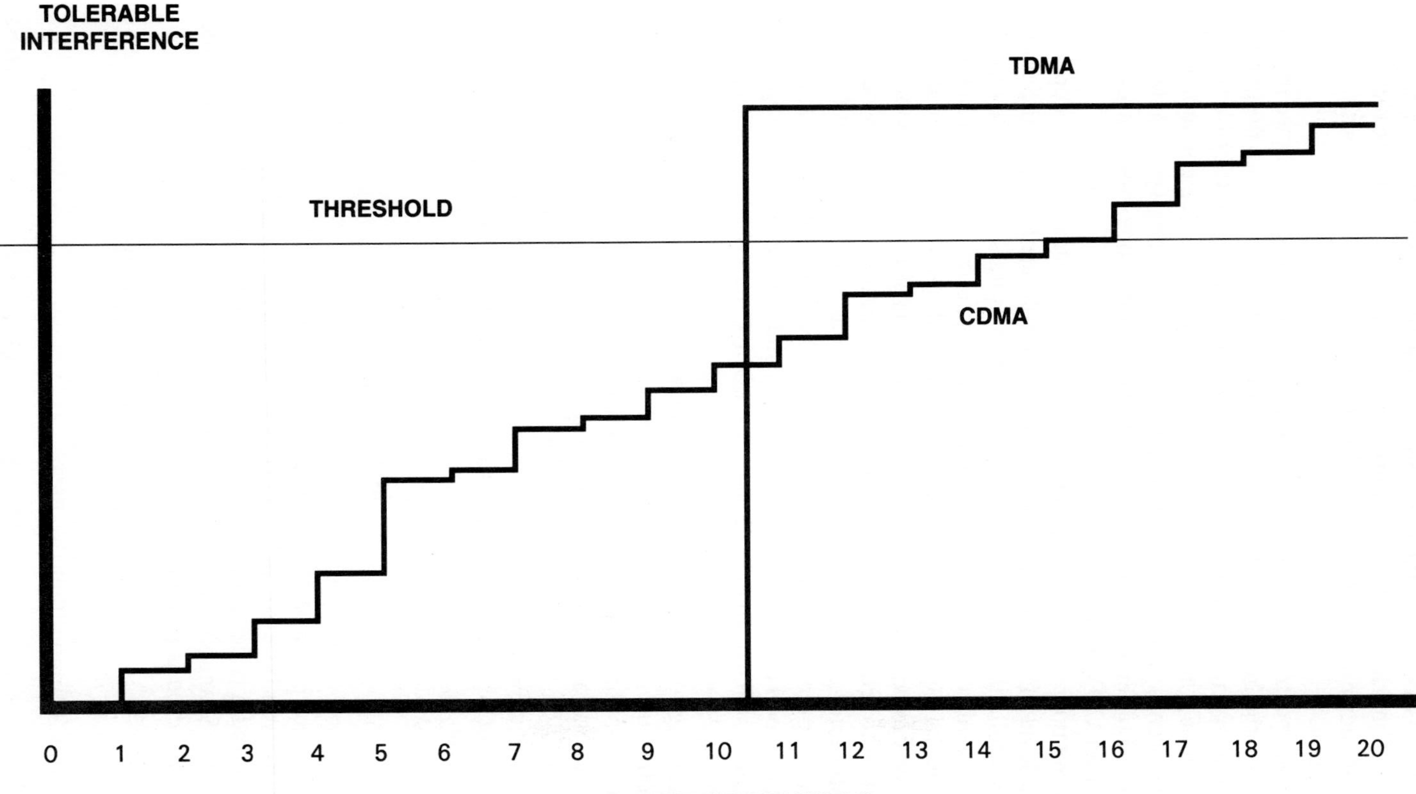

Figure 6.4. TDMA versus CDMA.

number of users beyond the dimension limit without causing an intolerable amount of interference to reception of a mobile unit at the cell-site receiver. Thus, as shown in Figure 6.4, the TDMA system has a "brick wall" limit on capacity.

Spread-spectrum radios can tolerate some interference, as shown in Figure 6.4, so the introduction of each additional active radio raises the overall level of interference to the base station receivers receiving CDMA signals from mobile transmitters. Each mobile radio can introduce a unique level of interference, reflecting its cell-site power level, timing synchronization relative to other signals at the cell site, and specific code cross-correlation with other CDMA signals.

The number of CDMA channels allowed in the star network depends on the level of total interference that can be tolerated. Unlike the time-dimension-limited TDMA system, the CDMA system is limited by interference, and consequently the quality of the radio design plays a key role in its overall capacity. Certainly, a well-designed radio will have a required bit error probability with a higher level of interference than a poorly designed radio. Forward error-correction coding techniques can also increase the threshold of tolerable interference and, thus, increase overall CDMA capacity. Spread-spectrum CDMA systems, therefore, place a greater premium on good overall mobile radio design and overall system design than conventional narrowband FDMA and TDMA multiple-access radio systems.

Returning to Figure 6.4, suppose that at the cell site the signal level of all mobile users is the same and interference between radios is modeled as Gaussian noise. This is the case with A-CDMA, in which we assume that each radio has a required bit error probability that defines a required energy-per-bit-to-noise ratio given by E_b/N_0. This E_b/N_0 defines the threshold shown in Figure 6.4. Given these assumptions, the relationship between the number of users M, the processing gain PG, and the required E_b/N_0 is given by

$$M = \frac{\text{PG}}{E_b/N_0} \tag{6.1}$$

which is a special case of (5.2) in Part 5, Chapter 5.

For a given bit error probability, the required E_b/N_0 depends on how well the radio is designed and how much error-correction coding is used. The ideal Shannon limit in white Gaussian noise shows that error-free communication is possible [22] for

$$E_b/N_0 = \ln 2 = 0.69 = -1.59 \text{ dB}. \tag{6.2}$$

For this Shannon limit, we have

$$M = 1.44 \times \text{PG}. \tag{6.3}$$

This theoretical Shannon limit shows that spread-spectrum A-CDMA systems can have more users per cell than traditional systems, which are limited by the number of dimensions, such as non-overlapping frequency bands (FDMA) or time slots (TDMA). Of course, with practical coded A-CDMA radios in a cell, it may be difficult to accommodate this many users in a single cell. FDMA and TDMA systems, however, use up to 20 percent of this theoretical capacity to ensure the practical isolation between non-interfering channels.

6.5.1 Data versus Voice Applications

For data applications, the bit error probabilities are typically less than 10^{-5}, and consequently the threshold of tolerable interference shown in Figure 6.4 may be lower than that in digital voice applications, resulting in fewer CDMA channels. Another way to increase CDMA capacity for voice applications is to use voice activation circuits that cut off radio transmit power when there is no voice activity. Since the average voice activity factor is 35 percent, using such circuits in a CDMA system dramatically lowers the noise floor or allows proportionally more active voice channels.

Owing to the higher tolerance to error and the option of voice activation, the spread-spectrum CDMA's capacity advantage is greater with digital voice systems than with data networks.

6.5.2 Power Control

For an interference-limited CDMA system, each active mobile transmitter produces some level of interference in receivers of other mobile radio signals at the cell site. Therefore, mobile radios should not transmit any more power than is necessary for satisfactory performance. Power control of mobile radios would ensure that for a fixed number of active radios, the interference caused by each radio is minimal and approximately equal. Another benefit of power control is that the life of usable battery time is extended for mobile spread-spectrum radios.

Generally, for spread-spectrum CDMA systems, cell-site radios provide "master" control of "slave" mobile radios. Although power control and voice activation circuits may be complex, they are typically implemented in digital processing chips for which the cost keeps dropping as technology advances.

6.5.3 Time Synchronization and Orthogonal Codes

Another factor affecting the level of interference experienced by base station receivers is the time synchronization of all mobile radios. If all mobile radio signals arriving at the cell site are synchronized to within a fraction of a chip-time interval, then it is possible to reduce the level of mutual interference dramatically. For such synchronized CDMA

(S-CDMA) star networks, the use of orthogonal codewords effectively reduces interference to zero, given sufficient orthogonal codes for distribution among mobile radios. Even with some timing errors, interference can be significantly reduced with a careful selection of codewords and time synchronization of all radios in a cell.

Codes (collection of codewords) used for such S-CDMA applications have been studied extensively and are discussed in Part 1, Chapter 5, Section 5.7. With S-CDMA, the number of non-interfering spread-spectrum mobile radios can be roughly the same as with TDMA. This is so because for the same time and bandwidth, the number of orthogonal dimensions is also the same, regardless of whether the dimensions use orthogonal frequencies (FDMA), time slots (TDMA), or spreading codes (S-CDMA). In practice, differences reflect implementation. (As we shall see in Section 6.7, S-CDMA systems can exceed the dimension limit by using more complex optimal multiple-access receivers.) With S-CDMA, it is theoretically possible to have as many non-interfering mobile users as with FDMA or TDMA. If this is truly the case, why does spread-spectrum CDMA offer more capacity? As illustrated by Qualcomm, the answer is that the 100 percent frequency of reuse allowed with spread-spectrum systems can be applied to a network of many cells in a high-density area.

6.5.4 The Outbound Channel

Up to now, the discussion of spread-spectrum CDMA focused on the reception of mobile radio transmitters at the cell site. Normally, for large cells with large multipath delays, it may be difficult to time-synchronize mobile transmitters so that their signals arrive at the cell site within a fraction of a chip time. Such synchronization in the inbound direction becomes even more difficult as the data rate increases, and, in data networks, the data rate is usually very high. Thus, the inbound channel may be characterized as asynchronous CDMA (A-CDMA), with mutual interference characterized by random delays and larger delay multipath components relative to the chip-time interval. Such A-CDMA channels are usually analyzed by making an equivalent noise model of the mutual interference. With S-CDMA channels with small, random time offsets, performance analysis is usually performed for specific codes.

The outbound channel (cell site to mobile radios) performs very differently from the inbound channel. Since transmitters for the outbound channel are all located at the cell site, all radio signals to mobile radios can be easily synchronized. Each mobile radio then receives from the cell site the radio signals synchronized in time, or S-CDMA. Since the outbound channel can be synchronized, orthogonal codewords are typically used for transmissions from the cell site to mobile radios. Of course, multipath can result in interference in the mobile receivers.

For large cells such as in the digital cellular IS-95 standard radios, the inbound channel is A-CDMA and the outbound channel is S-CDMA.

Consider the S-CDMA outbound channel in wireless LAN applications in which a wired LAN can be accessed by wireless laptop computers. On average, the amount of data outbound (LAN server to mobile laptop) is about 10 times as much as the data inbound. Hence, for inbound channels, typically only one mobile laptop can transmit at any given time, using carrier-sensed multiple access (CSMA) protocols. With S-CDMA on the more critical outbound channel, a much higher overall capacity can be achieved. The S-CDMA channel is limited by the multipath conditions in the propagation paths from the cell site on the wired LAN to the mobile laptop units.

6.5.5 Frequency of Reuse and Antenna Sectorization

The primary advantage of direct-sequence spread-spectrum radios is that they allow reuse of the same frequency in adjacent cells in a multicellular network. Because narrowband radios are not designed to withstand much interference, narrowband radios in adjacent cells cannot share the same frequency band. If, as discussed above, the number of mobile users per cell is roughly the same for the same bandwidth per cell, a direct-sequence spread-spectrum radio system can employ frequency of reuse to attain a higher overall network capacity.

Figure 6.3 illustrates an idealized array of cells in a high-density network of many cells. In this configuration, each cell has six neighboring cells. For narrowband radios, each cell would have available only one-seventh of the total available bandwidth, while the direct-sequence spread-spectrum radios with 100 percent frequency of reuse would have available the entire bandwidth available in each cell. If a spread-spectrum system has as many mobile radios per bandwidth in each cell as a narrowband radio system, its overall capacity would be 7 times greater than that of the narrowband system.

The actual achievable capacity depends on the tradeoff between many parameters in a network of direct-sequence radios. These parameters include the type of direct-sequence spread-spectrum modulation, processing gain, coding gain, level of network synchronization, data rates, use of power control, specific code selection, and voice activation. Environmental issues include cell size and multipath/propagation conditions. In Section 6.6, we present an example of a radio system for an idealized microcellular network for voice personal communication service applications in which S-CDMA is used in both inbound and outbound directions.

6.5.6 Narrowbeam and Delay-Line Antennas

For a large network of microcells, one of the key advantages of having complete frequency of reuse is the elimination of the complicated frequency-management planning required when conventional narrowband radios are used. Also, spread-spectrum radios afford far greater flexibility with antennas. Because these radios are less sensitive to interference, sectorized antennas, which can increase a cell's capacity, can be used at a cell site with fewer constraints on overlap in sector antenna beams. Fixed and adaptive multibeam antennas can also be more easily employed with spread-spectrum radios. Moreover, owing to their inherent ability to overcome multipath delays greater than a chip-time interval, distributed antennas on a long cable facilitate covering all areas inside a building [16]. Again, these advantages are *inherent* in direct-sequence spread-spectrum radios.

Since slow frequency-hopping spread-spectrum radios are merely narrowband radios with time-varying center frequencies, they do not have the same frequency of reuse capability of direct-sequence spread-spectrum radios. Therefore, the higher overall capacity possible with direct-sequence radios in a multicellular network is not achievable with slow frequency-hopping radios. Fast frequency-hopping spread-spectrum radios with coding and interleaving can attain the same kind of capacity advantage as direct-sequence radios. However, the low cost requirements of commercial radios make such fast frequency-hopping systems less practical.

6.6 SPREAD-SPECTRUM CDMA FOR PCS AND PCN

Personal communication networks (PCNs) and personal communication services (PCSs) refer to a broad range of wireless communication applications and services. Initially, PCNs and PCSs were generally perceived as low-cost pocket telephone handsets that could, in a single unit, replace a home cordless telephone, wireless office telephone, wireless pay phone, cellular phone, and the planned worldwide Low Earth Orbiting (LEO) satellite mobile phones. With the rapidly growing use of paging and messaging devices, laptop computers, and personal digital assistants (PDAs), there is an increasing need for personal wireless data communication as well. PCSs, which now include all wireless personal communication devices, are distinguished by their personal nature, which allows universal personal communications services anywhere, anytime, to anyone, in any form.

For some PCS applications that require a very high density of mobile voice handsets in an area covered by many cells, the spread-spectrum CDMA type of design is ideal. Here, we examine in some detail a Cylink system design similar to that of the IS-95 digital cellular spread-spectrum CDMA standard but optimized for microcells with roaming mobile users [23]. It serves as another illustration of a high-capacity direct-sequence spread-spectrum CDMA system design with computer simulations of the overall system performance.

In many high-density PCS applications, the cells in a multicell network are expected to be less than 200 m in diameter. In such microcells, multipath delay differences are quite small, and mobile radio transmissions can be tightly controlled by the base stations. Multipath delays, especially for indoor applications, are typically less than 0.2 μsec [24, 25] for such microcells. Qualcomm designed its spread-spectrum CDMA system (IS-95) under the restrictions of existing mobile cellular applications in which cell areas and multipath delays are large, and mobile users can move rapidly in automobiles.

This spread-spectrum radio system designed for PCS assumes no restrictions on channelization. It illustrates the key advantages of using spread-spectrum CDMA to achieve higher capacity for digital voice applications in a high density of microcells. Although this design follows the paradigm introduced by Qualcomm, this design is simpler. We compare it with the digital European cordless telephone (DECT) standard for PCS in Europe. DECT is the European standard for PCS analogous to GSM, the European digital cellular standard.

In this PCS application, spread-spectrum radios can be used to achieve synchronous code division multiple access (S-CDMA) in both directions within each microcell. Synchronization is not necessarily maintainable between radios from different microcells, so the spread-spectrum processing gain and error-control coding are used primarily for overcoming interference between radios from different microcells. By carefully selecting the amount of processing gain for these spread-spectrum radios, we can practically achieve a high-capacity system in which each microcell uses S-CDMA and achieves 100 percent frequency of reuse. Since orthogonal codewords are used in this system, it is less sensitive to power control.

Consider a star network in which all remote radios are time-synchronized to within a fraction of a chip-time arrival at the base station. In these illustrations, M remote radios each transmit a spread-spectrum radio signal with a binary spreading code of L chips per data bit.

6.6.1 Binary Orthogonal Codes

From Welch's bound (see Part 1, Chapter 5, Section 5.7.2), we know that the number of binary orthogonal codewords of length L is less than or equal to L. On the other hand, it's easy to find L orthogonal codewords of length L. One of the most common is given when $L = 2^n$ for any integer n, which yields $M = L$ orthogonal codewords generated by the Hadamard matrices. This shows that, in the binary case, the S-CDMA scheme can achieve as many non-interfering channels as in a TDMA scheme.

6.6.2 S-CDMA Equivalent to Bit-Level TDMA

The idea of using a matched filter in direct-sequence spread-spectrum receivers is based on the fact that such filters are known to be optimum for signal detection in white Gaussian noise. In our S-CDMA system, however, we are limited not by noise but rather by interference caused by other spread-spectrum signals. Here, we consider an alternative to the matched filters based on Ruprecht [26].

Rather than assign a unique orthogonal codeword to each mobile unit in a microcell, an alternative S-CDMA scheme is to assign to each mobile unit a common codeword with a unique time slot. Suppose we have three mobile units, each using a common spreading codeword. As illustrated in Figure 6.5, if each mobile radio uses a different time offset from the basic reference derived from the base station's broadcast signals, then the common inphase and quadrature codeword-matched filters will have at their outputs differing peaks, owing to the different offset transmissions of each mobile unit.

As shown in Figure 6.5 with the in-phase matched filter, signals from the different mobile unit signals can then be separated at the output of the common matched filter. This method for achieving a set of orthogonal signals is referred to as the *time-slotted S-CDMA technique*. Recall that the RAKE processor in Qualcomm's system is designed to separate the different multipath signals from a mobile unit if the multipath delays are longer than the chip time. Such a RAKE processor combines the outputs to take advantage of this path diversity.

Note that this time-slotted S-CDMA technique also requires time synchronization and that orthogonality is provided by time-slot assignment similar to that in TDMA. The output of the matched filter is essentially a TDMA signal at the bit level. Thus, in a microcell, there are as many S-CDMA orthogonal signals as TDMA signals. The important difference is that in a high-density application with many microcells in a network, S-CDMA can tolerate more interference from other microcells and thus allow

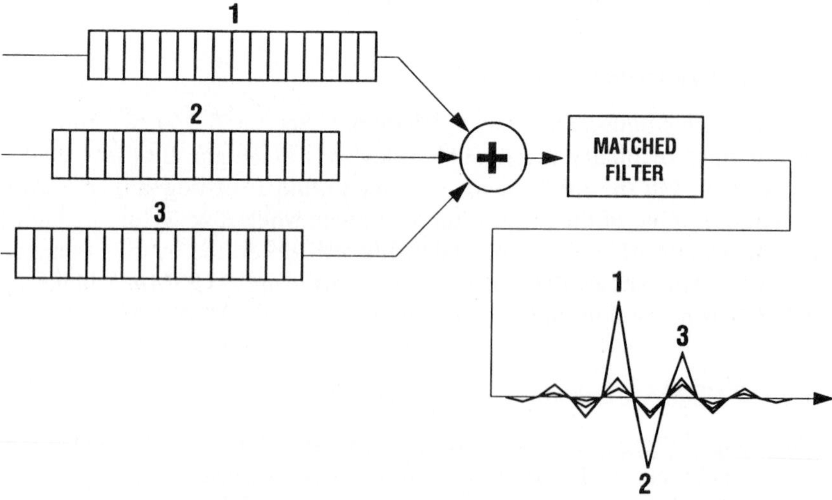

Figure 6.5. Time-slotted S-CDMA with matched filters.

greater frequency of reuse, which results in an overall higher capacity when it is measured in the number of mobile units per high-density area.

This slotted S-CDMA system has the advantage that only one set of in-phase and quadrature matched filters is needed for all the mobile units assigned to the base station. The problem, however, is that with matched filters, signals are not completely orthogonal. In general, each signal's matched filter output has some non-zero terms that contribute to interference at other time slots. This is illustrated in Figure 6.5.

Ruprecht [25] noted that the matched filter is optimum for detecting signals in white Gaussian noise but not necessarily for other situations. For example, he considered an application in which spread-spectrum signals function as sounders (or radar signals) used to determine propagation channel characteristics (or target characteristics). In particular, if such spread-spectrum signals are used for estimating multipaths in a channel, it is important that pulses from different paths not interfere in the measurements.

In the interest of minimizing mutual interference between pulses from different multipath returns, Ruprecht determined that the maximum-likelihood estimation of multipath channels would use filters that are inverse to the transmitted spread-spectrum pulse signal rather than matched filters.

Suppose we regard a codeword as an impulse response of a filter which, of course, is of finite duration. The ideal inverse filter is a real-valued waveform of infinite duration. Naturally, by definition, when a codeword enters the inverse filter, the output is ideally a delta function. A similar discrete time version can also be shown to give only a single non-zero output sample for the discrete time-inverse filter.

If such an ideal inverse filter is used in place of the matched filter, no interference of the time-shifted signals is seen at the filter output. Thus, in theory, inverse filters in a time slotted S-CDMA system produce truly orthogonal signals at the output of the inverse filter.

As discussed earlier, this time slotted S-CDMA technique can be considered as a bit-level TDMA scheme in which the CDMA signals are converted to TDMA signals. The inverse filter for the common codeword treated as an impulse response, however, has infinite duration. Ruprecht considered various levels of time truncation for the inverse filter and found that in most cases truncation to 3 times the codeword duration resulted in "slight" interference among signals at the filter output samples. He also conducted an exhaustive search for short codewords and their truncated inverse filters and found the best ones when white Gaussian noise is in the channel.

Although the use of a truncated inverse filter results in a single filter rather than a bank of matched filters for separating all mobile units' signals at the base station, implementation of such filters is complicated because, unlike codewords, they are not binary levels. Many ways exist for developing easier-to-implement approximations to the inverse filters at the cost of some mutual interference.

6.6.3 A High-Density Voice PCS System

We consider here an S-CDMA high-density network of microcells for a voice application of PCS similar in principle to the IS-95 digital cellular standard but less complex and optimized for microcellular networks. There are two fundamental differences between the high-density network of microcells and the IS-95 digital cellular standard:

- Full-duplex operation is achieved by using time division duplexing (TDD) rather than the FDD dictated by the given cellular frequency band allocation.
- A 32-kbps voice compression is assumed rather than the lower-data-rate compression techniques for digital cellular, which require more digital signal processing with more time delays.

Both these differences reduce cost and complexity. Using TDD is consistent with PCS bands which are generally not allocated as separate transmit and receive bands, as in the cellular bands. Using 32-kbps voice compression reduces processing delays and implementation costs.

In this analysis, we assume a network of evenly distributed microcell sites and randomly distributed mobile voice radios. We assume the network is time-synchronized so that all cell sites have a common time reference (obtained, e.g., from GPS receivers). Each active mobile unit is slave to the corresponding cell-site radios and therefore synchronized to the basic network clock. Of course, in practical systems, time errors will occur and will affect overall performance and capacity. Note that conventional TDMA systems also require a similar network time synchronization. Because of this assumed network synchronization, all base stations transmit TDD packetized bursts followed by all the mobile units transmitting their packetized bursts.

Figure 6.6 illustrates cell sites simultaneously transmitting their packetized bursts. Note that during this time interval, each mobile unit receives the data burst from its assigned cell sites together with interference from other cell sites. Signals that are transmitted by their assigned cell site and are intended for other mobile units assigned to the same cell site use orthogonal codewords.

During the inbound time frame, all mobile units transmit their packets to their cell sites. As shown in Figure 6.7, each cell-site receiver must handle reception of all the mobile unit signals assigned to its cell under interference from all mobile units in other cells.

In this analysis, we assume S-CDMA for both inbound and outbound channels. For microcells in which multipath time delays are smaller and

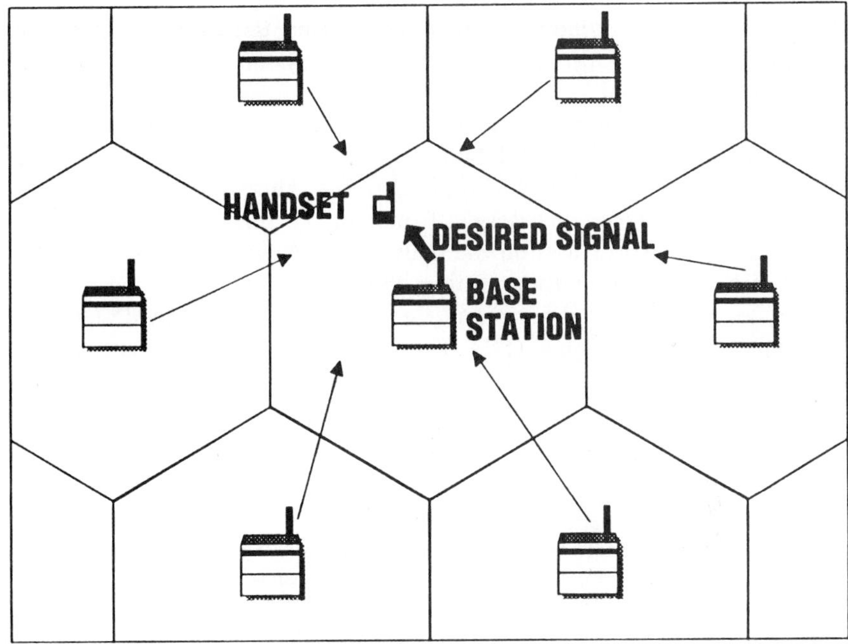

Figure 6.6. Outbound simulation model (base to handset).

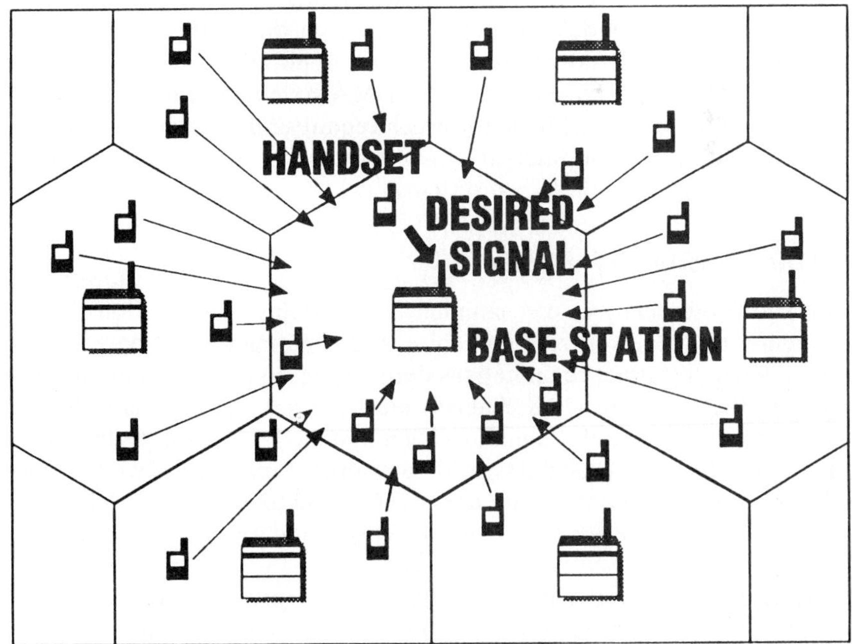

Figure 6.7. Inbound simulation model (handset to base).

mobility is limited to roaming by pedestrians using these mobile units, this assumption is valid as long as all multipath delays are small compared to the chip-time interval.

Given ideal synchronization of cell sites, consider a direct-sequence spread-spectrum QPSK modulation in which we assume that interference derives from other similar synchronized radios. Here, we examine an example in which interference derives from cross-correlation stemming from the specific codewords used in the network. Propagation delays and time offsets are taken into consideration in this simulation.

The system considered here is a spread-spectrum S-CDMA design with full-duplex operation using TDD. The following are its signal carrier features:

A PCS S-CDMA System

Type of modulation	DS/QPSK
Voice transmission	32 kbps ADPCM digital voice
Data transmission	4.8 kbps signaling channel
Processing gain	32 chips/bit
QPSK symbol burst rate	1.536 M symbols/sec

The S-CDMA system requires time synchronization for the network of microcells on the order of a burst chip-time interval, which is 651 nanoseconds (nsec). This delay is much larger than the multipath delays expected for microcells, especially for indoor applications. The digital European cordless telephone (DECT), a TDMA system to be discussed later, has a burst bit rate of 1.152 mbps, which requires time synchronization on the order of a bit time interval of 868 nsec. Thus, time synchronization issues are similar for these two systems.

6.6.3.1 Bit-Error Probabilities

Most textbook analyses of communication systems are based on the assumption that receiver front-end noise is the limiting performance factor. Even when performance limitations derive from other sources of interference in the communication channel, most analyses approximate this interference as noise. For communication systems, the usual performance measure is bit error probability, with interference modeled as white Gaussian noise with spectral density denoted N_0. The bit error probability, P_b, is typically expressed in terms of the ratio of the energy per bit, E_b, to noise, E_b/N_0.

Except for a few cases, it is generally difficult to arrive at an exact closed-form expression for the bit error probability of a communication system, even under the assumption of white Gaussian noise interference. When interference is not modeled as white Gaussian noise, analysis is even more difficult. For this reason, very few expressions for bit error probability are given for interference that is not white Gaussian noise.

For coherent BPSK, the bit error probability against white Gaussian noise is well known and is given by

$$P_b = Q(\sqrt{2E_b/N_0}) \tag{6.4}$$

where $Q(x)$ is the Gaussian integral function

$$Q(x) = \frac{1}{\sqrt{2\pi}} \int_x^\infty e^{-t^2/2}\, dt. \tag{6.5}$$

For this ideal noise-limited case, we have the following required values of E_b/N_0:

$$\frac{E_b}{N_0} = \begin{cases} 4.32 \text{ dB}, & \text{for } P_b = 10^{-2} \\ 6.79 \text{ dB}, & \text{for } P_b = 10^{-3} \\ 8.40 \text{ dB}, & \text{for } P_b = 10^{-4} \\ 9.59 \text{ dB}, & \text{for } P_b = 10^{-5}. \end{cases} \tag{6.6}$$

By using differentially coherent detection of DBPSK (assuming, again, that the limiting factor is white Gaussian noise), the bit error probability is given by the simple expression

$$P_b = \tfrac{1}{2} e^{-E_b/N_0}. \tag{6.7}$$

For this idealized case, the required E_b/N_0 is as follows:

$$\frac{E_b}{N_0} = \begin{cases} 5.92 \text{ dB}, & \text{for } P_b = 10^{-2} \\ 7.93 \text{ dB}, & \text{for } P_b = 10^{-3} \\ 9.30 \text{ dB}, & \text{for } P_b = 10^{-4} \\ 10.34 \text{ dB}, & \text{for } P_b = 10^{-5}. \end{cases} \tag{6.8}$$

Note that the difference between coherent detection and differentially coherent detection is less than 2 dB.

The above bit error probability expressions also apply to spread-spectrum communication systems of the direct-sequence type when the basic modulation is BPSK and the interference is white Gaussian noise. For our spread-spectrum system, however, the performance limitation is due to interference from other similar spread-spectrum radios.

In general, applications are characterized by a high density of users with mobile units roaming in an area with many microcells. This situation is idealized in Figure 6.8. In the S-CDMA system design, during the outbound frame, each mobile unit will be receiving signals from its assigned base station, as shown in Figure 6.6. It could also be receiving interference from neighboring base stations. For the inbound case, all the mobile units will be sending interfering signals to neighboring base stations. However, thanks to our use of orthogonal codes in the S-CDMA system, there is no interference among the radios within a microcell.

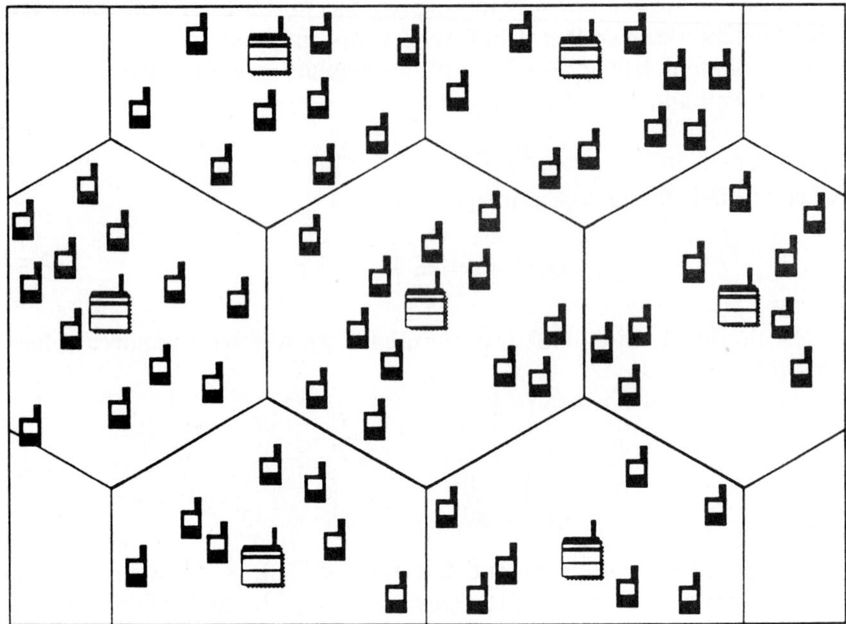

Figure 6.8. Simulation model (random distribution).

In Appendix 6B, we derive bounds on the bit error probability for our spread-spectrum system when interference derives from other similar spread-spectrum signals in a network of microcells. In general, obtaining exact expressions for the bit error probabilities is difficult, and we must resort to using easy-to-evaluate upper bounds on them even though upper bounds give worst case analyses, since the true error probabilities are less then the more easily computed upper bounds.

We show in Appendix 6B that in the interference-limited case, the bit error probability bound for direct-sequence BPSK signals is given by

$$P_b < \tfrac{1}{2}e^{-\mathrm{SJR}} \tag{6.9}$$

where SJR is the signal-to-interference ratio

$$\mathrm{SJR} = A^2/J_0 \tag{6.10}$$

with

$$J_0 = \sum_k C_k^2. \tag{6.11}$$

Here C_k is the cross-correlation of the interfering signal's codeword with the receiver's codeword, and A is the signal amplitude. Note that this expression is exactly the same as the bit error probability for differentially coherent detection of DBPSK signals if we replace N_0 by $J_0/2$.

The results in Appendix 6B are for the direct-sequence spread-spectrum coherent BPSK modulation with coherent demodulation. The corresponding results for differentially coherent demodulation of DBPSK are expected to be within 2 dB of the bit error bounds given here. The DQPSK system may add an additional decibel of required energy per bit to interference. Using convolutional codes with Viterbi decoding will improve this performance by 4 to 6 dB.

6.6.3.2 Computer Simulations

A computer program has been developed to calculate the signal-to-interference ratios for the idealized network of direct-sequence S-CDMA spread-spectrum radios. It allows various parameters to be changed to examine the effects of different codewords, power attenuation constants, voice activation factors, and numbers of randomly placed mobile handsets throughout the network. Naturally, the greater the power attenuation factor assumed, the lower the mutual interference between radios. A 35 percent voice activation level was also assumed.

Figure 6.9 shows a contour plot of the signal-to-interference ratio, SJR, for a mobile handset as a function of its location. As shown in Figure 6.9, the interference for mobile units derives from the cell sites of other microcells. The lack of symmetry is explained by the specific choice of codewords in each of the microcells in this model. Here, we assume six active voice channels per microcell. Modified five-stage LFSR sequences were used. The propagation attenuation is assumed to be the inverse third power of distance.

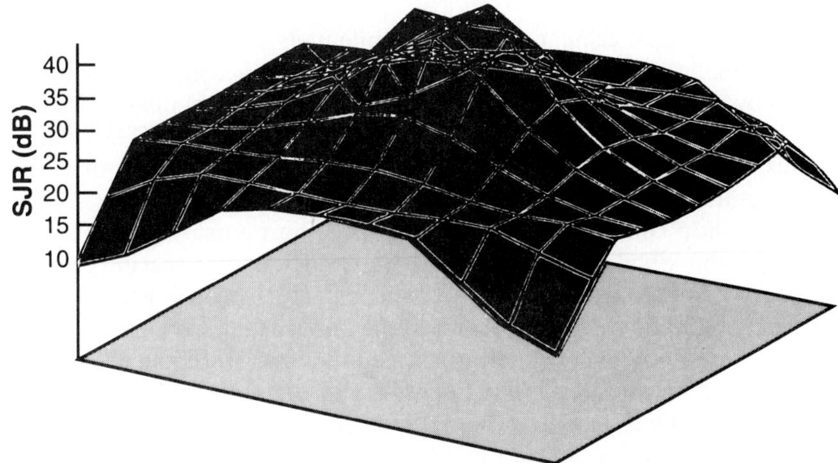

Figure 6.9. Three-dimensional contour SJR plot for handset.

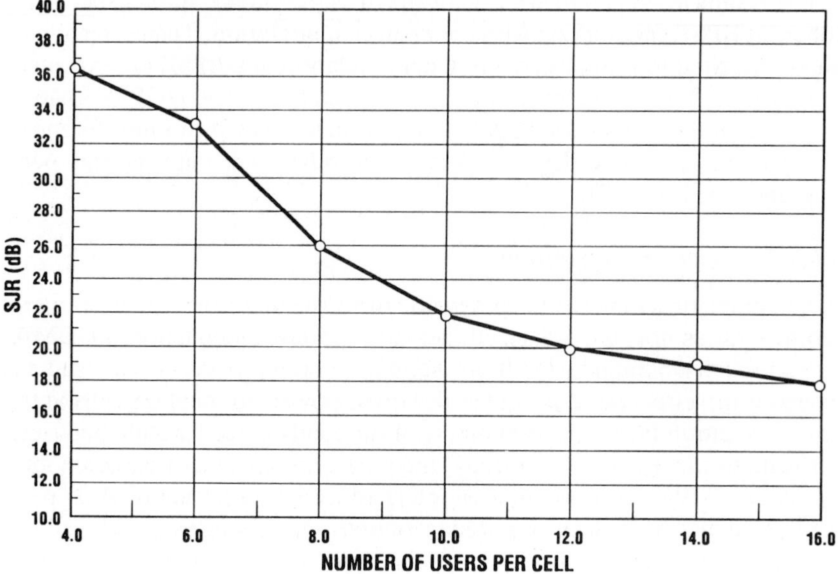

Figure 6.10. SJR versus number of users per cell.

For the mobile-to-cell-site channel, the SJR at the cell-site receiver depends on the particular distribution of mobile handsets throughout the network. Figure 6.10 illustrates a typical example as a function of the number of randomly distributed mobile handsets per microcell for the inbound direction.

6.6.3.3 Other System Issues

In the IS-95 digital cellular standard, mobile units synchronize on the cell site by locking onto the strongest pilot signal which is continuously transmitted by each of the cell sites. In this TDD structure, a similar broadcast pilot signal can be sent by each cell site at the beginning of its TDD burst. In this TDD design, the cell-site packetized bursts are longer than the mobile units' packetized bursts to accommodate the additional time needed to send a short common broadcast burst. This short burst serves as a pilot signal for the mobile units for maintaining a lock on the specific cell-site signal. For initial acquisition, one of the cell-site signals is used for this purpose. As in IS-95, this signal aids in the initial acquisition and provides paging information to the mobile units. Cell sites using different codewords for this purpose are used instead of offsets of the same PN sequence, as in the Qualcomm system. To achieve the rapid acquisition needed for TDD systems, each receiver should use matched filters rather than the serial correlators typically used with longer PN sequences.

Soft handoff can be achieved by using a RAKE receiver processor as in the IS-95 system. Another alternative is to allow the receiver to track more than one signal with different codewords. With programmable matched filters, this can be done in practice with very few additional gates in a custom chip design.

6.6.3.4 Comparison with DECT

For PCS applications, the current DECT system, using TDMA, serves as a baseline for comparison with the S-CDMA system described here. DECT has been under development in Europe for several years and represents the state of the art for PCS using conventional TDMA radios. These PCS systems, which involve users carrying portable or mobile handsets while roaming in an area covered by many microcells, are designed for microcells of up to approximately 200 m in diameter. The most important criterion for comparison is capacity, as measured by the total number of simultaneous voice users in a given high-density area (1 km^2, for example), in which the number of microcell sites and the total bandwidth within each area are constant. The comparison should also assume that overall complexity and cost are roughly equivalent, although these can be difficult to measure.

As pointed out earlier, the design philosophy regarding spread-spectrum radios is different: Now interference is tolerated, and the primary issue is to design to a tolerable level of interference. This new design criterion for a network of microcells adds another design dimension that does not apply with conventional narrowband radios and places a much stronger emphasis on the quality of radios developed and the overall system design and signal coordination. Radios that tolerate greater interference afford more flexibility in designing a network of microcells, which is especially important since it facilitates the implementation of various antenna techniques at the base stations, which can in turn dramatically increase microcell capacity.

DECT Standard

Within the 1.88–1.90 GHz band are 10 FDMA carriers. In each, 12 digital voice channels use TDMA for multiple-access and TDD for full-duplex operation, giving a total of 120 voice channels. The spacing between the FDMA carriers is 1.728 MHz.

Type of modulation	GMSK
Voice transmission	32 kbps ADPCM digital voice
Data transmission	4.8 kbps signaling channel
Duplex voice channels per carrier	12
Time frame	10 msec
Time slot per channel (including guard space)	0.417 msec
Number of time slots per frame	24
Burst bit rate	1.152 Mbps
Output power	250-mW burst peak

Note that with 24 time slots, the guard times needed between slots account for 23.3 percent of the total time frame. Each voice channel with TDD, overhead, and time gaps uses 96 kbps of the 1156-kbps burst rate.

This DECT design permits 12 voice users in every 1.728 MHz of bandwidth. By normalizing to 1 MHz, we have 6.94 active voice users per megahertz of bandwidth. In a large network of densely packed microcells, the available total bandwidth per cell will be reduced by a factor of $\frac{1}{7}$ because adjacent microcells cannot share the same frequency band. The frequency-of-reuse limitation of conventional narrowband radios can reduce overall capacity for the area covered by all microcells by as much as one-seventh. Thus, this DECT system used in a high density of microcells averages only one active channel per megahertz per cell.

In the above S-CDMA example, we see that the bandwidth is roughly the same, but the potential number of active voice channels per cell is much larger for signal-to-interference ratios as high as 15 dB. This can be seen in the number of users allowed in the simulation results shown in Figures 6.9 and 6.10, in which 100 percent frequency of reuse is assumed.

6.7 HIGHER-CAPACITY OPTIMAL RECEIVERS

Up to this point, we have assumed that the receivers were designed for interference like noise and that a signal-to-interference threshold limited performance. In fact, interference experienced in the CDMA system is quite different from noise, and this fact can be exploited to achieve better performance and to increase capacity beyond the dimensional limit defined by the number of orthogonal codewords.

In Part 5, Chapter 5, spread-spectrum multiple-access concepts were discussed. Section 5.3.3 showed research results on optimum receivers that simultaneously demodulate all multiple-access signals. Here, the receiver treats multiple-access signals as one larger composite signal and attempts to demodulate all the signals with one optimal processor. Theoretical Shannon limits show that spread-spectrum radios in a multiple-access system permit capacity beyond what is possible with completely orthogonal signals. That is, it is possible to exceed the capacity limit set by the number of orthogonal coordinates such as frequency slots (frequency dimensions) in FDMA and time slots (time dimensions) in TDMA.

Most of these earlier studies were primarily theoretical, although some more practical suboptimal receiver structures were considered. With the recent renewed interest in spread-spectrum radios and their potential capacity advantage, there has been a dramatic increase in the number of papers examining optimal and suboptimal CDMA receiver structures with higher overall capacity [19, 27–40].

Interference is now viewed differently than in the past. Most early studies assume a receiver design based on the classical theory of noise interference.

In most high-density radio networks, capacity is limited not by noise but by mutual interference. With spread-spectrum multiple-access signals, the so-called interference is not noise, but is other similar signals. Unlike classic receivers designed to reduce noise, more complex optimal receivers take advantage of the specific nature of multiple-access signals to achieve much higher capacity.

For example, even in its simplest form, one can take advantage of the fact that the interference signal, unlike noise, possesses some non-random components that remain constant for each bit time interval. Suggested approaches have included adaptive noise cancellation and adaptive filtering techniques such as those used in telephone channel equalization [39, 40]. More advanced but complex techniques can improve performance to increase overall capacity further.

6.8 SUMMARY

A wide range of commercial wireless products are being developed in response to the 1985 FCC Part 15 ruling which eliminates the need for licensing in specific bands for operation with spread-spectrum radios with up to 1 W of power. The FCC Part 15 rule has been a catalyst for many innovative wireless applications.

Qualcomm's application of spread-spectrum radios for a digital cellular phone system also served to stimulate interest in spread-spectrum radios. It introduced a new way of designing high-density multicell digital voice networks [41].

More research is being devoted to the use of new types of optimal receivers that take advantage of the fact that the "interference" is not random noise but rather other CDMA signals with characteristics that can be exploited to achieve better performance and higher capacity. Most of this work has been directed to direct-sequence spread-spectrum systems, with most of the complexity in the form of digital signal processing.

The key issues associated with commercial applications of spread-spectrum radios are complexity and cost. As pointed out by Viterbi [2], "Doubtless, CDMA is conceptually more difficult to understand. But difficulty of concept should not be confused with difficult of implementation." Indeed, most of the complexity in direct-sequence spread-spectrum radios in a CDMA network resides in the digital processing, which is implementable in digital chips. Today, all kinds of complex processing are readily available in the form of low-cost digital chips in everyday products.

Practical commercial applications for spread-spectrum radios are now becoming better understood. Their primary advantages are their greater robustness compared to narrowband radios and their potentially higher overall capacity in multicell networks. Spread-spectrum radios are well suited to play key roles in a world becoming increasingly wireless.

6.9 REFERENCES

[1] A. J. Viterbi, "When not to spread spectrum—A sequel," *IEEE Comm. Mag.*, vol. 23, pp. 12–17, Apr. 1985.

[2] A. J. Viterbi, "Wireless digital communication: A view based on three lessons learned," *IEEE Comm. Mag.*, vol. 29, no. 9, pp. 33–36, Sept. 1991.

[3] G. R. Cooper and R. W. Nettleton, "A spread-spectrum technique for high-capacity mobile communications," *IEEE Trans. Veh. Tech.*, vol. 27, no. 4, pp. 264–275, Nov. 1978.

[4] A. J. Viterbi, "A processing satellite transponder for multiple access by low-rate mobile users," *Proc. Dig. Satellite Comm. Conf.*, Montreal, Canada, Oct. 1978.

[5] D. J. Goodman, P. S. Henry, and V. K. Prabu, "Frequency-hopped multilevel FSK for mobile radio," *Bell Syst. Tech. J.*, vol. 59, pp. 1267–1275, Sept. 1980.

[6] G. L. Turin, "Introduction to spread-spectrum antimultipath techniques and their applications to urban digital radio," *Proc. IEEE*, vol. 68, no. 3, pp. 328–353, Mar. 1980.

[7] A. J. Viterbi, "Bandwidth efficiency in coded networks of fixed and mobile users," presented at IEEE Communication Theory Workshop, Tucson, Arizona, April 1982.

[8] E. B. Parker, "Satellite micro earth stations—A small investment with big returns," *Data Comm.*, p. 97, Jan. 1983.

[9] E. B. Parker, "Micro earth stations as personal computer accessories," *Proc. IEEE*, vol. 72, no. 11, pp. 1526–1531, Nov. 1984.

[10] E. B. Parker, "History of VSAT networks," chapter 3 in *The Book on VSATs*, A. Malkin and Y. Gat, eds., Tel Aviv, Israel: Gilat Communication Systems Ltd., 1991.

[11] J. J. Spilker, Jr., *Digital Communications by Satellite*, Englewood Cliffs, NJ: Prentice-Hall, 1977, p. 508.

[12] J. P. Freret, "Applications of spread spectrum radio to wireless terminal communications," *Proc. NTC '80*, vol. 4, pp. 69.7.1–69.7.4.

[13] M. Kavehrad and B. Ramamurthi, "Direct-sequence spread spectrum with DPSK modulation and diversity for indoor wireless communications," *IEEE Trans. Comm.*, vol. 35, no. 2, pp. 224–236, Feb. 1987.

[14] M. Kavehrad and P. J. McLane, "Spread spectrum for indoor digital radio," *IEEE Comm. Mag.*, vol. 25, no. 6, June 1987.

[15] K. S. Gilhousen, I. M. Jacobs, R. Padovani, A. J. Viterbi, L. A. Weaver, Jr., and C. E. Wheatley, III, "On the capacity of a cellular CDMA system," *IEEE Trans. Veh. Tech.*, vol. 40, no. 2, pp. 303–312, May 1991.

[16] A. Salmasi and K. Gilhousen, "On the system design aspects of code division multiple access applied to digital cellular and personal communications networks," *Proc. IEEE Veh. Tech. Conf.*, pp. 57–62, May 1991.

[17] A. J. Viterbi, "Very low rate convolutional codes for maximum theoretical performance of spread spectrum multiple access channels," *IEEE J. Select. Areas Comm.*, vol. 8, no. 4, May 1990.

[18] W. C. Y. Lee, "Overview of cellular CDMA," *IEEE Trans. Veh. Tech.*, vol. 40, no. 2, pp. 291–301, May 1991.

[19] N. Abramson, *Multiple Access Communications*, New York: IEEE Press, 1993.

[20] D. C. Cox, "Wireless network access for personal communications," *IEEE Comm. Mag.*, pp. 96–115, Dec. 1992.

[21] J. L. Massey and T. Mittelholzer, "Investigations on an optimal code family to be used in synchronous high capacity CDMA communication systems," Report to ESTEC on technical assistance for the CDMA communication system analysis, Institute for Signal and Information Processing, ETH-Zurich, Switzerland, July 1990.

[22] A. J. Viterbi and J. K. Omura, *Principles of Digital Communication and Coding*, New York: McGraw-Hill, 1979.

[23] J. K. Omura, "Spread spectrum radios for personal communication services," *IEEE 2d Int. Symp. Spread Spectrum Tech. Appl.* (ISSSTA '92), Yokohama, Japan, Nov. 29–Dec. 2, 1992.

[24] D. M. J. Devasirvatham, "Time delay spread measurements of 850 MHz radio waves in building environments," *Proc. GLOBECOM-85*, New Orleans, Dec. 1985.

[25] H. Hashemi, "The indoor radio propagation channel," *Proc. IEEE*, vol. 81, no. 7, pp. 943–968, July 1993.

[26] J. Ruprecht, "Periodic binary input sequences for multi-user maximum-likelihood estimation of multipath channels," *1990 Int. Symp. Infor. Theory Appl.*, Paper 55-1, Nov. 1990.

[27] K. S. Schneider, "Optimum detection of code division multiplexed signals," *IEEE Trans. Aerosp. Electron. Syst.*, vol. 15, pp. 181–185, Jan. 1979.

[28] S. Verdu, "Minimum probability of error for asynchronous gaussian multiple-access channels," *IEEE Trans. Inform. Theory*, vol. 32, pp. 85–96, Jan. 1986.

[29] S. Verdu, "Optimum multi-user asymptotic efficiency," *IEEE Trans. Comm.*, vol. 34, pp. 890–897, Sept. 1986.

[30] R. Lupas and S. Verdu, "Linear multiuser detectors for synchronous code-division multiple-access channels," *IEEE Trans. Inform. Theory*, vol. 35, pp. 123–136, Jan. 1989.

[31] M. K. Varanasi and B. Aazhang, "Near-optimum detection in synchronous code-division multiple-access systems," *IEEE Trans. Comm.*, vol. 39, pp. 725–736, May 1991.

[32] H. V. Poor and S. Verdu, "Single-user detectors for multiuser channels," *IEEE Trans. Comm.*, vol. 36, pp. 50–60, Jan. 1988.

[33] R. Lupas and S. Verdu, "Near-far resistance of multiuser detectors in asynchronous channels," *IEEE Trans. Comm.*, vol. 38, no. 4, pp. 496–508, Apr. 1990.

[34] M. K. Varanasi and B. Aazhang, "Multistage detection in asynchronous code-division multiple access communications," *IEEE Trans. Comm.*, vol. 38, no. 4, pp. 509–519, Apr. 1990.

[35] Z. Xie, R. T. Short, and C. K. Rushforth, "A family of suboptimum detectors for coherent multiuser communications," *IEEE J. Select. Areas Comm.*, vol. 8, pp. 683–690, May 1990.

[36] Y. C. Yoon, R. Kohno, and H. Imai, "A spread-spectrum multi-access system with a cascade of co-channel interference cancellers for multipath fading channels," *Proc. IEEE 2d Int. Symp. Spread Spectrum Tech. Appl.*, pp. 87–90, Dec. 1992.

[37] S. Tachikawa, "Performance of M-ary spread spectrum multiple access communication systems using co-channel interference cancellation techniques," *Proc. IEEE 2d Int. Symp. Spread Spectrum Tech. Appl.*, pp. 95–98, Dec. 1992.

[38] P. B. Rapajic and B. S. Vucetic, "Linear asynchronous code-division multiple

access single-user receiver," *Proc. IEEE 2d Int. Symp. Spread Spectrum Tech. Appl.*, pp. 99–102, Dec. 1992.
[39] M. Abdulrahman, D. D. Falconer, and A. U. H. Sheikh, "Equalization for interference cancellation in spread spectrum multiple access systems," *IEEE 42d Trans. Veh. Tech. Conf.*, pp. 71–74, 1992.
[40] M. Abdulrahman, A. U. H. Sheikh, and D. D. Falconer, "DFE convergence for interference cancellation in spread spectrum multiple access systems," *IEEE 43d Trans. Veh. Tech. Conf.*, pp. 807–810, 1993.
[41] A. J. Viterbi, *Principles of Spread Spectrum Multiple Access Communication*, Englewood Cliffs, NJ: Prentice-Hall, in press.

APPENDIX 6A. MULTIPATH AND DIVERSITY

In this appendix, we investigate the Rayleigh fading channel model and the use of diversity techniques to overcome some of the deep fade problems typically encountered in these radio channels.

Rayleigh Fading Model

The biggest limitation to mobile radio performance is propagation impairment owing to multipath. Typically, a continuous wave (CW) channel input signal of the form

$$A \cos \omega_0 t \tag{6A.1}$$

where A is a constant has at the output of a multipath channel a signal of the form

$$R \cos (\omega_0 t + \phi) \tag{6A.2}$$

where R is a random amplitude variable and ϕ is a random phase variable. The phase term is almost always accurately modeled as having a uniform probability density over all phases.

The mathematical model for the random amplitude variable is less certain, and the results are very sensitive to this model. As illustrated in Figure 6A.1, the most common assumption is that in-phase and quadrature components of the signal experience several independent amplitudes so that the sum of the independent in-phase amplitude terms contributing to amplitude is given by the random variable X, while the corresponding quadrature term is another independent random variable Y. The Central Limit Theorem states that if the number of independent random multipath reflections is large, X and Y can be modeled as independent Gaussian random variables. It is important to note that the accuracy of this Gaussian approximation is highest near the mean values of these random variables and declines as the approximation departs from mean values.

The amplitude random variable is given by

$$R = \sqrt{X^2 + Y^2} \tag{6A.3}$$

where X and Y are often approximated as Gaussian random variables. If X or Y or both have non-zero mean values, then R is called a *Rician*

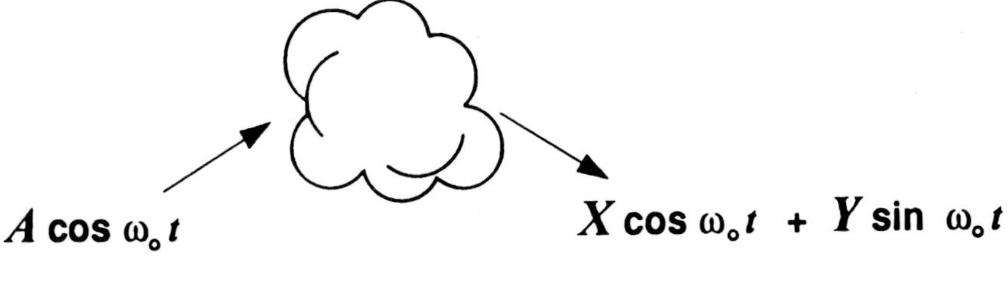

$$X = \sum_k A_k \qquad Y = \sum_k B_k$$

$$R = \sqrt{X^2 + Y^2}$$

Figure 6A.1. Rayleigh fading.

random variable (after Steve Rice of Bell Laboratories, who first used this model around 1940). With zero mean values for X and Y, then R is known as a *Rayleigh* random variable.

The worst case assumes that R is a Rayleigh random variable. Therefore, if there are no strong direct components in X and Y, we can assume that they are zero-mean Gaussian random variables. Without loss in generality, we normalize by assuming that X and Y are independent zero-mean Gaussian random variables with unit variance. Then R is the classical Rayleigh random variable with probability density

$$f(r) = re^{-r^2/2} \tag{6A.4}$$

and the probability distribution function

$$F(r) = 1 - e^{-r^2/2} \tag{6A.5}$$

for all $r \geq 0$. For this normalized case, we have the expected value of $R^2/2$ given by

$$E\left[\frac{R^2}{2}\right] = 1. \tag{6A.6}$$

Note that this corresponds to the case of normalizing the average power of the channel output signal

$$\begin{aligned} E[[R \cos (\omega_0 t + \phi)]^2] &= E[R^2]\, E[\cos^2 (\omega_0 t + \phi)] \\ &= \frac{E[R^2]}{2} \\ &= 1. \end{aligned} \tag{6A.7}$$

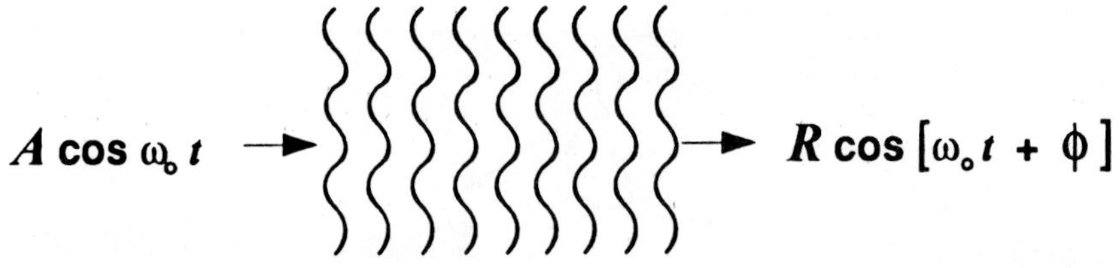

$A \cos \omega_0 t \rightarrow$ $\rightarrow R \cos[\omega_0 t + \phi]$

$$R = \prod_k A_k = A_0 e^{\sum_k Z_k} = A_0 e^x$$

$$X \sim N(O, \sigma^2)$$

Figure 6A.2. Log normal fading.

Another model sometimes considered is the log normal fading statistics for the output amplitude of a propagation channel. In Figure 6A.2, a signal is assumed to consist of many independent amplitude variations, with the resultant signal amplitude a product of many random terms.
The product of such terms forms the total random amplitude

$$R = \prod_k A_k \tag{6A.8}$$

in which each term has the form

$$A_k = A_0 e^{Z_k} \tag{6A.9}$$

where Z_k is a random variable. We then have

$$R = A_0 \exp\left(\sum_k Z_k\right). \tag{6A.10}$$

Again, the Central Limit Theorem is applied, this time to the exponent term:

$$X = \sum_k Z_k. \tag{6A.11}$$

This Gaussian approximation for the random amplitude exponent results in the log normal model.

The log normal model tends to be more accurate for optical communications with narrow beams. Long radio paths with many reflections and focussed antenna beams sometimes show this behavior. For indoor applications with radios at 1 GHz, the Rayleigh fading model is more commonly used and is used in the remainder of this appendix.

Upper Bound on $F(r)$

It is easy to show that, in general,

$$1 - e^{-r^2/2} \le \frac{r^2}{2} \tag{6A.12}$$

for all $r \ge 0$. This bound is tightest when r is close to zero. The proof of this bound is seen by showing that the function

$$g(r) = \frac{r^2}{2} - (1 - e^{-r^2/2}) \tag{6A.13}$$

has a minimum value at $r = 0$ of $g(0) = 0$.

This bound is useful for evaluating the probability of deep fades owing to this Rayleigh fading model. We normalized the fade term to

$$E\left[\frac{R^2}{2}\right] = 1$$
$$= 0 \text{ dB} \tag{6A.14}$$

and now we want to know the probability of a deep fade, specifically, the probability that

$$\frac{R^2}{2} \le x \text{ dB}. \tag{6A.15}$$

By converting to decibels, we have

$$\frac{r^2}{2} = 10^{x/10}. \tag{6A.16}$$

Thus, the desired probability is

$$\Pr\left[\frac{R^2}{2} \le x \text{ dB}\right] = F(\sqrt{2 \times 10^{x/10}})$$
$$\le 10^{x/10}. \tag{6A.17}$$

By using this bound, the following table gives the probability of deep fades with a single Rayleigh random variable.

Fade Threshold x, dB	Probability	Probability Bound
0	6.321×10^{-1}	1.0
−10	9.516×10^{-2}	10^{-1}
−20	9.950×10^{-3}	10^{-2}
−30	9.995×10^{-4}	10^{-3}
−40	9.999×10^{-5}	10^{-4}
−50	10^{-5}	10^{-5}
−60	10^{-6}	10^{-6}

This shows that starting with an average signal channel output power of 0 dB, the probability of getting into deep fades decreases as shown here. The simple bound is accurate for the deeper-fade cases of interest, as summarized in this table.

Dynamics of Fading

Note that choosing the mathematical model of a Rayleigh random variable for the amplitude owing to multipath always gives a non-zero probability of hitting a deep fade level. Consequently, one must accept some level of fade, either a "hit" or loss of the signal at the receiver. The only question is, How often can we accept such hits? The answer depends on the time dynamics of the fading process.

In a study of fading, we should model the stochastic process for $R(t)$, the time-varying Rayleigh fading amplitude. Typically, a person walks at a rate less than 5 km/hr. With a carrier frequency of 1 GHz, the carrier signal wave length is 30 cm. Thus, a person roaming and talking with a mobile unit will typically experience less than 10 nulls per second.

Typical measurements taken by Cylink in an office building with a single antenna are shown in Figure 6A.3. Here, the transmitter is a spread-spectrum signal of 1 M chips per second. These measurements confirm that this rate of 10 multipath nulls per second is somewhat high. Even in these short measurements, deep nulls of 20-dB drop from the average can be observed.

As the spread-spectrum signal becomes wider, the effects of frequency diversity begin to appear, and signals will show fewer deep nulls than a CW or narrowband signal. In fact, a wider signal can be thought of as consisting of many different CW components, which make for frequency-selective multipath fading. That is, cancellation of multipath signals at one frequency does not mean a cancellation of signals at another frequency. Although spread-spectrum signals may show fewer deep nulls, frequency diversity effects will not be too evident with the 2-MHz bandwidth signals in these measurements except to reduce the depth of the nulls.

If we must accept some loss of signal, we need to assume some statistical dynamics for the fading process. Based on the discussion above, suppose that we have a statistically independent sample of $R(t)$ once every 100 msec. This corresponds to the maximum of 10 fades per second. In 1 minute's time, we estimate that there will be 600 independent amplitude random variables while a person walks at 5 km/hr. Suppose we let these independent random Rayleigh variables be $R(t_k)$ for $k = 1, 2, \ldots, 600$. What is the probability that in 1 minute the fade drops to x dB at least once? This is the event that $\{R(t_k) \le r\}$ for one or more independent sample

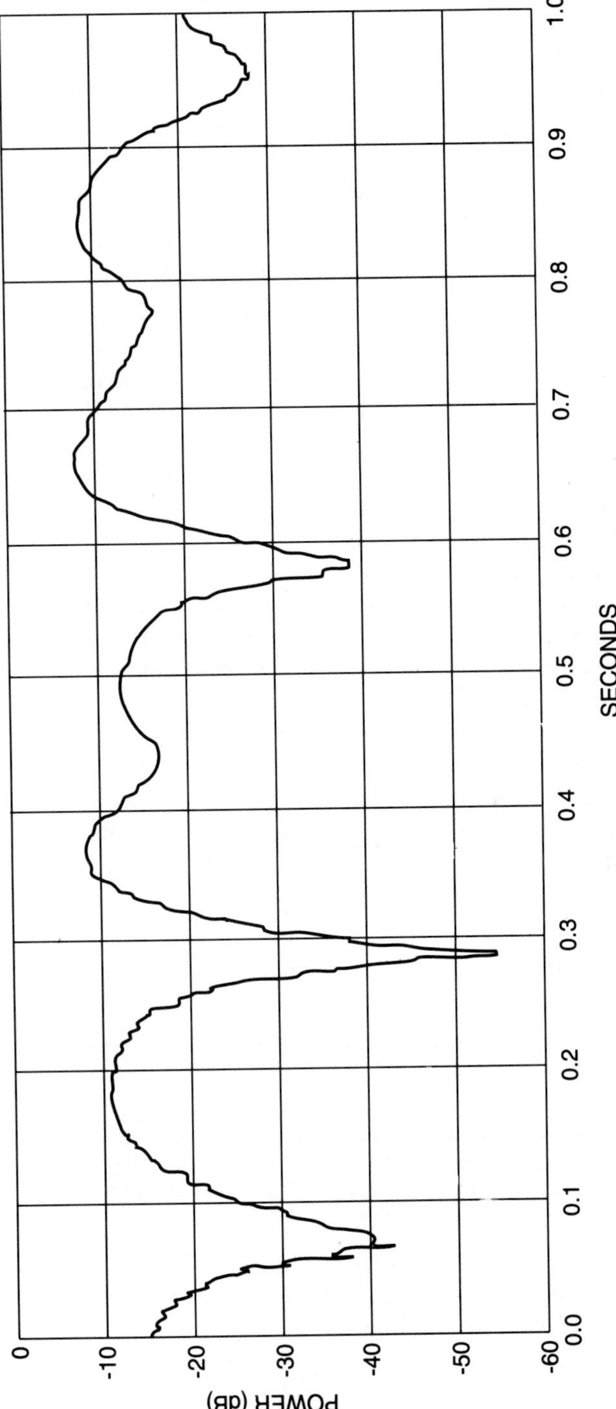

Figure 6A.3. Single antenna.

times given by indices $k = 1, 2, \ldots, 600$. We use the simple union bound for this:

$$\begin{aligned}
\Pr\left[\min_{1 \le k \le 600} R(t_k) \le r\right] &= \Pr\left[\bigcup_{k=1}^{600} \{R(t_k) \le r\}\right] \\
&\le \sum_{k=1}^{600} \Pr\left[R(t_k) \le r\right] \\
&= 600F(r) \\
&\le 600 \times 10^{x/10}. \qquad (6A.18)
\end{aligned}$$

Note that for $x = -30$ dB, the probability is less than 0.6 that such a fade will occur in 1 minute. For $x = -40$ dB, the probability is less than 0.06 or, on average, no more than once every 16 minutes of roaming and talking. Of course, this is based on the simple union bound and gives a more pessimistic probability than a more precise calculation of the true probabilities, which will be smaller.

It seems that if we allow ourselves an average of one −40-dB fade once every 16 minutes, then we must compensate for the Rayleigh fading channel by 40 dB of power control. This assumes no diversity and does not take into account any of the frequency diversity effects that occur with spread-spectrum signals.

Note that in comparing this application with the cellular radio application in which the radio can be in an automobile traveling at 100 km/hr, the rate of change may be more than 20 times faster than the roaming pace in PCS applications. This means that deep fades occur more often with cellular applications, and thus the IS-95 design must overcome deeper fades to achieve the same rate of deep fades as a PCS system.

Impact of Diversity

The results above are based on a single-channel output signal. In practice, we may have more than one-channel output, with diversity owing to

- Antenna diversity in which two or more receiver antennas are used.
- Frequency diversity in which a wideband signal experiences frequency-selective fading. Fast frequency-hopping spread-spectrum systems can also exhibit frequency diversity.
- Path diversity in which multipath owing to different delays may be resolved as separate signals at the in-phase and quadrature spread-spectrum codeword-matched filter outputs.
- Time diversity in which different time samples are interleaved in an error-correction coding technique.

The purpose of diversity is to obtain more than one output signal with independent random amplitudes in each signal. Suppose there are N independent random variables owing to N diversity signals. Suppose $R_1, R_2, \ldots, R_N$ are the independent random amplitudes for these N diversity signals.

There are many ways to combine the N output signals. The simplest technique is to take the signal with the largest amplitude. If we follow this rule, then the diversity random amplitude is the random variable given by the largest of the N random amplitudes:

$$R = \text{Max}\,\{R_1, R_2, \ldots, R_N\}. \tag{6A.19}$$

The probability distribution for this is

$$\begin{aligned} F_N(r) &= \Pr\,[R \leq r] \\ &= \Pr\left[\bigcap_{n=1}^{N} \{R_n \leq r\}\right]. \end{aligned} \tag{6A.20}$$

Diversity is not useful unless the signal amplitudes are independent. Assuming $R_1, R_2, \ldots, R_N$ are independent and identically distributed, we have the result that

$$F_N(r) = F(r)^N \tag{6A.21}$$

where $F(r)$ is the probability distribution of each amplitude.

Assuming the same normalized Rayleigh random variables where

$$\begin{aligned} F(r) &= 1 - e^{-r^2/2} \\ &\leq \frac{r^2}{2} \end{aligned} \tag{6A.22}$$

for all $r \geq 0$, we get the distribution for the diversity random variable as

$$\begin{aligned} F_N(r) &= (1 - e^{-r^2/2})^N \\ &\leq \left(\frac{r^2}{2}\right)^N. \end{aligned} \tag{6A.23}$$

Noting that

$$\frac{r^2}{2} = 10^{x/10} \tag{6A.24}$$

where x is the threshold level in decibels, we get the following table for $N = 1, 2, 3,$ and 4.

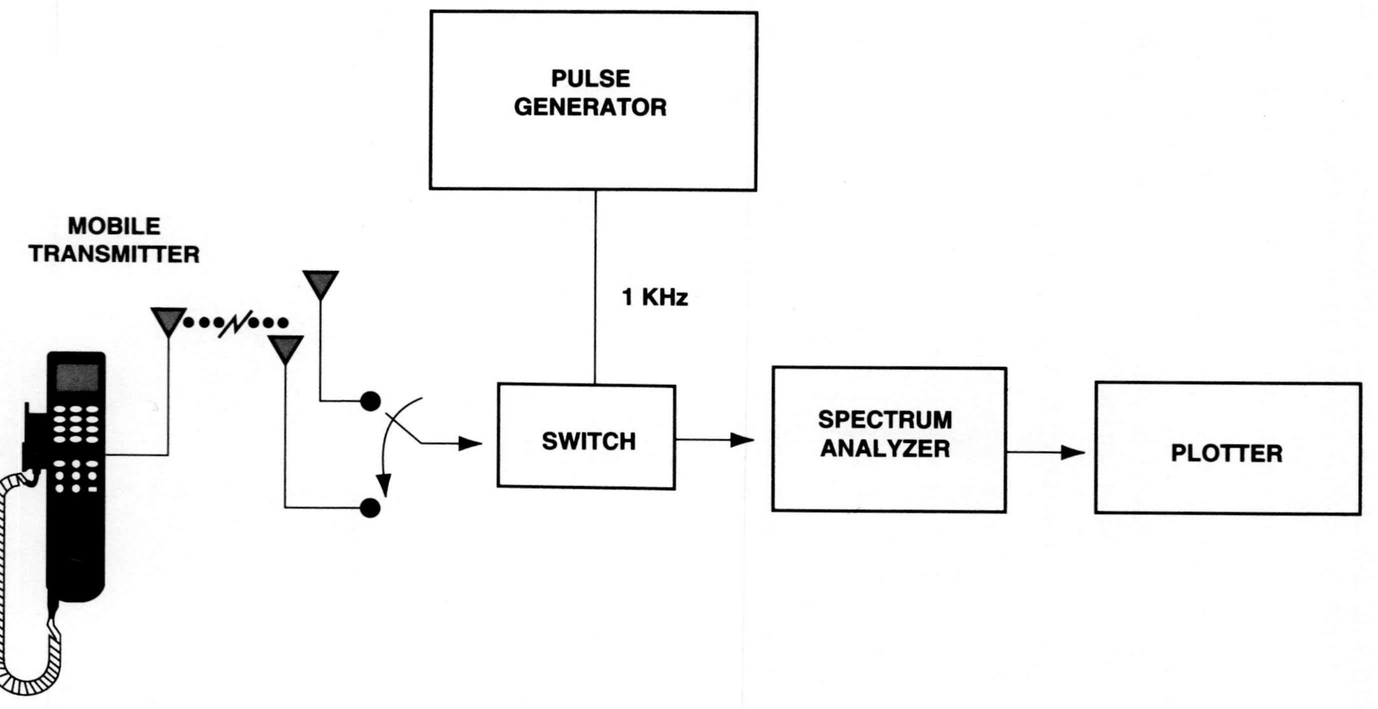

Figure 6A.4. Experiment with diversity antennas.

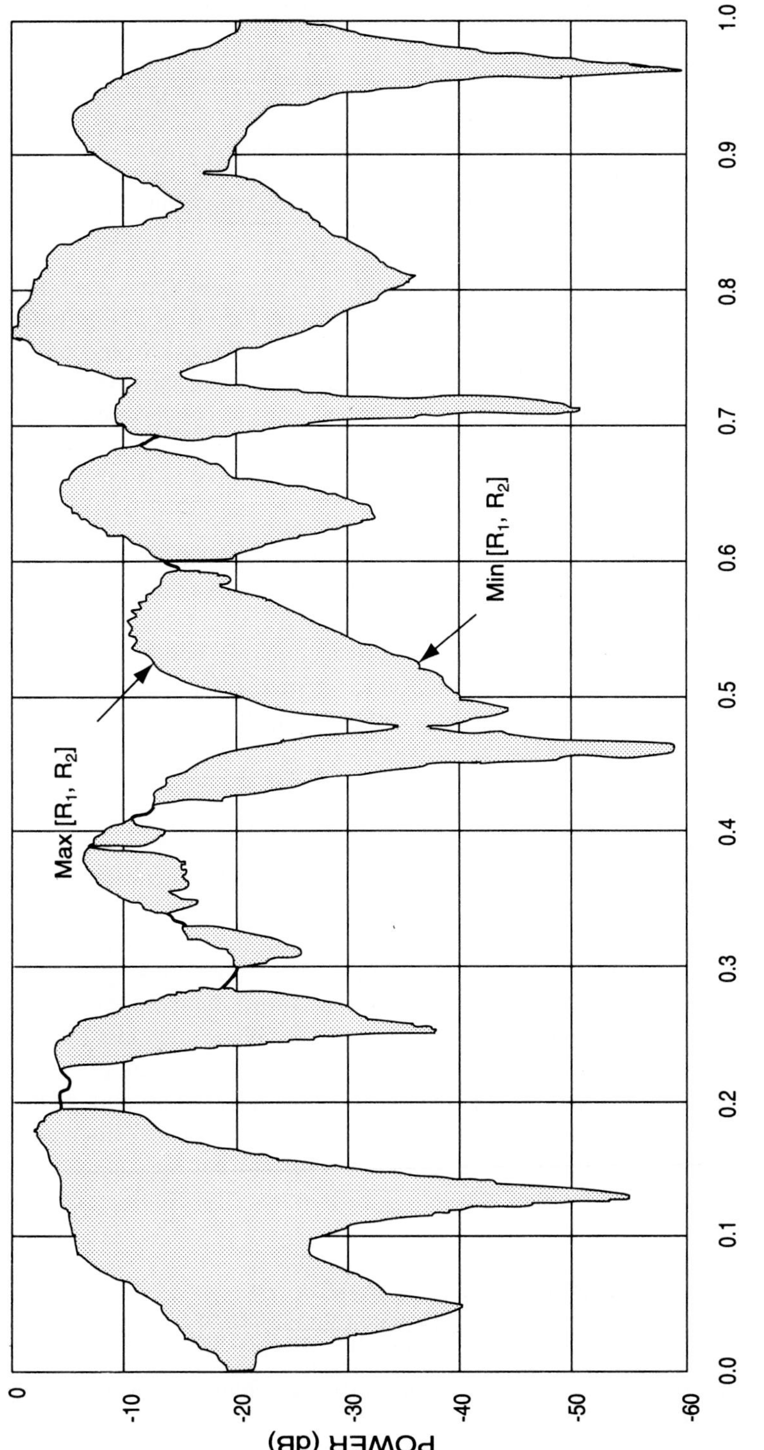

Figure 6A.5. Diversity antennas.

Fade Threshold, dB	Probability Bound			
	$N = 1$	$N = 2$	$N = 3$	$N = 4$
−10	10^{-1}	10^{-2}	10^{-3}	10^{-4}
−20	10^{-2}	10^{-4}	10^{-6}	10^{-8}
−30	10^{-3}	10^{-6}	10^{-9}	10^{-12}
−40	10^{-4}	10^{-8}	10^{-12}	10^{-16}
−50	10^{-5}	10^{-10}	10^{-15}	10^{-20}

Recall that before, with no diversity ($N = 1$), we saw that a deep fade threshold of −40 dB averaged no more than one fade every 16 minutes. With dual diversity ($N = 2$), the same average occurrence would have a fade threshold of −20 dB. This means that to avoid more than one deeper fade every 16 minutes, power control circuits need to cover fades of only 20 dB down from the average signal power level.

Antenna Diversity

Figure 6A.4 shows the experimental set for Cylink's diversity antenna measurements with a 1 M chip-per-second spread-spectrum transmitter signal. The pulse generator switches between the two antennas at a 1-kHz rate. This 1-MHz chip rate is close to the chip rate considered by the Qualcomm cellular and Cylink PCS voice systems. The resulting graph shows the two antennas' received signal levels but does not indicate which antenna has the stronger signal.

Figure 6A.5 shows a typical measured signal power of a spread-spectrum radio for two diversity antennas. The top envelope represents $\text{Max}\{R_1, R_2\}$, while the bottom envelope represents $\text{Min}\{R_1, R_2\}$. Note that, for the most part, the maximum has nulls that seem to follow a pattern consistent with the probabilities described above.

Measurements taken by Cylink seem to confirm that diversity antennas require about 20 dB of power control to overcome fading owing to multipath inside buildings. Deep fades beyond this control limit will be allowed to cause loss of signal but will do so infrequently. When such loss of signal occurs in a deep fade, recovery is generally very quick and the effects are short noise bursts. In today's analog cordless telephones and cellular phones, such noise bursts are very common and generally much more frequent than expected here. Experience with current spread-spectrum voice modems confirms this behavior.

APPENDIX 6B. ERROR BOUNDS FOR INTERFERENCE-LIMITED CHANNELS

Appendix 6B follows the presentation in Part 1, Chapter 4, Appendix 4A and Part 2, Chapter 1, Section 1.2.

We assume ideal coherent detection of DS/BPSK with the spreading codeword-matched filter output sampled at the correct time for the intended spread-spectrum signal with energy per bit of E_b. Without interference, the output sample of the matched filter is A if a 0 data bit is sent and $-A$ if the data bit is a 1. Assuming interference I at the spreading codeword-matched filter output sample when a 1 bit is sent, the bit error probability is given by the general expression

$$P_b = \Pr[-A + I \geq 0] \tag{6B.1}$$

based on the probability distribution of the interference random variable I.

Although we can assume that the probability density function of the random interference variable I is symmetric about the origin, it is generally difficult to obtain an error expression for such interference caused by other signals in the microcell network, given the difficulty in obtaining a closed-form expression.

We derive an easy-to-evaluate Chernoff bound expression on this bit error probability that allows us to avoid computing probability densities for the interference I. This bound uses the step function $U_{-1}(x)$ given by

$$U_{-1}(x) = \begin{cases} 1, & x \geq 0 \\ 0, & x < 0 \end{cases} \tag{6B.2}$$

and the inequality

$$U_{-1}(x) \leq e^{rx}, \qquad \text{for any } r \geq 0. \tag{6B.3}$$

The above inequality is used to obtain an upper bound on the bit error probability

$$\begin{aligned} \Pr[-A + I \geq 0] &= E[U_{-1}(-A + I)] \\ &\leq E[e^{r(-A+I)}] \\ &= e^{-rA}E[e^{rI}], \end{aligned} \tag{6B.4}$$

where the expectation, E, is taken over all the random variables in the interference term I.

When all data bits are equally likely and I has a probability density symmetric about the origin, another factor of $\frac{1}{2}$ can be applied to the final average bit error probability to yield the final Chernoff bound

$$P_b \leq \frac{1}{2} e^{-rA}E[e^{rI}], \tag{6B.5}$$

where the expectation, E, is taken over all random variables in the interference term I and r is any positive real number.

Outbound Channel

Consider a mobile unit and a base station with an active voice channel. The outbound channel is the TDD burst originating from the base station to the mobile unit. During this outbound burst, the mobile unit is assumed to be synchronized with and receiving a coherent DS/BPSK signal from the base station. Since it uses orthogonal codewords, the mobile unit receives no interference from this base station at the output sample time of its codeword-matched filter.

However, this mobile unit will receive interference from other base station transmissions (see Figure 6.6), which appear at the output sample of the mobile unit's codeword-matched filter. If we consider only one interference base station, interference has the form

$$I = \left(\sum_k a_k C_k\right)(\cos\phi) + \left(\sum_j b_j D_j\right)(\sin\phi) \tag{6B.6}$$

where C_k is the cross-correlation owing to the k-th codeword used by the interfering base station in its in-phase coordinate and D_j is the cross-correlation owing to the j-th codeword used by the same interfering base station in its quadrature coordinate. Here, we mean the cross-correlation with the codeword of the mobile unit taken at the time corresponding to the time delay difference between the two base stations and the mobile unit. Here, ϕ is a fixed arbitrary phase difference between the two base station signals.

The parameters C_k and D_j are taken to be fixed cross-correlation constants. The only random variables here are the binary data bits on these interfering spread-spectrum signals. They are given by the independent binary random variables a_k and b_j, which take on values of ± 1 with equal probability. The expectation, E, is taken over only these binary random variables. For the moment, we shall retain ϕ as a constant.

Since the binary random variables are independent, we have

$$\begin{aligned} E[e^{rI}] &= E\left[\exp\left[r\left(\sum_k a_k C_k\right)(\cos\phi) + r\left(\sum_j b_j D_j\right)(\sin\phi)\right]\right] \\ &= E\left[\exp\left[r\left(\sum_k a_k C_k\right)(\cos\phi)\right]\right] \\ &\quad \times E\left[\exp\left[r\left(\sum_j b_j D_j\right)(\sin\phi)\right]\right] \end{aligned} \tag{6B.7}$$

and

$$E\left[\exp\left[r\left(\sum_k a_k C_k\right)(\cos\phi)\right]\right] = \prod_k E[e^{ra_kC_k}\cos\phi]$$

$$= \prod_k \frac{e^{rC_k \cos\phi} + e^{-rC_k \cos\phi}}{2}$$

$$= \prod_k \cosh(rC_k \cos\phi). \tag{6B.8}$$

Next we use the inequality

$$\cosh x \leq e^{x^2/2} \tag{6B.9}$$

to obtain the bound

$$E[e^{rI}] \leq \exp\left\{\frac{1}{2}r^2\left[\left(\sum_k C_k^2\right)(\cos^2\phi) + \left(\sum_j D_j^2\right)(\sin^2\phi)\right]\right\}. \tag{6B.10}$$

At this point, we make one simplifying assumption about the base station signals. We assume that the interference terms of the interfering base station's in-phase and quadrature coordinates are identical and, consequently, that each base station will "balance" out the load into its in-phase and quadrature transmissions. Thus, we assume that

$$\sum_k C_k^2 = \sum_j D_j^2 \tag{6B.11}$$

and define the term J_0 as

$$J_0 = \sum_k C_k^2 + \sum_j D_j^2. \tag{6B.12}$$

Then

$$E[e^{rI}] \leq e^{r^2 J_0/4} \tag{6B.13}$$

and the total bound becomes

$$P_b \leq \frac{1}{2}\exp\left\{\frac{-4rA + r^2 J_0}{4}\right\} \tag{6B.14}$$

which is valid for any $r \geq 0$. The value of r that minimizes the bound is easily found to be

$$r^* = \frac{2A}{J_0} \tag{6B.15}$$

which then gives the final form of the upper bound

$$P_b = \frac{1}{2}e^{-A^2/J_0}. \tag{6B.16}$$

Note that since $A^2/2 = E_b$, this Chernoff bound is exactly the same as the ideal differentially coherent demodulated DBPSK bit error rate against white Gaussian noise with noise spectral density of $N_0 = J_0/2$. Thus, we have the natural measure of E_b/N_0 given by

$$E_b/N_0 = A^2/J_0 \tag{6B.17}$$

where J_0 is the sum of the squares of all correlation values of interference at the output sample of the mobile unit's codeword-matched filter.

The "balance" assumption that

$$\begin{aligned} J_0 &= \sum_k C_k^2 + \sum_j D_j^2 \\ &= 2\sum_k C_k^2 \\ &= 2\sum_j D_j^2 \end{aligned} \tag{6B.18}$$

eliminated the phase term ϕ from the bound.

Note that by following the above discussion, interference signals from several base stations would give basically the same result where J_0 is the sum of the squares of the cross-correlation values of all interfering signals from all other base stations.

The Chernoff bound derived here applies to the outbound channel in the S-CDMA system examined in Section 6.6.3, a bound that depends only on the assumption that data bits on all radios in the network are independent binary random variables. There is no assumption about noise or equivalent noise models.

Inbound Channel

We now consider the receiver at a base station that is coherently demodulating a DS/BPSK signal from a mobile unit. This mobile unit uses a unique spreading codeword to transmit digital voice with TDD bursts to the base station. We assume that all mobile units in active communication with the same base station are synchronized in time, use orthogonal codewords, and, therefore, do not interfere with each other at the base station. Thus, as shown in Figure 6.7, each base station receives interference only from the mobile units of neighboring base stations.

This base station samples the output of a matched filter corresponding to the mobile unit's codeword. Here, interference is caused by mobile units transmitting in other microcells. The interference is given by

$$I = \sum_k a_k C_k \cos \phi_k \tag{6B.19}$$

where C_k is the cross-correlation term for the interfering codewords with the codeword of the mobile unit transmitting to the base station. The random data bits modulating these interfering signals are given by a_k, while the random phase terms are given by ϕ_k. All these terms are assumed to be independent random variables, with phase random variables having uniform probability density over all phases.

Recall that from the Chernoff bound we have the term

$$\begin{aligned} E[e^{rA}] &= E\left[\exp\left(r \sum_k a_k C_k \cos \phi_k\right)\right] \\ &= \prod_k E[\exp(r a_k C_k \cos \phi_k)] \\ &= \prod_k I_0(rC_k) \end{aligned} \tag{6B.20}$$

where

$$\begin{aligned} I_0(x) &= \frac{1}{2\pi} \int_0^{2\pi} e^{x \cos \phi}\, d\phi \\ &= \sum_{k=0}^{\infty} \frac{(x/2)^{2k}}{(k!)^2} \end{aligned} \tag{6B.21}$$

is the modified Bessel function of order 0. Since $k! \geq 1$, we have the simple bound

$$\begin{aligned} I_0(x) &\leq \sum_{k=0}^{\infty} \frac{(x/2)^{2k}}{k!} \\ &= e^{(x/2)^2}. \end{aligned} \tag{6B.22}$$

Using this inequality in the previous equation results in

$$E[e^{rI}] \leq \exp\left(\frac{1}{4} r^2 \sum_k C_k^2\right). \tag{6B.23}$$

As in the previous section, we define J_0 as the sum of the squares of all the interfering cross-correlation terms. Here, it is defined as

$$J_0 = \sum_k C_k^2 \tag{6B.24}$$

The bit error probability is bounded by

$$P_b \leq \frac{1}{2} \exp\left\{\frac{-4rA + r^2 J_0}{4}\right\} \tag{6B.25}$$

Again, choosing $r \geq 0$ that minimizes this bound gives the final form

$$P_b \leq \frac{1}{2} e^{-A^2/J_0} \tag{6B.26}$$

which is the same form as in the outbound channel.

It is interesting to note that two different assumptions yield the same upper bound for the bit error probability for the S-CDMA interference-limited channel. For the outbound channel, interference to each mobile unit is caused by transmissions of other base stations. It is assumed that each base station balances its transmitted signals over both in-phase and quadrature coordinates.

For the inbound channel, each base station receives interference from all mobile units in other microcells. Here, the phase of each microcell signal is random and independent of other signal phases.

The fact that the bound is the same under differing conditions supports our intuition that the error bound developed here is quite robust and will be useful in many interference-limited cases. These bounds assume coherent DS/BPSK signals. With an appropriate adjustment, this same bound applies to the differentially coherent DS/DBPSK and DS/QPSK signals.

All the interference is in J_0, which is the sum of the squares of each of the interfering signal's cross-correlation with the receiver's codeword. These cross-correlation terms are evaluated at the synchronized sample time of the receiver in question. Timing errors and other impairments can be evaluated by adding their effects to the terms given in J_0. Signals within a microcell, e.g., may have some timing errors and may contribute to the cross-correlation terms summed in J_0. The analysis is still the same. The usefulness of this new bound lies in the fact that various assumptions about the interference can be easily evaluated as long as cross-correlation values can be computed.

INDEX

ABOUT THE AUTHORS

MARVIN K. SIMON, an internationally recognized expert on spread-spectrum systems, is a senior scientist at Jet Propulsion Laboratory.

JIM K. OMURA is founder and chairman of Cylink Corporation, which designs and manufactures spread-spectrum radios.

ROBERT A. SCHOLTZ is director of the Communications Science Institute of the University of Southern California.

BARRY K. LEVITT is technical leader of the Communications Concepts Research Group at Jet Propulsion Laboratory.